Ernest L. Mackie,
    March 4, 1939.

HIGHER MATHEMATICS

*With Applications to
Science and Engineering*

HIGHER MATHEMATICS

With Applications to Science and Engineering

BY

RICHARD STEVENS BURINGTON

Assistant Professor of Mathematics
The Case School of Applied Science

AND

CHARLES CHAPMAN TORRANCE

Instructor in Mathematics
The Case School of Applied Science

FIRST EDITION

McGRAW-HILL BOOK COMPANY, INC.

NEW YORK AND LONDON

1939

THE MAPLE PRESS COMPANY, YORK, PA.

PREFACE

This book is an outgrowth of a series of courses in advanced calculus and related subjects, given by the authors at The Case School of Applied Science, and designed primarily to meet the growing needs of students interested in the applications of mathematics to physics and engineering. To this end, special care has been taken to emphasize physical meanings of notations and relationships occurring in the subject. Applications to many branches of physics and engineering are given. These applications have been included as integral parts of the explanations of the several mathematical topics, and exercises involving them will be found in every chapter.

In keeping with the growing demand for rigor, every effort has been made to foster in the student the habit of carefully examining the operations he is performing. Stress has been placed on the precise mathematical interpretations of the concepts studied and on the conditions that must be met for a given theorem or formula to be valid, and no pains have been spared to make every proof complete. Thus, the present treatment is suited to students of pure mathematics.

In a subject as extended as the one in this book, it is hardly possible to acknowledge in every case indebtedness to specific books and papers. However, in the various references that appear throughout the book and in the bibliography every effort has been made to indicate the principal sources.

To Dr. Robert F. Rinehart of the Department of Mathematics at The Case School of Applied Science the authors are greatly indebted for having written the section on Algebra in Chap. VI.

The authors wish to express their sincere appreciation to Dean T. M. Focke of The Case School of Applied Science for his continued encouragement in the preparation of this manuscript. They take pleasure in acknowledging their indebtedness to President William E. Wickenden and Dr. Eckstein Case of The

Case School of Applied Science, who have made it possible to complete the manuscript at this time.

The senior author wishes to acknowledge his debt to his wife Jennet for her long and persevering efforts in the preparation of the manuscript.

R. S. BURINGTON,
C. C. TORRANCE.

CLEVELAND, OHIO,
January, 1939.

CONTENTS

CHAPTER III

CONTENTS

CHAPTER IV

PAGE

CHAPTER V

CONTENTS

HIGHER MATHEMATICS

CHAPTER I

DIFFERENTIAL CALCULUS

PART A. ELEMENTARY REVIEW

1. Introduction. In this chapter we shall first briefly review certain important topics in elementary differential calculus, and then we shall give an introduction to the theory of partial differentiation. Extensive applications of the various topics considered to physics, engineering, and geometry will be found in the exercises throughout the chapter.

2. Functions. The concept of a function is of fundamental importance. We shall first consider a real function of a real variable x.

A *real variable* is a symbol having real numbers for values.

A real variable may be a single letter, say x, or a formula in terms of a real variable x, or any notation to which are attached real values, such as $|x|$ and P_n, where $|x|$ denotes the numerical value of the real number x and where P_n denotes the nth prime number. The term real variable is also applied to anything having real values, such as physical quantities (temperature, pressure, density, acceleration, potential, etc.). It is evident that any quantity having real values can always be represented by a real variable. In this chapter, whenever we speak of a variable we shall always mean a real variable.

A *real independent variable* is a symbol for an arbitrary real number.

Before we define a function we make a precautionary remark. The student has perhaps learned to think of a variable as being a function of x if the variable has a definite value for each value of x. But this concept of a function is inadequate, for according to it, $\log_{10} x$, $\tan x$, $\sqrt{x(3 - x)}$, and $(-2)^x$ are *not* functions of the independent variable x since they do *not* have a definite

1

real value for *each* value of x. Thus, $\log_{10} x$ has a definite real value only when $x > 0$; tan x has a definite real value only when x is not an odd multiple of $\pi/2$ radians; $\sqrt{x(3 - x)}$ has a definite real value only when x is a number in the interval $0 \leqq x \leqq 3$; and $(-2)^x$ has a definite real value only when x is such a rational number that, when written in the form $x = p/q$ with p and q relatively prime integers, q is odd. These examples show that a variable may have a definite value for *certain* values of x, i.e., for some particular *set of values* of x, though not for each value of x. The difficulty with the preceding definition of a function may be remedied by requiring the variable in question to have a definite value for only some set D of values of x, where D may be an interval or a number of intervals or a part of the rational numbers or any other set of real numbers.

DEFINITION 2.1.   *If a variable has exactly one real value for each value of the variable x in some set D of real numbers, then this variable is called a real single-valued function of x defined over D (where by "defined over D" we mean "with value determined for each value of x in D").*

DEFINITION 2.2.   *The domain of definition of a function of x is the set of all values of x at which the function is defined.*

For example, the domain of definition of $\log_{10} x$ is the set of all positive numbers; the domain of definition of tan x is the set of all real numbers other than the odd multiples of $\pi/2$; the domain of definition of $\sqrt{x(3 - x)}$ is the set of numbers in the interval $0 \leqq x \leqq 3$; and the domain of definition of $(-2)^x$ is the set of all rational numbers p/q (in lowest terms) with q odd.

It should be noted that x is not necessarily an independent variable in Definition 2.1, but may itself be a function of another variable. On the other hand, in Definition 2.2, x must be free to take on all real values.

We shall give three examples to illustrate the meaning of Definition 2.1. First, let us consider the hot filament of an X-ray tube. Suppose the position of a point P of the filament (assumed to be of negligible thickness) is determined by its distance x from one end of the filament. If the filament is 2 cm. long, then the temperature T of the filament is a function of x in that T has a definite value for each value of x from 0 to 2. We denote the value of T at the point $x = a$ by $T(a)$, and we read* this symbol "the value

---

* If the student is asked to quote the symbol $T(a)$ orally, he should say "the value of T at $x = a$" and not some abbreviated translation of his own

of T at $x = a$." If the temperature of the filament (in degrees centigrade) at each end is 100, at the middle is 900, and if the temperature drops off linearly from the middle to each end, then $T(0) = T(2) = 100$, $T(1) = 900$, $T(\frac{1}{2}) = 500$, $T(0.1) = 180$, and $T(1.2) = 740$. This last equation, for example, should be read "the value of T at $x = 1.2$ is 740." If we wish to consider the value of T at an arbitrary or variable point of the filament, then we use the symbol $T(x)$ which we read "the value of T at an arbitrary* value of x." It is evident that T may be represented by the formula $800x + 100$ for values of x between 0 and 1. Thus the statement

$$T(x) = 800x + 100 \qquad \text{when} \qquad 0 \leqq x \leqq 1$$

means "the value of T at an arbitrary value of x is $800x + 100$ when x is between 0 and 1." To represent the value of T from 0 to 2, we write

$$T(x) = \begin{cases} 800x + 100 & \text{when} \qquad 0 \leqq x \leqq 1, \\ 1700 - 800x & \text{when} \qquad 1 \leqq x \leqq 2, \end{cases} \tag{1}$$

meaning that the value of T at an arbitrary value of x is $800x + 100$ when x is between 0 and 1, and is $1700 - 800x$ when x is between 1 and 2. The fact that two formulas are used to represent T does not mean that the temperature of the filament is simultaneously two functions of x. The temperature along the filament is one definite function of x, and it is possible to represent it by a single, though rather complicated, formula. In relation (1), the symbol $T(x)$ does *not* denote the formula $800x + 100$ or the formula $1700 - 800x$ or even both of the formulas at once; $T(x)$ has only the meaning already ascribed to it. We shall often meet with functions which are most conveniently described with the aid of two or more simple formulas instead of one complicated formula.

As our second example of a function, let us consider a formula in x, such as $\sqrt{\sin \pi x}$. It is convenient to denote a given formula by a single letter, say f, g, F, or ϕ, in exactly the same way that we denoted the temperature in the preceding example by T; in fact, we use f or some other letter as the name of a given formula. If f denotes a given formula in x, then the formula f is a real single-valued function of x when f has exactly one real value for each value of x in some set D of real numbers. Thus $\sqrt{\sin \pi x}$ is a real single-valued function of x, whereas $\sqrt{x - 2} + \sqrt{1 - x}$ is not (since it has a definite real value for no value of x), and $\sin^{-1} x$ is not (since it has many values for each value of x between -1 and 1).

If f denotes a single-valued function of x, then we denote the value of the function f for the value $x = a$ by $f(a)$, and we read this symbol "the value of

---

invention, such as "T, a." The practice of attaching cryptic readings to notation, particularly to save time or effort, is one of the most prolific sources of difficulty in the whole of mathematics, for such a practice effectively prevents the student from learning to think in terms of the meaning of the notation used. The student should be especially careful to avoid this mistake when reading by himself.

* It is implied, of course, that this value is one at which T is defined.

f when $x = a$," or if we think of the values of x as represented by points on the x-axis, we read it "the value of f at $x = a$." Thus, if f denotes $\sqrt{\sin \pi x}$, then $f(\frac{1}{2}) = 1$ and $f(\frac{1}{6}) = 1/\sqrt{2}$. The symbol $f(x)$ is read "the value of f for an arbitrary value of x." Thus *we use f as the name of a function, while we use $f(x)$ to denote an arbitrary value of the function.* This distinction is important, and failure to observe it may cause much confusion later on (see Ex. XIX, 1b and 1e).

For our last example, let us consider the equation

$$x + y^2 = 3^y. \tag{2}$$

Although this equation cannot be "solved" for y in terms of x in any simple way, yet it is readily seen from the graph (Fig. 1) of this equation that, for each value x_0 of x, there exists exactly one value y_0 of y such that the pair of numbers (x_0, y_0) is a solution of (2). [Each line $x = x_0$ meets the graph of (2) in exactly one point.] Hence, (2) determines a definite value of y for each value of x, that is, (2) deter-

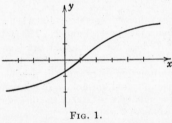

Fig. 1.

mines y as a single-valued *implicit* function of x defined for all values of x. We denote the value of y corresponding to the value $x = a$ by $y(a)$, and we read this symbol "the value of y when $x = a$." Thus $y(1) = 0$, $y(5) = 2$, and $y(-\frac{2}{3}) = -1$. If we think of y, not only as a variable having values, but also as a symbol denoting a function of x [viz., the function that would be obtained if (2) could somehow be solved for y in terms of x], then the notation $y(a)$ has exactly the same significance as the notation $f(a)$ in the preceding example.

If a variable has two or more values for each value of x in some set D of real numbers, then this variable is called a multiple-valued function of x. Thus, $\cos^{-1} x$, $\tan^{-1} x$, and the other inverse trigonometric functions are multiple-valued functions of x. Again, the equation $x^2 + y^2 = 1$ determines y as a multiple-valued function of x. (If x_0 is any number such that $-1 < x_0 < 1$, the line $x = x_0$ meets the graph of the equation $x^2 + y^2 = 1$ in two points.) A given multiple-valued function may be represented by two or more single-valued functions, so that the properties of the multiple-valued function may be determined by analyzing the properties of the respective single-valued functions. Hence we shall be particularly concerned in this chapter with single-valued functions.

If f denotes a single-valued function of x, and if x_0 is a value of x at which f is defined, then the pair of numbers $[x_0, f(x_0)]$ may be regarded as the rectangular coordinates of a point in a plane.

If x_0 is regarded as ranging through all values of x at which f is defined, then the set of all points $[x_0, f(x_0)]$ is called the *graph* of f. Thus the number $f(x_0)$ is represented by the ordinate up to the graph of f erected at the point $x = x_0$ on the x-axis. We may state this idea in another way: the significance of each point P on the graph of f is that the two coordinates of P always represent a value x_0 of x and the corresponding value $f(x_0)$ of f.

If f is a single-valued function of x, and if Δx (read "delta x") denotes the change in the value of x in going from a value x_0 to another value x_1, so that $\Delta x = x_1 - x_0$, then $f(x_0 + \Delta x) - f(x_0)$ *represents the change in the value of f in going from $x = x_0$ to*

$x = x_0 + \Delta x$. Furthermore, $\dfrac{f(x_0 + \Delta x) - f(x_0)}{\Delta x}$ *represents the*

ratio of the change in f to the change in x, or the mean change in f per

unit change in x, or the mean rate of change of f with respect to x, in going from $x = x_0$ to $x = x_0 + \Delta x$. (By the mean change in f per unit change in x is meant the change f would undergo per unit change in x were f changing at a constant rate from the value $f(x_0)$ to the value $f(x_0 + \Delta x)$, that is, if in Fig. 2 the graph of

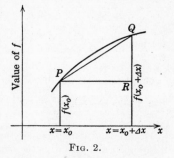

Fig. 2.

f were the chord $\overline{PQ}$ instead of the curve shown.) It is evident that $f(x_0 + \Delta x) - f(x_0)$ is represented by the line segment $\overline{RQ}$ in Fig. 2 and that $\dfrac{f(x_0 + \Delta x) - f(x_0)}{\Delta x}$ represents the slope of the chord $\overline{PQ}$.

EXERCISES I

1. If $f(x) = x^4 - x^2 + 5$, find $f(0), f(1), f(-1), f(kx_0)$. If $f(xy)$ denotes the result of substituting xy for x in the formula for f, find $f(xy)$ and $f(x) \cdot f(y)$. Are the results equal? Find $f(x + y)$ and $f(x) + f(y)$. Are the results equal? Find $f(x/y)$ and $f(x)/f(y)$.

2. If $f(x) = \dfrac{x + a}{x - a}$, find $f(a + b)$, $\dfrac{f(a + b)}{f(a - b)}$, $f\left(\dfrac{a + b}{a - b}\right)$, $f\left(\dfrac{1}{a}\right) + f\left(\dfrac{1}{b}\right)$ and $f\left(\dfrac{1}{a} + \dfrac{1}{b}\right)$. What is the domain of definition of f?

3. If $f(x) = x + \dfrac{1}{x}$, find $f(a) + \dfrac{1}{f(a)}$ and $f\left(a + \dfrac{1}{a}\right)$.

4. If $f(x) = x^2$, show that
$$[f(a + b)]^2 + [f(a - b)]^2 = 2f(a^2 + b^2) + 8f(ab).$$

5. If $f(x) = \dfrac{e^x - e^{-x}}{2}$, where $e = 2.718 \ldots$, show that
$$f(\log_e (u + \sqrt{u^2 + 1})) = u.$$

6. If $f(x) = \dfrac{e^x - e^{-x}}{e^x + e^{-x}}$, show that $f\left(\dfrac{1}{2} \log_e \dfrac{1 + u}{1 - u}\right) = u.$

7. If $f(x) = \log_a x$, show that $f(x) + f(y) = f(xy)$. If $f(x) = a^x$, show that $f(x) f(y) = f(x + y)$.

8. If $F(x) = 2x\sqrt{1 - x^2}$, show that $F(\sin \theta) = F(\cos \theta) = \sin 2\theta$.

9. If $F(x) = 2x^2 - 1$, show that $F(\cos \theta) = \cos 2\theta$.

10. Find the value of $\dfrac{f(x_0 + \Delta x) - f(x_0)}{\Delta x}$ when $f(x)$ is given by the following formulas:

(a) $x^2 - 3x$.

(b) $\dfrac{3x}{2 - x}$.

(c) $\sqrt{5 - 2x^2}$.

(d) $x^{1/2} - a^{1/2}$.

(e) $\cos x$.

(f) $\sin^4 (1 - 3x^2)$.

(g) $\log_{10} x$.

(h) $\log_b \tan 2x$.

(i) 2^x.

(j) $10^{\sin^{-1} x}$.

Graph formulas (a), (b), (c), (e), (g), and (i). Represent $f(x_0), f(x_0 + \Delta x)$, $f(x_0 + \Delta x) - f(x_0)$, and $\dfrac{f(x_0 + \Delta x) - f(x_0)}{\Delta x}$ on these graphs when $x_0 = 1$ and $\Delta x = \frac{1}{2}$.

11. (a) If T is the temperature of a certain quantity of gas in degrees Fahrenheit and if $p(T)$ is the unit pressure of the gas in pounds per square inch at temperature T, give the complete physical interpretation of the quantity $\dfrac{p(T_0 + \Delta T) - p(T_0)}{\Delta T}$, i.e., state the meaning of $p(T_0)$, $p(T_0 + \Delta T)$, $p(T_0 + \Delta T) - p(T_0)$, and the given fraction. [For example, $p(T_0)$ represents the unit pressure at the temperature T_0 and $\dfrac{p(T_0 + \Delta T) - p(T_0)}{\Delta T}$ represents the mean change in unit pressure per degree change in temperature in going from the temperature T_0 to the temperature $T_0 + \Delta T$.]

(b) If x represents distance in centimeters along the filament of an X-ray tube and if $T(x)$ is the temperature of the filament in degrees centigrade at the point x, give the complete physical interpretation of the quantity $\dfrac{T(x_0 + \Delta x) - T(x_0)}{\Delta x}$. (The fraction itself represents the mean change in temperature per centimeter along the filament from the point x_0 to the point $x_0 + \Delta x$.)

(c) If x represents distance in inches along a radio antenna and if $D(x)$ is the density of electric charge at the point x, give the complete physical interpretation of the quantity $\dfrac{D(x_0 + \Delta x) - D(x_0)}{\Delta x}$.

(d) If p represents unit pressure in pounds per square inch and if $E(p)$ is the voltage needed to make an electric spark jump 1 in. in air at pressure p, interpret $\dfrac{E(p_0 + \Delta p) - E(p_0)}{\Delta p}$ completely.

(e) If t represents time in seconds and if $A(t)$ is the number of grams of a chemical substance existing at time t, interpret $\dfrac{A(t_0 + \Delta t) - A(t_0)}{\Delta t}$ completely.

(f) Give three other physical examples of functions and discuss them in the manner indicated in the preceding parts of this question.

12. Does the equation $x^2 + y^3 = 5$ determine y as a single-valued function of x? If so, what is the domain of definition of y? Find $y(0)$, $y(1)$, and $y(-2)$.

13. If $\text{Sin}^{-1} y + \text{Tan}^{-1} y = x$, find $y(0)$ and $y(\tfrac{3}{4}\pi)$, remembering that $\text{Sin}^{-1} y$ and $\text{Tan}^{-1} y$, written with capital letters, denote principal values. What is the domain of definition of y when determined as a function of x by this equation?

14. For what values of x does the equation $x + y^2 = 2y$ define y as a single-valued function of x?

15. Graph the function f when $f(x) = \sqrt{\sin \pi x}$, showing the portion of the graph between $x = -4$ and $x = 6$. What is the domain of definition of f?

16. Graph the function f when

$$f(x) = \begin{cases} x^2 & \text{when} \quad x \geqq 0, \\ -2x & \text{when} \quad x < 0. \end{cases}$$

Does the symbol $f(x)$ denote x^2 or $-2x$ or both of these formulas simultaneously? Describe a physical situation in which f is involved as some physical quantity.

17. Graph the function f when

$$f(x) = \begin{cases} \tfrac{1}{2}(\pi + x) & \text{when} \quad -\pi \leqq x < 0, \\ 0 & \text{when} \quad x = 0, \\ \tfrac{1}{2}(\pi - x) & \text{when} \quad 0 < x \leqq \pi. \end{cases}$$

It is possible to represent f by the single formula

$$f(x) = \left| \sin x + \frac{\sin 2x}{2} + \frac{\sin 3x}{3} + \cdots \right|,$$

where the symbol $|\ |$ denotes "numerical value of" and where only values of x in the interval $-\pi \leqq x \leqq \pi$ are considered. If

$$g(x) = \begin{cases} \tfrac{1}{2}(\pi + x) & \text{when} \quad -\pi \leqq x \leqq 0, \\ \tfrac{1}{2}(\pi - x) & \text{when} \quad 0 \leqq x \leqq \pi, \end{cases}$$

then g may be represented by the single formula

$$g(x) = \frac{2}{\pi}\left(\cos x + \frac{\cos 3x}{3^2} + \frac{\cos 5x}{5^2} + \cdots \right),$$

where $-\pi \leq x \leq \pi$. Although the values of f and g differ at only the single point $x = 0$, yet f and g are represented by different formulas and must be regarded as distinct functions.

18. Graph the function f when $f(x) = \dfrac{1}{1 - 2^x} + \dfrac{1}{1 - 2^{-x}}$. What is the domain of definition of f? If g is represented by the formula $g(x) = 1$ for all values of x, are f and g the same function?

This exercise illustrates the following fact: *If two functions f and g have different domains of definition, then f and g must be regarded as distinct, even though f and g have the same values wherever both functions are defined.*

19. If D is the domain of definition of the function f and if E is the domain of definition of the function g, what is the domain of definition of the function $f + g$? Of the function $f \cdot g$? of f/g? [Recall that division by zero is never permitted, so that the symbol $f(a)/g(a)$ is meaningless when $g(a) = 0$.] For what values of x is $f[g(x)]$ defined? (Note that $f[g(a)]$ is meaningless unless a is such a value of x in E that $g(a)$ is a number in D.)

3. The Limit of a Function. We now wish to develop an accurate formulation of the concept "limit of a function." We first give two simple examples.

The function $(\sin x)/x$ has no value at $x = 0$, $0/0$ not being a number. But if we tabulate values of x and $(\sin x)/x$ as x gets close to 0, and plot the resulting data, we obtain the following results:

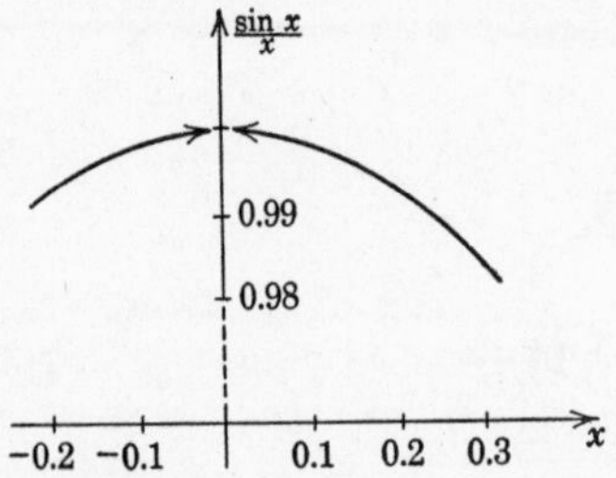

Fig. 3.

x	$\sin x$	$\dfrac{\sin x}{x}$
0.5	0.47943	0.9589
0.3	0.29552	0.9851
0.2	0.19867	0.9933
0.1	0.09983	0.9983
0.05	0.0499792	0.99958
0.01	0.009999983	0.9999983
-0.01	-0.009999983	0.9999983
-0.05	-0.0499792	0.99958
-0.1	-0.09983	0.9983

It would appear from the table and the graph that, as x approaches 0 (x being either positive or negative), the value of $(\sin x)/x$ approaches the number 1. (It will be proved in Ex. IV, 21 that this surmise is correct.) If we use the symbol $\rightarrow$ to denote "approaches," then the value of $(\sin x)/x \rightarrow 1$ as $x \rightarrow 0$.

(This result, of course, depends on the fact that we have measured x in radians.)

As another example, we note that the function $(1 + x)^{1/x}$ has no value at $x = 0$. But it would seem from the table and graph below that the value of $(1 + x)^{1/x} \to 2.718 \cdots$ as $x \to 0$. (It will be proved in Ex. IV, 23 that this surmise is correct.) The student will do well to compute more values of this function, using a large table of logarithms.

x	$(1 + x)^{1/x}$
0.1	2.5938
0.03	2.6786
0.01	2.7048
0.001	2.7169
0.0001	2.7181
. . . .	. . .
−0.0001	2.7184
−0.001	2.7196
−0.01	2.7320

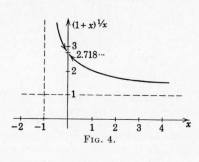

Fig. 4.

These examples show that if f is a function of x and if the value of x is approaching a number a, then the value of f may approach a number A. (In the preceding examples, $a = 0$ and A is respectively 1 and $2.718 \cdots$.) We wish to analyze the meaning of this statement in detail, and we first raise the question, what is meant by the word *approach?*

A. *We define the word "approach" to mean "become and remain arbitrarily close to."*

We give two examples to show why it is necessary to say "become *and remain* arbitrarily close to." Suppose the independent variable x is made to vary as follows: x decreases from $\frac{1}{2}$ to 0.1 (taking on all values in between), increases back up to $\frac{1}{2}$, decreases to 0.01, increases back up to $\frac{1}{2}$, decreases to 0.001, increases back up to $\frac{1}{2}$, decreases to 0.0001, etc. While x *gets* arbitrarily close to 0, it does not *remain* there, and one would not say that x approached 0 in the sense intended.

Again, consider the function $(\cos x)\left(\cos \dfrac{1}{x}\right)$ whose graph is shown in Fig. 5. This function has no value at $x = 0$ and is such that its graph oscillates infinitely many times in the neighborhood of $x = 0$. While the value of $\cos x \cos (1/x)$ *gets* arbitrarily close to 1 (and also to −1) as x approaches 0, it does not *remain* there, and one would not say that the value of cos x cos $(1/x)$ approached 1 (or -1) in the sense intended when x approaches 0.

It is often thought that a variable V, when approaching a number A, can never attain the value A. While this is sometimes the case, as with $(\sin x)/x$ and $(1 + x)^{1/x}$ when x is approaching 0, it is not always so.

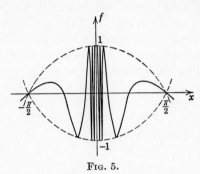

Fig. 5.

B. *When we say that a variable V is approaching a number A, there is no implication that V can never reach or equal A, nor is there any implication that V must eventually attain the value A.*

For example, it is readily proved that the graph of x^2 cos $(1/x)$ oscillates between the two parabolas $y = x^2$ and $y = -x^2$, the number of oscillations becoming infinite as x approaches 0. It follows that the value of x^2 cos $(1/x)$ becomes and remains arbitrarily close to 0 as x approaches 0. However, as x^2 cos $(1/x)$ approaches 0 in this manner, it actually reaches and takes on the value 0 infinitely many times.

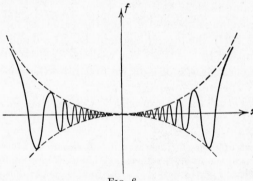

Fig. 6.

Again, suppose x varies as follows: x decreases from 1 to -0.1 (taking on all values in between), increases to 0.01, decreases to -0.001, increases to 0.0001, etc. Since x becomes and remains arbitrarily close to 0, it is approaching 0; but in approaching 0 in this manner, it takes on the value 0 infinitely many times. This manner of approach is illustrated physically by a pendulum coming to rest.

In considering the behavior of a function f as $x \rightarrow a$, we have always allowed x to approach a in an arbitrary manner so long

as x remained in the domain of definition of the function f.
The following example shows the desirability of restricting the
manner in which x may approach a.   Suppose

$$f(x) = \left| \sin x + \frac{\sin 2x}{2} + \frac{\sin 3x}{3} + \cdots \right|.$$

(See Ex. I, **17**.)   This function is defined for all values of x and,
in particular, has the value 0 at $x = 0$.   (This value is indicated
in Fig. 7 by the large dot at the origin.)   If x approaches 0 in
the manner indicated in the preceding paragraph, then we

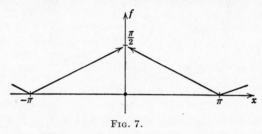

FIG. 7.

cannot say that the value of f approaches $\pi/2$ as $x \to 0$, for the
value of f does not become *and remain* arbitrarily close to $\pi/2$.
But if we deliberately exclude 0 as a possible value of x as x
approaches 0, then the value of f approaches $\pi/2$ as $x \to 0$.
Thus, as $x \to a$, it is possible for the value of a function f to
approach a number A when x remains different from a but not
when x is free to take on the value a.   It follows that, by restricting x to remain different from a, we can more fully analyze the
behavior of a function f "near" $x = a$.   Hence we lay down
the following principle:

C. *In considering the behavior of a function f as $x \to a$, we
restrict x to remain different from a.*

It is evident from Fig. 5 that the value of the function
$\cos x \cos (1/x)$ approaches no number A as $x \to 0$.   Again, as
$x \to 0$ (but remaining $\neq 0$), the value of the function

$$|\sin x + \tfrac{1}{2} \sin 2x + \cdots|$$

approaches a number which is different from the value of this
function at $x = 0$.   Thus,

D. *As $x \to a$, the value of a function f need not approach any
number A; if the value of f does approach a number A as $x \to a$,
and if f is defined at $x = a$, then A and $f(a)$ may be distinct.*

We have an immediate corollary from C and D:

E. *In considering the question as to whether or not the value of a function f approaches a number A as $x \to a$, it is immaterial whether or not f is defined at $x = a$, and if f is defined at $x = a$ it is immaterial what the number $f(a)$ may be.*

We are now in a position to define the limit of a function.

DEFINITION 3.1A.   *If the value of a function f approaches a number A as x approaches a (but remaining $\neq a$), then this number A is denoted by the symbol $\lim_{x \to a} f(x)$ which is read "the number approached by the value of f as $x \to a$." The number $\lim_{x \to a} f(x)$ is referred to as the limit of f as $x \to a$.*

For example, $\lim_{x \to 0} (\sin x)/x = 1$, i.e., the number approached by the value of $(\sin x)/x$ as $x \to 0$ is 1.   Again,

$$\lim_{x \to 0} (1 + x)^{1/x} = 2.718 \cdots ,$$

$\lim_{x \to 0} |\sin x + \frac{1}{2} \sin 2x + \cdots| = \pi/2$, and $\lim_{x \to 0} [\cos x \cdot \cos (1/x)]$ does not exist.

EXERCISES II

1. The graphs of a number of functions are shown below.   In each case state whether or not $\lim_{x \to 0} f(x)$ exists, and if it does, state its value.

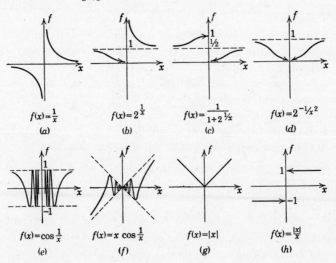

$f(x) = \frac{1}{x}$ $f(x) = 2^{\frac{1}{x}}$ $f(x) = \frac{1}{1 + 2^{1/x}}$ $f(x) = 2^{-1/x^2}$

(a)   (b)   (c)   (d)

$f(x) = \cos \frac{1}{x}$ $f(x) = x \cos \frac{1}{x}$ $f(x) = |x|$ $f(x) = \frac{|x|}{x}$

(e)   (f)   (g)   (h)

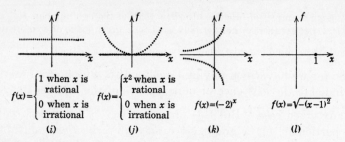

$$f(x) = \begin{cases} 1 \text{ when } x \text{ is rational} \\ 0 \text{ when } x \text{ is irrational} \end{cases}$$

(i)

$$f(x) = \begin{cases} x^2 \text{ when } x \text{ is rational} \\ 0 \text{ when } x \text{ is irrational} \end{cases}$$

(j)

$$f(x) = (-2)^x$$

(k)

$$f(x) = \sqrt{-(x-1)^2}$$

(l)

2. The graphs of a number of functions are shown below. In each case state whether or not $\lim_{x \to a} f(x)$ exists, and if it does, estimate its value.

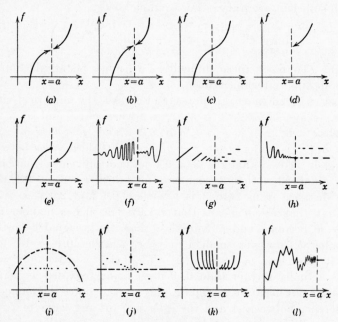

(a) (b) (c) (d)

(e) (f) (g) (h)

(i) (j) (k) (l)

3. Graph the function $[x]$, where $[x]$ denotes the largest integer not greater than x. For what values of a does $\lim_{x \to a} [x]$ exist?

4. Show that the function f such that $f(x) = 1$ when x is rational and $f(x) = 0$ when x is irrational, may be represented by the single formula $f(x) = \lim_{n \to \infty} [\cos^2\{\pi(n!)x\}]$, where $[\cdots]$ denotes "greatest integer contained in" (see Ex. 3). What formula represents the function in Ex. 1j?

The two functions mentioned in this exercise, as well as functions like $(-2)^x$ and $\cos(1/x)$, illustrate the fact that it may be impossible to represent accurately the behavior of a function by means of a graph.

5. Give examples of functions to show that, of the two numbers $f(a)$ and $\lim_{x \to a} f(x)$, both, either, or neither may exist for a given value of a; moreover, if both these numbers exist, they may be the same or distinct.

So far we have been relying largely on the graph of a function to indicate the existence or nonexistence of the number $\lim_{x \to a} f(x)$ in any given case. But this procedure is very limited in scope. In particular, (1) a graph gives only an *indication*, and not a *proof*, of the existence of the number $\lim_{x \to a} f(x)$, and (2) the method fails completely when the graph of a function cannot be drawn with sufficient accuracy. For example, does

$$\lim_{x \to 0} \left(\sin \frac{1}{x} + \frac{1}{2} \sin \frac{2}{x} + \frac{1}{3} \sin \frac{3}{x} + \cdots \right)$$

exist? To meet these difficulties we must restate Definition 3.1a in a more technical form.

Let us recall that $|x|$ denotes, and is read, the numerical value of x. Thus, $|3| = |-3| = 3$; $|x| = x$ when $x \geqq 0$ and $|x| = -x$ when $x < 0$; $|x - a| = x - a$ if $x \geqq a$ and $|x - a| = a - x$ if $x < a$. It is evident that $|x - a|$ represents the *distance* between x and a. To say that $x - 3 < 0.1$ does not prevent x from being any number less than 3, such as -50, but if $|x - 3| < 0.1$, then the distance from x to 3 is less than 0.1 and $2.9 < x < 3.1$. To say that $x \to a$ means that x varies in such a manner that $|x - a|$ becomes and remains less than any assignable positive number δ, however small δ may be, whether 0.1 or 10^{-10}, or $10^{-(10^{10})}$, or less. (We say that a number is positive only when it is actually greater than 0, 0 itself being regarded as neither positive nor negative.) Again, $|f(x) - A|$ denotes the numerical difference between A and the *value* of f for any value of x, and the condition $|f(x) - A| < 0.01$ is equivalent to the condition $A - 0.01 < f(x) < A + 0.01$. It is evident that Definition 3.1a can be put in the following form:

F. *If $|f(x) - A|$ becomes and remains less than any assignable positive number ϵ when x varies in any manner so that $|x - a|$ becomes and remains less than any assignable positive number δ but without ever becoming 0, then $A = \lim_{x \to a} f(x)$.*

We wish to simplify this form of the definition of a limit so that we do not need to think of x as actually varying in any

particular manner and so that we do not need to use the words
"become and remain." Let f be a given function, such as the
one whose graph is shown in Fig. 8a, let ϵ be a given small positive
number, say 0.01, and let the lines $y = A - \epsilon$ and $y = A + \epsilon$
be drawn. It is evident that, for values of x near $x = a$, the
graph of f remains within the horizontal strip formed by these
two lines. In fact, there exists a small positive number δ,
indicated in Fig. 8b, such that the following assertion holds:
*If we consider only that portion of the graph of f lying in the vertical
strip between the lines $x = a - \delta$ and $x = a + \delta$ but not on
the line $x = a$, then this portion of the graph of f remains within the*

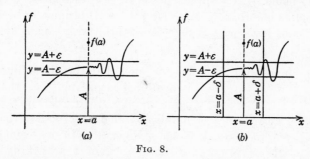

Fig. 8.

horizontal strip between the lines $y = A - \epsilon$ and $y = A + \epsilon$. The
fact that x is restricted to be different from a and to lie between
$a - \delta$ and $a + \delta$ is expressed by the condition $0 < |x - a| < \delta$;
the fact that, for these values of x, the graph of f remains between
the lines $y = A - \epsilon$ and $y = A + \epsilon$ is expressed by the condition
$|f(x) - A| < \epsilon$. Hence the italicized assertion may be expressed
by the formula

$$|f(x) - A| < \epsilon \quad \text{for all values}$$
$$\text{of } x \text{ such that} \quad 0 < |x - a| < \delta. \quad (1)$$

[Note the similarity between (1) and paragraph F.]

It is evident that, the smaller is the *given* number ϵ in (1), the
smaller must δ be taken for (1) to hold; in other words, the
narrower is the given horizontal strip in Fig. 8a, the narrower
must be the vertical strip in Fig. 8b. Again, the more irregular
is the graph of f near $x = a$, the smaller must be δ for any given
number ϵ. In short, formula (1) holds for a given number
ϵ *only when δ is sufficiently small.* We now raise a fundamental

question: However small ϵ may be in (1), does there always exist a sufficiently small positive number δ such that (1) holds? It is seen in Fig. 9 that, no matter how small δ is taken, (1) cannot hold for the number ϵ shown. Hence, for some functions f the answer to our question is negative. We now show that

G. $\lim\limits_{x \to a} f(x) = A$ *when, and only when, the answer to the above question is affirmative.*

Suppose first that the function f is such that the above question is answered affirmatively. Let ϵ be an arbitrarily small positive number. By hypothesis, there exists a positive number δ such that (1) holds. As x approaches a, $|x - a|$ ultimately becomes *and remains* less than δ. By (1), $|f(x) - A|$ ultimately becomes and remains less than ϵ. Since ϵ was arbitrarily small, $\lim\limits_{x \to a} f(x)$ exists and is A.

Now suppose the function f is such that the above question

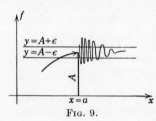

Fig. 9.

is answered negatively, i.e., that for some number ϵ there exists no positive number δ sufficiently small so that (1) holds (see Fig. 9). In this event there exist values $\bar{x}$ of x arbitrarily close to a and distinct from a such that $|f(\bar{x}) - A| > \epsilon$. If x approaches a in such a manner as to take on these values $\bar{x}$, then $|f(x) - A|$ cannot become *and remain* less than ϵ, that is, the value of f does not approach A as a limit. This completes the proof of Theorem G.

Because (1) does not involve the idea of approach, it is customary to use (1) to *define* $\lim\limits_{x \to a} f(x)$. Theorem G shows that the following definition is equivalent to Definition 3.1a.

DEFINITION 3.1B. *Let f be a real single-valued function of x and let A and a be real numbers. If, for each positive number ϵ, however small, there exists a positive number δ such that*

$$|f(x) - A| < \epsilon \quad \text{for all values} \atop \text{of } x \text{ such that} \quad 0 < |x - a| < \delta, \quad (1)$$

then A is denoted by either $\lim\limits_{x \to a} f(x)$ or $\lim\limits_{x = a} f(x)$, and A is referred to as "the limit of f at $x = a$."

Although this definition does not involve the idea of approach, the symbol $\lim_{x \to a} f(x)$ is often used because it suggests our original intuitive concept of a limit.

For condition (1) to hold, the function f must be *defined* for all values of x such that $0 < |x - a| < \delta$. This implies that, for a function f to have a limit at $x = a$, f must be defined over the whole of some interval about $x = a$, except perhaps at $x = a$ itself. This condition is usually met by the common elementary functions and, for the sake of simplicity, will be assumed in the discussion to follow. See Exs. IV, 6 and 27, in this connection.

Example 1. Does $\lim_{x \to 4} (3x - 2)$ exist? If so, what is its value?

We first observe that neither the existence nor the value of this limit can be determined from the fact that $3x - 2 = 10$ when $x = 4$; the intuitive feeling that if a function f has a value at $x = a$, then this value must be $\lim_{x \to a} f(x)$ is shown to be erroneous by the function

$$|\sin x + \tfrac{1}{2} \sin 2x + \tfrac{1}{3} \sin 3x + \cdots|$$

which has the value 0 and the limit 1 at $x = 0$ (see Fig. 7 and paragraph E). Thus, if it turns out that $\lim_{x \to 4} (3x - 2)$ exists and is 10, this result must be regarded merely as a coincidence.

In using Definition 3.1b to determine the existence of $\lim_{x \to 4} (3x - 2)$, we first think of ϵ as being a *given* number, arbitrarily small, with the lines $y = A - \epsilon$ and $y = A + \epsilon$ drawn on the graph of $3x - 2$; then we inquire if a number δ exists which is sufficiently small that (1) holds. We shall prove that $\lim_{x \to 4} (3x - 2)$ exists by showing that there exists a formula for δ in terms of ϵ such that, however small ϵ may be, this formula gives a value of δ sufficiently small that (1) holds.

In (1), let $f(x) = 3x - 2$ and let $A = 10$. Since

$$|(3x - 2) - 10| = |3x - 12| = 3|x - 4|,$$

it follows that, if ϵ is any given positive number, $|(3x - 2) - 10| < \epsilon$ when* $3|x - 4| < \epsilon$, i.e., when $|x - 4| < \epsilon/3$. Thus (1) holds when we take $\delta = \epsilon/3$. This proves that $\lim_{x \to 4} (3x - 2)$ exists and is 10. The fact that we showed (1) holds even when $x = 4$ is of significance in the next section.

Example 2. Show that $\lim_{x \to 3} x^2$ exists and is 9.

Remarks similar to those made in Example 1 may also be made here. In (1) let $f(x) = x^2$ and let $A = 9$. Since $|\alpha\beta| = |\alpha| \cdot |\beta|$ when α and β are

---

* By "when" we mean "for all values of x such that."

real numbers,

$$|x^2 - 9| = |(x + 3)(x - 3)| = |x + 3| \cdot |x - 3|. \tag{2}$$

Since $|x + 3| < 7$ when $|x - 3| < 1$, it follows that

$$|x + 3| \cdot |x - 3| < 7|x - 3| \qquad \text{when} \qquad |x - 3| < 1. \tag{3}$$

Again, if ϵ is any given positive number,

$$7|x - 3| < \epsilon \qquad \text{when} \qquad |x - 3| < \frac{\epsilon}{7}. \tag{4}$$

It follows by (2), (3), and (4) that $|x^2 - 9| < \epsilon$ when $|x - 3| < \delta$, where δ is the smaller of 1 and $\epsilon/7$. This proves that $\lim\limits_{x \to 3} x^2$ exists and is 9.

Example 3. Show that $\lim\limits_{x \to -1} (x^2 - 5x) = 6$.

Since $|\alpha \pm \beta| \leqq |\alpha| + |\beta|$ when α and β are real numbers,

$$|(x^2 - 5x) - 6| = |(x^2 - 1) - (5x + 5)| \leqq |x^2 - 1| + |5x + 5|. \tag{5}$$

Let ϵ be any positive number. It is readily shown by the methods of Examples 1 and 2 that

$$|x^2 - 1| < \frac{\epsilon}{2} \qquad \text{when} \qquad |x + 1| < \delta_1, \tag{6}$$

where δ_1 is the smaller of 1 and $\epsilon/6$, and that

$$|5x + 5| < \frac{\epsilon}{2} \qquad \text{when} \qquad |x + 1| < \delta_2, \qquad \text{where} \qquad \delta_2 = \frac{\epsilon}{10}. \tag{7}$$

It follows by (5), (6), and (7) that

$$|(x^2 - 5x) - 6| < \epsilon \qquad \text{when} \qquad |x + 1| < \delta,$$

where δ is the smaller of δ_1 and δ_2.

Example 4. Show that $\lim\limits_{x \to 0} 2^{-1/x^2} = 0$ (see Ex. II, 1d).

It is evident that

$$|2^{-1/x^2} - 0| = |2^{-1/x^2}| = \frac{1}{2^{1/x^2}}, \qquad \text{where} \qquad x \neq 0. \tag{8}$$

Let ϵ be any positive number <1 and let $\epsilon = 1/2^n$, i.e., $n = -\log_2 \epsilon$. Since $n > 0$,

$$\frac{1}{2^{1/x^2}} < \frac{1}{2^n} \qquad \text{when} \qquad \frac{1}{x^2} > n, \qquad \text{i.e., when} \qquad 0 < x^2 < \frac{1}{n},$$

$$\text{i.e., when} \qquad 0 < |x| < \frac{1}{\sqrt{n}}. \tag{9}$$

In this result we can write $|x - 0|$ instead of $|x|$, and it follows by (8) and (9) that

$|2^{-1/x^2} - 0| < \epsilon$ when $0 < |x - 0| < \dfrac{1}{\sqrt{n}}$,   where $n = -\log_2 \epsilon$.

If $\epsilon \geqq 1$, $|2^{-1/x^2} - 0| < \epsilon$ for all $x \neq 0$.

Example 5. Show that $\lim\limits_{\theta \to 0} \cos \theta = 1$.

Let ϵ be any positive number $\leqq 2$. Let O be the center of a circle of radius 1, let $\overline{BC}$ be the chord perpendicular to the radius OA at the distance ϵ from A, and let $\delta = \angle AOB$. It is evident that $|\cos \theta - 1| < \epsilon$ when $|\theta - 0| < \delta$. If $\epsilon > 2$, then $|\cos \theta - 1| < \epsilon$ for all θ.

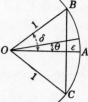

Fig. 10.

EXERCISES III

Show that the following limits exist and have the values indicated:

1. $\lim\limits_{x \to 2} (1 - 4x) = -7$.

2. $\lim\limits_{x \to c} (ax + b) = ac + b$, where $a \neq 0$.

3. $\lim\limits_{x \to c} b = b$.

4. $\lim\limits_{x \to -2} 3x^2 = 12$.

5. $\lim\limits_{x \to 3} (2x^2 - x) = 15$.

6. $\lim\limits_{x \to 1} (2x - 3x^2) = -1$.

7. $\lim\limits_{x \to 5} \sqrt{x} = \sqrt{5}$. $\left(\text{Write } |\sqrt{x} - \sqrt{5}| = \left| \dfrac{x - 5}{\sqrt{x} + \sqrt{5}} \right|. \right)$

8. $\lim\limits_{x \to 2} \sqrt{3x - 1} = \sqrt{5}$.

9. $\lim\limits_{x \to 2} x^3 = 8$.

10. $\lim\limits_{\theta \to a} \cos \theta = \cos a$.

11. $\lim\limits_{\theta \to a} \sin \theta = \sin a$.

12. $\lim\limits_{x \to 0} x \cos \dfrac{1}{x} = 0$. $\left(\left| \cos \dfrac{1}{x} \right| \leqq 1 \text{ for all } x \neq 0. \right)$

13. $\lim\limits_{x \to 0} x^2 \sqrt{x(4 - x)} = 0$. [Find the maximum value of $\sqrt{x(4 - x)}$.]

14. $\lim\limits_{x \to 2} 1/x = \frac{1}{2}$.

15. $\lim\limits_{x \to 1} 1/(3x + 2) = \frac{1}{5}$.

16. In connection with Example 2 above, show ϵ and δ on the graph of x^2.

17. By applying Definition 3.1b, examine each of the functions in Exs. II, 1 and 2 for the existence of a limit at the points indicated. (In each case draw the lines $y = A \pm \epsilon$ and the corresponding lines $x = a \pm \delta$.)

We close this section with two general theorems about limits.

THEOREM 3.1. *A function f can have at most one limit at a point $x = a$.*

Suppose f had two different limits A and A' at $x = a$. If ϵ is taken to be less than $\frac{1}{2}|A - A'|$, then it is impossible for (1) to hold for both A and A', i.e., the graph of f cannot remain within both of the horizontal strips bounded by the pairs of lines $y = A \pm \epsilon$, $y = A' \pm \epsilon$.

THEOREM 3.2. *If f and g are functions such that $\lim\limits_{x \to a} f(x)$ and $\lim\limits_{x \to a} g(x)$ exist, then*

(a) $\lim\limits_{x \to a} [f(x) \pm g(x)]$ *exists and equals* $\lim\limits_{x \to a} f(x) \pm \lim\limits_{x \to a} g(x)$.

(b) $\lim\limits_{x \to a} [f(x) \cdot g(x)] = \lim\limits_{x \to a} f(x) \cdot \lim\limits_{x \to a} g(x)$ *(where, in writing* " $=$ ", *we imply the existence of the first limit).*

(c) $\lim\limits_{x \to a} \dfrac{f(x)}{g(x)} = \dfrac{\lim\limits_{x \to a} f(x)}{\lim\limits_{x \to a} g(x)}$, *provided that* $\lim\limits_{x \to a} g(x) \neq 0$.

We first note that, if α and β are real numbers,

$$|\alpha \pm \beta| \leq |\alpha| + |\beta| \tag{10}$$

and

$$|\alpha\beta| = |\alpha| \cdot |\beta|. \tag{11}$$

Let $\lim\limits_{x \to a} f(x) = A$ and $\lim\limits_{x \to a} g(x) = B$. To prove part (a) we must show that, if ϵ is any positive number, there exists a positive number δ such that

$$|[f(x) \pm g(x)] - (A \pm B)| < \epsilon \quad \text{when} \quad 0 < |x - a| < \delta. \tag{12}$$

By (10),

$$|[f(x) \pm g(x)] - (A \pm B)|$$
$$= |[f(x) - A] \pm [g(x) - B]| \leq |f(x) - A| + |g(x) - B|. \tag{13}$$

By hypothesis, ϵ being given, there exist positive numbers δ_1 and δ_2 such that

$$|f(x) - A| < \frac{\epsilon}{2} \quad \text{when} \quad 0 < |x - a| < \delta_1 \quad \text{and}$$

$$|g(x) - B| < \frac{\epsilon}{2} \quad \text{when} \quad 0 < |x - a| < \delta_2. \tag{14}$$

Let δ denote the smaller of δ_1 and δ_2. Then (12) follows from (13) and (14).

To prove part (b), we must show that, if ϵ is any positive number, there exists a positive number δ such that

$$|f(x) \cdot g(x) - AB| < \epsilon \qquad \text{when} \qquad 0 < |x - a| < \delta. \qquad (15)$$

By (10) and (11)

$$|f(x) \cdot g(x) - AB| = |f(x)[g(x) - B] + B[f(x) - A]|$$
$$\leq |f(x)| \cdot |g(x) - B| + |B| \cdot |f(x) - A|. \qquad (16)$$

Suppose $B \neq 0$. By hypothesis, ϵ being given, there exists a number $\delta_1 > 0$ such that

$$|f(x) - A| < \frac{\epsilon}{2|B|} \qquad \text{when} \qquad 0 < |x - a| < \delta_1. \qquad (17)$$

Hence, if $M = |A| + \frac{\epsilon}{2|B|}$, it follows that

$$|f(x)| < M \qquad \text{when} \qquad 0 < |x - a| < \delta_1. \qquad (18)$$

By hypothesis, there exists a number $\delta_2 > 0$ such that

$$|g(x) - B| < \frac{\epsilon}{2M} \qquad \text{when} \qquad 0 < |x - a| < \delta_2. \qquad (19)$$

Let δ denote the smaller of δ_1 and δ_2. Then (15) follows from (16), (17), (18), and (19) since

$$|f(x)| \cdot |g(x) - B| + |B| \cdot |f(x) - A| < M\frac{\epsilon}{2M} + |B|\frac{\epsilon}{2|B|} = \epsilon$$
$$\text{when} \qquad 0 < |x - a| < \delta.$$

We leave it to the student to consider the case $B = 0$ (see Exs. III, 12 and 13).

By part (b),

$$\lim_{x \to a} [f(x)/g(x)] = \lim_{x \to a} [f(x) \cdot 1/g(x)] = \lim_{x \to a} f(x) \cdot \lim_{x \to a} 1/g(x).$$

Thus, to prove part (c) we need only to show that

$$\lim_{x \to a} 1/g(x) = 1/\lim_{x \to a} g(x),$$

provided that $\lim_{x \to a} g(x) \neq 0$; that is, we must show that, if ϵ is any positive number, there exists a positive number δ such that

$$\left|\frac{1}{g(x)} - \frac{1}{B}\right| < \epsilon \quad \text{when} \quad 0 < |x - a| < \delta, \quad \text{where} \quad B \neq 0. \qquad (20)$$

By (11),

$$\left|\frac{1}{g(x)} - \frac{1}{B}\right| = \left|\frac{B - g(x)}{B \cdot g(x)}\right| = \frac{|g(x) - B|}{|B| \cdot |g(x)|}. \tag{21}$$

Since $B \neq 0$, $|B| > 0$. By hypothesis, there exists a number $\delta_2 > 0$ such that $|g(x) - B| < |B|/2$ when $0 < |x - a| < \delta_2$. Hence

$$|g(x)| > \frac{|B|}{2} \qquad \text{when} \qquad 0 < |x - a| < \delta_2. \tag{22}$$

By hypothesis, ϵ being given, there exists a number $\delta_2' > 0$ such that

$$|g(x) - B| < \frac{B^2\epsilon}{2} \qquad \text{when} \qquad 0 < |x - a| < \delta_2'. \tag{23}$$

Let δ denote the smaller of δ_2 and δ_2'. Then (20) follows from (21), (22), and (23), since

$$\frac{|g(x) - B|}{|B| \cdot |g(x)|} < \frac{|g(x) - B|}{|B| \cdot |B|/2} < \frac{B^2\epsilon/2}{|B| \cdot |B|/2} = \epsilon \qquad \text{when}$$
$$0 < |x - a| < \delta.$$

Parts (a) and (b) of this theorem may evidently be extended to any finite number of terms or factors. For example,

$$\lim_{x \to a} [f(x) \cdot g(x) \cdot h(x)]$$

may be dealt with by letting $F(x) = f(x) \cdot g(x)$ and quoting part (b) twice.

In all of these proofs we have assumed that f and g are defined over some interval I about $x = a$ (except perhaps at $x = a$ itself) and that all of the δ's are taken small enough to remain within I. (See Ex. IV, 27.)

4. Continuous Functions. As mentioned above, a function f may have neither a value nor a limit at a point $x = a$. A particularly important situation arises when f has both a value and a limit at $x = a$ and these two numbers are the same.

DEFINITION 4.1. *If f denotes a real, single-valued function of x, and if at $x = a$; (1) $f(a)$ exists; (2) $\lim_{x \to a} f(x)$ exists; and (3) $\lim_{x \to a} f(x) = f(a)$, then f is said to be continuous at $x = a$. If f is*

continuous at each point* $x = a$ of some set D of real numbers, then
f is said to be continuous over D.   If f is not continuous at $x = a$,
then f is said to be discontinuous at $x = a$, and a is called a point
of discontinuity of f.

The outstanding property of a continuous function is given by
THEOREM 4.1.   *If a function f is continuous at $x = a$, then*
$\lim\limits_{x \to a} f(x)$ *exists and may be evaluated directly as $f(a)$; or in brief,*
$\lim\limits_{\Delta x \to 0} f(a + \Delta x) = f(a)$, *where $a + \Delta x = x$.*

It is this property that the student is prone to assume unjusti-
fiably when he first studies the concept of a limit.

THEOREM 4.2.   *A function f is continuous at $x = a$ when, and
only when* (1) $f(a)$ *exists, and* (2) *for each positive number ϵ there
exists a positive number δ such that*

$$|f(x) - f(a)| < \epsilon \qquad \text{when} \qquad |x - a| < \delta.$$

The proof of this theorem is left to the student in Ex. IV, 1.
It should be observed that in this theorem x is no longer restricted
to be unequal to a.   In simple language, this theorem means
that if f is continuous at $x = a$, then the value of f differs from
$f(a)$ by an arbitrarily small amount so long as x does not get too
far from a.

THEOREM 4.3.   *If f and g are functions of x continuous at
$x = a$, then $f \pm g$ and $f \cdot g$ are continuous at $x = a$, and f/g is
continuous at $x = a$ provided that $g(a) \neq 0$.*

By hypothesis, $\lim\limits_{x \to a} f(x) = f(a)$ and $\lim\limits_{x \to a} g(x) = g(a)$.   By
Theorem 3.2a, $\lim\limits_{x \to a} [f(x) \pm g(x)]$ exists and equals $f(a) \pm g(a)$.
Hence $f \pm g$ is continuous at $x = a$.   The other parts of this
theorem are proved in a similar manner.

THEOREM 4.4.   *Let g be a function of x continuous at $x = a$ and
let f be a function of u continuous at $u = A$, where $A = g(a)$.
If $u = g(x)$, then $f[g(x)]$ is continuous at $x = a$.*

Since $f(A)$ exists and since $g(a) = A$, $f[g(a)]$ exists.   We must
show that, if ϵ is any positive number, there exists a positive

---

* We use the word *point* because of its suggestiveness in connection with
the graph of f.   Strictly speaking, *point* should be regarded as synonymous
with *real number*.   But it is often helpful to think of a number as represented by a "point" on the x-axis.

number δ such that

$$|f[g(x)] - f[g(a)]| < \epsilon \qquad \text{when} \qquad |x - a| < \delta. \qquad (1)$$

By hypothesis, ϵ being given, there exists a positive number η such that

$$|f(u) - f(A)| < \epsilon \qquad \text{when} \qquad |u - A| < \eta. \qquad (2)$$

Likewise, corresponding to this number η there exists a positive number δ such that

$$|g(x) - g(a)| < \eta \qquad \text{when} \qquad |x - a| < \delta. \qquad (3)$$

If we now think of u as determined by the relation $u = g(x)$, then (2) becomes

$$|f[g(x)] - f[g(a)]| < \epsilon \qquad \text{when} \qquad |g(x) - g(a)| < \eta. \qquad (4)$$

But by (3), $|g(x) - g(a)| < \eta$ when $|x - a| < \delta$. Hence (1) obtains.

We now give a number of examples to illustrate the concept of continuity.

Example 1. If m is a positive integer, and if $f(x) = x^m$, then f is continuous at every value of x.

Let a be an arbitrary value of x. Then $f(a) = a^m$, so that $f(a)$ exists. By Theorem 3.2b,

$$\lim_{x \to a} f(x) = \lim_{x \to a} x^m = \lim_{x \to a} x \cdot \lim_{x \to a} x \cdot \dots \cdot \lim_{x \to a} x = a \cdot a \cdots a = a^m = f(a).$$

Hence f is continuous at $x = a$. Since a is arbitrary, f is everywhere continuous.

Example 2. If n is a positive integer, and if $f(x) = x^{1/n}$, where $x \geq 0$, then f is continuous at all values of $x \geq 0$. (In order that f may be single-valued, we regard $x^{1/n}$ as denoting the positive real nth root of x.)

Let a be an arbitrary non-negative value of x. Then $f(a) = a^{1/n}$, so that $f(a)$ exists. By the identity

$$\alpha^{\frac{1}{n}} - \beta^{\frac{1}{n}} = \frac{\left(\alpha^{\frac{1}{n}} - \beta^{\frac{1}{n}}\right)\left(\alpha^{\frac{n-1}{n}} + \alpha^{\frac{n-2}{n}}\beta^{\frac{1}{n}} + \cdots + \alpha^{\frac{1}{n}}\beta^{\frac{n-2}{n}} + \beta^{\frac{n-1}{n}}\right)}{\left(\alpha^{\frac{n-1}{n}} + \alpha^{\frac{n-2}{n}}\beta^{\frac{1}{n}} + \cdots + \alpha^{\frac{1}{n}}\beta^{\frac{n-2}{n}} + \beta^{\frac{n-1}{n}}\right)}$$

$$= \frac{\alpha - \beta}{\alpha^{\frac{n-1}{n}} + \cdots + \beta^{\frac{n-1}{n}}}, \qquad (5)$$

where $\alpha \geq 0$, $\beta \geq 0$, and α and β are not both zero, it follows that, if ϵ is any positive number, if $x \geq 0$, and if $a > 0$, then

$$\left| x^{\frac{1}{n}} - a^{\frac{1}{n}} \right| = \left| \frac{x - a}{x^{\frac{n-1}{n}} + \cdots + a^{\frac{n-1}{n}}} \right|$$

$$\leqq \left| \frac{x - a}{a^{\frac{n-1}{n}}} \right| < \epsilon \qquad \text{when} \qquad |x - a| < \epsilon \cdot a^{\frac{n-1}{n}}.$$

Thus f is continuous at $x = a$. In the case where $a = 0$,

$$|x^{1/n} - 0| = |x^{1/n}| < \epsilon \qquad \text{when} \qquad |x - 0| = |x| < \epsilon^n.$$

Hence f is continuous at $x = 0$.

It is evident that if n is an odd positive integer, then $x^{1/n}$ is defined and continuous for all values of x.

Example 3. If N is a positive rational number m/n (in lowest terms), and if $f(x) = x^N$, where $x \geqq 0$, then f is continuous at all values of $x \geqq 0$.

Since $f(x) = (x^{1/n})^m$, it follows by Examples 1 and 2 and Theorem 4.4 that f is continuous at all non-negative values of x.

It is evident that if n is odd, then f is everywhere continuous.

Example 4. If N is a rational number, and if $f(x) = x^N$, where $x > 0$, then f is continuous at all positive values of x.

The case where N is positive has already been considered in Example 3. If N is negative, let $N = -M$. Then $f(x) = 1/x^M$. The continuity of f follows from Theorem 4.3 and Example 3. If $N = 0$, then f has the constant value 1 and hence is continuous.

This result may be extended for special values of N as indicated in Examples 1, 2, 3.

Example 5. If $p(x) = a_0 + a_1x + a_2x^2 + \cdots + a_nx^n$, where n is a nonnegative integer, where $a_0, a_1, \ldots, a_n$ are real constants and where $a_n \neq 0$, then p is called a polynomial of degree n. If $f(x) = p(x)/q(x)$, where p and q are polynomials, then f is continuous at all values of x except those at which q has the value 0.

This follows immediately from Example 1 and Theorem 4.3.

Example 6. If $f(x) = \cos x$ and $g(x) = \sin x$, then f and g are continuous at all values of x.

This result follows immediately from Exs. III, 10 and 11.

Example 7. If $f(x) = \log_b x$, where $x > 0$, $b > 0$, and $b \neq 1$, then f is continuous at every positive value of x.

We here consider the case $b > 1$, leaving the case $b < 1$ to Ex. 12 below. We first show that $\lim\limits_{u \to 1} \log_b u = \log_b 1 = 0$, using the fact that

$$\log_b \alpha < \log_b \beta \qquad \text{when} \qquad \alpha < \beta \qquad \text{and} \qquad b > 1. \qquad (6)$$

If ϵ is any positive number, then

$$|\log_b u - \log_b 1| = |\log_b u| < \epsilon \qquad \text{when} \qquad -\epsilon < \log_b u < \epsilon,$$

i.e.,

$$\text{when } \log_b \frac{1}{b^\epsilon} < \log_b u < \log_b b^\epsilon \quad \left(\text{since } \log_b \frac{1}{b^\epsilon} = -\epsilon \text{ and } \log_b b^\epsilon = \epsilon \right),$$

i.e.,

$$\text{when } \frac{1}{b^\epsilon} < u < b^\epsilon \qquad \text{[by (6)].}$$

But $1/b^\epsilon < 1 < b^\epsilon$ since $b > 1$. Hence $1 - (1/b^\epsilon) > 0$ and $b^\epsilon - 1 > 0$. If we take δ as the smaller of $1 - (1/b^\epsilon)$ and $b^\epsilon - 1$, then u meets the condition $1/b^\epsilon < u < b^\epsilon$ when $|u - 1| < \delta$. Hence

$$|\log_b u - \log_b 1| < \epsilon \qquad \text{when} \qquad |u - 1| < \delta.$$

It follows that $\log_b u$ is continuous at $u = 1$.

Since $u = x/a$ is continuous at $x = a$, it follows by Theorems 3.2 and 4.4 and Ex. III, 3, that

$$\lim_{x \to a} \log_b x = \lim_{x \to a} \log_b \left(a \cdot \frac{x}{a} \right) = \lim_{x \to a} \log_b a + \lim_{x \to a} \log_b \frac{x}{a} = \log_b a,$$

where $a > 0$ but otherwise arbitrary. This proves the continuity of $\log_b x$ when $b > 1$.

Example 8. A function is discontinuous at $x = a$ when it fails to meet any one of the three conditions in Definition 4.1. Thus, the functions $(x^3 - 5)/2x$, $(\sin x)/x$, ctn x, and $(1 + x)^{1/x}$ are discontinuous at $x = 0$ because they are not defined at $x = 0$. The function $[x]$ is discontinuous at every integer value of x because this function has no limit at these values of x. The function $|\sin x + \frac{1}{2} \sin 2x + \frac{1}{3} \sin 3x + \cdots|$ is discontinuous at $x = 0$ because its value there is not the same as its limit there.

We conclude this section with an extension of the concept of a limit.

Definition 4.2a. *If, as $x \to a$ (but remaining $\neq a$), the value of a function f becomes and remains greater than any assignable number N, however large, then f is said to increase without bound. This behavior of f is indicated by the notation $\lim\limits_{x \to a} f(x) \to +\infty$, which is read "the value of f increases without bound as $x \to a$."*

This definition may evidently be put in the alternative form of

Definition 4.2b. *If, for each positive number N, however large, there exists a positive number δ such that*

$$f(x) > N \qquad \text{when} \qquad 0 < |x - a| < \delta,$$

then this situation is indicated by the notation $\lim\limits_{x \to a} f(x) \to +\infty$.

Example 9. It is evident that $\lim\limits_{x \to 4} 1/(x - 4)^2 \to +\infty$. But it is *not* the case that $\lim\limits_{x \to 2} 1/(x - 2) \to +\infty$ nor is it the case that $\lim\limits_{x \to \pi/2} \tan x \to +\infty$.

EXERCISES IV

1. Prove Theorem 4.2. (First show that if a function f meets the conditions in Definition 4.1, it also meets those in Theorem 4.2. Then show that if f meets the conditions in Theorem 4.2, it also meets those in Definition 4.1.) Illustrate the meaning of Theorem 4.2 by a graph.

2. Show directly by Theorem 4.2, and without quoting any other theorem or example, that the following functions are continuous at $x = a$, where a is any value of x at which the respective functions are defined. State explicitly the values of x at which these functions are continuous.

(a) $5x + 4$.   (b) $6x^2$.   (c) $x^2 - 5x + 7$.   (d) $\sqrt{2x}$.

(e) $\sqrt[3]{1 - 2x}$.   (f) $\dfrac{1}{x + 4}$.   (g) $\dfrac{x - 1}{x^2}$.   (h) $|x|$.

3. (a) For each of the functions in Ex. II, 1, state whether or not the function is continuous at $x = 0$.

(b) For each of the functions in Ex. II, 2, state whether or not the function is continuous at $x = a$.

(c) State whether or not the following functions are continuous at $x = 0$:

(1) $f(x) = \begin{cases} x \cos(1/x) & \text{when } x \neq 0, \\ 1 & \text{when } x = 0. \end{cases}$

(2) $f(x) = \begin{cases} x \cos(1/x) & \text{when } x \neq 0, \\ 0 & \text{when } x = 0. \end{cases}$
   (3) $f(x) = \begin{cases} 2^{-1/x^2} & \text{when } x \neq 0, \\ 1 & \text{when } x = 0. \end{cases}$

(4) $f(x) = \begin{cases} (\sin x)/x & \text{when } x \neq 0, \\ 1 & \text{when } x = 0. \end{cases}$
   (5) $f(x) = (1 + x)^{1/x}$.

(6) $f(x) = \begin{cases} (1 + x)^{1/x} & \text{when } x \neq 0, \\ 1 & \text{when } x = 0. \end{cases}$

(7) $f(x) = \begin{cases} \frac{1}{2}(\pi + x) & \text{when } -\pi \leq x \leq 0, \\ \frac{1}{2}(\pi - x) & \text{when } \quad 0 \leq x \leq \pi. \end{cases}$ (See Ex. I, 17.)

(8) $f(x) = \begin{cases} x + 3 & \text{when } x \geq 2, \\ x - 1 & \text{when } x < 2. \end{cases}$
   (9) $f(x) = \dfrac{1}{1 - 2^x} + \dfrac{1}{1 - 2^{-x}}$.

(10) $f(x) = |x|/x$.
   (11) $f(x) = \begin{cases} |x|/x & \text{when } x \neq 0, \\ 0 & \text{when } x = 0. \end{cases}$

(12) $f(x) = \dfrac{1}{2 - |x|}$.
   (13) $f(x) = \begin{cases} x^2 & \text{when } x > 0, \\ -2x & \text{when } x < 0. \end{cases}$

4. Do the following limits exist? If so, prove and evaluate.

$$\text{(a)} \quad \lim_{x \to 1} \frac{5x}{\sqrt[3]{1 - 2x}}.$$

Solution. The functions $5x$ and $1 - 2x$ are continuous at all values of x and the function $u^{1/3}$ is continuous at all values of u. By Theorem 4.4, $\sqrt[3]{1 - 2x}$ is continuous at $x = 1$. By Theorem 4.3, $\dfrac{5x}{\sqrt[3]{1 - 2x}}$ is continuous at $x = 1$ since the value of $\sqrt[3]{1 - 2x}$ at $x = 1$ is not 0.   Hence, by

Theorem 4.1, $\lim\limits_{x \to 1} \dfrac{5x}{\sqrt[3]{1 - 2x}} = \dfrac{5(1)}{\sqrt[3]{1 - 2(1)}} = -5.$

(b) $\lim\limits_{x \to 1} \dfrac{x - 1}{x^2 + 4}.$ (c) $\lim\limits_{x \to 3} (\cos x)\sqrt{1 - x^2}.$ (d) $\lim\limits_{x \to 3} (\cos x)\sqrt{x^2 - 1}.$

(e) $\lim\limits_{x \to 0} \log_{10} \cos x.$ (f) $\lim\limits_{x \to 2} \dfrac{x + 1}{x^2 - 4}.$ (g) $\lim\limits_{x \to 0} \sin^2 |x|.$

5. With the aid of the theorems and examples in Sec. 4, show that if $f(x)$ is continuous at $x = a$, then

(a) $[f(x)]^n$ is continuous at $x = a$.   State the conditions on n and a.

(b) $\cos f(x)$ is continuous at $x = a$, i.e.,

$$\lim_{x \to a} \cos f(x) = \cos\left[\lim_{x \to a} f(x)\right] = \cos f(a).$$

(c) $\sec f(x)$ is continuous at $x = a$.   State the conditions on a.

(d) $\log_b f(x)$ is continuous at $x = a$, i.e.,

$$\lim_{x \to a} \log_b f(x) = \log_b\left[\lim_{x \to a} f(x)\right] = \log_b f(a).$$

State the conditions on x, a, and b.

6. If a function f is defined only for values of $x > a$ then, as remarked after Definition 3.1b, $\lim\limits_{x \to a} f(x)$ does not exist because f is not defined on both sides of $x = a$.   Yet in some cases it would seem natural to ascribe a limit to f at $x = a$.   To meet this situation we introduce *one-sided limits* and *one-sided continuity*.

Definition 4.3.   *If, for each positive number ϵ, however small, there exists a positive number δ such that*

$$|f(x) - A| < \epsilon \quad \text{when} \quad 0 < x - a < \delta,$$

then A is denoted by $\lim\limits_{x \to a+} f(x)$ and is referred to as the right-hand limit of f at $x = a$.

This definition is applicable even when f is defined for values of $x < a$.

Define the left-hand limit of f at $x = a$.   Define the right and left continuity of f at $x = a$.   Discuss the functions of Exs. II, 1 and 2, as to one-sided limits and one-sided continuity.

Show that if $\lim\limits_{x \to a+} f(x)$ and $\lim\limits_{x \to a-} f(x)$ exist and are equal, then $\lim\limits_{x \to a} f(x)$ exists and has the common value of the one-sided limits.

The concept of one-sided continuity allows us to introduce the following definition:

If a function f is defined only over the interval $a \leqq x \leqq b$, we say that f is continuous over this interval if f is continuous at each interior point of the interval and if f is right continuous at a and left continuous at b.

7. Show that Definitions 4.2a and 4.2b are equivalent.

8. Define the notation $\lim_{x \to a} f(x) \to -\infty$.

9. Evaluate:

(a) $\lim_{x \to 0} 1/x^2$.

(b) $\lim_{x \to -\frac{1}{2}} \dfrac{1}{2x + 1}$.

(c) $\lim_{x \to -3} \dfrac{2x}{(x + 3)^4}$.

(d) $\lim_{x \to 0} \left[\left(\dfrac{1}{x^2} \right) + \cos \left(\dfrac{1}{x} \right) \right]$.

(e) $\lim_{x \to 1} \dfrac{\cos x}{\sqrt{1 - x^2}}$.

(f) $\lim_{x \to 2} \dfrac{x}{(x - 2)^3(x + 1)}$.

(g) $\lim_{x \to -2} \log_{10} (x^2 - 4)$.

(h) $\lim_{x \to 0} (1/x^2) \cos (1/x)$.

(i) $\lim_{x \to 0} (1/x^2) \cos^2 (1/x)$.

(j) $\lim_{x \to 0} \csc x$.

(k) $\lim_{x \to 0} \tan (1/x)$.

(l) $\lim_{x \to -1} (1 + x)^{1/x}$.

10. The following definition is frequently useful:

Definition 4.4. *If, for each positive number ϵ, however small, there exists a sufficiently large positive number N such that*

$$|f(x) - A| < \epsilon \qquad when \qquad x > N,$$

then A is denoted by $\lim_{x \to +\infty} f(x)$ and is referred to as the limit of f as x increases without bound.

Define the symbol $\lim_{x \to -\infty} f(x)$. Define the symbol $\lim_{x \to +\infty} f(x) \to +\infty$. Give examples to illustrate these definitions fully. Show that $\lim_{x \to 0+} f(x)$ exists when and only when $\lim_{y \to +\infty} \varphi(y)$ exists and that these limits are equal, where $y = 1/x$ and $\varphi(y) = f(1/y)$. State and prove the análogue of Theorem 3.2 for the case where $x \to +\infty$. Evaluate:

$$\lim_{x \to +\infty} 2^{-x}; \qquad \lim_{x \to +\infty} x \sin x; \qquad \lim_{x \to +\infty} x \csc x; \qquad \lim_{x \to +\infty} x(1 + \cos^2 x).$$

11. Prove relations (10) and (11) following Theorem 3.2.

12. Complete the proof of Example 7 by discussing the case $0 < b < 1$.

13. Extend Theorem 4.4 to the case where g merely has a limit A at $x = a$. Extend the results of Ex. 5 by means of this result.

14. If k is a constant, show directly that $\lim_{x \to a} k \cdot f(x) = k \lim_{x \to a} f(x)$ without quoting Theorem 3.2.

15. If $\lim\limits_{x \to a} f(x) = 0$ and if there exist numbers M and η such that $M > |g(x)|$ when $0 < |x - a| < \eta$, show that $\lim\limits_{x \to a} [f(x) \cdot g(x)] = 0$.

Give an example to show that this theorem need not hold when there exist no such numbers M and η.

16. (a) Show that $\lim\limits_{x \to a} \dfrac{1}{f(x)} = 0$ when and only when $\lim\limits_{x \to a} |f(x)| \to +\infty$.

(b) Show that $\lim\limits_{x \to 0} \dfrac{f(x)}{x}$ can exist only when $\lim\limits_{x \to 0} f(x) = 0$. Give an example to show that $\lim\limits_{x \to 0} \dfrac{f(x)}{x}$ may fail to exist even when $\lim\limits_{x \to 0} f(x) = 0$.

17. If $\lim\limits_{x \to a} f(x)$ and $\lim\limits_{x \to a} [f(x) + g(x)]$ exist, show that $\lim\limits_{x \to a} g(x)$ exists and evaluate it. If $\lim\limits_{x \to a} f(x)$ and $\lim\limits_{x \to a} [f(x) \cdot g(x)]$ exist, under what condition does $\lim\limits_{x \to a} g(x)$ exist?

18. If $f(x) \leq g(x) \leq h(x)$ over some interval about $x = a$ (except perhaps at $x = a$), and if $\lim\limits_{x \to a} f(x) = \lim\limits_{x \to a} h(x)$, then $\lim\limits_{x \to a} g(x)$ exists and equals $\lim\limits_{x \to a} f(x)$. State and prove an analogous result for the case $x \to +\infty$.

19. Show that if F and G are functions of x which may be represented in the form $F(x) = \varphi(x) \cdot f(x)$, $G(x) = \varphi(x) \cdot g(x)$, where $\varphi(x) \neq 0$ in some interval about $x = a$ except perhaps at $x = a$, and if $\lim\limits_{x \to a} \dfrac{f(x)}{g(x)}$ exists, then $\lim\limits_{x \to a} \dfrac{F(x)}{G(x)}$ exists and equals $\lim\limits_{x \to a} \dfrac{f(x)}{g(x)}$. [It must be remembered that $\dfrac{F(x)}{G(x)}$ and $f(x)/g(x)$ are *not* always equal if $\varphi(a) = 0$.]

For example, the fraction $\dfrac{x^2 - 4x + 3}{x^2 - 7x + 12}$ may be written as $\dfrac{(x - 3)(x - 1)}{(x - 3)(x - 4)}$, and by the preceding result, $\lim\limits_{x \to 3} \dfrac{x^2 - 4x + 3}{x^2 - 7x + 12} = \lim\limits_{x \to 3} \dfrac{x - 1}{x - 4} = -2$.

20. Show that if f is a function of x and if $\lim\limits_{x \to a} f(x)$ exists and is > 0, then there exists an interval I about $x = a$ over which the value of f remains > 0 except perhaps at $x = a$ itself. A similar situation exists when $\lim\limits_{x \to a} f(x) < 0$.

21. Show that $\lim\limits_{\theta \to 0} \dfrac{\sin \theta}{\theta} = 1$ when θ is measured in radians.

Solution. In Fig. 11 let AB be an arc of a circle with center O and radius r, and let BC and AD be perpendicular to OA. Suppose $\theta = \angle AOB$ is such that $0 < \theta < \pi/2$. Since area $\triangle OCB <$ area sector $OAB <$ area $\triangle OAD$, it follows that

$$\frac{r^2}{2} \sin \theta \cos \theta < \frac{r^2}{2}\theta < \frac{r^2}{2} \tan \theta.$$

If we divide this inequality by the positive number $(r^2/2) \sin \theta$ we see that

$$\cos\theta < \frac{\theta}{\sin\theta} < \sec\theta. \tag{7}$$

It is readily shown that (7) also holds when $-\pi/2 < \theta < 0$. If we take reciprocals of the quantities in (7) we find that

$$\sec\theta > \frac{\sin\theta}{\theta} > \cos\theta. \tag{8}$$

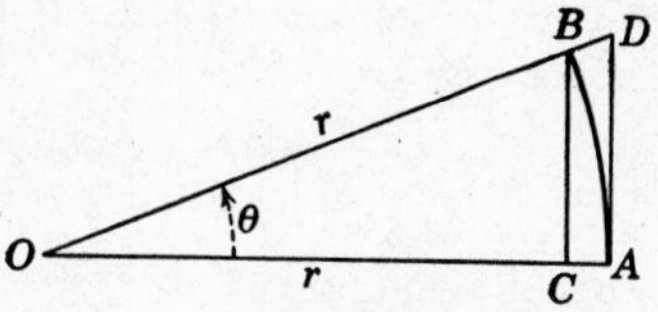

FIG. 11.

By Example 6 and Ex. 5c, $\cos\theta$ and $\sec\theta$ are continuous at $\theta = 0$. Hence, if ϵ is any positive number, there exist positive numbers δ_1 and δ_2 such that

$$\sec\theta - 1 < \epsilon \text{ when } |\theta - 0| < \delta_1, \text{ and } 1 - \cos\theta < \epsilon \text{ when } |\theta - 0| < \delta_2. \tag{9}$$

By (8) and (9),

$$\left|\frac{\sin\theta}{\theta} - 1\right| < \epsilon \qquad \text{when} \qquad 0 < |\theta - 0| < \delta,$$

where δ is the smallest of δ_1, δ_2, and $\pi/2$.

22. Evaluate $\lim\limits_{\theta\to 0} (\sin\theta)/\theta$ when θ is measured in degrees.

23. Show that $\lim\limits_{x\to 0} (1 + x)^{1/x} = e$, where $e = 2.718 \cdots$.

Solution. Let us first consider the case where $x = 1/n$, n being a positive integer. By the binomial theorem,

$$\begin{aligned}(1+x)^{1/x} &= \left(1 + \frac{1}{n}\right)^n = 1 + n\frac{1}{n} + \frac{n(n-1)}{2!}\left(\frac{1}{n}\right)^2 \\ &\quad + \frac{n(n-1)(n-2)}{3!}\left(\frac{1}{n}\right)^3 + \cdots + \frac{n(n-1)\cdots(1)}{n!}\left(\frac{1}{n}\right)^n \\ &= 1 + 1 + \frac{1 - \frac{1}{n}}{2!} + \frac{\left(1 - \frac{1}{n}\right)\left(1 - \frac{2}{n}\right)}{3!} + \cdots \\ &\quad + \frac{\left(1 - \frac{1}{n}\right)\left(1 - \frac{2}{n}\right)\cdots\left(1 - \frac{n-1}{n}\right)}{n!},\end{aligned} \tag{10}$$

and

$$\begin{aligned}\left(1 + \frac{1}{n+1}\right)^{n+1} &= 1 + 1 + \frac{1 - \frac{1}{n+1}}{2!} + \frac{\left(1 - \frac{1}{n+1}\right)\left(1 - \frac{2}{n+1}\right)}{3!} + \cdots \\ &\quad + \frac{\left(1 - \frac{1}{n+1}\right)\left(1 - \frac{2}{n+1}\right)\cdots\left(1 - \frac{n-1}{n+1}\right)}{n!} \\ &\quad + \frac{\left(1 - \frac{1}{n+1}\right)\left(1 - \frac{2}{n+1}\right)\cdots\left(1 - \frac{n-1}{n+1}\right)\left(1 - \frac{n}{n+1}\right)}{(n+1)!}.\end{aligned} \tag{11}$$

Since each term of (10) is less than or equal to the corresponding term in (11) and since (11) has one more (positive) term than (10),

$$\left(1 + \frac{1}{n}\right)^n < \left(1 + \frac{1}{n+1}\right)^{n+1}.$$

Thus *the value of* $\left(1 + \dfrac{1}{n}\right)^n$ *increases with* n. Let e be the sum of the convergent infinite series

$$e = 1 + 1 + \frac{1}{2!} + \frac{1}{3!} + \frac{1}{4!} + \frac{1}{5!} + \cdots = 2.71828\ 18284\ 59045 \cdots. \qquad (12)$$

Since each term of (10) is less than or equal to the corresponding term in (12),

$$\left(1 + \frac{1}{n}\right)^n < e \qquad (13)$$

for every positive integer n. We shall now show that

$$\lim_{n \to +\infty} \left(1 + \frac{1}{n}\right)^n = e$$

even though, for all large integer values of n, the latter terms of (10) are very small compared with the corresponding terms of (12). Let

$$S_m = 1 + 1 + \frac{1}{2!} + \frac{1}{3!} + \frac{1}{4!} + \cdots + \frac{1}{m!},$$

and let

$$s_{n,m} = 1 + 1 + \frac{1 - \dfrac{1}{n}}{2!} + \frac{\left(1 - \dfrac{1}{n}\right)\left(1 - \dfrac{2}{n}\right)}{3!} + \cdots$$
$$+ \frac{\left(1 - \dfrac{1}{n}\right)\left(1 - \dfrac{2}{n}\right) \cdots \left(1 - \dfrac{m-1}{n}\right)}{m!}, \quad (m \leqq n)$$

i.e., $s_{n,m}$ is the sum of the first $(m + 1)$ terms of (10). For any positive number ϵ, however small, there exists an integer m_0 such that

$$e - S_{m_0} < \frac{\epsilon}{2}. \qquad (14)$$

For this number m_0 there exists a value n_0 of n so large that

$$S_{m_0} - s_{n_0, m_0} < \frac{\epsilon}{2}. \qquad (15)$$

By (14) and (15), $e - s_{n_0, m_0} < \epsilon$, and as $s_{n_0, m_0} \leqq \left(1 + \dfrac{1}{n_0}\right)^{n_0}$, it follows that

$$e - \left(1 + \frac{1}{n_0}\right)^{n_0} < \epsilon.$$

By (13) and the fact that $\left(1 + \dfrac{1}{n}\right)^n$ increases with n,

$$\left| e - \left(1 + \frac{1}{n}\right)^n \right| < \epsilon \qquad \text{when} \qquad n > n_0,$$

that is, $\lim\limits_{n \to +\infty} \left(1 + \dfrac{1}{n}\right)^n = e.$

Now let y be any real number > 1 and let n be the greatest integer contained in y, i.e., $n = [y]$. Then

$$n \leqq y < n + 1,$$

$$1 + \frac{1}{n} \geqq 1 + \frac{1}{y} > 1 + \frac{1}{n+1},$$

$$\left(1 + \frac{1}{n}\right)^y \geqq \left(1 + \frac{1}{y}\right)^y > \left(1 + \frac{1}{n+1}\right)^y,$$

and therefore

$$\left(1 + \frac{1}{n}\right)^{n+1} > \left(1 + \frac{1}{y}\right)^y > \left(1 + \frac{1}{n+1}\right)^n.$$

But

$$\lim_{n \to +\infty} \left(1 + \frac{1}{n}\right)^{n+1} = \lim_{n \to +\infty} \left[\left(1 + \frac{1}{n}\right)^n \left(1 + \frac{1}{n}\right) \right]$$

$$= \lim_{n \to +\infty} \left(1 + \frac{1}{n}\right)^n \lim_{n \to +\infty} \left(1 + \frac{1}{n}\right) = e \cdot 1 = e;$$

likewise $\lim\limits_{n \to +\infty} \left(1 + \dfrac{1}{n+1}\right)^n = \lim\limits_{n \to +\infty} \dfrac{\left(1 + \dfrac{1}{n+1}\right)^{n+1}}{1 + \dfrac{1}{n+1}} = e.$ Hence it

may be shown by the method of Ex. 18 that $\lim\limits_{y \to +\infty} \left(1 + \dfrac{1}{y}\right)^y$ exists and equals e. By Ex. 10, $\lim\limits_{x \to 0+} (1 + x)^{1/x} = e$, where $x = 1/y$.

Finally, let y be any real number < -1 and write $y = -z$. Then

$$\lim_{y \to -\infty} \left(1 + \frac{1}{y}\right)^y = \lim_{z \to +\infty} \left(\frac{z}{z-1}\right)^z$$

$$= \lim_{z \to +\infty} \left[\left(1 + \frac{1}{z-1}\right)^{z-1}\left(1 + \frac{1}{z-1}\right)\right] = e.$$

Hence $\lim_{x \to 0-} (1 + x)^{1/x} = e$, and by Ex. 6 and the preceding paragraph, $\lim_{x \to 0} (1 + x)^{1/x}$ exists and is e.

24. The following definition has many important applications:

DEFINITION 4.5. *If f is a single-valued function of x, if R is the set of all values of f, and if, for each value of y in R, the equation $y = f(x)$ has exactly one solution in x, then this equation determines x as a single-valued function of y over R, say $x = \varphi(y)$, and φ is called the inverse of f.*

(a) Illustrate the meaning of this definition graphically. In how many points can a line $y = A$ meet the graph of f if φ is single-valued? Which functions of Exs. II, 1 and 2, have single-valued inverses?

(b) Show that if f is defined and continuous over the interval $a \leqq x \leqq b$ and has a single-valued inverse φ, then φ is also continuous.

Hint: Let M and m be the maximum and minimum values of f for values of x in the interval $c - \epsilon \leqq x \leqq c + \epsilon$. Because f is continuous, it takes on every value from m to M as x varies from $c - \epsilon$ to $c + \epsilon$ (see Theorem 8.5 of Chap. IX). Establish the continuity of φ at $y = C = f(c)$ by choosing δ with reference to m and M and using the fact that φ is single-valued.

25. For each of the following functions φ, state the domain of definition of φ, graph φ, and show by the preceding exercise that φ is continuous at each point of its domain of definition.

(a) $\text{Cos}^{-1} x$. (The capital letter C indicates that we are considering only principal values of this function.) What is the domain of definition of the inverse of this function?

(b) $\text{Sin}^{-1} x$. (c) $\text{Tan}^{-1} x$. (d) b^x, where $b > 0$ and $b \neq 1$.

(e) Extend the results of this exercise as indicated in Ex. 5.

26. Show that if $\lim_{x \to a} \log_b f(x)$ exists and is A, then $\lim_{x \to a} f(x)$ exists and is b^A.

HINT: Write $f(x) = b^{\log_b f(x)}$ and use Exs. 25d and 13.

27. Suppose we alter condition (1) in Definition 3.1b to read

$$|f(x) - A| < \epsilon \qquad \text{for all values of } x \text{ at which } f \text{ is defined}$$
$$\text{such that } 0 < |x - a| < \delta, \quad (1')$$

so that it is not implied, as with (1), that f is defined for all values of $x \neq a$ in some interval about $x = a$. Then Definition 3.1b has a much wider application. For example, $\lim_{x\to 0} \sqrt{x \sin (1/x)}$ exists and is 0. But Theorem 3.1 is false, for if f is defined at only the single point $x = a$, that is,

$$f(x) = \sqrt{-(x-a)^2},$$

then *every* number A meets condition (1′). Again, Theorem 3.2 fails when f and g are defined at no common point so that $f + g$ and $f \cdot g$ do not exist. To meet these difficulties we introduce

Definition 4.6. *Let D be a set of real numbers. If the number a is such that every interval about a, however small, contains at least one number in D other than a, then a is called an accumulation point of D.*

For example, 0 is an accumulation point of the set of numbers $1/n$, where n is a positive integer, and also of the set of numbers $0 \leq x \leq 1$. It is immaterial whether a belongs to D or not.

Give examples of sets having accumulation points. Show that a finite set can have no accumulation point. Restate and prove Theorems 3.1 and 3.2 using

Definition 4.7. *If f is a function of x, if a is an accumulation point of the domain of definition of f, and if for each $\epsilon > 0$ there exists a $\delta > 0$ such that (1′) holds, then A is denoted by $\lim_{x\to a} f(x)$.*

Generalize the concept of continuity, showing that it is unnecessary to use the idea of an accumulation point. Review Sec. 4 and the above exercises with these generalizations in mind. Note that we tacitly assumed a generalization of Definition 4.4 in Ex. 23. Discuss the function

$$f(x) = \begin{cases} x \text{ when } x \text{ is rational and } 0 \leq x \leq 1, \\ 2 - x \text{ when } x \text{ is irrational and } 1 < x < 2 \end{cases}$$

in connection with Ex. 24b, noting that f is continuous with a single-valued inverse.

5. The Derivative of a Function. Let f denote a function of x. As was pointed out in Sec. 2, the quantity $\dfrac{f(x_0 + \Delta x) - f(x_0)}{\Delta x}$ represents the mean rate of change of the value of f with respect to x when x varies from $x = x_0$ to $x = x_0 + \Delta x$. We now wish to study further the properties of this quantity.

Since x_0 is constant, $\dfrac{f(x_0 + \Delta x) - f(x_0)}{\Delta x}$ is a function of the one variable Δx, and as such is subject to the discussion of the preceding sections. In particular, $\dfrac{f(x_0 + \Delta x) - f(x_0)}{\Delta x}$ is discontinuous at $\Delta x = 0$ because its value is not defined at $\Delta x = 0$. Moreover, $\lim\limits_{\Delta x \to 0} \dfrac{f(x_0 + \Delta x) - f(x_0)}{\Delta x}$ may or may not exist. For a given function f, this limit may exist for some values of x_0, but not for others.* Suppose for the present that x_0 takes on only those values for which this limit exists. Let f' denote that function of x whose value, for each such number x_0, is the number $\lim\limits_{\Delta x \to 0} \dfrac{f(x_0 + \Delta x) - f(x_0)}{\Delta x}$. If we recall that the symbol $f'(x_0)$ denotes, and is read, the value of f' for the value x_0 of x, then, for each such number x_0, $f'(x_0) = \lim\limits_{\Delta x \to 0} \dfrac{f(x_0 + \Delta x) - f(x_0)}{\Delta x}$. With this discussion in mind, we may introduce

DEFINITION 5.1. *Let f denote a real, single-valued function of x. The derivative of f with respect to x is that function f' of x such that*

$$f'(x_0) = \lim\limits_{\Delta x \to 0} \frac{f(x_0 + \Delta x) - f(x_0)}{\Delta x} \tag{1}$$

at all points x_0 where the limit exists, and such that f' is defined for no other values of x.

According to the second remark after Definition 3.1b, $f'(x_0)$ cannot exist unless f is defined over some interval about $x = x_0$. Hence we shall regard the existence of $f'(x_0)$ as implying that f is defined over some interval about $x = x_0$. See Exs. IV, 27, and V, 5.

In this definition of f', we use x_0, rather than merely x, to emphasize the fact that *only* Δx is to vary in the limit (1); the limit (1) would be meaningless if both x and Δx varied simultaneously.

If there is no value x_0 for which the limit (1) exists, then the function f is said to have no derivative.

To *differentiate* a function f is to find its derivative f'. A function f is said to be *differentiable* if it has a derivative, and it is said to be *differentiable at $x = x_0$* if $f'(x_0)$ exists.

---

* In case the student has acquired the idea that this limit "almost always" exists, it should be mentioned that, for most functions f, this limit exists for *no* value of x_0; it is only when f is a very "simple" function, like a polynomial, that this limit exists for all values of x_0.

Various other symbols for f' are in common use; for example, $f' = f_x = D_x f = df/dx = \lim\limits_{\Delta x \to 0} \Delta f/\Delta x$, where Δf is defined by the relation

$$\Delta f = f(x_0 + \Delta x) - f(x_0).$$

The following example illustrates the way the derivative of a function may sometimes be determined:

Example 1.   Find $f' = D_x f$ when $f(x) = x^2/(3 - 2x)$, $x \neq \frac{3}{2}$.
Solution.   By Definition 5.1,

$$f'(x_0) = \lim_{\Delta x \to 0} \frac{f(x_0 + \Delta x) - f(x_0)}{\Delta x} \qquad \text{(provided this limit exists)}$$

$$= \lim_{\Delta x \to 0} \frac{\dfrac{(x_0 + \Delta x)^2}{3 - 2(x_0 + \Delta x)} - \dfrac{x_0^2}{3 - 2x_0}}{\Delta x}$$

(where x_0 and $x_0 + \Delta x$ are $\neq \frac{3}{2}$)

$$= \lim_{\Delta x \to 0} \frac{-2x_0^2 + 6x_0 - 2x_0\Delta x + 3\Delta x}{(3 - 2x_0)[3 - 2(x_0 + \Delta x)]} \qquad \text{(by Ex. IV, 19)}$$

$$= \frac{-2x_0^2 + 6x_0}{(3 - 2x_0)^2} \qquad \text{when} \qquad x_0 \neq \frac{3}{2}. \quad \text{(by Theorem 4.1)}$$

Hence

$$D_x \frac{x^2}{3 - 2x} = \frac{6x - 2x^2}{(3 - 2x)^2}, \qquad x \neq \frac{3}{2}.$$

The following formulas of differentiation may be derived by the method illustrated in Example 1. In these formulas g and h denote differentiable functions of x.

TABLE I

(1) $D_x c = 0$, where c is a constant.   (2) $D_x(g \pm h) = D_x g \pm D_x h$.

(3) $D_x(g \cdot h) = g \cdot D_x h + h \cdot D_x g$.   (4) $D_x \dfrac{g}{h} = \dfrac{h \cdot D_x g - g \cdot D_x h}{h^2}$.

(5) If g is a function of u, and if $u = h(x)$, then $D_x g = D_u g \cdot D_x u$.

(5a) $D_u v = 1/D_v u$.   (6) $D_x(h)^n = n(h)^{n-1} \cdot D_x h$.

(7) $D_x \cos h = -\sin h \cdot D_x h$.   (8) $D_x \sec h = \sec h \cdot \tan h \cdot D_x h$.

(9) $D_x \sin h = \cos h \cdot D_x h$.   (10) $D_x \csc h = -\csc h \cdot \operatorname{ctn} h \cdot D_x h$.

(11) $D_x \tan h = \sec^2 h \cdot D_x h$.   (12) $D_x \operatorname{ctn} h = -\csc^2 h \cdot D_x h$.

(13) $D_x \cos^{-1} h = -\dfrac{1}{\sqrt{1 - h^2}} D_x h$.   (14) $D_x \sec^{-1} h = \dfrac{1}{h\sqrt{h^2 - 1}} D_x h$.

(15) $D_x \sin^{-1} h = \dfrac{1}{\sqrt{1 - h^2}} D_x h$.   (16) $D_x \csc^{-1} h = -\dfrac{1}{h\sqrt{h^2 - 1}} D_x h$.

(17) $D_x \tan^{-1} h = \dfrac{1}{1 + h^2} D_x h$.   (18) $D_x \operatorname{ctn}^{-1} h = -\dfrac{1}{1 + h^2} D_x h$.

(19) $D_x \log_e h = \dfrac{1}{h} D_x h.$ (20) $D_x \log_a h = \dfrac{1}{h} \log_a e \cdot D_x h.$

(21) $D_x e^h = e^h \cdot D_x h.$ (22) $D_x a^h = a^h \log_e a \cdot D_x h.$

More complete lists are found in various mathematical tables.

By way of example, we shall derive a few of the above formulas. We first prove the following theorem which will be needed for these derivations:

Theorem 5.1. *If f is a function of x, and if f' is defined at $x = x_0$ [i.e., if $f'(x_0)$ exists], then f is continuous at $x = x_0$.*

If f were not continuous at $x = x_0$, then the quantity

$$f(x_0 + \Delta x) - f(x_0)$$

would not approach 0 as $\Delta x \to 0$ and $\lim\limits_{\Delta x \to 0} \dfrac{f(x_0 + \Delta x) - f(x_0)}{\Delta x}$ could not exist (see Ex. IV, 16b).

The converse of this theorem is false, for there exist functions f which are continuous at $x = x_0$, but such that $f'(x_0)$ does not exist. For example, if $f(x) = |x|$ (see Ex. II, 1g), then $f'(0)$ does not exist, for $\dfrac{f(0 + \Delta x) - f(0)}{\Delta x} = \dfrac{|0 + \Delta x| - |0|}{\Delta x} = \dfrac{|\Delta x|}{\Delta x}.$

But $\dfrac{|\Delta x|}{\Delta x} = 1$ when $\Delta x > 0$ and $\dfrac{|\Delta x|}{\Delta x} = -1$ when $\Delta x < 0.$

Hence $\lim\limits_{\Delta x \to 0} \dfrac{|\Delta x|}{\Delta x}$ does not exist. On the other hand, it follows directly from Theorem 4.2 that $|x|$ is continuous at $x = 0$. In fact, there are many functions known which are everywhere continuous and have a derivative nowhere.

Theorem 5.2. *If $f(x) = g(x) \cdot h(x)$, and if $g'(x_0)$ and $h'(x_0)$ exist, then $f'(x_0)$ exists and equals $g(x_0) \cdot h'(x_0) + h(x_0) \cdot g'(x_0)$.*

By Definition 5.1

$$
\begin{aligned}
f'(x_0) &= \lim_{\Delta x \to 0} \frac{f(x_0 + \Delta x) - f(x_0)}{\Delta x} \qquad \text{(provided this limit exists)}\\[2mm]
&= \lim_{\Delta x \to 0} \frac{g(x_0 + \Delta x) \cdot h(x_0 + \Delta x) - g(x_0) \cdot h(x_0)}{\Delta x}\\[2mm]
&= \lim_{\Delta x \to 0} \frac{\begin{aligned}g(x_0 + \Delta x) \cdot h(x_0 + \Delta x) &- g(x_0 + \Delta x) \cdot h(x_0)\\ &+ g(x_0 + \Delta x) \cdot h(x_0) - g(x_0) \cdot h(x_0)\end{aligned}}{\Delta x}\\[2mm]
&= \lim_{\Delta x \to 0} \left[g(x_0 + \Delta x)\frac{h(x_0 + \Delta x) - h(x_0)}{\Delta x} \right.\\
&\qquad\qquad \left. + h(x_0)\frac{g(x_0 + \Delta x) - g(x_0)}{\Delta x} \right]. \quad (2)
\end{aligned}
$$

By hypothesis, $g'(x_0)$ exists, so that g is continuous at $x = x_0$. By Theorem 4.1, $\lim\limits_{\Delta x \to 0} g(x_0 + \Delta x)$ exists and is $g(x_0)$. By hypothesis, $\lim\limits_{\Delta x \to 0} \dfrac{h(x_0 + \Delta x) - h(x_0)}{\Delta x}$ and $\lim\limits_{\Delta x \to 0} \dfrac{g(x_0 + \Delta x) - g(x_0)}{\Delta x}$ exist. By Ex. III, 3, $\lim\limits_{\Delta x \to 0} h(x_0) = h(x_0)$. Hence, by Theorem 3.2, the limit (2) exists and may be written as

$$f'(x_0) = \lim_{\Delta x \to 0} g(x_0 + \Delta x) \cdot \lim_{\Delta x \to 0} \frac{h(x_0 + \Delta x) - h(x_0)}{\Delta x}$$

$$+ \lim_{\Delta x \to 0} h(x_0) \cdot \lim_{\Delta x \to 0} \frac{g(x_0 + \Delta x) - g(x_0)}{\Delta x}$$

$$= g(x_0) \cdot h'(x_0) + h(x_0) \cdot g'(x_0).$$

If follows from this theorem that formula (3) in Table I is valid at each value x_0 of x where $D_x g$ and $D_x h$ are defined.

Theorem 5.3. *If $f(x) = g(x)/h(x)$, if $h(x_0) \neq 0$, and if $g'(x_0)$ and $h'(x_0)$ exist, then $f'(x_0)$ exists and equals*

$$\frac{h(x_0) \cdot g'(x_0) - g(x_0) \cdot h'(x_0)}{[h(x_0)]^2}.$$

By Definition 5.1

$$f'(x_0) = \lim_{\Delta x \to 0} \frac{f(x_0 + \Delta x) - f(x_0)}{\Delta x} \qquad \text{(provided this limit exists)}$$

$$= \lim_{\Delta x \to 0} \frac{\dfrac{g(x_0 + \Delta x)}{h(x_0 + \Delta x)} - \dfrac{g(x_0)}{h(x_0)}}{\Delta x},$$

where* by hypothesis $h(x_0) \neq 0$ and where by Theorem 5.1 and Ex. IV, 20, $h(x_0 + \Delta x) \neq 0$ for $|\Delta x|$ sufficiently small. It follows that

$$f'(x_0) = \lim_{\Delta x \to 0} \frac{h(x_0)g(x_0 + \Delta x) - g(x_0)h(x_0 + \Delta x)}{h(x_0)h(x_0 + \Delta x)\Delta x}$$

$$= \lim_{\Delta x \to 0} \left\{ \frac{1}{h(x_0)h(x_0 + \Delta x)} \left[h(x_0)\frac{g(x_0 + \Delta x) - g(x_0)}{\Delta x} \right. \right.$$

$$\left. \left. - g(x_0)\frac{h(x_0 + \Delta x) - h(x_0)}{\Delta x} \right] \right\}.$$

---

* This remark is necessary in order to show that the preceding fraction has a definite value for each value of Δx considered. The student must be ever on his guard against using notation which may appear to be meaningful, but which is actually meaningless for some or all values of the variable involved; in particular, he must be certain that the denominator of a fraction never becomes zero.

An argument similar to that used in the preceding proof shows that this limit exists and has the value stated in the theorem. It follows from this theorem that formula (4) in the above table holds wherever f, g', and h' are defined.

THEOREM 5.4. *If $f(x) = [h(x)]^n$, where n is a positive integer, and if $h'(x_0)$ exists, then $f'(x_0)$ exists and equals $n[h(x_0)]^{n-1} \cdot h'(x_0)$.*

We first note that if α and β are real numbers, and if n is a positive integer, then

$$\alpha^n - \beta^n = (\alpha - \beta)(\alpha^{n-1} + \alpha^{n-2}\beta + \cdots + \alpha\beta^{n-2} + \beta^{n-1}). \quad (3)$$

By Definition 5.1

$$f'(x_0) = \lim_{\Delta x \to 0} \frac{f(x_0 + \Delta x) - f(x_0)}{\Delta x} \qquad \text{(provided this limit exists)}$$

$$= \lim_{\Delta x \to 0} \frac{[h(x_0 + \Delta x)]^n - [h(x_0)]^n}{\Delta x}$$

$$= \lim_{\Delta x \to 0} \left[\frac{h(x_0 + \Delta x) - h(x_0)}{\Delta x} \{[h(x_0 + \Delta x)]^{n-1} \right.$$

$$\left. + [h(x_0 + \Delta x)]^{n-2}h(x_0) + \cdots + [h(x_0)]^{n-1}\} \right] \quad \text{(by (3))}. \quad (4)$$

By hypothesis, $\lim\limits_{\Delta x \to 0} \dfrac{h(x_0 + \Delta x) - h(x_0)}{\Delta x}$ exists. Since h is continuous at $x = x_0$, it follows by Ex. IV, 5, and Theorem 4.1 that $\lim\limits_{\Delta x \to 0} [h(x_0 + \Delta x)]^{n-1}$, $\lim\limits_{\Delta x \to 0} [h(x_0 + \Delta x)]^{n-2}$, etc., exist and equal $[h(x_0)]^{n-1}$, $[h(x_0)]^{n-2}$, etc., respectively. By Theorem 3.2, the limit (4) exists and may be written as

$$f'(x_0) = \lim_{\Delta x \to 0} \frac{h(x_0 + \Delta x) - h(x_0)}{\Delta x} \left\{ \lim_{\Delta x \to 0} [h(x_0 + \Delta x)^{n-1} \right.$$

$$\left. + h(x_0) \cdot \lim_{\Delta x \to 0} [h(x_0 + \Delta x)]^{n-2} + \cdots + [h(x_0)]^{n-1} \right\}$$

$$= h'(x_0)\{[h(x_0)]^{n-1} + [h(x_0)]^{n-1} + \cdots + [h(x_0)]^{n-1}\}.$$

Since there are n terms in the second factor of this last expression

$$f'(x_0) = n[h(x_0)]^{n-1}h'(x_0).$$

It follows from this theorem that, for positive integer values of n, formula (6) in the above table is valid at each value x_0 of x at which $D_x h$ is defined. This theorem may be extended by the methods illustrated in Examples 2, 3, and 4 of Sec. 4 to the case where n is any rational number (see Ex. V, 1e and 5).   In the special case where h is merely x, formula (6) evidently reduces to $D_x x^n = n x^{n-1}$.

Because students often have difficulty understanding the significance of formula (5) in Table I, we have carried out the preceding derivation without the use of this formula.   Hence we may use formula (6) as an illustration of formula (5) in the following way.   If, in formula (5), g denotes u^n, then (5) assumes the form

$$D_x u^n = D_u u^n \cdot D_x u = n u^{n-1} D_x u.$$

But this is just formula (6) when written in terms of u instead of h.

In the preceding theorem, we considered the nth power of a function h of x.   Let us now consider an arbitrary function g of the function h; for example, g may denote a trigonometric or logarithmic function of h.   The following theorem provides a general method for finding $D_x g(h)$.

THEOREM 5.5.   *Suppose g is a function of a variable u, and suppose $u = h(x)$.   Let $f(x) = g[h(x)]$.   If $h'(x_0)$ and $g'(u_0)$ exist, where $u_0 = h(x_0)$ and $g' = D_u g$, then $f'(x_0)$ exists and equals $g'(u_0) \cdot h'(x_0)$.*

By the remark following Definition 5.1, there exists an interval $u_0 - \epsilon < u < u_0 + \epsilon$ over which g is defined.   By Theorem 5.1, h is continuous at $x = x_0$.   Hence there exists a $\delta > 0$ such that

$$|h(x) - u_0| < \epsilon \qquad \text{when} \qquad |x - x_0| < \delta.$$

By Ex. I, 19, $g[h(x)]$ is defined when $|x - x_0| < \delta$.   By Definition 5.1

$$f'(x_0) = \lim_{\Delta x \to 0} \frac{f(x_0 + \Delta x) - f(x_0)}{\Delta x} \qquad \text{(provided this limit exists)}$$
$$= \lim_{\Delta x \to 0} \frac{g[h(x_0 + \Delta x)] - g[h(x_0)]}{\Delta x}.$$

{It may help to understand this notation to think of $g[h(x)]$ as $\cos\ h(x)$ or $\log\ h(x)$.}   Let $u_0 + \Delta u = h(x_0 + \Delta x)$, where $u_0 = h(x_0)$.   Then

$$\Delta u = h(x_0 + \Delta x) - h(x_0) \tag{5}$$

and

$$\frac{g[h(x_0 + \Delta x)] - g[h(x_0)]}{\Delta x} = \frac{g(u_0 + \Delta u) - g(u_0)}{\Delta x} = \varphi(\Delta u)\frac{\Delta u}{\Delta x}, \quad (6)$$

where

$$\varphi(\Delta u) = \begin{cases} \dfrac{g(u_0 + \Delta u) - g(u_0)}{\Delta u} & \text{when} \quad \Delta u \neq 0, \\ g'(u_0) & \text{when} \quad \Delta u = 0. \end{cases} \quad (7)$$

[While Δx is arbitrary and may be restricted to be $\neq 0$, Δu is determined by (5) and cannot be *supposed* $\neq 0$. Hence in defining φ we must allow for the case $\Delta u = 0$. See footnote, p. 39.] It follows that

$$f'(x_0) = \lim_{\Delta x \to 0} \left[\varphi(\Delta u)\frac{\Delta u}{\Delta x} \right]. \text{ (provided this limit exists)} \quad (8)$$

Since h is continuous at $x = x_0$, Δu is a continuous function of Δx and $\Delta u \to 0$ as $\Delta x \to 0$. Hence, φ being continuous at $\Delta u = 0$, it follows by Theorem 4.4 that $\lim\limits_{\Delta x \to 0} \varphi(\Delta u) = \varphi(0) = g'(u_0)$. By (5), $\lim\limits_{\Delta x \to 0} \Delta u/\Delta x = h'(x_0)$. Hence the limit (8) exists and

$$f'(x_0) = \lim_{\Delta x \to 0} \varphi(\Delta u) \cdot \lim_{\Delta x \to 0} \frac{\Delta u}{\Delta x} = g'(u_0) \cdot h'(x_0).$$

Formula (5) of Table I follows from this theorem.

Theorem 5.6. *If $f(x) = \cos h(x)$, and if $h'(x_0)$ exists, then $f'(x_0)$ exists and equals $-\sin h(x_0) \cdot h'(x_0)$.*

Let $u = h(x)$ and let $g(u) = \cos u$. By Definition 5.1

$$g'(u_0) = \lim_{\Delta u \to 0} \frac{g(u_0 + \Delta u) - g(u_0)}{\Delta u} \quad \text{(provided this limit exists)}$$

$$= \lim_{\Delta u \to 0} \frac{\cos (u_0 + \Delta u) - \cos u_0}{\Delta u}$$

$$= \lim_{\Delta u \to 0} \frac{-2 \sin \left(u_0 + \dfrac{\Delta u}{2} \right) \sin \dfrac{\Delta u}{2}}{\Delta u}$$

$$\left(\text{since } \cos \alpha - \cos \beta = -2 \sin \frac{\alpha + \beta}{2} \sin \frac{\alpha - \beta}{2} \right)$$

$$= \lim_{\Delta u \to 0} \left[-\sin \left(u_0 + \frac{\Delta u}{2} \right) \frac{\sin \dfrac{\Delta u}{2}}{\Delta u/2} \right]. \quad (9)$$

By Example 6 of Sec. 4 and Theorem 4.1,

$$\lim_{\Delta u \to 0} \sin \left(u_0 + \frac{\Delta u}{2} \right) = \sin u_0.$$

By Ex. IV, 21, $\lim_{\Delta u \to 0} \dfrac{\sin \dfrac{\Delta u}{2}}{\Delta u / 2} = 1.$ By Theorem 3.2, the limit (9) exists and equals $-\sin u_0$. Hence

$$D_u \cos u = -\sin u.$$

If we now apply formula (5) of Table I

$$D_x \cos u = D_u \cos u \cdot D_x u = -\sin u \cdot D_x u.$$

This is formula (7) written in terms of u instead of h.

THEOREM 5.7. *If* $f(x) = \log_b h(x)$, *and if* $h'(x_0)$ *exists, then* $f'(x_0)$ *exists and equals* $\dfrac{1}{h(x_0)} h'(x_0) \log_b e$.

Let $u = h(x)$ and let $g(u) = \log_b u$. By Definition 5.1,

$$g'(u_0) = \lim_{\Delta u \to 0} \frac{g(u_0 + \Delta u) - g(u_0)}{\Delta u} \qquad \text{(provided this limit exists)}$$

$$= \lim_{\Delta u \to 0} \frac{\log_b (u_0 + \Delta u) - \log_b (u_0)}{\Delta u}$$

$$= \lim_{\Delta u \to 0} \left[\frac{1}{\Delta u} \log_b \frac{u_0 + \Delta u}{u_0} \right]$$

$$= \lim_{\Delta u \to 0} \left\{ \frac{1}{u_0} \left[\frac{u_0}{\Delta u} \log_b \left(1 + \frac{\Delta u}{u_0} \right) \right] \right\}$$

$$= \lim_{\Delta u \to 0} \left[\frac{1}{u_0} \log_b \left(1 + \frac{\Delta u}{u_0} \right)^{u_0 / \Delta u} \right].$$

Let $\Delta t = \Delta u / u_0$. Then $\Delta t \to 0$ as $\Delta u \to 0$ and this last limit becomes

$$g'(u_0) = \frac{1}{u_0} \lim_{\Delta t \to 0} \log_b \left[(1 + \Delta t)^{1/\Delta t} \right]. \tag{10}$$

From Ex. IV, 23, $\lim_{\Delta t \to 0} (1 + \Delta t)^{1/\Delta t} = e$. By Ex. IV, 5 and 13, (10) may be written as

$$g'(u_0) = \frac{1}{u_0} \log_b \left[\lim_{\Delta t \to 0} (1 + \Delta t)^{1/\Delta t} \right] = \frac{1}{u_0} \log_b e.$$

Formula (20) of Table I follows from this result with the aid of formula (5). Formula (19) is the special case of (20) arising when we take $b = e$. Because of the simplicity of (19), it is customary to use e as the logarithmic base. Logarithms to the base e are called *natural* logarithms. Whenever we write a logarithm without indicating the base, as log x, it is assumed that the base is e.

Theorem 5.8. *If $y = f(x)$, if f is single-valued, continuous, and has a single-valued inverse φ, so that $x = \varphi(y)$, and if $f'(x_0)$ exists and is $\neq 0$, then $\varphi'(y_0)$ exists and equals $1/f'(x_0)$, where $y_0 = f(x_0)$. This result is summarized in the formula $D_y x = 1/D_x y$.*

Let $y_0 + \Delta y = f(x_0 + \Delta x)$, where $y_0 = f(x_0)$. Then

$$\Delta y = f(x_0 + \Delta x) - f(x_0). \tag{11}$$

Moreover, $x_0 = \varphi(y_0)$, $x_0 + \Delta x = \varphi(y_0 + \Delta y)$, and

$$\Delta x = \varphi(y_0 + \Delta y) - \varphi(y_0). \tag{12}$$

By Definition 5.1 and (12)

$$\varphi'(y_0) = \lim_{\Delta y \to 0} \frac{\Delta x}{\Delta y} \qquad \text{(provided this limit exists)}$$

$$= \lim_{\Delta y \to 0} \frac{1}{\Delta y / \Delta x}, \tag{13}$$

where Δy is assumed $\neq 0$ and where it follows that $\Delta x \neq 0$ since f is single-valued. [If $\Delta x = 0$ in (12), then φ has the same value x_0 for two values of y, i.e., f has two values y for this value x_0.] By Ex. IV, 24b, φ is continuous at $y = y_0$, and by (12), $\Delta x \to 0$ as $\Delta y \to 0$. By hypothesis and (11), $\lim_{\Delta x \to 0} \Delta y / \Delta x$ exists and is $\neq 0$. Thus, (13) may be written as

$$\varphi'(y_0) = \frac{1}{\displaystyle\lim_{\Delta x \to 0} \frac{\Delta y}{\Delta x}} = \frac{1}{f'(x_0)}.$$

Theorem 5.9. *If $f(x) = \mathrm{Cos}^{-1} h(x)$, and if $h'(x)$ exists, then $f'(x)$ exists and equals $\dfrac{-1}{\sqrt{1 - [h(x)]^2}} h'(x)$.*

Let $u = h(x)$ and let $v = \mathrm{Cos}^{-1} u$. Then $u = \cos v$. Since $D_v \cos v$ exists, it follows by Theorem 5.8 that $D_u \mathrm{Cos}^{-1} u$ exists and is given by

$$D_u \operatorname{Cos}^{-1} u = D_u v = \frac{1}{D_v u} = \frac{1}{D_v \cos v} = \frac{-1}{\sin v} = \frac{-1}{\sqrt{1 - \cos^2 v}}$$

$$= \frac{-1}{\sqrt{1 - u^2}},$$

where $\sin v = +\sqrt{1 - \cos^2 v}$ since $0 \leq v \leq \pi$.   Formula (13) of Table I follows from this result with the aid of formula (5).

The derivative of the derivative of a function f is called the *second derivative* of f.   If a function is differentiated n times, the result is called the nth derivative.   Thus

$$D_x[D_x f(x)] = D_x^2 f(x) = f''(x) = \frac{d^2}{dx^2} f(x),$$

$$D_x[D_x^2 f(x)] = D_x^3 f(x) = f'''(x) = \frac{d^3}{dx^3} f(x),$$

and in general

$$D_x[D_x^{n-1} f(x)] = D_x^n f(x) = f^{(n)}(x) = \frac{d^n}{dx^n} f(x).$$

EXERCISES V

1. Find the derivatives with respect to x of each of the following functions, using the fundamental method illustrated in Example 1:

(a) $x^3 - 2x$.   (b) $\dfrac{2x - 1}{1 - 3x}$.   (c) $\dfrac{1 + 4x}{x^2}$.

(d) $\sqrt{x}$.   (e) $\sqrt{h(x)}$.   (f) $\sqrt[3]{1 - 2x}$.

2. Derive all the formulas in Table I which have not already been discussed.

Suggestions.   For formulas (1) and (2), see Theorem 5.2; for (9), see Theorem 5.6 and use the formula $\sin \alpha - \sin \beta = 2 \cos \frac{1}{2}(\alpha + \beta) \sin \frac{1}{2}(\alpha - \beta)$; for (8), (10), (11), and (12), express the respective functions in terms of $\cos h$ and $\sin h$, and use (3) and (4); for (14)—(18), (21), and (22), see Theorem 5.9; for (6), where n is any real number, let $y = [h(x)]^n$.   Then, if* $h(x) > 0$

$$y = e^{\log_e [h(x)]^n} = e^{n \log_e h(x)},$$

and $D_x y$ may be computed by (19) and (21).   If $h(x) < 0$, then $[h(x)]^n$ may have either sign; in either case let $h(x) = -k(x)$.   Give an example to show that if $h(x_0) = 0$ and n is not a positive integer, then $y'(x_0)$ need not exist.

---

* We do not use the well-known device of computing $D_x \log_e y$ by (5) because (5) presupposes the existence of $D_x y$.

3. Find the derivative with respect to x of each of the following functions:

(a) $(2 - 3x^2)^7$.

(b) $(x^2 + 1)^4(1 - 5x)^6$.

(c) $\sqrt[3]{a^2 - x^2}$.

(d) $\dfrac{\sin^2 \pi x}{1 + \cos x}$.

(e) $\sqrt{\dfrac{1 - x}{1 + x}}$.

(f) $\tan^5 7x - \mathrm{Cos}^{-1} 3x$.

(g) $x^2 \csc 3x + \mathrm{ctn}^3 7x$.

(h) $\sec (\mathrm{Sin}^{-1} 2x)$.

(i) $be^{ax} \sin mx$.

(j) $\log \sin \left(\dfrac{\pi}{2} - x^2 \right)$.

(k) $e^{-x^2} \mathrm{Tan}^{-1} \dfrac{x}{x + 1}$.

(l) $\dfrac{1}{b(ax + b)} - \dfrac{1}{b^2} \log \dfrac{ax + b}{x}$.

(m) $\dfrac{1}{\sqrt{b}} \log \dfrac{\sqrt{ax + b} - \sqrt{b}}{\sqrt{ax + b} + \sqrt{b}}$.

(n) $\dfrac{1}{2}\left(x\sqrt{a^2 - x^2} + a^2 \mathrm{Sin}^{-1} \dfrac{x}{a} \right)$.

(o) $\dfrac{1}{a\sqrt{b^2 + c^2}} \log \tan \dfrac{1}{2}\left(ax + \tan^{-1} \dfrac{c}{b} \right)$.

(p) $\dfrac{e^{ax}}{a^2 + b^2} (a \sin bx - b \cos bx)$.   (q) $x \, \mathrm{Cos}^{-1} ax - \dfrac{1}{a}\sqrt{1 - a^2x^2}$.

(r) $\log_{10} \log_{10} ax$.

(s) $x^{\sin x}$.   (Let $y = x^{\sin x}$ and find $D_x \log y$.)

(t) $\log_x (x + 4)$.   (Use the formula $\log_b a = (\log_c a)/(\log_c b)$.

(u) Derive the formula $D_x f(x) = f(x)D_x \log f(x)$.   Use this formula to check your results in (d), (e), (k), (s).

4. Interpret $D_x f$ as an instantaneous *rate* and illustrate with physical examples (see end of Sec. 1 and Ex. I, 11).

5. Extend Definition 5.1 and the preceding theorems as indicated in Ex. IV, 6 and 27.

6. Find the second and third derivatives of the functions of Ex. 1a, c, i, j, and r.

7. Show by mathematical induction that

$$D_x^n \cos x = \cos \left(x + \frac{n\pi}{2} \right).\qquad(14)$$

Solution.   The proof consists of two steps: (1) show that (14) holds when $n = 1$; and (2) show that if (14) holds for some value k of n, then (14) holds also when $n = k + 1$.

(1) By the relation

$$- \sin \alpha = \cos \left(\alpha + \frac{\pi}{2} \right)\qquad(15)$$

it follows that

$$D_x \cos x = - \sin x = \cos \left(x + \frac{\pi}{2} \right).$$

Hence (14) holds when $n = 1$.

(2) If k is a value of n such that $D_x^k \cos x = \cos\left(x + \dfrac{k\pi}{2}\right)$, then by (15),

$$D_x^{k+1} \cos x = D_x(D_x^k \cos x) = D_x \cos\left(x + \frac{k\pi}{2}\right) = -\sin\left(x + \frac{k\pi}{2}\right)$$

$$= \cos\left(x + \frac{k+1}{2}\pi\right). \tag{16}$$

Hence (14) holds when $n = k + 1$.

That this argument constitutes a proof of (14) may be seen as follows: by step (1) we may set $k = 1$ in (16) and conclude that (14) holds when $n = 2$. We may now set $k = 2$ in (16) and conclude that (14) holds when $n = 3$. We may now set $k = 3$ in (16), etc. This process may evidently be repeated arbitrarily many times.

Show by mathematical induction that

(a) $D_x^n \sin x = \sin\left(x + \dfrac{n\pi}{2}\right).$

(b) $D_x^n \log (1 + x) = \dfrac{(-1)^{n-1}(n-1)!}{(1+x)^n}.$ $(0! = 1)$

(c) $D_x^n e^{ax} = a^n e^{ax}.$

(d) $D_x^n(ax + b)^k = a^n \cdot k(k-1)(k-2) \cdots (k - n + 1) \cdot (ax + b)^{k-n}.$

8. (a) By induction prove Leibnitz's theorem that

$$D_x^n(u \cdot v) = D_x^n u \cdot v + nD_x^{n-1}u \cdot D_x v + \frac{n(n-1)}{2!}D_x^{n-2}u \cdot D_x^2 v + \cdots + u \cdot D_x^n v.$$

(b) Using this result, find the second and third derivatives of $e^x \sin x$ and $x^3 \log x$.

(c) Generalize Leibnitz's theorem for products of three or more factors.

9. Find the nth derivative of

(a) $e^{ax} \sin bx.$ (b) $\sqrt{a^2 - x^2}.$ [Write this as $(a + x)^{\frac{1}{2}}(a - x)^{\frac{1}{2}}.$]

(c) $\mathrm{Tan}^{-1} x.$ $\left[D_x \mathrm{Tan}^{-1} x = \dfrac{1}{x^2 + 1}. \right.$

$\left. \dfrac{1}{x^2 + 1} = (x + i)^{-1} (x - i)^{-1}, \text{ where } i = \sqrt{-1}. \right]$

10. Suppose $f(x) = \begin{cases} x \cos (1/x) & \text{when } x \neq 0, \\ 0 & \text{when } x = 0. \end{cases}$ (See Ex. III, 12.)

Calculate $\dfrac{f(0 + \Delta x) - f(0)}{\Delta x}$ and show that $f'(0)$ does not exist even though f is continuous at $x = 0$.

11. Find $D_x y$ from the relation $x^3 - xy^2 - y^3 = 1$.

Solution. This problem is discussed in detail in Sec. 19. For the present it is sufficient to perform the following steps:

(1) Regard y as denoting that function of x which would be obtained if the given equation were solved for y in terms of x.

(2) Differentiate both members of the given equation with respect to x and equate the results.

(3) Solve the resulting equation for $D_x y$.

If we follow this procedure we find that

$$D_x(x^3 - xy^2 - y^3) = D_x 1,$$
$$3x^2 - [x \cdot D_x y^2 + y^2 \cdot (1)] - D_x y^3 = 0,$$
$$3x^2 - x \cdot 2y D_x y - y^2 - 3y^2 \cdot D_x y = 0,$$
$$D_x y = \frac{3x^2 - y^2}{2xy + 3y^2}.$$

Find $D_x y$ from the relations

(a) $x - x^3 y^2 + y^5 = 4.$ (b) $x \sin y + y \sin x = 1.$ (c) $y = \cos xy$

12. Find $D_x^2 y$ from the relations

(a) $ax^2 + 2bxy + cy^2 = 1.$ (b) $x^3 + y^3 = 3axy.$ (c) $e^{x+y} = x.$

13. (a) If $x = \varphi(u)$ and $y = \psi(u)$, and if y is determined as a function of x, $y = f(x)$, show that

$$D_x y = \frac{D_u y}{D_u x},$$

stating the conditions under which this result holds (see Theorem 5.5).

(b) By differentiating the preceding result with respect to x, show that

$$D_x^2 y = \frac{D_u(D_u y / D_u x)}{D_u x} = \frac{D_u^2 y \cdot D_u x - D_u y \cdot D_u^2 x}{(D_u x)^3}.$$

(c) Show that the formula

$$D_x^2 y = -\frac{D_y^2 x}{(D_y x)^3}$$

results as a special case of part (b) when $u = y$.

(d) Starting from the relation $D_x y = D_z y \cdot D_x z$, show that

$$D_x^2 y = D_x^2 z \cdot D_z y + (D_x z)^2 \cdot D_z^2 y.$$

14. Find $D_x y$ and $D_x^2 y$ if

(a) $x = \alpha(\alpha^2 + 3\alpha + 3),\ y = 3\alpha(\alpha + 1).$

(b) $x = a \cos \theta,\ y = b \sin \theta.$

(c) $x = a(\theta - \sin \theta),\ y = a(1 - \cos \theta).$

15. Make the indicated change of variable in each of the following equations:

(a) $(1 - y^2)\dfrac{d^2y}{dx^2} + y\left(\dfrac{dy}{dx}\right)^2 + (1 - y^2)^{3/2} = 0;$ $y = \cos z.$

$$Ans. \quad \frac{d^2z}{dx^2} - 1 = 0.$$

(b) $\dfrac{d^2y}{dx^2} + \dfrac{2x}{1 + x^2}\dfrac{dy}{dx} + \dfrac{y}{(1 + x^2)^2} = 0;$ $x = \tan z.$

$$Ans. \quad \frac{d^2y}{dz^2} + y = 0.$$

(c) $(1 - x^2)\dfrac{d^2y}{dx^2} - 2x\dfrac{dy}{dx} + n(n + 1)y = 0;$ $x = \sin \theta.$

(d) $(1 - x^2)\left[\dfrac{d^2y}{dx^2} - \dfrac{1}{y}\left(\dfrac{dy}{dx}\right)^2\right] - x\dfrac{dy}{dx} + y = 0;$ $y = e^z,$ $x = \cos \theta.$

16. If $x = r \cos \theta$, $y = r \sin \theta$, and if $r = F(\theta)$, show that

$$\frac{dy}{dx} = \frac{\sin \theta \dfrac{dr}{d\theta} + r \cos \theta}{\cos \theta \dfrac{dr}{d\theta} - r \sin \theta}.$$

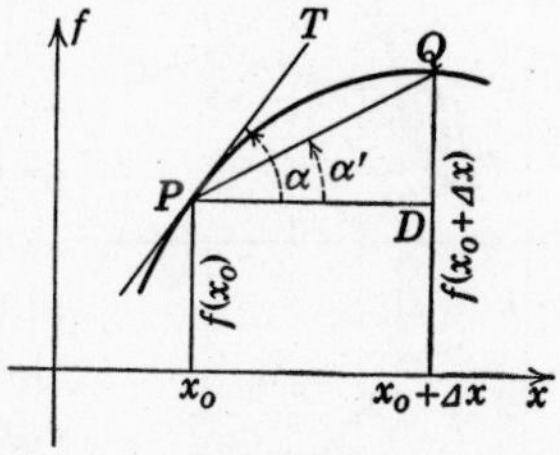

6. Interpretations and Applications of the Derivative. *Slope.*

FIG. 12.

Let f be a function of x, and let $[x_0, f(x_0)]$ and

$$[x_0 + \Delta x, f(x_0 + \Delta x)]$$

be two points P and Q on the graph of f. With reference to Fig. 12 it is evident that $\overline{DQ} = \Delta f = f(x_0 + \Delta x) - f(x_0)$ and that the slope of the chord $\overline{PQ}$ is $\tan \alpha' = \Delta f/\Delta x$, where α' is the angle of inclination of $\overline{PQ}$. If the chord $\overline{PQ}$ approaches a limiting position $\overline{PT}$ as $\Delta x \to 0$ and $Q \to P$, then the slope of the line $\overline{PT}$ is

$$\tan \alpha = \lim_{\Delta x \to 0} \frac{\Delta f}{\Delta x} = f'(x_0),$$

where α is the angle of inclination of $\overline{PT}$. If we call $\overline{PT}$ the *tangent line* to the graph of f at P, then we may state the following result:

If f is a function of x, then $f'(x_0)$ represents the slope of the tangent to the graph of f at the point $[x_0, f(x_0)]$.

We define the slope of a curve at a point P to be the slope of the tangent line to the curve at P.

Since the equation of the line through the point (x_0, y_0) with slope m is $y - y_0 = m(x - x_0)$, it is seen that the equation of the tangent to the curve $y = f(x)$ at the point (x_0, y_0) is

$$y - y_0 = f'(x_0)(x - x_0).$$

The fact that $f'(x_0)$ represents the slope of the tangent to the graph of f at $x = x_0$ enables us to solve the following problem: Given the graph G of a function f for which no formula is known. Plot the graph of f'. (This situation occurs, for example, whenever a smooth curve is drawn through a series of points plotted from experimental data.)

Suppose the graph G is as shown in the upper half of Fig. 13.

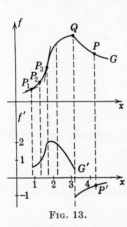

Let $P_1, P_2, P_3, \cdots$ be a number of points on G. At each of these points draw the tangent to G and estimate its slope. Project $P_1, P_2, P_3, \cdots$ onto the lower x-axis and at the points so obtained erect ordinates of lengths equal to these estimated slopes. Through the ends of these ordinates draw a smooth curve G'. Then G' is the graph of f'. (Note that if G has a corner Q, then G has no genuine tangent at Q. But, by considering separately the parts of G to the right and left of Q, it is possible to draw *right* and *left* tangents at Q. The slopes of both these tangents are plotted.)

Fig. 13.

This graphical analysis brings out the following fact: If the graphs G and G' of a function f and its derivative f' are plotted, the *ordinate* of a point P' on G' represents the *slope* of the tangent to G at the point P having the same abscissa as P'.

EXERCISES VI

1. Find the equations of the tangent and normal to each of the following curves at the points indicated:
   (a) $y = x^3$ at $(2, 8)$.
   (b) $x^2 + 2y^2 - 3xy + x - 1 = 0$ at $(1, 1)$.
   (c) $x^2y^2 = 4a^2(2a - y)$ at the point where $x = 2a$.
   (d) $Ax^2 + 2Hxy + By^2 + 2Fx + 2Gy + C = 0$ at (x_1, y_1).
   (e) $x = (\alpha + 1)^3$, $y = (\alpha - 1)^3$ at $\alpha = 2$.
2. (a) Find all the points on the curve $y = x^3$ where the slope is 4. Plot.

(b) Determine the points on the curve $x^{2/3} + y^{2/3} = a^{2/3}$ at which the tangents are perpendicular to the line $x - 2y + 3 = 0$.   Plot.

(c) Show that the circle $x^2 + y^2 = 8ax$ and the cissoid $y^2(2a - x) = x^3$ meet at an angle of $45°$ at each of two points distinct from the origin.   Plot.

(d) Show that the tangents to the curve $x^3 + y^3 = 3axy$ at the point where it intersects the parabola $y^2 = ax$ are parallel to the y-axis.   Plot.

3. Plot the graph of f' when the graph of the function f is as indicated in the following figures:

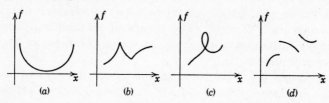

| (a) | (b) | (c) | (d) |

4. Sketch the graphs of the derivatives of the functions of Exs. II, 1 and 2.

5. If β is the angle made by a curve $y = f(x)$ or $r = F(\theta)$ with a line from the origin, show that $\tan \beta = \dfrac{x\dfrac{dy}{dx} - y}{x + y\dfrac{dy}{dx}} = \dfrac{r}{\dfrac{dr}{d\theta}}$.

Increasing and Decreasing Functions.   Let f be a function of x. We say that f is *increasing* at the point $x = x_0$ if there exists an interval I about this point such that, for each point x_1 of I,

$$\begin{cases} f(x_1) > f(x_0) \text{ when } x_1 > x_0, \text{ and} \\ f(x_1) < f(x_0) \text{ when } x_1 < x_0, \end{cases} \tag{1}$$

and we say that f is *decreasing* at $x = x_0$ if under the same circumstances

$$\begin{cases} f(x_1) < f(x_0) \text{ when } x_1 > x_0, \text{ and} \\ f(x_1) > f(x_0) \text{ when } x_1 < x_0. \end{cases} \tag{2}$$

For example, if $f(x) = \sin x$, then f is increasing at $x = \pi/6$ since condition (1) is met when I is taken sufficiently small. It is assumed in this definition and the following theorem that f is defined over the whole of some interval about $x = x_0$.

THEOREM 6.1.   *Let f be a function of x and let x_0 be a value of x at which $f'(x_0)$ exists.   If $f'(x_0) > 0$, then f is increasing at $x = x_0$; if $f'(x_0) < 0$, then f is decreasing at $x = x_0$.*

If $f'(x_0) > 0$, then by Ex. IV, 20, there exists an interval I about $x = x_0$ such that, for each $x_1 \neq x_0$ in I, $\dfrac{\Delta f}{\Delta x} = \dfrac{f(x_1) - f(x_0)}{x_1 - x_0}$

remains > 0. But when $\dfrac{f(x_1) - f(x_0)}{x_1 - x_0}$ is positive, $f(x_1) - f(x_0)$
and $(x_1 - x_0)$ have the same sign, i.e., condition (1) holds
when x_1 is in I. The second part of the theorem is proved in a
similar manner.

In geometric language, this theorem states that a function is
increasing at any point where the slope of its graph is positive and
is decreasing at any point where the slope of its graph is negative.

Maxima and Minima. The theory of maxima and minima
has many important applications in various branches of mathematics and physics.

DEFINITION 6.1. *Let f be a function of x. We say that f has a
relative maximum at the point $x = x_0$ if there exists an interval I
about this point such that, for each point x_1 of I, $f(x_0) \geqq f(x_1)$.
We say that f has a relative minimum at the point $x = x_0$ if there
exists an interval I about this point such that, for each point x_1 of I,
$f(x_0) \leqq f(x_1)$.*

It is evident that if f is increasing or decreasing at a point
$x = x_0$, then f cannot have a relative maximum or minimum at
$x = x_0$.

THEOREM 6.2. *If f is a function of x, then f' has the value
0 at each point $x = x_0$ where* (a) *f has a relative maximum or
minimum,* (b) *f' is defined, and* (c) *the domain of definition of f
extends over some interval about $x = x_0$.*

Suppose f has a relative maximum at $x = x_0$. Then there
exists an interval I about this point such that, for each point
x_1 of I, $f(x_0) \geqq f(x_1)$. If $f'(x_0)$ were positive, then by Theorem
6.1, (1) and hypothesis (c) there would exist values $x_1 > x_0$
in I such that $f(x_0) < f(x_1)$. Hence $f'(x_0)$ is not positive. It
follows in similar manner that $f'(x_0)$ is not negative. Therefore
$f'(x_0) = 0$. The case where f has a relative minimum at $x = x_0$
is treated in an analogous manner.

By Theorem 6.2, each value x_0 of x [meeting conditions (b)
and (c)] at which f has a relative maximum or minimum is a solution of the equation $f'(x) = 0$. Hence the set of all values
x_0 of x [meeting conditions (b) and (c)] at which f has a relative
maximum or minimum is contained in the set of all solutions of
the equation $f'(x) = 0$. However, the equation $f'(x) = 0$ may
have one or more solutions x_0 at which f has neither a relative
maximum nor minimum, as is illustrated by the function x^3.

It follows that the procedure for determining the points [meeting conditions (b) and (c)] where f has a relative maximum or minimum is to find the set of all solutions of the equation $f'(x) = 0$ and then to investigate the nature of f at each of these solutions by means of Theorem 6.3 or 6.4 or some stronger theorem.

THEOREM 6.3.   *Let f be a function of x and let x_0 be a value of x such that f' is defined in some interval about x_0.   (a) If $f'(x_0) = 0$ and if f' is increasing at x_0, then f has a relative minimum at x_0.   (b)   If $f'(x_0) = 0$ and if f' is decreasing at x_0, then f has a relative maximum at x_0 (see Fig. 14).   (c) If $f'(x_0) = 0$, but f' is positive* (or negative) at every other point of some interval about x_0, then f has neither a relative maximum nor minimum at x_0.

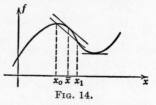

FIG. 14.

From the hypotheses of part (b) it follows by (1) that

$$f'(\bar{x}) < 0 \text{ when } \bar{x} > x_0 \qquad \text{and} \qquad f'(\bar{x}) > 0 \text{ when } \bar{x} < x_0, \quad (3)$$

where $\bar{x}$ is restricted to lie in a sufficiently small interval I about x_0.   Let x_1 be any point of I.   The slope of the chord through the points $[x_0, f(x_0)]$ and $[x_1, f(x_1)]$ is $\dfrac{f(x_1) - f(x_0)}{x_1 - x_0}$.   By the theorem of the mean (see Sec. 10), there exists a point $\bar{x}$ between x_0 and x_1 such that the tangent at $\bar{x}$ is parallel to this chord, i.e.,

$$f'(\bar{x}) = \frac{f(x_1) - f(x_0)}{x_1 - x_0}.$$

If $x_1 > x_0$, then $\bar{x} > x_0$, and by (3), $f'(\bar{x}) < 0$.   Hence $f(x_1) - f(x_0)$ and $x_1 - x_0$ have opposite signs, and because $x_1 > x_0$, $f(x_1) < f(x_0)$.   It may be shown in a similar way that $f(x_1) < f(x_0)$ when $x_1 < x_0$.   Thus $f(x_1) < f(x_0)$ wherever x_1 may be in I (other than at x_0).   This proves part (b).   Parts (a) and (c) may be proved in a similar manner.

The truth of Theorem 6.3 is intuitively evident from Fig. 14; part (c) of the theorem is illustrated by the function x^3 with $x_0 = 0$.

It should be noted that a function may have a relative maximum or minimum at a point without having a finite derivative at that point.   For example, the function $2 + (x - 3)^{2/3}$ has a relative minimum at $x = 3$, and yet this function does not have a finite derivative at $x = 3$ (see Fig. 15a). Thus one cannot detect all relative maxima and minima by Theorem 6.3.

Definition 6.1 may be extended to the case where f is defined

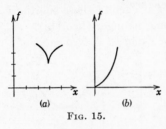

(a)   (b)

Fig. 15.

on only one side of the point $x = x_0$. But in this event the point x_0 may be a relative maximum or minimum of f even though $f'(x_0) \neq 0$. For example, the function $f(x) = x + \sqrt{x^3}$, which is defined for only nonnegative x, has a relative minimum at $x = 0$, and yet $f'(0) = 1$ (see Fig. 15b). This example shows that Theorem 6.2 is false when condition (c) is omitted.

Example 1. Find the relative maxima and minima of the function f when $f(x) = 2x^3 - 3x^2 - 12x + 6$.

Solution. $f'(x) = 6(x - 2)(x + 1)$. Hence $f'(x) = 0$ when $x = 2$ and $x = -1$. Furthermore, f' is decreasing at $x = -1$, since $f'(x) > 0$ when $x < -1$ and $f'(x) < 0$ when $-1 < x < 2$. Thus f has a relative maximum at $x = -1$. Similar reasoning shows that f has a relative minimum at $x = 2$. These results may be checked by graphing f.

Theorem 6.3 may be put into a more convenient form by observing that, according to Theorem 6.1, f' is increasing at x_0 when $f''(x_0) > 0$ and f' is decreasing at x_0 when $f''(x_0) < 0$. If we incorporate these results into Theorem 6.3, we obtain

THEOREM 6.4. *Let f be a function of x and let x_0 be a value of x such that $f''(x_0)$ exists.* (a) *If $f'(x_0) = 0$ and if $f''(x_0) > 0$, then f has a relative minimum at x_0.* (b) *If $f'(x_0) = 0$ and if $f''(x_0) < 0$, then f has a relative maximum at x_0.*

With reference to the graph of f, it is seen that f'' is positive wherever the graph is *concave upward*, and f'' is negative wherever the graph is *concave downward*.

In Example 1 above, $f''(x) = 6(2x - 1)$, and f' is shown to be decreasing at $x = -1$ by the fact that $f''(-1) < 0$.

Theorem 6.4 sometimes fails to locate a relative maximum or minimum that may be detected by Theorem 6.3. For example, if $f(x) = x^4$, then $f'(x) = 0$ only when $x = 0$. But $f''(x) = 0$ when $x = 0$ and Theorem 6.4 provides no information. On the other hand, $f'(x) > 0$ when $x > 0$ and $f'(x) < 0$ when $x < 0$. Hence f' is increasing at $x = 0$ and Theorem 6.3 shows that f has a relative minimum at $x = 0$.

Inflection Points. We define a *point of inflection* on a curve to be a point at which the slope of the curve has a relative maximum or minimum. If the equation of the curve is of the form $y = f(x)$, then the points of inflection may be found by maximizing and minimizing f'. We leave it to the student to discuss the exceptional cases, such as that arising when the maximum slope is infinite.

EXERCISES VII

1. Locate all maximum and minimum points (if any) on the graph of each of the following functions. Justify your results by giving conclusive tests. Plot.

(a) $x^3 - 6x^2 + 9x + 1$.   (b) $x^3(x + 4)^2$.

(c) $(\log x)/x$.   (d) $\sin x + \cos 2x$.

(e) $(x + 1)^{2/3}(x - 5)^2$.   (f) $x/(1 - x^2)$.

(g) $x^3 - 3x^2 + 3x + 7$.   (h) $x/(x^2 + a^2)^{5/2}$.

(i) x^6.   (j) e^{-x^2}.

2. In a certain triangle two sides are given. What should the value of the angle between them be in order that the area of the triangle may be a maximum?

3. Find the altitude of the right circular cylinder of maximum volume that can be inscribed in a given right circular cone.

4. Find the altitude of the right circular cone of maximum volume that can be inscribed in a given sphere.

5. A fisherman is at A which is 3 miles from the nearest point B on a straight shore LM. He wishes to reach in minimum time a point C situated on shore 6 miles from B. How far from C should he land if he can row at the rate of 4 miles an hour, can walk at the rate of 5 miles an hour and he loses 5 min. in docking his boat?

6. Let OM and ON be two straight tracks intersecting at right angles at O. A rod AB of length l moves so that A slides along OM and B slides along ON. A second rod PS is

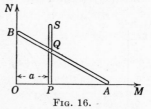

FIG. 16.

rigidly attached to OM at P so that $\overline{OP} = a$ and PS is parallel to ON. Both AB and PS are grooved and a pin Q slides along these rods at their point of intersection. Find the position of AB such that distance $\overline{PQ}$ is a maximum. (See Fig. 16.)

7. In the preceding problem let PS rotate about P and let the pin Q be fixed on PS at a distance $\overline{PQ} = b$. Find the position of AB such that the angle OPS is a maximum. What are the conditions on a, b, and l under which this mechanism will work?

8. Find the minimum distance from the point $(3, 1)$ to the parabola $y = x^2$.

9. A water tank stands on level ground and the water surface is H ft. above the ground. A jet of water issues from a small hole in the side of the tank, the hole being h ft. below the water surface. For what value of h will the range of the jet be a maximum? (The lateral velocity of the jet is $\sqrt{2gh}$. The jet falls according to the law $s = \frac{1}{2}gt^2$.)

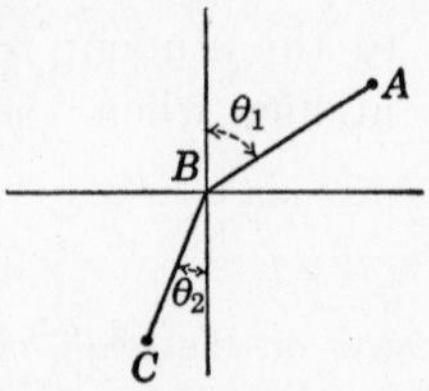

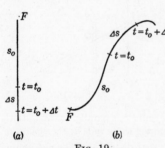

10. The speed of light in air is v_1 and in glass is v_2. A ray of light starts at A in air, meets the surface of a plate of glass at B, and is refracted to C within the plate. Show that the position of B must be such that

$$\frac{\sin \theta_1}{\sin \theta_2} = \frac{v_1}{v_2}$$

Fig. 17.

in order that the time of travel from A to C be a minimum.

11. A light ray AC is bent by a prism. Using the law of refraction given in Ex. 10, show that the angular deflection is a minimum when $\theta = \psi$.

12. Find the points of inflection of:

(a) $y = x^4 + 2x^3 - 12x^2 + 7x - 9$.
(b) $y = (x - 3)^4 + 7$.
(c) $y = 8a^3/(x^2 + 4a^2)$.
(d) $y = \sin^2 x$.

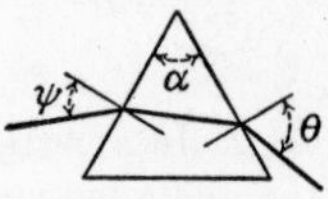

Fig. 18.

7. Velocity, Acceleration, Radius of Curvature.

Suppose a point particle P is moving along a path C, suppose s is the distance along C to P from some fixed point F on C, and suppose s is determined as a function of the time t by the relation $s = f(t)$. If $s_0 = f(t_0)$ and $s_0 + \Delta s = f(t_0 + \Delta t)$, then

$$\Delta s = f(t_0 + \Delta t) - f(t_0)$$

is the distance traveled during the interval of time Δt. Hence the mean speed of P over the interval Δs is $\Delta s/\Delta t$ and the instantaneous speed of P at $t = t_0$ is

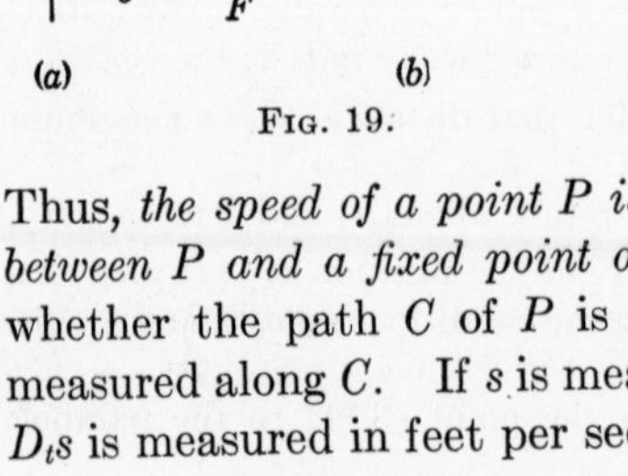

Fig. 19.

$$\lim_{\Delta t \to 0} \frac{\Delta s}{\Delta t} = D_t s. \tag{1}$$

Thus, *the speed of a point P is the rate of change of the distance s between P and a fixed point on the path of P.* It is immaterial whether the path C of P is straight or curved so long as s is measured along C. If s is measured in feet and t in seconds, then $D_t s$ is measured in feet per second.

When P moves along a plane curve, its rectangular coordinates x and y are given by equations of the form

$$x = \varphi(t), \qquad y = \psi(t). \tag{2}$$

We shall assume that φ and ψ are differentiable. It is evident that $D_t x$ is the speed of the projection P_1 of P upon the x-axis and $D_t y$ is the speed of the projection P_2 of P upon the y-axis. We speak of $D_t x$ and $D_t y$ as the x-component and y-component of the velocity of P. We write

$$v_x = D_t x = x' = \dot{x}, \qquad v_y = D_t y = y' = \dot{y}.$$

The vector* $\mathbf{V}$ whose x and y-components at any time t are v_x and v_y is called the *velocity vector* of P.

THEOREM 7.1. *The length (or magnitude) v of the velocity vector $\mathbf{V}$ of a point P is the speed of P at any time t, and the direction of $\mathbf{V}$ is always along the tangent to the path of P.*

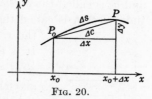

Fig. 20.

Let s, x, and y have the significance indicated above, let equations (2) represent the path of P, and let Δc be the length of the chord through the positions of P at $t = t_0$ and $t = t_0 + \Delta t$.
Then

$$(\Delta c)^2 = (\Delta x)^2 + (\Delta y)^2,$$

$$(\Delta s)^2\left(\frac{\Delta c}{\Delta s}\right)^2 = (\Delta x)^2 + (\Delta y)^2, \tag{3}$$

and

$$\left(\frac{\Delta s}{\Delta t}\right)^2\left(\frac{\Delta c}{\Delta s}\right)^2 = \left(\frac{\Delta x}{\Delta t}\right)^2 + \left(\frac{\Delta y}{\Delta t}\right)^2.$$

If we assume the path of P to be such that $\lim\limits_{\Delta s \to 0} \Delta c/\Delta s = 1$ (this assumption being met by most curves occurring in practice), and if we let $\Delta t \to 0$, then

$$(D_t s)^2 = (D_t x)^2 + (D_t y)^2 = v_x^2 + v_y^2. \tag{4}$$

It is evident that $D_t s$ is the length v of the vector $\mathbf{V}$.

To show that the vector $\mathbf{V}$ has the same direction as the tangent line at any point of the curve (2), let θ be the inclination of $\mathbf{V}$

---

* By a vector we here mean merely a directed line segment.

to the x-axis (see Fig. 21).   Then by Ex. V, 13a,

$$\tan \theta = \frac{v_y}{v_x} = \frac{D_t y}{D_t x} = D_x y = \tan \varphi,$$

where φ is the inclination of the tangent to the curve (2).   Hence
V lies along the tangent at each point of the curve (2).

It should be noted in passing that $v_x = v \cos \theta$ and $v_y = v \sin \theta$.
It is readily seen that $\lim\limits_{\Delta t \to 0} \Delta v_x / \Delta t = D_t v_x = D_t^2 x$ represents
the rate of change of v_x with respect to t and that $D_t v_y = D_t^2 y$
represents the rate of change of v_y with respect to t.   We write

$$a_x = D_t v_x = D_t^2 x = x'' = \ddot{x}, \qquad a_y = D_t v_y = D_t^2 y = y'' = \ddot{y}.$$

The vector **A** whose x- and y-components at any time t are a_x
and a_y is called the *acceleration vector* of P; the length (or magnitude) a of **A** is called the *acceleration* of P; a_x and a_y are called
the x and y-components of acceleration of P.
It is evident that the acceleration a of P is
$\sqrt{a_x^2 + a_y^2}$ and that the direction α of **A** is
given by the relation $\tan \alpha = a_y/a_x$.   Example
1 below shows that the vector **A** does not
always lie along the tangent to the path of P.

Fig. 21.

(For a more detailed treatment of this topic, see Ex. X, 9 of
Chap. VI.)

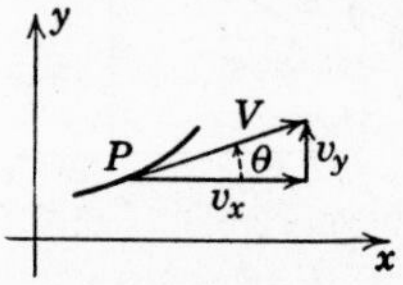

Let l be a half-line rotating about a fixed point O, let l_0 be a
fixed half-line through O, and let ψ be the angle of rotation from
l_0 to l measured in radians.   We call $D_t \psi$ the *angular velocity* of l and $D_t^2 \psi$ the *angular acceleration* of l.

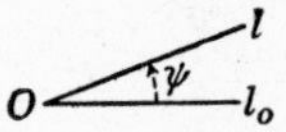

Fig. 22.

Example 1.   A particle P moves around a circle of radius
r with the constant speed of 2 revolutions per second.   Find
the velocity and acceleration of P at any time t.

Solution.   The position of P may be represented parametrically by the
equations $x = r \cos \psi$, $y = r \sin \psi$.   Then (see Fig. 23).

$$v_x = -r \sin \psi \cdot D_t \psi, \qquad v_y = r \cos \psi \cdot D_t \psi.$$

But $D_t \psi = 4\pi$, so that $v_x = -4\pi r \sin \psi$, $v_y = 4\pi r \cos \psi$.   The speed v of
P is $\sqrt{v_x^2 + v_y^2} = 4\pi r$, and the direction angle θ of the velocity vector **V**
is given by the relation

$$\tan \theta = \frac{v_y}{v_x} = -\operatorname{ctn} \psi.$$

Again,

$$a_x = -16\pi^2 r \cos \psi, \qquad a_y = -16\pi^2 r \sin \psi.$$

The acceleration a of P is $\sqrt{a_x^2 + a_y^2} = 16\pi^2 r$ and the direction angle α of the acceleration vector $\mathbf{A}$ is given by the relation $\tan \alpha = a_y/a_x = \tan \psi$. Thus $\mathbf{A}$ is directed toward the center of the circle. The values of v and a may be combined to show that $a = v^2/r$.

The quantity $D_t v = D_t^2 s$ represents the rate of change of the speed v and is called the *tangential acceleration* of P. This name is justified by

THEOREM 7.2. *If $\mathbf{A}_T$ is the component of the acceleration vector $\mathbf{A}$ along the tangent to the path of P, then the magnitude a_T of $\mathbf{A}_T$ is $D_t^2 s$.*

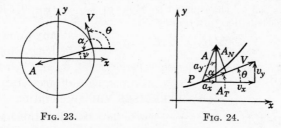

FIG. 23.   FIG. 24.

With reference to Fig. 24 it is seen that

$$a_T = a \cos (\alpha - \theta) = a (\cos \alpha \cos \theta + \sin \alpha \sin \theta)$$
$$= a\left(\frac{a_x}{a} \cos \theta + \frac{a_y}{a} \sin \theta\right) = a_x \cos \theta + a_y \sin \theta.$$

On the other hand,

$$D_t^2 s = D_t v = D_t \sqrt{v_x^2 + v_y^2} = \frac{1}{\sqrt{v_x^2 + v_y^2}}(v_x a_x + v_y a_y)$$
$$= a_x \frac{v_x}{v} + a_y \frac{v_y}{v} = a_x \cos \theta + a_y \sin \theta.$$

These results show that $a_T = D_t^2 s$.

An immediate corollary of this theorem is that $\mathbf{A}$ is perpendicular to $\mathbf{V}$ whenever $D_t v = 0$, i.e., whenever the speed of P is constant. The component $\mathbf{A}_N$ of $\mathbf{A}$ normal to $\mathbf{V}$ may be thought of as arising from the change of direction of $\mathbf{V}$ along the path of P, and $\mathbf{A}_N$ need not be zero even though the magnitude v of $\mathbf{V}$ is constant. (See Ex. IX, 3.) It is seen that

$$a_N = (1/v) (a_y v_x - a_x v_y).$$

If the path of P is a straight line, then $a = D_t^2 s$, for if we choose the x-axis along the path of P, $v_y = a_y = 0$, so that $a_N = 0$.

Example 2. A line l is rotating about the point $(1, 3)$ (coordinates being in feet). Let A and B be the points of intersection of l with the x- and y-axes. If A is approaching the origin O at the rate of 10 ft. per second, find the speed of B when $\overline{OA} = 2$.

Solution. The solution of this problem is based on two fundamental principles: (1) Represent the speed of each point by a derivative according to the remark following (1); and (2) To evaluate a derivative, say $D_t y$, get an equation in y and differentiate it with respect to t.

Following the first of these principles, let $\overline{OA} = r$ and let $\overline{OB} = s$. Then $D_t r = -10$ ($D_t r$ is negative because r is decreasing) and $D_t s$ is the quantity to be found. Following the second of these principles, we must get an equation in s to evaluate $D_t s$. In this case we have a pair of similar triangles and $r/1 = s/(s-3)$. This equation simplifies to $rs - 3r - s = 0$. If we differentiate this equation with respect to t, we find that

$$r \cdot D_t s + s \cdot D_t r - 3D_t r - D_t s = 0.$$

But $D_t r = -10$, and at the instant in question, $r = 2$ and $s = 6$. Hence $D_t s = 30$ ft. per second.

EXERCISES VIII

1. A point (x, y) moves according to the relations $x = t^2$, $y = 2t$, where x and y are measured in feet and the time t in seconds. Find, when $t = 2$ sec., (a) the coordinates of the point reached; (b) the magnitude and direction of the velocity vector; (c) the magnitude and direction of the acceleration vector of the point; (d) the tangential and normal accelerations.

2. The motion of a projectile is given by the equations

$$x = v_0(\cos \theta)t, \qquad y = v_0(\sin \theta)t + 16t^2,$$

where v_0 is the initial speed of the projectile, θ the angle of projection with the horizon, and t the time of flight in seconds. At $t = 2$ sec., find the magnitude and direction of the velocity and acceleration vectors, if $v_0 = 100$ ft. per second and $\theta = 30°$. Show that the path of the projectile is a parabola.

3. A point P is moving along the parabola $y = x^2$ so that $D_t x = 5$. Find $D_t y$ and the speed of P at the instant when $x = 2$. Also find the angular velocity of OP at this instant, O being the origin.

4. A point P is moving along the hyperbola $x^2 - y^2 = 7$ with speed 5. Find $D_t x$ and $D_t y$ at the instant when P is at $(4, 3)$. Also find the angular velocity of OP at this instant.

5. Two straight railroad tracks cross each other at right angles, one track running north and south and the other track east and west. At a certain instant, a train is traveling east 40 m.p.h. 10 miles east of the intersection O, while another train is traveling north 50 m.p.h. 8 miles north of O. Find the rate at which the trains are separating from each other at the instant under consideration.

6. A rod of length 30 ft. is constrained to move in such a manner that its ends A and B follow perpendicular tracks OE and ON, respectively. If the end A is pulled away from O at the rate of 3 ft. per minute, find (a) how fast

B moves along ON when A is 18 ft. from O; (b) at what position A and B will be moving at the same rates; (c) at what position B will be moving 6 ft. per minute.

7. A wheel of radius r rotates about its center with an angular speed of ω rad. per second, while the center moves along the x-axis with speed v ft. per second. Find the velocity vector of a point on the perimeter of the wheel.

8. A car wheel of radius a rolls along a straight track. A point P on the circumference of the wheel then describes a cycloid with equations

$$x = a(\phi - \sin \phi), \qquad y = a(1 - \cos \phi),$$

where ϕ is the angle through which the wheel has rotated. Find the magnitude and direction of the velocity and acceleration vectors of the point P.

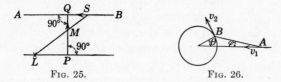

FIG. 25.   FIG. 26.

Show that the velocity vector always lies along the line joining P with the highest point of the wheel.

9. A man M is walking along a straight path PQ toward Q at the rate of 5 ft. per second and casts a shadow S on the wall AB from the light L. How fast is S moving when M is 20 ft. from the wall, if $\overline{PQ} = 60$ ft. and $\overline{LP} = 40$ ft.?

10. The end A of a connecting rod in an engine slides along a straight track and the end B is carried by a rotating crank. If v_1 and v_2 are the speeds of A and B in their paths, show that

$$v_1 = \frac{\sin (\varphi + \theta)}{\cos \varphi} v_2.$$

FIG. 27.

(Since the connecting rod is not changing length, the components of v_1 and v_2 along AB are equal. These components may be computed directly by trigonometric relations.)

11. Solve Ex. 5 without the use of derivatives. (By trigonometry, find the components of the velocities of the two trains along the line joining the trains.)

12. A man M walks across a circular stage 100 ft. in diameter at the rate of 5 ft. per second. He casts a shadow S on the wall from a light L as shown in Fig. 27. Find the speed of S along the wall when M is three-quarters of the way across. (Find $D_t\alpha$ using $\triangle OML$. Note that $\beta = 2\alpha$. Express s in terms of β.)

13. Starting from (3), derive the following relations:

$$1 = (D_s x)^2 + (D_s y)^2. \tag{5}$$
$$(D_x s)^2 = 1 + (D_x y)^2. \tag{6}$$
$$(D_y s)^2 = (D_y x)^2 + 1. \tag{7}$$
$$D_x s = \sec \alpha, \qquad D_y s = \csc \alpha. \tag{8}$$
$$D_s x = \cos \alpha, \qquad D_s y = \sin \alpha. \tag{9}$$

State the functional relations between x, y, and s in each case. (The time t is not involved in these formulas.) α is the inclination of the tangent to the curve C along which the point (x, y) moves. What assumptions are made in (8) and (9) as to the direction in which s is measured along the curve C? When would minus signs be needed in (8) and (9)?

Let C be a curve in the xy-plane, let θ be the inclination of the tangent to C at any point on C, and let s denote the arc length measured along C from some fixed point on C. Then $\Delta\theta/\Delta s$ represents the mean change in direction of C per unit of distance along C and $D_s\theta$ is the rate of change of θ with respect to s. The value of $D_s\theta$ at any point P on C is called the *curvature K* of C at P. It is evident that C is flat when the curvature is small and that C bends sharply when the curvature is large. Since $\theta = \tan^{-1} D_x y$, it follows by Ex. V, 13a, and (6) that

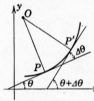

Fig. 28.

$$K = D_s\theta = D_s(\tan^{-1} D_x y) = \frac{D_x(\tan^{-1} D_x y)}{D_x s}$$

$$= \frac{D_x^2 y}{1 + (D_x y)^2} \cdot \frac{1}{\sqrt{1 + (D_x y)^2}} = \frac{D_x^2 y}{[1 + (D_x y)^2]^{3/2}}.$$

If C is a circle of radius a, then K may be computed directly from Fig. 28 as follows: since the central angle at O is $\Delta\theta$ and since $\Delta s = a\Delta\theta$, we have at once that $\Delta\theta/\Delta s = 1/a$. Thus $\Delta\theta/\Delta s$ is constant and

$$K = D_s\theta = \frac{1}{a}.$$

The circle whose radius is $1/K$ and which is tangent to the concave side of a curve C at P is called the *circle of curvature* of C at P, and the radius of this circle is called the *radius of curvature R* of C at P. It is evident that $R = 1/K$.

EXERCISES IX

1. Find the curvatures of the following curves:

(a) $y = x^2$.   (b) $y = \log x$.   (c) $y = e^x$.   (d) $y = \sin x$.

2. If the equations of a curve are $x = \varphi(t)$, $y = \psi(t)$, where t denotes time, show that

$$K = \frac{x'y'' - y'x''}{[x'^2 + y'^2]^{3/2}}.$$

(See Ex. V, 13b.)

3. If a point P moves along a path C with constant speed, i.e.,

$$D_t^2 s = D_t v = 0,$$

show that the acceleration a of P is $a = v^2/R$.

Suggestion. Let P be an arbitrary point on C. Choose axes with origin at P and x-axis along the tangent to C at P. By the remark following Theorem 7.2, $a = y''$ at P. Moreover, $y' = 0$ at P. The desired formula follows from Ex. 2.

4. Find the curvature of the cycloid $x = a(\theta - \sin \theta)$, $y = a(1 - \cos \theta)$. In particular, what is the curvature at the point where $\theta = 30°$?

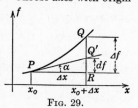

FIG. 29.

8. The Differential of a Function. Let f be a function of the independent variable x having a derivative at $x = x_0$. We define the symbol df by the formula

$$df = f'(x_0) \cdot \Delta x,$$

and we call df the *differential* of f at $x = x_0$.

It is seen from Fig. 29 that

$$RQ' = (\tan \alpha) \Delta x = f'(x_0) \cdot \Delta x.$$

Hence $df = RQ'$, or in words, *df represents the change in the ordinate up to the tangent line at $x = x_0$ arising from the change Δx in x.*

Since

$$f'(x_0) = \lim_{\Delta x \to 0} \frac{\Delta f}{\Delta x},$$

where $\Delta f = f(x_0 + \Delta x) - f(x_0)$, it follows that $\Delta f/\Delta x$ is "approximately" equal to $f'(x_0)$ when $|\Delta x|$ is small. Hence Δf is "approximately" $f'(x_0) \cdot \Delta x$, that is df is "*approximately*" Δf when $|\Delta x|$ *is small.* Thus $f(x_0 + \Delta x)$ is "approximately" $f(x_0) + df$.

Example 1. Find by means of differentials the approximate change in value of $3x^2$ when x changes from 10 to 10.1. Also find the actual change in value of $3x^2$.

Solution. Let $x_0 = 10$, $\Delta x = 0.1$, and $f(x) = 3x^2$. Then

$$f'(x_0) = 6x_0 = 60,$$

and $df = f'(x_0) \cdot \Delta x = 60(0.1) = 6$. Again,

$$\Delta f = 3(x_0 + \Delta x)^2 - 3x_0^2 = 3(10.1)^2 - 3(10)^2 = 6.03.$$

In the case where $f(x) = x$, then $f'(x) = 1$, and

$$dx = f'(x) \cdot \Delta x = 1 \cdot \Delta x = \Delta x.$$

This proves

Theorem 8.1. *The differential of an independent variable x is equal to the increment of the variable; i.e., $dx = \Delta x$. The differential of f is $df = f'(x)\,dx$.*

Suppose $y = f(x)$ and $x = \phi(t)$, where t is an independent variable. Then $y = f[\phi(t)] \equiv F(t)$ is a function of t. If $f(x)$ and $\phi(t)$ are differentiable functions, then we find by formula (5) of Table I, that $F'(t) = f'(x) \cdot \phi'(t)$. Hence the differential of y is

$$dy = F'(t) \cdot \Delta t = f'(x) \cdot \phi'(t) \cdot \Delta t. \tag{1}$$

But the differential of x is equal to $dx = \phi'(t) \cdot \Delta t$. Therefore

$$dy = f'(x)\,dx. \tag{2}$$

This proves

Theorem 8.2. *The differential of f is equal to $df = f'(x)\,dx$, irrespective of whether x is the independent variable or not.*

From (2), we have

$$f'(x) = \frac{df(x)}{dx},$$

that is, the first derivative of f is equal to the ratio of the differential of f to the differential of x. This property motivates the use of the symbol $df(x)/dx$ for the derivative $f'(x)$.

EXERCISES X

1. By means of a differential, find approximately the change in the value of $x^3 + 10x^2$ when x changes from 13 to 12.98. Find the actual change in the value of this function and find the error of the approximation.

2. Find approximately the amount by which x may change from 12 in order that the value of $3x^2 + 5x - 7$ may change by no more than 0.2.

3. Find an approximate value of $f(x) = 2x/\sqrt{x^2 + 16}$ when $x = 3.02$. [Note that $f(3.02)$ is approximately $f(3) + df$.]

4. Find an approximate value of sin 31°.

5. Find an approximate value of $\log_e 1.05$.

6. If $y = x^{3/2}$ and if $x = 4t^2$, find dx when $t = 2$ and $dt = 0.01$, and use this result to find dy. Check the result by expressing y in terms of t and computing dy directly.

7. Show that the volume of a thin spherical shell is approximately the area of either its inner or outer surface multiplied by its thickness.

8. Show that the volume of a thin cylindrical shell is approximately the area of either its inner or outer surface multiplied by its thickness.

9. Find an approximate formula for the volume of a thin conical shell bounded by two circular cones having a common vertex, a common axis, and equal heights.

9. Rolle's Theorem.

The following theorem is needed to prove the Theorem of the Mean in Sec. 10.

THEOREM 9.1 (*Rolle's Theorem*).   *If f is a function of x defined and continuous over the interval $a \leq x \leq b$, if f′ is defined over the interval $a < x < b$, and if $f(a) = f(b) = 0$, then there exists at least one value ξ of x, $a < \xi < b$, such that $f'(\xi) = 0$.*

By Theorem 8.3 of Chap. IX there exists a value ξ of x, $a < \xi < b$, at which f has either a relative maximum or a relative minimum. By hypothesis, f' is defined at $x = \xi$ and f is defined in some interval about $x = \xi$. By Theorem 6.2, $f'(\xi) = 0$.

We leave it to the student to state and interpret Theorem 9.1 geometrically with the aid of a graph. We give some examples to bring out the significance of the hypotheses in this theorem.

Example 1. If $f(x) = \begin{cases} (1/x) - 1 \text{ when } 0 < x \leq 1, \\ 0 \text{ when } x = 0, \end{cases}$ then there exists no value ξ of x such that $f'(\xi) = 0$. The difficulty is that f is discontinuous at $x = 0$, even though the hypotheses of Theorem 9.1 are met in all other respects.

Example 2. If $f(x) = x^{2/3} - 1$ when $-1 \leq x \leq 1$, then there exists no value ξ of x such that $f'(\xi) = 0$. The difficulty is that f' is not defined at $x = 0$.

Example 3. If $f(x) = x \sin 1/x$ when $0 < x \leq \epsilon$ and $f(0) = 0$, where ϵ is any positive number of the form $1/n\pi$, then there exists a value ξ of x, $0 < \xi < \epsilon$, such that $f'(\xi) = 0$. It is immaterial that $f'(0)$ does not exist.

Theorem 9.1 illustrates nicely the fact that the hypotheses of a theorem must be carefully stated in order that the theorem may be valid.

10. Theorem of the Mean.

We now take up a theorem which has many important applications.

THEOREM 10.1 (*Theorem of the Mean*).   *If f is a function of x defined and continuous over the interval $a \leq x \leq b$, and if f′ is* *defined over the interval $a < x < b$, then there exists at least one value ξ of x, $a < \xi < b$, such that*

$$f'(\xi) = \frac{f(b) - f(a)}{b - a}.$$

We observe from Fig. 30 that, if y is the function whose graph is the straight line PQ, then $f - y$ has the value 0 at $x = a$ and $x = b$. We shall show that the present theorem results when Rolle's theorem is applied to the function $f - y$. Let

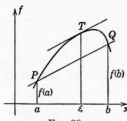

FIG. 30.

$$y = f(a) + \frac{f(b) - f(a)}{b - a}(x - a) \quad (1)$$

(the formula for y being constructed by finding the equation of the line PQ) and let us construct the auxiliary function E so that

$$E(x) = f(x) - y = f(x) - f(a) - \frac{f(b) - f(a)}{b - a}(x - a). \quad (2)$$

It is evident from Theorem 4.3 that E is defined and continuous over the interval $a \leqq x \leqq b$. Since $E'(x) = f'(x) - \dfrac{f(b) - f(a)}{b - a}$, E' is defined over the interval $a < x < b$. Moreover,

$$E(a) = E(b) = 0.$$

Hence E meets the conditions of Rolle's theorem and there exists a value ξ of x, $a < \xi < b$, such that $E'(\xi) = 0$, that is,

$$f'(\xi) - \frac{f(b) - f(a)}{b - a} = 0.$$

Thus our theorem is proved.

In geometric language, Theorem 10.1 states that, if f meets the given conditions, then there exists a point $x = \xi$ on the graph of f between the points $x = a$ and $x = b$ at which the slope of the tangent is equal to the slope of the chord through the points where $x = a$ and $x = b$.

THEOREM 10.2. *If $f'(x) = 0$ for all values of x in the interval $a \leqq x \leqq b$, then $f(x)$ is constant over this interval.*

Since f' is defined over the interval $a \leqq x \leqq b$, it follows by Theorem 5.1 that f is continuous over this interval and meets the conditions of Theorem 10.1. Let x_1 be any value of x such that $a < x_1 \leqq b$. By Theorem 10.1, there exists a value ξ of x such that

$$f'(\xi) = \frac{f(x_1) - f(a)}{x_1 - a},$$

where $a < \xi < x_1$. By hypothesis, $f'(\xi) = 0$. Hence

$$f(x_1) = f(a).$$

Since x_1 is arbitrary, f has the constant value $f(a)$ over the interval $a \leqq x \leqq b$.

THEOREM 10.3. *If g and h are functions of x such that*

$$g'(x) \equiv h'(x)$$

or all values of x in the interval $a \leqq x \leqq b$, then $g(x) - h(x)$ is constant over this interval.

Let $f(x) \equiv g(x) - h(x)$. Then $f'(x) = 0$ for all values of x in the interval $a \leqq x \leqq b$. By Theorem 10.2, $f(x)$ is constant over this interval.

The construction of indefinite integrals in Chap. II is based on this theorem.

EXERCISES XI

1. Give the geometrical interpretations of Theorems 9.1, 10.2, and 10.3.

2. Find ξ so that $f'(\xi) = \dfrac{f(b) - f(a)}{b - a}$ in the following cases:

(a) $f(x) = x^3$; $a = 1$, $b = 2$.
(b) $f(x) = \sqrt{x^2 - 4}$; $a = 2$, $b = 3$.
(c) $f(x) = \sin 2x$; $a = 0$, $b = \pi/4$.
(d) $f(x) = e^x$; $a = 0$, $b = 1$.

3. Construct examples similar to Examples $1 - 3$ of Sec. 9 to show the significance of the hypotheses of Theorems 10.1 and 10.3.

4. Show that Theorem 10.1 may be written in the form

$$f(b) = f(a) + (b - a) \cdot f'(a + \theta (b - a)),$$

where θ is a number such that $0 < \theta < 1$.

5. Prove Theorem 10.3 when $g'(x) \equiv h'(x)$ over the interval $a < x < b$ or over an infinite interval.

11. Indeterminate Forms.
If $f(x) = g(x)/h(x)$ and if

$$g(a) = h(a) = 0,$$

then the function f is said to assume the *indeterminate form*

$0/0$ at $x = a$. We wish to develop a method for evaluating $\lim\limits_{x \to a} g(x)/h(x)$ when this limit exists. We assume that the student is already familiar with the elementary method indicated in Ex. IV, 19.

THEOREM 11.1 (*Cauchy's Theorem*). *If the functions g and h meet the conditions of Theorem 10.1, if there exists no value x_1 of x, $a < x_1 < b$, such that both $g'(x_1)$ and $h'(x_1)$ are 0, and if*

$$h(b) - h(a) \neq 0,$$

then there exists at least one value ξ of x, $a < \xi < b$, such that $h'(\xi) \neq 0$ and

$$\frac{g'(\xi)}{h'(\xi)} = \frac{g(b) - g(a)}{h(b) - h(a)}.$$

The auxiliary function

$$E(x) = g(x) - g(a) - \frac{g(b) - g(a)}{h(b) - h(a)}[h(x) - h(a)]$$

meets all the conditions of Rolle's theorem. Hence there exists a value ξ of x, $a < \xi < b$, such that $E'(\xi) = 0$, that is,

$$g'(\xi) - \frac{g(b) - g(a)}{h(b) - h(a)} h'(\xi) = 0.$$

If $h'(\xi)$ were 0, $g'(\xi)$ would also be 0. But by hypothesis, $g'(\xi)$ and $h'(\xi)$ are not both 0. Hence $h'(\xi) \neq 0$ and the theorem follows at once.

THEOREM 11.2 (*L'Hôpital's Rule*). *Let g and h be two functions of x such that there exists an interval I about $x = a$ over which (1) $h(x) \neq 0$ when $x \neq a$, (2) g and h are continuous, and (3) except perhaps at $x = a$, g' and h' are defined and do not vanish simultaneously. If $g(a) = h(a) = 0$, and if $\lim\limits_{x \to a} g'(x)/h'(x)$ exists, then $\lim\limits_{x \to a} g(x)/h(x)$ exists and equals $\lim\limits_{x \to a} g'(x)/h'(x)$.*

If in Theorem 11.1 we set $g(a) = h(a) = 0$ and $b = x$, it follows that

$$\frac{g(x)}{h(x)} = \frac{g'(\xi)}{h'(\xi)}, \ a < \xi < x, \text{ or}^* \ x < \xi < a; x \text{ in } I \text{ and } \neq a.$$

---

* The case $x < \xi < a$ results by interchanging b and a in Theorem 11.1

The theorem results immediately from the fact that $\xi \to a$ as $x \to a$ and that $\lim\limits_{\xi \to a} g'(\xi)/h'(\xi)$ exists.

It is evident that

$$\text{if } \lim_{x \to a} g'(x)/h'(x) \to \pm \infty, \text{ then } \lim_{x \to a} g(x)/h(x) \to \pm \infty.$$

It follows from this theorem that if g' and h' are continuous at $x = a$ and if $h'(a) \neq 0$, then $\lim\limits_{x \to a} g(x)/h(x) = g'(a)/h'(a)$. If however, $g'(a) = h'(a) = 0$, then we may apply Theorem 11.2 to the function $g'(\xi)/h'(\xi)$ and (with suitable hypotheses) obtain the result that $\lim\limits_{\xi \to a} g'(\xi)/h'(\xi) = \lim\limits_{\eta \to a} g''(\eta)/h''(\eta)$. If g'' and h'' are continuous at $x = a$ and $h''(a) \neq 0$, then

$$\lim_{\xi \to a} g'(\xi)/h'(\xi) = g''(a)/h''(a).$$

But if $g''(a) = h''(a) = 0$, then Theorem 11.2 may be applied again to evaluate this limit in terms of the third derivatives. This process may be repeated as many times as necessary.

Example 1. Find $\lim\limits_{x \to 1} \dfrac{\log x^3}{2(x^2 - 1)}$.

The function $\dfrac{\log x^3}{2(x^2 - 1)}$ assumes the indeterminate form $\dfrac{0}{0}$ at $x = 1$. By Theorem 11.2, $\lim\limits_{x \to 1} \dfrac{\log x^3}{2(x^2 - 1)} = \lim\limits_{x \to 1} \dfrac{3/x}{4x} = \dfrac{3}{4}$.

Example 2. Find $\lim\limits_{x \to 0} \dfrac{e^{3x} + e^{-3x} - 2}{5x^2}$.

At $x = 0$, $\dfrac{e^{3x} + e^{-3x} - 2}{5x^2}$ assumes the form $\dfrac{0}{0}$. By Theorem 11.2, $\lim\limits_{x \to 0} \dfrac{e^{3x} + e^{-3x} - 2}{5x^2} = \lim\limits_{x \to 0} \dfrac{3e^{3x} - 3e^{-3x}}{10x}$. At $x = 0$, $\dfrac{3e^{3x} - 3e^{-3x}}{10x}$ assumes the form $0/0$. If we apply Theorem 11.2 again, we find that

$$\lim_{x \to 0} \frac{e^{3x} + e^{-3x} - 2}{5x^2} = \lim_{x \to 0} \frac{3e^{3x} - 3e^{-3x}}{10x} = \lim_{x \to 0} \frac{9e^{3x} + 9e^{-3x}}{10} = \frac{9}{5}.$$

We give a few examples to show how other types of indeterminate forms may be evaluated by the preceding method.

Example 3. If $\lim\limits_{x \to a} g(x) = 0$ and $\lim\limits_{x \to a} |h(x)| \to +\infty$, then the product $g(x) \cdot h(x)$ is said to be of the indeterminate form $0 \cdot \infty$ at $x = a$. It is sometimes possible to evaluate $\lim\limits_{x \to a} [g(x) \cdot h(x)]$ by writing it in the form

$\lim\limits_{x \to a} \dfrac{g(x)}{1/h(x)}$, where $\dfrac{g(x)}{1/h(x)}$ is of the form $\dfrac{0}{0}$ at $x = a$. Thus,

$$(x^3 - 27) \csc (x - 3)$$

is of the form $0 \cdot \infty$ at $x = 3$, and

$$\lim_{x \to 3} [(x^3 - 27) \csc (x - 3)] = \lim_{x \to 3} \frac{x^3 - 27}{\sin (x - 3)} = \lim_{x \to 3} \frac{3x^2}{\cos (x - 3)} = 27.$$

Example 4. If $\lim\limits_{x \to a} |g(x)| \to + \infty$ and $\lim\limits_{x \to a} |h(x)| \to + \infty$, then the quotient $g(x)/h(x)$ is said to be of the indeterminate form ∞ / ∞ at $x = a$. It is sometimes possible to evaluate $\lim\limits_{x \to a} g(x)/h(x)$ by writing it in the form

$\lim\limits_{x \to a} \dfrac{1/h(x)}{1/g(x)}$, where $\dfrac{1/h(x)}{1/g(x)}$ is of the form $\dfrac{0}{0}$ at $x = a$. Thus, $\dfrac{\operatorname{ctn} \sqrt{x}}{\operatorname{ctn} x}$ is of the

form $\dfrac{\infty}{\infty}$ at $x = 0$, and $\lim\limits_{x \to 0} \dfrac{\operatorname{ctn} \sqrt{x}}{\operatorname{ctn} x} = \lim\limits_{x \to 0} \dfrac{\tan x}{\tan \sqrt{x}} = \lim\limits_{x \to 0} \dfrac{2\sqrt{x} \sec^2 x}{\sec^2 \sqrt{x}} = 0.$

Example 5. If $\lim\limits_{x \to a} |g(x)| \to + \infty$ and $\lim\limits_{x \to a} |h(x)| \to + \infty$, then another method for evaluating $\lim\limits_{x \to a} g(x)/h(x)$ is as follows: let x be a point between x_1 and a. Then (under suitable hypotheses) we may write Theorem 11.1 in the form

$$\frac{g(x) - g(x_1)}{h(x) - h(x_1)} = \frac{g(x)}{h(x)} \cdot \frac{1 - [g(x_1)/g(x)]}{1 - [h(x_1)/h(x)]} = \frac{g'(\xi)}{h'(\xi)},$$ where ξ is between x_1 and x.

Hence,

$$\frac{g(x)}{h(x)} = \frac{g'(\xi)}{h'(\xi)} \cdot \frac{1 - [h(x_1)/h(x)]}{1 - [g(x_1)/g(x)]}.$$

Suppose $\lim\limits_{\xi \to a} g'(\xi)/h'(\xi)$ exists and equals A. Since ξ is always between x_1 and a, it follows that, by taking x_1 sufficiently close to a, $g'(\xi)/h'(\xi)$ will remain arbitrarily close to A no matter how x varies between x_1 and a. With x_1 so determined and fixed, it follows that by taking x sufficiently close to a, $|g(x)|$ and $|h(x)|$ can be made arbitrarily large so that the fraction

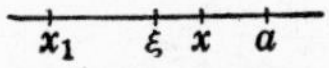

FIG. 31.

$\dfrac{1 - [h(x_1)/h(x)]}{1 - [g(x_1)/g(x)]}$ can be made arbitrarily close to 1 (see Ex. IV, 16a). Hence $g(x)/h(x)$ can be made arbitrarily close to A, that is,

$$\lim_{x \to a} \frac{g(x)}{h(x)} \text{ exists and equals } \lim_{x \to a} \frac{g'(x)}{h'(x)}.$$

This result may be regarded as an extension of L'Hôpital's rule. It is evident that if $\lim\limits_{x \to a} g'(x)/h'(x) \to \pm \infty$, then $\lim\limits_{x \to a} g(x)/h(x) \to \pm \infty$.

If $f(x) = x \log x$, then f is of the form $0 \cdot \infty$ at $x = 0$. If we write f as $\dfrac{x}{1/\log x}$ to put it in the form $\dfrac{0}{0}$, it turns out that L'Hôpital's rule is of no help. But if we write f as $\dfrac{\log x}{1/x}$ to put it in the form $\dfrac{\infty}{\infty}$, then the preceding result shows that

$$\lim_{x \to 0} \frac{\log x}{1/x} = \lim_{x \to 0} \frac{1/x}{-1/x^2} = \lim_{x \to 0} (-x) = 0.$$

Example 6. To evaluate $\lim\limits_{x \to \infty} g(x)/h(x)$ when $g(x)/h(x)$ assumes either the form $0/0$ or the form ∞/∞, let $x = 1/y$, where $y > 0$. It follows by Theorem 11.2 and Example 5 that

$$\lim_{x \to \infty} \frac{g(x)}{h(x)} = \lim_{y \to 0+} \frac{g(1/y)}{h(1/y)} = \lim_{y \to 0+} \frac{g'(1/y) \cdot (-1/y^2)}{h'(1/y) \cdot (-1/y^2)} = \lim_{y \to 0+} \frac{g'(1/y)}{h'(1/y)}$$
$$= \lim_{x \to \infty} \frac{g'(x)}{h'(x)}.$$

Thus

$$\lim_{x \to \infty} \frac{x^2}{e^{x^2}} = \lim_{x \to \infty} \frac{2x}{e^{x^2} \cdot 2x} = \lim_{x \to \infty} \frac{1}{e^{x^2}} = 0.$$

Example 7. The indeterminate form $\infty - \infty$ may sometimes be evaluated by reducing it to the form $0/0$ or ∞/∞. Thus, $(2x/\pi) \sec x - \tan x$ assumes the form $\infty - \infty$ at $x = \pi/2$, and

$$\lim_{x \to \pi/2} \left(\frac{2x}{\pi} \sec x - \tan x \right) = \lim_{x \to \pi/2} \frac{(2x/\pi) - \sin x}{\cos x}$$
$$= \lim_{x \to \pi/2} \frac{(2/\pi) - \cos x}{-\sin x} = -\frac{2}{\pi}.$$

Example 8. The indeterminate forms 0^0, 1^∞, and ∞^0 may sometimes be reduced to the forms $0/0$ or ∞/∞ by taking the logarithm of the given function. Thus, $\lim\limits_{x \to \infty} (1 + 3/x)^x$ is of the form 1^∞. But

$$\lim_{x \to \infty} \log \left(1 + \frac{3}{x} \right)^x = \lim_{x \to \infty} x \log \left(1 + \frac{3}{x} \right) = \lim_{x \to \infty} \frac{\log \left(1 + \dfrac{3}{x} \right)}{\dfrac{1}{x}}$$

$$= \lim_{x \to \infty} \frac{-\dfrac{3}{x^2}}{\left(1 + \dfrac{3}{x} \right)\left(-\dfrac{1}{x^2} \right)} = \lim_{x \to \infty} \frac{3}{1 + \dfrac{3}{x}} = 3.$$

By Ex. IV, 26, $\lim\limits_{x \to \infty} \left(1 + \dfrac{3}{x}\right)^x$ exists and equals e^3.

Example 9. Algebraic devices are sometimes useful. Thus,

$$\lim_{x \to \infty} \frac{2x - 3}{x + 1} = \lim_{x \to \infty} \frac{2 - \dfrac{3}{x}}{1 + \dfrac{1}{x}} = 2.$$

EXERCISES XII

1. Evaluate the following:

(a) $\lim\limits_{x \to 1} \dfrac{\sin \pi x}{x - 1}$.

(b) $\lim\limits_{\theta \to 0} \dfrac{\sin a\theta}{b\theta}$.

(c) $\lim\limits_{x \to \pi/4} \dfrac{1 + \sec 2x}{\tan 2x}$.

(d) $\lim\limits_{x \to \infty} x^n/e^x,\ n > 0$.

(e) $\lim\limits_{x \to 0} (1 + 2x)^{1/3x}$.

(f) $\lim\limits_{x \to \infty} (1 + 2x)^{1/3x}$.

(g) $\lim\limits_{x \to 0} x^{2x}$.

(h) $\lim\limits_{x \to 0} \left(\dfrac{1}{x} - \csc x\right)$.

(i) $\lim\limits_{x \to 0} x \log^2 x$.

(j) $\lim\limits_{x \to 0} x \log^n x,\ n > 0$.

(k) $\lim\limits_{x \to 0} x^{-n}e^{-1/x^2},\ n > 0$.

(l) $\lim\limits_{x \to 0} (7^x - 5^x)/x$.

(m) $\lim\limits_{x \to \infty} e^x/e^{x^2}$.

(n) $\lim\limits_{x \to 0} \log x/\operatorname{ctn} x$.

(o) $\lim\limits_{x \to 0} \sin x \cdot \log x$.

(p) $\lim\limits_{x \to \infty} \dfrac{x \cos 1/x}{x + 1}$.

(q) $\lim\limits_{x \to \infty} \dfrac{a_0 + a_1 x + a_2 x^2 + \cdots + a_m x^m}{b_0 + b_1 x + b_2 x^2 + \cdots + b_n x^n}$, where $a_m \neq 0,\ b_n \neq 0$.

2. Find $f'(0)$ when

(a) $f(x) = \begin{cases} \dfrac{\sin x}{x} \text{ when } x \neq 0, \\ 1 \text{ when } x = 0. \end{cases}$

(b) $f(x) = \begin{cases} (1 + x)^{1/x} \text{ when } x \neq 0, \\ e \text{ when } x = 0. \end{cases}$

3. Why is it that $\lim\limits_{x \to \infty} (\sin^2 x)/\cos^2 x$ cannot be evaluated by L'Hôpital's rule to obtain the result -1? Does this limit exist? Can L'Hôpital's rule be applied to evaluate $\lim\limits_{x \to 0} x^2/|\sin x|$, even though $|\sin x|$ has no derivative at $x = 0$? Find this limit.

4. Give a geometric interpretation of Cauchy's theorem and of the function E used in the proof of this theorem.

5. Show that the hypotheses in L'Hôpital's rule may be altered in the following way when $h'(a) \neq 0$: if $g(a) = h(a) = 0$, and if $g'(a)$ and $h'(a)$ exist with $h'(a) \neq 0$, then $\lim\limits_{x \to a} g(x)/h(x) = g'(a)/h'(a)$.

Suggestion. Show that $g(x)/h(x)$ may be written in the form

$$\frac{g(x)}{h(x)} = \frac{g(a + \Delta x)}{h(a + \Delta x)} = \frac{\dfrac{g(a + \Delta x) - g(a)}{\Delta x}}{\dfrac{h(a + \Delta x) - h(a)}{\Delta x}}, \qquad \text{where} \qquad x = a + \Delta x,$$

and apply Theorem 3.2c.

The only advantage of the more complicated form of L'Hôpital's rule is that it sometimes enables us to deal with the case where $h'(a)$ is 0 or does not exist.

6. Using the notation of Definition 3.1b give in complete detail the proof sketched in Example 5.   (Cf. the proof of Theorem 3.2b.)

12. Infinitesimals.   If the value of a variable is approaching zero, then the variable is sometimes called an *infinitesimal*. Thus, if the value of x is approaching 1, then log x and ctn $\frac{1}{2}\pi x$ are infinitesimals.   If the function f is continuous at $x = x_0$, then $\Delta f = f(x_0 + \Delta x) - f(x_0)$ is an infinitesimal when $\Delta x \to 0$.

It is sometimes desirable to compare two infinitesimals.   Let β be such a function of α that $\lim_{\alpha \to 0} \beta(\alpha) = 0$.   Then β is said to be an infinitesimal of the *same order* as α if $\lim_{\alpha \to 0} \beta/\alpha$ exists, is finite, and is not zero.   If $\lim_{\alpha \to 0} \beta/\alpha = 0$, then β is said to be an infinitesimal of *higher order* than α (the intuitive idea being that β is approaching 0 "more rapidly" than α), and if $\lim_{\alpha \to 0} \alpha/\beta = 0$, then β is said to be an infinitesimal of *lower order* than α.   If $\lim_{\alpha \to 0} \beta/\alpha^n$ exists and is not zero, then β is said to be an infinitesimal of the nth order relative to α.

Example 1.   When $x \to 0$, x and sin x are infinitesimals of the same order, for by Sec. 11, $\lim_{x \to 0} (\sin x)/x = \lim_{x \to 0} (\cos x)/1 = 1$.

Example 2.   When $x \to 0$, sin $x - x$ is of higher order than x, for $\lim_{x \to 0} (\sin x - x)/x = \lim_{x \to 0} (\cos x - 1)/1 = 0$.   In fact, sin $x - x$ is of the third order relative to x, for

$$\lim_{x \to 0} \frac{\sin x - x}{x^3} = \lim_{x \to 0} \frac{\cos x - 1}{3x^2} = \lim_{x \to 0} \frac{-\sin x}{6x} = \lim_{x \to 0} \frac{-\cos x}{6} = -\frac{1}{6}.$$

If two infinitesimals α and β are of the same order with $\lim_{\alpha \to 0} \alpha/\beta = 1$, then evidently one may be used to *approximate* the other.   It is for this reason that infinitesimals have been used to so great an extent in the applications of calculus to problems in geometry and physics.   Thus, the student may have frequently replaced sin x by x for purposes of approximation (when x is small and measured in radians), such as in studying the motion of a pendulum when the oscillations are small.

EXERCISES XIII

1. Let $\widehat{PQ}$ be an arc of a circle and let α be the central angle (measured in radians) subtended by $\widehat{PQ}$.

(a) Show that α and the length of the chord $\overline{PQ}$ are infinitesimals of the same order when $\alpha \to 0$.

(b) Show that the difference between the arc length and chord length from P to Q is of the third order relative to α when $\alpha \to 0$.

(c) If the tangent line is drawn to the circle at P and if a line is drawn from Q perpendicular to this tangent and meeting it at T, then $\overline{QT}$ is an infinitesimal of higher order than the arc $\widehat{PQ}$ when $\alpha \to 0$, and the length of the tangent $\overline{PT}$ is an infinitesimal of the same order.

(d) Let M be the intersection of the tangents to the circle at P and Q, and let the line joining M and the center of the circle meet the chord $\overline{PQ}$ at S and the arc $\widehat{PQ}$ at R. Find the order of $\overline{MR} - \overline{RS}$ relative to α when $\alpha \to 0$.

2. In the triangle ABC, suppose that the angle θ at A is an infinitesimal, and suppose that the sides $\overline{AB}$ and $\overline{AC}$ differ by an infinitesimal of the same order as θ.

(a) If the area of the triangle is approximated by the formula $\frac{1}{2}(\overline{AB})^2 \cdot \theta$, what is the order of the error relative to θ?

(b) If the area of the triangle is approximated by the formula $\frac{1}{2}(\overline{AB})(\overline{AC}) \cdot \theta$, what is the order of the error relative to θ?

3. Find the order of infinitesimal neglected when the volume of a spherical shell is approximated by the formula $4\pi r^2 h$, where h is the infinitesimal thickness of the shell and

(a) r is the inner radius.   (b) r is the outer radius.
(c) r is the mean radius.

4. Let α and β be two infinitesimals with β a function of α. Also, let α' and β' be two infinitesimals which differ respectively from α and β by infinitesimals of higher order than α and β, respectively. Show that if either $\lim_{\alpha \to 0} \beta/\alpha$ or $\lim_{\alpha' \to 0} \beta'/\alpha'$ exists, then both limits exist and are equal. Show that if either β/α or β'/α' increases without bound as $\alpha \to 0$ and $\alpha' \to 0$, then the other does also. Generalize this result.

13. Taylor's Theorem.   It is evident that if

$$P_n(x) = A_0 + \frac{A_1}{1!}(x - a) + \frac{A_2}{2!}(x - a)^2$$

$$+ \cdots + \frac{A_n}{n!}(x - a)^n, \quad (1)$$

where A_0, A_1, . . . , A_n, and a are real numbers, then

$$P_n'(x) = A_1 + A_2(x - a) + \cdots + \frac{A_n}{(n - 1)!}(x - a)^{n-1},$$

$$P_n''(x) = \quad A_2 \quad + \cdots + \frac{A_n}{(n - 2)!}(x - a)^{n-2}, \quad (2)$$

. . . .

$$P_n^{(n)}(x) = \qquad\qquad A_n.$$

By (1) and (2) we have the very useful result that

$$P_n(a) \quad = A_0, \qquad P_n'(a) = A_1, \qquad P_n''(a) = A_2,$$
$$P_n'''(a) = A_3, \qquad \cdots, \qquad P_n^{(n)}(a) = A_n. \quad (3)$$

Let f be a function of x having n derivatives at $x = a$ (such as $\cos x$), and in (1) let us take $A_0 = f(a)$, $A_1 = f'(a)$, $A_2 = f''(a)$, $\cdots$, $A_n = f^{(n)}(a)$. Then

$$P_n(x) = f(a) + \frac{f'(a)}{1!}(x - a) + \frac{f''(a)}{2!}(x - a)^2$$

$$+ \cdots + \frac{f^{(n)}(a)}{n!}(x - a)^n, \quad (4)$$

and by (3),

$$P_n(a) = f(a), \qquad P_n'(a) = f'(a),$$
$$P_n''(a) = f''(a), \qquad \cdots, \qquad P_n^{(n)}(a) = f^{(n)}(a). \quad (5)$$

Thus, at $x = a$, the values of P_n and its first n derivatives are respectively equal to the values of f and its first n derivatives. (Cf. Examples 1 and 2 below.) We raise the following fundamental question: How close does the polynomial P_n in (4) approximate the function f in the neighborhood of $x = a$, that is, how close are the graphs of P_n and f near $x = a$? One might expect the approximation to be good, since, by (5), the two graphs have the same ordinate and slope at $x = a$, the slopes are changing at the same rate at $x = a$, etc.

To determine the accuracy of P_n as an approximation of f, we shall derive a formula for the difference $f(x) - P_n(x)$. Suppose f has $n + 1$ derivatives defined over the interval $a \leq x \leq b$. Then, since a polynomial has arbitrarily many derivatives, the auxiliary function

$$\varphi(x) \equiv f(x) - P_n(x) - \lambda(x - a)^{n+1} \quad (6)$$

has $n + 1$ derivatives defined over the interval $a \leqq x \leqq b$, where in (6) we choose λ as that constant such that $\varphi(b) = 0$, that is, such that

$$\varphi(b) = f(b) - P_n(b) - \lambda(b - a)^{n+1} = 0. \tag{7}$$

By Theorem 5.1, φ and its first n derivatives are continuous. Moreover, by (5),

$$\varphi(a) = 0, \qquad \varphi'(a) = 0, \qquad \varphi''(a) = 0, \cdots,$$
$$\varphi^{(n)}(a) = 0, \qquad \text{and} \qquad \varphi(b) = 0. \tag{8}$$

We shall now apply Rolle's theorem to the function φ and its successive derivatives. Since $\varphi(a) = \varphi(b) = 0$, there exists a value c_1 of x, $a < c_1 < b$, such that $\varphi'(c_1) = 0$. Since

$$\varphi'(a) = \varphi'(c_1) = 0,$$

there exists a value c_2 of x, $a < c_2 < c_1$, such that $\varphi''(c_2) = 0$. Repetition of this argument shows that $\varphi'''(x), \cdots, \varphi^{(n)}(x)$, and $\varphi^{(n+1)}(x)$ vanish at values $c_3, \cdots, c_n$, and ξ of x such that $a < \xi < c_n < \cdots < c_3 < c_2 < c_1 < b$. Upon differentiating (6), we find that

$$\varphi^{(n+1)}(x) \equiv f^{(n+1)}(x) - 0 - (n + 1)! \cdot \lambda. \tag{9}$$

But $\varphi^{(n+1)}(\xi) = 0$ for some value ξ of x between a and b, so that

$$f^{(n+1)}(\xi) - (n + 1)! \cdot \lambda = 0, \qquad a < \xi < b. \tag{10}$$

If we solve (10) for λ and substitute in (7), we find that

$$f(b) - P_n(b) - \frac{f^{(n+1)}(\xi)}{(n + 1)!}(b - a)^{n+1} = 0. \tag{11}$$

If we evaluate $P_n(b)$ by (4), we obtain the result that

$$f(b) = f(a) + \frac{f'(a)}{1!}(b - a) + \frac{f''(a)}{2!}(b - a)^2$$
$$+ \cdots + \frac{f^{(n)}(a)}{n!}(b - a)^n + \frac{f^{(n+1)}(\xi)}{(n + 1)!}(b - a)^{n+1}, \tag{12}$$

where $a < \xi < b$. Formula (12) is known as *Taylor's formula* or *theorem*. It is readily shown that (12) holds when $b < a$, ξ being such that $b < \xi < a$.

It is convenient to denote the last term of (12) by R_n, that is,

$$R_n = \frac{f^{(n+1)}(\xi)}{(n+1)!}(b-a)^{n+1}. \tag{13}$$

The expression R_n is called the *remainder* and represents the error made when $P_n(b)$ is used to approximate $f(b)$. *If we can show that* $\lim_{n \to \infty} R_n = 0$, *then, and only then, do we know that* $P_n(b)$ *can be made to approximate* $f(b)$ *arbitrarily closely by taking* n *sufficiently large.* In this connection, it is a matter of practical importance to know how large we must take n in order that R_n may be numerically less than a given "allowable error" ϵ. Suppose there exists a number M such that $|f^{(n+1)}(\xi)| < M$ for all values of ξ between a and b. [While it is usually impossible to determine ξ in (12), it is often a simple matter to determine such a number M.] Then R_n is numerically less than

$$\frac{M}{(n+1)!}|b-a|^{n+1}.$$

If we can choose n so that $\dfrac{M}{(n+1)!}|b-a|^{n+1} < \epsilon$, then $P_n(b)$ approximates $f(b)$ to within an amount less than ϵ.

Taylor's theorem may be written in many ways; for example, if in (12) we replace b by x, we have

$$f(x) = f(a) + \frac{f'(a)}{1!}(x-a) + \frac{f''(a)}{2!}(x-a)^2$$
$$+ \cdots + \frac{f^{(n)}(a)}{n!}(x-a)^n + R_n, \tag{14}$$

where

$$R_n = \frac{f^{(n+1)}(\xi)}{(n+1)!}(x-a)^{n+1}, \ \xi \text{ between } a \text{ and } x. \tag{15}$$

If in (12) we replace b by $a + x$ and ξ by $a + \theta x$, where $0 < \theta < 1$, we find that

$$f(a+x) = f(a) + \frac{f'(a)}{1!}x + \frac{f''(a)}{2!}x^2$$
$$+ \cdots + \frac{f^{(n)}(a)}{n!}x^n + R_n, \tag{16}$$

where

$$R_n = \frac{f^{(n+1)}(a + \theta x)}{(n + 1)!} x^{n+1}, \qquad 0 < \theta < 1.$$

(Lagrange's form of remainder)   (17)

If $a = 0$ in (16), we have *Maclaurin's formula* or *theorem:*

$$f(x) = f(0) + \frac{f'(0)}{1!}x + \frac{f''(0)}{2!}x^2 + \cdots + \frac{f^{(n)}(0)}{n!}x^n + R_n, \quad (18)$$

where

$$R_n = \frac{f^{(n+1)}(\theta x)}{(n + 1)!} x^{n+1}, \qquad 0 < \theta < 1. \tag{19}$$

Example 1. Expand e^{2x} by Maclaurin's theorem.
Solution. It is seen that

$$f(x) = e^{2x}; f'(x) = 2e^{2x}; f''(x) = 2^2 e^{2x}; \cdots ,$$
$$f^{(n)}(x) = 2^n e^{2x}; f^{(n+1)}(x) = 2^{n+1} e^{2x}.$$
$$f(0) = 1; f'(0) = 2; f''(0) = 2^2; \cdots ; f^{(n)}(0) = 2^n;$$
$$f^{(n+1)}(\theta x) = 2^{n+1} e^{2(\theta x)}.$$

By (18) we have

$$e^{2x} = 1 + \frac{2}{1!}x + \frac{2^2}{2!}x^2 + \cdots + \frac{2^n}{n!}x^n + \frac{2^{n+1}e^{2\theta x}}{(n + 1)!} x^{n+1}, \qquad 0 < \theta < 1. \quad (20)$$

Let x be assigned a value b. Then $R_n = \dfrac{(2b)^{n+1}}{(n + 1)!} e^{2\theta b}$. Since $0 < \theta < 1$, it follows that $e^{2\theta b} < M$, where $M = e^{2b}$ if $b > 0$ and $M = 1$ if $b < 0$. Thus, for a given value of n, $\dfrac{(2b)^{n+1}}{(n + 1)!} M$ is an *upper bound* of the numerical value of R_n. For example, if $b = 0.05$ and $n = 4$, we know that the remainder is not larger than $\dfrac{0.00001}{120} e^{0.1}$. If we replace $e^{0.1}$ by a larger quantity whose decimal value we know, such as $\sqrt{e} = 1.64$, we know that the remainder is not larger than $(0.00001/120)(1.64) < 0.0000002$. Hence, by (20) with $x = 0.05$ and $n = 4$,

$$e^{0.1} = 1 + 2(0.05) + 2(0.05)^2 + \tfrac{4}{3}(0.05)^3 + \tfrac{2}{3}(0.05)^4 = 1.1051708$$
to within 0.0000002.

To show that $|R_n|$ can be made arbitrarily small by taking n sufficiently large, let us consider the factor $(2b)^{n+1}/(n + 1)!$ in R_n. Let n_0 be such a positive integer that $|2b/n_0| < \tfrac{1}{2}$. When $n > n_0$, all factors in the product

$$\frac{(2b)^{n+1}}{(n + 1)!} = \left(\frac{2b}{1}\right)\left(\frac{2b}{2}\right) \cdots \left(\frac{2b}{n_0}\right) \cdots \left(\frac{2b}{n}\right)\left(\frac{2b}{n + 1}\right) \quad \text{after the } n_0\text{th are}$$

numerically $<\frac{1}{2}$. Hence $|(2b)^{n+1}/(n+1)!| < |2b/1| \cdots |2b/n_0|(\frac{1}{2})^{n+1-n_0}$

when $n > n_0$. But $\lim\limits_{n \to \infty} (\frac{1}{2})^{n+1-n_0} = 0$. Therefore $\lim\limits_{n \to \infty} \dfrac{(2b)^{n+1}}{(n+1)!} = 0$.

Because the factor $e^{2\theta b}$ never exceeds M, it follows by Ex. IV, 15, that, for any given value of b, n can be taken suffici-
ently large that $|R_n|$ becomes arbitrarily
small. However, the larger is b the larger
must we take n to make $|R_n|$ less than a
given number ϵ. In other words, it is impossible to find any one value of n suffi-
ciently large that $|R_n| < \epsilon$ simultaneously for
all values of b. This kind of a situation will
be discussed in detail when we take up the
concept of *uniform convergence*.

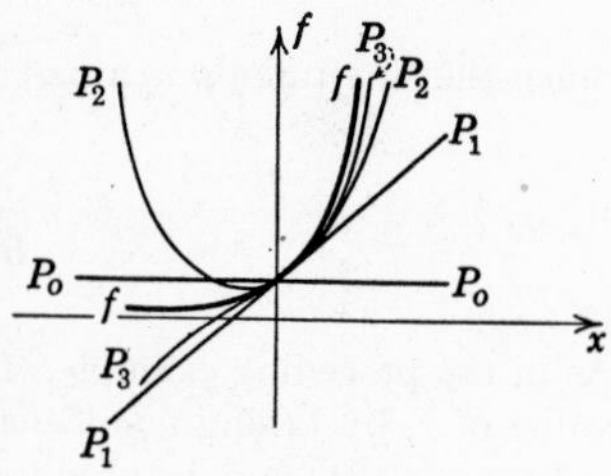

Fig. 32.

In Fig. 32 are shown the graphs of
$f(x) = e^{2x}$ and of the polynomials P_0, P_1, P_2, and P_3. The manner in which
P_n approximates f more and more closely as $n \to \infty$ is clearly indicated.

Example 2. Expand $\sin x$ about $a = \pi/6$ rad. by Taylor's theorem.

Solution. It follows by Ex. V, 7, that

$$f(x) = \sin x, \qquad\qquad f\left(\frac{\pi}{6}\right) = \frac{1}{2},$$

$$f'(x) = \cos x = \sin\left(x + \frac{\pi}{2}\right), \qquad f'\left(\frac{\pi}{6}\right) = \frac{\sqrt{3}}{2},$$

$$f''(x) = -\sin x = \sin(x + \pi), \qquad f''\left(\frac{\pi}{6}\right) = -\frac{1}{2},$$

$$f'''(x) = -\cos x = \sin\left(x + \frac{3\pi}{2}\right), \qquad f'''\left(\frac{\pi}{6}\right) = -\frac{\sqrt{3}}{2},$$

$$\cdots \cdots \cdots \cdots \cdots$$

$$f^{(n)}(x) = \sin\left(x + \frac{n\pi}{2}\right), \qquad f^{(n)}\left(\frac{\pi}{6}\right) = \sin\left(\frac{\pi}{6} + \frac{n\pi}{2}\right),$$

$$f^{(n+1)}(x) = \sin\left(x + \frac{n+1}{2}\pi\right). \qquad f^{(n+1)}(\xi) = \sin\left(\xi + \frac{n+1}{2}\pi\right).$$

By (14) we have

$$\sin x = \frac{1}{2} + \frac{\sqrt{3}}{2}\left(x - \frac{\pi}{6}\right) + \frac{-\frac{1}{2}}{2!}\left(x - \frac{\pi}{6}\right)^2 + \cdots$$

$$+ \frac{\sin\left(\dfrac{\pi}{6} + \dfrac{n\pi}{2}\right)}{n!}\left(x - \frac{\pi}{6}\right)^n + R_n, \quad (21)$$

where

$$R_n = \frac{\sin\left(\xi + \frac{n+1}{2}\pi\right)}{(n+1)!}\left(x - \frac{\pi}{6}\right)^{n+1}, \; \xi \text{ between } \frac{\pi}{6} \text{ and } x.$$

Since the sine function cannot be numerically greater than 1,

$$|R_n| \leqq \frac{\left|x - \frac{\pi}{6}\right|^{n+1}}{(n+1)!}.$$

As in the preceding example, $|R_n|$ can be made arbitrarily small, for a given value of x, by taking n sufficiently large.

Formula (21) may be used to approximate the values of $\sin x$ to any degree of accuracy. Thus, $\sin 31°$ may be computed to as many decimals as desired by setting $x = 31(\pi/180)$ radians in (21):

$$\sin 31° = \sin \frac{31\pi}{180} = \frac{1}{2} + \frac{\sqrt{3}}{2}\frac{\pi}{180} - \frac{1}{4}\left(\frac{\pi}{180}\right)^2 - \cdots$$

$$+ \frac{\sin\left(\frac{\pi}{6} + \frac{n\pi}{2}\right)}{n!}\left(\frac{\pi}{180}\right)^n + R_n,$$

where

$$|R_n| \leqq \frac{(\pi/180)^{n+1}}{(n+1)!}.$$

If we take $n = 4$, $R_n \leqq 0.000,000,000,01$, and $\sin 31° = 0.515,038,0749$ correct to ten decimals.

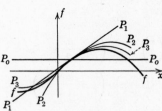

FIG. 33.

In Fig. 33 are shown the graphs of $f(x) = \sin x$ and of the polynomials $P_0, P_1, P_2,$ and P_3.

The next example illustrates the case where R_n does not approach zero as $n \to \infty$.

Example 3. Expand the function f about $x = 0$ when

$$f(x) = \begin{cases} e^{-1/x^2} & \text{when} \quad x \neq 0, \\ 0 & \text{when} \quad x = 0. \end{cases}$$

Solution. It is evident that f is continuous at $x = 0$ (see Sec. 3, Example 4). Moreover, $f'(x) = (2/x^3)e^{-1/x^2}$ when $x \neq 0$, and

$$f'(0) = \lim_{\Delta x \to 0}\frac{f(0 + \Delta x) - f(0)}{\Delta x} = \lim_{\Delta x \to 0}\left(\frac{1}{\Delta x}e^{-1/(\Delta x)^2}\right).$$

By Ex. XII, 1k, this last limit exists and is 0. Moreover, by Ex. XII, 1k, $\lim_{x \to 0} f'(x) = 0$. Hence f' is defined and continuous at all values of x.

We shall prove by induction that

$$f^{(n)}(x) = \begin{cases} \dfrac{Q_n(x)}{x^{3n}}e^{-1/x^2} & \text{when} \quad x \neq 0, \\ 0 & \text{when} \quad x = 0, \end{cases} \tag{22}$$

where Q_n is a polynomial of degree less than $3n$ (see Ex. V, 7).

We have already shown that (22) holds when $n = 1$. Let N be a value of n for which (22) holds. We shall show that (22) holds when $n = N + 1$. If in (22) we set $n = N$ and differentiate, we find that

$$f^{(N+1)}(x) = \frac{Q_{N+1}(x)}{x^{3(N+1)}}e^{-1/x^2}, \qquad x \neq 0,$$

where $Q_{N+1}(x) = (2 - 3Nx^2)Q_N(x) + x^3 Q'_N(x)$. Since Q_{N+1} is a polynomial of degree less than $3(N + 1)$, (22) holds for the case $n = N + 1$ when $x \neq 0$. But by Ex. XII, 1k,

$$f^{(N+1)}(0) = \lim_{\Delta x \to 0} \frac{f^{(N)}(0 + \Delta x) - f^{(N)}(0)}{\Delta x} = \lim_{\Delta x \to 0} \frac{Q_N(\Delta x)}{(\Delta x)^{3N+1}}e^{-1/(\Delta x)^2} = 0,$$

so that (22) holds when $n = N + 1$ and $x = 0$. Thus (22) is established for all positive integer values of n.

If we expand f by Maclaurin's theorem about $x = 0$, we find that

$$f(x) = 0 + 0 \cdot x + 0 \cdot x^2 + \cdots + 0 \cdot x^n + R_n.$$

Thus, for every value of n and x, the remainder is equal to the value of the original function f itself, and P_n, for all n, is identically zero (see Fig. 34).

Our next example shows how the remainder may behave in different ways for different values of x.

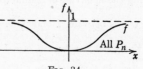

FIG. 34.

Example 4. Expand $\sqrt{x}$ about $a = 1$ by Taylor's theorem.

Solution. It is seen that

$$f(x) = x^{1/2}, \qquad\qquad f(1) = 1,$$
$$f'(x) = \tfrac{1}{2}x^{-1/2}, \qquad\qquad f'(1) = \tfrac{1}{2},$$
$$f''(x) = \tfrac{1}{2}(-\tfrac{1}{2})x^{-3/2}, \qquad\qquad f''(1) = \tfrac{1}{2}(-\tfrac{1}{2}),$$

$$\cdots\cdots\cdots\cdots\cdots\cdots\cdots$$

$$f^{(n)}(x) = \frac{1}{2}\left(-\frac{1}{2}\right)\left(-\frac{3}{2}\right)\cdots \qquad f^{(n)}(1) = \frac{1}{2}\left(-\frac{1}{2}\right)\cdots\left(-\frac{2n-3}{2}\right),$$
$$\left(-\frac{2n-3}{2}\right)x^{-\frac{2n-1}{2}},$$

$$f^{(n+1)}(x) = \frac{1}{2}\left(-\frac{1}{2}\right)\left(-\frac{3}{2}\right)\cdots \qquad f^{(n+1)}(\xi) = \frac{1}{2}\left(-\frac{1}{2}\right)\cdots$$
$$\left(-\frac{2n-1}{2}\right)x^{-\frac{2n+1}{2}}. \qquad\qquad \left(-\frac{2n-1}{2}\right)\xi^{-\frac{2n+1}{2}}.$$

By (14) we have

$$\sqrt{x} = 1 + \frac{1}{2}(x - 1) - \frac{1}{2} \cdot \frac{1}{4}(x - 1)^2 + \frac{1 \cdot 3}{2 \cdot 4} \cdot \frac{1}{6}(x - 1)^3$$

$$- \frac{1 \cdot 3 \cdot 5}{2 \cdot 4 \cdot 6} \cdot \frac{1}{8}(x - 1)^4 + \cdots$$

$$+ (-1)^{n+1}\frac{1 \cdot 3 \cdot 5 \cdots (2n - 3)}{2 \cdot 4 \cdot 6 \cdots (2n - 2)} \cdot \frac{1}{2n}(x - 1)^n + R_n, \quad (23)$$

where

$$R_n = (-1)^{n+2}\frac{1 \cdot 3 \cdot 5 \cdots (2n - 1)}{2 \cdot 4 \cdot 6 \cdots (2n)} \cdot \frac{1}{2n + 2}\xi^{-\frac{2n+1}{2}}(x - 1)^{n+1},$$

$$\xi \text{ between 1 and } x.$$

In (23) let us set $x = b$ and let us determine the behavior of R_n as $n \to \infty$. Let us write R_n in the form

$$R_n = (-1)^{n+2}\frac{1 \cdot 3 \cdot 5 \cdots (2n - 1)}{2 \cdot 4 \cdot 6 \cdots (2n)} \cdot \frac{1}{2n + 2}\sqrt{\xi}\left(\frac{b - 1}{\xi}\right)^{n+1}.$$

Since $\lim\limits_{n \to \infty} \dfrac{1 \cdot 3 \cdot 5 \cdots (2n - 1)}{2 \cdot 4 \cdot 6 \cdots (2n)} \cdot \dfrac{1}{2n + 2} = 0$, it is a question of determining the behavior of the factor $\sqrt{\xi}\left(\dfrac{b - 1}{\xi}\right)^{n+1}$. Since ξ is between 1 and b, $\sqrt{\xi}$ is between 1 and $\sqrt{b}$. If $1 < b < 2$, then $0 < b - 1 < 1$, and since $1 < \xi$, $0 < \dfrac{b - 1}{\xi} < b - 1 < 1$. Hence $\lim\limits_{n \to \infty}\left(\dfrac{b - 1}{\xi}\right)^{n+1} = 0$, so that $\lim\limits_{n \to \infty} R_n = 0$. Again, if $\frac{1}{2} < b \leqq 1$, then $0 \leqq 1 - b < \frac{1}{2} < \xi$, so that $0 \leqq \dfrac{1 - b}{\xi} < \dfrac{1 - b}{\frac{1}{2}} < 1$. Here also $\lim\limits_{n \to \infty} R_n = 0$. Hence $\lim\limits_{n \to \infty} R_n = 0$ when $\frac{1}{2} < b < 2$. But if $b > 2$, then ξ may be so close to 1 that $\dfrac{b - 1}{\xi} > 1$ and $\lim\limits_{n \to \infty}\left(\dfrac{b - 1}{\xi}\right)^{n+1} \to + \infty$. In this case the behavior of R_n as $n \to \infty$ can be determined only by further investigation. Again, if $0 \leqq b < \frac{1}{2}$, then $\frac{1}{2} < |b - 1|$, and if $\xi < \frac{1}{2}$, then $\dfrac{|b - 1|}{\xi} > 1$ and the behavior of R_n is indeterminate as in the preceding case. However, it can be shown, for example, that $\lim\limits_{n \to \infty} P_n(0) = 0$, and since $\sqrt{0} = 0$, it follows that $\lim\limits_{n \to \infty} R_n = 0$ when $b = 0$. On the other hand, it can be shown that $\lim\limits_{n \to \infty} P_n(b)$ does not exist when $b > 2$, and since $\sqrt{b}$ exists, it follows that $\lim\limits_{n \to \infty} R_n$ does not exist when $b > 2$.

In Fig. 35 are shown the graphs of $\sqrt{x}$ and P_0, P_1, P_2, P_3, and P_4. It would seem from the figure that the polynomials P_n approximate $\sqrt{x}$ more and more closely as $n \to \infty$ for values of x in the interval $0 \leqq x \leqq 2$, but not for other values of x. This surmise can in fact be shown to be true.

EXERCISES XIV

1. Expand each of the following functions about the values of x indicated, and in each case include the remainder R_n.

(a) e^{-3x}, $a = 0$.   (b) $\cos x$, $a = \pi/3$.
(c) $\sin 2x$, $a = 0$.   (d) $x^{\frac{1}{3}}$, $a = 1$.
(e) $\log_e (1 + x)$, $a = 0$.   (f) $\log_{10} (1 + x)$, $a = 0$.
(g) $\log_e (1 + x)/(1 - x)$, $a = 0$.   (Write $\log_e (1 + x)/(1 - x)$ as
          $\log_e (1 + x) - \log_e (1 - x)$ and use part (e).)
(h) b^x, $b > 0$, about $a = 0$.   (i) $\tan x$, $a = 0$.
(j) $\tan x$, $a = \pi/4$.
(k) $\sin (1 - x^2)$, $a = 1$.   (Expand $\sin u$ about $u = 0$, and substitute
          $u = 1 - x^2$ in the result.)
(l) e^{-x^2}, $a = 0$.   (m) $\log \sin x$, $a = \pi/2$.
(n) $\sqrt{1 - x^2}$, $a = 0$.   (o) $\mathrm{Tan}^{-1} x$, $a = 0$.   (See Ex. V, 9.)
(p) $\mathrm{Sin}^{-1} x$, $a = 0$.   (q) $(1 + x)^m$, $a = 0$.
(r) $c_0 + c_1 x + c_2 x^2 + \cdots + c_n x^n$ about $x = a$.
(s) $\sinh x$, $a = 0$.   (t) $\cosh x$, $a = 0$.
(u) $\tanh x$, $a = 0$.   (v) $\sinh^{-1} x$, $a = 0$.

See Chap. II, Sec. 5 for the definitions of the functions in parts s, t, u, and v.

2. (a) How many terms are needed to compute e to six decimals if the Maclaurin development for e^x is used?

(b) How many terms are needed to compute $\log_e 1.5$ to five decimals if the Maclaurin development for $\log_e (1 + x)$ is used?

3. (a) Compute $\sin 30'$ correct to six decimals.

(b) Compute $\cos 62°$ correct to six decimals.

(c) Compute $\mathrm{Sin}^{-1} 0.1$ correct to the nearest second.

(d) Compute $\mathrm{Tan}^{-1} \frac{1}{5}$ and $\mathrm{Tan}^{-1} \frac{1}{239}$. From the relation

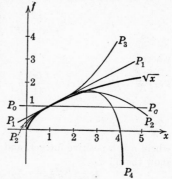

Fig. 35.

$$\frac{\pi}{4} = \mathrm{Tan}^{-1} 1 = 4 \, \mathrm{Tan}^{-1} \frac{1}{5} - \mathrm{Tan}^{-1} \frac{1}{239}$$

compute $\pi/4$ to seven decimal places. How many terms would be needed to find $\mathrm{Tan}^{-1} 1$ to this accuracy by direct computation?

4. (a) In the result of Ex. 1g, show that the remainder R_{n-1} is less than $\dfrac{2x^n}{n(1 - x)^n}$, where in this formula $0 \leqq x < 1$.

(b) With the aid of the preceding result, compute $\log_e 2$ correct to five decimals.   (Use $x = \frac{1}{3}$ in Ex. 1g.)

(c) How many terms would be needed to find $\log_e 2$ to this accuracy by Ex. 1e?

(d) Compute $\log_e \frac{5}{3}$ correct to six decimals by Ex. 1g.

5. (a) From the Maclaurin expansion for $(1 + x)^p$, where p is any real number, show that

$$|R_n| < \left| \frac{p(p-1) \cdots (p-n)}{(n+1)!} x^{n+1} \right| \quad \text{when} \quad x > 0 \quad \text{and} \quad n+1 > p,$$

and

$$|R_n| < \left| \frac{p(p-1) \cdots (p-n)}{(n+1)!} \frac{x^{n+1}}{(1+x)^{n+1-p}} \right| \quad \text{when} \quad -1 < x < 0$$
$$\text{and} \quad n+1 > p.$$

(b) Compute $\sqrt{102}$ correct to five decimals.

(c) Compute $\sqrt[5]{251}$ correct to five decimals.

6. (a) Find the Maclaurin development of the function f when

$$f(x) = \begin{cases} \sin x + e^{-1/x^2} & \text{when} \quad x \neq 0, \\ 0 & \text{when} \quad x = 0. \end{cases}$$

(b) Find $\lim\limits_{n \to \infty} R_n$ and discuss the behavior of P_n as $n \to \infty$.

7. By considering the auxiliary function

$$\varphi(x) = F(x) - \left(\frac{b-x}{b-a} \right)^p F(a),$$

where

$$F(x) \equiv -f(b) + f(x) + \frac{f'(x)}{1!}(b-x) + \frac{f''(x)}{2!}(b-x)^2 + \cdots$$
$$+ \frac{f^{(n)}(x)}{n!}(b-x)^n,$$

where n is a positive integer, and where p is an arbitrary positive number, show that

$$f(b) = f(a) + \frac{f'(a)}{1!}(b-a) + \frac{f''(a)}{2!}(b-a)^2 + \cdots$$
$$+ \frac{f^{(n)}(a)}{n!}(b-a)^n + R_n,$$

where

$$R_n = \frac{f^{(n+1)}(\xi)}{p(n!)}(b-a)^p(b-\xi)^{n-p+1}, \quad a < \xi < b. \quad \text{(Schlömilch's form.)}$$

8. From Ex. 7, obtain Lagrange's form of the remainder

$$R_n = \frac{f^{(n+1)}(\xi)}{(n+1)!}(b - a)^{n+1}, \qquad a < \xi < b,$$

Cauchy's form

$$R_n = \frac{f^{(n+1)}(\xi)}{n!}(b - a)(b - \xi)^n, \qquad a < \xi < b,$$

and the following modified forms:

$$R_n = \frac{f^{(n+1)}(a + \theta h)}{p(n!)}h^{n+1}(1 - \theta)^{n-p+1}, \qquad 0 < \theta < 1,$$
$$R_n = \frac{f^{(n+1)}(a + \theta h)}{n!}h^{n+1}(1 - \theta)^n, \qquad 0 < \theta < 1.$$

9. Write the remainder in four different forms in the case where $\sin x$ is expanded about $a = 0$.

10. Show that

$$(1 + x)^k = 1 + \frac{k}{1!}x + \frac{k(k - 1)}{2!}x^2 + \cdots$$
$$+ \frac{k(k - 1) \cdots (k - n + 1)}{n!}x^n + R_n,$$

where

$$R_n = \frac{k(k - 1) \cdots (k - n)}{p(n!)} \cdot \frac{(1 - \theta)^{n-p+1}}{(1 + \theta x)^{n-k+1}}x^{n+1}, \qquad 0 < \theta < 1,$$

for all values of x when $n < k - 1$, and for all x such that $-1 < x$ when $n > k - 1$.

PART B.   PARTIAL DIFFERENTIATION

14. Functions of Several Variables. We now take up the problem of extending to functions of several variables the concepts and theorems developed in the preceding sections.

Let x and y be two real variables. We shall speak of a pair of values of x and y as a *point*. We shall denote a point $x = a$, $y = b$ by the symbol (a, b), where in this symbol it is understood that the first value a relates to x and the second value b relates to y. If values of x and y are represented by rectangular coordinates in a plane, then a point, as we have defined the word, is represented in the usual way by a geometric "point." We shall use the word point interchangeably in both the geometric sense and in the sense just now defined. By the xy-plane we shall mean the set of all points (x, y), where x and y are assumed independent.

Let us recall from Sec. 2 that a *real variable* is a symbol having real numbers for values. Thus, the formula $x^2 - 3xy$ is a real variable in that it is a symbol having real values when x and y have real values, that is, $x^2 - 3xy$ has a definite real value at each point (x, y). However, the variable $\sqrt{x + y}$ is defined at only those points (x, y) such that $x + y \geqq 0$; the variable $\log_e [1 - (x^2 + y^2)]$ is defined at only those points (x, y) such that $1 - (x^2 + y^2) > 0$, that is, at only those points inside the circle $x^2 + y^2 = 1$; and the variable y^x is defined only if either $y > 0$ and x is arbitrary, or $y = 0$ and $x \neq 0$, or $y < 0$ and x is rational with an odd denominator. With these examples in mind, we may define a function of x and y.

DEFINITION 14.1. *Let x and y be two real variables. If a variable has exactly one real value at each point (x, y) in some set D of points (x, y), then this variable is called a real single-valued function of x and y defined over D.*

If x and y are *independent* variables, so that x and y may be assigned all possible pairs of values, and if D is the set of all points (x, y) at which a function of x and y is defined, then D is called the *domain of definition* of this function.

Thus, for example, the domain of definition, D, of the function $\log_e [1 - (x^2 + y^2)]$ is the interior of the circle $x^2 + y^2 = 1$.

In Definition 14.1, x and y need not be independent, but they may themselves be functions of other variables.

If f denotes a function of x and y, then $f(x, y)$ denotes, and is read, the value of f at the point (x, y).

As an example of a function of two variables, let us consider the temperature T at a certain instant of the "plate" in a three-electrode vacuum tube. Suppose the plate is a rectangle $ABCD$, 2 cm. long, 1 cm. wide, and of negligible thickness. Let x and y be the rectangular coordinates of a point P in the plate, where the origin is at A and where x is measured parallel to the length AB of the plate. It follows that T is a function of x and y in that T has a definite value at

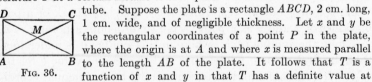

FIG. 36.

each point (x, y) in the plate. We denote the value of T at the point (a, b) by $T(a, b)$, and we read this symbol "the value of T at (a, b)." If the temperature of the plate (in degrees centigrade) at the center M is 100, along the edges is 0, and drops off linearly from the center to each point on each edge, then $T(1, \frac{1}{2}) = 100$, $T(\frac{1}{2}, \frac{1}{4}) = T(\frac{1}{2}, \frac{1}{3}) = T(1, \frac{1}{4}) = 50$, and $T(0, \frac{1}{2}) = T(2, 1) = 0$. This last equation, for example, should be read "the value of T at $(2, 1)$ is 0." The symbol $T(x, y)$ denotes, and is read, "the value of T at an arbitrary point (x, y)." It is evident that

$$T(x, y) = \begin{cases} 200y \text{ when } (x, y) \text{ is in triangle } ABM, \\ 100x \text{ when } (x, y) \text{ is in triangle } ADM, \\ 100(2 - x) \text{ when } (x, y) \text{ is in triangle } BCM, \\ 200(1 - y) \text{ when } (x, y) \text{ is in triangle } CDM, \end{cases}$$

where we read this relation "the value of T at an arbitrary point (x, y) is $200y$ when (x, y) is in the triangle ABM," etc. The fact that T is represented by several formulas in no way contradicts the fact that T is one definite function of x and y defined over the entire rectangle $ABCD$; it is possible to represent T by a single, but rather complicated, formula.

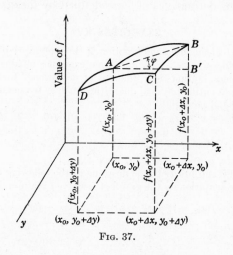

Fig. 37.

If f denotes a function of x and y, and if $f(x_0, y_0)$ denotes the value of f at (x_0, y_0), where (x_0, y_0) is a point at which f is defined, then the triple of numbers $[x_0, y_0, f(x_0, y_0)]$ may be regarded as the rectangular coordinates of a point in space. If (x_0, y_0) ranges over all points at which f is defined, then the set of all points $[x_0, y_0, f(x_0, y_0)]$ is called the *graph* of f. Thus the number $f(x_0, y_0)$ is represented by the length of the line segment erected perpendicular to the xy-plane at (x_0, y_0) and extending up to the graph of f.

If f is a function of x and y, then $f(x_0 + \Delta x, y_0) - f(x_0, y_0)$ represents the change in the value of f in going from the point (x_0, y_0) to the point $(x_0 + \Delta x, y_0)$. Furthermore,

$$\frac{f(x_0 + \Delta x, y_0) - f(x_0, y_0)}{\Delta x}$$

represents the mean* change in f per unit change in x, or the mean rate of change of f with respect to x, in going along the line from the point (x_0, y_0) to the point $(x_0 + \Delta x, y_0)$. It is evident that $f(x_0 + \Delta x, y_0) - f(x_0, y_0)$ is represented by the line segment $\overline{BB'}$ in Fig. 37 and that $\dfrac{f(x_0 + \Delta x, y_0) - f(x_0, y_0)}{\Delta x} = \tan \varphi$. Several other quantities of this sort are discussed in Ex. 4 below. The significance of these quantities should be thoroughly understood, for the various derivatives of f are defined by means of them.

EXERCISES XV

1. Define a real single-valued function of three real variables x, y, and z; of n real variables x_1, x_2, . . . , x_n. Give examples of functions of three and four variables, stating their domains of definition. Include examples of functions representing physical quantities, such as temperature, pressure, density, stress, and potential.

2. If $f(x, y) = x^2 - xy + 3y^2$, find $f(1, 0)$, $f(0, -2)$, $f(-1, 1)$, and $f(-3, -1)$.

3. If $f(x, y, z) = x^2 + y^2 + z^2$ and $F(x, y, z) = xy + yz + zx$, show that $f(x, y, z) + 2F(x, y, z) = [f(\sqrt{x}, \sqrt{y}, \sqrt{z})]^2$.

4. State fully and precisely the meaning of the following quantities and show their representation on the graph of f, where f is a function of x and y:

$$f(x_0, y_0 + \Delta y) - f(x_0, y_0); \quad f(x_0 + \Delta x, y_0 + \Delta y) - f(x_0, y_0);$$

$$\frac{f(x_0, y_0 + \Delta y) - f(x_0, y_0)}{\Delta y}; \quad \frac{f(x_0 + \Delta x, y_0 + \Delta y) - f(x_0, y_0)}{\sqrt{(\Delta x)^2 + (\Delta y)^2}};$$

[note that $\sqrt{(\Delta x)^2 + (\Delta y)^2}$ is the distance between the points (x_0, y_0) and $(x_0 + \Delta x, y_0 + \Delta y)$]; $\quad \dfrac{f(x_0 + \Delta x, y_0 + \Delta y) - f(x_0, y_0)}{\Delta x}$.

5. State the physical meaning of each of the quantities at the end of Sec. 14 and in Ex. 4 when $f(x, y)$ represents:

(a) the elevation at (x, y) on a topographical map, where x, y, and elevation are measured in feet.

(b) the temperature at (x, y) over a portion of the xy-plane, where x and y are measured in inches and temperature in degrees centigrade.

* See the end of Sec. 2 for the significance of the word mean.

(c) If p, v, and T denote the unit pressure, volume, and temperature of a certain quantity of gas (pounds, inches, and degrees centigrade being the units) and if p is a function of v and T, so that $p(v_0, T_0)$ denotes the unit pressure when $v = v_0$ and $T = T_0$, state the physical meaning of the various quantities analogous to those discussed in parts (a) and (b).

(d) If R is the resistance in ohms of an electric arc, if I is the current in amperes through this arc, if g is the number of milligrams of metallic vapor in this arc, and if R is a function of I and g, so that $R(I, g)$ denotes the resistance when the current is I and the amount of vapor present is g, state the physical meaning of the various quantities analogous to those discussed in parts (a) and (b).

For example, in part (b), $\dfrac{f(x_0 + \Delta x,\ y_0) - f(x_0,\ y_0)}{\Delta x}$ denotes the mean change in temperature per inch along the line from (x_0, y_0) to $(x_0 + \Delta x, y_0)$, that is, the mean rate of change of temperature with respect to x along this line segment. Again, $\dfrac{p(v_0,\ T_0 + \Delta T) - p(v_0,\ T_0)}{\Delta T}$ denotes the mean change of unit pressure per degree change in temperature, or the mean rate of change of unit pressure with respect to temperature, in going from the state (v_0, T_0) (i.e., the state in which $v = v_0$ and $T = T_0$) to the state $(v_0, T_0 + \Delta T)$ with the volume remaining at v_0. (Why is this last phrase necessary?)

6. Let $T(x, y, z)$ represent the temperature at (x, y, z) at a certain instant in a block of ice. State the physical meaning of each of the following quantities: $T(x_0, y_0, z_0)$; $T(x_0 + \Delta x, y_0, z_0) - T(x_0, y_0, z_0)$;

$$\frac{T(x_0 + \Delta x,\ y_0,\ z_0) - T(x_0,\ y_0,\ z_0)}{\Delta x};\quad \frac{T(x_0,\ y_0,\ z_0 + \Delta z) - T(x_0,\ y_0,\ z_0)}{\Delta z};$$

$$\frac{T(x_0,\ y_0 + \Delta y,\ z_0 + \Delta z) - T(x_0,\ y_0,\ z_0)}{\sqrt{(\Delta y)^2 + (\Delta z)^2}}.$$

7. Find the values of the quantities at the end of Sec. 14 and in Ex. 4 when (a) $f(x, y) = x^2 - 3xy$; (b) $f(x, y) = \dfrac{x + y}{x - 2y}$; (c) $f(x, y) = \sqrt{3x - y^2}$.

8. A common method for representing geometrically a function f of x and y is to show its contour lines in the xy-plane. This is done by plotting the curves

$$f(x, y) = \text{constant}$$

and attaching to each curve the corresponding value of the constant. For example, if $f(x, y) = x^2 + y$, the contour lines are the curves $x^2 + y = c$. In Fig. 38 these contours are shown for $c = 2$, 1, 0, -1, and -2. The surface $z = f(x, y)$ may be visualized by imagining the contour lines placed at the proper levels.

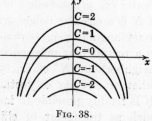

FIG. 38.

Draw a contour map for each of the following functions:

(a) $f(x, y) = 1/(x + y)$;　　　　　　(b) $f(x, y) = x^2 + y^2$;
(c) $f(x, y) = (x^2 + y^2)/2x$;　　　　(d) $f(x, y) = 2xy/(x^2 - y^2)$;
(e) $f(x, y) = y/(x^2 + 1)$;　　　　　(f) $f(x, y) = x^2 - 2y^2$.

Give several examples of the use of such representations of functions in engineering and scientific work.

9. The function φ is such that

$$\varphi(x, y) = \begin{cases} 1/x & \text{when} & x < 0 & \text{and} & x^2 + y^2 \leqq 1, \\ x^2 + 3y & \text{when} & x \geqq 0, & y \geqq 0, & \text{and} & x + y < 1, \\ 0 & \text{when} & 0 < x \leqq 1 & \text{and} & -1 \leqq y < 0. \end{cases}$$

Evaluate: $\varphi(0, 0)$; $\varphi(-1, 0)$; $\varphi(0, 1)$; $\varphi(\frac{1}{4}, \frac{1}{2})$; $\varphi(\frac{1}{4}, -\frac{1}{2})$; $\varphi(0, -\frac{1}{2})$. Draw a figure indicating the domain of definition of φ.

10. Define a multiple-valued function of x and y. If $z = \tan^{-1}(y/x)$, is z a multiple-valued function of x and y? Describe the graph of z. Does the equation $x^2 + y^2 + z^2 = 1$ define z as a multiple-valued function of x and y? For what values of x and y is z single-valued?

11. Let ρ and θ be the polar coordinates (taken in the usual manner) of the point (x, y). Describe the surfaces (a) $z = \rho^2 \sin 2\theta$; (b) $z = \tan 2\theta$. Compare this latter surface with the surface of Ex. 8d.

15. Continuous Functions. Let δ and η be arbitrary positive numbers. By a *neighborhood* of a point (x_0, y_0) we shall mean either the set of all points (x, y) such that

$$(x - x_0)^2 + (y - y_0)^2 < \delta,$$

i.e., the interior of a circle with center (x_0, y_0) and radius δ, or else the set of all points (x, y) such that $x_0 - \delta < x < x_0 + \delta$ and $y_0 - \eta < y < y_0 + \eta$, i.e., the interior of a rectangle with center (x_0, y_0) and edges of lengths 2δ and 2η. It is evident that, if N is a circular neighborhood of the point (x_0, y_0), there exists a rectangular neighborhood N' of (x_0, y_0) within N, and if N is a rectangular neighborhood of (x_0, y_0), there exists a circular neighborhood N' of (x_0, y_0) within N. Thus it is immaterial whether circular or rectangular neighborhoods are considered. It is readily possible to introduce other kinds of neighborhoods, such as triangular or elliptical, without in any way altering the ideas and theorems to be developed below. The only detail of consequence is that, if N is any kind of a neighborhood of

(x_0, y_0), N must contain (x_0, y_0) in its interior, and not on its boundary.*

DEFINITION 15.1. *If f is a real single-valued function of x and y, if A is a real number, and if, for each positive number ϵ, however small, there exists a neighborhood N of the point (a, b) such that $|f(x, y) - A| < \epsilon$ for all points (x, y) in N other than (a, b), then A is denoted by either $\lim\limits_{\substack{x \to a \\ y \to b}} f(x, y)$ or $\lim\limits_{\substack{x = a \\ y = b}} f(x, y)$, and A is referred to as the limit of f at (a, b).*

DEFINITION 15.2. *If f is a real single-valued function of x and y, and if at the point (a, b), (1) $f(a, b)$ exists, (2) $\lim\limits_{\substack{x \to a \\ y \to b}} f(x, y)$ exists, and (3) $\lim\limits_{\substack{x \to a \\ y \to b}} f(x, y) = f(a, b)$, then f is said to be continuous at (a, b).*

DEFINITION 15.3. *If f is a real single-valued function of x and y, and if $f(x, y_0)$, which is a function of x alone, is continuous at $x = x_0$, then f is said to be continuous in x at (x_0, y_0). Continuity in y is similarly defined.*

EXERCISES XVI

1. Interpret Definitions 15.1, 15.2, and 15.3 geometrically with the aid of the graph of f.

2. Show that $\lim\limits_{\substack{x \to a \\ y \to b}} f(x, y) = A$ when and only when the value of f at (x, y) becomes and remains arbitrarily close to A as $x \to a$ and $y \to b$ in any manner whatever, that is, as the point (x, y) approaches the point (a, b) along any path whatever so long as the point (x, y) remains distinct from (a, b).

3. Extend the theorems, examples, and exercises in and following Secs. 3 and 4 to functions of x and y.

4. Extend Definitions 15.1 and 15.2 to a function of 3 variables; to a function of n variables. Discuss the concept *neighborhood* in connection with these definitions. Extend the results of the preceding exercises to functions of n variables.

5. Let $f(r, \theta) = \begin{cases} (1/r) \sin 2\theta & \text{when } r \neq 0, \\ 0 & \text{when } r = 0. \end{cases}$

Show that f, when represented as a function of x and y, is continuous in x at $(0, 0)$ and also in y at $(0, 0)$, but that f is not continuous at $(0, 0)$. Sketch the graph of f.

* The subjects called *point set theory* and *topology* deal with questions such as the following: What are all the geometric figures that may be used as neighborhoods of a point (x_0, y_0)? What is meant by the interior of such a figure when its boundary is not a simple closed curve?

16. Partial Derivatives. Let f denote a function of x and y, and let the point (x, y) move along some path in the xy-plane. As (x, y) moves, the value of f at (x, y) varies, i.e., $f(x, y)$ changes. It is our object to find the value at the point (x_0, y_0) of the rate* of change of the value of f at (x, y) as the point (x, y) moves along some path in the xy-plane. To illustrate the meaning of this concept, let (x_0, y_0) be a certain point and let C_1, C_2, C_3, and C_4 be different curves in the xy-plane through (x_0, y_0). If $f(x, y)$ represents the temperature at (x, y) at a certain instant, and if the temperature is high near P in the figure and low along the y-axis, then $f(x, y)$ increases rapidly as the point (x, y) moves along C_1 in the direction indicated, $f(x, y)$ increases slowly along C_2 in the direction indicated, $f(x, y)$ is constant along some curve C_3, and $f(x, y)$ decreases rapidly along C_4 in the direction shown. Thus, at the point (x_0, y_0) the value of f changes at different rates along different curves through this point. It is consequently meaningless to speak merely of "the rate of change of f at (x_0, y_0)." It is always necessary to know the path C of the point (x, y) and to say "the value at (x_0, y_0) of the rate of change of $f(x, y)$ as the point (x, y) moves along C."

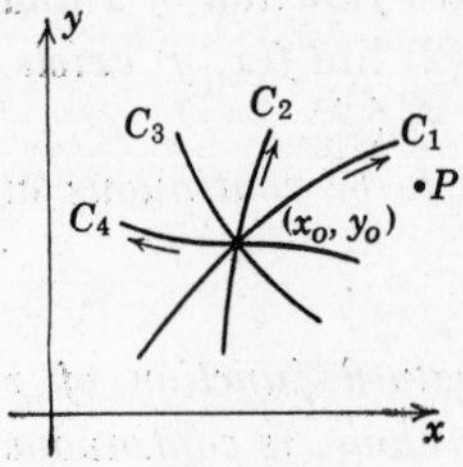

Fig. 39.

In developing a method for determining the rate of change of a given function f along a given curve C we shall consider three cases:

Case 1.   The curve C is the straight line $y = y_0$.

Case 2.   The curve C is the straight line $x = x_0$.

Case 3.   The curve C is any curve other than a straight line parallel to one of the axes.

Case 1.   Let (x_0, y_0) be a fixed point on the line $y = y_0$. The change in the value of f over a short interval along the line $y = y_0$ from (x_0, y_0) to $(x_0 + \Delta x, y_0)$ is then $f(x_0 + \Delta x, y_0) - f(x_0, y_0)$ and the mean rate of change of f with respect to x over this interval is $\dfrac{f(x_0 + \Delta x, y_0) - f(x_0, y_0)}{\Delta x}$. As $\Delta x \to 0$, the point $(x_0 + \Delta x, y_0)$ moves along the line $y = y_0$ to the point (x_0, y_0), and

---

* This rate may be with respect to any of various variables. In this paragraph it is tacitly assumed that the rate is measured with respect to the distance the point (x, y) moves along its path.

$$\lim_{\Delta x \to 0} \frac{f(x_0 + \Delta x, y_0) - f(x_0, y_0)}{\Delta x}$$

represents the value at (x_0, y_0) *of the instantaneous rate of change of* $f(x, y)$ *with respect to* x *along the line* $y = y_0$.

DEFINITION 16.1. *Let* f *be a real single-valued function of* x *and* y. *The partial derivative of* f *with respect to* x *is that function* f_x *of* x *and* y *such that*

$$f_x(x_0, y_0) = \lim_{\Delta x \to 0} \frac{f(x_0 + \Delta x, y_0) - f(x_0, y_0)}{\Delta x} \tag{1}$$

at all points (x_0, y_0) *where the limit exists, and such that* f_x *is defined nowhere else.*

Inasmuch as y has the constant value y_0 during the limit process involved in (1), it can be said that, during this limit process, f is a function of the one variable x; this is indicated by the notation $f(x, y_0)$. If we introduce the symbol

$$\frac{d}{dx} f(x, y_0) \bigg]_{x_0}$$

to denote the value of $(d/dx) f(x, y_0)$ at $x = x_0$, then it follows by Definition 5.1 that

$$\frac{d}{dx} f(x, y_0) \bigg]_{x_0} = \lim_{\Delta x \to 0} \frac{f(x_0 + \Delta x, y_0) - f(x_0, y_0)}{\Delta x}. \tag{2}$$

As an immediate consequence of (1) and (2) we have

THEOREM 16.1. $f_x(x_0, y_0) = (d/dx)f(x, y_0)]_{x_0}$.

It follows from this theorem that f_x may be formally computed by differentiating f with respect to x in the usual way while treating y as a constant.

To illustrate this discussion, let $f(x, y) = 3x^2 + 5xy$. By (1),

$$f_x(x_0, y_0) = \lim_{\Delta x \to 0} \frac{3(x_0 + \Delta x)^2 + 5(x_0 + \Delta x)y_0 - (3x_0^2 + 5x_0 y_0)}{\Delta x}$$

$$= 6x_0 + 5y_0.$$

Again, if we use the elementary differentiation rules and Theorem 16.1, we find that

$$f_x(x_0, y_0) = \frac{d}{dx}(3x^2 + 5xy_0) \bigg]_{x_0} = 6x_0 + 5y_0.$$

It follows in either case that $f_x(x, y) = 6x + 5y$.

The function f_x is also denoted by the symbol $\partial f/\partial x$. It would be natural to use the symbol df/dx, but it is conventional to use ∂ rather than d because f is a function of more than one variable. The reason for this convention will soon be seen. The symbol f_x is most useful when it is desired to indicate the value of this function at a particular point, such as $f_x(x_0 + \Delta x, y_0)$; the symbol $\partial/\partial x$ is often used when differentiation is regarded merely as an operation on f to obtain another function. Thus,

$$(\partial/\partial x)\ (3x^2 + 5xy) = 6x + 5y.$$

EXERCISES XVII

1. Find f_x, both by (1) and by Theorem 16.1, when f is given by the following formulas:

(a) $x^2y - 4y^3$; (b) $\dfrac{1}{2x - 3y}$; (c) $\sqrt{x^2 - 3xy^2}$; (d) $\sin x \cos y$.

2. Define the partial derivative of f with respect to y, i.e., define the function $f_y = \partial f/\partial y$. State the analogue of Theorem 16.1 and the formal rule for computing f_y. State the significance of $f_y(x_0, y_0)$ as a rate. Find, by two methods, f_y for the functions of the preceding exercise. Note that this exercise provides the solution to Case 2 above.

3. State the physical significance of $f_x(x_0, y_0)$ and $f_y(x_0, y_0)$ when $f(x, y)$ represents (a) temperature at the point (x, y) in the xy-plane, (b) elevation at the point (x, y) on a topographic map, (c) unit pressure at (x, y) in the xy-plane.

4. On the graph of f show the lines whose slopes are $f_x(x_0, y_0)$ and $f_y(x_0, y_0)$; also, show the angles φ and ψ whose tangents are these numbers.

5. Using only Theorem 16.1, find $\partial/\partial x$ and $\partial/\partial y$ of: (a) $\sin^3 (x - y^2)$; (b) $e^{-x/y}$; (c) $(\log x)/(\log y)$; (d) $\sqrt{1 - \sqrt{2x - y^2}}$; (e) $y \operatorname{Sin}^{-1} (y/x)$; (f) $\operatorname{Tan}^{-1} [(x - y)/(x + y)]$; (g) $\log \log^2 \sec (x^2 - y)$; (h) x^y.

6. Find the partial derivatives with respect to x and y of each of the following functions:

(a) $\sin (4x^2 - 3y)$;

(b) $\cos (3xy)$;

(c) $3x/(2x - y^2)$;

(d) $e^{-\tan xy}$;

(e) $\sqrt{(2x - 3y)^2 + 4y^3 - 5x}$;

(f) $\log (3x^5y - y^2)^{3/2}$.

7. If f and g are functions of x and y, express $(\partial/\partial x)(f \cdot g)$ in terms of f_x and g_x.

Solution. When y is constant, f and g are functions of x alone; hence $f \cdot g$ is the product of two functions of x alone and may be differentiated with respect to x by the ordinary product formula. Therefore, by Theorem 16.1,

$$\frac{\partial}{\partial x}(f \cdot g) = f \cdot g_x + g \cdot f_x = f\frac{\partial g}{\partial x} + g\frac{\partial f}{\partial x}.$$

Express $\partial/\partial x$ and $\partial/\partial y$ of the following functions in terms of f_x, f_y, g_x, and g_y:

(a) $3f + 2g$. (b) f^2. (c) $f \cdot \sqrt{g}$.

(d) $f/(f + g)$. (e) e^{-f}. (f) $f \cdot \sin^2 g$.

(g) $\log \tan f$. (h) $\operatorname{Sin}^{-1} f$.

8. Define the functions f_x, f_y, and f_z when f is a function of x, y, and z. If $f(x, y, z)$ represents the temperature of a substance at the point (x, y, z), state the physical significance of $f_x(x_0, y_0, z_0)$, $f_y(x_0, y_0, z_0)$, and $f_z(x_0, y_0, z_0)$. State the analogue of Theorem 16.1 and the formal rule for finding f_x, f_y, and f_z. Find f_x, f_y, and f_z when $f(x, y, z) = xy - 2y^3 z$ and when

$$f(x, y, z) = xz \cos (y^2 + z^2).$$

9. Suppose that x, y, and z are independent variables. Evaluate $\partial x/\partial y$, $\partial z/\partial x$, $\partial f(x)/\partial y$, and $\partial \varphi(x, y)/\partial z$.

10. Let u be a function of x and y, v a function of y and z, and w a function of x. Find

(a) $\dfrac{\partial u^2}{\partial x}$. (b) $\dfrac{\partial (u/v)}{\partial y}$.

(c) $\dfrac{\partial (u \tan v)}{\partial z}$. (d) $\dfrac{\partial}{\partial y}(xu + yv^2 + zw^3)$.

(e) $\dfrac{\partial}{\partial z} \log \left(u + \sqrt{v} + \dfrac{1}{w} \right)$. (f) $\dfrac{\partial}{\partial x} ue^{-w^2}$.

11. If $z = \sin [(x - y)/(x + y)]$, show that $x(\partial z/\partial x) + y(\partial z/\partial y) = 0$.

12. If $z = x^2 y e^{y/x}$, show that $x(\partial z/\partial x) + y(\partial z/\partial y) = 3z$.

13. If g and h are functions of x and y such that $g_x(x, y) = h_x(x, y)$ for all points (x, y) in the rectangle $a \leq x \leq b$, $c \leq y \leq d$, show that $g(x, y) - h(x, y)$ is a function of y alone over this rectangle; i.e., show that there exists a function φ of y such that

$$g(x, y) \equiv h(x, y) + \varphi(y).$$

State the analogous result in the case where $g_y(x, y) = h_y(x, y)$. Extend these results to the case where g and h are functions of x, y, and z (see Theorems 10.3 and 16.1).

17. Higher Partial Derivatives. If f is a function of x and y, and if f has partial derivatives with respect to x and y, then these derivatives are also functions of x and y, and may have partial derivatives which are called the *second partial derivatives* of f. These partial derivatives are denoted by the symbols

$$\frac{\partial}{\partial x}\left(\frac{\partial f}{\partial x}\right) = \frac{\partial^2 f}{\partial x^2} = f_{xx}, \qquad \frac{\partial}{\partial x}\left(\frac{\partial f}{\partial y}\right) = \frac{\partial^2 f}{\partial x\, \partial y} = f_{xy},$$

$$\frac{\partial}{\partial y}\left(\frac{\partial f}{\partial x}\right) = \frac{\partial^2 f}{\partial y\, \partial x} = f_{yx}, \qquad \frac{\partial}{\partial y}\left(\frac{\partial f}{\partial y}\right) = \frac{\partial^2 f}{\partial y^2} = f_{yy}.$$

It should be noted that the symbol f_{yx} indicates differentiation first with respect to x and then with respect to y.

Example 1. If $f(x, y) = x^3 - 5xy^2$, then

$$f_x(x, y) = 3x^2 - 5y^2, \qquad f_{xx}(x, y) = 6x, \qquad f_{xy}(x, y) = -10y,$$
$$f_y(x, y) = -10xy, \qquad f_{yx}(x, y) = -10y, \qquad f_{yy}(x, y) = -10x.$$

In this example it happens that $f_{yx} = f_{xy}$. We raise the question, will this always be the case for every function f? It is evident that

$$f_{yx}(x_0, y_0) = \lim_{k \to 0} \frac{f_x(x_0, y_0 + k) - f_x(x_0, y_0)}{k} =$$

$$\lim_{k \to 0} \left\{ \lim_{h \to 0} \frac{[f(x_0 + h, y_0 + k) - f(x_0, y_0 + k)] - [f(x_0 + h, y_0) - f(x_0, y_0)]}{hk} \right\}, (1)$$

$$f_{xy}(x_0, y_0) = \lim_{h \to 0} \frac{f_y(x_0 + h, y_0) - f_y(x_0, y_0)}{h} =$$

$$\lim_{h \to 0} \left\{ \lim_{k \to 0} \frac{[f(x_0 + h, y_0 + k) - f(x_0 + h, y_0)] - [f(x_0, y_0 + k) - f(x_0, y_0)]}{hk} \right\}, (2)$$

provided these limits exist. Since the fractions in the right members of (1) and (2) are the same, it follows that $f_{yx}(x_0, y_0) = f_{xy}(x_0, y_0)$ when, and only when, the limits with respect to h and k may be interchanged. The following example shows that the order in which the limits are taken cannot always be inverted, so that $f_{yx}(x_0, y_0)$ is not always equal to $f_{xy}(x_0, y_0)$.

Example 2. Let

$$f(x, y) = \begin{cases} xy\dfrac{x^2 - y^2}{x^2 + y^2} & \text{when} \qquad (x, y) \neq (0, 0), \\ 0 \text{ at } (0, 0). \end{cases}$$

Then

$$f_x(0, y_0) = \lim_{\Delta x \to 0} \frac{f(0 + \Delta x, y_0) - f(0, y_0)}{\Delta x} = \lim_{\Delta x \to 0} \frac{(\Delta x) y_0 \dfrac{\overline{\Delta x}^2 - y_0^2}{\overline{\Delta x}^2 + y_0^2} - 0}{\Delta x} = -y_0,$$

$$f_y(x_0, 0) = \lim_{\Delta y \to 0} \frac{f(x_0, 0 + \Delta y) - f(x_0, 0)}{\Delta y} = \lim_{\Delta y \to 0} \frac{x_0 (\Delta y) \dfrac{x_0^2 - \overline{\Delta y}^2}{x_0^2 + \overline{\Delta y}^2} - 0}{\Delta y} = x_0.$$

It follows from these results that

$$f_{yx}(0, 0) = \lim_{\Delta y \to 0} \frac{f_x(0, 0 + \Delta y) - f_x(0, 0)}{\Delta y} = \lim_{\Delta y \to 0} \frac{-\Delta y - 0}{\Delta y} = -1,$$

$$f_{xy}(0, 0) = \lim_{\Delta x \to 0} \frac{f_y(0 + \Delta x, 0) - f_y(0, 0)}{\Delta x} = \lim_{\Delta x \to 0} \frac{\Delta x - 0}{\Delta x} = 1.$$

Thus $f_{yx}(0, 0) \neq f_{xy}(0, 0)$. The following theorem provides a criterion that $f_{yx}(x_0, y_0) = f_{xy}(x_0, y_0)$.

THEOREM 17.1. *Let f denote a real single-valued function of x and y. If f_{yx} is defined over some rectangular neighborhood N of (x_0, y_0) and is continuous at (x_0, y_0), and if $f_{xy}(x_0, y_0)$ exists, then $f_{xy}(x_0, y_0) = f_{yx}(x_0, y_0)$.*

We first observe that, because f_{yx} is defined over N, f_x and f are also defined over N. Again, the existence of $f_{xy}(x_0, y_0)$ implies the existence of $f_y(x_0, y_0)$.

We shall evaluate $f_{xy}(x_0, y_0)$ by means of the right member of (2). Let $(x_0 + h, y_0 + k)$ be a point of N with $h \neq 0$ and $k \neq 0$, and let $\varphi(x) = f(x, y_0 + k) - f(x, y_0)$. Then φ has an x-derivative defined from x_0 to $x_0 + h$ inclusive (N being rectangular). By Theorem 10.1, there exists a number λ, $0 < \lambda < 1$, such that

$$[f(x_0 + h, y_0 + k) - f(x_0 + h, y_0)] - [f(x_0, y_0 + k) - f(x_0, y_0)]$$
$$= \varphi(x_0 + h) - \varphi(x_0) = h \cdot \varphi'(x_0 + \lambda h)$$
$$= h\left[\frac{d}{dx}f(x, y_0 + k) - \frac{d}{dx}f(x, y_0)\right]_{x_0 + \lambda h}$$
$$= h[f_x(x_0 + \lambda h, y_0 + k) - f_x(x_0 + \lambda h, y_0)], \quad (3)$$

the last result following by Theorem 16.1. By hypothesis, the function $f_x(x_0 + \lambda h, y)$ of the variable y has a y-derivative defined from y_0 to $y_0 + k$ inclusive, and by Theorem 10.1, there exists a number μ, $0 < \mu < 1$, such that

$$h[f_x(x_0 + \lambda h, y_0 + k) - f_x(x_0 + \lambda h, y_0)]$$
$$= h[kf_{yx}(x_0 + \lambda h, y_0 + \mu k)]. \quad (4)$$

By (2), (3), (4), and the continuity of f_{yx} at (x_0, y_0),

$$f_{xy}(x_0, y_0) = \lim_{h \to 0}\left[\lim_{k \to 0} f_{yx}(x_0 + \lambda h, y_0 + \mu k)\right] = f_{yx}(x_0, y_0).$$

It is apparent that Theorem 17.1 remains valid when the roles of x and y are interchanged.

Higher derivatives of f are defined in an obvious manner. Thus, $\partial^{p+q}f/\partial^p x \, \partial^q y$ denotes the function obtained from f by differentiating partially q times with respect to y and p times with respect to x. If f and its derivatives are continuous, the order of differentiation with respect to x and y is immaterial; for example,

$$\frac{\partial^3 f}{\partial^2 x \, \partial y} = \frac{\partial}{\partial x}\left(\frac{\partial^2 f}{\partial x \, \partial y}\right) = \frac{\partial}{\partial x}\left(\frac{\partial^2 f}{\partial y \, \partial x}\right) = \frac{\partial^2}{\partial x \, \partial y}\left(\frac{\partial f}{\partial x}\right)$$

$$= \frac{\partial^2}{\partial y \, \partial x}\left(\frac{\partial f}{\partial x}\right) = \frac{\partial^3 f}{\partial y \, \partial^2 x}.$$

EXERCISES XVIII

1. If $f(x, y) = \tan (y + kx) + (y - kx)^{3/2}$, show that $\dfrac{\partial^2 f}{\partial x^2} = k^2 \dfrac{\partial^2 f}{\partial y^2}$.

2. If $z = x \, \mathrm{Tan}^{-1} \dfrac{y}{x} + xe^{y/x}$, show that $x^2\dfrac{\partial^2 z}{\partial x^2} + 2xy\dfrac{\partial^2 z}{\partial x \, \partial y} + y^2\dfrac{\partial^2 z}{\partial y^2} = 0$.

3. If $z = \log (x^2 + y^2)$, show that $\dfrac{\partial^2 z}{\partial x^2} + \dfrac{\partial^2 z}{\partial y^2} = 0$.

4. Show that $\dfrac{\partial^2 z}{\partial y \, \partial x} = \dfrac{\partial^2 z}{\partial x \, \partial y}$ when (a) $z = \dfrac{\sqrt{x^2 - y^2}}{x}$; (b) $z = e^{\frac{x+y}{x-y}}$.

5. If $f(x, y, z) = (x^2 + y^2 + z^2)^{-1/2}$, show that $\dfrac{\partial^2 f}{\partial x^2} + \dfrac{\partial^2 f}{\partial y^2} + \dfrac{\partial^2 f}{\partial z^2} = 0$.

6. If $V = e^{a\phi} \cos (a \log r)$, show that $\dfrac{\partial^2 V}{\partial r^2} + \dfrac{1}{r}\dfrac{\partial V}{\partial r} + \dfrac{1}{r^2}\dfrac{\partial^2 V}{\partial \phi^2} = 0$.

7. If $u = e^{xy}$, show that $\dfrac{\partial^2 u}{\partial x^2} + \dfrac{\partial^2 u}{\partial y^2} = \dfrac{1}{u}\left[\left(\dfrac{\partial u}{\partial x}\right)^2 + \left(\dfrac{\partial u}{\partial y}\right)^2\right]$.

8. In Example 2 above, find $f_{yx}(0, 0)$ and $f_{xy}(0, 0)$ directly by (1) and (2). Construct another function to illustrate the point of Example 2.

18. Total Derivatives. We now take up Case 3 of Sec. 16. (See Ex. XVII, 2 for Case 2.) Let f be a single-valued function* of x and y, and let C be an arbitrary curve in the domain of definition of f and having the parametric equations†

$$x = p(u), \qquad y = q(u). \tag{1}$$

We shall assume f, p, and q to be differentiable. As u varies, the point (x, y) moves along C according to (1). Hence the value of f at the moving point (x, y) varies with u, that is, $f(x, y)$ is a function of u. We wish to determine the value at (x_0, y_0) of the rate of change of $f(x, y)$ with respect to u as (x, y) moves along C.

---

* To make this discussion vivid, think of $f(x, y)$ as representing the temperature at (x, y).

† It may be helpful to think of u as representing arc length along C.

The point on C at which $u = u_0$ has the coordinates

$$x_0 = p(u_0), \qquad y_0 = q(u_0), \qquad (2_1)$$

and the point on C where $u = u_0 + \Delta u$ has the coordinates

$$x_0 + \Delta x = p(u_0 + \Delta u), \qquad y_0 + \Delta y = q(u_0 + \Delta u). \qquad (2_2)$$

Hence f has the value $f(x_0,\ y_0)$ when $u = u_0$ and it has the value $f(x_0 + \Delta x,\ y_0 + \Delta y)$ at $u = u_0 + \Delta u$. Also, the change in the value of f over the short interval along C from $(x_0,\ y_0)$ to $(x_0 + \Delta x,\ y_0 + \Delta y)$ is $f(x_0 + \Delta x,\ y_0 + \Delta y) - f(x_0,\ y_0)$, and the mean rate of change of f with respect to u over this interval is

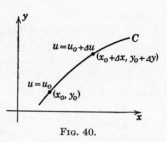

FIG. 40.

$\dfrac{f(x_0 + \Delta x,\ y_0 + \Delta y) - f(x_0,\ y_0)}{\Delta u}$. As $\Delta u \to 0$, $\Delta x \to 0$ and $\Delta y \to 0$

according* to (2_2) and the point $(x_0 + \Delta x,\ y_0 + \Delta y)$ moves along C to the point $(x_0,\ y_0)$. Hence

$$\lim_{\Delta u \to 0} \frac{f(x_0 + \Delta x,\ y_0 + \Delta y) - f(x_0,\ y_0)}{\Delta u} \qquad (3)$$

(provided this limit exists) represents the value at $(x_0,\ y_0)$ of the instantaneous rate of change of $f(x, y)$ with respect to u as (x, y) moves along C. We shall now show that $\dfrac{df(x,\ y)}{du}\bigg]_{u_0}$ (i.e., the value of $\dfrac{df(x,\ y)}{du}$ at $u = u_0$) is equal to the limit (3), and then we shall evaluate (3).

As the point (x, y) moves along C, $f(x, y)$ is given by the formula $f[p(u),\ q(u)]$ according to (1). Hence

$$\frac{df(x,\ y)}{du}\bigg]_{u_0} = \frac{df[p(u),\ q(u)]}{du}\bigg]_{u_0}$$

$$= \lim_{\Delta u \to 0} \frac{f[p(u_0 + \Delta u),\ q(u_0 + \Delta u)] - f[p(u_0),\ q(u_0)]}{\Delta u}.$$

(Note that we write $\dfrac{df(x,\ y)}{du}$, and not $\dfrac{\partial f(x,\ y)}{\partial u}$, because f is now

---

* Since p and q are differentiable, they are also continuous.

regarded as a function of the single independent variable u.)
It follows by (2_1) and (2_2) that we may express the preceding
result in the form

$$\frac{df(x, y)}{du}\bigg]_{u_0} = \lim_{\Delta u \to 0} \frac{f(x_0 + \Delta x, y_0 + \Delta y) - f(x_0, y_0)}{\Delta u}. \qquad (4)$$

To evaluate the limit in (3) and (4), let us subtract and add
$f(x_0, y_0 + \Delta y)$ in the numerator of the fraction in the right-hand
member of (4). Then this member becomes

$$\lim_{\Delta u \to 0} \left[\frac{f(x_0 + \Delta x, y_0 + \Delta y) - f(x_0, y_0 + \Delta y)}{\Delta u} \right.$$
$$\left. + \frac{f(x_0, y_0 + \Delta y) - f(x_0, y_0)}{\Delta u} \right]. \qquad (5)$$

In case Δx and $\Delta y \neq 0$ when $\Delta u \neq 0$, we may write (5) in the
form

$$\lim_{\Delta u \to 0} \left[\frac{f(x_0 + \Delta x, y_0 + \Delta y) - f(x_0, y_0 + \Delta y)}{\Delta x} \cdot \frac{\Delta x}{\Delta u} \right.$$
$$\left. + \frac{f(x_0, y_0 + \Delta y) - f(x_0, y_0)}{\Delta y} \cdot \frac{\Delta y}{\Delta u} \right]; \qquad (6)$$

the general case where Δx or Δy may be 0 when $\Delta u \neq 0$ may be
treated by the device used in the proof of Theorem 5.5. By
Theorem 3.2, we may write (6) as

$$\lim_{\Delta u \to 0} \frac{f(x_0 + \Delta x, y_0 + \Delta y) - f(x_0, y_0 + \Delta y)}{\Delta x} \cdot \lim_{\Delta u \to 0} \frac{\Delta x}{\Delta u}$$
$$+ \lim_{\Delta u \to 0} \frac{f(x_0, y_0 + \Delta y) - f(x_0, y_0)}{\Delta y} \cdot \lim_{\Delta u \to 0} \frac{\Delta y}{\Delta u}, \qquad (7)$$

provided the various limits exist. Since we assumed p and q
to be differentiable, and since $\Delta x = p(u_0 + \Delta u) - p(u_0)$ and
$\Delta y = q(u_0 + \Delta u) - q(u_0)$ by (2_1) and (2_2), the second and
fourth limits in (7) exist and equal $\dfrac{dx}{du}\bigg]_{u_0}$ and $\dfrac{dy}{du}\bigg]_{u_0}$. We next
consider the third limit in (7), i.e.,

$$\lim_{\Delta u \to 0} \frac{f(x_0, y_0 + \Delta y) - f(x_0, y_0)}{\Delta y}, \qquad (8)$$

wherein $\Delta y = q(u_0 + \Delta u) - q(u_0)$. Since $\dfrac{dq}{du}\bigg]_{u_0}$ exists, it follows by Theorem 5.1 that q is continuous at $u = u_0$. Hence, as $\Delta u \to 0$, Δy also $\to 0$ in (8). But

$$\text{as } \Delta y \to 0, \quad \frac{f(x_0,\, y_0 + \Delta y) - f(x_0,\, y_0)}{\Delta y} \to f_y(x_0,\, y_0).$$

Therefore the limit (8) has the value $f_y(x_0,\, y_0)$.

It remains to consider the first limit in (7). Let

$$\varphi(x) = f(x,\, y_0 + \Delta y),$$

where for the moment Δy is constant. By Theorems 10.1 and 16.1,

$$\frac{f(x_0 + \Delta x,\, y_0 + \Delta y) - f(x_0,\, y_0 + \Delta y)}{\Delta x} = \frac{\varphi(x_0 + \Delta x) - \varphi(x_0)}{\Delta x}$$

$$= \varphi'(x_0 + \theta \cdot \Delta x)$$

$$= \frac{d}{dx} f(x,\, y_0 + \Delta y)\bigg]_{x_0 + \theta \cdot \Delta x}$$

$$= f_x(x_0 + \theta \cdot \Delta x,\, y_0 + \Delta y),$$

where $0 < \theta < 1$. Having established this result for arbitrary values of Δx and Δy, we may now think of Δx and Δy as variable, θ being a function of Δx and Δy. It follows that if f_x is continuous, then

$$\lim_{\Delta u \to 0} \frac{f(x_0 + \Delta x,\, y_0 + \Delta y) - f(x_0,\, y_0 + \Delta y)}{\Delta x}$$

$$= \lim_{\Delta u \to 0} f_x(x_0 + \theta \cdot \Delta x,\, y_0 + \Delta y) = f_x(x_0,\, y_0),$$

since $\Delta x \to 0$ and $\Delta y \to 0$ as $\Delta u \to 0$.

We have now evaluated all the limits in (7) and we may summarize our results in

THEOREM 18.1. *If f is a real single-valued function of x and y having first partial derivatives with respect to x and y, if at least one of these partial derivatives is continuous,[*] and if x and y are defined as differentiable functions of u by the equations $x = p(u)$, $y = q(u)$, then*

$$\frac{df(x,\, y)}{du}\bigg]_{u_0} = f_x(x_0,\, y_0) \cdot \left(\frac{dx}{du}\right)_{u_0} + f_y(x_0,\, y_0) \cdot \left(\frac{dy}{du}\right)_{u_0}. \tag{A}$$

[*] The proof was given for the case where f_x is continuous, but the proof is easily modified to meet the case where f_y is continuous.

When expressed in general notation, (A) assumes the form

$$\frac{df(x, y)}{du} = \frac{\partial f(x, y)}{\partial x} \frac{dx}{du} + \frac{\partial f(x, y)}{\partial y} \frac{dy}{du}, \tag{9}$$

where we have written $f(x, y)$ instead of merely f in order to show explicitly that f depends on x and y (see Sec. 23). With regard to the interpretation of (9), it should be observed that

(a) It is implied in the notation $\dfrac{df(x, y)}{du}$ that x and y have been determined as functions of u, say $x = p(u)$, $y = q(u)$, so that, as u varies, the point (x, y) moves along that curve C whose parametric equations are $x = p(u)$, $y = q(u)$.

(b) The notation $\dfrac{df(x, y)}{du}$ represents the rate of change of $f(x, y)$ with respect to u as the point (x, y) moves along the curve C in (a).

(c) Even though x and y have been determined as functions of u in (a), $\dfrac{\partial f(x, y)}{\partial x}$ and $\dfrac{\partial f(x, y)}{\partial y}$ are computed by regarding x and y as independent with either y or x constant.

We call $\dfrac{df(x, y)}{du}$ the *total derivative* of f with respect to u.

Formula (A) reduces to a particularly important form when it is supposed that the parametric equations of C are expressed in terms of the arc length s of C, i.e., that $u = s$ in (1). By (9) of Sec. 7, $\dfrac{dx}{ds}\bigg]_{s_0} = \cos \alpha$ and $\dfrac{dy}{ds}\bigg]_{s_0} = \sin \alpha$, where α is the inclination of the tangent line to C at the point $s = s_0$. If these values are substituted in (A), this formula assumes the special form

$$\frac{df(x, y)}{ds}\bigg]_{s_0} = f_x(x_0, y_0) \cos \alpha + f_y(x_0, y_0) \sin \alpha. \tag{A'}$$

Formula (9) may be greatly generalized. Suppose, for example, that f is a function of x and y, and that $x = p(u, v, w)$, $y = q(u, v, w)$. Since f is expressible as a function of u, v, and w, i.e., $f(x, y) = f(p(u, v, w), q(u, v, w))$, f may have partial derivatives with respect to u, v, and w. We may evidently write $\dfrac{\partial f(p(u, v, w), q(u, v, w))}{\partial u}$ in the abbreviated form $\dfrac{\partial f(x, y)}{\partial u}$. But there is nothing in this last notation to indicate that x and y depend on v and w. We introduce the notation $\left.\dfrac{\partial f(x,\ y)}{\partial u}\right)_{v,w}$ to show that (a) x and y have been determined as functions of u, v, and w; and (b) v and w are regarded as constant during the computation of the derivative in question. Two special cases of this notation should be kept in mind: The symbol $\dfrac{\partial f(x,\ y)}{\partial u}$ indicates by the absence of any subscript that u is the only independent variable; as indicated above, it is customary in this case to write $\dfrac{df(x,\ y)}{du}$ instead of $\dfrac{\partial f(x,\ y)}{\partial u}$. Again, if x and y are themselves the independent variables, then this is indicated by the notation $\left.\dfrac{\partial f(x,\ y)}{\partial x}\right)_{y}$; however, if no ambiguity can arise, the subscript y may be omitted as in Sec. 16. According to this notation, (9) would be written in the alternative form

$$\frac{df(x,\ y)}{du} = \left.\frac{\partial f(x,\ y)}{\partial x}\right)_{y} \cdot \frac{dx}{du} + \left.\frac{\partial f(x,\ y)}{\partial y}\right)_{x} \cdot \frac{dy}{du}. \tag{9'}$$

With this notation in mind, we may state

THEOREM 18.2. *If f is a function of a finite number n_1 of variables x, y, z, $\cdots$, and if each of these variables is a function of a finite number n_2 of variables u, v, w, $\cdots$ (n_1 and n_2 being entirely independent), then*

$$\left.\frac{\partial f(x,\ y,\ z,\ \cdots)}{\partial u}\right)_{v,w,\ldots} = \left.\frac{\partial f(x,\ y,\ z,\ \cdots)}{\partial x}\right)_{y,z,\ldots} \left.\frac{\partial x}{\partial u}\right)_{v,w,\ldots}$$

$$+ \left.\frac{\partial f(x,\ y,\ z,\ \cdots)}{\partial y}\right)_{x,z,\ldots} \left.\frac{\partial y}{\partial u}\right)_{v,w,\ldots} + \cdots,$$

$$\left.\frac{\partial f(x,\ y,\ z,\ \cdots)}{\partial v}\right)_{u,w,\ldots} = \left.\frac{\partial f(x,\ y,\ z,\ \cdots)}{\partial x}\right)_{y,z,\ldots} \left.\frac{\partial x}{\partial v}\right)_{u,w,\ldots} \tag{B}$$

$$+ \left.\frac{\partial f(x,\ y,\ z,\ \cdots)}{\partial y}\right)_{x,z,\ldots} \left.\frac{\partial y}{\partial v}\right)_{u,w,\ldots} + \cdots,$$

where the dots at the end of each line indicate a finite number of terms.

The proof of (B) will be taken up in Ex. 14 below.

EXERCISES XIX

1. Let $x = p(u)$ and $y = q(u)$ be the parametric equations of a curve C in the xy-plane. Let $f(x, y)$ represent the temperature of a substance at the point (x, y). Give the physical interpretation of $\dfrac{df(x, y)}{du}$ in the following cases:

(a) u represents arc length s along C.

Ans. If s is measured in inches, and f in degrees centigrade, then the value of $\dfrac{df(x, y)}{ds}$ at any point P on C represents the change in temperature per inch along C at P.

(b) u is the time t in seconds. (Think of a small thermometer moving along C with a known speed. Does the fact that the thermometer reading $f(x, y)$ is changing along C and is a function of t in any way indicate that the temperature at a fixed point P is changing, i.e., that f is a function of t?)

(c) $u = x$.

(d) u is the distance r from the origin to the point (x, y).

(e) Repeat (a), (b), (c), and (d), taking f to represent the elevations on a topographic map and regarding the point (x, y) as representing on the map an automobile climbing a mountain road. (In $\dfrac{df(x, y)}{dt}$, x and y are functions of t. Hence the elevation $f(x, y)$ of the automobile is a function of t. Does this imply that f is a function of t, i.e., that there is an earthquake?)

(f) Repeat (a), (b), (c), and (d) for two other physical interpretations of f.

2. If u is the time t in seconds, if $f(x, y)$ represents the elevation of an automobile at (x, y) as in Ex. 1e, and if x, y, and f are measured in feet, show that in formula (9′) the quantity $\left. \dfrac{\partial f(x, y)}{\partial x} \right)_y \dfrac{dx}{dt}$ is the part of the vertical velocity of the automobile in feet per second due to the component of the velocity of the automobile parallel to the x-axis. Interpret the last term of (9′). State the meaning of (9′) as a whole. Repeat this discussion for the case where f represents the temperature of a substance.

3. When the point (x, y) traces out the curve C of Ex. 1, what is the locus C' of the point $[x, y, f(x, y)]$? Show C' on the graph of f. What is the significance of C' in the case where f has the interpretation of Ex. 1e?

4. Suppose that u is the arc length s along the curve C of Ex. 1. Show that $\dfrac{df(x, y)}{ds} = \tan \theta$, where θ is the inclination to the xy-plane of the tangent to the curve C' of Ex. 3.

Suggestion. Note that

$$\left. \frac{df(x, y)}{ds} \right]_{s_0} = \lim_{\Delta s \to 0} \left[\frac{f(x_0 + \Delta x, y_0 + \Delta y) - f(x_0, y_0)}{\sqrt{(\Delta x)^2 + (\Delta y)^2}} \cdot \frac{\sqrt{(\Delta x)^2 + (\Delta y)^2}}{\Delta s} \right].$$

Assume C to be such that the limit of the last factor is 1. See Ex. XV, 4.

5. (a) Suppose that $f(x, y) = x^2 - xy$ and that the curve C is the line through the point $(1, 3)$ with slope $\tan \alpha = -1$. Then $\cos \alpha = -1/\sqrt{2}$, $\sin \alpha = -1/\sqrt{2}$, and by (A'),

$$\frac{df(x, y)}{ds}\Bigg]_{1,3} = (-1)\left(-\frac{1}{\sqrt{2}}\right) + (-1)\left(\frac{1}{\sqrt{2}}\right) = 0.$$

This result indicates that the rate of change of $f(x, y)$ with respect to s as (x, y) moves along C is zero at $(1, 3)$. Check this result by graphing the values of f at the following points on C: $(\frac{1}{2}, \frac{7}{2})$, $(\frac{3}{4}, \frac{13}{4})$, $(1, 3)$, $(\frac{5}{4}, \frac{11}{4})$, and $(\frac{3}{2}, \frac{5}{2})$.

(b) Find $\dfrac{df(x, y)}{ds}\Bigg]_{0,1}$ when $f(x, y) = x + 2y$ and C is the curve $x^2 + y^2 = 1$. Check this result by graphing the values of f at several points on C near $(0, 1)$. (Cf. Ex. 4.)

(c) Find $\dfrac{df(x, y)}{ds}\Bigg]_{1,1}$ when $f(x, y) = \sqrt{2}y/x$ and C is the curve $y = x^2$. Check this result graphically.

6. In the adjoining figure PX, PY, and PZ are parallel to the coordinate axes; PQ and PR are the traces of a plane on the XZ- and YZ-planes; PT is a line in the plane PQR; the lines a, b, and h are parallel to PZ. Show that

$$h = \frac{an + bm}{n + m}$$

and that

$$\tan \theta = \frac{h}{r} = \tan \varphi \cos \alpha$$
$$+ \tan \psi \sin \alpha. \quad (10)$$

Suppose that the plane PQR is tangent to the graph of $z = f(x, y)$ at P and that

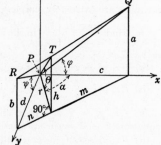

Fig. 41.

the line PT is tangent to the curve C' of Ex. 3. Show by Ex. 4 and Ex. XVII, 4 that formula (10) is merely formula (A') written in trigonometric notation.

7. If $f(x, y) = x^2 - 3xy$ and if the curve C has the equations $x = u - 2$ $y = u^2 + 5$, find $\dfrac{df(x, y)}{du}$ by two methods.

Solution by Formula (9). Substitution in (9) leads to the result that

$$\frac{df(x, y)}{du} = (2x - 3y)\frac{dx}{du} + (-3x)\frac{dy}{du}. \quad (11)$$

Note that the equations of C are not used in applying formula (9); they are used only to calculate dx/du and dy/du. It is seen that

$$\frac{dx}{du} = 1, \qquad \frac{dy}{du} = 2u, \tag{12}$$

and that these results may be substituted in (11) to obtain the desired formula.

Solution by Direct Differentiation. In the formula for f we may think of x and y as functions of u and differentiate f as a function of u by the elementary formulas. Thus,

$$\frac{df(x, y)}{du} = \frac{d(x^2)}{du} - 3\frac{d(xy)}{du} = 2x\frac{dx}{du} - 3\left(x\frac{dy}{du} + y\frac{dx}{du}\right)$$

$$= (2x - 3y)\frac{dx}{du} - 3x\frac{dy}{du}. \tag{13}$$

Note again that the equations of C are not used in this differentiation, and are used only to calculate dx/du and dy/du. Since (11) and (13) are the same, the final result, after substitution of (12), must be the same. In the exercises below it is best to carry out the computations (11) and (13) first, check these results, and then to make the substitution (12).

A third method for solving this problem would be to substitute the formulas for x and y in the formula for f and then differentiate. The reader will find by trial that this method is to be recommended only when the formulas are extremely simple.

8. Find $\dfrac{df(x, y)}{du}\bigg]_{u=2}$ in the following cases by the two methods described in Ex. 7.

　(a) $f(x, y) = x^3y - y^4$; $x = 1/u$ and $y = \log u$.

　(b) $f(x, y) = \dfrac{x + y}{x - y}$; $x = \sqrt{u}$ and $y = e^u$.

　(c) $f(x, y) = \sqrt{x - y}$; x and y are defined as functions of u by the equations $u - 2 = \sin(xu)$ and $u - 2 = \log(y + u)$.

　(d) $f(x, y) = \operatorname{Sin}^{-1}(y/x)$; x and y are defined as functions of u by the equations $x^u = u + 2$ and $\operatorname{Tan}^{-1}(u/2) + \operatorname{Tan}^{-1}(y/2) = \pi/4$.

9. Let us consider the special case of (9) where $u = x$. The relations $x = p(u)$ and $y = q(u)$ reduce to $x = x$ (this being the formula for x in terms of the independent variable x) and $y = q(x)$. Formula (9) becomes

$$\frac{df(x, y)}{dx} = \frac{\partial f(x, y)}{\partial x}\bigg)_y + \frac{\partial f(x, y)}{\partial y}\bigg)_x \cdot \frac{dy}{dx}$$

since $\dfrac{dx}{dx} = 1$. What do $\dfrac{df(x, y)}{dx}$ and $\dfrac{\partial f(x, y)}{\partial x}\bigg)_y$ represent? Make clear the difference in significance of these derivatives by giving in each case the equation of the curve along which the point (x, y) moves [see paragraph (b) following Theorem 18.1]. In which of these derivatives is y variable during the limit process defining the derivative and in which is it constant?

Does the symbol $\dfrac{df(x, y)}{dx}$ have any significance if y is not a function of x? Carry through this entire discussion for the case $u = y$.

10. Using the results of the preceding exercise, find $\dfrac{df(x, y)}{dx}$ and $\dfrac{df(x, y)}{dy}$ when $f(x, y) = e^{x/y}$ and x and y are related by the equation $x^4 - xy^3 = y$; also when $f(x, y) = \sqrt{x^2 - y^2}$ and $\sqrt{x} + \sqrt{y} = xy$. Check your results by differentiating f directly as a function of one variable by the methods of elementary calculus.

11. If the coordinates of the point (x, y, z) are determined by the equations

$$x = p(u), \qquad y = q(u), \qquad z = r(u) \tag{14}$$

in terms of the parameter u, so that, as u varies, the point (x, y, z) traces out a curve C in space, then equations (14) are called the *parametric* equations of C. If f denotes a function of x, y, and z with continuous partial derivatives, show that

$$\frac{df(x, y, z)}{du} = \frac{\partial f}{\partial x}\bigg)_{y,z} \cdot \frac{dx}{du} + \frac{\partial f}{\partial y}\bigg)_{x,z} \cdot \frac{dy}{du} + \frac{\partial f}{\partial z}\bigg)_{x,y} \cdot \frac{dz}{du}.$$

[Carry out the derivation in the following steps: (1) state the analogues of equations (2_1), (2_2), and (4) of the preceding article; (2) subtract and add $f(x_0, y_0 + \Delta y, z_0 + \Delta z)$ and $f(x_0, y_0, z_0 + \Delta z)$ in the numerator of the new equation (4) to get the analogue of (7); (3) apply the theorem of the mean to the first and third factors of the new equation (7) to get the analogue of (A). The discussion of the limits carries over verbatim and need not be repeated.] Interpret $\dfrac{df(x, y, z)}{du}$ as in Ex. 1a, b, c, d. [Remember that C is now a curve in space and that $f(x, y, z)$ is defined throughout space (or a portion of it)].

12. State the formula for $(d/du)f(x_1, x_2, \cdots, x_n)$. [Note that there are as many terms in this formula as there are variables x_i.]

13. If the rectangular coordinates (x, y) of a point P are determined by the equations

$$x = p(u, v), \qquad y = q(u, v),$$

then u and v may be regarded as a second pair of coordinates of the point P (see Sec. 23). For example, if

$$x = r \cos \theta, \qquad y = r \sin \theta, \tag{15}$$

then r and θ are the *polar* coordinates of P. Again, if

$$x = \tfrac{1}{2}(u - v), \qquad y = \sqrt{uv}, \tag{16}$$

then u and v are the *parabolic* coordinates of P.

If f denotes a function of x and y, show that

$$\frac{\partial f(x, y)}{\partial u}\bigg)_v = \frac{\partial f(x, y)}{\partial x}\bigg)_y \cdot \frac{\partial x}{\partial u}\bigg)_v + \frac{\partial f(x, y)}{\partial y}\bigg)_x \cdot \frac{\partial y}{\partial u}\bigg)_v.$$

[The procedure is seen to be exactly parallel to that indicated in the preceding section when it is remembered that v has the constant value v_0 throughout the computation. The right member of (4) is unaltered. Hence (7) is unaltered and it is merely a question of interpreting the second and fourth limits in (7) as partial derivatives.]

Interpret $\dfrac{\partial f(x, y)}{\partial u}\bigg)_v$ when (a) $u = r$ and $v = \theta$ in (15).   (b) u and v are the parameters in (16).   In each case state the path of the point (x, y).

State the formula for $\dfrac{\partial f(x, y)}{\partial v}\bigg)_u$.   If $x = p(u, v, w)$, $y = q(u, v, w)$, state the formula for $\dfrac{\partial f(x, y)}{\partial u}\bigg)_{v,w}$.

14. Prove Theorem 18.2.

Solution. Let x, y, $\cdots$ be called the first set of variables, and let u, v, $\cdots$ be called the second set of variables.   Exercise 12 shows that

$$\frac{\partial f(x, y, \cdots)}{\partial u}$$

$$= \frac{\partial f(x, y, \cdots)}{\partial x}\bigg)_{y,\dots} \cdot \frac{\partial x}{\partial u} + \frac{\partial f(x, y, \cdots)}{\partial y}\bigg)_{x,\dots} \cdot \frac{\partial y}{\partial u} + \cdots,$$

where the right-hand member contains as many terms as there are variables of the first set—one term corresponding to each variable.   Exercise 13 shows that these terms are in no way altered, either as to form or number, because of the additional variables v, $\cdots$ of the second set; it is necessary merely to affix the proper set of subscripts to the second factors in each term.   On the other hand, Exercise 13 shows that there is a formula of this same type for each of the derivatives $\dfrac{\partial f(x, y, \cdots)}{\partial v}$, $\cdots$.

15. Let $f(x, y, z) = xz^2 + y \sin (x + z)$.   Find by formula (B):

(a) df/du when $x = u$, $y = u^2$, $z = \sqrt{u}$.

(b) $\dfrac{\partial f}{\partial u}\bigg)_v$ when $x = uv$, $y = u^2 + v^2$, $z = \sqrt{u + v}$.

(c) $\dfrac{\partial f}{\partial u}\bigg)_{v,w}$ when $x = uvw$, $y = u^2 + v^2 + w^2$, $z = \sqrt{u + v + w}$.

(d) $\dfrac{\partial f}{\partial w}\bigg)_{u,v}$ when x, y, and z are defined as in (c).

16. Let $f(x, y, z) = xyz \log (x + y + z)$. Express the following in terms of the derivatives of x, y, and z:

(a) $\dfrac{df}{du}$; (b) $\dfrac{\partial f}{\partial v}\Big)_u$; (c) $\dfrac{\partial f}{\partial p}\Big)_{q,r,s,t}$; (d) $\dfrac{\partial f}{\partial x}\Big)_{y,z,u,v}$.

17. If $u = e^{x^2-xy+3y^2}$, where $x = r \cos (s - t)$ and $y = r \sin (s - t)$, find by two methods, as in Ex. 7:

(a) $\dfrac{\partial u}{\partial r}\Big)_{s,t}$; (b) $\dfrac{\partial u}{\partial s}\Big)_{r,t}$; (c) $\dfrac{\partial u}{\partial t}\Big)_{r,s}$; (d) $\dfrac{\partial u}{\partial r}\Big)_s$; (e) $\dfrac{du}{dr}$.

18. If $u = [\operatorname{Sin}^{-1} (xy)] [\operatorname{Sin}^{-1} (xz)]$, find:

(a) $\dfrac{du}{dt}$; (b) $\dfrac{\partial u}{\partial r}\Big)_s$; (c) $\dfrac{\partial u}{\partial s}\Big)_r$; (d) $\dfrac{\partial u}{\partial \alpha}\Big)_{\beta,\gamma,\delta}$.

19. Given a function $f(x, y, z)$, where x, y, and z are functions of u and v, and where u and v are functions of t. Find $\dfrac{df(x, y, z)}{dt}$ by two applications of formula (B).

20. It often happens that a variable, say x, appears in both the first and second sets of variables (see Ex. 9). This should cause no confusion if formula (B) is followed explicitly and if this variable is treated like each of the other variables of the first set and also like each of the other variables of the second set. For example, in the formula for $\dfrac{\partial f(x, y, z, \cdots)}{\partial u}\Big)_{x,v,\ldots}$, the second factor of the first term is $\dfrac{\partial x}{\partial u}\Big)_{x,v,\ldots}$, where x is being differentiated as a variable of the first set. Since x is a subscript, it is regarded as constant. Hence $\dfrac{\partial x}{\partial u}\Big)_{x,v,\ldots} = 0$.

Evaluate:

(a) $\dfrac{\partial f(x, y, z)}{\partial u}\Big)_x$. (b) $\dfrac{\partial f(x, y, z)}{\partial x}\Big)_u$. (c) $\dfrac{\partial f(x, y, z)}{\partial x}\Big)_z$. (d) $\dfrac{df(x, y, z)}{dz}$.

(e) $\dfrac{\partial f(x, y, u, v)}{\partial u}\Big)_x$. (f) $\dfrac{\partial f(x, y, u, v)}{\partial u}\Big)_{x,v}$. (g) $\dfrac{\partial}{\partial y}(x^2 - xz + yz)\Big)_z$.

(h) $\dfrac{\partial}{\partial y}(x^2 - xz + yz)\Big)_u$. (i) $\dfrac{\partial}{\partial y}(x^2 - xz + yz - w^2)\Big)_x$.

(j) $\dfrac{\partial}{\partial v}(x^2 - y^2 + xu - yv)\Big)_{x,u}$.

21. If $f(x, y, u, v) = x^2y + y^3u - xv^4$, find: (a) $\dfrac{\partial f}{\partial x}\Big)_{y,u,v}$; (b) $\dfrac{\partial f}{\partial x}\Big)_{u,v}$;

(c) $\dfrac{\partial f}{\partial x}\Big)_v$; (d) $\dfrac{df}{dx}$; (e) $\dfrac{\partial f}{\partial u}\Big)_{x,y}$; (f) $\dfrac{\partial f}{\partial u}\Big)_x$; (g) $\dfrac{df}{du}$; (h) $\dfrac{\partial f}{\partial v}\Big)_{x,y}$.

22. The elevation E of each point P on the surface of a rough ocean is $E(x, y, t)$, where (x, y) is the projection of P on a fixed horizontal plane M and where t denotes time (units in feet and seconds). The path of a small boat sailing over the water is given by the equations $x = p(t)$, $y = q(t)$, $z = E(x, y, t)$. Find dz/dt and interpret each quantity appearing in the result and interpret the result as a whole (see Ex. 2). Under what conditions would the equations $x = p(t)$, $y = q(t)$ represent the projection of the wake of the boat on the plane M?

23. The temperature T at any point P of a substance and at any time t is $T(x, y, z, t)$. Find and completely interpret the formula for dT/dt when the point (x, y, z) moves along the path $x = p(t)$, $y = q(t)$, $z = r(t)$.

24. Let v be the volume of a certain quantity of gas, T its temperature, p its unit pressure, and E its total energy. The following relations occur in

thermodynamics: $v = \Phi(T, p)$, $p = F(T, E)$. Find and interpret $\left.\dfrac{\partial v}{\partial T}\right)_E$

and $\left.\dfrac{\partial v}{\partial E}\right)_T$. Is p regarded as constant or variable when one is computing

$\left.\dfrac{\partial v}{\partial T}\right)_E$? When one is computing $\left.\dfrac{\partial v}{\partial T}\right)_p$?

25. By repeated use of formula (B), find $(d/dx) f(x, y, z)$ when y is given as a function of x and z, and z is given as a function of x.

26. Given $f(x, y, u, v)$ with y a function of x and v, with u a function of y and v, and with x a function of v. Find $(d/dv) f(x, y, u, v)$.

27. Given $f(x, y, u, v)$ with y a function of x, u, v; with v a function of u

and w; and with x a function of v and w. Find $\left.\dfrac{\partial f}{\partial u}\right)_w$.

28. Find: (a) $\left.\dfrac{\partial}{\partial x} f(x + y, \quad x - y)\right)_y$; (b) $\left.\dfrac{\partial}{\partial y} f(\sqrt{xy}, \quad \sqrt{x} + \sqrt{y})\right)_x$;

(c) $\left.\dfrac{\partial}{\partial x} f\left(x^2 + y^2, e^{xy}, \dfrac{x + y}{x - y} \right)\right)_y$; (d) $\left.\dfrac{\partial}{\partial y} f(\sin xy, \log (x - y))\right)_x$. [In prob-

lems of this type it may be helpful to introduce new variables; for example, in part (a) let $u = x + y$, $v = x - y$, and express the result in terms of f_u and f_v.]

29. (a) If $z = f(xy)$, show that $x\dfrac{\partial z}{\partial x} - y\dfrac{\partial z}{\partial y} = 0$.

(b) If $z = f\left(\dfrac{y}{x}\right)$, show that $x\dfrac{\partial z}{\partial x} + y\dfrac{\partial z}{\partial y} = 0$.

30. (a) If $x = p(u)$ and $y = q(u)$, find $\dfrac{d^2 f(x, y)}{du^2}$.

Solution. Since $\dfrac{df(x, y)}{du} = f_x\dfrac{dx}{du} + f_y\dfrac{dy}{du}$, it follows that

$$\frac{d^2f}{du^2} = \frac{d}{du}\left(f_x\frac{dx}{du} + f_y\frac{dy}{du}\right) = \left(\frac{d}{du}f_x\right)\frac{dx}{du} + f_x\frac{d^2x}{du^2} + \left(\frac{d}{du}f_y\right)\frac{dy}{du} + f_y\frac{d^2y}{du^2}.$$

Since f_x and f_y are functions of x and y, their derivatives with respect to u are found in exactly the same way as df/du. Thus,

$$\frac{d}{du}f_x = \frac{\partial f_x}{\partial x}\cdot\frac{dx}{du} + \frac{\partial f_x}{\partial y}\cdot\frac{dy}{du} = \frac{\partial^2 f}{\partial x^2}\cdot\frac{dx}{du} + \frac{\partial^2 f}{\partial x\,\partial y}\cdot\frac{dy}{du},$$

and a similar formula exists for $(d/du)f_y$. Substitution of these results in d^2f/du^2 gives

$$\frac{d^2f}{du^2} = \frac{\partial^2 f}{\partial x^2}\left(\frac{dx}{du}\right)^2 + 2\frac{\partial^2 f}{\partial y\,\partial x}\frac{dx}{du}\frac{dy}{du} + \frac{\partial^2 f}{\partial y^2}\left(\frac{dy}{du}\right)^2 + \frac{\partial f}{\partial x}\frac{d^2x}{du^2} + \frac{\partial f}{\partial y}\frac{d^2y}{du^2}.$$

(b) If $x = p(u, v)$ and $y = q(u, v)$, find $\partial^2 f/\partial u^2$, $\partial^2 f/\partial v\,\partial u$, and $\partial^2 f/\partial v^2$.

(c) If $x = p(u)$, $y = q(u)$, $z = r(u)$, find $\dfrac{d^2f(x,\ y,\ z)}{du^2}$.

31. If $z = \varphi(x + iy) + \psi(x - iy)$, show that $\dfrac{\partial^2 z}{\partial x^2} + \dfrac{\partial^2 z}{\partial y^2} = 0$, where $i^2 = -1$ and where i is treated like a numerical coefficient when differentiating.

USEFUL FORMULAS

32. (a) If $x = r \cos \phi$ and $y = r \sin \phi$, show that

$$\left(\frac{\partial f}{\partial x}\right)^2 + \left(\frac{\partial f}{\partial y}\right)^2 = \left(\frac{\partial f}{\partial r}\right)^2 + \frac{1}{r^2}\left(\frac{\partial f}{\partial \phi}\right)^2, \tag{17}$$

where f is a function of x and y. [Note that formula (B) is applicable to the terms in the right-hand member of (17). If f is regarded as a function of r and ϕ, (17) could be obtained by working with the left member, but the computation is more difficult.] In (17) the subscripts indicating the independent variables have been omitted; this is commonly done in those cases where the context itself indicates what they should be.

(b) If $x = r \sin \phi \cos \theta$, $y = r \sin \phi \sin \theta$, $z = r \cos \phi$, show that

$$\left(\frac{\partial f}{\partial x}\right)^2 + \left(\frac{\partial f}{\partial y}\right)^2 + \left(\frac{\partial f}{\partial z}\right)^2 = \left(\frac{\partial f}{\partial r}\right)^2 + \frac{1}{r^2}\left(\frac{\partial f}{\partial \phi}\right)^2 + \frac{1}{r^2 \sin^2 \phi}\left(\frac{\partial f}{\partial \theta}\right)^2,$$

where f is a function of x, y, and z.

33. (a) If $x = r \cos \phi$ and $y = r \sin \phi$, show that

$$\frac{\partial^2 f}{\partial x^2} + \frac{\partial^2 f}{\partial y^2} = \frac{\partial^2 f}{\partial r^2} + \frac{1}{r}\frac{\partial f}{\partial r} + \frac{1}{r^2}\frac{\partial^2 f}{\partial \phi^2},$$

where f is a function of x and y.

(b) If $x = r \sin \phi \cos \theta$, $y = r \sin \phi \sin \theta$, $z = r \cos \phi$, show that

$$\frac{\partial^2 f}{\partial x^2} + \frac{\partial^2 f}{\partial y^2} + \frac{\partial^2 f}{\partial z^2} = \frac{\partial^2 f}{\partial r^2} + \frac{1}{r^2} \frac{\partial^2 f}{\partial \phi^2} + \frac{1}{r^2 \sin^2 \phi} \frac{\partial^2 f}{\partial \theta^2} + \frac{2}{r} \frac{\partial f}{\partial r} + \frac{\operatorname{ctn} \phi}{r^2} \frac{\partial f}{\partial \phi},$$

where f is a function of x, y, and z.

34. If $f(x, y)$ and $g(x, y)$ are such that $\partial f/\partial x = \partial g/\partial y$ and $\partial f/\partial y = -\partial g/\partial x$, and if $x = r \cos \phi$ and $y = r \sin \phi$, show that

$$\frac{\partial f}{\partial r} = \frac{1}{r} \frac{\partial g}{\partial \phi} \quad \text{and} \quad \frac{1}{r} \frac{\partial f}{\partial \phi} = -\frac{\partial g}{\partial r}.$$

Under the preceding hypotheses show that the quantity in Ex. 33a is 0.

35. If $x = f(u, v)$ and $y = g(u, v)$ are such that $\partial f/\partial u = \partial g/\partial v$ and $\partial f/\partial v = -\partial g/\partial u$, and if F is a function of x and y, show by Ex. 30b that

$$\frac{\partial^2 F}{\partial u^2} + \frac{\partial^2 F}{\partial v^2} = \left(\frac{\partial^2 F}{\partial x^2} + \frac{\partial^2 F}{\partial y^2}\right)\left[\left(\frac{\partial f}{\partial u}\right)^2 + \left(\frac{\partial f}{\partial v}\right)^2\right].$$

36. If (x, y, z) and (X, Y, Z) are the coordinates of a point P with respect to two sets of rectangular axes with a common origin O and based on the same unit of length, it can be shown that

$$\begin{aligned} x &= a_1 X + b_1 Y + c_1 Z, \\ y &= a_2 X + b_2 Y + c_2 Z, \\ z &= a_3 X + b_3 Y + c_3 Z, \end{aligned} \tag{T}$$

where a_1, b_1, and c_1 are the direction cosines of the X-, Y-, and Z-axes with respect to the x-axis, a_2, b_2, and c_2 those with respect to the y-axis, and a_3, b_3, and c_3 those with respect to the z-axis. Show that

$$\left(\frac{\partial f}{\partial x}\right)^2 + \left(\frac{\partial f}{\partial y}\right)^2 + \left(\frac{\partial f}{\partial z}\right)^2 = \left(\frac{\partial f}{\partial X}\right)^2 + \left(\frac{\partial f}{\partial Y}\right)^2 + \left(\frac{\partial f}{\partial Z}\right)^2,$$

where f is a function of x, y, and z. [Recall the formula

$$\cos \theta = \cos \alpha_1 \cos \alpha_2 + \cos \beta_1 \cos \beta_2 + \cos \gamma_1 \cos \gamma_2 \tag{18}$$

for the angle between two lines.]

37. Let the point (x, y, z) move along a curve C in space. If s is the arc length along C and if t denotes times, show that

$$\left(\frac{ds}{dt}\right)^2 = \left(\frac{dx}{dt}\right)^2 + \left(\frac{dy}{dt}\right)^2 + \left(\frac{dz}{dt}\right)^2.$$

(Cf. Sec. 7.) If α, β, and γ are the direction angles of a tangent to C, show that

$$\frac{dx}{ds} = \cos \alpha, \qquad \frac{dy}{ds} = \cos \beta, \qquad \frac{dz}{ds} = \cos \gamma.$$

Suggestion. Let (x_0, y_0, z_0) and $(x_0 + \Delta x, y_0 + \Delta y, z_0 + \Delta z)$ be two points on C, let Δc be the length of the chord joining these points, and let α' be the direction angle of this chord with the x-axis. Then $\Delta x = (\Delta c) \cos \alpha'$ and $\Delta x/\Delta s = (\Delta c/\Delta s) \cos \alpha'$. The first of the above results is obtained by taking limits under suitable hypotheses. Use these results to extend formula (A') to a function $f(x, y, z)$.

38. *Euler's Theorem for Homogeneous Functions.* If a function $f(x, y, z)$ is such that $f(\lambda x, \lambda y, \lambda z) = \lambda^n f(x, y, z)$, then f is said to be *homogeneous of order n.* Thus, $x^2 - xy$, $e^{y/x}$, $\sqrt{x + y}$, and $(x - y)/xy$ are homogeneous of orders 2, 0, $\frac{1}{2}$, and -1, respectively. Prove

Theorem. If a function $f(x, y, z)$ is homogeneous and differentiable, then

$$x\frac{\partial f}{\partial x} + y\frac{\partial f}{\partial y} + z\frac{\partial f}{\partial z} = nf(x, y, z).$$

Suggestion. Differentiate the relation $f(\lambda x, \lambda y, \lambda z) = \lambda^n f(x, y, z)$ with respect to λ by the method of Ex. 28 and in the result set $\lambda = 1$.

Extend this result to a function of arbitrarily many variables. Also, extend this result to higher derivatives.

39. *Theorem of the Mean for a Function of Two Variables.* Let f be a function of x and y; let (a, b) and $(a + h, b + k)$ be two points. Construct the function $g(t) = f(a + th, b + tk)$. Apply Theorem 10.1 to the quantity $g(1) - g(0)$ to show that

$$f(a + h, b + k) - f(a, b) = hf_x(a + \theta h, b + \theta k) + kf_y(a + \theta h, b + \theta k),$$

where $0 < \theta < 1$. State this result as a theorem, and include in the hypotheses of the theorem all the conditions f must meet.

19. Differentiation of Implicit Functions. In order that the content of this section may be more easily understood, let us first consider the following physical situation.

A solid metallic hemisphere has its base in the xy-plane. Heat is being applied to this hemisphere over a portion H of its base (see Fig. 42) so that each point of H is kept at the temperature $100°C$. The rest of the base not in H is insulated so that there is no transfer of heat across it. The entire spherical surface is kept at $0°C$. Let $T(x, y, z)$ represent the temperature (at a certain instant) at the point (x, y, z) in the hemisphere. Let A denote a certain temperature between $0°$ and $100°$. It is evident that $T(a, b, c) = A$ only at certain points (a, b, c); in other words, the equation $T(x, y, z) = A$ is satisfied only for certain points (a, b, c). We say that the set of values a, b, c of x, y, z is a *solution* of the equation $T(x, y, z) = A$ if the number $T(a, b, c)$ is the number A, that is, if $T(a, b, c) = A$. In this illustration, what is the locus of the points representing the solutions of the equation $T(x, y, z) = 0$? Of the equation $T(x, y, z) = 100$? Of $T(x, y, z) = 10$? Of $T(x, y, 0) = 10$? Of $T(0, y, z) = 10$? Of $T(x, y, a/2) = 10$, where a is the radius of the hemisphere. Of $T(x, y, a/2) = 90$? Of $T(0, y, z) = 90$? Of $T(a/4, y, z) = 90$? How many solutions exist of the equation $T(a/4, y, 0) = 90$? Of $T(0, y, a/2) = 10$? Of $T(x, a/2, a/4) = 50$? Of $T(a/2, 0, z) = 95$? Of $T(a/2, 0, z) = 10$?

Now let (x_0, y_0) be an arbitrary point in the base of the hemisphere. Does there exist a *unique* solution of the equation $T(x_0, y_0, z) = A$? (The word *unique* is always used in mathematics in the sense "one and only one" and never in the sense "peculiar" or "unusual.") To put the question another way, does there exist a unique point $z = z_0$ on the line $x = x_0, y = y_0$ at which the temperature is A? It seems intuitively evident that there exists such a unique point if (x_0, y_0) is not too near the circumference of the base; otherwise, there is no such point. In other words, there exists such a unique point when and only when (x_0, y_0) lies in a certain region D of the base of the hemisphere. Moreover, the extent of D depends on A, D being H when $A = 100$ and D being the entire base when $A = 0$.

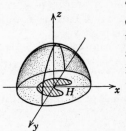

FIG. 42.

Again, does there exist a unique solution of the equation $T(x_0, y, z_0) = A$? It seems evident that for most points (x_0, z_0) there are four, two, or no solutions, though for certain points (x_0, z_0) there are three or one.

This illustration brings out three things: (1) In discussing the solutions of an equation $f(x, y, z) = A$, it is quite unnecessary to think of f as being represented by a formula or to think of the equation as being "solved" for one of the variables in terms of the other two. (2) An equation $f(x, y, z) = A$ does not necessarily have a unique solution in one of the variables for given values of the other two variables, but may have either no solution or several solutions. (3) An equation $f(x, y, z) = A$ may have a unique solution in *z for each point (x, y) of some region D of the xy-plane* without having a unique solution in z for each point (x, y) of the entire xy-plane.

The discussion of this illustration should be kept carefully in mind during the reading of this section. It will be helpful to think of f as representing the temperature of the above hemisphere, and to think of D as a portion of the base of this hemisphere.

Let f be a single-valued function of the independent variables x, y, and z. We wish to give a precise meaning to the statement that the equation $f(x, y, z) = A$ defines z as a single-valued function of x and y, where A is a constant. To make this meaning precise, we must avoid using any phrase like "solve for" or "in terms of," and instead we must use the terminology of Definition 14.1. We shall state this meaning in two ways: first, in a simple, direct manner which has rather limited application, and second, in a more technical form of wide application.

Suppose f is a single-valued function of x, y, and z such that, for each point (x_0, y_0) *in some region D of the xy-plane, the equation*

$$f(x_0, y_0, z) = A \tag{1}$$

has one and only one solution $z = z_0$. Then, for each point (x_0, y_0) in D, the value of z is uniquely determined as the number z_0 which satisfies (1). Since z has exactly one real value at each point (x_0, y_0) in D, it follows by Definition 14.1 that z is a single-valued function of x and y defined over D. Let φ denote the function* of x and y which represents the value of z, so that

$$z = \varphi(x, y). \tag{2}$$

Then, from the manner in which the value of z is determined, φ is such that, for each point (x_0, y_0) in D,

---

* If z can be represented by a "formula" in x and y, i.e., the formula that would be obtained if the equation $f(x, y, z) = A$ could be "solved" for z, then φ denotes this formula. For example, if $x + 2y + 3z = 1$, then $z = \varphi(x, y) = (\frac{1}{3})(1 - x - 2y)$. But *if there exists no such "formula" for z, and this is usually the case, what does φ denote?*

To answer this question we must generalize Definition 2.1 as follows: Let D be any set of elements a, b, c, $\cdots$ whatever. Also, let S be any set of elements p, q, r, $\cdots$ whatever. If in any manner there is associated with each element of D an element of S, then the *abstract correspondence* associating elements of S with elements of D is called a *function*. If φ represents this correspondence, then $\varphi(a)$ denotes, and is read, the element of S associated by φ with a.

In the present connection, φ denotes the correspondence between points (x, y) of D and values of z.

$$\varphi(x_0, y_0) = z_0,$$

where z_0 is the solution of (1). Hence, for *every* point (x_0, y_0) in D,

$$f[x_0, y_0, \varphi(x_0, y_0)] = A. \tag{3}$$

This discussion is summarized in the following definition.*

DEFINITION 19.1A. *If f is a single-valued function of x, y, and z such that, for each point (x, y) in some region D of the xy-plane, the equation*

$$f(x, y, z) = A \tag{4}$$

has one and only one solution in z, then we say that this equation defines z as a single-valued implicit function φ of x and y over D, i.e., $z = \varphi(x, y)$, and φ is such that $f[x, y, \varphi(x, y)] = A$ for each point (x, y) of D.

This definition may be stated in geometric language: If on each line $x = x_0$, $y = y_0$ intersecting D there exists exactly one point $z = z_0$ at which the value of f is A, i.e., if on each such line there exists exactly one point $z = z_0$ on the *graph* of (4), then equation (4) defines z as a single-valued function of x and y over D. The student should construct various physical examples (analogous to the above hemisphere) to bring out the significance of this definition.

Let us now return to the discussion of the above hemisphere. It is evident that the equation $T(x, y, z) = A$ does *not* define x as a single-valued function of y and z. However, if we were to cut off a small portion R of the hemisphere around the point $(a, 0, 0)$ without altering the values of T within R, then, *considering only R as though the rest of the hemisphere did not exist*, the equation $T(x, y, z) = A$ defines x as a single-valued function of y and z.

We may state this idea in more general form as follows: Suppose equation (4) defines z as a *multiple-valued* function of x and y, i.e., for certain points (x, y), equation (4) has two or more solutions in z. There may exist a region R of space such that, when f is considered as defined *only in R*, equation (4) defines z as a single-valued function of x and y. By this device of making z single-valued we are able to discuss the continuity of z, the derivatives of z, and so on. We are now in a position to generalize Definition 19.1a.

DEFINITION 19.1B. *Let R be a region of space and let D be a region of the xy-plane. Suppose f is a single-valued function of x, y, and z such that, for each point (x_0, y_0) in D, the equation*

* The significance of (3) is illustrated by substituting $z = \frac{1}{3}(1 - x - 2y)$ in the equation $x + 2y + 3z = 1$.

$$f(x_0, y_0, z) = A \tag{1}$$

has one and only one solution $z = z_0$ such that the point (x_0, y_0, z_0) is in R. Then we say that within the region R the equation $f(x, y, z) = A$ defines z as a single-valued implicit function of x and y over D.

We leave it to the student to state this definition in geometric language. It is evident that the situation described in this definition can exist only when D is contained in the projection of R on the xy-plane. In fact, for a given region R the maximum possible extent of D is the projection on the xy-plane of that portion of the graph of the equation $f(x, y, z) = A$ contained in R. Likewise, if the region R is to be such that within it the equation $f(x, y, z) = A$ defines z as a single-valued function of x and y, R must not contain two points on the graph of this equation having the same projection on the xy-plane.

We shall now derive a formula for $\dfrac{\partial z}{\partial x}\bigg)_y$ in the case where z is determined as a differentiable function of x and y by the equation $f(x, y, z) = A$. We first note the following comparisons: if f is a function of the *independent* variables x, y, and z, then the value of f varies (in general) with x, y, and z, and if f is differentiable, $\dfrac{\partial f}{\partial x}\bigg)_{y,z}$, $\dfrac{\partial f}{\partial y}\bigg)_{x,z}$, and $\dfrac{\partial f}{\partial z}\bigg)_{x,y}$ are (in general) all different from zero. But if z is determined as a function of x and y over the region D by the equation $f(x, y, z) = A$, then, for *each* point (x, y) in D, z always has just such a value that the value of f is always A. Thus, as the point (x, y) moves in any manner in D, z varies in just such a way that the value of f remains constant and equal to A. Hence, for example, $\dfrac{\partial f(x, y, z)}{\partial x}\bigg)_y = 0$.

We know by formula (B) that, if f and z are differentiable,

$$\frac{\partial f(x, y, z)}{\partial x}\bigg)_y = \frac{\partial f}{\partial x}\bigg)_{y,z} + \frac{\partial f}{\partial z}\bigg)_{x,y} \frac{\partial z}{\partial x}\bigg)_y. \tag{5}$$

If z is determined by the equation $f(x, y, z) = A$, then we know from the preceding paragraph that the value of the left member of (5) is zero, while the first term of the right member is, in general, not zero. Hence

$$\frac{\partial f}{\partial x}\bigg)_{y,z} + \frac{\partial f}{\partial z}\bigg)_{x,y} \cdot \frac{\partial z}{\partial x}\bigg)_y = 0. \tag{6}$$

As mentioned above, $\dfrac{\partial f}{\partial z}\bigg)_{x,y}$ is, in general, not zero. If we specifically assume f to be such that $\dfrac{\partial f}{\partial z}\biggr)_{x,y} \neq 0$, then we may write (6) in the form

$$\frac{\partial z}{\partial x}\biggr)_y = -\frac{\dfrac{\partial f}{\partial x}\biggr)_{y,z}}{\dfrac{\partial f}{\partial z}\biggr)_{x,y}}. \qquad (7)$$

This is the formula desired. Other formulas of this nature are given in the exercises below.

EXERCISES XX

1. State in both geometric and nongeometric language exactly what is meant by saying that the equation $f(x, y, z) = A$ defines x as a single-valued function of y and z.

Let f be a single-valued function of a finite number of independent variables $x, y, \cdots, u$. Under what conditions does the equation $f(x, y, \cdots, u) = A$ define u as a single-valued function of $x, y, \cdots$?

2. What does Eq. (2) represent with reference to the hemisphere discussed in the preceding section?

3. What is the difference in significance between the first two derivatives in Eq. (5)? In particular, state the functional relationships among the variables x, y, and z; state whether x, y, and z are constant or variable during the calculation of these derivatives; state the equations of the curve along which the point (x, y, z) moves.

4. The discussion in the preceding section may be summarized by the following formal rule for calculating $\dfrac{\partial z}{\partial x}\biggr)_y$. Regard the equation $f(x, y, z) = A$ as defining z as a function of x and y. By formula (B) differentiate both sides of this equation with respect to x. Equate the results and solve for $\dfrac{\partial z}{\partial x}\biggr)_y$. Why is it correct (according to this rule) to say that, since $f(x, y, z) = A$, $\dfrac{\partial f(x, y, z)}{\partial x}\biggr)_y = \dfrac{\partial A}{\partial x}\biggr)_y = 0$, but usually incorrect to say that $\dfrac{\partial f(x, y, z)}{\partial x}\biggr)_{y,z} = \dfrac{\partial A}{\partial x}\biggr)_{y,z} = 0$? Under what circumstance would this last statement be correct?

5. If $f(x, y, z) = A$, find: (a) $\dfrac{\partial z}{\partial y}\biggr)_x$; (b) $\dfrac{\partial y}{\partial x}\biggr)_z$; (c) $\dfrac{\partial x}{\partial z}\biggr)_y$.

6. Find $\dfrac{\partial u}{\partial x}\biggr)_y$ and $\dfrac{\partial x}{\partial y}\biggr)_u$ from the following relations:

(a) $x^2 - xy + yu^2 - 3 = 0$; (b) $xe^y (\sin u) - 1 = 0$;

(c) $x + y + u = 1/xyu$; (d) $u = f(x + u, y - u)$;

(e) $f(x + y + u) = g(xyu)$; (f) $xu^2 + f\left(\dfrac{y + u}{x^2 + u^2}\right) = 0$.

7. Show that if y is determined as a differentiable function of x by the relation $f(x, y) = A$, then $\dfrac{dy}{dx} = -\dfrac{f_x(x, y)}{f_y(x, y)}$. Use this result to obtain dy/dx in the following cases:

(a) $(x^2/a^2) + (y^2/b^2) = 1$; (b) $ax^2 + 2bxy + cy^2 = d$;

(c) $e^x + e^y = 2xy$; (d) $\text{Tan}^{-1} 3x^2y = x^{-3}y^{-5}$;

(e) $ye^{-3x^2y} = \cos 5x$; (f) $y/x = \log (x^2 + y^2)$.

Check these results by the methods of elementary calculus.

8. If $z = f(x, y)$ and $\varphi(x, y) = 0$, find dz/dx.

9. Find $\dfrac{\partial y}{\partial v}\bigg)_{x,z,u}$ and $\dfrac{\partial u}{\partial z}\bigg)_{x,y,v}$ by means of the relation

$$f(x, y, z, u, v) = A.$$

10. A certain law of thermodynamics is represented by the relation $pv^{1.41} = C$, where p and v denote the unit pressure and volume of a certain quantity of gas, and where C is a constant. Find the rate of change of volume with respect to pressure when the pressure is p_0.

11. The characteristic equation of a certain substance is represented by the equation $F(p, v, T) = 0$, where p, v, and T, respectively, denote the unit pressure, volume and temperature of the substance. Show that

$$\frac{\partial p}{\partial v}\bigg)_T \cdot \frac{\partial v}{\partial T}\bigg)_p \cdot \frac{\partial T}{\partial p}\bigg)_v = -1.$$

State the physical significance of each factor in this relation and also of the entire relation.

12. Given a function $f(x, y, z)$ and given that the equation $\varphi(x, y, z) = 0$ determines each of the variables as a function of the other two. Is it true that $\dfrac{\partial f}{\partial y}\bigg)_x = \dfrac{\partial f}{\partial z}\bigg)_x \cdot \dfrac{\partial z}{\partial y}\bigg)_x$?

13. Let $f(x, y, u)$ and $g(x, y, u)$ be two functions of the independent variables x, y, and u. If we form the equations

$$f(x, u, v) = A \qquad \text{and} \qquad g(x, u, v) = B, \tag{8}$$

then these equations (generally) determine u and v each as a function of x. (See Theorem 20.2 below.) This is intuitively evident when we think of the equation $f(x, u, v) = A$ as being solved for v, giving $v = \varphi(x, u)$, and the result substituted in the equation $g(x, u, v) = B$, giving $g[x, u, \varphi(x, u)] = B$. This last equation may be solved for u in terms of x, giving $u = p(x)$; if this result is substituted in $v = \varphi(x, u)$, the resulting equation may be solved for v in terms of x, giving $v = q(x)$. It follows that $u = p(x)$, $v = q(x)$ are the parametric equations of the curve of intersection C of the two surfaces with equations (8). If f and g are differentiable, then we may write

$$\frac{d}{dx} f(x, u, v) = \frac{d}{dx} A = 0, \qquad \frac{d}{dx} g(x, u, v) = \frac{d}{dx} B = 0.$$

Evaluate these derivatives by formula (B) to obtain two equations containing du/dx and dv/dx, as well as the various partial derivatives of f and g. Solve these equations for du/dx and dv/dx in terms of the remaining quantities to show that

$$\frac{du}{dx} = - \frac{\begin{vmatrix} f_x & f_v \\ g_x & g_v \end{vmatrix}}{\begin{vmatrix} f_u & f_v \\ g_u & g_v \end{vmatrix}} \quad \text{and} \quad \frac{dv}{dx} = - \frac{\begin{vmatrix} f_u & f_x \\ g_u & g_x \end{vmatrix}}{\begin{vmatrix} f_u & f_v \\ g_u & g_v \end{vmatrix}}.$$

What quantity must be $\neq 0$?

14. Find dy/dx and dz/dx from the relations

$$x^2 + y^2 + z^2 = 3,$$
$$xy + yz + xz = 3.$$

Evaluate these derivatives at $(1, 1, 1)$ and $(1, 2, 3)$. Why is the first result indeterminate and the second meaningless?

15. Find $\dfrac{\partial u}{\partial x}\bigg)_{y,\dots}$ and $\dfrac{\partial v}{\partial x}\bigg)_{y,\dots}$ from the relations

$$f(x, y, \cdots, u, v) = A, \qquad g(x, y, \cdots, u, v) = B. \tag{9}$$

Use determinants to represent these results. What quantity must be $\neq 0$? What special form do these results assume when equations (9) have the following form:

$$x = F(u, v), \qquad y = G(u, v).$$

16. Find $\dfrac{\partial x}{\partial v}\bigg)_{u}$ and $\dfrac{\partial y}{\partial v}\bigg)_{u}$ from the relations

$$x^2 + y^2 + u^2 + v^2 = 4,$$
$$xyuv = 1.$$

What is the significance of the indeterminacy of these derivatives at $(1, 1, 1, 1)$?

17. Find $\dfrac{\partial u}{\partial x}\bigg)_{y,\dots}$, $\dfrac{\partial v}{\partial x}\bigg)_{y,\dots}$, and $\dfrac{\partial w}{\partial x}\bigg)_{y,\dots}$ from the relations

$$f(x, y, \cdots, u, v, w) = A,$$
$$g(x, y, \cdots, u, v, w) = B,$$
$$h(x, y, \cdots, u, v, w) = C.$$

Use determinants to represent these results.   What quantity must be $\neq 0$?

18. Find $\dfrac{\partial u}{\partial x}\Big)_{y,z}$ from the relations

$$
\begin{aligned}
x &= u + v + w, \\
y &= u^2 + v^2 + w^2, \\
z &= u^3 + v^3 + w^3.
\end{aligned}
$$

Does $\dfrac{\partial u}{\partial x} = \dfrac{1}{\partial x/\partial u}$?   What subscripts are implied in these derivatives?

19. If $f(x, y, u, v) = A$ and if u and v are functions of x and y, does

$$
\frac{dy}{dx} = -\frac{\dfrac{\partial f}{\partial x}\Big)_y}{\dfrac{\partial f}{\partial y}\Big)_x}?
$$

How may $\dfrac{\partial f}{\partial x}\Big)_y$ and $\dfrac{\partial f}{\partial y}\Big)_x$ be evaluated?

20. With reference to a certain quantity of fluid, let p, v, T, ϕ, and H, respectively, denote the unit pressure, volume, temperature, entropy, and total heat added to the gas to bring it to the state (p, v, T, ϕ).   (Note that H is not the internal energy of the gas.)   The following thermodynamic magnitudes are of frequent use:

Specific heat at constant volume: $C_v = \dfrac{\partial H}{\partial T}\Big)_v = T\dfrac{\partial \phi}{\partial T}\Big)_v$.

Specific heat at constant pressure: $C_p = \dfrac{\partial H}{\partial T}\Big)_p = T\dfrac{\partial \phi}{\partial T}\Big)_p$.

Latent heat of expansion: $L_v = \dfrac{\partial H}{\partial v}\Big)_T = T\dfrac{\partial \phi}{\partial v}\Big)_T$.

Coefficient of cubic expansion: $\alpha_v = \dfrac{1}{v}\dfrac{\partial v}{\partial T}\Big)_p$.

Isothermal modulus of elasticity: $E_T = -v\dfrac{\partial p}{\partial v}\Big)_T$.

Adiabatic modulus of elasticity: $E_\phi = -v\dfrac{\partial p}{\partial v}\Big)_\phi$.

(a) Write each of these definitions in words.   For example, C_v is the instantaneous rate at which heat is added to the fluid per degree rise of temperature when the volume is kept constant; α_p is the instantaneous rate of change of volume per degree rise of temperature for a unit of volume when the pressure is kept constant.

(b) What notations represent the instantaneous value of the following rates: change in volume per unit change in entropy when the temperature remains constant; change in volume per unit change in entropy for a unit volume when the temperature remains constant; change in temperature per unit change in volume for a unit volume when the pressure remains constant.

(c) If p, v, and T are related as in Ex. 11, show that $\alpha_p E_T$ is equal to the rate of increase of pressure with respect to temperature when the volume is constant.

(d) If p, v, T, and ϕ are related by the equations

$$f(p, v, T, \phi) = A, \qquad g(p, v, T, \phi) = B,$$

show that $E_\phi/E_T = C_p/C_v$.

(e) If p, v, T, and ϕ are related as in part (d), and if $\left(\dfrac{\partial T}{\partial v}\right)_\phi = \left(\dfrac{\partial p}{\partial \phi}\right)_v$, show that $\left(\dfrac{\partial \phi}{\partial p}\right)_T = -\left(\dfrac{\partial v}{\partial T}\right)_p$.

21. If the equations $f(x, y, u, v) = A$ and $g(x, y, u, v) = B$ determine u and v as functions of x and y, and also determine x and y as functions of u and v, show that

$$\frac{\partial u}{\partial x}\frac{\partial x}{\partial u} + \frac{\partial u}{\partial y}\frac{\partial y}{\partial u} = 1, \qquad \frac{\partial u}{\partial x}\frac{\partial x}{\partial v} + \frac{\partial u}{\partial y}\frac{\partial y}{\partial v} = 0.$$

Generalize these results to $2n$ variables.

20. Some Implicit Function Theorems. We have already discussed in Sec. 19 the question as to when the equation $f(x, y, z) = A$ defines z as a single-valued function of x and y. But the criterion given is sometimes difficult to apply in a practical case. We now wish to develop a more convenient criterion that the equation $f(x, y, z) = A$ defines z as a single-valued function of x and y.

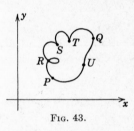

Fig. 43.

As a preliminary example, let us consider the equation $F(x, y) = A$ with the graph C shown in Fig. 43. This equation determines y as a single-valued function of x in a small neighborhood of P, but in no neighborhood, however small, of Q or R. (Within every small neighborhood of Q or R a line $x = x_0$ generally meets the graph in either two or no points. Remember that every neighborhood of a point contains this point in its interior.) By Ex. XX, 7,

$$D_x y]_{x_0, y_0} = -\frac{F_x(x_0, y_0)}{F_y(x_0, y_0)}. \tag{1}$$

It is evident from (1) that if $F_y(x_0, y_0) \neq 0$, then $D_x y]_{x_0, y_0}$ has exactly one finite value. Therefore, if $F_y(x_0, y_0) \neq 0$, (x_0, y_0) cannot be the point Q (at which $D_x y$ is infinite), nor can (x_0, y_0) be the point R (at which $D_x y$ has two values). We are thus led to the question, is the condition $F_y(x_0, y_0) \neq 0$ sufficient to ensure that (x_0, y_0) is necessarily a point in some neighborhood of which y is defined as a single-valued function of x by the equation $F(x, y) = A$? Or might (x_0, y_0) be at S where $D_x y$ has one finite value, but near which y is not a single-valued function of x? These questions are answered in Theorem 20.1a below.

It must not be supposed that F_y *cannot* be zero at a point near which the equation $F(x, y) = A$ defines y as a single-valued function of x. It is evident from (1) that F_y is zero at T and U ($D_x y$ being infinite at these points), and yet y is a single-valued function of x in a small neighborhood of each of these points. The conclusion to be drawn (presupposing Theorem 20.1a) is that the condition $F_y(x_0, y_0) \neq 0$ is unnecessarily strong.

THEOREM 20.1A. *Let f be a real single-valued function of a finite number of independent variables $x, y, \cdots, u$. If $(x_0, y_0, \cdots, u_0)$ is a solution of the equation*

$$f(x, y, \cdots, u) = A \qquad (2)$$

such that (1) *f and f_u are defined and continuous over some neighborhood N of the point $(x_0, y_0, \cdots, u_0)$, and* (2)

$$f_u(x_0, y_0, \cdots, u_0) \neq 0,$$

then within some neighborhood $\bar{N}$ of $(x_0, y_0, \cdots, u_0)$ within N equation (2) *defines u as a single-valued continuous function of $x, y, \cdots, $ say $u = \varphi(x, y, \cdots)$, and the domain of definition of u extends over the whole of some neighborhood D of $(x_0, y_0, \cdots)$ in the space of points $(x, y, \cdots)$.*

In this and the following theorems, we follow the convention that, when we indicate a partial derivative by subscript notation, such as f_u or $f_u(x, y, \cdots, u)$, we shall always understand that this derivative is computed while regarding all of the variables $x, y, \cdots, u$ as independent with all of them constant except the variable of differentiation.

In proving this theorem, we shall suppose for simplicity that there are only two variables x and u; the proof may be extended directly to the general case. We shall also suppose $f_u(x_0, u_0)$ to be positive; the case where it is negative is entirely analogous.

Since f_u is positive and continuous at (x_0, u_0), there exists within N a rectangular neighborhood $\bar{N}$ of (x_0, u_0) such that* f_u *is defined and remains positive over* $\bar{N}$. Since $f_u(x_0, u_0)$ is positive, $f(x_0, u)$ is an increasing function of u at $u = u_0$. Hence, for any two values u_1 and u_2 sufficiently close to u_0 with $u_1 < u_0 < u_2$ and such that (x_0, u_1) and (x_0, u_2) are within $\bar{N}$, it follows by Theorem 6.1 that

$$f(x_0, u_1) < A < f(x_0, u_2),$$

where $A = f(x_0, u_0)$. Since $f(x, u_1)$ is a continuous function of x at $x = x_0$, and since $f(x_0, u_1) < A$, there exist values x_1' and x_2' sufficiently close to x_0 with $x_1' < x_0 < x_2'$ such that (x_1', u_1) and (x_2', u_1) are within $\bar{N}$ and such that at each point of the line segment from (x_1', u_1) to (x_2', u_1) the value of f remains less than A. Likewise there exist values x_1'' and x_2'' with $x_1'' < x_0 < x_2''$ such that (x_1'', u_2) and (x_2'', u_2) are within $\bar{N}$ and such that at each point of the line segment from (x_1'', u_2) to (x_2'', u_2) the value of f remains greater than A. Let x_1 denote the greater of x_1' and x_1'', and let x_2 denote the smaller of x_2' and x_2''. Since $\bar{N}$ is rectangular, the entire rectangle with vertices (x_1, u_1), (x_2, u_1), (x_2, u_2), and (x_1, u_2) lies within $\bar{N}$.

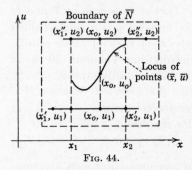

Fig. 44.

The interval† $x_1 < x < x_2$ serves as the neighborhood D of x_0 mentioned in the theorem, and the rectangle† $\bar{N}$ serves as the neighborhood N of the theorem, for let $\bar{x}$ denote an arbitrary value of x in the interval $x_1 < x < x_2$. Since

$$f(\bar{x}, u_1) < A < f(\bar{x}, u_2),$$

and since $f(\bar{x}, u)$ is a continuous function of u over the interval $u_1 \leqq u \leqq u_2$, the value of f, while increasing from $f(\bar{x}, u_1)$ to

---

* This is the only property of f_u that we shall use. Hence it would be sufficient to hypothesize this property instead of the continuity of f_u. But in most cases arising in practice it is more convenient to apply the theorem as stated, for the continuity of f_u is usually easier to establish than the invariance of sign of f_u over $\bar{N}$.

† There is no implication that this is the largest possible neighborhood of the required sort.

$f(\bar{x}, u_2)$, must pass through the value A at some value* $u = \bar{u}$, so that $f(\bar{x}, \bar{u}) = A$, where $u_1 < \bar{u} < u_2$. Since f_u is positive over $\bar{N}$, $f(\bar{x}, u)$ is an increasing function of u over the segment S of the line $x = \bar{x}$ within N, and there exists *at most one* value $\bar{u}$ within S such that $f(\bar{x}, \bar{u}) = A$. Thus the equation $f(x, u) = A$ determines a unique value $u = \bar{u}$ in the interval $u_1 < u < u_2$ for each value $x = \bar{x}$ in the interval $x_1 < x < x_2$; that is, within $\bar{N}$ the equation $f(x, u) = A$ determines u as a single-valued function of x, say $u = \varphi(x)$, and the domain of definition of u extends over the interval $x_1 < x < x_2$.

The continuity of u at $x = x_0$ is immediate: the preceding argument shows that, no matter how close u_1 and u_2 may be taken to u_0, there exists an interval about x_0 over which $\varphi(x)$ remains between u_1 and u_2. The continuity of u at any other point of the interval $x_1 < x < x_2$ follows in an analogous manner.

It should be noted that in the preceding proof we did not use all of our hypothesis as to the continuity of f; we used merely the fact that $f(x, u)$ is continuous in u when x is constant and that $f(x, u)$ is continuous in x when u is constant (see Definition 15.3).

THEOREM 20.1B. *If in Theorem 20.1a it is further supposed that f_x is defined and continuous over N, then u_x is defined and continuous over D, and is given by the formula*

$$u_x(x, y, \cdot \cdot \cdot) = -\frac{f_x(x, y, \cdot \cdot \cdot, u)}{f_u(x, y, \cdot \cdot \cdot, u)},$$

where $(x, y, \cdot \cdot \cdot)$ is any point of D, and $u = \varphi(x, y, \cdot \cdot \cdot)$.

As in the preceding proof we shall assume that there are only two variables x and u, and we shall use the notation introduced during the preceding proof. Let $\bar{x}$ be an arbitrary value of x in the interval $x_1 < x < x_2$, let $\bar{u} = \varphi(\bar{x})$, and let

$$\bar{u} + \Delta u = \varphi(\bar{x} + \Delta x).$$

Since $f(x, u)$ has the constant value A for all x in the interval $x_1 < x < x_2$ when $u = \varphi(x)$, it follows that

$$f(\bar{x} + \Delta x, \bar{u} + \Delta u) - f(\bar{x}, \bar{u})$$

has the constant value zero. Hence

$$\lim_{\Delta x \to 0} \frac{f(\bar{x} + \Delta x, \bar{u} + \Delta u) - f(\bar{x}, \bar{u})}{\Delta x} \tag{3}$$

---

* See Theorem 8.5, Chap. IX.

exists and equals zero. But (3) may be written in the form

$$\lim_{\Delta x \to 0} \left[\rho(\Delta x,\, \Delta u) \cdot \frac{\Delta u}{\Delta x} + \frac{f(\bar{x} + \Delta x,\, \bar{u}) - f(\bar{x},\, \bar{u})}{\Delta x} \right], \qquad (4)$$

where

$$\rho(\Delta x,\, \Delta u) = \begin{cases} \dfrac{f(\bar{x} + \Delta x,\, \bar{u} + \Delta u) - f(\bar{x} + \Delta x,\, \bar{u})}{\Delta u} & \text{when} \quad \Delta u \neq 0, \\[2ex] f_u(\bar{x} + \Delta x,\, \bar{u}) & \text{when} \quad \Delta u = 0. \end{cases}$$

By Theorem 10.1, $\rho(\Delta x,\, \Delta u) = f_u(\bar{x} + \Delta x,\, \bar{u} + \theta \cdot \Delta u)$, where $0 < \theta < 1$. Since φ is continuous, $\Delta u \to 0$ as $\Delta x \to 0$, and since f_u is continuous, $\lim_{\Delta x \to 0} \rho(\Delta x,\, \Delta u)$ exists and equals $f_u(\bar{x},\, \bar{u})$. By hypothesis, $\lim_{\Delta x \to 0} \dfrac{f(\bar{x} + \Delta x,\, \bar{u}) - f(\bar{x},\, \bar{u})}{\Delta x}$ exists and equals $f_x(\bar{x},\, \bar{u})$. Since the limit (4) exists and $f_u(\bar{x},\, \bar{u}) \neq 0$, $\lim_{\Delta x \to 0} \Delta u / \Delta x$ must exist, that is $\lim_{\Delta x \to 0} \dfrac{\varphi(\bar{x} + \Delta x) - \varphi(\bar{x})}{\Delta x} = \varphi_x(\bar{x})$ exists (see Ex. IV, 17). Thus (4) may be written as $f_u(\bar{x},\, \bar{u}) \cdot \varphi_x(\bar{x}) + f_x(\bar{x},\, \bar{u})$. Since the value of (4) is zero, it follows that

$$\varphi_x(\bar{x}) = u_x(\bar{x}) = -\frac{f_x(\bar{x},\, \bar{u})}{f_u(\bar{x},\, \bar{u})}.$$

The continuity of u_x follows at once from the representation $u_x = -f_x / f_u$ and the continuity of f_x and f_u.

It should be noted that we used the existence and continuity of f_x only at points on the graph of φ.

We now wish to extend Theorems 20.1a and 20.1b to the case where we have two equations

$$F(x, y,\, \cdots,\, u, v) = A, \qquad G(x, y,\, \cdots,\, u, v) = B. \quad (5)$$

As a preliminary example, we first discuss the case where equations (5) assume the special form

$$x = f(u, v), \qquad y = g(u, v), \qquad\qquad (6)$$

f and g being single-valued. *Suppose f and g are such that, for each point* (x_0, y_0) *in some region D of the xy-plane, the equations*

$$x_0 = f(u, v), \qquad y_0 = g(u, v) \qquad\qquad (7)$$

have one and only one solution $u = u_0$, $v = v_0$. Since u and v each have exactly one real value at each point (x_0, y_0) in D, it follows by Definition 14.1

that u and v are each a single-valued function of x and y defined over D. Let φ and ψ denote the functions of x and y which represent the values of u and v, so that

$$u = \varphi(x, y), \qquad v = \psi(x, y). \tag{8}$$

Then φ and ψ are such that, for each point (x_0, y_0) in D,

$$\varphi(x_0, y_0) = u_0, \qquad \psi(x_0, y_0) = v_0,$$

where u_0 and v_0 satisfy (7). Hence, for every point (x_0, y_0) in D,

$$x_0 = f[\varphi(x_0, y_0), \psi(x_0, y_0)], \qquad y_0 = g[\varphi(x_0, y_0), \psi(x_0, y_0)]. \tag{9}$$

We say that equations (6) define u and v as single-valued *implicit* functions of x and y when u and v are determined as functions of x and y in the manner indicated above. We leave it to the student to generalize this discussion along the line of Definition 19.1b, and to extend this discussion to Eqs. (5).

The following example illustrates the preceding discussion: If

$$x = \frac{u}{v}, \qquad y = \frac{1 - u}{v}, \tag{10}$$

then

$$u = \frac{x}{x + y}, \qquad v = \frac{1}{x + y}. \tag{11}$$

Thus Eqs. (10) determine u and v as single-valued functions of x and y over the entire xy-plane except for the line $x + y = 0$. The significance of (9) is illustrated by substituting formulas (11) in (10).

The condition given above that Eqs. (6) determine u and v as functions of x and y may be difficult to apply in a particular case. We shall now develop a criterion which is sometimes more convenient to use.

Suppose the graphs of Eqs. (7) are plotted on the same axes. Then u_0 and v_0 are the coordinates of the point P_0 of intersection of the two graphs. The graph of the equation $x_0 = f(u, v)$ is really the section of the surface $x = f(u, v)$ cut by the plane $x = x_0$. If f is a continuous function, the surface $x = f(u, v)$ is such that nearby sections $x = x_0$ and $x = x_1$ are nearly alike; that is, the contours (see Fig. 45)

$$x_0 = f(u, v), \qquad x_1 = f(u, v)$$

are close together when x_0 and x_1 are nearly equal. Likewise, the contours

$$y_0 = g(u, v) \qquad y_1 = g(u, v)$$

are close together when y_0 and y_1 are nearly equal. If the curves (7) intersect at an angle $\neq 0$, then, in general, the curves

$$x_1 = f(u, v), \qquad y_1 = g(u, v) \tag{12}$$

will intersect at a single point P_1 near P_0, i.e., Eqs. (6) have a unique solution $u = u_1$, $v = v_1$ near the solution $u = u_0$, $v = v_0$. Thus Eqs. (6) define u and v as single-valued continuous functions of x and y for values of

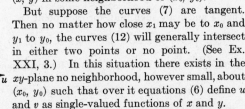

x and y near x_0 and y_0, that is, for all points (x, y) in some neighborhood of (x_0, y_0).

But suppose the curves (7) are tangent. Then no matter how close x_1 may be to x_0 and y_1 to y_0, the curves (12) will generally intersect in either two points or no point. (See Ex. XXI, 3.) In this situation there exists in the xy-plane no neighborhood, however small, about (x_0, y_0) such that over it equations (6) define u and v as single-valued functions of x and y.

Fig. 45.

Again, suppose one of the curves (7) intersects the other at a node. Then the curves (12) will generally intersect in two points, so that here also Eqs. (6) fail to define u and v as single-valued functions of x and y over any neighborhood, however small, of (x_0, y_0).

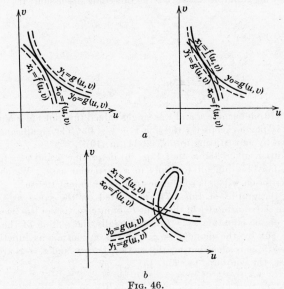

a

b

Fig. 46.

If f and g are differentiable at (u_0, v_0), then it follows from Ex. XX, 7, that the equation of the line tangent to the curve $x_0 = f(u, v)$ at the point (u_0, v_0) is

$$f_u(u_0, v_0) \cdot (u - u_0) + f_v(u_0, v_0) \cdot (v - v_0) = 0, \tag{13}$$

and the equation of the line tangent to the curve $y_0 = g(u, v)$ at the point (u_0, v_0) is

$$g_u(u_0, v_0) \cdot (u - u_0) + g_v(u_0, v_0) \cdot (v - v_0) = 0, \tag{14}$$

provided that $f_u(u_0, v_0)$ and $f_v(u_0, v_0)$ are not both zero and that $g_u(u_0, v_0)$ and $g_v(u_0, v_0)$ are not both zero. The angle ϕ between these two lines is determined by the relation*

$$\tan \phi = \frac{f_u(u_0, v_0)g_v(u_0, v_0) - f_v(u_0, v_0)g_u(u_0, v_0)}{f_u(u_0, v_0)g_u(u_0, v_0) + f_v(u_0, v_0)g_v(u_0, v_0)}.$$

Let

$$J\left(\frac{f, g}{u, v}\right) \equiv \begin{vmatrix} f_u(u, v) & f_v(u, v) \\ g_u(u, v) & g_v(u, v) \end{vmatrix} \equiv f_u(u, v)g_v(u, v) - f_v(u, v)g_u(u, v).$$

The determinant $J\left(\dfrac{f, g}{u, v}\right)$ is called the *Jacobian* of the functions f and g.

It is evident that if $J\left(\dfrac{f, g}{u, v}\right)_0 \neq 0$, where $J\left(\dfrac{f, g}{u, v}\right)_0$ denotes the value of J at (u_0, v_0), then $\tan \phi \neq 0$ and the curves (7) cannot be tangent at (u_0, v_0). Moreover, if $J\left(\dfrac{f, g}{u, v}\right)_0 \neq 0$, then $f_u(u_0, v_0)$ and $f_v(u_0, v_0)$ cannot both be zero. It follows from the discussion of Eq. (1) that the curve $x_0 = f(u, v)$ cannot have a node at (u_0, v_0). Likewise, the curve $y_0 = g(u, v)$ cannot have a node at (u_0, v_0). Thus the condition $J\left(\dfrac{f, g}{u, v}\right)_0 \neq 0$ prevents the existence of each of the situations described above in which Eq. (6) failed to define u and v as single-valued functions of x and y. We are led to the question, is the condition $J\left(\dfrac{f, g}{u, v}\right)_0 \neq 0$ sufficient to ensure that Eqs. (6) define u and v as single-valued functions of x and y over some neighborhood of (x_0, y_0)? The answer to this question is provided by Theorem 20.2a below. As in the case of Theorem 20.1a, it must *not* be supposed that Eqs. (6) cannot define u and v as functions of x and y over a neighborhood of the point (x_0, y_0) when $J\left(\dfrac{f, g}{u, v}\right)_0 = 0$.

---

* The right member of this relation cannot be of the form 0/0, for suppose

$$f_u g_v - f_v g_u = 0, \tag{15}$$
$$f_u g_u + f_v g_v = 0, \tag{16}$$

where we omit the notation (u_0, v_0) for brevity. By hypothesis, f_u and f_v are not both zero; suppose $f_u \neq 0$. If we eliminate f_v from (15) and (16), we find that $f_u(g_u^2 + g_v^2) = 0$. Since $f_u \neq 0$, it follows that $g_u^2 + g_v^2 = 0$, and hence that $g_u = g_v = 0$. But g_u and g_v are not both zero. The same contradiction results when $f_v \neq 0$. This contradiction shows that (15) and (16) cannot both be true.

THEOREM 20.2A.   *Let f and g be real single-valued functions of a finite number of independent variables* x, y, $\cdots$, u, v. *If* $(x_0, y_0, \cdots, u_0, v_0)$ *is a solution of the equations*

$$f(x, y, \cdots, u, v) = A, \qquad g(x, y, \cdots, u, v) = B \quad (17)$$

such that (1) f, g, f_u, f_v, g_u, *and* g_v *are defined and continuous over some neighborhood* N *of the point* $(x_0, y_0, \cdots, u_0, v_0)$, *and* (2) $J\left(\dfrac{f, g}{u, v}\right)_0 \neq 0$, *where* $J\left(\dfrac{f, g}{u, v}\right) \equiv \begin{vmatrix} f_u & f_v \\ g_u & g_v \end{vmatrix}$, *then within some neighborhood* $\bar{N}$ *of* $(x_0, y_0, \cdots, u_0, v_0)$ *equations* (17) *define* u *and* v *as single-valued continuous functions of* x, y, $\cdots$, *and the domains of definition of* u *and* v *extend over the whole of some neighborhood* D *of* $(x_0, y_0, \cdots)$ *in the space of points* $(x, y, \cdots)$.

Since $J\left(\dfrac{f, g}{u, v}\right)_0 \neq 0$,

$$f_v(x_0, y_0, \cdots, u_0, v_0) \qquad \text{and} \qquad g_v(x_0, y_0, \cdots, u_0, v_0)$$

cannot both be zero; suppose $g_v(x_0, y_0, \cdots, u_0, v_0) \neq 0$. It follows by Theorems 20.1a and 20.1b that within some neighborhood N_1 of $(x_0, y_0, \cdots, u_0, v_0)$ within N the equation $g(x, y, \cdots, u, v) = B$ defines v as a single-valued continuous function of x, y, $\cdots$, u, say $v = \theta(x, y, \cdots, u)$, and the domain of definition of v extends over the whole of some neighborhood D_1 of $(x_0, y_0, \cdots, u_0)$. Moreover, v_u is defined and continuous over D_1 and equals $-g_u/g_v$.

Since θ is continuous, and since N_1 is within N,

$$f(x, y, \cdots, u, \theta(x, y, \cdots, u))$$

is defined and continuous over D_1. By Theorem 18.2,

$$\left.\frac{\partial f(x, y, \cdots, u, \theta)}{\partial u}\right)_{x,y,\ldots}$$

exists and is given by the formula

$$\left.\frac{\partial f(x, y, \cdots, u, \theta)}{\partial u}\right)_{x,y,\ldots} = \left.\frac{\partial f(x, y, \cdots, u, v)}{\partial u}\right)_{x,y,\ldots,v}$$
$$+ \left.\frac{\partial f(x, y, \cdots, u, v)}{\partial v}\right)_{x,y,\ldots,u} \left.\frac{\partial v}{\partial u}\right)_{x,y,\ldots} = \frac{J}{g_v},$$

where $v_u = -g_u/g_v$. Since J and g_v are continuous,

$$f_u(x, y, \cdots, u, \theta)$$

is defined and continuous over D_1; moreover, the value of $f_u(x, y, \cdots, u, \theta)$ at $(x_0, y_0, \cdots, u_0)$ is not zero since $J \neq 0$ at $(x_0, y_0, \cdots, u_0, v_0)$. It follows by Theorems 20.1a and 20.1b that within some neighborhood N_2 of $(x_0, y_0, \cdots, u_0)$ within D_1 the equation $f(x, y, \cdots, u, \theta) = A$ defines u as a single-valued continuous function of $x, y, \cdots$, say

$$u = \varphi(x, y, \cdots),$$

and the domain of definition of u extends over the whole of some neighborhood D of $(x_0, y_0, \cdots)$. If in the relation

$$v = \theta(x, y, \cdots, u)$$

we write $u = \varphi(x, y, \cdots)$, then v is defined as a single-valued continuous function of $x, y, \cdots$, say $v = \psi(x, y, \cdots)$, and the domain of definition of v extends over D. Finally, the neighborhood $\bar{N}$ of the theorem may be taken as the part of N_1 whose projection on the $(x, y, \cdots, u)$-hyperplane lies within N_2.

THEOREM 20.2B. *If in Theorem 20.2a it is further supposed that f_x and g_x are defined and continuous over N, then u_x and v_x are defined and continuous over D, and are given by the formulas*

$$u_x(x, y, \cdots) = -\frac{J\left(\dfrac{f, g}{x, v}\right)}{J\left(\dfrac{f, g}{u, v}\right)}, \qquad v_x(x, y, \cdots) = -\frac{J\left(\dfrac{f, g}{u, x}\right)}{J\left(\dfrac{f, g}{u, v}\right)},$$

where $(x, y, \cdots)$ is any point of D, and $u = \varphi(x, y, \cdots)$, $v = \psi(x, y, \cdots)$ in the notation of the preceding proof.

Let $(\bar{x}, \bar{y}, \cdots)$ be a point of D, with $\bar{u} = \varphi(\bar{x}, \bar{y}, \cdots)$, $\bar{v} = \psi(\bar{x}, \bar{y}, \cdots)$. By virtue of the way D was determined in the preceding proof, $g_v(\bar{x}, \bar{y}, \cdots, \bar{u}, \bar{v}) \neq 0$ and the value of J at $(\bar{x}, \bar{y}, \cdots \bar{u}, \bar{v})$ is $\neq 0$. Since f has the constant value A when $u = \varphi(x, y, \cdots)$, $v = \psi(x, y, \cdots)$,

$$\lim_{\Delta x \to 0} \frac{f(\bar{x} + \Delta x, \bar{y}, \cdots, \bar{u} + \Delta u, \bar{v} + \Delta v) - f(\bar{x}, \bar{y}, \cdots, \bar{u}, \bar{v})}{\Delta x}$$

$$(18)$$

exists and equals zero. But (18) may be broken up into parts as was (3), and the fraction $\Delta v/\Delta x$ which appears in the process may be written as

$$\frac{\Delta v}{\Delta x} = \frac{\theta(\bar{x} + \Delta x, \bar{y}, \cdots, \bar{u} + \Delta u) - \theta(\bar{x}, \bar{y}, \cdots, \bar{u})}{\Delta x}.$$

This fraction may also be broken up. In view of the fact that $\theta_x = -g_x/g_v$ and $\theta_u = -g_u/g_v$, $\lim\limits_{\Delta x \to 0} \Delta u/\Delta x$ may be proved to exist as in Theorem 20.1b. The remainder of the proof is evident.

The following extension of Theorem 20.2 may be proved by induction. (See Ex. 4 and 5 below.)

Theorem 20.3. *Let $f_1, f_2, \cdots, f_n$ be real single-valued functions of a finite number of independent variables $x_1, x_2, \cdots, x_p$; $u_1, u_2, \cdots, u_n$. If $(x_1^{(0)}, \cdots, x_p^{(0)}; u_1^{(0)}, \cdots, u_n^{(0)})$ is a solution of the equations*

$$
\begin{aligned}
f_1(x_1, \cdots, x_p; u_1, \cdots, u_n) &= A_1, \\
f_2(x_1, \cdots, x_p; u_1, \cdots, u_n) &= A_2, \cdots, \\
f_n(x_1, \cdots, x_p; u_1, \cdots, u_n) &= A_n
\end{aligned}
\tag{19}
$$

such that $f_1, \cdots, f_n$ and all their first partial derivatives are defined and continuous over some neighborhood N of the point $(x_1^{(0)}, \cdots, u_n^{(0)})$, and if at this point the Jacobian

$$
J\left(\frac{f_1, f_2, \cdots, f_n}{u_1, u_2, \cdots, u_n}\right)_0 =
\begin{vmatrix}
\dfrac{\partial f_1}{\partial u_1} & \dfrac{\partial f_1}{\partial u_2} & \cdots & \dfrac{\partial f_1}{\partial u_n} \\
\dfrac{\partial f_2}{\partial u_1} & \dfrac{\partial f_2}{\partial u_2} & \cdots & \dfrac{\partial f_2}{\partial u_n} \\
\cdots \cdots \cdots \cdots \cdots \\
\dfrac{\partial f_n}{\partial u_1} & \dfrac{\partial f_n}{\partial u_2} & \cdots & \dfrac{\partial f_n}{\partial u_n}
\end{vmatrix}_0 \neq 0,
\tag{20}
$$

then within some neighborhood $\bar{N}$ of $(x_1^{(0)}, \cdots, u_n^{(0)})$ Eqs. (19) define $u_1, \cdots, u_n$ as single-valued functions of $x_1, \cdots, x_p$ having continuous first partial derivatives, and the domains of definition of $u_1, \cdots, u_n$ and all their first derivatives extend over the whole of some neighborhood D of $(x_1^{(0)}, \cdots, x_p^{(0)})$ in the space of points $(x_1, \cdots, x_p)$; furthermore,

$$
\frac{\partial u_i}{\partial x_j} = -\frac{J\left(\dfrac{f_1, f_2, \cdots, f_n}{u_1, \cdots, u_{i-1}, x_j, u_{i+1}, \cdots, u_n}\right)}{J\left(\dfrac{f_1, f_2, \cdots, f_n}{u_1, u_2, \cdots, u_n}\right)}.
$$

Suppose that Eqs. (19) are of the special form

$$x_1 = \varphi_1(u_1, \cdots, u_n), \qquad x_2 = \varphi_2(u_1, \cdots, u_n), \qquad \cdots,$$
$$x_n = \varphi_n(u_1, \cdots, u_n), \quad (21)$$

where in (19)

$$f_i(x_1, \cdots, x_p; u_1, \cdots, u_n) = \varphi_i(u_1, \cdots, u_n) - x_i, \text{ and}$$
$$A_i = 0.$$

Then the Jacobian (20) assumes the form

$$J\left(\frac{\varphi_1, \cdots, \varphi_n}{u_1, \cdots, u_n}\right) = \begin{vmatrix} \dfrac{\partial \varphi_1}{\partial u_1} & \cdots & \dfrac{\partial \varphi_1}{\partial u_n} \\ \cdots \cdots \cdots \cdots \\ \dfrac{\partial \varphi_n}{\partial u_1} & \cdots & \dfrac{\partial \varphi_n}{\partial u_n} \end{vmatrix}.$$

If $J\left(\dfrac{\varphi_1, \cdots, \varphi_n}{u_1, \cdots, u_n}\right) \neq 0$, then Eqs. (21) define $u_1, \cdots, u_n$ as single-valued functions of $x_1, \cdots, x_n$ over some region of the space of points $(x_1, \cdots, x_n)$, that is,

$$u_1 = \psi_1(x_1, \cdots, x_n), \qquad \cdots, u_n = \psi_n(x_1, \cdots, x_n). \quad (21')$$

The functions ψ_i are called the *inverses* of the functions φ_j, and the operation of obtaining (21') from (21) is called an *inversion*. It can be shown (see Ex. 14 below) that if

$$J\left(\frac{\varphi_1, \cdots, \varphi_n}{u_1, \cdots, u_n}\right) \neq 0,$$

then $J\left(\dfrac{\psi_1, \cdots, \psi_n}{x_1, \cdots, x_n}\right) \neq 0$. Hence equations (21') may be inverted back to (21). If $u_1, \cdots, u_n$ and $x_1, \cdots, x_n$ are regarded as two systems of coordinates in n-dimensional space, then (21) and (21') determine either set of coordinates in terms of the other, and (21) and (21') are said to define a *transformation of coordinates*. In partic- ular, consider the transformation

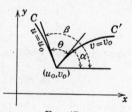

FIG. 47.

$$\begin{cases} x = \varphi_1(u, v), \\ y = \varphi_2(u, v), \end{cases} \quad \text{with inverse} \quad \begin{cases} u = \psi_1(x, y), \\ v = \psi_2(x, y). \end{cases}$$

If C is the *parametric curve* $u = u_0$, i.e., the curve with equation $u_0 = \psi_1(x, y)$ and with parametric equations

$$\begin{cases} x = \varphi_1(u_0, v), \\ y = \varphi_2(u_0, v), \end{cases}$$

if C' is the parametric curve $v = v_0$, and if u and v represent arc lengths along C' and C, respectively, then the angle θ between C and C' at this point of intersection is given by

$$\sin \theta = \sin (\beta - \alpha) = \cos \alpha \sin \beta - \cos \beta \sin \alpha$$

$$= \frac{\partial x}{\partial u} \frac{\partial y}{\partial v} - \frac{\partial x}{\partial v} \frac{\partial y}{\partial u} = J\left(\frac{x, y}{u, v}\right). \tag{22}$$

Thus, if $J\left(\dfrac{x, y}{u, v}\right) \neq 0$, then $\theta \neq 0$, and the parametric curves cannot be tangent. If u and v are arbitrary parameters, then

$$\sin \theta = \frac{dx}{ds} \frac{dy}{d\sigma} - \frac{dx}{d\sigma} \frac{dy}{ds} = J\left(\frac{x, y}{u, v}\right) \frac{du}{ds} \frac{dv}{d\sigma}, \tag{22'}$$

where s and σ are arc lengths along C' and C, where u is a function of s alone along C', and v is a function of σ alone along C. These results will be used in Sec. 19 of Chap. II.

Consider the transformation

$$\begin{cases} x = \varphi_1(u, v, w), \\ y = \varphi_2(u, v, w), \\ z = \varphi_3(u, v, w), \end{cases} \quad \text{with inverse} \quad \begin{cases} u = \psi_1(x, y, z), \\ v = \psi_2(x, y, z), \\ w = \psi_3(x, y, z). \end{cases}$$

Let the parametric curves

$$C: \begin{cases} u = u_0, \\ v = v_0, \end{cases} \qquad C': \begin{cases} u = u_0, \\ w = w_0, \end{cases} \qquad C'': \begin{cases} v = v_0, \\ w = w_0, \end{cases}$$

have direction cosines

$$(l, m, n), \qquad (L, M, N), \qquad (\lambda, \mu, \nu),$$

respectively, at the point $P_0 = (u_0, v_0, w_0)$. If (a, b, c) are the direction cosines of the normal **A** to the plane containing the tangents to C and C' at P, then

$$al + bm + cn = 0, \quad aL + bM + cN = 0, \quad a^2 + b^2 + c^2 = 1,$$

and

$$a = \frac{mN - nM}{k}, \qquad b = \frac{nL - lN}{k}, \qquad c = \frac{lM - mL}{k},$$

where

$$k = [(mN - nM)^2 + (nL - lN)^2 + (lM - mL)^2]^{1/2}$$
$$= [1 - (lL + mM + nN)^2]^{1/2}.$$

If θ is the angle between C and C', and if α is the angle between $\mathbf{A}$ and C'', then

$$\cos \alpha \sin \theta = \cos \alpha \sqrt{1 - \cos^2 \theta}$$
$$= (a\lambda + b\mu + c\nu)\sqrt{1 - (lL + mM + nN)^2}$$
$$= (mN - nM)\lambda + (nL - lN)\mu + (lM - mL)\nu$$
$$= J\left(\frac{x, y, z}{u, v, w}\right), \tag{22''}$$

provided that u, v, w are arc-lengths along C'', C', C. (Note that $l = \partial x/\partial w$, etc. If u, v, w are arbitrary, J must be multiplied by $\dfrac{du}{ds_1}\dfrac{dv}{ds_2}\dfrac{dw}{ds_3}$.) Thus, if $J\left(\dfrac{x, y, z}{u, v, w}\right) \neq 0$, it follows that $\cos \alpha \sin \theta \neq 0$, $\theta \neq 0°$ and $\alpha \neq 90°$, and the three curves C, C', C'' must intersect each other at angles $\neq 0°$.

Example 1. For the transformation

$$x = r \cos \theta, \qquad y = r \sin \theta, \tag{23}$$
$$J\left(\frac{x, y}{r, \theta}\right) = \begin{vmatrix} \cos \theta & -r \sin \theta \\ \sin \theta & r \cos \theta \end{vmatrix} = r.$$

Hence, in the neighborhood of any solution x_0, y_0, r_0, θ_0 such that $r_0 \neq 0$, Eqs. (23) define r and θ as single-valued functions of x and y. If we restrict θ to be in the interval $-\pi/2 < \theta \leqq \pi/2$ (cf. Definition 19.1b), then equations (23) have the single-valued inverse

$$r = \sqrt{x^2 + y^2} \text{ when } x > 0, \qquad r = y \text{ when } x = 0,$$
$$r = -\sqrt{x^2 + y^2} \text{ when } x < 0, \qquad \theta = \text{Tan}^{-1}\frac{y}{x},$$

provided that $r \neq 0$, i.e., that both x and y are not 0.

Example 2. For the transformation

$$u = x^2 - 2y, \qquad v = x + y, \tag{24}$$
$$J\left(\frac{u, v}{x, y}\right) = \begin{vmatrix} 2x & -2 \\ 1 & 1 \end{vmatrix} = 2x + 2.$$

Hence in the neighborhood of any solution x_0, y_0, u_0, v_0 such that $J \neq 0$, i.e., $x \neq -1$, Eqs. (24) define x and y as single-valued functions of u and v. In Fig. 48 it is seen that the curves (24) are tangent at $x = -1$ but everywhere else cross at an angle $\neq 0$. If we restrict x to be ≥ -1 or ≤ -1

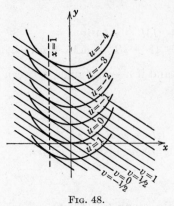

(cf. Definition 19.1b), then u and v determine a unique point (x, y) (the curve $u = u_0$ meets the curve $v = v_0$ in only one point), and (24) has a single-valued inverse; u and v are called *parametric coordinates* of the point (x, y). If (24) is

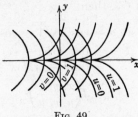

Fig. 48.   Fig. 49.

solved for x and y, it is seen that the domain of definition of the inverse of (24) is given by the relation $u + 2v \geq -1$.

Example 3. For the transformation

$$u = x - y^{2/3}, \qquad v = x + y^2, \tag{25}$$

$J\left(\dfrac{u, v}{x, y}\right) = 2y + \dfrac{2}{3y^{1/3}}.$ Hence J is never 0. Yet it is seen from Fig. 49 that the transformation (25) does not have a single-valued inverse unless we restrict y to be ≥ 0 or ≤ 0 (cf. Definition 19.1b). Since u and v determine a unique point (x, y) (under suitable restrictions), u and v are called *parametric coordinates* of the point (x, y).

Example 4. Our last illustration is based on the physical properties of superheated steam. By the *degrees of superheat* of a sample of steam at pressure p is meant the temperature of the steam above the boiling point of water at pressure p. Thus, steam at atmospheric pressure with a temperature of 250°F. has 38° superheat. By the *total heat* of steam is meant the total quantity of heat that must be added to one pound of water to vaporize it and bring it to a given state of superheat and pressure. Suppose the temperature T and the total heat H of steam are given by the relations

$$T = F(p, S), \qquad H = \phi(p, S), \tag{26}$$

where p denotes pressure and S degrees of superheat. The question arises, is the state of steam uniquely determined by the values of T and H, that is, does (26) have a single-valued inverse? It is known of the functions F and ϕ that $J\left(\dfrac{F, \phi}{p, S}\right)$ is never 0. Hence the curves (26) are never tangent, and in the neighborhood of any solution p_0, S_0, T_0, H_0, (26) has a unique inverse. We leave it to the student to decide how it may be determined whether or not (26) has a unique inverse for all values of p and S.

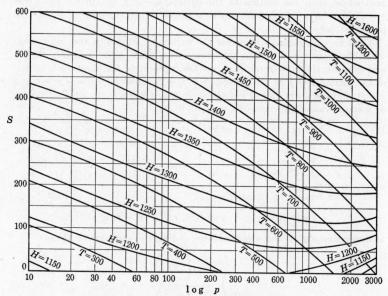

Fig. 50.—Pressure-superheat steam chart.

EXERCISES XXI

1. Give the details of the proofs of Theorems 20.1a and 20.1b for the case $f(x, y, u) = A$.

2. Give examples of functions $f(x, u)$ to illustrate the need of the phrase "within some neighborhood $\bar{N}$" in Theorem 20.2a when N is the entire xu-plane.

3. Give examples to show how equations (6) may define u and v as single-valued functions of x and y in some neighborhood of a point at which

$$J = \begin{vmatrix} f_u & f_v \\ g_u & g_v \end{vmatrix} \text{ equals zero.}$$

4. Extend Theorem 20.2 to the case where three equations define three variables u, v, and w as functions of the remaining variables.

Suggestion. If the Jacobian $J = \begin{vmatrix} f_u & f_v & f_w \\ g_u & g_v & g_w \\ h_u & h_v & h_w \end{vmatrix} \neq 0$, then the minor of some element in the first column, say f_u, is not zero. By Theorem 20.2, v and w are determined as functions of the remaining variables. The proof now follows the same lines as in Theorem 20.2.

5. Prove Theorem 20.3 by induction.

6. Theorem 20.1 may be stated in simple geometric language for a function $f(x, y)$ in the following way: if the section of the surface $z = f(x, y)$ cut by the plane $x = x_0$ has at the point (y_0, z_0) a definite, finite, and non-zero slope, then the section of the surface $z = f(x, y)$ cut by the plane $z = z_0$ is a curve which defines y as a single-valued function of x near the point (x_0, y_0).

The following surfaces illustrate the variety of situations that may occur when the section $x = x_0$ does not have at the point (y_0, z_0) a definite, finite, and nonzero slope. Sketch each surface, determine the slope (if it exists) of the section $x = 0$ at the point $y = 0$, $z = 0$, show the sections $x = 0$ and $z = 0$, and state whether or not the section $z = 0$ is a curve which defines y as a single-valued function of x near $(0, 0)$.

(1) $z = x - y^2$.   (5) $z = x^2 - y^3$.   (9) $z = \sqrt[3]{x^2 + y^2}$.

(2) $z = x^2 - y^2$.   (6) $z = (x - y)^2$.   (10) $z = y^2/(1 - x^2)$.

(3) $z = x^3 - y^2$.   (7) $z = x^2 + y^2$.   (11) $z = \sqrt{y^2/(1 - x^2)}$.

(4) $z = x - y^3$.   (8) $z = \sqrt{x^2 + y^2}$.   (12) $z = \sqrt[3]{y^2/(1 - x^2)}$.

7. If we regard the equations

$$x = f_1(u, v), \qquad y = f_2(u, v), \qquad z = f_3(u, v)$$

as determining z, u, and v as functions of x and y, show by Ex. 4 that

$$\frac{\partial z}{\partial x}\bigg)_y = \frac{J\left(\dfrac{f_3, f_2}{u, v}\right)}{J\left(\dfrac{f_1, f_2}{u, v}\right)}$$

and find $\dfrac{\partial z}{\partial y}\bigg)_x$.

8. If $u = f_1(x, y, z)$, $v = f_2(x, y, z)$, $w = f_3(x, y, z)$, show that under suitable assumptions

$$\frac{\partial u}{\partial x}\bigg)_{v,w} \cdot J\left(\frac{v, w}{y, z}\right) = J\left(\frac{u, v, w}{x, y, z}\right).$$

9. If $u_1 = f_1(x_1, \cdots, x_n)$, $\cdots$, $u_n = f_n(x_1, \cdots, x_n)$, show that

$$\frac{\partial u_1}{\partial x_1}\bigg)_{u_2,\dots,u_n} \cdot J\left(\frac{u_2, \cdots, u_n}{x_2, \cdots, x_n}\right) = J\left(\frac{u_1, \cdots, u_n}{x_1, \cdots, x_n}\right).$$

(See Chap. VI, Sec. 4 for the use of Cramer's rule.)

10. (a) If $f(x, y, z) = 0$, $g(x, y, z) = 0$ are the equations of a curve C in space, show that (with certain exceptions) the equations of the tangent line to C at (x_0, y_0, z_0) are

$$\frac{x - x_0}{J\left(\dfrac{f, g}{y, z}\right)_0} = \frac{y - y_0}{J\left(\dfrac{f, g}{z, x}\right)_0} = \frac{z - z_0}{J\left(\dfrac{f, g}{x, y}\right)_0}.$$

(b) Discuss the geometrical situations arising when one or more of the Jacobians are equal to zero.

11. (a) In Example 2 above, plot the points $u = 1, v = 1; u = 2, v = -1;$ $u = -2, v = 0$. If u and v are represented as the rectangular coordinates of a point in the uv-plane, plot several of the curves $x = x_0$ and $y = y_0$ in the uv-plane.

(b) In Example 4 above, what are the pressure and superheat of steam when $T = 400, H = 1250; T = 900, H = 1450; T = 300, H = 1150.$ Sketch a few graphs to represent the inverse of (26).

12. Discuss the transformation

$$x = \tfrac{1}{2}(u - v), \qquad y = \sqrt{uv}$$

in which u and v are called *parabolic coordinates.*

13. Discuss the transformation

$$u = x^2 - y, \qquad v = \frac{y - 2}{x - 1}.$$

14. (a) Show that if

$$x = f(u, v), \qquad y = g(u, v)$$

with $J\left(\dfrac{f, g}{u, v}\right) \neq 0$, and if

$$u = \varphi(x, y), \qquad v = \psi(x, y),$$

then $J\left(\dfrac{\varphi, \psi}{x, y}\right) = \dfrac{1}{J\left(\dfrac{f, g}{u, v}\right)}.$

(b) Extend this result to n functions of n variables.

15. (a) Show that if

$$x = f(u, v), \qquad y = g(u, v),$$

and

$$u = \varphi(r, s), \qquad v = \psi(r, s),$$

then

$$J\left(\frac{x, y}{r, s}\right) = J\left(\frac{x, y}{u, v}\right) \cdot J\left(\frac{u, v}{r, s}\right).$$

(b) Extend this result to n variables. Show that the results of Ex. 14 are special cases of these results.

16. If ξ and η are functions of the three variables x, y, z and if $x, y,$ and z are functions of the two independent variables u and v, show that

$$J\left(\frac{\xi, \eta}{u, v}\right) = J\left(\frac{\xi, \eta}{x, y}\right)J\left(\frac{x, y}{u, v}\right) + J\left(\frac{\xi, \eta}{y, z}\right)J\left(\frac{y, z}{u, v}\right) + J\left(\frac{\xi, \eta}{z, x}\right)J\left(\frac{z, x}{u, v}\right).$$

21. Functional Dependence. To introduce the concept of functional dependence, let us consider the following simple example: Suppose

$$u = f(x, y), \qquad v = g(x, y), \tag{1}$$

where f and g have continuous first partial derivatives. We say that u and v are *functionally related* if, for each point (x, y) of some region D of the xy-plane, u and v always comprise a solution of an equation of the form

$$\psi(u, v) = 0, \tag{2}$$

where ψ is differentiable and such that ψ_u and ψ_v are never* simultaneously 0 at any point (u, v). If we differentiate (2) with respect to x and y, we find that

$$\begin{aligned} \psi_u f_x + \psi_v g_x = 0, \\ \psi_u f_y + \psi_v g_y = 0. \end{aligned} \tag{3}$$

Since ψ_u and ψ_v are never simultaneously 0, we may eliminate ψ_u and ψ_v from (3) to obtain the result that

$$\begin{vmatrix} f_x & g_x \\ f_y & g_y \end{vmatrix} \equiv J\left(\frac{u, v}{x, y}\right) \equiv 0. \tag{4}$$

We have thus shown that if *u and v are functionally dependent over D, then their Jacobian (4) is identically zero over D.*

The converse of this theorem is also true, namely, *if the Jacobian (4) is identically 0 over D, then u and v are functionally dependent.* If f_x, f_y, g_x, g_y are all identically zero, then f and g are constants (see Ex. V, 13). This case is of no interest and we pass over it. Suppose $f_x(x_0, y_0) \neq 0$. By Theorem 20.1, the equation $u = f(x, y)$ determines x as a differentiable function of u and y, say $x = \varphi(u, y)$, in some neighborhood of (x_0, u_0, y_0). By (1), $v = g[\varphi(u, y), y]$ and

$$\left(\frac{\partial v}{\partial y}\right)_u = \left(\frac{\partial g}{\partial x}\right)_y \left(\frac{\partial x}{\partial y}\right)_u + \left(\frac{\partial g}{\partial y}\right)_x. \tag{5}$$

Since $u = f(x, y)$,

$$\left(\frac{\partial u}{\partial y}\right)_u = 0 = \left(\frac{\partial f}{\partial x}\right)_y \left(\frac{\partial x}{\partial y}\right)_u + \left(\frac{\partial f}{\partial y}\right)_x. \tag{6}$$

* This restriction can be considerably weakened.

Since f_x is continuous and $f_x(x_0, y_0) \neq 0$, $f_x(x, y) \neq 0$ over some neighborhood N of (x_0, y_0) and (6) may be solved for $\dfrac{\partial x}{\partial y}\Big)_u$ at all points in N. If we substitute this result in (5), we find that

$$\frac{\partial v}{\partial y}\bigg)_u = \frac{-\dfrac{\partial g}{\partial x}\bigg)_y \dfrac{\partial f}{\partial y}\bigg)_x + \dfrac{\partial g}{\partial y}\bigg)_x \dfrac{\partial f}{\partial x}\bigg)_y}{\dfrac{\partial f}{\partial x}\bigg)_y} = \frac{J}{f_x}.$$

By hypothesis, $J \equiv 0$. Hence $\dfrac{\partial v}{\partial y}\Big)_u \equiv 0$ wherever $f_x \neq 0$. Thus v is a function of u alone in some neighborhood of u_0, say $v = \varphi(u)$, and u and v are functionally dependent.

These results are summarized in

THEOREM 21.1. *If $u = f(x, y)$ and $v = g(x, y)$, where f and g have continuous first partial derivatives, then u and v are functionally dependent when, and only when, $J\left(\dfrac{u,\, v}{x,\, y}\right) \equiv 0$ over some region of the xy-plane.*

Example. The functions

$$u = e^{3x/y}, \qquad v = \log y - \log x$$

are functionally dependent, for

$$J\left(\frac{u,\, v}{x,\, y}\right) \equiv \begin{vmatrix} \dfrac{3}{y}e^{3x/y} & -\dfrac{3x}{y^2}e^{3x/y} \\[2mm] -\dfrac{1}{x} & \dfrac{1}{y} \end{vmatrix} \equiv 0.$$

It turns out that $v - \log 3 + \log \log u = 0$.

When Theorem 21.1 is extended to n variables, we obtain

THEOREM 21.2. *If*

$$u_1 = f_1(x_1, x_2, \cdots, x_n), \qquad u_2 = f_2(x_1, x_2, \cdots, x_n),$$
$$\cdots, \qquad u_n = f_n(x_1, x_2, \cdots, x_n), \quad (7)$$

where all the functions f_i have continuous first partial derivatives, then $u_1, \cdots, u_n$ are functionally dependent when, and only when,

$$J\left(\frac{u_1,\, \cdots,\, u_n}{x_1,\, \cdots,\, x_n}\right) \equiv 0 \text{ over some region } D \text{ of the space of points}$$

$(x_1, \cdots, x_n)$.

If there exists a functional relation

$$\psi(u_1, \cdots, u_n) = 0,$$

such that $\psi_{u_1}, \cdots, \psi_{u_n}$ are never all simultaneously 0, then

$$\frac{\partial \psi}{\partial u_1} \frac{\partial u_1}{\partial x_1} + \cdots + \frac{\partial \psi}{\partial u_n} \frac{\partial u_n}{\partial x_1} = 0,$$

$$\cdots \cdots \cdots \cdots \cdots \cdots \cdots \qquad (8)$$

$$\frac{\partial \psi}{\partial u_1} \frac{\partial u_1}{\partial x_n} + \cdots + \frac{\partial \psi}{\partial u_n} \frac{\partial u_n}{\partial x_n} = 0,$$

and elimination of the derivatives $\partial \psi / \partial u_1, \cdots, \partial \psi / \partial u_n$ from
(8) leads to the result that $J\left(\begin{matrix} u_1, & \cdots, & u_n \\ x_1, & \cdots, & x_n \end{matrix}\right) \equiv 0.$

Conversely, suppose $J \equiv 0$ throughout some region D, and suppose some derivative of one of the u's is not 0 in D, say $\partial u_1 / \partial x_1$. Then the first of the equations (7) defines x_1 as a function of $u_1, x_2, \cdots, x_n$ in D, say $x_1 = \varphi(u, x_2, \cdots, x_n)$. Then by (7),

$$u_2 = f_2[\varphi(u_1, x_2, \cdots, x_n), x_2, \cdots, x_n], \qquad \cdots,$$
$$u_n = f_n[\varphi(u_1, x_2, \cdots, x_n), x_2, \cdots, x_n].$$

If we follow the same procedure as in the proof of Theorem 21.1, we find that

$$J\left(\begin{matrix} u_2, & \cdots, & u_n \\ x_2, & \cdots, & x_n \end{matrix}\right)_{u_1} = \frac{J}{\left.\dfrac{\partial u_1}{\partial x_1}\right)_{x_2,\dots,x_n}}.$$

Since $J \equiv 0$ in D, $J\left(\begin{matrix} u_2, & \cdots, & u_n \\ x_2, & \cdots, & x_n \end{matrix}\right)_{u_1} \equiv 0$ in D. Thus our problem is reduced to the case of $n - 1$ functions in $n - 1$ variables. The theorem follows at once by induction.

EXERCISES XXII

1. Determine which of the following sets of functions are functionally dependent:

(a) $x = u - v + 3$, $y = u^2 - 2uv + v^2 + 7$.

(b) $x = 3u + 4v - w$, $y = 2u - v + 3w$, $z = 6u + 8v - 2w - 1$.

(c) $u = \sin(x - y)$, $v = \cos^{1/2}(x - y)$.

(d) $x = u^2 + v^2$, $y = u^2 - v^2$.

2. Carry out in detail the proof of Theorem 21.2 for the case $n = 3$.

3. If w is a function of u and v such that $\varphi(u^2 - v^2, v^2 - w^2) = 0$, show that $vw\dfrac{\partial w}{\partial u} + uw\dfrac{\partial w}{\partial v} = uv.$

4. Consider the pair of lines

$$u = a_1x + b_1y + c_1 = 0,$$
$$v = a_2x + b_2y + c_2 = 0.$$

(a) Prove that if $J\left(\dfrac{u, v}{x, y}\right) \neq 0$, the lines intersect in exactly one point.

(b) Prove that if $J\left(\dfrac{u, v}{x, y}\right) = 0$, with at least one of the elements of J in

each row not zero, the lines are parallel.

(c) Find a criterion for distinguishing between the case where u and v are coincident, and the case where u and v are parallel but not coincident.

5. Extend Ex. 4 to the case where there are three planes

$$u = a_1x + b_1y + c_1z + d_1 = 0,$$
$$v = a_2x + b_2y + c_2z + d_2 = 0,$$
$$w = a_3x + b_3y + c_3z + d_3 = 0.$$

22. Normal Derivative.

In formula (A') of Sec. 18, namely,

$$\frac{df(x, y)}{ds}\bigg]_{x_0,y_0} = f_x(x_0, y_0) \cos \alpha + f_y(x_0, y_0) \sin \alpha, \qquad (A')$$

$\dfrac{df(x, y)}{ds}\bigg]_{x_0,y_0}$ represents the value at (x_0, y_0) of the rate of change

of $f(x, y)$ with respect to the distance s transversed by the point (x, y) while moving along the curve C with equations $x = p(s)$, $y = q(s)$. It was pointed out at the beginning of Sec. 16 that,

at the *fixed* point (x_0, y_0), $\dfrac{df(x, y)}{ds}\bigg]_{x_0,y_0}$ may have different values

according as the point (x, y) moves along different curves C, s of course always being measured along the curve traversed by

(x, y). Since $\dfrac{df(x, y)}{ds}\bigg]_{x_0,y_0}$ has a definite value for each curve C

through (x_0, y_0), $\dfrac{df(x, y)}{ds}\bigg]_{x_0,y_0}$ is a *function* of the curves C through

(x_0, y_0). But we can say even more than this.

In formula (A'), the coefficients $f_x(x_0, y_0)$ and $f_y(x_0, y_0)$ are in no way related to the curve C, for they are determined entirely by the function f and the point (x_0, y_0). Hence, for a given function f and a given point (x_0, y_0), the only variable in (A') is α, that is, *the value of* $\dfrac{df(x, y)}{ds}$ *at* (x_0, y_0) *depends only on* α. This fact is of such fundamental importance that we shall elaborate upon it.   Let C and $\bar{C}$ be any two curves in the xy-plane through the point (x_0, y_0) and having there the common angle of inclination α, and let s and $\bar{s}$ represent the arc lengths along C and $\bar{C}$.

Formula (A') shows that $\dfrac{df(x, y)}{ds}\Big]_{x_0, y_0}$ equals $\dfrac{df(x, y)}{d\bar{s}}\Big]_{x_0, y_0}$,

where (x, y) moves along C in $\dfrac{df(x, y)}{ds}$ and along $\bar{C}$ in $\dfrac{df(x, y)}{d\bar{s}}$.   In

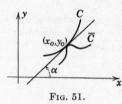

FIG. 51.

other words, the value at (x_0, y_0) of the rate of change of $f(x, y)$ with respect to arc length is the same for all curves having the same direction at (x_0, y_0).   This *common*

value of $\dfrac{df(x, y)}{ds}\Big]_{x_0, y_0}$ for all curves C with

direction α at (x_0, y_0) is called the space rate of change of f at (x_0, y_0) in the direction α, or, in more technical language, the *directional derivative* of f at (x_0, y_0) in the direction α.   *To determine the directional derivative of f at (x_0, y_0) in any*

given direction α, it is necessary merely to find $\dfrac{df(x, y)}{ds}\Big]_{x_0, y_0}$ *by*

formula (A') *for the proper value of α.*

Since, for a given function f, the value of $\dfrac{df(x, y)}{ds}$ at the fixed

point (x_0, y_0) depends only on α, $\dfrac{df(x, y)}{ds}\Big]_{x_0, y_0}$ is a function of the

one variable α and may be denoted by $f_{s_0}(\alpha)$, the subscript s_0 indicating that f has been differentiated with respect to s and the derivative evaluated at (x_0, y_0).   We know from elementary calculus that $f_{s_0}(\alpha)$ has a maximum at $\alpha = \alpha_0$ if α_0 is a solution

of the equation $\dfrac{d}{d\alpha}f_{s_0}(\alpha) = 0$ such that $\dfrac{d^2}{d\alpha^2}f_{s_0}(\alpha)\Big]_{\alpha_0} < 0$.   By

formula (A'),

$$\frac{d}{d\alpha}f_{s_0}(\alpha) = -f_x(x_0, y_0)\sin\alpha + f_y(x_0, y_0)\cos\alpha. \tag{1}$$

The various solutions α_0 of the equation $\dfrac{d}{d\alpha}f_{s_0}(\alpha) = 0$ are evidently given by the formula

$$\tan\alpha_0 = \frac{f_y(x_0, y_0)}{f_x(x_0, y_0)}, \tag{2}$$

the case where α_0 is an odd multiple of $\pi/2$ being treated in the usual formal way. Furthermore,

$$\frac{d^2}{d\alpha^2} f_{s_0}(\alpha) \bigg]_{\alpha_0} = -[f_x(x_0, y_0) \cos \alpha_0 + f_y(x_0, y_0) \sin \alpha_0]. \quad (3)$$

If this expression has a negative value, α_0 maximizes $f_{s_0}(\alpha)$; if this expression has a positive value, α_0 minimizes $f_{s_0}(\alpha)$. The case where (3) has the value zero is taken up in Ex. 5 below.

Equation (2) always has exactly two solutions α_0 and α_0' between 0 and 2π rad., and $\alpha_0' = \alpha_0 \pm \pi$. Since

$$\cos \alpha_0' = \cos (\alpha_0 \pm \pi) = -\cos \alpha_0$$

and

$$\sin \alpha_0' = \sin (\alpha_0 \pm \pi) = -\sin \alpha_0,$$

the values of (3) for α_0 and α_0' are numerically equal but of opposite sign. Hence either α_0 or α_0', say α_0, is a value of α for which $f_{s_0}(\alpha)$ has a maximum and the other, α_0', is a value of α for which $f_{s_0}(\alpha)$ has a minimum [unless (3) has the value zero for both α_0 and α_0']. $f_{s_0}(\alpha)$ has no other maximum or minimum value for α between 0 and 2π.

DEFINITION 22.1. *Let α_0 denote the unique direction at (x_0, y_0) in which $\dfrac{df(x, y)}{ds}\bigg]_{x_0,y_0}$ is a maximum, let C be any curve in the xy-plane through (x_0, y_0) with slope $\tan \alpha_0$ there, and let n, instead of s, denote the arc-length of such a curve C. Then the symbol $\dfrac{df(x, y)}{dn}\bigg]_{x_0,y_0}$ indicates by the letter n that the point (x, y) moves along some curve C having slope $\tan \alpha_0$ at (x_0, y_0); $\dfrac{df(x, y)}{dn}\bigg]_{x_0,y_0}$ is called the normal derivative of f at (x_0, y_0).*

Since α_0 maximizes $\dfrac{df(x, y)}{ds}\bigg]_{x_0,y_0}$, it follows that $\dfrac{df(x, y)}{dn}\bigg]_{x_0,y_0}$ is the maximum value of $\dfrac{df(x, y)}{ds}\bigg]_{x_0,y_0}$. The reason for calling $\dfrac{df(x, y)}{dn}\bigg]_{x_0,y_0}$ the "normal" derivative lies in the following theorem which will be proved in Ex. 7 below.

Theorem 22.1. *If $f(x, y)$ is a given function, if (x_0, y_0) is a given point, and if α_0 is determined by equation (2), then a line with direction angle α_0 is normal to the curve $f(x, y) = k$, where*

$$k = f(x_0, y_0).$$

In successive columns of the following table are shown the various possible combinations of signs of $f_x(x_0, y_0)$ and $f_y(x_0, y_0)$. When these two quantities are both positive (second column), it

$f_y(x_0, y_0)$	+	+	−	−
$f_x(x_0, y_0)$	+	−	−	+
α_0	I	II	III	IV

follows by (2) that $\tan \alpha_0$ is positive, and hence that α_0 is in the first or third quadrant. By the above definition, α_0 maximizes $f_{s_0}(\alpha)$. Hence (3) represents a negative number, that is,

$$f_x(x_0, y_0) \cos \alpha_0 + f_y(x_0, y_0) \sin \alpha_0$$

is a positive number. Since $f_x(x_0, y_0)$ and $f_y(x_0, y_0)$ were supposed positive, the signs of $\cos \alpha_0$ and $\sin \alpha_0$ show that α_0 cannot be in the third quadrant. Therefore α_0 must be in the first quadrant as indicated in the table. It is left to the student in Ex. 4 below to carry through this argument for the remaining columns of the table.

It follows from the table that $\sin \alpha_0$ and $\cos \alpha_0$ always have the same sign as $f_y(x_0, y_0)$ and $f_x(x_0, y_0)$, respectively. From this fact and (2) it follows that the formulas

$$\cos \alpha_0 = \frac{f_x(x_0, y_0)}{\sqrt{[f_x(x_0, y_0)]^2 + [f_y(x_0, y_0)]^2}},$$
$$\sin \alpha_0 = \frac{f_y(x_0, y_0)}{\sqrt{[f_x(x_0, y_0)]^2 + [f_y(x_0, y_0)]^2}} \tag{4}$$

determine $\cos \alpha_0$ and $\sin \alpha_0$ in sign and magnitude. Substitution of these formulas in (A') leads to the result that

$$\frac{df(x, y)}{dn}\bigg]_{x_0, y_0} = \sqrt{[f_x(x_0, y_0)]^2 + [f_y(x_0, y_0)]^2}. \tag{5}$$

It is seen from (2) and (5) that $\dfrac{df(x,\, y)}{dn}\bigg]_{x_0,y_0}$ is represented in direction and magnitude by the vector whose x- and y-components are $f_x(x_0,\, y_0)$ and $f_y(x_0,\, y_0)$. In vector analysis, this vector is denoted by **grad** f and is called the *gradient* of f.

EXERCISES XXIII

1. (a) Find $\dfrac{df(x,\, y)}{ds}\bigg]_{1,2}$ when $f(x,\, y) = x^2 - 3xy$ and the point $(x,\, y)$ moves along the curve C with equation $y = x^2 - x + 2$.

Suggestion. To evaluate $\cos \alpha = dx/ds$ and $\sin \alpha = dy/ds$, find $\tan \alpha = dy/dx$ from the equation of C.

(b) Repeat (a) when the equation of C is $y = 3 - (1/x)$; when the equation of C is $y = 2 + \log x$; when it is known of C merely that its slope at $(1,\, 2)$ is 1.

2. Find the direction α_0 of the normal derivative of $f(x,\, y) = x^2 - 3xy$ at $(1,\, 2)$, and find $\dfrac{df(x,\, y)}{dn}\bigg]_{1,2}$ both by (5) and (A').

3. Find the directional derivative of $f(x,\, y) = \sqrt{x - y}$ at the point $(2,\, -2)$ in the direction $\alpha = 150°$. Find the direction of the normal derivative of this function at $(2,\, -2)$ and find $\dfrac{df(x,\, y)}{dn}\bigg]_{2,-2}$.

4. Show that the signs of $f_x(x_0,\, y_0)$ and $f_y(x_0,\, y_0)$ determine the quadrant in which α_0 lies as indicated in the above table.

5. Show that (1) and (3) can both have the value zero only when

$$f_x(x_0,\, y_0) = f_y(x_0,\, y_0) = 0. \qquad (\star)$$

[Set (3) equal to zero and eliminate α_0 from the resulting equation and (2)].

In case (1) and (3) are both zero, so that $(\star)$ holds, $\dfrac{df(x,\, y)}{ds}\bigg]_{x_0,y_0} = 0$ in every direction, and α_0 is indeterminate. The full significance of condition $(\star)$ is discussed in Sec. 25.

6. If in formula (2) we think of $(x_0,\, y_0)$ as an arbitrary point, then we may omit the subscripts and the formula

$$\tan \alpha_0 = \frac{f_y(x,\, y)}{f_x(x,\, y)}$$

determines α_0 at each point $(x,\, y)$. In this formula, x and y are independent. But suppose we determine y as such a function of x that the graph of y is a curve C whose slope at *each* point $(x,\, y)$ on it is $\tan \alpha_0$. Two things are evident: (1) y must be such a function of x that

$$\frac{dy}{dx} = \frac{f_y(x,\, y)}{f_x(x,\, y)} \qquad (6)$$

since dy/dx represents the slope of C and since $\tan \alpha_0 = f_y(x, y)/f_x(x, y)$. Conversely, every* solution y of Eq. (6) has for a graph a curve with slope equal to $\tan \alpha_0$ at each point on it. It therefore follows that the set S of all solutions of (6) defines exactly the set of all curves with slope $\tan \alpha_0$ at each point on them. (2) At *each* point (x, y) on any particular curve C of the set S the directional derivative of f is a maximum in the direction of C since the slope of C at (x, y) is $\tan \alpha_0$. Hence n may be used to denote the arc length of C and $df(x, y)/dn$ is the normal derivative of f at each point of C. [Note that this last assertion was true in Definition 22.1 for only the particular point (x_0, y_0) on C.] Thus the curves of the set S comprise all the loci that may be traced out by a point P moving so that the value of f at P is always changing at the maximum possible rate.

Methods for integrating Eq. (6) will be given in Chap. III. However, there is one particularly simple case where the integration may be effected at once. If $dy/dx = \varphi(x)/\psi(y)$, write this relation in the form $\psi(y) \, dy = \varphi(x) \, dx$ and integrate† both sides. Integrate Eq. (6) by this method in the following cases and state the significance of the solutions:

(1) $f(x, y) = xy$. [The solution of (6) in this case is $x^2 - y^2 = c$, where c is an arbitrary constant. For each value of c this equation defines a curve

C such that, at any point P of C, $\dfrac{df(x, y)}{ds}\bigg]_P$ is a maximum in the direction

of C.]

(2) $f(x, y) = x^2 + y^2$.

Solution. $\log y = \log x + \log c$, where the constant of integration is written as $\log c$. This solution reduces to $y = cx$.

(3) $f(x, y) = (x^2 + y^2)^{-\frac{1}{2}}$.

(4) $f(x, y) = \log (x - y)$.

Check the interpretation of part (1) in the following manner: Let $c = 3$. Find the slope of $x^2 - y^2 = 3$ at $(2, 1)$, find $\tan \alpha_0$ at $(2, 1)$ by formula (2)

of Sec. 22, and compare results. Find $\dfrac{df(x, y)}{dn}\bigg]_{2,1}$ by (5) of Sec. 22, find

$\dfrac{df(x, y)}{ds}\bigg]_{2,1}$ by (A′) when (x, y) moves along the curve $x^2 - y^2 = 3$, and compare results.

7. (a) Find a formula for the direction α_1 in which $\dfrac{df(x, y)}{ds}\bigg]_{x_0, y_0} = 0$.

Show that $\tan \alpha_1$ is the slope of the curve $f(x, y) = k$ at the point (x_0, y_0). Show that the directions α_0 and α_1 are at right angles. Prove Theorem 22.1.

(b) Check Theorem 22.1 by plotting on the same axes a few of the curves C of Ex. 6 and a few of the curves $f(x, y) = k$ in the case where $f(x, y)$ is the function of part (1) of the preceding exercise. Repeat this check by taking $f(x, y)$ as the functions of parts (2) and (4) of the preceding exercise. [To

---

*It will be shown in Chap. III that Eq. (6) has a one-parameter family of solutions.

† See Chap. II, Part A.

plot log $(x - y) = k$, write this equation in the form $x - y = e^k = k'$, and choose various values of k'.]

(c) Why does the equation $(x^2 + y^2)^{-\frac{1}{2}} = k$ represent the same set of curves as the equation $x^2 + y^2 = k$? [Note the last sentence of part (b).] Why are the solutions of parts (2) and (3) the same in Ex. 6? What would have been the solution to part (4) of Ex. 6 if $f(x, y)$ had been sin $(x - y)$? $\sqrt{x - y}$? $\varphi(x - y)$, where φ is an arbitrary function? State a general theorem which is exemplified by the answers to the preceding questions.

8. In Exs. 6 and 7 it was shown that at any point (x, y) the direction along which a function $f(x, y)$ changes most rapidly is always orthogonal to the direction along which f is constant. This result has many important physical applications, a few of which we now state. At any point in a material substance the flow of heat is always in the direction along which the temperature changes most rapidly; hence the flow of heat in a thin flat sheet of material substance is always along the set of curves orthogonal to the set of curves of constant temperature (isothermals). At any point of an electric field the force acting on a charged particle is always in the direction along which the potential of the field changes most rapidly; hence in a plane electric field the force acting on a charged particle is always orthogonal to the curves of constant potential (equipotential curves). If something of variable concentration is diffusing through space, such as a solid as it dissolves in a liquid which is not being stirred, the flow at any point is always in the direction along

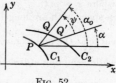

FIG. 52.

which the density changes most rapidly; hence the paths of diffusion in a thin flat layer of material are orthogonal to the curves of constant density.

Suppose the functions $f(x, y)$ of Ex. 6 represent temperature, potential, and concentration in connection with physical situations of the sort just now described. Give the physical interpretations of the curves plotted in Ex. 7b.

9. Show that $\dfrac{df}{ds}\bigg)_{x_0,y_0} = \dfrac{df}{dn}\bigg)_{x_0,y_0}$ cos ψ, where ψ is the angle between the directions along which df/ds and df/dn are taken. (If df/ds is taken in the direction α, then $\psi = \alpha_0 - \alpha$. Expand cos ψ and evaluate df/dn, cos α_0, and sin α_0 by formulas (4) and (5) of Sec. 22.)

Note that if $\psi = 90°$, we obtain the result found in Ex. 7a. Also note that df/ds is a maximum when $\psi = 0$.

Check the above formula by means of the results of Exs. 1, 2, 3 above.

The above formula may be "derived" geometrically by drawing the graphs C_1 and C_2 of the equations $f(x, y) = k_1$, $f(x, y) = k_2$, where $k_2 - k_1$ is numerically small, taking PQ orthogonal to C_1, noting that (see Fig. 52)

$$k_2 - k_1 = \frac{df}{dn}\bigg)_P \cdot \overline{PQ} = \frac{df}{ds}\bigg)_P \cdot \overline{PQ'}$$

approximately, and assuming the sector PQQ' to be approximately a right triangle so that $\overline{PQ} = \overline{PQ'}$ cos ψ.

10. Show by the preceding exercise that the sum of the squares of the directional derivatives of $f(x, y)$ at a point P along any two perpendicular directions is always the square of the normal derivative of $f(x, y)$ at P.

11. Find the directional derivative of $f(x, y)$ along the curve $x = p(u)$, $y = q(u)$, where $u \neq s$.

12. Find a formula for the normal derivative in polar coordinates. (See Ex. XIX, 32.) Show that $\dfrac{df(r, \theta)}{ds} = \dfrac{\partial f}{\partial r} \cos \psi + \dfrac{1}{r} \dfrac{\partial f}{\partial \theta} \sin \psi$, where ψ is the angle between the direction in which df/ds is taken and the direction θ.

13. If T represents a temperature distribution over a plane area, then dT/dn is called the *temperature gradient*. Find the temperature gradient at $(1, \pi/4)$ when $T(r, \theta) = (\sin 2\theta)/r^2$. In what direction is it taken?

14. Derive the formula

$$\frac{df(x, y, z)}{ds}\bigg]_{x_0, y_0, z_0} = f_x(x_0, y_0, z_0) \cos \alpha + f_y(x_0, y_0, z_0) \cos \beta$$

$$+ f_z(x_0, y_0, z_0) \cos \gamma, \quad (7)$$

where $x = p(s)$, $y = q(s)$, $z = r(s)$ are the parametric equations of a curve in space with arc length s, and where α, β, γ are the direction angles of this curve at the point (x_0, y_0, z_0). Show that $\dfrac{df(x, y, z)}{ds}\bigg]_{x_0, y_0, z_0}$ may be regarded as determining a directional derivative in space.

15. Find the direction along which $\dfrac{df(x, y, z)}{ds}\bigg]_{x_0, y_0, z_0}$ is a maximum and find this maximum value.

Solution. It will be shown in Sec. 25 that the coordinates α_0, β_0, of a point where a function $g(\alpha, \beta)$ has a maximum are determined as a solution of the pair of equations $g_\alpha(\alpha, \beta) = 0$, $g_\beta(\alpha, \beta) = 0$. (We omit all reference to second derivatives for the sake of simplicity.) Let us apply this result to (7), regarding γ as a function of α and β determined by the relation

$$\cos^2 \alpha + \cos^2 \beta + \cos^2 \gamma = 1. \quad (8)$$

Differentiation of (7) gives

$$\frac{\partial}{\partial \alpha}\left(\frac{df}{ds}\bigg]_{x_0, y_0, z_0}\right) = -f_x(x_0, y_0, z_0) \sin \alpha - f_z(x_0, y_0, z_0) \sin \gamma \frac{\partial \gamma}{\partial \alpha},$$

$$\frac{\partial}{\partial \beta}\left(\frac{df}{ds}\bigg]_{x_0, y_0, z_0}\right) = -f_y(x_0, y_0, z_0) \sin \beta - f_z(x_0, y_0, z_0) \sin \gamma \frac{\partial \gamma}{\partial \beta}. \quad (9)$$

Before we set these expressions equal to zero, let us simplify them. Differentiation of (8) with respect to α and β gives

$$-2 \cos \alpha \sin \alpha - 2 \cos \gamma \sin \gamma \frac{\partial \gamma}{\partial \alpha} = 0,$$

$$-2 \cos \beta \sin \beta - 2 \cos \gamma \sin \gamma \frac{\partial \gamma}{\partial \beta} = 0.$$

If we solve these identities for $\sin \gamma(\partial\gamma/\partial\alpha)$ and $\sin \gamma(\partial\gamma/\partial\beta)$, substitute in (9), and then set (9) equal to zero, letting $(\alpha_0, \beta_0, \gamma_0)$ denote a solution of the equations so obtained, we find that

$$\cos \alpha_0 = \frac{f_x(x_0, y_0, z_0)}{f_z(x_0, y_0, z_0)} \cos \gamma_0, \qquad \cos \beta_0 = \frac{f_y(x_0, y_0, z_0)}{f_z(x_0, y_0, z_0)} \cos \gamma_0.$$

These formulas, when substituted in (8), show that

$$\cos \alpha_0 = \frac{f_x(x_0, y_0, z_0)}{\sqrt{f_x^2 + f_y^2 + f_z^2}}, \qquad \cos \beta_0 = \frac{f_y(x_0, y_0, z_0)}{\sqrt{f_x^2 + f_y^2 + f_z^2}},$$
$$\cos \gamma_0 = \frac{f_z(x_0, y_0, z_0)}{\sqrt{f_x^2 + f_y^2 + f_z^2}}, \tag{10}$$

where (x_0, y_0, z_0) has been omitted from the denominators for brevity. Formulas (10) determine by means of the direction angles $\alpha_0, \beta_0, \gamma_0$ the direction in which $\dfrac{df}{ds}\bigg]_{x_0, y_0, z_0}$ is a maximum. If we substitute (10) in (7), we find that the normal derivative is given by the formula

$$\frac{df}{dn}\bigg]_{x_0, y_0, z_0} = \sqrt{[f_x(x_0, y_0, z_0)]^2 + [f_y(x_0, y_0, z_0)]^2 + [f_z(x_0, y_0, z_0)]^2}, \tag{11}$$

where $\dfrac{df}{dn}\bigg]_{x_0, y_0, z_0}$ is the maximum value of $\dfrac{df}{ds}\bigg]_{x_0, y_0, z_0}$ and where n has the same significance as in Definition 22.1.

Compare these results with those obtained above for a function of two variables. Define **grad** f.

16. By reasoning as in Ex. 6, derive and interpret the systems of equations

$$\frac{dx}{ds} = \frac{f_x(x, y, z)}{\sqrt{f_x^2 + f_y^2 + f_z^2}}, \qquad \frac{dy}{ds} = \frac{f_y(x, y, z)}{\sqrt{f_x^2 + f_y^2 + f_z^2}}, \qquad \frac{dz}{ds} = \frac{f_z(x, y, z)}{\sqrt{f_x^2 + f_y^2 + f_z^2}}$$

and

$$\frac{dy}{dx} = \frac{f_y(x, y, z)}{f_x(x, y, z)}, \qquad \frac{dz}{dx} = \frac{f_z(x, y, z)}{f_x(x, y, z)}. \tag{12}$$

What is meant by a solution of the system (12)? How does such a solution define a *curve* in space? What is the significance of the curves determined by (12)?

Methods for integrating (12) will be given in Chap. III. Show that $y = ax$, $z = bx$, where a and b are constants, is a solution of (12) when $f(x, y, z) = x^2 + y^2 + z^2$.

17. Show that $\dfrac{df}{ds}\bigg]_{x_0, y_0, z_0} = \dfrac{df}{dn}\bigg]_{x_0, y_0, z_0} \cos \psi$, where ψ is the angle between the directions along which df/ds and df/dn are taken. Extend the result of Ex. 10.

Suggestion. Recall that $\cos \psi = \cos \alpha \cos \alpha_0 + \cos \beta \cos \beta_0 + \cos \gamma \cos \gamma_0$. See Ex. 9.

18. Show by Ex. 17 that the surfaces $f(x, y, z) = k$ are orthogonal to every curve represented by a solution of (12). Note that the numerical example of Ex. 16 illustrates this result. Extend the discussion of Ex. 8 to physical situations in space.

19. Illustrate all the results of Exs. 14 to 18 by means of the function $f(x, y, z) = xyz$. In Exs. 14 and 15, take (x_0, y_0, z_0) as the point $(1, 2, 3)$; in Exs. 14 and 17 take $\alpha = \beta = \pi/4$, $\gamma = \pi/2$. Integrate equations (12), using Ex. 6, (1) as a clue to guess the solutions.

20. Find a formula for the normal derivative of a function defined over three-dimensional space in polar coordinates. (See Ex. XIX, 32.)

21. Find a formula for the normal derivative of a function defined in cylindrical coordinates (r, ϕ, z), where $x = r \cos \phi$, $y = r \sin \phi$, $z = z$.

22. Extend all the above results to functions of n variables.

23. Point Functions. Invariance of Directional Derivative.

In this section we shall show that the directional derivative is an invariant. However, before considering this matter we must first distinguish between a point function and a function of several variables.

If a physical situation determines at each point of space the value of some physical quantity Q, such as temperature, density, potential, stress, acceleration, $\cdots$, then we may indicate the direct connection between the values of Q and the actual points P of space by representing the value of Q at P by $Q(P)$. The notation $Q(P)$ stresses the fact that the values of Q are correlated directly with points P quite independently of any coordinate system which may be used to locate P, and without the aid of any formula.

DEFINITION 23.1. *If, by any means, the values of some quantity f are determined at, and correlated directly with, the actual points of some portion of space, then f is called a point function.*

The following examples illustrate this idea: (1) If at each point P near a certain magnet the field has a definite strength F measured in some system of units, then F is a point function and we denote the value of F at P by $F(P)$. (2) Let C be a family of curves in space such that exactly one curve of the family passes through each point of space, and such that each curve has a definite curvature K at each point P on it. Then $K(P)$ is a point function defined by this family of curves. The value of K is quite independent of any coordinate system used to locate P.

We should note that the concept point function is quite in contrast to that of a function f of three variables (such as a formula) where the value of the quantity f is determined for each set of values of the three variables. Thus, the value of f for the values a, b, c of three variables is denoted by $f(a, b, c)$. This symbol in no way implies that a, b, and c are the coordinates of a point with reference to any coordinate system; or if a, b, c are the coordinates of a point, the symbol in no way indicates the particular coordinate system in mind. The actual symbols used for the three variables under consideration are irrelevant; for whether we write $f(x, y, z)$, or $f(u, v, w)$, or $f(\xi, \eta, \zeta)$ is immaterial, since these symbols all denote the same number when (x, y, z), (u, v, w), and (ξ, η, ζ) denote the same set of numbers.

Now suppose that $f(P)$ is a given point function and suppose that we introduce a rectangular coordinate system (x, y, z), a polar system (r, ϕ, θ), and some other system (λ, μ, ν) for representing points P, where now, in contrast with the preceding paragraph, we use a definite set of letters to refer to a definite coordinate system. If f_r is the function of three variables (formula) such that $f(P) = f_r(x, y, z)$ when P and (x, y, z) denote the same point, then f_r is said to represent the point function f in the (x, y, z) coordinate system. Similarly, if f_p and f_c are the functions of three variables such that $f(P) = f_p(r, \phi, \theta)$ and $f(P) = f_c(\lambda, \mu, \nu)$ when P and (r, ϕ, θ) or P and (λ, μ, ν) denote the same point, then f_p and f_c represent f in the (r, ϕ, θ) and (λ, μ, ν) systems. It is evident that f_r, f_p, and f_c are all different and that none of these functions can be identified with f itself; for example, if f_r represents the temperature at P, no formula for the temperature of a certain substance can be identified with the temperature itself. Furthermore, f_p can be determined from f_r by the equations relating x, y, and z with r, ϕ, and θ; f_c may be obtained in a similar manner from either f_r or f_p. However, it is inconvenient to retain the various subscripts on the letter f and it is customary to omit them. But then we have the paradoxical situation that

$$f(P) = f(x, y, z) = f(r, \phi, \theta) = f(\lambda, \mu, \nu) \tag{1}$$

in which (x, y, z), (r, ϕ, θ), and (λ, μ, ν), while representing the same *point*, do *not* represent the same *set of numbers* (see the preceding paragraph) and in which the letter f denotes *four* different functions, namely, the original point function f and three different functions of three variables. In particular, $f(x, y, z)$ denotes $f_r(x, y, z)$. However, the notation $f(x, y, z)$ admits the reading "the value of the point function f at the point (x, y, z)" just as $f(P)$ denotes "the value of f at P." In this sense, $f(P)$ and $f(x, y, z)$ mean exactly the same thing, i.e., the value of f at a certain point, the only difference between the two symbols being the notations used to denote a particular point. Hence each of the last three symbols in (1) is used to denote the value of both the point function f and a function of three variables. The advantages of this double use of notation are (1) the use of the same letter f in the symbols $f(x, y, z)$, $f(r, \phi, \theta)$ and $f(\lambda, \mu, \nu)$ emphasizes the fact that the various functions of three variables denoted by these symbols all represent the same point function f, and (2) it avoids the necessity of specifically introducing different letters to denote these different functions of three variables.

We are now in a position to consider the invariance of a directional derivative. Let $f(P)$ be a point function defined in space and let C be a curve in space with arc length s. If we think of P as moving along C, then $df(P)/ds$ represents the rate of change of f along C with respect to s; in fact,

$$\frac{df(P)}{ds}\bigg]_{P_0} = \lim_{\Delta s \to 0} \frac{f(P) - f(P_0)}{\Delta s},$$

where P approaches P_0 along C and where Δs is the arc length along C between P_0 and P. Thus, once the unit of length is determined, $df(P)/ds$ has an absolute significance independent of any coordinate system. Hence $df(P)/ds$ is a point function. But to calculate $df(P)/ds$ it is necessary to introduce coordinates and use formula (A′) or some other such formula. The following question inevitably arises: If we introduce two different rectangular coordinate systems (x, y, z) and (X, Y, Z) to calculate $df(P)/ds$, will we necessarily obtain the same result? Obviously not, for the two systems may be based on different units of length. Will the calculated value of $df(P)/ds$ depend on any other feature of the coordinate systems used, such as the origin selected or the orientation of the axes?

To answer this question, consider two rectangular systems (x, y, z) and (X, Y, Z) based on the same unit of length and with a common origin.   Then formula (T) of Ex. XIX, 36, gives the relations between (x, y, z) and (X, Y, Z).   Let the direction angles of the curve C of the preceding paragraph at the point P_0 be α, β, γ with respect to the (x, y, z) system and let these angles be A, B, C with respect to the (X, Y, Z) system.   It is left to the student in Ex. 7 to show that

$$f_x(P_0) \cos \alpha + f_y(P_0) \cos \beta + f_z(P_0) \cos \gamma$$
$$= f_X(P_0) \cos A + f_Y(P_0) \cos B + f_Z(P_0) \cos C. \quad (2)$$

It is also left to the student to show that this relation holds when one coordinate system is a translation of the other.   It follows that this relation holds for any two rectangular systems based on the same unit of length.

Because the quantity $f_x(P) \cos \alpha + f_y(P) \cos \beta + f_z(P) \cos \gamma$ has the same value for all rectangular systems based on the same unit of length, α, β, and γ always being determined with reference to the coordinate system denoted by (x, y, z), we speak of this quantity as an *invariant with respect to such systems*.   (Is it an invariant with respect to *all* rectangular systems?)   It is one of the fundamental objectives of mathematical analysis to discover invariants since these quantities in physical or geometrical applications have absolute physical or geometric interpretations which are independent of the coordinate system used to express them.

EXERCISES XXIV

1. Given a point function f.   Why has the symbol $f(1, 2, \pi)$ no value? How may it be given infinitely many values?   What is the significance of this symbol when f is a given function of three variables?   In this case can it have more than one value?   Does its value depend in any way upon the interpretation of the three variables as coordinates of a point?

2. Given a formula f_v in three variables (or more generally, a function f_v of three variables).   When and how does f_v *define* a point function f? Exactly what does f denote?   (Of course, f denotes the point function determined by f_v.   But answer the question without using the word function and do not suppose that f_v represents a physical quantity.   See footnote, p. 115.)

3. Suppose that the notations (p, q, r) and (u, v, w) refer to two given coordinate systems.   If f is a function of three variables, then $f(p, q, r)$ and $f(u, v, w)$, while representing the *same* function of three variables, may be regarded as defining *different* point functions.   Under what conditions with regard to the points (p, q, r) and (u, v, w) will these two point functions have the same value?

4. In a certain coordinate system the coordinates (u, v, w) of each point P are related to the rectangular coordinates (x, y, z) of P by the equations

$$u = x(x + y), \qquad v = (x + y)(x + z), \qquad w = x(x + z).$$

Do the functions $v\left(\dfrac{1}{w} - \dfrac{1}{u}\right)$ and $\dfrac{y - z}{x}$ represent the same point function?

5. Given a point function f defined in space and a curve C in space represented in two different ways by parametric equations involving two different parameters u and u'. Compare $f(u)$ and $f(u')$.

6. Given the surface S whose parametric equations in a rectangular coordinate system are $x = \varphi_1(u, v)$, $y = \varphi_2(u, v)$, and $z = \varphi_3(u, v)$. Let f be a point function. Discuss fully the notations $f(u, v)$ and $f(u', v')$, where u' and v' provide a second representation of S.

7. Prove formula (2) in Sec. 23.

HINT.   Note that $f_X(P_0) = \dfrac{\partial f(X, Y, Z)}{\partial X}\bigg]_{P_0}$. But $f(X, Y, Z) \equiv f(x, y, z)$ when (X, Y, Z) and (x, y, z) represent the same point since f is a point function. Hence $\dfrac{\partial f(X, Y, Z)}{\partial X}\bigg]_{P_0} = \dfrac{\partial f(x, y, z)}{\partial X}\bigg]_{P_0}$. This last derivative may be evaluated by formula (B). The quantities $f_Y(P_0)$ and $f_Z(P_0)$ are treated similarly. The combined coefficient of $f_x(P_0)$ reduces to cos α by (18) of Ex. XIX, 36.

8. Show that the normal derivative and the direction in which it is taken are invariants with respect to rectangular coordinate systems based on the same unit of length.

HINT.   To show the invariance of the normal derivative, note Ex. XIX, 36.   To show the invariance of the direction of the normal derivative, express cos A_0, cos B_0, and cos C_0 in the (X, Y, Z) system, evaluate cos α_0, cos β_0, and cos γ_0 in terms of A_0, B_0, C_0, and the direction angles of the (x, y, z) axes with reference to the (X, Y, Z) system, and show that the results reduce to the usual formulas for cos α_0, cos β_0, and cos γ_0 in the (x, y, z) system.

9. If f is a point function, if C is a curve in space, and if u is a parameter determining the position of the point P on C, show that $df(P)/du$ is an invariant when calculated in *any* coordinate system.

24. Differentials.   Let $f(x, y, \cdots)$ be a function of a finite number of independent variables $x, y, \cdots$.   Since each of the variables $x, y, \cdots$ is independent, $\Delta x, \Delta y, \cdots$ may be assigned arbitrary values; that is, $\Delta x, \Delta y, \cdots$ are independent variables.*

---

* We do not assume that $\Delta x, \Delta y, \cdots$ are small or are approaching zero. In certain applications it is necessary to assume that these variables are arbitrarily large.

We define the differential df of f by the relation

$$df = f_x(x, y, \cdots) \Delta x + f_y(x, y, \cdots) \Delta y + \cdots . \qquad (1)$$

(cf. Sec. 8). It should be noted that the value of df depends, not only upon the values of Δx, Δy, $\cdots$, but also upon the values of x, y, $\cdots$ at which the partial derivatives of f are evaluated. Thus, the value of df at the point $(x_0, y_0, \cdots)$ is $df = f_x(x_0, y_0, \cdots) \Delta x + f_y(x_0, y_0, \cdots) \Delta y + \cdots$.

If $f(x, y, \cdots)$ is merely the quantity x, then it follows by (1) that $dx = \Delta x$. Similarly, $dy = \Delta y$, $\cdots$. Thus the differential of an *independent* variable is the same as its increment. Hence we may write (1) in the form

$$df = f_x(x, y, \cdots) \, dx + f_y(x, y, \cdots) \, dy + \cdots , \qquad (2)$$

where x, y, $\cdots$ are *independent* variables. Now suppose that x, y, $\cdots$ are not independent but functions of a finite number of independent variables u, v, $\cdots$. It follows directly from (2) that, $f(x, y, \cdots)$ being regarded as a function of the independent variables u, v, $\cdots$,

$$df = \frac{\partial f}{\partial u} \, du + \frac{\partial f}{\partial v} \, dv + \cdots .$$

But the coefficients of du, dv, $\cdots$, may be evaluated by formula (B). Hence

$$df = \left[\frac{\partial f}{\partial x} \frac{\partial x}{\partial u} + \frac{\partial f}{\partial y} \frac{\partial y}{\partial u} + \cdots \right] du$$
$$+ \left[\frac{\partial f}{\partial x} \frac{\partial x}{\partial v} + \frac{\partial f}{\partial y} \frac{\partial y}{\partial v} + \cdots \right] dv + \cdots$$
$$= \frac{\partial f}{\partial x} \left(\frac{\partial x}{\partial u} \, du + \frac{\partial x}{\partial v} \, dv + \cdots \right)$$
$$+ \frac{\partial f}{\partial y} \left(\frac{\partial y}{\partial u} \, du + \frac{\partial y}{\partial v} \, dv + \cdots \right) + \cdots . \qquad (3)$$

It follows by another direct application of (2) that

$$dx = \frac{\partial x}{\partial u} \, du + \frac{\partial x}{\partial v} \, dv + \cdots ,$$
$$dy = \frac{\partial y}{\partial u} \, du + \frac{\partial y}{\partial v} \, dv + \cdots , \qquad \cdots .$$

It is evident that (3) reduces to (2) by virtue of these relations. This proves

THEOREM 24.1.   *If $f(x, y, \cdots)$ is a differentiable function of a finite number of variables $x, y, \cdots$, then, whether $x, y, \cdots$ are independent or not,*

$$df = f_x(x, y, \cdots)\, dx + f_y(x, y, \cdots)\, dy + \cdots.$$

Higher Differentials.   For certain types of work, some people prefer to use differentials. We shall let d^2f, d^3f, $\cdots$, d^nf denote differentials of f of the second, third, $\cdots$, and nth order, respectively, where

$$d^2f = d(df),\ d^3f = d(d^2f),\ \cdots,\ d^nf = d(d^{n-1}f).$$

If f is an independent variable, we define

$$d^2f = 0,\ d^3f = 0,\ \cdots,\ d^nf = 0.$$

Consider a differentiable function f of the two variables x and y. Then

$$df = \frac{\partial f}{\partial x}\, dx + \frac{\partial f}{\partial y}\, dy, \tag{4}$$

$$d^2f = d(df) = d\!\left(\frac{\partial f}{\partial x}\right) dx + \frac{\partial f}{\partial x}\, d(dx) + d\!\left(\frac{\partial f}{\partial y}\right) dy + \frac{\partial f}{\partial y}\, d(dy). \tag{5}$$

Since

$$
\begin{aligned}
d\!\left(\frac{\partial f}{\partial x}\right) &= \frac{\partial}{\partial x}\!\left(\frac{\partial f}{\partial x}\right) dx + \frac{\partial}{\partial y}\!\left(\frac{\partial f}{\partial x}\right) dy = \frac{\partial^2 f}{\partial x^2}\, dx + \frac{\partial^2 f}{\partial y\, \partial x}\, dy, \\
d\!\left(\frac{\partial f}{\partial y}\right) &= \frac{\partial}{\partial x}\!\left(\frac{\partial f}{\partial y}\right) dx + \frac{\partial}{\partial y}\!\left(\frac{\partial f}{\partial y}\right) dy = \frac{\partial^2 f}{\partial x\, \partial y}\, dx + \frac{\partial^2 f}{\partial y^2}\, dy,
\end{aligned}
\tag{6}
$$

Eq. (5) may be written in the form

$$d^2f = \frac{\partial^2 f}{\partial x^2}\,(dx)^2 + 2\frac{\partial^2 f}{\partial x\, \partial y}\, dx\, dy + \frac{\partial^2 f}{\partial y^2}\,(dy)^2 + \frac{\partial f}{\partial x}\, d^2x + \frac{\partial f}{\partial y}\, d^2y.$$

Similar expressions may be found for $d^3f, \cdots, d^nf$. If x is an independent variable $d^2x = 0$; likewise if y is independent, $d^2y = 0$.

EXERCISES XXV

1. If $f(x, y) = x^2 - 3xy$, find df when $x = 2$, $y = 3$, $\Delta x = 0.05$, and $\Delta y = -0.02$. Also find Δf, where $\Delta f = f(x + \Delta x, y + \Delta y) - f(x, y)$.

2. If $b = \dfrac{\sin B}{\sin A}\, a$, and if A, B, and a are measured to be 30°, 45°, and 250, respectively, find the error db in the calculated value of b due to errors $dA = 0.002$ rad., $dB = -0.003$ rad., and $da = -0.005$.

3. (a) If $a = \sqrt{b^2 + c^2 - 2bc \cos A}$, and if b, c, and A are measured to be 12, 15, and 30°, respectively, find da when $db = 0.1$, $dc = -0.2$, and $dA = 0.04$ rad. [These measured values of b, c, and A are to be used in parts (b) and (c) of this problem.]

(b) Find the maximum value of da when $db = \pm 0.1$, $dc = \pm 0.2$, and $dA = \pm 0.04$ rad. by selecting the signs properly.

(c) What is the largest value dA may have in order that da may not be greater than 0.01 when $db = dc = 0.001$?

(d) Find dA when $b = 12 + 0.002T^2$, $c = 15 - 0.05T$, and $a = 20$, where T represents temperature in degrees centigrade, given that T is originally 0 and that $dT = 10$. (First compute da, db, and dc.)

4. If $z = x^2 - y^2$, where $x = u + v$, $y = 2u - v$, find dz when $u = 1$, $v = -2$, $du = 0.1$, and $dv = 0.05$ by two methods: (a) by computing dz in terms of dx and dy, and (b) by substitution of x and y directly in the formula for z.

5. Let us consider equation (2) when there are only two variables x and y. On the graph of $f(x, y)$ show the geometric representation of $f_y(x_0, y_0)\, dy$, $f_x(x_0, y_0)\, dx$, and $f_x(x_0, y_0 + dy)\, dx$. (Remember that, in the notation of Ex. XVII, 4, $f_x(x_0, y_0) = \tan \varphi$ and $f_y(x_0, y_0) = \tan \psi$.) What quantities are approximated by

$$f_y(x_0, y_0)\, dy,\ f_x(x_0, y_0 + dy)\, dx,\ \text{and}\ f_y(x_0, y_0)\, dy + f_x(x_0, y_0 + dy)\, dx$$

when dx and dy are small? (See Sec. 8.) How does df differ from this last quantity? What three sources of error are involved in the use of df as an approximation of the quantity $f(x_0 + dx,\ y_0 + dy) - f(x_0, y_0)$? Show that the point $(x_0 + dx,\ y_0 + dy,\ f(x_0, y_0) + df)$ lies in the plane tangent to the graph of f at $[x_0,\ y_0,\ f(x_0, y_0)]$.

6. If f is a point function, is the differential df a point function? Is it a function of six variables? If it is neither of these things, what is it? Can df be described in any sense as an invariant? If so, prove.

HINT. Consider df as being evaluated at a *point pair* $(P; P')$, where P is in the space (u, v, w) and P' is in the space (du, dv, dw). What are the equations for the change of coordinates in the two spaces?

7. Prove: If df is known to be equal to

$$df = X_1\, dx_1 + X_2\, dx_2 + \cdots + X_n\, dx_n,$$

where $X_1, \cdots, X_n$ are functions of $x_1, \cdots, x_n$, then $\partial f / \partial x_i = X_i$, where the partial derivative is taken holding all the x's fixed but x_i $(i = 1, \cdots, n)$.

8. Let $x = r \cos \theta$, $y = r \sin \theta$. Calculate dx, dy, d^2x, d^2y for: (a) the case when r and θ are independent variables; and (b) the case when $r = e^{3t}$ and $\theta = \log (4s + 3t)$, where s and t are independent variables.

9. Develop an expression for d^3f in case f is a function of two variables x and y; for d^nf.

10. Show that if $y = \varphi(x)$, $x = r \cos \theta$, $y = r \sin \theta$, with θ the independent variable, then

$$\frac{d^2y}{dx^2} = \frac{r^2 \, d\theta^3 + 2 \, d\theta \, dr^2 - r \, d^2r \, d\theta}{(\cos \theta \, dr - r \sin \theta \, d\theta)^3}.$$

25. Taylor's Theorem. Maxima and Minima. Let $f(x, y)$ be a function of x and y having partial derivatives of all orders up to and including order $n + 1$. Let $\phi(t) = f(a + th, \, b + tk)$. (See Ex. XIX, 39.) By Maclaurin's theorem,

$$\phi(t) = \phi(0) + \phi'(0)t + \frac{\phi''(0)}{2!}t^2 + \cdots + \frac{\phi^{(n)}(0)}{n!}t^n$$
$$+ \frac{\phi^{(n+1)}(\theta t)}{(n+1)!}t^{n+1}, \qquad 0 < \theta < 1. \quad (1)$$

But

$$\phi'(t) = hf_x + kf_y,$$
$$\phi''(t) = h^2 f_{xx} + 2hk f_{xy} + k^2 f_{yy}$$
$$= \left(h\frac{\partial}{\partial x} + k\frac{\partial}{\partial y} \right)^2 f,$$

where $\left(h\dfrac{\partial}{\partial x} + k\dfrac{\partial}{\partial y} \right)$ is to be expanded formally as a polynomial and the result applied as an operator to f. It is seen that

$$\phi^{(n)}(t) = \left(h\frac{\partial}{\partial x} + k\frac{\partial}{\partial y} \right)^n f, \qquad \phi^{(n)}(0) = \left(h\frac{\partial}{\partial x} + k\frac{\partial}{\partial y} \right)^n f \bigg]_{a,b}.$$

If we now set $t = 1$ in equation (1), we find that

$$f(a + h, \, b + k) = f(a, b) + [hf_x(a, b) + kf_y(a, b)]$$
$$+ \frac{1}{2!}\left[h^2 f_{xx}(a, b) + 2hk f_{xy}(a, b) + k^2 f_{yy}(a, b) \right]$$
$$+ \cdots + \frac{1}{n!}\left(h\frac{\partial}{\partial x} + k\frac{\partial}{\partial y} \right)^n f \bigg]_{a,b} + R_n, \quad (2)$$

where

$$R_n = \frac{1}{(n+1)!}\left(h\frac{\partial}{\partial x} + k\frac{\partial}{\partial y} \right)^{n+1} f \bigg]_{a+\theta h, b+\theta k}, \qquad 0 < \theta < 1.$$

Formula (2) is called *Taylor's theorem for a function of two variables.* The special case resulting when $a = b = 0$ is called *Maclaurin's theorem.*

The function $f(x, y)$ is said to have a *relative minimum* at (a, b) if, for every point (x, y) in some neighborhood about (a, b), $f(x, y) \geqq f(a, b)$. A relative maximum is defined in a similar way. It is evident that $f(x, y)$ can have a relative maximum or minimum at (a, b) only if $f(x, b)$ and $f(a, y)$ have relative maxima or minima at $x = a$ and $y = b$, respectively, that is, if $f_x(a, b) = f_y(a, b) = 0$. *Hence, all the points (a, b) at which f has a relative maximum or minimum are found among the solutions of the equations*

$$f_x(x, y) = 0, \qquad f_y(x, y) = 0.$$

(We omit the discussion of technicalities in this paragraph.)

Suppose now that the point (a, b) is such that

$$f_x(a, b) = f_y(a, b) = 0.$$

To determine whether or not f has a relative maximum or minimum at (a, b), let us write (2) for the case $n = 1$:

$$f(a + h, b + k) = f(a, b) + 0 + \frac{1}{2!}[h^2 f_{xx}(a + \theta h, b + \theta k)$$
$$+ 2hk f_{xy}(a + \theta h, b + \theta k) + k^2 f_{yy}(a + \theta h, b + \theta k)]. \qquad (3)$$

It is evident that f has a relative minimum at (a, b) if there exists some neighborhood N of (a, b) such that, for each point $(a + h, b + k)$ in N other than (a, b), the last term of (3) is > 0; a similar statement holds with regard to a relative maximum of f at (a, b).

A convenient test for determining the sign of the last term of (3) is obtained by observing that, if $Q(h, k) = Ah^2 + 2Bhk + Ck^2$, then

$$Q(h, k) = \frac{1}{A}[(Ah + Bk)^2 + (AC - B^2)k^2]. \qquad (4)$$

The form of (4) shows that if $AC - B^2 > 0$, then $Q(h, k)$ has the same sign as A regardless of the values of h and k unless $h = k = 0$. Incidentally, if $AC - B^2 > 0$, A and C must have the same sign and neither can be zero; hence $1/A$ is finite in (4). Let us apply this result to the last term of (3). If

$$f_{xx}(a, b)f_{yy}(a, b) - [f_{xy}(a, b)]^2 > 0, \qquad (5)$$

and if f_{xx}, f_{yy}, and f_{xy} are continuous at (a, b), then

$$f_{xx}(a + \theta h, b + \theta k)f_{yy}(a + \theta h, b + \theta k)$$
$$- [f_{xy}(a + \theta h, b + \theta k)]^2 > 0$$

over some neighborhood N of (a, b), and the sign of the last term of (3) is the sign of $f_{xx}(a, b)$. This proves

THEOREM 25.1. *If $f(x, y)$ has continuous second derivatives, if $f_x(a, b) = f_y(a, b) = 0$, and if (5) holds, then f has a relative minimum at (a, b) if $f_{xx}(a, b) > 0$, and f has a relative maximum at (a, b) if $f_{xx}(a, b) < 0$.*

EXERCISES XXVI

1. Expand by Maclaurin's theorem:

(a) $\sin(xy)$. (b) $e^x \cos y$. (c) $\sqrt{x - y}$. (d) $\log(x + y)$.

2. Derive Taylor's theorem for a function of x, y, and z.

3. Examine for maxima and minima:

(a) $x^2 y + xy^2 - x$. (b) $x^2 + y^2 + x + y$. (c) $x^3 + 3x^2 - 2xy + 5y^2 - 4y^3$.

4. Find the shortest distance between the lines

$$\begin{cases} y = x + 1 \\ z = 2x \end{cases} \quad \text{and} \quad \begin{cases} y = 2 - x \\ z = 2 + x \end{cases}$$

5. Apply Theorem 25.1 to Ex. XXIII, 15.

6. If $u = f(x, y, z)$, where x, y, z are connected by the relation

$$\phi(x, y, z) = 0,$$

show that, to determine the maxima and minima of f, the relations

$$\frac{\partial u}{\partial x}\bigg)_y = 0, \qquad \frac{\partial u}{\partial y}\bigg)_x = 0$$

may be replaced by the relations

$$\phi(x, y, z) = 0, \quad \begin{vmatrix} f_x & f_z \\ \phi_x & \phi_z \end{vmatrix} = 0, \quad \begin{vmatrix} f_y & f_z \\ \phi_y & \phi_z \end{vmatrix} = 0. \tag{6}$$

Suggestion. Evaluate $\dfrac{\partial u}{\partial x}\bigg)_y$ and $\dfrac{\partial u}{\partial y}\bigg)_x$ by formula (B), and in the results substitute for $\dfrac{\partial z}{\partial x}\bigg)_y$ and $\dfrac{\partial z}{\partial y}\bigg)_x$ the values of these quantities found by means of the relation $\phi(x, y, z) = 0$.

7. Show that equations (6) are obtained when one seeks the maxima and minima of $U = f(x, y, z) + \lambda \phi(x, y, z)$, where λ is a constant to be determined by the relation $\partial U / \partial z = 0$.

The device of finding the maxima and minima of u in Ex. 6 by introducing the function U and the constant λ is called the method of *Lagrange's multipliers*.

8. Extend the results of Exs. 6 and 7 to the case where $u = f(x, y, z, w)$ with $\phi(x, y, z, w) = 0$, $\psi(x, y, z, w) = 0$.

9. Find the "stationary" values of u when $u = xyz$ with $x + y + z = 1$.

CHAPTER II

INTEGRAL CALCULUS

PART A. INDEFINITE INTEGRALS

1. Introduction. In this chapter we shall first briefly review some of the elementary methods for finding indefinite integrals, and then we shall give an introduction to line, surface, and volume integrals. Following this we shall develop the theory of Riemann integration. Finally we shall take up the question of evaluating improper integrals. In Part B of this chapter we shall place particular emphasis upon the physical applications of definite integrals.

2. The Indefinite Integral of a Function f(x). We say that a function* $F(x)$ is an *integral* of a function $f(x)$ if $D_x F(x) = f(x)$. Thus, $x^3 + 7$, x^3, and $x^3 - 2$ are integrals of $3x^2$ since $D_x(x^3 + 7)$, $D_x x^3$, and $D_x(x^3 - 2)$ are each equal to $3x^2$. Again, $\log x$ and $\log 5x$ are integrals of $1/x$ since $D_x \log x$ and $D_x \log 5x$ are each equal to $1/x$.

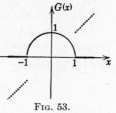

Fig. 53.

An integral of $f(x)$ is sometimes defined to be a function $F(x)$ such that $dF(x) = f(x)\,dx$. In this sense, x^3 is an integral of $3x^2$ since $d(x^3) = 3x^2\,dx$. This definition of an integral is evidently equivalent to the one given above.

If $F(x)$ is an integral of $f(x)$ and if C_0 is any real number, then $F(x) + C_0$ is also an integral of $f(x)$. Thus, *if $f(x)$ has an integral $F(x)$, then $f(x)$ has infinitely many integrals.* However, it is *not* generally the case that *all* integrals of $f(x)$ are obtained by giving C all real values in the formula $F(x) + C$. For example, if $f(x) = -x/\sqrt{1 - x^2}$, this function being defined only over the interval $-1 < x < 1$, then one integral of $f(x)$ is

---

* In this section we consider only real single-valued functions of a real variable.

163

the function $F(x) = \sqrt{1 - x^2}$, where $-1 < x < 1$. Another integral of $f(x)$ is the function $G(x)$ such that (see Fig. 53)

$$G(x) = \begin{cases} \sqrt{1 - x^2} \text{ when } -1 < x < 1, \\ x \text{ when } x \text{ is rational with } |x| \geq 1, \\ 0 \text{ for all other } x, \end{cases}$$

since $D_xG(x) = f(x)$ in the interval $-1 < x < 1$ and since $G(x)$ is discontinuous, and hence nondifferentiable, outside this interval. (Cf. Chap. I, Theorem 5.1.) In fact, $G(x)$ could have been defined as any nondifferentiable function outside the interval $-1 < x < 1$. It is evident that $G(x)$ is not representable as $F(x) + C$ for any value of C. But for our present purposes the nondifferentiable part of $G(x)$ is of little interest and we shall consider only those integrals $F(x)$ of a function $f(x)$ which have the same* domain of definition as $f(x)$. Thus, we shall consider integrals of $-x/\sqrt{1 - x^2}$ like $\sqrt{1 - x^2} + C_0$, but not like $G(x)$.

DEFINITION 2.1. *We denote an arbitrary integral of $f(x)$ [having the same domain of definition as $f(x)$] by $I_x f(x)$; we call $I_x f(x)$ the indefinite integral of $f(x)$.*

If $f(x)$ has at least one integral, then $f(x)$ is called *integrable*.

THEOREM 2.1. *Let $f(x)$ be an integrable function of x whose domain of definition is a single interval I, finite or infinite in length. If $F(x)$ is any integral of $f(x)$, then*

$$\mathbf{I}_x f(x) = F(x) + C, \tag{1}$$

where (1) is to be interpreted as asserting that any integral whatever of $f(x)$ is representable as $F(x) + C$ by proper choice of the number C, (i.e., that every integral of $f(x)$ may be obtained by giving C all real values in the formula $F(x) + C$).

* This restriction, while satisfactory for those functions ordinarily met with in practice, would be unsuitable in a technical treatment of this subject. Thus, let $F(x)$ be the function such that $F(x) = x^4$ when x is rational and $F(x) = 0$ when x is irrational; let $f(x) = D_xF(x)$. Then $f(x) = 0$ when $x = 0$ and $f(x)$ is defined nowhere else. (Cf. Chap. I, Ex. II, 1j and 1l.) While $f(x)$ has at least one integral, e.g., $F(x)$, it is seen that $f(x)$ has no integral $G(x)$ with the same domain of definition as $f(x)$, for the domain of definition of $f(x)$ is the single point $x = 0$ and no function $G(x)$ defined only at $x = 0$ can have a derivative. Hence the above restriction removes from consideration all integrals of $f(x)$.

Let $G(x)$ be an arbitrary integral of $f(x)$. It is readily seen by Theorem 10.3 and Ex. XI, 5 of Chap. I that $G(x) - F(x) \equiv C_0$, so that $G(x) \equiv F(x) + C_0$. Hence $G(x)$ is obtained by giving C the value C_0 in the formula $F(x) + C$. Since $G(x)$ is an arbitrary instance of $I_x f(x)$, (1) holds.

The fact that $F(x)$ was an arbitrary integral of $f(x)$ in Theorem 2.1 implies that, if $G(x)$ is any integral of $f(x)$ other than $F(x)$, then $I_x f(x) = G(x) + C$. Likewise, since $\log C$ takes on all real values when C takes on all positive values, $I_x f(x) = F(x) + \log C$. It is evident that infinitely many other formulas for representing $I_x f(x)$ may be constructed. No inconsistency arises when we write

$$I_x f(x) = F(x) + C,\; I_x f(x) = G(x) + C,\; I_x f(x) = F(x) + \log C,$$

etc., if we do not regard $I_x f(x)$ as *being* or *denoting* any of the formulas $F(x) + C$, etc., and if instead we interpret each of these relations as indicated in Theorem 2.1. To obtain any particular integral of $f(x)$, different values of C must, of course, be used in the various formulas $F(x) + C$, $F(x) + \log C$, etc.

Example 1. If $f(x) = x/\sqrt{1 - x^2}$, then $f(x)$ is defined over the single interval $-1 < x < 1$ and, by Theorem 2.1,

$$I_x \left(x/\sqrt{1 - x^2} \right) = -\sqrt{1 - x^2} + C$$

since $-\sqrt{1 - x^2}$ is an integral of $f(x)$.

Example 2. If $f(x) = \cos 2x$, then $f(x)$ is defined over the entire x-axis and $I_x \cos 2x = \frac{1}{2} \sin 2x + C$.

We give three examples to illustrate the fact that Theorem 2.1 is false whenever the domain of definition of $f(x)$ is not a single interval (see Ex. I, 3).

Example 3. If $f(x) = -1/x^2$, then $f(x)$ is defined for all x except $x = 0$, and the domain of definition of $f(x)$ is not a single interval. One integral of $f(x)$ is the function $F(x) = 1/x$, and another integral of $f(x)$ is the function $G(x)$ such that

$$G(x) = \begin{cases} \dfrac{1}{x} \text{ when } x > 0, \\[2mm] \dfrac{1}{x} + 2 \text{ when } x < 0, \end{cases}$$

or more generally,

$$G(x) = \begin{cases} \dfrac{1}{x} + C_1 \text{ when } x > 0, \\[2mm] \dfrac{1}{x} + C_2 \text{ when } x < 0, \end{cases}$$

where $C_1 \neq C_2$.   There exists no *single* number C_0 such that

$$G(x) = F(x) + C_0.$$

Hence $G(x)$ is not among the functions represented by the formula $F(x) + C$ and it is *not* the case that $I_x(-1/x^2) = (1/x) + C$.

Example 4.   If $f(x) = \csc^2 \pi x$, then $f(x)$ is undefined for integer values of x. While an integral of $f(x)$ is $-(1/\pi) \operatorname{ctn} \pi x$, it is not the case that

$$I_x \csc^2 \pi x = -\frac{1}{\pi} \operatorname{ctn} \pi x + C,$$

for an integral of $f(x)$ not represented by this formula is the function $G(x) = -(1/\pi) \operatorname{ctn} \pi x + [x]$, where $[x]$ denotes the greatest integer not larger than x.

Example 5.   If $f(x) = (2/x^3)e^{-1/x^2}$, then $f(x)$ is undefined at $x = 0$ and an integral of $f(x)$ not represented by the formula $e^{-1/x^2} + C$ is the function $G(x)$ such that $G(x) = e^{-1/x^2}$ when $x > 0$ and $G(x) = e^{-1/x^2} + 1$ when $x < 0$.   This example illustrates the fact that Theorem 2.1 may fail even when $f(x)$ does not become infinite and has a limit at *every* point $x = a$.

To *integrate* $f(x)$ is to find a representation of $I_x f(x)$.   In the symbol $I_x f(x)$, $f(x)$ is called the *integrand*.   When integrating $f(x)$ by Theorem 2.1, the *constant of integration* C should always be included, for it is by evaluating C properly that we obtain an integral which has a specified value for a given value of x. (This will appear later to be of great importance in the applications of integrals.)   For example, to find the integral of $3x^2$ which has the value 5 when $x = 2$, we first find $I_x 3x^2 = x^3 + C$, and then we determine C from the equation $2^3 + C = 5$.   The function $x^3 - 3$ is the desired integral.

3. Properties of Indefinite Integrals.   In this section we shall list a few of the elementary properties of indefinite integrals.

I. *If $f(x)$ is an integrable function of x, then $D_x[I_x f(x)] = f(x)$.* This follows immediately from the concept of an integral and Definition 2.1.

II. *If $f(x)$ and $g(x)$ are integrable and have for their domain of definition the single interval I, then the function $\varphi(x) = f(x) + g(x)$ is integrable and**

---

* Since the integrals in (1) are indefinite, a constant C should be added to the right member of (1).   But it is customary to omit this constant and to interpret the symbol $=$ as meaning "differs by only a constant from."   This comment also applies to other equations involving integrals, such as (4), (5), (8), and (11) below.

$$I_x[f(x) + g(x)] = I_x f(x) + I_x g(x). \tag{1}$$

Let $F(x)$ and $G(x)$ be integrals of $f(x)$ and $g(x)$. By Theorem 2.1, $I_x f(x) = F(x) + C_1$ and $I_x g(x) = G(x) + C_2$. Hence

$$I_x f(x) + I_x g(x) = F(x) + G(x) + C_3, \tag{2}$$

where $C_3 = C_1 + C_2$. But

$$D_x[F(x) + G(x)] = D_x F(x) + D_x G(x) = f(x) + g(x).$$

Hence $[F(x) + G(x)]$ is an integral of $[f(x) + g(x)]$ and, by Theorem 2.1,

$$I_x[f(x) + g(x)] = F(x) + G(x) + C_4. \tag{3}$$

Since the right members of (2) and (3) differ by only a constant, (1) holds.

III. *If $f(x)$ is an integrable function whose domain of definition is a single interval and if k is any constant, then $kf(x)$ is integrable and*

$$I_x[kf(x)] = k\left[I_x f(x)\right]. \tag{4}$$

This property may be proved in the same manner as the preceding property.

Example 1. By (1) and (4) it follows that

$$I_x(4x^6 + 5\cos 3x) = I_x 4x^6 + I_x 5\cos 3x = 4 I_x x^6 + 5 I_x \cos 3x$$

$$= \frac{4x^7}{7} + \frac{5}{3}\sin 3x + C.$$

As indicated above, $I_u g(u)$ denotes an arbitrary integral of $g(u)$ when u is independent. But if u is a function of x, say $u = h(x)$, then we regard $I_u g(u)$ as denoting any function of x that may be obtained by integrating $g(u)$ with respect to u and substituting $u = h(x)$ in the result. Thus, if $I_u g(u) = G(u) + C$ when u is independent, then $I_u g(u) = G[h(x)] + C$ when $u = h(x)$.

In the following three properties we shall assume that all of the functions involved meet the conditions of Theorem 2.1.

IVa. *If $f(x)$ can be written in the form $f(x) = g(u) \cdot D_x u$ by properly choosing u as a differentiable function of x, say $u = h(x)$, and if $g(u)$ is integrable, then $f(x)$ is integrable and*

$$\mathbf{I}_x f(x) = \mathbf{I}_x [g(u) \cdot D_x u] = \mathbf{I}_u g(u), \tag{5}$$

where $I_u g(u)$ is interpreted as stated above.

Let $G(u)$ be an integral of $g(u)$. Since $u = h(x)$,

$$\mathbf{I}_u g(u) = G[h(x)] + C. \tag{6}$$

Since $D_x G[h(x)] = D_u G(u) \cdot D_x u = g(u) \cdot D_x u = f(x)$, $G[h(x)]$ is an integral of $f(x)$ and

$$\mathbf{I}_x f(x) = G[h(x)] + C'. \tag{7}$$

Since the right members of (6) and (7) differ by only a constant, (5) holds.

Example 2. If $f(x) = (6x + 5)\sqrt{3x^2 + 5x + 4}$, we take

$$u = 3x^2 + 5x + 4,$$

so that $D_x u = 6x + 5$. Then $f(x) = u^{1/2} D_x u$, $g(u)$ in (5) being $u^{1/2}$. By (5),

$$\mathbf{I}_x f(x) = \mathbf{I}_x [u^{1/2} D_x u] = \mathbf{I}_u u^{1/2} = \tfrac{2}{3} u^{3/2} + C = \tfrac{2}{3}(3x^2 + 5x + 4)^{3/2} + C.$$

Example 3. If $f(x) = xe^{x^2}$, we take $u = x^2$, so that $D_x u = 2x$. Then

$$\mathbf{I}_x xe^{x^2} = \mathbf{I}_x [\tfrac{1}{2} e^u D_x u] = \tfrac{1}{2} \mathbf{I}_u e^u = \tfrac{1}{2} e^u + C = \tfrac{1}{2} e^{x^2} + C.$$

IVb. *Let x be a differentiable function of u, say $x = \varphi(u)$, with u in turn a differentiable function of x, say $u = h(x)$. If $f(x)$ is such that $f[\varphi(u)] \cdot D_u \varphi(u)$ is integrable, then $f(x)$ is integrable and*

$$\mathbf{I}_x f(x) = \mathbf{I}_u [f(x) \cdot D_u x] = \mathbf{I}_u \{f[\varphi(u)] \cdot D_u \varphi(u)\}, \tag{8}$$

where the right member of (8) is interpreted as indicated above.

Let $\Phi(u)$ be an integral of $f[\varphi(u)] \cdot D_u \varphi(u)$. Since $u = h(x)$,

$$\mathbf{I}_u \{f[\varphi(u)] \cdot D_u \varphi(u)\} = \Phi[h(x)] + C. \tag{9}$$

By Theorem 5.8 of Chap. I,

$$D_x \Phi[h(x)] = D_u \Phi(u) \cdot D_x u = f[\varphi(u)] \cdot D_u x \cdot D_x u = f(x).$$

Hence $\Phi[h(x)]$ is an integral of $f(x)$ and

$$\mathbf{I}_x f(x) = \Phi[h(x)] + C'. \tag{10}$$

Since the right members of (9) and (10) differ by only a constant, (8) results.

Example 4. If $f(x) = \sqrt{a^2 - x^2}$, it is not evident how $f(x)$ may be expressed in the form (5). There is no general rule for determining $\varphi(u)$ in (8), but we try $x = a \sin u$ as $\varphi(u)$ since $f(x)$ simplifies upon making this substitution. As $D_u x = D_u \varphi(u) = a \cos u$, it follows by (8) that

$$\mathbf{I}_x \sqrt{a^2 - x^2} = \mathbf{I}_u [\sqrt{a^2 - a^2 \sin^2 u} \cdot a \cos u] = \mathbf{I}_u a^2 \cos^2 u$$

$$= \frac{a^2}{2} \mathbf{I}_u (1 + \cos 2u) = \frac{a^2}{2}\left(u + \frac{1}{2} \sin 2u \right) + C$$

$$= \frac{a^2}{2}\left[\mathrm{Sin}^{-1} \frac{x}{a} + \frac{x\sqrt{a^2 - x^2}}{a^2} \right] + C.$$

It should be noted that, in using (5), x need not be expressible in terms of u, whereas in using (8), x and u must be expressible in terms of each other. This accounts for the fact that the hypotheses of IVa and IVb are stated differently.

V. *If $f(x)$ can be written in the form $f(x) = g(x) \cdot h(x)$, where $g(x)$ is integrable and $h(x)$ is differentiable, and if $G(x)$ is any integral of $g(x)$, then*

$$\mathbf{I}_x f = \mathbf{I}_x (g \cdot h) = G \cdot h - \mathbf{I}_x (G \cdot D_x h), \tag{11}$$

provided that $G \cdot D_x h$ is integrable.

The proof of this property is based on the fact that

$$D_x[G \cdot h - \mathbf{I}_x (G \cdot D_x h)] = (D_x G)h + G \cdot D_x h - D_x \mathbf{I}_x (G \cdot D_x h)$$

$$= gh + G \cdot D_x h - G \cdot D_x h = gh = f.$$

[We have written f, g, and h instead of $f(x)$, $g(x)$, and $h(x)$ merely for simplicity.]

We leave it to the reader to show that the generality of (11) is not increased by replacing $G(x)$ by $G(x) + C$ in its right member; in other words, it is always sufficient to take as $G(x)$ some one particular integral of $g(x)$.

Not only can $G(x)$ be *any* integral of $g(x)$ in (11), but it is often possible to choose $G(x)$ so that the last integration in (11) is simplified.   This is brought out in

Example 5.   Find $I_x \log (x + 3)$.   Unless we happen to know an integral of $\log (x + 3)$, we should not take $g(x)$ as $\log (x + 3)$.   Hence we choose

$$g(x) = 1, \qquad h(x) = \log (x + 3),$$

so that

$$G(x) = x + k, \qquad D_x h(x) = \frac{1}{x + 3},$$

where k is some number to be determined.   By (11),

$$I_x \log (x + 3) = (x + k) \log (x + 3) - I_x \left(\frac{x + k}{x + 3} \right).$$

If we choose $k = 3$, the integration of the last term is simple, and we find that

$$I_x \log (x + 3) = (x + 3) \log (x + 3) - x + C.$$

4. Elementary Integration.   Since $D_u \dfrac{u^{n+1}}{n + 1} = u^n$, it follows that*

$$I_u \, u^n = \frac{u^{n+1}}{n + 1} + C. \qquad (n \neq -1) \quad (1)$$

Again, since $D_x \dfrac{[h(x)]^{n+1}}{n + 1} = [h(x)]^n \cdot D_x h(x)$, it follows that

$$I_x \{[h(x)]^n \cdot D_x h(x)\} = \frac{[h(x)]^{n+1}}{n + 1} + C. \quad (n \neq -1) \quad (2)$$

When (1) and (2) are compared, it would seem that (2) is more general than (1).   Hence in constructing a table of integrals it would seem that we should include (2) rather than (1).   But it is sufficient to include (1) because (2) may be derived from (1) in the following way: Let $u = h(x)$.   Then by (5) of property IVa,

$$I_x \{[h(x)]^n \cdot D_x h(x)\} = I_u \, u^n = \frac{u^{n+1}}{n + 1} + C = \frac{[h(x)]^{n+1}}{n + 1} + C.$$

* In this section and in Table II we leave it to the student to modify integral formulas wherever necessary in the light of Examples 3, 4, 5 of Sec. 2 and Ex. I, 3.

This device is very important, and the student should become so familiar with it that he performs it automatically.   For example,

$$\mathbf{I}_u \cos u = \sin u + C$$

becomes

$$\mathbf{I}_x [\cos h(x) \cdot D_x h(x)] = \sin h(x) + C, \tag{3}$$

and in general,

$$\mathbf{I}_u g(u) = G(u) + C \tag{4}$$

becomes

$$\mathbf{I}_x \{g[h(x)] \cdot D_x h(x)\} = G[h(x)] + C. \tag{5}$$

The student should write out Table II below in terms of $h(x)$.

Examples.   By (2),

$$\mathbf{I}_x (\cos^2 5x \sin 5x) = -\tfrac{1}{5}\mathbf{I}_x [(\cos 5x)^2(-5 \sin 5x)] = -\tfrac{1}{15} \cos^3 5x + C,$$

where

$$h(x) = \cos 5x.$$

The coefficient -5 is introduced into the second factor of the integrand in order that this factor may be represented as $D_x h(x)$.   By property III, this coefficient is compensated for by introducing the coefficient $-\tfrac{1}{5}$ before $\mathbf{I}_x$. As another example, we have by (3),

$$\mathbf{I}_x \left[(\cos \sqrt{x})\frac{1}{\sqrt{x}} \right] = 2\mathbf{I}_x \left[(\cos \sqrt{x})\frac{1}{2\sqrt{x}} \right] = 2 \sin \sqrt{x} + C,$$

where

$$h(x) = \sqrt{x}.$$

By (4), (5), and formula (3) of Table II,

$$\mathbf{I}_x (3e^{\sin^2 x} \sin x \cos x) = \tfrac{3}{2}\mathbf{I}_x [e^{\sin^2 x} (2 \sin x \cos x)] = \tfrac{3}{2}e^{\sin^2 x} + C,$$

where

$$h(x) = \sin^2 x.$$

These examples show that, when the integral formulas are written in terms of $h(x)$, it is unnecessary to apply property IVa in each individual problem.

We write the following integral formulas in the historical notation $\int f(u)\, du$ instead of $I_u f(u)$. These formulas may all be verified by differentiation. With regard to the formulas involving hyperbolic functions, see Sec. 5.

TABLE II

1. $\displaystyle\int u^n\, du = \frac{u^{n+1}}{n+1} + C,\, n \neq -1.$ 2. $\displaystyle\int \frac{1}{u}\, du = \log_e u + C.$

3. $\displaystyle\int e^u\, du = e^u + C.$ 4. $\displaystyle\int a^u\, du = a^u \log_a e + C.$

5. $\displaystyle\int \cos u\, du = \sin u + C.$

6. $\displaystyle\int \sec u\, du = \log\,(\sec u + \tan u) + C.$

7. $\displaystyle\int \sin u\, du = -\cos u + C.$

8. $\displaystyle\int \csc u\, du = -\log\,(\csc u + \operatorname{ctn} u) + C.$

9. $\displaystyle\int \tan u\, du = -\log \cos u + C.$ 10. $\displaystyle\int \operatorname{ctn} u\, du = \log \sin u + C.$

11. $\displaystyle\int \sec u \tan u\, du = \sec u + C.$ 12. $\displaystyle\int \csc u \operatorname{ctn} u\, du = -\csc u + C.$

13. $\displaystyle\int \sec^2 u\, du = \tan u + C.$ 14. $\displaystyle\int \csc^2 u\, du = -\operatorname{ctn} u + C.$

15. $\displaystyle\int \frac{1}{a^2 + u^2}\, du = \frac{1}{a} \operatorname{Tan}^{-1} \frac{u}{a} + C.$ 16. $\displaystyle\int \frac{1}{a^2 - u^2}\, du = \frac{1}{a} \tanh^{-1} \frac{u}{a} + C.$

17. $\displaystyle\int \frac{1}{\sqrt{a^2 - u^2}}\, du = \operatorname{Sin}^{-1} \frac{u}{a} + C.$

18. $\displaystyle\int \frac{1}{u\sqrt{u^2 - a^2}}\, du = \frac{1}{a} \operatorname{Sec}^{-1} \frac{u}{a} + C.$

19. $\displaystyle\int \frac{1}{\sqrt{u^2 - a^2}}\, du = \pm \cosh^{-1} \frac{u}{a} + C.$

20. $\displaystyle\int \frac{1}{u\sqrt{a^2 - u^2}}\, du = \mp \frac{1}{a} \operatorname{sech}^{-1} \frac{u}{a} + C.$

21. $\displaystyle\int \frac{1}{\sqrt{a^2 + u^2}}\, du = \sinh^{-1} \frac{u}{a} + C.$

22. $\displaystyle\int \frac{1}{u\sqrt{a^2 + u^2}}\, du = -\frac{1}{a} \operatorname{csch}^{-1} \frac{u}{a} + C.$

Many integrals may be reduced to the above forms by simple devices.

Example 1. Find $\int \dfrac{1}{\sqrt{6 - 8x - 2x^2}} \, dx$.

This integral may be reduced to formula 17 by completing the square within the radical after factoring out the coefficient 2 of x^2.

$$\int \frac{1}{\sqrt{6 - 8x - 2x^2}} \, dx = \frac{1}{\sqrt{2}} \int \frac{1}{\sqrt{7 - (x + 2)^2}} \, dx$$

$$= \frac{1}{\sqrt{2}} \operatorname{Sin}^{-1} \frac{x + 2}{\sqrt{7}} + C.$$

Example 2. Find $\int \dfrac{x + 6}{x^2 - 4x + 7} \, dx$.

This integral may be evaluated by breaking up the numerator into two parts such that one part is the derivative of the denominator.

$$\int \frac{x + 6}{x^2 - 4x + 7} \, dx = \frac{1}{2} \int \frac{2x + 12}{x^2 - 4x + 7} \, dx = \frac{1}{2} \left[\int \frac{2x - 4}{x^2 - 4x + 7} \, dx \right.$$

$$\left. + \int \frac{16}{x^2 - 4x + 7} \, dx \right] = \frac{1}{2} \log (x^2 - 4x + 7) + \frac{8}{\sqrt{3}} \operatorname{Tan}^{-1} \frac{x - 2}{\sqrt{3}} + C.$$

EXERCISES I

1. Prove formulas 1 to 15, 17, 18 of Table II.
2. Integrate by means of properties II, III, IV, and Table II.

(1) $\displaystyle\int \left(\sqrt{5x - 7} + \frac{2a}{\sqrt{3x}} - \frac{b}{x^2} + \sqrt[3]{5x^2} \right) dx.$

(2) $\displaystyle\int \left[(4x - 9)^5 + \frac{3ax}{b^2 + c^2x^2} \right] dx.$

(3) $\displaystyle\int \left(\frac{\log^5 7x}{3x} + \cos^3 5x \sin 5x \right) dx.$

(4) $\displaystyle\int [x(a^2 + b^2x^2)^{1/2} + (a^{2/3} - x^{2/3})^3] \, dx.$

(5) $\displaystyle\int \left[\frac{7}{9x^2 + 16} + (\tan 2x - 1)^2 \right] dx.$

(6) $\displaystyle\int \left(\frac{2x}{\sqrt[3]{6 - 5x^2}} + \frac{1}{\sqrt{9 - 16x^2}} \right) dx.$

(7) $\displaystyle\int\left(x\sqrt{3x^2+7}+\frac{7x}{9x^2+16}\right)dx.$

(8) $\displaystyle\int\left(\frac{4x^3-5x}{x+1}+\frac{x}{x^2+3x+10}\right)dx.$ (Divide out the first fraction.)

(9) $\displaystyle\int\left(\frac{2x-1}{2x+3}+\frac{x+1}{\sqrt{x}}\right)dx.$

(10) $\displaystyle\int\left[\frac{(x+3)(5x-1)}{x}+x^4(x^5+7)^{\frac12}\right]dx.$

(11) $\displaystyle\int\left[\frac{1}{3\sqrt{x}+1}+\frac{\sin(x^{\frac13})}{x^{\frac23}}\right]dx.$ (In the first fraction let $x=u^2$.)

(12) $\displaystyle\int\left[7(6)^{2x}+\frac{x^3}{x+1}\right]dx.$

(13) $\displaystyle\int\left(\frac{5x^2}{\sqrt{3x+4}}+\frac{1}{x^2-2x+5}\right)dx.$

(14) $\displaystyle\int(x\cos x^2+x\cos x^2\sin x^2)\,dx.$

(15) $\displaystyle\int(x^5\sqrt{2x^6-1}+\sec^2 3x)\,dx.$

(16) $\displaystyle\int(\csc 2\theta+\sin^2 3\theta+\tan 7\theta)\,d\theta.$

(17) $\displaystyle\int\left(\tan^2\frac{3\theta}{2}+\sec 5\theta+\frac{1}{\sin 4\theta}\right)d\theta.$

(18) $\displaystyle\int(\tan 3x+\operatorname{ctn} 3x)^2\,dx.$ (19) $\displaystyle\int\left(\cos^2 3x+\frac{x+1}{9x^2+7}\right)dx.$

(20) $\displaystyle\int\left(\frac{x^\pi+e^{3x}}{7}+\sin 7x\cos 7x\right)dx.$

(21) $\displaystyle\int\left(\frac{4x-3}{x^2+2x+7}+\frac{x}{\sqrt{1-9x^4}}\right)dx.$

(22) $\displaystyle\int\left(\sin^3\frac{x}{2}+\sec^4\frac{x}{2}+\cos^4\frac{x}{2}\right)dx.$

(23) $\displaystyle\int(5e^{\tan 7x}\sec^2 7x-7^{3x})\,dx.$ (24) $\displaystyle\int(e^{-\sin^2 3x}\sin 6x-e^2)\,dx.$

(25) $\displaystyle\int\left(\operatorname{ctn}^3 7x+\tan^3\frac{2x}{7}\sec\frac{2x}{7}\right)dx.$

(26) $\displaystyle\int[\cos 3x\cos 2x+(\cos 3x)^{-\frac75}\sin 3x]\,dx.$

(27) $\int (\operatorname{ctn}^2 3\theta + \csc^3 5\theta \operatorname{ctn} 5\theta) \, d\theta.$ (28) $\int \left(\frac{1}{3x^2 + 4x + 7} + \operatorname{ctn} 2x \right) dx.$

(29) $\int \left(\frac{2}{\sqrt{2 + x - x^2}} + \tan^4 x \right) dx.$

(30) $\int \left(\frac{2}{x\sqrt{4x^2 - 9}} + \sin^2 x \cos^5 x \right) dx.$

(31) $\int \left(\frac{1}{2x^2 + 6x + 25} + \cos^3 4x \right) dx.$

(32) $\int \left(\frac{1}{x\sqrt{9x^2 + 12x + 2}} + x \sec^4 x^2 \right) dx.$

(33) $\int \left(\sin^2 3x \cos^2 3x + \frac{1}{\sqrt{3 + 4x - 4x^2}} \right) dx.$

(34) $\int \left(\frac{1}{9x^2 + 12x + 5} + \frac{\cos^3 5x}{\sin^2 5x} \right) dx.$

(35) $\int \left(\tan^6 x \sec^4 x + x\sqrt{9 - 4x^2} \right) dx.$

(36) $\int \left(\frac{7x}{1 - 7x^2} + \tan^5 x \sec^3 x \right) dx.$ (37) $\int \left(\frac{1}{e^{3x} + 1} + \csc^2 3x \right) dx.$

(38) $\int \left(\frac{1}{\sqrt{5 - 4x - 4x^2}} + \operatorname{ctn}^5 2x \right) dx.$

(39) $\int (\cos^5 2x + \sin^6 2x) \, dx.$ (40) $\int \left(\frac{1}{\sqrt{2ax - x^2}} + \cos^4 5x \right) dx.$

(41) $\int \left(\frac{1}{1 - \cos 2x} + \frac{\sin^3 2x}{\cos^4 2x} \right) dx.$

(42) $\int \left(\frac{1}{1 + \cos x} + \cos^2 3x \sin^4 3x \right) dx.$

(43) $\int (\sec^5 x \tan x + \cos^3 5x\sqrt{\sin 5x}) \, dx.$

(44) $\int \left(\frac{e^{\operatorname{Tan}^{-1} x}}{1 + x^2} + 10^{3x} + 7^{\log_7 x^2} \right) dx.$

3. Generalize Theorem 2.1 in the light of Examples 3, 4, 5 of Sec. 2.

5. Hyperbolic Functions.   In the previous section we encountered hyperbolic functions.   Since these functions appear very frequently in the scientific literature and are quite useful, we shall devote a short section to them.   We define the hyperbolic cosine, sine, tangent, secant, cosecant, and cotangent as follows:

$$\cosh u = \frac{e^u + e^{-u}}{2}. \qquad \operatorname{sech} u = \frac{2}{e^u + e^{-u}}.$$

$$\sinh u = \frac{e^u - e^{-u}}{2}. \qquad \operatorname{csch} u = \frac{2}{e^u - e^{-u}}. \tag{1}$$

$$\tanh u = \frac{e^u - e^{-u}}{e^u + e^{-u}}. \qquad \operatorname{ctnh} u = \frac{e^u + e^{-u}}{e^u - e^{-u}}.$$

The following elementary identities result immediately from the definitions of the hyperbolic functions:

$\cosh^2 u - \sinh^2 u = 1.$

$\operatorname{sech}^2 u + \tanh^2 u = 1.$

$\operatorname{ctnh}^2 u - \operatorname{csch}^2 u = 1.$

$\cosh (u \pm v) = \cosh u \cosh v \pm \sinh u \sinh v.$

$\sinh (u \pm v) = \sinh u \cosh v \pm \cosh u \sinh v.$

$\tanh (u \pm v) = \dfrac{\tanh u \pm \tanh v}{1 \pm \tanh u \tanh v}.$

$\cosh 2u = \cosh^2 u + \sinh^2 u = 2 \cosh^2 u - 1 = 2 \sinh^2 u + 1.$

$\sinh 2u = 2 \cosh u \sinh u.$

$\tanh 2u = \dfrac{2 \tanh u}{1 + \tanh^2 u}.$

$$\cosh \frac{u}{2} = \sqrt{\frac{\cosh u + 1}{2}}. \tag{2}$$

$\sinh \dfrac{u}{2} = \pm \sqrt{\dfrac{\cosh u - 1}{2}}.$

$\tanh \dfrac{u}{2} = \pm \sqrt{\dfrac{\cosh u - 1}{\cosh u + 1}} = \dfrac{\cosh u - 1}{\sinh u} = \dfrac{\sinh u}{\cosh u + 1}.$

$\cosh u + \cosh v = 2 \cosh \left(\dfrac{u + v}{2} \right) \cosh \left(\dfrac{u - v}{2} \right).$

$\cosh u - \cosh v = 2 \sinh \left(\dfrac{u + v}{2} \right) \sinh \left(\dfrac{u - v}{2} \right).$

$\sinh u \pm \sinh v = 2 \sinh \left(\dfrac{u \pm v}{2} \right) \cosh \left(\dfrac{u \mp v}{2} \right).$

$$D_x \cosh u = \sinh u \, D_x u.$$
$$D_x \sinh u = \cosh u \, D_x u.$$
$$D_x \tanh u = \operatorname{sech}^2 u \, D_x u.$$
$$D_x \operatorname{sech} u = - \operatorname{sech} u \tanh u \, D_x u. \tag{3}$$
$$D_x \operatorname{csch} u = - \operatorname{csch} u \operatorname{ctnh} u \, D_x u.$$
$$D_x \operatorname{ctnh} u = - \operatorname{csch}^2 u \, D_x u.$$

If $u = \cosh x$, then x is a function of u denoted by $x = \cosh^{-1} u$ and x is called the inverse hyperbolic cosine of u; if $u = \sinh x$, then $x = \sinh^{-1} u$; the other inverse hyperbolic functions are defined in a similar manner.

If $\quad x = \cosh^{-1} u$, $\quad$ then $\quad u = \cosh x = \dfrac{e^x + e^{-x}}{2}$. Hence

$u = \dfrac{(e^x)^2 + 1}{2e^x}$, $e^x = u \pm \sqrt{u^2 - 1}$, and $x = \log (u \pm \sqrt{u^2 - 1})$.

Thus $\cosh^{-1} u = \log (u \pm \sqrt{u^2 - 1})$, where $u \geqq 1$. Similar computations with the other inverse hyperbolic functions lead to the following results:

$$\cosh^{-1} u = \log (u \pm \sqrt{u^2 - 1}), \text{ where } u \geqq 1.$$

$$\sinh^{-1} u = \log (u + \sqrt{u^2 + 1}).$$

$$\tanh^{-1} u = \frac{1}{2} \log \frac{1 + u}{1 - u}, \text{ where } u^2 < 1.$$

$$\operatorname{sech}^{-1} u = \log \left(\frac{1}{u} \pm \sqrt{\frac{1}{u^2} - 1} \right), \text{ where } 0 < u \leqq 1. \quad (4)$$

$$\operatorname{csch}^{-1} u = \log \left(\frac{1}{u} + \sqrt{\frac{1}{u^2} + 1} \right).$$

$$\operatorname{ctnh}^{-1} u = \frac{1}{2} \log \frac{u + 1}{u - 1}, \text{ where } u^2 > 1.$$

The student will better understand the significance of the inverse hyperbolic functions if he will compute $\cosh [\log (u \pm \sqrt{u^2 - 1})]$, $\tanh \left(\dfrac{1}{2} \log \dfrac{1 + u}{1 - u} \right)$, etc., directly by (1). (Cf. Exs. I, 5 and 6, of Chap. I.)

The following formulas result directly from (4):

$$D_x \cosh^{-1} u = \frac{\pm 1}{\sqrt{u^2 - 1}} D_x u.$$

$$D_x \sinh^{-1} u = \frac{1}{\sqrt{u^2 + 1}} D_x u.$$

$$D_x \operatorname{sech}^{-1} u = \frac{\mp 1}{u\sqrt{1 - u^2}} D_x u. \quad (5)$$

$$D_x \operatorname{csch}^{-1} u = \frac{-1}{u\sqrt{1 + u^2}} D_x u.$$

$$D_x \tanh^{-1} u = \frac{1}{1 - u^2} D_x u = D_x \operatorname{ctnh}^{-1} u.$$

EXERCISES II

1. Prove formulas 16, 19 to 22 of Table II.
2. Using definitions (1) in Sec. 5, prove each of the identities (2).
3. Graph the functions in (1) and by means of these graphs sketch the graphs of the functions in (4).
4. Prove formulas (3), (4), and (5).
5. Construct a table of integrals for the hyperbolic functions to correspond to formulas 5 to 14 in Table II.
6. In Table II express each integral involving an inverse hyperbolic function in terms of the equivalent logarithm given in (4).
7. Show that

$$e^u = \cosh u + \sinh u, \qquad e^{-u} = \cosh u - \sinh u.$$

Evaluate:

8. $\displaystyle\int \frac{1}{\sqrt{5x^2 + 3}}\, dx.$ 9. $\displaystyle\int \frac{1}{\sqrt{x^2 - 4x + 1}}\, dx.$

10. $\displaystyle\int \frac{1}{x\sqrt{9x^2 - 18x + 14}}\, dx.$ 11. $\displaystyle\int \frac{1}{2 - 15x - 9x^2}\, dx.$

12. The circular trigonometric functions may be defined as follows:

$$\cos \theta = \frac{e^{i\theta} + e^{-i\theta}}{2}. \qquad \sec \theta = \frac{2}{e^{i\theta} + e^{-i\theta}}.$$

$$\sin \theta = \frac{e^{i\theta} - e^{-i\theta}}{2i}. \qquad \csc \theta = \frac{2i}{e^{i\theta} - e^{-i\theta}}. \qquad (6)$$

$$\tan \theta = \frac{e^{i\theta} - e^{-i\theta}}{i(e^{i\theta} + e^{-i\theta})}. \qquad \operatorname{ctn} \theta = \frac{i(e^{i\theta} + e^{-i\theta})}{e^{i\theta} - e^{-i\theta}}.$$

Assuming that formulas (6) hold for any complex number θ, show that

$$\begin{aligned}
\cosh (ix) &= \cos x, & \cos (ix) &= \cosh x, \\
\sinh (ix) &= i \sin x, & \sin (ix) &= i \sinh x, \\
\tanh (ix) &= i \tan x, & \tan (ix) &= i \tanh x.
\end{aligned} \qquad (7)$$

Show by (7) that the well-known trigonometric identities result when $u = ix$, $v = iy$ are substituted in (2). Show that

$$e^{i\theta} = \cos \theta + i \sin \theta, \qquad e^{-i\theta} = \cos \theta - i \sin \theta$$

Relation between Circular and Hyperbolic Geometry. The locus defined by the parametric equations

$$\begin{aligned}
x &= a \cos \theta, \\
y &= a \sin \theta,
\end{aligned} \qquad (8)$$

is the circle $x^2 + y^2 = a^2$. If $\theta = 0$, then $x_0 = a$ and $y_0 = 0$; if $\theta = \theta_1$, then $x_1 = a \cos \theta_1$ and $y_1 = a \sin \theta_1$. Let A and B be the points $(a, 0)$ and

(x_1, y_1).   The area K of the circular sector AOB is $K = (\theta_1/2)\,a^2$, where θ_1 is measured in radians.   Since $\theta_1 = \cos^{-1}(x_1/a)$, it follows that

$$\theta_1 = \frac{2K}{a^2} = \cos^{-1}\frac{x_1}{a}.$$

Hence, *if $a = 1$, the parameter θ in (8) is twice the area of the circular sector AOB.*

The locus defined by the parametric equations

$$\begin{aligned} x &= a\cosh u, \\ y &= a\sinh u, \end{aligned} \tag{9}$$

is one branch of the hyperbola $x^2 - y^2 = a^2$.   If $u = 0$, then $x_0 = a$ and $y_0 = 0$; if $u = u_1$, then $x_1 = a\cosh u_1$ and $y_1 = a\sinh u_1$.   Let A and B' be

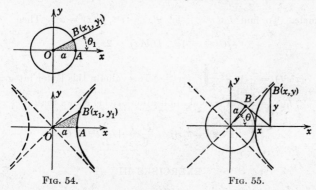

FIG. 54.   FIG. 55.

the points $(a, 0)$ and (x_1, y_1).   The area K of the hyperbolic sector AOB' can be shown by the methods of Sec. 13 below to be

$$K = \frac{a^2}{2}\log\left(\frac{x_1 + \sqrt{x_1^2 - a^2}}{a}\right) = \frac{a^2}{2}\cosh^{-1}\frac{x_1}{a}.$$

Since $u_1 = \cosh^{-1}\dfrac{x_1}{a}$, it follows that

$$u_1 = \frac{2K}{a^2} = \cosh^{-1}\frac{x_1}{a}.$$

Hence, *if $a = 1$, the parameter u in (9) is twice the area of the hyperbolic sector AOB'.*

The hyperbola $x^2 - y^2 = a^2$ may be represented parametrically as

$$\begin{aligned} x &= a\sec\theta, \\ y &= a\tan\theta, \end{aligned} \tag{10}$$

where θ is the same angle as in (8).   By (9) and (10) it follows that

$$\cosh u = \sec\theta, \qquad \sinh u = \tan\theta,$$

where $-\pi/2 < \theta < \pi/2$. From these relations and (1) it is seen that

$$\text{sech } u = \cos \theta, \qquad \text{csch } u = \text{ctn } \theta,$$
$$\tanh u = \sin \theta, \qquad \text{ctnh } u = \csc \theta.$$

The relation $\sinh u = \tan \theta$ determines θ as a function of u, i.e., $\theta = \text{Tan}^{-1} \sinh u$. This function is called the *gudermannian* of u and is denoted by $\theta = gd\ u$.

6. Integration by Parts. Formula (11) of Sec. 3 is called the formula for *integration by parts*. While we have already given an example to show the significance of this formula, we shall give another example to show how (11) may be repeatedly used to evaluate a given integral.

Example. To find $I_x (x^2 e^{3x})$, let $g(x) = e^{3x}$, $h(x) = x^2$. Then

$$G(x) = \tfrac{1}{3}e^{3x}, \ D_x h(x) = 2x,$$

and $\displaystyle I_x (x^2 e^{3x}) = \frac{x^2}{3}e^{3x} - \frac{2}{3} I_x (xe^{3x})$. To evaluate this latter integral, let $\bar{g}(x) = e^{3x}$, $\bar{h}(x) = x$. A second application of (11) shows that

$$I_x (x^2 e^{3x}) = \frac{x^2}{3}e^{3x} - \frac{2x}{9}e^{3x} + \frac{2}{27}e^{3x} + C.$$

EXERCISES III

Integrate:

1. $\displaystyle \int x \cos 2x\ dx.$

2. $\displaystyle \int \log(3x + 1)\ dx.$

3. $\displaystyle \int xe^{-5x}\ dx.$

4. $\displaystyle \int e^{4x} \sin 3x\ dx.$

5. $\displaystyle \int \frac{x^3}{\sqrt{4x^2 + 9}}\ dx.$

6. $\displaystyle \int x \sin x \cos x\ dx.$

7. $\displaystyle \int x^2 e^{ax}\ dx.$

8. $\displaystyle \int x \log 2x\ dx.$

9. $\displaystyle \int xe^x \sin(e^x)\ dx.$

10. $\displaystyle \int x^2 \sin \tfrac{3}{2}x\ dx.$

11. $\displaystyle \int x \tan^{-1} 3x\ dx.$

12. $\displaystyle \int \sec^3 x\ dx.$

13. $\displaystyle \int \cos^{-1} ax\ dx.$

14. $\displaystyle \int \frac{\log x}{x^2}\ dx.$

7. Integration of Rational Fractions. In this section we shall
develop a procedure for finding the integral of a rational fraction
$f(x)/g(x)$, where $f(x)$ and $g(x)$ are polynomials in x with $g(x) \neq 0$.
Since this method depends on certain properties of polynomials
and fractions, we shall begin with a résumé of these properties.

A *polynomial of degree n* in x is a function $P(x)$ of the form

$$P(x) = a_0 + a_1x + a_2x^2 + \cdots + a_nx^n, \tag{1}$$

where n is a nonnegative integer, a_0, a_1, $\cdots$, a_n are complex
numbers,* and $a_n \neq 0$. For example, $x^4 - 3x + 2$, $-5x$, and 7
are polynomials of degree 4, 1, and 0, respectively. We shall
regard 0 as a polynomial of degree 0. A polynomial $P(x)$ is
said to *vanish identically* $[P(x) \equiv 0]$ if it has the value 0 for
all complex values of x. Two polynomials $P_1(x)$ and $P_2(x)$ are
said to be *identically equal* $[P_1(x) \equiv P_2(x)]$ if their values are
equal for all complex values of x. It is evident that the sum, difference, and product of two polynomials are again polynomials.

A value r of x for which the value of $P(x)$ is 0 is called a *zero* of
$P(x)$ or a *solution* of the equation $P(x) = 0$. Thus, 3 is a zero
of $x^2 - 5x + 6$.

Theorem 7.1 *(Factor Theorem). Let $P(x)$ be a polynomial
$a_0 + a_1x + \cdots + a_nx^n$ of degree $n > 0$. If r is a zero of
$P(x)$, so that $P(r) = 0$, then $x - r$ is a factor of $P(x)$, that is,*

$$P(x) \equiv (x - r)Q(x), \tag{2}$$

where $Q(x)$ is a polynomial of degree $n - 1$.

Since $P(r) = 0$,

$$
\begin{aligned}
P(x) &\equiv P(x) - P(r) \\
&\equiv a_1(x - r) + a_2(x^2 - r^2) + \cdots + a_n(x^n - r^n),
\end{aligned} \tag{3}
$$

where $a_n \neq 0$. Each term of the right member of (3) has $x - r$
as a factor. [Cf. Chap. I, Sec. 5, formula (3).] Hence $x - r$ is a
factor of $P(x)$, and $P(x)$ may be written in the form (2). Since
the term of highest degree in $Q(x)$ is a_nx^{n-1} with $a_n \neq 0$, $Q(x)$
is of degree $n - 1$.

As an illustration of this theorem, we know that $x - 3$ is a
factor of $x^2 - 5x + 6$ because 3 is a zero of this polynomial.

---

* By a complex number we mean a number of the form $a + bi$, where
a and b are real numbers and $i^2 = -1$.

The converse of this theorem is also true, for if $x - r$ is a factor of $P(x)$, then $P(x)$ may be expressed in the form (2) and it is immediately evident that r is a zero of $P(x)$.

Theorem 7.2 (*Fundamental Theorem of Algebra*). *Every polynomial $P(x)$ of degree $n > 0$ has at least one zero.*

The proof of this theorem will be given in Chap. V.

Theorem 7.3. *If $P(x)$ is a polynomial*

$$a_0 + a_1 x + \cdots + a_n x^n$$

of degree $n > 0$, then there exists exactly one set of n complex numbers, $r_1, r_2, \cdots, r_n$ such that

$$P(x) \equiv a_n (x - r_1)(x - r_2) \cdots (x - r_n). \qquad (4)$$

By Theorem 7.2, $P(x)$ has at least one zero r_1, and by Theorem 7.1, $P(x) \equiv (x - r_1)Q(x)$. Repeated applications of Theorems 7.2 and 7.1 to $Q(x)$ lead to the result (4). Moreover, $P(x)$ cannot be factored in essentially any other way, for the right member of (4) shows that the *only* zeros of $P(x)$ are the numbers $r_1, \cdots, r_n$, and $x - r$ can be a factor of $P(x)$ only when r is a zero of $P(x)$ (converse of Theorem 7.1).

The numbers $r_1, \cdots, r_n$ of the preceding theorem need not all be distinct, as is illustrated by the polynomial $x^2 - 4x + 4$.

As an immediate consequence of Theorem 7.3 we have

Theorem 7.4. *A polynomial of degree $n > 0$ cannot have more than n distinct zeros.*

It follows from this theorem that if a polynomial $P(x)$ has the value 0 for all values of x, then this polynomial cannot be of positive degree, i.e., it must be merely a constant. This constant must evidently be 0. Hence we may state

Theorem 7.5. *A polynomial $P(x)$ vanishes identically when and only when all of its coefficients are zero.*

If two polynomials

$$a_0 + a_1 x + \cdots + a_m x^m \qquad \text{and} \qquad b_0 + b_1 x + \cdots + b_n x^n$$

are identically equal, then their difference vanishes identically. By Theorem 7.5, all the coefficients $a_0 - b_0$, $a_1 - b_1$, $\cdots$ in their difference are zero. Hence, corresponding coefficients of the two polynomials are equal. This proves

Theorem 7.6. *Two polynomials $a_0 + a_1 x + \cdots + a_m x^m$ and $b_0 + b_1 x + \cdots + b_n x^n$ are identically equal when and only when $m = n$ and $a_0 = b_0$, $a_1 = b_1$, $\cdots$, $a_m = b_m$.*

The two following theorems will be particularly useful:

THEOREM 7.7.   *Let $P(x)$ be a polynomial of degree $n > 0$ with real coefficients. If $r_1 = \alpha + \beta i$ is a zero of $P(x)$, where α and β are real numbers, then $r_2 = \alpha - \beta i$ is a zero of $P(x)$.*

In Eq. (1) set $x = \alpha + \beta i$. We may express the result in the form

$$P(\alpha + \beta i) = R(\alpha, \beta) + iS(\alpha, \beta), \tag{5}$$

where $R(\alpha, \beta)$ denotes the real part of $P(\alpha + \beta i)$ and where $S(\alpha, \beta)$ denotes the collected coefficient of i in $P(\alpha + \beta i)$ after $P(\alpha + \beta i)$ has been multiplied out and simplified. Since the coefficients of $P(x)$ are real, $R(\alpha, \beta)$ contains no odd powers of β and $S(\alpha, \beta)$ contains no even powers of β. Hence

$$P(\alpha - \beta i) = R(\alpha, \beta) - iS(\alpha, \beta). \tag{6}$$

If $x = \alpha + \beta i$ is a zero of $P(x)$, then $P(\alpha + \beta i) = 0$. By (5), $R(\alpha, \beta) = S(\alpha, \beta) = 0$. By (6), $P(\alpha - \beta i) = 0$, so that $\alpha - \beta i$ is a zero of $P(x)$.

THEOREM 7.8.   *If $P(x)$ is a polynomial of degree $n > 0$ with real coefficients, then $P(x)$ can be written as the product of linear and quadratic factors, where each factor has real coefficients and where no quadratic factor is factorable into linear factors with real coefficients, i.e.,*

$$P(x) \equiv a_n(x - r_1)(x - r_2) \cdots (x - r_k)(x^2 + c_1x + d_1)$$
$$(x^2 + c_2x + d_2) \cdots (x^2 + c_lx + d_l), \tag{7}$$

where $k + 2l = n$.

To each real zero $r_1, \cdots, r_k$ of $P(x)$ corresponds a real factor $(x - r_1), \cdots, (x - r_k)$ of $P(x)$ in (4). If $\alpha + \beta i$ is a zero of $P(x)$ with $\beta \neq 0$, then by Theorem 7.7, $\alpha - \beta i$ is another zero of $P(x)$, and the product

$$[x - (\alpha + \beta i)][x - (\alpha - \beta i)] \equiv x^2 - 2\alpha x + \alpha^2 + \beta^2$$

has real coefficients. Thus all factors in (4) having complex r's combine in pairs to give real quadratic factors of $P(x)$, and $P(x)$ reduces to the form (7).

We are now ready to take up the integration of rational fractions. A function of x is called a *rational fraction* if it is expressible as the ratio $f(x)/g(x)$ of two polynomials $f(x)$ and $g(x)$ with $g(x) \neq 0$. If the degree of $f(x)$ is less than the degree of

$g(x)$, then the fraction $f(x)/g(x)$ is called *proper;* otherwise the fraction is called *improper.* For example,

$$\frac{3x^2 + 7x + 1}{5x^3 - 9}$$

is a proper fraction, and

$$\frac{x^2 + x}{3x^2 - 1} \quad \text{and} \quad \frac{x^3 - 1}{x^2 + 2x + 4}$$

are improper fractions. If $f(x)$ and $g(x)$ have no common factor (other than a constant), then the fraction $f(x)/g(x)$ is said to be in *lowest terms.*

It is well known that by the process of long division every rational fraction $F(x)/g(x)$ can be expressed in the form

$$\frac{F(x)}{g(x)} \equiv P(x) + \frac{f(x)}{g(x)},$$

where $P(x)$ is a polynomial and where $f(x)/g(x)$ is proper. $[P(x) \equiv 0$ if $F(x)/g(x)$ is already proper.] Hence, *to evaluate* $\int \frac{F(x)}{g(x)}\, dx$ *when the integrand is a rational fraction, reduce the integrand to lowest terms, and if the integrand is improper, express the integral in the form*

$$\int \frac{F(x)}{g(x)}\, dx \equiv \int P(x)\, dx + \int \frac{f(x)}{g(x)}\, dx, \tag{8}$$

where $P(x)$ is a polynomial and where $f(x)/g(x)$ is proper.

We shall now show how the third integral in (8) may be evaluated by breaking up the fraction $f(x)/g(x)$ into a sum of simpler fractions called *partial fractions.*

THEOREM 7.9. *Let $f(x)/g(x)$ be a proper fraction. If $g(x)$ contains the factor $x - r$ exactly m times, so that*

$$g(x) \equiv (x - r)^m Q(x),$$

where $m \geqq 1$ and $Q(r) \neq 0$, then $f(x)/g(x)$ may be represented in the form

$$\frac{f(x)}{g(x)} \equiv \frac{A}{(x - r)^m} + \frac{h(x)}{(x - r)^{m-1}Q(x)}, \tag{9}$$

where A is a constant, $h(x)$ is a polynomial, and the last fraction *in* (9) *is proper. Moreover. A and* $h(x)$ *can be determined in exactly one way.*

Consider the identity

$$\frac{f(x)}{g(x)} \equiv \frac{A}{(x-r)^m} + \frac{f(x) - AQ(x)}{(x-r)^m Q(x)},\qquad(10)$$

where A is a constant to be determined. By Theorem **7.1** and its converse, the numerator $f(x) - AQ(x)$ has $(x - r)$ as a factor if and only if $f(r) - AQ(r) = 0$. Since $Q(r) \neq 0$, the preceding relation holds when and only when we take $A = f(r)/Q(r)$. Hence, when A is determined in this way, but in no other way, the factor $(x - r)$ may be divided out of the last fraction in (10) and (9) results. [Note that if $f(x)$ also has the factor $x - r$, then $f(r) = 0$ and $A = 0$. Thus the operation (9) merely removes the common factor $x - r$ from $f(x)$ and $g(x)$.]

It follows that if the operation (9) is performed on the fraction $\dfrac{h(x)}{(x-r)^{m-1}Q(x)}$, the result is that

$$\frac{h(x)}{(x-r)^{m-1}Q(x)} \equiv \frac{B}{(x-r)^{m-1}} + \frac{k(x)}{(x-r)^{m-2}R(x)}.$$

Hence, if the operation (9) is repeatedly performed, we find that

$$\frac{f(x)}{g(x)} \equiv \frac{A_{11}}{(x-r_1)^{m_1}} + \frac{A_{12}}{(x-r_1)^{m_1-1}} + \cdots + \frac{A_{1,m}}{x-r_1}$$
$$+ \frac{A_{21}}{(x-r_2)^{m_2}} + \cdots + \frac{A_{2,m_2}}{x-r_2} + \cdots + \frac{A_{k1}}{(x-r_k)^{m_k}}$$
$$+ \cdots + \frac{A_{k,m_k}}{x-r_k} + \frac{f_1(x)}{g_1(x)},\qquad(11)$$

where $g_1(x)$ contains no real linear factor. Since the successive coefficients A_{ij} are uniquely determined, $f(x)/g(x)$ has only one expression of this sort. Moreover, the order in which $r_1, r_2, \cdots, r_k$ are chosen is immaterial. For example, suppose r_2 had been taken first. If we add all the fractions in the right member of (11) except $A_{21}/(x - r_2)^{m_2}$, we find that

$$\frac{f(x)}{g(x)} \equiv \frac{A_{21}}{(x-r_2)^{m_2}} + \frac{h_1(x)}{(x-r_2)^{m_2-1}Q_1(x)}.$$

Since this result is of the form (9), A_{21} must be the number given by (9).

Example 1.   Resolve $\dfrac{x}{(x-2)^2(x+3)}$ into partial fractions.

By (10), $\dfrac{x}{(x-2)^2(x+3)} = \dfrac{A}{(x-2)^2} + \dfrac{x-A(x+3)}{(x-2)^2(x+3)}$, where $f(x) = x$

and $Q(x) = x + 3$.   But $A = \dfrac{f(2)}{Q(2)} = \dfrac{2}{5}$.   Hence

$$\frac{x}{(x-2)^2(x+3)} = \frac{\frac{2}{5}}{(x-2)^2} + \frac{\frac{3}{5}(x-2)}{(x-2)^2(x+3)}$$

$$= \frac{2}{5(x-2)^2} + \frac{3}{5}\frac{1}{(x-2)(x+3)}.$$

Another application of this procedure shows that

$$\frac{1}{(x-2)(x+3)} = \frac{1}{5}\left(\frac{1}{x-2} - \frac{1}{x+3}\right).$$

Hence

$$\frac{x}{(x-2)^2(x+3)} = \frac{2}{5(x-2)^2} + \frac{3}{25(x-2)} - \frac{3}{25(x+3)}.$$

THEOREM 7.10.   *Let* $f(x)/g(x)$ *be a proper fraction. If* $g(x)$ *contains the factor* $x^2 + cx + d$ *exactly* m *times, so that*

$$g(x) \equiv (x^2 + cx + d)^m Q(x),$$

where $x^2 + cx + d$ *does not have equal zeros,* $m \geq 1$, *and* $Q(r) \neq 0$ *when* r *is either zero of* $x^2 + cx + d$, *then* $f(x)/g(x)$ *may be represented in the form*

$$\frac{f(x)}{g(x)} \equiv \frac{Ax+B}{(x^2+cx+d)^m} + \frac{h(x)}{(x^2+cx+d)^{m-1}Q(x)}, \qquad (12)$$

where A *and* B *are constants, and the last fraction in* (12) *is proper. Moreover,* A, B, *and* $h(x)$ *can be determined in exactly one way.*

Consider the identity

$$\frac{f(x)}{g(x)} \equiv \frac{Ax+B}{(x^2+cx+d)^m} + \frac{f(x)-(Ax+B)\,Q(x)}{(x^2+cx+d)^m\,Q(x)}, \qquad (13)$$

where A and B are constants to be determined.   Let r_1 and r_2 be the distinct zeros of $x^2 + cx + d$.   By Theorem 7.1, the numerator $f(x) - (Ax+B)\,Q(x)$ has $x^2 + cx + d$ as a factor if and only if

$$f(r_1) - (Ar_1 + B) Q(r_1) = 0,$$
$$f(r_2) - (Ar_2 + B) Q(r_2) = 0.$$

The only solution of these equations is

$$A = \frac{f(r_1) Q(r_2) - f(r_2) Q(r_1)}{(r_1 - r_2) Q(r_1) Q(r_2)}, \quad B = \frac{r_1 Q(r_1) f(r_2) - r_2 Q(r_2) f(r_1)}{(r_1 - r_2) Q(r_1) Q(r_2)},$$

where the denominators of A and B are $\neq 0$ because $Q(r_1) \neq 0$, $Q(r_2) \neq 0$, and $r_1 \neq r_2$. Hence, when A and B are determined in this way, the factor $x^2 + cx + d$ may be divided out of the last fraction in (13) and (12) results.

It should be noted that $x^2 + cx + d$ has distinct zeros when it is one of the factors in (7), for

$$x^2 + cx + d \equiv [x - (\alpha + \beta i)][x - (\alpha - \beta i)]$$

with $\beta \neq 0$. Moreover, A and B are real, for let

$$f(r_1) = R_1(\alpha, \beta) + iS_1(\alpha, \beta), \quad Q(r_1) = R_2(\alpha, \beta) + iS_2(\alpha, \beta),$$

where $r_1 = \alpha + \beta i$. Then

$$f(r_2) = f(\alpha - \beta i) = R_1(\alpha, \beta) - iS_1(\alpha, \beta)$$

and $Q(r_2) = R_2(\alpha, \beta) - iS_2(\alpha, \beta)$. Since

$$(r_1 - r_2)A = \frac{f(r_1)}{Q(r_1)} - \frac{f(r_2)}{Q(r_2)},$$
$$2i\beta A = \frac{R_1 + iS_1}{R_2 + iS_2} - \frac{R_1 - iS_1}{R_2 - iS_2} = \frac{2i(R_2 S_1 - R_1 S_2)}{R_2^2 + S_2^2}.$$

Since i divides out, and R_1, S_1, R_2, S_2, and β are real with $\beta \neq 0$, A is real. It may be shown in a similar manner that B is real.

By Theorem 7.8, $g_1(x)$ in (11) may be broken up into quadratic factors as in (7). Hence the operation (12) may be repeatedly applied to $f_1(x)/g_1(x)$ in (11) with the result that

$$\frac{f(x)}{g(x)} \equiv \frac{A_{11}}{(x - r_1)^{m_1}} + \frac{A_{12}}{(x - r_1)^{m_1-1}} + \cdots + \frac{A_{1,m_1}}{x - r_1}$$

$$+ \cdots + \frac{A_{k1}}{(x - r_k)^{m_k}} + \cdots + \frac{A_{k,m_k}}{x - r_k} + \frac{B_{11}x + C_{11}}{(x^2 + c_1 x + d_1)^{n_1}}$$

$$+ \frac{B_{12}x + C_{12}}{(x^2 + c_1 x + d_1)^{n_1-1}} + \cdots + \frac{B_{1,n_1}x + C_{1,n_1}}{x^2 + c_1 x + d_1}$$

$$+ \cdots + \frac{B_{l1}x + C_{l1}}{(x^2 + c_l x + d_l)^{n_l}} + \cdots + \frac{B_{l,n_l}x + C_{l,n_l}}{x^2 + c_l x + d_l}. \tag{14}$$

This representation of $f(x)/g(x)$ is evidently the only possible one.

The coefficients A_{ij}, B_{ij}, and C_{ij} in (14) may be determined in three ways: (1) By the method indicated in the proofs of Theorems 7.9 and 7.10. (2) By clearing (14) of fractions, equating the coefficients of like powers of x (by virtue of Theorem 7.6), and solving the resulting equations. (3) By clearing (14) of fractions, substituting for x as many different values as there are unknown coefficients, and solving the resulting equations.

After the coefficients in (14) are determined, $\displaystyle\int \frac{f(x)}{g(x)}\, dx$ may be found as the sum of the integrals of the separate fractions in the right member of (14). All of these integrals may be evaluated by the methods discussed in the preceding sections together with the formulas

$$\int \frac{1}{(ax^2 + bx + c)^{n+1}}\, dx = \frac{2ax + b}{n(4ac - b^2)(ax^2 + bx + c)^n}$$
$$+ \frac{2(2n - 1)a}{n(4ac - b^2)} \int \frac{1}{(ax + bx + c)^n}\, dx.$$

$$\int \frac{x}{(ax^2 + bx + c)^{n+1}}\, dx = \frac{-(2c + bx)}{n(4ac - b^2)(ax^2 + bx + c)^n}$$
$$- \frac{b(2n - 1)}{n(4ac - b^2)} \int \frac{1}{(ax^2 + bx + c)^n}\, dx.$$

Examination of the results of these integrations leads us to

Theorem 7.11. *Every rational fraction $f(x)/g(x)$ with real coefficients may be integrated and the integral consists of the sum of only rational fractions, logarithms of rational fractions, and inverse tangents of rational fractions.*

Example 2. Find $\displaystyle\int \frac{2}{x^2 - 2x}\, dx.$

Since $x^2 - 2x = x(x - 2)$, we may write

$$\frac{2}{x^2 - 2x} \equiv \frac{A}{x} + \frac{B}{x - 2}.$$

Clearing of fractions, we find that

$$2 \equiv A(x - 2) + Bx. \tag{15}$$

To determine A and B by equating coefficients, we first collect like powers of x, obtaining

$$2 \equiv (A + B)x - 2A,$$

and then we set

$$A + B = 0, \qquad -2A = 2.$$

It follows that $A = -1$, $B = 1$. Or we may determine A and B by substituting two different values of x in (15), the values 2 and 0 being the most convenient since they make one or the other of the coefficients of A and B equal to 0. We find that

$$2 = 2B, \qquad 2 = -2A,$$

and as before, $A = -1$, $B = 1$. Hence

$$\int \frac{2}{x^2 - 2x}\, dx = \int \frac{-1}{x}\, dx + \int \frac{1}{x - 2}\, dx$$

$$= -\log x + \log (x - 2) + \log C = \log \frac{C(x - 2)}{x}.$$

Example 3. Find $\displaystyle \int \frac{2x^2 + 8x - 4}{x^2(x - 2)}\, dx.$

We may write

$$\frac{2x^2 + 8x - 4}{x^2(x - 2)} \equiv \frac{A}{x^2} + \frac{B}{x} + \frac{C}{x - 2}.$$

Hence

$$2x^2 + 8x - 4 \equiv A(x - 2) + Bx(x - 2) + Cx^2 \qquad (16)$$
$$\equiv (B + C)x^2 + (A - 2B)x - 2A,$$

and

$$B + C = 2, \qquad A - 2B = 8, \qquad -2A = -4,$$

so that $A = 2$, $B = -3$, $C = 5$. Thus

$$\int \frac{2x^2 + 8x - 4}{x^2(x - 2)}\, dx = \int \frac{2}{x^2}\, dx + \int \frac{-3}{x}\, dx + \int \frac{5}{x - 2}\, dx$$

$$= -\frac{2}{x} - 3 \log x + 5 \log (x - 2) + C$$

$$= -\frac{2}{x} + \log \frac{(x - 2)^5}{x^3} + C.$$

We might have determined A, B, and C in (16) by setting x equal to 2, 0, and some other value, say 1.

Example 4. Find $\displaystyle \int \frac{x^4 - 2x^3 + 3x^2 - 2x + 1}{x(x^2 + 1)^2}\, dx.$

We may write

$$\frac{x^4 - 2x^3 + 3x^2 - 2x + 1}{x(x^2 + 1)^2} \equiv \frac{A}{x} + \frac{Bx + C}{(x^2 + 1)^2} + \frac{Dx + E}{x^2 + 1}.$$

Hence

$$x^4 - 2x^3 + 3x^2 - 2x + 1 \equiv A(x^2 + 1)^2 + x(Bx + C) + x(x^2 + 1)(Dx + E).$$

We leave it to the student to show that $A = B = 1$, $C = D = 0$, $E = -2$. It follows that

$$\int \frac{x^4 - 2x^3 + 3x^2 - 2x + 1}{x(x^2 + 1)^2} \, dx = \int \frac{1}{x} \, dx + \int \frac{x}{(x^2 + 1)^2} \, dx + \int \frac{-2}{x^2 + 1} \, dx$$

$$= \log x - \frac{1}{2(x^2 + 1)} - 2 \operatorname{Tan}^{-1} x + C.$$

EXERCISES IV

Evaluate:

1. $\displaystyle\int \frac{dx}{x^3 + 8}.$

2. $\displaystyle\int \frac{dx}{a^2 - b^2 x^2}.$

3. $\displaystyle\int \frac{(2x^3 + x + 3)}{(x^2 + 1)^2} \, dx.$

4. $\displaystyle\int \frac{4 \, dx}{x^3 + 4x}.$

5. $\displaystyle\int \frac{x^3 + 1}{x(x - 1)^3} \, dx.$

6. $\displaystyle\int \frac{x^2 - 2x}{(x - 1)(x^2 + 1)^2} \, dx.$

7. $\displaystyle\int \frac{e^{2x} \, dx}{e^x + 1}.$

8. $\displaystyle\int \frac{5x^2 - 1}{(x^2 + 3)(x^2 - 2x + 5)} \, dx.$

9. $\displaystyle\int \frac{2(x - b)}{(x - p)^2 + q} \, dx.$

10. $\displaystyle\int \frac{2x + 3}{x^3 + x^2 - 2x} \, dx.$

11. $\displaystyle\int \frac{4 - 8x^2}{(4x^2 - 4x + 2)^2} \, dx.$

12. $\displaystyle\int \frac{2 + x^2 - 5x}{x^4 - 5x^2 + 4} \, dx.$

13. $\displaystyle\int \frac{x^2 + 3x + 3}{2x^3 + 5x^2 - 3x} \, dx.$

14. $\displaystyle\int \frac{1}{(9x^2 - 16)^2} \, dx.$

15. $\displaystyle\int \frac{dx}{(x - a)^m}, \; m \geq 1.$

16. $\displaystyle\int \frac{Bx + C}{x^2 + px + q} \, dx, \; p^2 - 4q < 0.$

17. $\displaystyle\int \frac{(Bx + C) \, dx}{(x^2 + px + q)^m}, \; m > 1, \; p^2 - 4q < 0.$

8. Integration by Substitution. To integrate by substitution we change the variable of integration by means of formula (8) in Sec. 3 (see Example 4 following this formula). While there is no general rule for determining $x = \varphi(u)$ in (8), we list below a few substitutions which are effective in certain cases.

Let $R(\alpha, \beta)$ be a rational fraction in α and β (i.e., the ratio of two polynomials in α and β). Then, for example, $R(\cos^2 x, \sin x)$

denotes the result of substituting $\alpha = \cos^2 x$, $\beta = \sin x$ in $R(\alpha, \beta)$. In particular, if $R(\alpha, \beta) = \dfrac{\alpha^2 - \beta}{2\beta^3}$, then

$$R(\cos^2 x, \sin x) = \frac{\cos^4 x - \sin x}{2 \sin^3 x}.$$

To integrate:

1. $\displaystyle\int \cos x \, R(\cos^2 x, \sin x) \, dx$; let $\sin x = z$, obtaining

$$\int R(1 - z^2, z) \, dz.$$

2. $\displaystyle\int \sin x \, R(\sin^2 x, \cos x) \, dx$; let $\cos x = z$, obtaining

$$-\int R(1 - z^2, z) \, dz.$$

3. $\displaystyle\int R(\sin x, \cos x) \, dx$; let $\tan \dfrac{x}{2} = z$, obtaining

$$\int R\left(\frac{2z}{1 + z^2}, \frac{1 - z^2}{1 + z^2}\right) \cdot \frac{2}{1 + z^2} \, dz.$$

4. $\displaystyle\int R(\tan x) \, dx$; let $\tan x = z$, obtaining $\displaystyle\int \frac{R(z)}{1 + z^2} \, dz$.

5. $\displaystyle\int R(x, \sqrt{a^2 - x^2}) \, dx$; let $x = a \sin z$, obtaining

$$\int R(a \sin z, a \cos z) \, a \cos z \, dz.$$

6. $\displaystyle\int R(x, \sqrt{a^2 + x^2}) \, dx$; let $x = a \tan z$, obtaining

$$\int R(a \tan z, a \sec z) \, a \sec^2 z \, dz.$$

7. $\displaystyle\int R(x, \sqrt{x^2 - a^2}) \, dx$; let $x = a \sec z$, obtaining

$$\int R(a \sec z, a \tan z) \, a \sec z \tan z \, dz.$$

These formulas all follow immediately from (8) in Sec. 3.   For example, if $\sin x = z$, then $D_x z = \cos x$, $D_z x = 1/\cos x$, and

$$\int \cos x \, R(\cos^2 x, \sin x) \, dx = \int \cos x \, R(\cos^2 x, \sin x) D_z x \, dz$$
$$= \int R(1 - z^2, z) \, dz.$$

In the above formulas, the substitution is made in such a way as to rationalize the integrand.   The principle of rationalizing the integrand often leads to the proper substitution.   For example, to evaluate $\displaystyle\int \frac{1}{\sqrt{x} + 1} \, dx$, let $\sqrt{x} = z$.   Then $x = z^2$, $D_z x = 2z$, and

$$\int \frac{1}{\sqrt{x} + 1} \, dx = \int \frac{1}{z + 1} 2z \, dz = 2 \int \left(1 - \frac{1}{z + 1}\right) dz$$
$$= 2[z - \log (z + 1)] + C$$
$$= 2[\sqrt{x} - \log (\sqrt{x} + 1)] + C.$$

Sometimes a purely artificial substitution is helpful, such as $x = \dfrac{1}{z}$ in $\displaystyle\int \frac{\sqrt{1 - x^2}}{x^4} \, dx$.   In all but the simplest cases, the only recourse is initiative and resourcefulness.

EXERCISES V

1. $\displaystyle\int \frac{dx}{(1 + x)^{3/2} + (1 + x)^{1/2}}.$

2. $\displaystyle\int \frac{x^3 \, dx}{(5 + 7x^2)^{3/2}}.$

3. $\displaystyle\int \frac{\sqrt{a^2 - x^2}}{x^4} \, dx.$

4. $\displaystyle\int \frac{dx}{x(16x^2 + 9)^{5/2}}.$

5. $\displaystyle\int \frac{dx}{x\sqrt{a^2 x^2 - b^2}}.$

6. $\displaystyle\int \frac{x \, dx}{\sqrt{4x - x^2}}.$

7. $\displaystyle\int \frac{\sqrt{9x^2 - 1}}{x} \, dx.$

8. $\displaystyle\int \sqrt{3 - 4x - 4x^2} \, dx.$

9. $\displaystyle\int \sqrt{a^2 - b^2 x^2} \, dx.$

10. $\displaystyle\int \frac{dx}{(16x^2 + 9)^{5/2}}.$

11. $\displaystyle\int \sqrt{1 + \cos 3x} \, dx.$

12. $\displaystyle\int \frac{a + b \sin x}{\cos^2 x} \, dx.$

13. $\displaystyle\int \frac{dx}{\sqrt{2x(1 - 2x)}}.$

14. $\displaystyle\int \sqrt{\frac{9 - 2x}{9 + 2x}} \, dx.$

15. $\displaystyle\int \frac{1 + \cos x}{\cos x(1 + \sin x)} \, dx.$

16. $\displaystyle\int \frac{x^{3/2} - x^{1/3}}{6x^{1/4}} \, dx.$

17. $\int \dfrac{dx}{(3x + 1)^{\frac{2}{3}} - (3x + 1)^{\frac{1}{2}}}$.

18. $\int \dfrac{x^{\frac{2}{3}} - x^{\frac{1}{4}}}{1 + x^{\frac{1}{2}}}\, dx$.

19. $\int \dfrac{\log^2 x\, dx}{x^{\frac{5}{2}}}$.

20. $\int \dfrac{dx}{a + b \cos x}$, $a^2 \neq b^2$.

21. $\int \dfrac{dx}{a + b \sin x}$, $a^2 \neq b^2$.

22. $\int \dfrac{dx}{a + b \cos x + c \sin x}$.

[22. Hint: $b \cos x + c \sin x = A \cos (x - \alpha)$, where $\tan \alpha = b/c$, $A = \sqrt{b^2 + c^2}$.]

23. $\int \tan^2 3x\, dx$.

24. $\int \dfrac{\cos x\, dx}{1 + \cos^2 x}$.

Develop a method for integrating:

25. $\int R(x, \sqrt{ax^2 + bx + c})\, dx$.

26. $\int R(x, \sqrt{ax + b}, \sqrt{cx + d})\, dx$.

27. Evaluate $\int \dfrac{dx}{(8 + 12x + 5x^2)\sqrt{2x^2 + 6x + 5}}$.

9. Integration by Tables. The indefinite integrals of many functions have been tabulated. The reader may utilize the preceding sets of exercises to obtain practice in the use of a table of integrals.

No table can give the integrals of all functions. In fact, there are many functions whose integrals can not be expressed in terms of the elementary functions with which the reader is familiar. Thus, there exists no way to represent $\int \dfrac{dx}{\sqrt{(1 - x^2)(1 - 9x^2)}}$ in terms of "elementary functions." Integrals of this sort will be studied later on.

10. The Symbol $I_x f(x)]_a^b$. We define the symbol $F(x)]_a^b$ by the formula

$$F(x)\Big]_a^b = F(b) - F(a), \qquad (1)$$

where $F(x)$ is any function of x defined at $x = a$ and $x = b$.

If $F(x)$ and $G(x)$ are any two integrals of a function $f(x)$ meeting the conditions of Theorem 2.1, then

$$F(x)\Big]_a^b = G(x)\Big]_a^b$$

since there exists a number C_0 such that $G(x) \equiv F(x) + C_0$ and since $G(b) - G(a) = [F(b) + C_0] - [F(a) + C_0] = F(b) - F(a)$.

Thus the number $F(x)]_a^b$ is the same for every integral $F(x)$ of $f(x)$.

DEFINITION 10.1. *If $f(x)$ meets the conditions of Theorem 2.1, then we define the symbol $I_x f(x)]_a^b$ by the relation*

$$I_x f(x) \Big]_a^b = F(x) \Big]_a^b = F(b) - F(a), \tag{2}$$

where $F(x)$ is any integral of $f(x)$.

In view of the relation between the symbol $I_x f(x)]_a^b$ and the definite integral of $f(x)$ defined in Sec. 13, page 207 it is customary to use the notation $\int_a^b f(x)\,dx$ instead of $I_x f(x)]_a^b$.

Example. $\displaystyle\int_1^4 x^2\,dx = \frac{x^3}{3}\Big]_1^4 = \frac{64}{3} - \frac{1}{3} = 21.$ The preceding discussion

is illustrated by the fact that we may also write

$$\int_1^4 x^2\,dx = \left(\frac{x^3}{3} + 17\right)\Big]_1^4 = 21.$$

If $x = \varphi(u)$, where $u = \alpha$ when $x = a$ and $u = \beta$ when $x = b$, then it follows by (8) of Sec. 3 that

$$\int_a^b f(x)\,dx = \int_\alpha^\beta [f(x)\,D_u x]\,du = \int_\alpha^\beta \{f[\varphi(u)]D_u\varphi(u)\}\,du. \tag{3}$$

EXERCISES VI

Evaluate:

1. $\displaystyle\int_2^3 \left(\sqrt{x} - \frac{1}{\sqrt{x}}\right)dx.$

2. $\displaystyle\int_0^1 \frac{e^x\,dx}{1 + e^x}.$

3. $\displaystyle\int_0^{\pi/2} \cos^2 x\,dx.$

4. $\displaystyle\int_0^2 x\cos \pi x\,dx.$

5. $\displaystyle\int_{-\frac{1}{2}}^{\frac{1}{2}} \frac{dx}{\sqrt{1 - x^2}}.$

6. $\displaystyle\int_{-\alpha}^{2\alpha} \frac{dx}{\alpha^2 + x^2}.$

7. Why are the symbols $\displaystyle\int_{-1}^1 x^{-\frac{1}{3}}\,dx$ and $\displaystyle\int_0^\pi \sec^2 x\,dx$ meaningless?

11. The Indefinite Integrals of a Function of Several Variables. The concept of an indefinite integral may be extended to functions of several variables. We say that a real single-valued function $F(x, y)$ is *an integral with respect to x* of a function $f(x, y)$ if $\dfrac{\partial F(x, y)}{\partial x} = f(x, y)$. An integral of $f(x, y)$ with respect to y

is defined in a similar manner.   We say that $f(x, y)$ is *integrable* with respect to x (or y) if $f(x, y)$ has at least one integral with respect to x (or y).

If $f(x, y) = x/\sqrt{1 - x^2 - y^2}$, this function being defined only when $x^2 + y^2 < 1$, i.e., only inside the circle $x^2 + y^2 = 1$, then an integral of $f(x, y)$ with respect to x is the function

$$F(x, y) = -\sqrt{1 - x^2 - y^2} + \cos y + 3 \text{ since } \frac{\partial F(x, y)}{\partial x} = f(x, y).$$

Other integrals of $f(x, y)$ may be constructed by extending $F(x, y)$ in a nondifferentiable manner as in Sec. 2.   However, we shall consider only those integrals of a function $f(x, y)$ which have the same domain of definition as $f(x, y)$.

DEFINITION 11.1.   *We denote an arbitrary integral of $f(x, y)$ with respect to x [having the same domain of definition as $f(x, y)$] by $\int f(x, y)\ \partial x$, and we call $\int f(x, y)\ \partial x$ the indefinite integral of $f(x, y)$ with respect to x.*

The indefinite integral of $f(x, y)$ with respect to y is similarly defined.

Before we state the fundamental formula for representing indefinite integrals, we must introduce a concept which will be used again in Part B of this chapter.

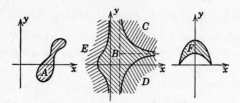

Fig. 56.

An *x-axial* region R of the xy-plane is a portion of the xy-plane such that, if l is any line meeting R and parallel to the x-axis, the part of l in R consists of a single interval, finite or infinite in length.   The term *y-axial* is similarly defined.   If R is both x-axial and y-axial, then R is called *axial*.   Thus, in Fig. 56, A, B, C, and D are axial, but E and F are not axial, though E is x-axial and F is y-axial.

THEOREM 11.1.   *Let $f(x, y)$ be a function integrable with respect to x whose domain of definition is an x-axial region D.   If $F(x, y)$ is any integral with respect to x of $f(x, y)$, then*

$$\int f(x, y) \, \partial x = F(x, y) + \varphi(y), \tag{1}$$

where $\varphi(y)$ is an arbitrary function of y defined over D, and where (1) *is to be interpreted as asserting that any integral whatever of* $f(x, y)$ *with respect to* x *is representable as* $F(x, y) + \varphi(y)$ *by a proper choice of* $\varphi(y)$.

It is seen that all the functions represented by the formula $F(x, y) + \varphi(y)$ are integrals of $f(x, y)$, for $\dfrac{\partial F(x, y)}{\partial x} = f(x, y)$ and $\dfrac{\partial \varphi(y)}{\partial x} = 0$ whatever $\varphi(y)$ may be. To show that the formula $F(x, y) + \varphi(y)$ represents *all* integrals of $f(x, y)$ [having the same domain of definition as $f(x, y)$], let $G(x, y)$ be any integral of $f(x, y)$ and let $y = y_0$ be the equation of any line l meeting D and parallel to the x-axis. Since D is x-axial, the part of l in D consists of a single interval I. Since

$$D_x F(x, y_0) \equiv D_x G(x, y_0)$$

in I, it follows by Theorem 10.3 and Ex. XI, 5 of Chap. I that $G(x, y_0) \equiv F(x, y_0) + C$. Since this result holds for each line $y = y_0$, C has a definite value for each value y_0 of y. Hence C is a function of y, say $C = H(y)$, and we may write

$$G(x, y_0) \equiv F(x, y_0) + H(y_0).$$

It follows that $G(x, y) \equiv F(x, y) + H(y)$, where $H(y)$ is a particular instance of $\varphi(y)$. Since $G(x, y)$ is an arbitrary integral of $f(x, y)$, (1) holds.

A similar theorem holds for $\int f(x, y) \, \partial y$. Thus,

$$\int \frac{x}{\sqrt{1 - x^2 - y^2}} \, \partial x = -\sqrt{1 - x^2 - y^2} + \varphi(y);$$

$$\int \frac{y}{\sqrt{1 - x^2 - y^2}} \, \partial y = -\sqrt{1 - x^2 - y^2} + \psi(x).$$

These integrals are computed by formula 1 of Table II while treating y or x as numerical constants. In general, $\int f(x, y) \, \partial x$ and $\int f(x, y) \, \partial y$ are evaluated by regarding x and y as independent; the methods of the preceding sections apply since the integrand is treated as a function of only one variable.

The discussion in Sec. 2 regarding different representations of $I_x f(x)$ may be extended to the present situation.

The following example illustrates the fact that Theorem 11.1 is false when the region D is not x-axial. Let D be the non-x-axial region consisting of the two squares shown in Fig. 57 and let $f(x, y) = 0$ at every point in D. One integral of $f(x, y)$ with respect to x is the function $F(x, y)$ such that $F(x, y) = 1$ at every point in D, $F(x, y)$ being defined nowhere else. Another integral is the function $G(x, y)$ such that

$$G(x, y) = \begin{cases} 3 \text{ at every point } (x, y) \text{ in } D \text{ for which } x < 0, \\ y \text{ at every point } (x, y) \text{ in } D \text{ for which } x > 0. \end{cases}$$

It is impossible to determine a function $\varphi(y)$ such that, for the entire region D, $G(x, y) = F(x, y) + \varphi(y)$. Hence it is not the case that $\int f(x, y) \, \partial x = F(x, y) + \varphi(y)$.

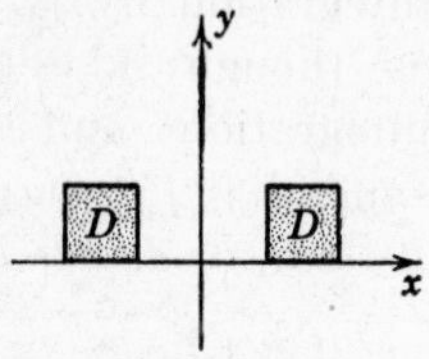

Properties I to V in Sec. 3 may be readily extended to functions of two variables.

In contrast with the symbol $\int f(x, y) \, \partial x$, we introduce the symbol $\int f(x, y) \, dx$ in

DEFINITION 11.2. *If y is a function of x, say* $y = q(x)$, *then $\int f(x, y) \, dx$ is defined by the relation*

FIG. 57.

$$\int f(x, y) \, dx = \int f[x, q(x)] \, dx,$$

provided this latter integral has meaning.

Symbols like $\int f(x, y) \, dy$, $\int f(x, y) \, du$, and $\int f(x, y, z) \, dx$ are similarly defined. In every case where an integral is written with d, rather than with ∂, the integrand must be expressed as a function of only the variable of integration before the integral can be evaluated. Thus, if $y = \sqrt{x + 1}$, then

$$\int xy^2 \, dx = \int x(x + 1) \, dx = \frac{x^3}{3} + \frac{x^2}{2} + C.$$

It is evident that $\int f(x, y) \, dx$ and $\int f(x, y) \, dy$ are entirely different functions. For example, if $y^2 = x$, then $\int (x + y^2) \, dx = x^2 + C$, whereas

$$\int (x + y^2) \, dy = \frac{2y^3}{3} + C.$$

Moreover, the functions $x^2 + C$ and $(2y^3/3) + C$ are not reducible to one another by means of the relation $y^2 = x$. However, we may change the variable of integration by means of

THEOREM 11.2.   *If x and y are differentiable functions of each other, say $x = \psi(y)$ and $y = \varphi(x)$, then*

$$\int f(x, y)\, dy = \int [f(x, y)\, D_x y]\, dx. \tag{2}$$

We leave the proof of this theorem to the reader.

If $F(x, y)$ is an integral of $f(x, y)$ with respect to x, then $\int_{p(y)}^{q(y)} f(x, y)\, \partial x$ is the function of y given by the formula

$$\int_{p(y)}^{q(y)} f(x, y)\, \partial x = F(x, y)\Big]_{x=p(y)}^{x=q(y)} = F[q(y), y] - F[p(y), y]. \tag{3}$$

Since $\int_{p(y)}^{q(y)} f(x, y)\, \partial x$ is a function of y, it may (under suitable conditions) be integrated with respect to y; we denote this integration by $\int_a^b \int_{p(y)}^{q(y)} f(x, y)\, \partial x\, dy$. This symbol is interpreted as though it were written $\int_a^b [\int_{x=p(y)}^{x=q(y)} f(x, y)\, \partial x]\, dy$, the inner integration and substitutions being performed first. The symbol $\int_a^b \int_{p(y)}^{q(y)} f(x, y)\, \partial x\, dy$ is referred to variously as a *repeated*, *iterated*, or *double integral*. Thus,

$$\int_0^2 \int_1^{y^2} (x - y)\, \partial x\, dy = \int_0^2 \left[\frac{x^2}{2} - xy\right]_{x=1}^{x=y^2} dy$$
$$= \int_0^2 \left(\frac{y^4}{2} - y^3 - \frac{1}{2} + y\right) dy = \frac{1}{5}.$$

Other integrals, such as $\int_a^b \int_{p(x)}^{q(x)} f(x, y)\, \partial y\, dx$ and

$$\int_a^b \int_{p(x)}^{q(x)} \int_{g(x,y)}^{h(x,y)} f(x, y, z)\, \partial z\, \partial y\, dx,$$

are computed in a similar manner.

EXERCISES VII

1. Evaluate: $\displaystyle\int (x^2 - y^2)\, \partial x$; $\displaystyle\int (x^2 - y^2)\, \partial y$; $\displaystyle\int \sin xy\, \partial x$; $\displaystyle\int xy e^{x^2+y^2}\, \partial y$; $\displaystyle\int \frac{1}{1 + x^2 + y^2}\, \partial x$; $\displaystyle\int xy^2 \log (x + y)\, \partial x$; $\displaystyle\int z\sqrt{x^2 + y^2 + z^2}\, \partial z$;

$$\int \sin^{-1} (x + y)\, \partial z.$$

2. Show that if $f(x, y)$ is defined over an x-axial region and is such that $f_x(x, y) \equiv 0$, then f is a function of y alone.   (See Ex. XVII, 13, of Chap. I.)

3. Find $\int f(x, y)\, dx$ when (a) $f(x, y) = xe^y$ and $y = x^2$; (b) $f(x, y) = \dfrac{1}{y - x}$ and $y = 2x^2 - 1$.   Find $\int f(x, y)\, dy$ when $f(x, y) = xy$ and $y = \sin x$.

4. Find $\int f(x, y)\, du$ when (a) $f(x, y) = x^2 - xy$ and $x = 1/u$, $y = 2u + 1$; (b) $f(x, y) = x^2 - xy$ and $x = \sin u$, $y = \cos u$; (c) $f(x, y) = x \sin y$ and $x = u^2$, $y = 2u$.

5. If $f(x, y) = 1/(y - x)^2$, then the functions

$$F(x, y) = \frac{1}{y - x}, \qquad G(x, y) = \begin{cases} \dfrac{1}{y - x} + 1 \text{ when } x > y, \\[2mm] \dfrac{1}{y - x} + y \text{ when } x < y, \end{cases}$$

are integrals of $f(x, y)$ with respect to x, but there exists no function $\varphi(y)$ such that $G(x, y) = F(x, y) + \varphi(y)$. Explain. Find representations for $\int f(x, y)\, \partial x$ and $\int f(x, y)\, \partial y$.

6. Find $\int f(x, y)\, \partial x$ and $\int f(x, y)\, \partial y$ when

(a) $f(x, y) = 1/(x^2 - y^2)$. (Consider the four parts into which the xy-plane is divided by the lines $x = \pm y$.)

(b) $f(x, y) = 1/(x^2 + y^2)$. (For $\int f(x, y)\, \partial x$ consider the cases $y \neq 0$ and $y = 0$).

(c) $f(x, y) = x/\sqrt{x^2 - y^2 - 1}$.

(d) $f(x, y)$ is the function discussed in connection with Fig. 57.

(e) Show how $\int f(x, y)\, \partial x$ may be represented by properly breaking up the domain of definition of $f(x, y)$ into x-axial regions. Show that Theorem 11.1 is never valid when the region D is not x-axial.

7. Define $\int f(x, y, z)\, \partial x$. Define an x-axial region in 3-dimensional space. State and prove Theorem 11.1 for a function $f(x, y, z)$.

8. Prove Theorem 11.2 by means of property IVb in Sec. 3. Verify this result when $f(x, y) = ye^z$ and $y = \sqrt{x}$.

9. (a) Under what conditions is it true that

$$\int f(x, y)\, du = \int [f(x, y)\, D_x u]\, dx = \int [f(x, y)\, D_y u]\, dy? \tag{4}$$

Verify this result when $f(x, y) = x^2 - xy$ and $x = 1/u$, $y = 2u + 1$.

(b) When is it true that $\int f(x, y, z)\, dx = \int [f(x, y, z)\, D_z x]\, dz$? Interpret and illustrate.

10. (a) Define and illustrate integrals of more complicated types, such as $\int f(x, y, z)\, \partial x$, where x and y are independent but $z = \varphi(x, y)$.

(b) Show that $\displaystyle \int \left[f(x, y, z) \frac{\partial z}{\partial y} \right] \partial y = \int f(x, y, z)\, \partial z$, where in both integrals x is constant but where $z = \varphi(x, y)$ in the first integral and $y = \psi(x, z)$ in the second.

11. Show that the value of $\int_{p(y)}^{q(y)} f(x, y)\, \partial x$ is independent of the integral $F(x, y)$ chosen in (3). State all the conditions that must be met by $f(x, y)$, y, and the "limits of integration" $p(y)$ and $q(y)$ in order that this result may be valid.

12. Evaluate:

(a) $\displaystyle\int_0^{2a}\int_0^{x^2} 2y\ \partial y\ dx.$
 (b) $\displaystyle\int_0^{2a}\int_0^{y^2} 2y\ \partial x\ dy.$

(c) $\displaystyle\int_0^1\int_{y^2}^1\int_0^{y-x} x\ \partial z\ \partial x\ dy.$
 (d) $\displaystyle\int_1^2\int_0^z\int_0^{x\sqrt{3}} \frac{x}{x^2+y^2}\ \partial y\ \partial x\ dz.$

(e) $\displaystyle\int_0^{\pi/2}\int_0^{\cos\theta} \rho\sin\theta\ \partial\rho\ d\theta.$
 (f) $\displaystyle\int_0^3\int_{-\sqrt{9-x^2}}^{\sqrt{9-x^2}}\int_0^x y\ \partial z\ \partial y\ dx.$

(g) $\displaystyle\int_0^{12}\int_0^{\pi/2}\int_0^{\cos\theta} \rho^2\sin\theta\ \partial\rho\ \partial\theta\ dz.$

(h) $\displaystyle\int_0^{\pi/2}\int_0^a\int_0^{\sqrt{a^2-r^2}} r(r\cos\theta + r\sin\theta + z)\ \partial z\ \partial r\ d\theta.$

13. Suppose that $\int [f(x,\ y)\ D_x y]\ dx = F(x) + C_1$ when $y = \varphi(x)$. Then

$$D_x F(x) = f(x,\ y)\ D_x y, \qquad \text{where} \qquad y = \varphi(x). \tag{5}$$

Again, suppose that $\int f(x,\ y)\ dy = \Phi(y) + C_2$ when $x = \theta(y)$, where θ and φ are both arbitrary and wholly independent of each other. It is evident that, in general, $F(x) \not\equiv \Phi[\varphi(x)] + C$, for Φ varies with θ, while F does not. Point out the fallacy in the following argument: After completing the integration to determine $\Phi(y)$, let us set $y = \varphi(x)$. Then $D_x\Phi[\varphi(x)] = D_y\Phi(y)\ D_x y$, where y is independent in $D_y\Phi(y)$, and where $y = \varphi(x)$ in $D_x y$. But $D_y\Phi(y) = f(x,\ y)$ [just as in (5)], and in this result we may (as always) write $y = \varphi(x)$. Hence

$$D_x\Phi[\varphi(x)] = f(x,\ y)\ D_x y, \qquad \text{where} \qquad y = \varphi(x). \tag{6}$$

By (5) and (6), $F(x)$ and $\Phi[\varphi(x)]$ have the same x-derivative, and by Theorem 10.3 of Chap. 1, $F(x) \equiv \Phi[\varphi(x)] + C$.

12. Exact Differentials. While $\int f(x,\ y)\ dx$ is meaningless unless y is a function of x, say $y = \varphi(x)$, yet it is sometimes possible to represent the quantity $\int f(x,\ y)\ dx + \int g(x,\ y)\ dy$ by a formula even when $\varphi(x)$ is not explicitly given. We wish to see when and how this may be done.

It was shown in Sec. 18 of Chap. I that, if y is a differentiable function of x, say $y = \varphi(x)$, then

$$\frac{df(x,\ y)}{dx} = f_x(x,\ y) + f_y(x,\ y)\ D_x y. \tag{1}$$

Since the two members of (1) denote the same function of x, y being given as a function of x, it follows that*

---

* Throughout this discussion we assume that the conditions of Theorems 2.1 and 11.1 are always met.

$$\int \frac{df(x,\,y)}{dx}\,dx = \int [f_x(x,\,y) + f_y(x,\,y)\,D_x y]\,dx$$

$$= \int f_x(x,\,y)\,dx + \int [f_y(x,\,y)\,D_x y]\,dx. \quad (2)$$

If the relation $y = \varphi(x)$ determines x as a function of y, say $x = \psi(y)$, then the last integral of (2) may be written as

$$\int f_y(x,\,y)\,dy$$

by virtue of Theorem 11.2. Since $\displaystyle\int \frac{df(x,\,y)}{dx}\,dx = f(x,\,y) + C$, it follows that (2) may be written in the form*

$$\int f_x(x,\,y)\,dx + \int f_y(x,\,y)\,dy = f(x,\,y) + C, \quad (3)$$

where in both members of (3), $y = \varphi(x)$ and $x = \psi(y)$. In no event are x and y to be thought of as independent in the right member of (3).

Example 1. If $f(x,\,y) = xy$, then $f_x(x,\,y) = y$, $f_y(x,\,y) = x$, and (3) becomes

$$\int y\,dx + \int x\,dy = xy + C. \quad (4)$$

To evaluate the left member of (4), x and y *must* be functions of each other. Suppose $y = x^2$, so that $x = \sqrt{y}$. Then the left member of (4) becomes $(x^3/3) + (2y^{3/2}/3) + C$. If in this formula we substitute $y = x^2$, the result is the same as that obtained by substituting $y = x^2$ in $f(x,\,y) = xy$. If we had taken $y = \log x$, so that $x = e^y$, then the left member of (4) becomes $(x \log x - x) + e^y + C$. Substitution of $y = \log x$ in this result and in $f(x,\,y) = xy$ leads to the same function of x. Thus, no matter how y may be represented as a function of x in (3), direct evaluation of the two members of (3) always leads to equivalent results.

As an immediate consequence of (3) we have

THEOREM 12.1. *The expression $\int M(x,\,y)\,dx + \int N(x,\,y)\,dy$ may be evaluated by the formula*

$$\int M(x,\,y)\,dx + \int N(x,\,y)\,dy = f(x,\,y) + C \quad (5)$$

when there exists a function $f(x,\,y)$ such that

$$f_x(x,\,y) = M(x,\,y), \qquad f_y(x,\,y) = N(x,\,y). \quad (6)$$

---

* It must be remembered that $\int f_x(x,\,y)\,dx \neq f(x,\,y) + C$. However, $\int f_x(x,\,y)\,\partial x = f(x,\,y) + \lambda(y)$.

For example,

$$\int (x^3 + y^2)\, dx + \int (2xy + \cos y)\, dy = \frac{x^4}{4} + xy^2 + \sin y + C,$$

for $\dfrac{\partial}{\partial x}\left(\dfrac{x^4}{4} + xy^2 + \sin y + C\right) = x^3 + y^2$, and

$$\frac{\partial}{\partial y}\left(\frac{x^4}{4} + xy^2 + \sin y + C\right) = 2xy + \cos y.$$

It is customary to write $\int M(x, y)\, dx + \int N(x, y)\, dy$ merely as $\int M(x, y)\, dx + N(x, y)\, dy$, it being implied that x and y are always inverse functions of each other in the two parts of the integral. We say that $M(x, y)\, dx + N(x, y)\, dy$ is an *exact differential* if and only if $\dfrac{\partial M(x, y)}{\partial y} \equiv \dfrac{\partial N(x, y)}{\partial x}$. We now prove

THEOREM 12.2. *A necessary and sufficient condition that there exist a function $f(x, y)$ such that*

$$\int M(x, y)\, dx + N(x, y)\, dy = f(x, y) + C$$

is that $M(x, y)\, dx + N(x, y)\, dy$ be exact. If $M\, dx + N\, dy$ is exact, the function $f(x, y)$ is given by the formula

$$f(x, y) = \int M(x, y)\, \partial x = m(x, y) + \varphi(y),$$

where $m(x, y)$ is any integral of M with respect to x, and where

$$\varphi(y) = \int \left[N(x, y) - \frac{\partial m(x, y)}{\partial y} \right] dy,$$

$N - (\partial m/\partial y)$ *being independent of x.*

To prove the theorem we seek the conditions under which we may determine a function $f(x, y)$ such that (6) holds. We observe that *every* function $f(x, y)$, such that $f_x(x, y) \equiv M(x, y)$, is represented by

$$f(x, y) = \int M(x, y)\, \partial x = m(x, y) + \varphi(y), \qquad (7)$$

where m is any integral of M with respect to x, and where it remains merely to determine $\varphi(y)$ so that

$$f_y(x, y) \equiv \frac{\partial}{\partial y}[m(x, y) + \varphi(y)] = N(x, y), \qquad (8)$$

i.e., so that

$$\frac{d\varphi(y)}{dy} \equiv N(x, y) - \frac{\partial m(x, y)}{\partial y}. \tag{9}$$

$\left[\vphantom{\frac{\partial^2}{\partial x}}\right.$ We assume that $\int M(x, y)\, \partial x$, $\int N(x, y)\, \partial y$, and $\dfrac{\partial M(x, y)}{\partial y}$ exist, and that $\dfrac{\partial^2 m(x, y)}{\partial x\, \partial y}$ exists and is continuous. $\left.\vphantom{\frac{\partial^2}{\partial x}}\right]$ It is apparent that $\varphi(y)$ can be determined so that (9) holds when and only when $N - (\partial m/\partial y)$ is a function of y alone. But $N - (\partial m/\partial y)$ is a function of y alone if and only if

$$\frac{\partial}{\partial x}\left[N(x, y) - \frac{\partial m(x, y)}{\partial y}\right] \equiv \frac{\partial N(x, y)}{\partial x} - \frac{\partial^2 m(x, y)}{\partial x\, \partial y} \equiv 0. \tag{10}$$

(Cf. Ex. VII, 2.)   By Theorem 17.1 of Chap. I,
$\dfrac{\partial^2 m(x, y)}{\partial x\, \partial y} = \dfrac{\partial}{\partial y}\left[\dfrac{\partial m(x, y)}{\partial x}\right] = \dfrac{\partial M(x, y)}{\partial y}.$ Hence (10) holds when and only when

$$\frac{\partial M(x, y)}{\partial y} \equiv \frac{\partial N(x, y)}{\partial x}. \tag{11}$$

It follows from (9) that $\varphi(y)$ is determined as stated in the theorem.

Example 2.   In the case of $\int(x^3 + y^2)\, dx + (2xy + \cos y)\, dy$, $M_y \equiv N_x \equiv 2y$, and $f(x, y) = \int(x^3 + y^2)\, \partial x = (x^4/4) + xy^2 + \varphi(y)$, where

$$\varphi(y) = \int [(2xy + \cos y) - 2xy]\, dy = \int \cos y\, dy = \sin y + C.$$

Hence

$$\int [(x^3 + y^2)\, dx + (2xy + \cos y)\, dy] = \frac{x^4}{4} + xy^2 + \sin y + C.$$

Example 3.   In the case of $\int y\, dx + x^2y^2\, dy$,

$$M_y(x, y) \equiv 1, \qquad N_x(x, y) \equiv 2xy^2,$$

$M_y \not\equiv N_x$, and $\int y\, dx + x^2y^2\, dy$ cannot be evaluated by (3).

Definition 12.1.   *Let (a, b) and (c, d) be two pairs of values of x and y with $a \neq c$ and $b \neq d$. If $y = q(x)$ and $x = p(y)$, q and p being mutual inverses, and if q is such that*

$$b = q(a), \qquad d = q(c), \tag{12}$$

[so that $a = p(b)$ and $c = p(d)$], then

$$\int_{a,b}^{c,d} [M(x, y)\, dx + N(x, y)\, dy]$$

$$= \int_a^c M[x, q(x)]\, dx + \int_b^d N[p(y), y]\, dy. \quad (13)$$

Because of condition (12), we may write (13) in the form

$$\int_{a,b}^{c,d} [M(x, y)\, dx + N(x, y)\, dy]$$

$$= \int_a^c M[x, q(x)]\, dx + \int_a^c N[x, q(x)]\, D_x q(x)\, dx. \quad (14)$$

If $M\, dx + N\, dy$ is exact, there exists a function $f(x, y)$ such that

$$\int \{M[x, q(x)]\, dx + N[x, q(x)]\, D_x q(x)\, dx\} = f[x, q(x)] + C,$$

and

$$\int_a^c \{M[x, q(x)]\, dx + N[x, q(x)]\, D_x q(x)\, dx\} = f[x, q(x)]\Big]_a^c$$

$$= f(x, y)\Big]_{x=a,y=b}^{x=c,y=d}. \quad (15)$$

This proves

Theorem 12.3. *If $M(x, y)\, dx + N(x, y)\, dy$ is exact, then*

$$\int_{a,b}^{c,d} [M(x, y)\, dx + N(x, y)\, dy] = f(x, y)\Big]_{x=a,y=b}^{x=c,y=d}, \quad (16)$$

where $f(x, y)$ is determined as in Theorem 12.2.

Because the right member of (16) is independent of the choice of p and q we have

Theorem 12.4. *If $M\, dx + N\, dy$ is exact, then*

$$\int_{a,b}^{c,d} M\, dx + N\, dy$$

is independent of the path joining (a, b) and (c, d).

It must be remembered that the preceding theorems are valid only when all the conditions of Theorems 2.1 and 11.1 are met. (See Example 4 and Fig. 103 in Sec. 18.)

EXERCISES VIII

Test the following for exactness and, when possible, evaluate:

1. $\displaystyle\int (2x - y)\, dx + (3y^2 - x)\, dy.$

2. $\int \dfrac{1}{x+y}\,dx + \dfrac{1}{x+y}\,dy.$ 3. $\int ye^{xy}\,dx + xe^{xy}\,dy.$

4. $\int \dfrac{1}{(x-y)^2}\,dx + \dfrac{1}{(x-y)^2}\,dy.$ 5. $\int \dfrac{-y}{x^2+y^2}\,dx + \dfrac{x}{x^2+y^2}\,dy.$

6. $\int [x + \log (x+y)]\,dx + [\sin y + \log (x+y)]\,dy.$

7. $\int \left(e^x + \sqrt{\dfrac{y}{x}} \right) dx + \left(\dfrac{1}{y} + \sqrt{\dfrac{x}{y}} \right) dy.$

8. $\int [\cos x + \cos (x-y)]\,dx - [\cos y + \cos (x-y)]\,dy.$

9. $\int (x + xe^{x^2-y^2})\,dx + (e^y + ye^{x^2-y^2})\,dy.$

10. Show that $\int M(x)\,dx + N(y)\,dy$ may be evaluated by integrating each term separately as in Sec. 4 and adding the results.

11. State the significance of the result of Ex. 1. Illustrate your answer by the method indicated in Example 1 taking:

(a) $y = x^2$.   (b) $y = \sqrt{x}$.   (c) $y = \sin x$.
(d) $y = e^x$.   (e) $x^2 + y^2 = 1$.

12. Evaluate $\int_{0,0}^{2,4} y\,dx + x\,dy$ by (13), taking:

(a) $y = x^2$.   (b) $y = 2x$.   (c) $y = x^3/2$.
(d) $y = 2\sqrt{2x}$.   (e) $y = x + 2$.

Why is this last result meaningless? (f) Show that $\int_{0,0}^{2,4} y\,dx + x\,dy$ is exact and evaluate by (16). Compare all of your results. (g) Evaluate $\int_{0,0}^{2,4} y\,dx - x\,dy$ by (13) using the preceding formulas for y. Are your results all the same? Why?

13. Evaluate by various methods, as in Ex. 12:

(a) $\int_{0,1}^{1,0} (x-y)\,dx + (y^2-x)\,dy.$ (b) $\int_{2,0}^{3,1} 2xy\,dx + x^2\,dy.$
(c) $\int_{-1,-1}^{1,0} y^2\,dx + x^2\,dy.$

14. If x, y, and z are determined as functions of each other, i.e.,
$x = p_1(y) = p_2(z)$, $y = q_1(x) = q_2(z)$, and $z = r_1(x) = r_2(y)$, show that

$$\int P(x, y, z)\,dx + Q(x, y, z)\,dy + R(x, y, z)\,dz = f(x, y, z) + C \quad (17)$$

when $P \equiv f_x$, $Q \equiv f_y$, and $R \equiv f_z$. Show that the function $f(x, y, z)$ exists when and only when

$$P_y \equiv Q_x, \qquad P_z \equiv R_x, \qquad Q_z \equiv R_y, \tag{18}$$

and develop a procedure for finding $f(x, y, z)$ when (18) holds. The differential $P\,dx + Q\,dy + R\,dz$ is called *exact* when (18) holds.

Define the symbol $\int_{a_1,b_1,c_1}^{a_2,b_2,c_2} P\, dx + Q\, dy + R\, dz$, stating the analogue of (12).

State and prove an extension of Theorems 12.3 and 12.4.

15. Evaluate $\int_{0,0,0}^{1,2,3} (x + 2xz + 2yz)\, dx + (2y + 2xz)\, dy + (x^2 + 2xy)\, dz$.

16. Evaluate

$$\int_{1,0,0}^{0,1,1} (x + y + z)^{1/2}\, dx + (x + y + z)^{1/2}\, dy + (x + y + z)^{1/2}\, dz.$$

17. Evaluate

$$\int [\sin (x + z) + (x + y) \cos (x + z)]\, dx + \sin (x + z)\, dy$$
$$+ (x + y) \cos (x + z)\, dz.$$

PART B. DEFINITE INTEGRALS

13. Construction and Evaluation of Definite Integrals. To construct the definite integral of a function $f(x)$ over an interval $a \leq x \leq b$ we must first define the limit of a sequence of numbers. Let $a_1, a_2, \cdots, a_n, \cdots$ be a infinite sequence of real numbers.

Fig. 58.

We say that this sequence has the limit A if the successive terms of the sequence become and remain arbitrarily close to A. It may be shown (cf. property G of Sec. 3, Chap. I) that this definition may be expressed in the following form:

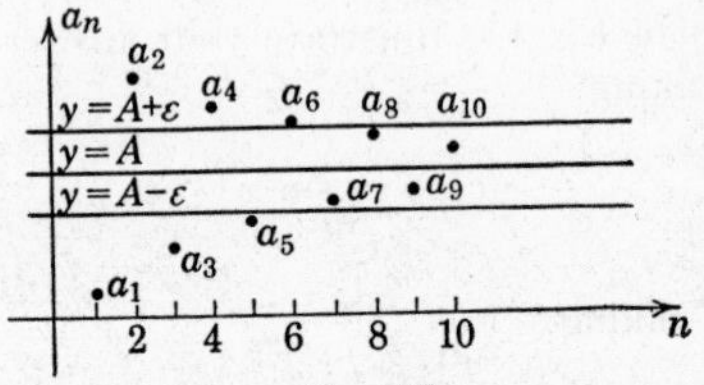

Definition 13.1. *Let $a_1, a_2, \cdots, a_n, \cdots$ be a sequence of arbitrary real numbers. If, for every positive number ϵ, however small, there exists a positive integer n_0 such that*

$$|a_n - A| < \epsilon \quad \text{for all} \quad n > n_0,$$

then the sequence $a_1, a_2, \cdots$ is said to have the limit A. We denote A by $\lim_{n \to \infty} a_n$.

This definition may be interpreted geometrically as indicated in Fig. 58. The similarity of this definition with Definition 3.1b of Chap. I should be noted. See Chap. IV for a detailed discussion of the properties of sequences.

Examples. According to Definition 13.1, we see that:

1. The sequence $3\frac{1}{2}, 3\frac{1}{3}, 3\frac{1}{4}, 3\frac{1}{5}, \cdots, 3 + (1/n), \cdots$ has the limit 3.
2. The sequence 2.1, 2.9, 2.01, 2.99, 2.001, 2.999, $\cdots$ has no limit.

3. If α is any constant angle, then the sequence $1, \cos \alpha, 1, \cos \dfrac{\alpha}{2}, 1,$

$\cos \dfrac{\alpha}{3}, 1, \cos \dfrac{\alpha}{4}, \cdots$ has the limit 1.

4. The sequence $2^{1/2}$, $2^{1/3}$, $2^{1/4}$, $2^{1/5}$, $2^{1/6}$, $\cdots$ has the limit 1.

5. The sequence $2^{1/2}$, 5, $2^{1/3}$, $2^{1/4}$, 5, $2^{1/5}$, $2^{1/6}$, $2^{1/7}$, $2^{1/8}$, 5, $2^{1/9}$, $\cdots$ has no limit.

We may now define a definite integral.

DEFINITION 13.2.   *Let $f(x)$ be a real single-valued function defined over the interval $a \leqq x \leqq b$. Perform the following operations:*

I.   *Subdivide the interval from $x = a$ to $x = b$ into an arbitrary finite number n_1 of nonoverlapping* subintervals I_1, I_2, $\cdots$, I_{n_1} of lengths $\Delta_1 x$, $\Delta_2 x$, $\cdots$, $\Delta_{n_1} x$ which need not be equal.*

II.   *In each interval I_i choose an arbitrary number x_i; thus, x_1 is a number in I_1, x_2 is a number in I_2, etc.*

III.   *Form the sum*

$$S_1 = \sum_{i=1}^{n_1} f(x_i)\,\Delta_i x$$
$$= f(x_1)\,\Delta_1 x + f(x_2)\,\Delta_2 x + \cdots + f(x_{n_1})\,\Delta_{n_1} x. \tag{1}$$

IV.   *By repeated applications of steps I to III, construct an infinite sequence*

$$S_1 = \sum_{i=1}^{n_1} f(x_i)\,\Delta_i x, \qquad S_2 = \sum_{i=1}^{n_2} f(x_i)\,\Delta_i x, \qquad \cdots ,$$

$$S_k = \sum_{i=1}^{n_k} f(x_i)\,\Delta_i x, \qquad \cdots \tag{2}$$

in any manner such that

$$\lim_{k \to \infty} \delta_k = 0, \tag{3}$$

where δ_k is the length of the longest interval in the sum S_k.

If $\lim\limits_{k \to \infty} S_k$ exists and has the same value for every possible construction of the sequence (2) meeting condition (3), then this limit is denoted by $\mathrm{S}_a^b f(x)\,dx$, i.e.,

$$\mathrm{S}_a^b f(x)\,dx = \lim_{k \to \infty} S_k. \tag{4}$$

We call $\mathrm{S}_a^b f(x)\,dx$ the definite integral (or Riemann sum) of $f(x)$

---

* It is permissible for two adjoining subintervals to have a common end point. An interval I_i may include both, either, or neither of its end points.

with respect to x from x = a to x = b, and we call a and b the limits of integration. We say that f(x) is summable from x = a to x = b if $S_a^b f(x) \, dx$ *exists.*

In step IV it is to be understood that the numbers x_i and $\Delta_i x$ in any one sum of (2) have no relation to the numbers x_i and $\Delta_i x$ in any other sum of (2); in other words, the sums of (2) are constructed independently except for condition (3) on δ_k.

In Part C of this chapter we determine the class of functions $f(x)$ for which $S_a^b f(x) \, dx$ exists; we mention in passing that

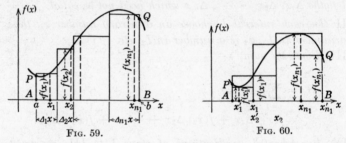

FIG. 59. FIG. 60.

$S_a^b f(x) \, dx$ exists when $f(x)$ is continuous over the interval $a \leqq x \leqq b$, and also in certain other cases.

Perhaps the simplest interpretation of (1) is obtained with the aid of the graph of $f(x)$. Suppose that the graph of $f(x)$ is a continuous curve and that the region $ABQP$ bounded by the graph of $f(x)$, the ordinates at $x = a$ and $x = b$, and the x-axis, has a finite area K. It is evident that $f(x_i) \, \Delta_i x$ represents the area of a rectangle of height $f(x_i)$ and base $\Delta_i x$, and that the sum (1) represents an approximation to the area K of $ABQP$.

We shall now show that

$$S_a^b f(x) \, dx = \text{area } K \text{ of } ABQP. \tag{5}$$

Construct the sums

$$S_1 = \sum_{i=1}^{n_1} f(x_i) \, \Delta_i x, \qquad s_1 = \sum_{i=1}^{n_1} f(x_i') \, \Delta_i x$$

as in Definition 13.2, where in S_1 each x_i is chosen so that $f(x_i)$ is the maximum value of f in the interval $\Delta_i x$, and where in s_1 each x_i' is chosen so that $f(x_i')$ is the minimum value of f in the interval $\Delta_i x$. Then (see Fig. 60)

$$s_1 \leqq \text{area } K \text{ of } ABQP \leqq S_1.$$

Construct in this manner two sequences S_1, S_2, $\cdots$ and s_1, s_2, $\cdots$ as in step IV of Definition 13.2. As mentioned above, $S_a^b f(x)\, dx$ exists because $f(x)$ is continuous. The existence of $S_a^b f(x)\, dx$ implies that $\lim_{k\to\infty} s_k$ and $\lim_{k\to\infty} S_k$ exist, and that

$$\lim_{k\to\infty} s_k = \lim_{k\to\infty} S_k = S_a^b f(x)\, dx. \tag{6}$$

On the other hand, $s_k \leq$ area K of $ABQP \leq S_k$ for each k, and

$$\lim_{k\to\infty} s_k \leq \text{area } K \text{ of } ABQP \leq \lim_{k\to\infty} S_k. \tag{7}$$

Equation (5) follows at once from (6) and (7).

In Sec. 14 we shall give several examples to show how (1) and (4) arise in connection with the computation of various physical and geometrical quantities.

Example 1. Find an approximate value of $S_1^2 x^2\, dx$.

Divide the interval from $x = 1$ to $x = 2$ into 10 parts of length 0.1, and let $x_1 = 1.0$, $x_2 = 1.1$, $x_3 = 1.2$, $\cdots$, $x_{10} = 1.9$. Then

$$s = \sum_{i=1}^{10} f(x_i)\, \Delta_i x = (1.0)^2(0.1) + (1.1)^2(0.1) + \cdots + (1.9)^2(0.1) = 2.185.$$

If instead we let $x_1 = 1.1$, $x_2 = 1.2$, $\cdots$, $x_{10} = 2.0$, then

$$S = \sum_{i=1}^{10} f(x_i)\, \Delta_i x = (1.1)^2(0.1) + (1.2)^2(0.1) + \cdots + (2.0)^2(0.1) = 2.485.$$

We see from the graph of $f(x) = x^2$ and (5) that, because of the way the x's were chosen in s and S,

$$2.185 \leq S_1^2 x^2\, dx \leq 2.485. \tag{8}$$

THEOREM 13.1 (*Fundamental Theorem of Integral Calculus*). Let $f(x)$ be a real single-valued function defined over the interval $a \leq x \leq b$. If* $S_a^b f(x)\, dx$ and $\int_a^b f(x)\, dx$ exist, then

$$S_a^b f(x)\, dx = \int_a^b f(x)\, dx. \tag{9}$$

Subdivide the interval from $x = a$ to $x = b$ into n_1 subintervals I_1, I_2, $\cdots$, I_{n_1} having a, $\bar{x}_1$, $\bar{x}_2$, $\cdots$, $\bar{x}_{n_1-1}$, b as successive endpoints. Let $F(x)$ be an arbitrary integral of $f(x)$, so that

* We mention in passing that this condition is always met when $f(x)$ is continuous over the interval $a \leq x \leq b$.

$D_x F(x) = f(x)$. Construct the sum (1) by choosing the numbers x_i in the following way: By Theorem 10.1 of Chap. I, there exists

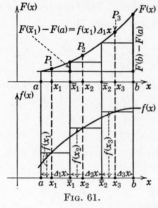

a value x_1 of x, $a < x_1 < \bar{x}_1$, such that

$$F(\bar{x}_1) - F(a) = F'(x_1)(\bar{x}_1 - a).$$

Take this value x_1 as the number x_1 in the sum (1). Since $F'(x_1) = f(x_1)$ and $\bar{x}_1 - a = \Delta_1 x$,

$$f(x_1) \Delta_1 x = F(\bar{x}_1) - F(a). \tag{10.1}$$

With the aid of Theorem 10.1 we may determine in a similar manner values x_2, x_3, $\cdots$, x_{n_1} within I_2, I_3, $\cdots$, I_{n_1} such that

Fig. 61.

$$f(x_2) \Delta_2 x = F(\bar{x}_2) - F(\bar{x}_1),$$
$$f(x_3) \Delta_3 x = F(\bar{x}_3) - F(\bar{x}_2), \qquad \cdots \tag{10.i}$$
$$f(x_{n_1}) \Delta_{n_1} x = F(b) - F(\bar{x}_{n_1-1}).$$

If we add all the equations (10.1) and (10.i), we find that

$$\sum_{i=1}^{n_1} f(x_i) \Delta_i x = f(x_1) \Delta_1 x + f(x_2) \Delta_2 x + \cdots + f(x_{n_1}) \Delta_{n_1} x$$
$$= F(b) - F(a). \tag{11}$$

Thus we have constructed the sum (1) in such a way that we have been able to evaluate it. If we construct each sum in the sequence (2) in this same manner, always determining the points x_i by the theorem of the mean as indicated above, then *every* sum S_k in (2) has the value $F(b) - F(a)$ as in (11). Hence

$$\lim_{k \to \infty} S_k = F(b) - F(a) = \int_a^b f(x)\, dx. \tag{12}$$

By hypothesis, $S_a^b f(x)\, dx$ exists. By Definition 13.2,

$$S_a^b f(x)\, dx = \lim_{k \to \infty} S_k,$$

so that (9) follows from (12).

It should be noted that the proof of this theorem is purely analytic and involves no reference to the graph of $f(x)$; in particular, no mention is made of the area of any figure. Hence

(9) holds no matter what interpretation, physical or geometrical, is given to $f(x)$ and $S_a^b f(x)\,dx$. However, the various steps of the proof may be interpreted geometrically with the aid of Fig. 61.

It was pointed out in Sec. 6 of Chap. I that, if $f(x) = D_x F(x)$, then *the slope of the tangent to the graph of $F(x)$ at $x = x_0$ is represented by the ordinate to the graph of $f(x)$ at $x = x_0$*. It now follows by (5) and (9) that *the area under the graph of $f(x)$ from $x = a$ to $x = b$ and above the x-axis is represented by the difference between the ordinates to the graph of $F(x)$ at $x = a$ and $x = b$*. This latter result provides a method for constructing the graph of $F(x)$ from the graph of $f(x)$: erect ordinates at various points between $x = a$ and $x = b$, and estimate the areas A_1, A_2, $\cdots$ of the

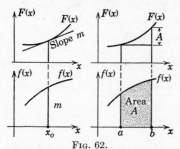
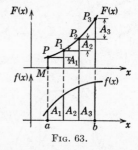

Fig. 62.   Fig. 63.

successive strips bounded by these ordinates and the graph of $f(x)$. Choose the initial ordinate MP at $x = a$ arbitrarily, and plot points P_1, P_2, $\cdots$ as indicated in Fig. 63 to obtain the graph of $F(x)$.

Theorem 13.1 provides a method for evaluating $S_a^b f(x)\,dx$ in the event that $\int_a^b f(x)\,dx$ exists. However, there exist functions $f(x)$ such that $S_a^b f(x)\,dx$ exists while $\int_a^b f(x)\,dx$ does not exist (see Ex. IX, 7) and in such cases $S_a^b f(x)\,dx$ must be evaluated by special devices (see Ex. IX, 8). Conversely, there exist functions $f(x)$ such that $\int_a^b f(x)\,dx$ exists while $S_a^b f(x)\,dx$ does not exist (see Hobson, "Theory of Functions of a Real Variable," 3d edition, Sec. 348). Moreover, the definition of $S_a^b f(x)\,dx$ can be extended to point functions (see Sec. 15), whereas the definition of $\int_a^b f(x)\,dx$ does not admit of such an extension. While it is common to denote $S_a^b f(x)\,dx$ by $\int_a^b f(x)\,dx$, it is seen that $S_a^b f(x)\,dx$ and $\int_a^b f(x)\,dx$ are essentially distinct in nature, and one should not try to merge them merely because they are sometimes equal in value.

Example 2. Find the area A bounded by the curves $Y = 10 + 3x - x^2$ and $y = x + 7$.

These curves intersect at points with abscissas $x = -1$ and $x = 3$. By (5), (see Fig. 64)

$$A = S_{-1}^{3} \, Y \, dx - S_{-1}^{3} \, y \, dx.$$

We may simplify this computation by (15) of Ex. 3:

$$A = S_{-1}^{3} \, (Y - y) \, dx = S_{-1}^{3} \, (3 + 2x - x^2) \, dx = \tfrac{32}{3}.$$

EXERCISES IX

1. As in Example 1, find approximate values of:

(a) $S_{2}^{3} \, x^2 \, dx.$ (b) $S_{-5}^{-1} \, \dfrac{1}{x} \, dx.$ (c) $S_{0}^{\pi} \, \sin x \, dx.$

(d) $S_{1}^{10} \, \log_{10} x \, dx.$ (e) $S_{0}^{1} \, e^{-x^2} \, dx.$

Check your results by (9). Sketch the areas represented by these integrals.

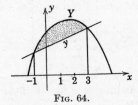
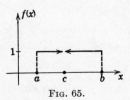

FIG. 64.   FIG. 65.

2. In Definition 13.2 it was assumed that $a \leqq b$. If $a > b$, we may define $S_{a}^{b} f(x) \, dx$ exactly as in Definition 13.2 if we interpret all the $\Delta_i x$'s as negative (inasmuch as x decreases in going from a to b). Show that

$$S_{a}^{b} f(x) \, dx = -S_{b}^{a} f(x) \, dx. \tag{13}$$

3. Let $f(x)$ and $g(x)$ be integrable and summable. Show by (9) that

$$S_{a}^{b} f(x) \, dx + S_{b}^{c} f(x) \, dx = S_{a}^{c} f(x) \, dx. \tag{14}$$

$$S_{a}^{b} [f(x) \pm g(x)] \, dx = S_{a}^{b} f(x) \, dx \pm S_{a}^{b} g(x) \, dx. \tag{15}$$

$$S_{a}^{b} kf(x) \, dx = k S_{a}^{b} f(x) \, dx, \qquad \text{where } k \text{ is a constant.} \tag{16}$$

[See Sec. 27 below for the case where $f(x)$ and $g(x)$ are not integrable.]

4. Find the areas bounded by the curves:

(a) $Y = x^2$ and $y = 2 - x.$ (b) $Y = x^4$ and $y = x^2.$
(c) $Y = x^3$ and $y = x.$ (d) $Y = x^3$ and $y = 2x - x^2.$
(e) $xy = 3$ and $x + 2y = 5.$

(f) $2x^2 - xy + 6 = 0$ and $y^2 = 15x + 79$.

(g) $y = \text{Sin}^{-1} x, y = \pi/2$, and $x = 0$.   (h) $y^2 - 2y + x = 0$ and $x = -3$.

[Take y as the independent variable in parts (g) and (h).]

5. Show that the area of the ellipse $(x^2/a^2) + (y^2/b^2) = 1$ is πab.

6. Find by a definite integral the area of a segment of a circle of radius a and altitude h.   Check your result by the methods of elementary geometry.

7. Show that the function

$$f(x) = \begin{cases} 1 & \text{when} & a \leqq x < c & \text{and when} & c < x \leqq b, \\ 0 & \text{when} & x = c \end{cases}$$

has no integral, and hence that $\int_a^b f(x)\, dx$ does not exist.   Show that $S_a^b f(x)\, dx$ exists and equals $b - a$.   (See Fig. 65.)

8. It will be shown in Part C of this chapter that*

$$S_a^b f(x)\, dx = S_a^b g(x)\, dx \tag{17}$$

if f and g differ in value at only a finite number of points or if g is defined at only a finite number of points where f is undefined.   It follows that, if we can construct a summable function g differing from f in the manner indicated and such that $\int_a^b g(x)\, dx$ exists, then we can evaluate $S_a^b f(x)\, dx$ by (17) and (9).   Thus, if in Ex. 7 we let $g(x) = 1$ for all x in the interval $a \leqq x \leqq b$, then

$$S_a^b f(x)\, dx = S_a^b g(x)\, dx = \int_a^b 1\, dx = b - a.$$

When possible, construct a suitable function $g(x)$ and evaluate:

(a) $\displaystyle S_0^1 x \log x\, dx.$ (b) $\displaystyle S_0^1 \frac{x}{\sqrt{1 - x^2}}\, dx.$

(c) $\displaystyle S_{-\pi/2}^{\pi/2} \frac{1 - \cos x}{\sin^2 x}\, dx.$ (d) $\displaystyle S_{-1}^1 \frac{1}{x^3} e^{-1/x^2}\, dx.$

9. Show that $S_0^1 f(x)\, dx$ does not exist when

$$f(x) = \begin{cases} 1 \text{ when } x \text{ is rational,} \\ 0 \text{ when } x \text{ is irrational.} \end{cases}$$

10. If $f(x) = -\log x$, show that $S_0^1 f(x)\, dx$ does not exist.

Suggestion.   Let $N_1, N_2, \cdots$ be a sequence of positive numbers such that $\lim_{k \to \infty} N_k \to +\infty$.   Remembering that $\lim_{x \to 0} (-\log x) \to +\infty$ and that $-\log x \geqq 0$ when $0 < x \leqq 1$, show that S_k in (2) can be made $> N_k$ by properly choosing x_1.   Since $\lim_{k \to \infty} N_k \to +\infty$, $\lim_{k \to \infty} S_k \to +\infty$ and $S_0^1 f(x)\, dx$ does not exist.   However, it will be seen later that the region bounded by $y = -\log x$, $x = 0$, $x = 1$, and $y = 0$ has the finite area 1.   This result indicates that Definition 13.2 is inadequate when $f(x)$ becomes infinite. (We shall discuss this difficulty in Part D of the present chapter.)

* Definition 13.2 may be extended to the case where $f(x)$ is undefined at a finite number of points in the interval $a \leqq x \leqq b$ if it is stipulated that the points x_i in (1) and (2) must be taken where $f(x)$ is defined.

11. We say that $f(x)$ is *unbounded* in the interval $a \leqq x \leqq b$ if there are points in this interval at which $|f(x)| > N$, however large N may be. Show that $S_a^b f(x) \, dx$ as given by Definition 13.2 never exists when $f(x)$ is unbounded and everywhere positive (or negative).

Show that, if $f(x)$ is everywhere positive (or negative), then $S_a^\infty f(x) \, dx$, $S_{-\infty}^b f(x) \, dx$, and $S_{-\infty}^{+\infty} f(x) \, dx$ never exist in the sense of Definition 13.2. However, integrals of these types are very common and useful when defined as in Sec. 31 below.

12. Let $f(x)$ be given by the following graphs. In each case, construct the graph of the integral $F(x)$ of $f(x)$ passing through $(0, 1)$. Estimate areas by means of small squares.

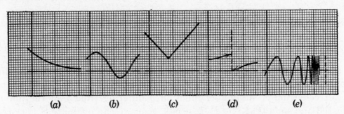

(a)	(b)	(c)	(d)	(e)

13. Using Theorem 10.1 of Chap. I in the manner indicated in the proof of Theorem 13.1, but applied to the entire interval from $x = a$ to $x = b$, prove

THEOREM 13.2 (*Theorem of the Mean for Integrals*). *If* $f(x)$ *is continuous over the interval* $a \leqq x \leqq b$, *then there exists a value* ξ *of* x, $a < \xi < b$, *such that*

$$(b - a)f(\xi) = S_a^b f(x) \, dx.$$

Illustrate the meaning of this theorem with the aid of a sketch and (5).

14. Elementary Applications of Definite Integrals.

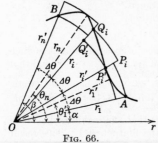

FIG. 66.

In this section we give a number of examples to show how definite integrals may be used to evaluate various physical and geometrical quantities.

Example 1. Find the area bounded by the continuous curve $r = f(\theta)$ and the radius vectors at $\theta = \alpha$ and $\theta = \beta$.

Subdivide the angle $\beta - \alpha$ into smaller angles* $\Delta\theta$. In each angle $\Delta\theta$ take values θ_i and θ_i' so that $r_i = f(\theta_i)$ and $r_i' = f(\theta_i')$ are the maximum and minimum values of $r = f(\theta)$ in the ith angle $\Delta\theta$. Draw arcs of circles with center 0 and radii r_i and r_i'. Then

* In this example we take the increments $\Delta_i \theta$ as equal merely for the sake of simplicity.

$$\text{Area sector } OP_iQ_i = \tfrac{1}{2}r_i^2\,\Delta\theta = \tfrac{1}{2}[f(\theta_i)]^2\,\Delta\theta,$$
$$\text{Area sector } OP_i'Q_i' = \tfrac{1}{2}[f(\theta_i')]^2\,\Delta\theta.$$

Construct the sums $S_n = \displaystyle\sum_{i=1}^{n}\tfrac{1}{2}[f(\theta_i)]^2\Delta\theta$ and $s_n = \displaystyle\sum_{i=1}^{n}\tfrac{1}{2}[f(\theta_i')]^2\,\Delta\theta$. Since $f(\theta)$ is continuous, $\tfrac{1}{2}[f(\theta)]^2$ is continuous, $S_\alpha^\beta\tfrac{1}{2}[f(\theta)]^2\,d\theta$ exists, $\lim\limits_{n\to\infty} S_n$ and $\lim\limits_{n\to\infty} s_n$ exist, and

$$\lim_{n\to\infty} s_n = \lim_{n\to\infty} S_n = \mathbf{S}_\alpha^\beta \tfrac{1}{2}[f(\theta)]^2\,d\theta. \tag{1}$$

On the other hand, $s_n \leqq$ area sector $OAB \leqq S_n$ for each n, and

$$\lim_{n\to\infty} s_n \leqq \text{area sector } OAB \leqq \lim_{n\to\infty} S_n. \tag{2}$$

It follows by (1) and (2) that

$$\text{Area sector } OAB = \mathbf{S}_\alpha^\beta \tfrac{1}{2}[f(\theta)]^2\,d\theta. \tag{3}$$

To illustrate: The circle $r = 2a\cos\theta$ is traced out when θ varies from 0 to π. Hence the area of this circle is $S_0^\pi \tfrac{1}{2}(2a\cos\theta)^2\,d\theta = \pi a^2$.

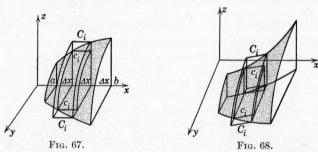

Fig. 67.   Fig. 68.

Example 2. A solid S is such that the area of the cross section of it cut by any plane $x = x_0$ is $A(x_0)$. Find the volume of that part of S between the planes $x = a$ and $x = b$.

Subdivide the solid S into laminas $L_1,\ \cdots\ ,L_n$ of thickness Δx by planes perpendicular to the x-axis. In each interval Δx choose x_i and x_i' so that $A(x_i)$ and $A(x_i')$ are the maximum and minimum values of $A(x)$ in the ith lamina. Suppose S is such that we can construct cylinders C_i and c_i of height Δx, having for cross sections the sections of S cut by the planes $x = x_i$ and $x = x_i'$, and such that L_i contains c_i and is contained in C_i. (See Figs. 67 and 68. The elements of these cylinders need not be parallel to the x-axis.) It follows that

$$\text{Volume } c_i \leqq \text{volume } L_i \leqq \text{volume } C_i. \tag{4}$$

But if we cannot construct C_i and c_i in this manner (see Fig. 69), then (4) may not hold and we must compute the volume of S by some other method (see Sec. 17). By Ex. X, 26, below, the volume of any cylinder is the product of its base and altitude. Hence (4) may be written as

$$A(x_i') \, \Delta x \leqq \text{volume } L_i \leqq A(x_i) \, \Delta x. \tag{5}$$

We leave it to the student to show that the volume V of S is

$$V = \underset{a}{\overset{b}{\textbf{S}}} A(x) \, dx. \tag{6}$$

[Cf. Example 1 and the proof of (5) in Sec. 13.]

For instance: A solid is such that any section of it perpendicular to the x-axis is a right triangle ABC, where A is on the curve $y = x^2$ in the xy-plane, B is on the line $z = x + 1$ in the xz-plane, and C is on the x-axis. To find

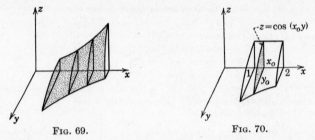

Fig. 69.   Fig. 70.

the volume V of this solid between the planes $x = 0$ and $x = 2$, we observe that $A(x) = \frac{1}{2}(x^2)(x + 1)$. Hence

$$V = \overset{2}{\underset{0}{\textbf{S}}} \tfrac{1}{2}(x^2)(x + 1) \, dx = \tfrac{10}{3}.$$

It is sometimes necessary to find $A(x)$ by integration. Thus, to find the volume V of the solid bounded by the surfaces $z = \cos xy$, $z = 0$, $y = 0$, $x = 1$, and $x = 2$, we first compute the area $A(x_0)$ of the section cut by the plane $x = x_0$:

$$A(x_0) = \overset{y_0}{\underset{0}{\textbf{S}}} \cos (x_0 y) \, dy = \int_0^{\pi/2x_0} \cos (x_0 y) \, dy,$$

where we express the upper limit of summation y_0 in terms of x_0 in order that A may be a function of x_0 alone. To obtain the formula $y_0 = \pi/2x_0$ we observe that the point $(x_0, y_0, 0)$ lies on the surface $z = \cos xy$. Hence $0 = \cos (x_0 y_0)$, $x_0 y_0 = \pi/2$, and $y_0 = \pi/2x_0$. It follows that

$$A(x) = \int_0^{\pi/2x} \cos xy \, \partial y$$

and

$$V = \overset{2}{\underset{1}{\textbf{S}}} A(x) \, dx = \int_1^2 \int_0^{\pi/2x} \cos xy \, \partial y \, dx = \log 2.$$

If the solid S is a volume of revolution, then cylindrical coordinates are sometimes useful. Suppose S is bounded by the surfaces $z = f(r)$, $z = 0$,

$r = a$, and $r = b$, and suppose $f(r)$ is continuous and nondecreasing from $r = a$ to $r = b$. Subdivide S into cylindrical shells $L_1, \cdots, L_n$, of thickness Δr. In each interval Δr choose r_i and r_i' so that $f(r_i)$ and $f(r_i')$ are the maximum and minimum values of $f(r)$ in the ith shell, and construct cylinders C_i and c_i of heights $f(r_i)$ and $f(r_i')$ as indicated in Fig. 71. Because $f(r)$ is non-decreasing, we may take r_i and r_i' as the outer and inner radii of the ith shell. It is seen that

$$2\pi r_i' f(r_i') \, \Delta r < \text{volume } c_i \leqq \text{volume } L_i \leqq \text{volume } C_i < 2\pi r_i f(r_i)\Delta r.$$

We leave it to the student to show that the volume V of S is

$$V = \mathrm{S}_a^b \, 2\pi r \, f(r) \, dr. \tag{7}$$

The case where $f(r)$ is nonincreasing between $r = a$ and $r = b$ is dealt with by considering the volume V' of the solid above $z = f(r)$ and below some plane $z = c$. The above argument shows that $V' = \mathrm{S}_a^b \, 2\pi r \, [c - f(r)] \, dr$, and (7) follows at once from (15) of Sec. 13. It is seen by (14) of Sec. 13

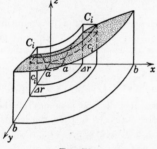

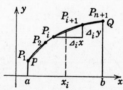

Fig. 71.   Fig. 72.

that (7) can be used for any function $f(r)$ with a finite number of maxima and minima between $r = a$ and $r = b$.

Thus, the volume V bounded by $z = r^2$, $z = 0$, $r = 1$, and $r = 3$ is

$$V = \mathrm{S}_1^3 \, 2\pi r(r^2) \, dr = 40\pi.$$

If the solid S is bounded above by $z = f(r)$ and below by $z = g(r)$, then by (15) of Sec. 13,

$$V = \mathrm{S}_a^b \, 2\pi r \, h(r) \, dr, \tag{7'}$$

where $h(r) = f(r) - g(r)$.

Example 3. Find the length of the curve $y = f(x)$ from $x = a$ to $x = b$ when $f'(x)$ exists and is continuous.

If C is any continuous arc from P to Q, then the length of C is defined as follows: *Let* $P_1, P_2, \cdots, P_n, P_{n+1}$ *be any set of* $n + 1$ *successive points on* C *with* $P_1 = P$ *and* $P_{n+1} = Q$, *and let* δ_n *denote the largest of all the chord lengths* $\overline{P_1P_2}, \cdots, \overline{P_nP_{n+1}}$. *If*

$$\lim_{\delta_n \to 0} \sum_{i=1}^{n} \overline{P_i P_{i+1}} = \lim_{\delta_n \to 0} (\overline{P_1 P_2} + \overline{P_2 P_3} + \cdots + \overline{P_n P_{n+1}}) \qquad (8)$$

always exists and has the same value for all choices of the points P_i, then the common value of this limit is called the length of C.

To evaluate the limit (8) when C has the equation $y = f(x)$, we may write

$$\overline{P_i P_{i+1}} = \sqrt{(\Delta_i x)^2 + (\Delta_i y)^2} = \sqrt{1 + \left(\frac{\Delta_i y}{\Delta_i x}\right)^2} \ \Delta_i x, \qquad (9)$$

where the notation is indicated in Fig. 72. By hypothesis, $f'(x)$ exists, and by Theorem 10.1 of Chap. 1, there exists a point x_i such that

$$f'(x_i) = \frac{\Delta_i y}{\Delta_i x}.$$

By (9),

$$\overline{P_i P_{i+1}} = \sqrt{1 + [f'(x_i)]^2} \ \Delta_i x. \qquad (10)$$

By hypothesis, $f'(x)$ is continuous. Hence $\sqrt{1 + [f'(x)]^2}$ is continuous, $S_a^b \sqrt{1 + [f'(x)]^2} \, dx$ exists, the limit (8) exists by virtue of (10) and Definition 13.2, the curve C has a length l, and

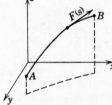

FIG. 73.

$$l = \mathbf{S}_a^b \sqrt{1 + [f'(x)]^2} \, dx. \qquad (11)$$

To illustrate: If C is the segment of the line $y = 2x$ from $x = 0$ to $x = 3$, then the length of C is $l = S_3^0 \sqrt{1 + 4} \, dx = 3\sqrt{5}$. This result checks with that obtained by elementary methods.

Example 4. Let C be a curve in space, let s denote arc length along C, let A and B be two points on C, and suppose that $s = a$ at A and $s = b$ at B. A point particle P moves along C and is acted on by a force such that the magnitude of its component in the direction of C at any position of P is $F(s)$. Find the work done on P by the force when P moves from A to B.

Divide the arc from A to B into subintervals of length Δs. In each interval Δs choose s_i and s_i' so that $F(s_i)$ and $F(s_i')$ are the maximum and minimum values of $F(s)$ in the ith interval Δs. If W_i is the actual work done by the force acting on P in the ith interval, then

$$F(s_i') \ \Delta s \leqq W_i \leqq F(s_i) \ \Delta s.$$

We leave it to the student to show that, if F is continuous, then the work done by the force on P in going from A to B is

$$W = \mathbf{S}_a^b F(s) \, ds. \qquad (12)$$

Thus, suppose an electric charge is carried along an arbitrary path $y = f(x)$ from the point (a, b) to the point (c, d), and suppose an electric field exerts a

constant force Φ on the charge in the direction of the positive end of the
x-axis.   Let s be measured along the path from (a, b).   The component of Φ
tangent to the path is $F = \Phi \cos \alpha$, where $\alpha = \tan^{-1} (dy/dx)$. Hence the
work done is (see (8) of Chapter I, Sec. 7)

$$W = \mathop{S}_{0}^{l} \Phi \cos \alpha \, ds = \int_{a}^{c} \Phi \left(\cos \alpha \, \frac{ds}{dx} \right) dx = \int_{a}^{c} \Phi \, dx = (c - a)\Phi.$$

It is seen that the work is independent of the path chosen from (a, b) to
(c, d).

Example 5.   Let R be a region on a plane vertical face of a vessel containing water.   Find the total force of the water on R, the height of the water
surface being given.

Subdivide R into strips $S_1, S_2, \cdot \cdot \cdot , S_n$ of width Δh by horizontal lines
at depths $h_0, h_1, \cdot \cdot \cdot , h_n$ below the water surface.   Let the width across

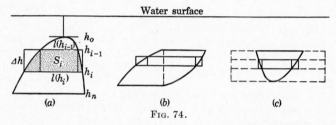

FIG. 74.

R at depth h be $l(h)$.   Suppose R is such that $l(h)$ increases with h, and also
such that, when we construct the rectangles r_i and R_i of height Δh with bases
$l(h_{i-1})$ and $l(h_i)$, respectively, S_i contains r_i and is contained in R_i [see Fig.
74 (a)].   Since the unit pressure at depth h is wh, where w is the density of
water,

$$(wh_{i-1}) \, l(h_{i-1}) \, \Delta h \le P_i \le (wh_i) \, l(h_i) \, \Delta h,$$

where P_i is the total force on S_i.   As in the preceding examples, it is seen
that, if $l(h)$ is continuous, the total force on R is

$$P = \mathop{S}_{a}^{b} wh \, l(h) \, dh, \qquad (13)$$

where a and b are the least and greatest depths of R.   If $l(h)$ decreases as h
increases [see Fig. 74 (c)], or if it is not the case that S_i contains r_i and is
contained in R_i [see Fig. 74 (b)], then (13) may be obtained by considering
the total force on a rectangle containing R [cf. the discussion of volumes of
revolution following (7)], or by breaking up R into smaller regions by vertical
lines.

As an illustration of (13), the total force on a gate valve 4 ft. in diameter
whose center is 50 ft. below the surface of a reservoir is

$$P = \mathop{S}_{48}^{52} wh2\sqrt{4 - (50 - h)^2} \, dh = 2w\int_{-2}^{2}(50 - y)\sqrt{4 - y^2} \, dy = 200\pi w.$$

EXERCISES X

1. Find the areas bounded by the following curves:
(a) $r = 2a \sin \theta$.   (b) $r = 3 - 2 \cos \theta$.   (c) $r = a \sin 2\theta$.
(d) $r = a \cos 3\theta$.   (e) $r^2 = 2a^2 \cos 2\theta$.   (f) $r = a \sin^2 (\theta/2)$.
(g) $r = \sec \theta + \tan \theta$ from $\theta = 0$ to $\theta = \pi/4$.
(h) $r^2 = a^2 b^2 / (a^2 \sin^2 \theta + b^2 \cos^2 \theta)$.
(i) the area common to $r = 3 \cos \theta$ and $r = 1 + \cos \theta$.
(j) the smaller part of the circle $r = 1$ cut off by $r = \theta$.

2. If $x = \varphi(t)$, $y = \psi(t)$ are the parametric equations of a curve C, if $x_1 = \varphi(t_1)$ and $x_2 = \varphi(t_2)$, and if the equations $x = \varphi(t)$, $y = \psi(t)$ define y as a single-valued function of x when t varies from t_1 to t_2, show that the area A bounded by C, the x-axis, and the ordinates at $x = x_1$ and $x = x_2$ is

$$A = \int_{t_1}^{t_2} (y\, D_t x)\, dt. \tag{14}$$

Using (14), find the areas bounded by:
   (a) One arch of the cycloid $x = a(\theta - \sin \theta)$, $y = a(1 - \cos \theta)$ and the x-axis.
   (b) The curve $x = a\theta$, $y = a(1 - \cos \theta)$ and the x-axis from $\theta = 0$ to $\theta = 2\pi$.
   (c) The hypocycloid $x = a \cos^3 \theta$, $y = a \sin^3 \theta$.
   (d) The loop of the curve $x^3 + y^3 = 3axy$. (Hint: Represent this curve by the parametric equations $x = 3at/(1 + t^3)$, $y = 3at^2/(1 + t^3)$.

3. Find the volumes of the following solids, using both the method of sections and the method of cylindrical shells whenever possible:
   (a) The solid obtained by rotating about the x-axis the area bounded by $y = x^2$, $y = 0$, and $x = 1$. [Hint: Use cylindrical shells concentric with the x-axis. Then $h(r) = 1 - \sqrt{r}$ in (7′).]
   (b) The solid obtained by rotating the area in (a) about the y-axis.
   (c) The solid obtained by rotating about the x-axis the area bounded by $y = \sin x$, $y = 0$, $x = 0$, and $x = \pi/2$.
   (d) The solid obtained by rotating the area in (c) about the y-axis.
   (e) The solid obtained by rotating about the x-axis the area bounded by $x^{2/3} + y^{2/3} = a^{2/3}$.
   (f) The solid obtained by rotating about the line $y = 4$ the area bounded by $y = x^2$ and $x = y^2$.
   (g) The solid obtained by rotating about the line $x = -2$ the area bounded by $x = y^2$ and $x = 1$.
   (h) The torus obtained by rotating the circle $x^2 + y^2 = a^2$ about the line $y = b$. $(b > a.)$
   (i) The solid bounded by $z = r$, $z = \sin r$, and the cylinder $r = \pi/2$.
   (j) The solid bounded by $(x^2/a^2) + (y^2/a^2) + (z^2/c^2) = 1$. (Write $r^2 = x^2 + y^2$.)
   (k) The solid bounded by $x^2 + y^2 + z^2 = 5$ and $x^2 + y^2 = 4z$.
   (l) The solid such that any section perpendicular to the x-axis is an equilateral triangle whose base is a chord of the circle $x^2 + y^2 = a^2$.

(m) The solid to the left of the plane $x = 5$ such that any section perpendicular to the x-axis is an isosceles triangle of height 10 whose base is a chord of the parabola $x = y^2$.

(n) The solid in the first octant to the left of the plane $x = 1$ such that any section perpendicular to the x-axis is a square whose base is a chord between the curves $y = x^2$ and $x = y^2$.

(o) The solid between the planes $x = 0$ and $x = 1$ such that any section perpendicular to the x-axis is a circle with center on the curve $y = \sin x$ and passing through the x-axis.

(p) The solid in the first octant to the left of the plane $x = 2$ such that the section cut by the plane $x = x_0$ is bounded by the curve $y = x_0 - z^2$.

(q) The solid in the first octant between the planes $x = 1$ and $x = 3$ and bounded by the surface $z = x \cos (y/x)$.

(r) The solid bounded by the surface $x^{1/2} + y^{1/2} + z^{1/2} = a^{1/2}$ and the coordinate planes.

4. If the area bounded by the curve $r = f(\theta)$ between $\theta = \alpha$ and $\theta = \beta$ is rotated about the polar axis, show that the volume of the solid obtained is

$$V = \int_\alpha^\beta \frac{2\pi}{3} r^3 \sin \theta \, d\theta. \tag{15}$$

Using (15), find the volumes obtained by rotating the following areas about the polar axis:

(a) The triangle bounded by $\theta = 0$, $\theta = \mathrm{Tan}^{-1} (a/h)$, and $r \cos \theta = h$.

(b) The circle $r = 2a \cos \theta$. (c) The cardioid $r = a(1 - \cos \theta)$.

5. Find the lengths of the following curves:

(a) $y^2 = x^3$ from $x = 0$ to $x = 4$.

(b) $y = \sqrt{a^2 - x^2}$ from $x = -a$ to $x = a$.

(c) $y = \log \cos x$ from $x = 0$ to $x = \pi/3$.

(d) The entire hypocycloid $x^{2/3} + y^{2/3} = a^{2/3}$.

(e) $y = (x^3/3) + x^2 + 5$ from $x = 0$ to $x = 3$.

6. Show that the length of the curve $r = g(\theta)$ from $\theta = \alpha$ to $\theta = \beta$ is

$$l = \int_\alpha^\beta \sqrt{r^2 + \left(\frac{dr}{d\theta}\right)^2} \, d\theta. \tag{16}$$

[HINT: change the variable of integration in (11) from x to θ by means of the relations $x = r \cos \theta$, $y = r \sin \theta$, remembering that $r = g(\theta)$.] Using (16), find the lengths of the following curves:

(a) The cardioid $r = a(1 - \cos \theta)$. (b) The circle $r = 2a \cos \theta$.

(c) $r = a \cos^3 (\theta/3)$.

(d) The spiral $r = \theta$ from $\theta = 0$ to $\theta = \pi$.

7. Show that the length of the curve $x = \varphi(t)$, $y = \psi(t)$ from $t = t_1$ to $t = t_2$ is

$$l = \int_{t_1}^{t_2} \sqrt{\left(\frac{dx}{dt}\right)^2 + \left(\frac{dy}{dt}\right)^2} \, dt. \tag{17}$$

Find the length of one arch of the cycloid $x = a(\theta - \sin \theta)$, $y = a(1 - \cos \theta)$. Show that the length of the ellipse $x = a \sin \varphi$, $y = b \cos \varphi$ is

$$4a \int_0^{\pi/2} \sqrt{1 - e^2 \sin^2 \varphi}\, d\varphi,$$

where e is the eccentricity of the ellipse and $b^2 = a^2(1 - e^2)$ (see Sec. 35 of Chap. V).

8. Show that the length of the space curve $y = \varphi(x)$, $z = \psi(x)$ from $x = a$ to $x = b$ is

$$l = \mathop{S}_a^b \sqrt{1 + \left(\frac{dy}{dx}\right)^2 + \left(\frac{dz}{dx}\right)^2}\, dx. \tag{18}$$

Find the length of the line $x = 2y = -z$ from $(0, 0, 0)$ to $(2, 1, -2)$, and check by elementary geometry. Write (18) with y the independent variable.

Show that the length of the space curve $x = \varphi(t)$, $y = \psi(t)$, $z = \theta(t)$ from $t = t_1$ to $t = t_2$ is

$$l = \mathop{S}_{t_1}^{t_2} \sqrt{\left(\frac{dx}{dt}\right)^2 + \left(\frac{dy}{dt}\right)^2 + \left(\frac{dz}{dt}\right)^2}\, dt. \tag{19}$$

9. The force F of attraction between two point particles of masses M and m distant r units apart is $F = k\,(mM/r^2)$. Find the work done by F when r varies from 2 to 1; from 10 to 1; from 1000 to 1; from "infinity" to 1; from 1 to 0.1; from 1 to 0.

10. The force F exerted by a spring is $F = kx$, where x is the extension of the spring beyond its natural length. For a certain spring $F = 100$ when $x = 5$. Find the work done in stretching the spring from $x = 2$ to $x = 6$.

11. A body falls according to the law $s = (g/k^2)(e^{-kt} + kt - 1)$. If the force F of resistance is $F = cv$, where $v = ds/dt$, find the work done against F when the body falls from $t = 0$ to $t = 10$.

12. If an electric current flows around a circular coil of wire of radius a, the force F exerted on a small magnet located on the axis of the coil and at distance x from the center of the coil is $F = kx/(a^2 + x^2)^{3/2}$. Find the work done by F when the magnet is brought from $x = a/2$ to $x = 0$.

13. The force F of repulsion between two positive electric point charges E and E' distant r units apart is $F = k(EE'/r^2)$. If E is fixed at the pole and if E' is carried along an arbitrary path $r = f(\theta)$ from the point (a, α) to the point (b, β), show that the work done is independent of the path and is equal to $kEE'\left(\dfrac{1}{b} - \dfrac{1}{a}\right)$, provided the path does not go through the pole.

$$\left[\text{Hint: If we write } s = \mathop{S}_\alpha^\theta \sqrt{r^2 + \left(\frac{dr}{d\theta}\right)^2}\, d\theta, \text{ then by Theorem 29.2,}\right.$$

$$\left.\frac{ds}{d\theta} = \sqrt{r^2 + \left(\frac{dr}{d\theta}\right)^2}. \text{ Also, see Ex. VI, 5 of Chap. I.}\right]$$

14. If an electric current flows along a long, straight wire, then a force $F = k/r$ is exerted on a small magnet distant r from the wire, the direction of F being perpendicular to the wire and to the radius vector r. If the wire is perpendicular to the $r\theta$-plane and goes through the pole, and if the magnet is carried along an arbitrary path $r = f(\theta)$ from the point (a, α) to the point (b, β), show that the work done is independent of the path and is equal to $k(\beta - \alpha)$, provided the path is traced out by the point (r, θ) as θ varies from α to β. Discuss the determination of α and β when the path goes around the wire more than once.

15. Show that the work done on a particle, when accelerated by a force F, is equal to the gain in kinetic energy of the particle. [HINT: Write

$$F = m\frac{dv}{dt} = m\frac{dv}{dx}\frac{dx}{dt} = mv\frac{dv}{dx}. \Big]$$

16. Show by (12) that, if gas expands in an engine cylinder according to the law $p = f(v)$, where p is the unit pressure and v the volume of the gas, then the work done on the piston by the gas is

$$W = \mathbf{S}_{v_1}^{v_2} p \, dv. \tag{20}$$

[HINT: If A is the piston area, then $F = pA$. In (12) let $s = v/A$.] Evaluate (20) when $pv^n = C$ with p_1, v_1, and p_2 given.

17. Show that (20) holds when the gas is contained in an expanding sphere.

18. If each particle of material in a volume V is raised (or lowered) to a certain horizontal plane H, show that the work done is

$$W = \mathbf{S}_{h_1}^{h_2} wh \, A(h) \, dh, \tag{21}$$

where w is the density of the material, h is the distance from the plane H to an arbitrary horizontal section of V, and $A(h)$ is the area of this section. Using (21), find:

(a) The work done on a turbine by the water in a hemispherical reservoir of 100 ft. radius when the reservoir is drained through the turbine, the turbine being 500 ft. below the original water level. How many 100-watt electric lights could be supplied by this turbine for 10 hr. if a watt-hour equals 2655 ft.-lb. of energy?

(b) The work done in building the great pyramid of Gizeh. [This pyramid was originally (about) 480 ft. high with a square base 750 ft. on a side. The stone in this pyramid weighs (about) 200 lb. per cubic foot.] If a slave did 500,000 ft.-lb. of work in a day, how many slaves would be needed to build this pyramid in ten years?

19. Find the force exerted by the water on a vertical trapezoidal dam 100 ft. long at the top, 40 ft. long at the bottom, and 30 ft. high, the water level being at the top of the dam. ($w = 62.4$ for water.)

20. A hole is torn in a ship's side, the hole being roughly an ellipse with axes 10 and 2 ft. long, respectively, the long axis horizontal and 8 ft. below the water line. Find the force exerted by the water on a patch over this hole.

21. The sides of a storage tank are vertical planes. Find the force exerted by the water on that part of a side bounded by the curves $y = x^2$, $y = 0$, and $x = 3$, the water level being 15 ft. above the line $y = 0$.

22. Derive a formula for the force of attraction between a point particle of mass M at the pole and a fine wire of mass m per foot, the wire being represented by the equation $r = f(\theta)$ and extending from $\theta = \alpha$ to $\theta = \beta$. Derive a formula for this force, using rectangular coordinates. (Use the law of attraction in Ex. 9.)

23. Derive a formula for the weight of the material in a volume V, the density ρ of the material being a function of x alone [see (6)]; of r alone [see (7)].

24. Derive a formula for the rate of flow of water in a circular pipe, given the velocity of the water as a function $f(r)$ of the distance r from the center of the pipe.

25. Derive a formula for the total amount of light falling from a point source S upon a plane area in the form of a circular ring, the source being on the line perpendicular to the plane of the ring and passing through the center of the ring. (The density of illumination at any point P of the ring is inversely proportional to the square of the distance from P to the source S and directly proportional to the cosine of the angle SPN, where PN is perpendicular to the plane of the ring.)

26. Show that the volume of any cylinder is the product of its base by its altitude.

27. *Average Values.* If $f(x)$ is a real function of x, *the average value $\bar{f}$ of $f(x)$ with respect to x* over a given interval $a \leqq x \leqq b$ is defined to be

$$\bar{f} = \frac{1}{b - a} \int_a^b f(x) \, dx.$$

Let $f(x) = 2$ for $-1 \leqq x < 0$, $f(x) = x + 2$ for $0 \leqq x < 2$, and $f(x) = 4(x - 3)^2$ for $2 \leqq x \leqq 3$. Find the average value of $f(x)$ over the interval $[-1, 3]$; over $[2, 3]$; over $[0, 2]$.

28. Find the average value of each of the following functions for the interval $-3 \leqq x \leqq 3$: x^2; $\cos (3x/2)$; $\sinh x$; $3x^4$; $\sin (x/2)$.

29. Repeat Ex. 28 for the interval $-3 \leqq x \leqq 0$; for $0 \leqq x \leqq 3$.

30. Find the average over $-2 \leqq x \leqq +2$ of the functions $2 \cos^3 x$; $(\cos 2x \sin^3 x - 2)$.

31. *Root-mean-square-Values.* By definition the *root-mean-square* value $\bar{\bar{f}}$ of $f(x)$ over the interval $a \leqq x \leqq b$ is

$$\bar{\bar{f}} = \text{r.m.s.} \, f = \sqrt{\frac{\int_a^b [f(x)]^2 \, dx}{(b - a)}}.$$

(a) Compute r.m.s. for the function given in Ex. 27.

(b) Compute r.m.s. for each of the functions in Ex. 28, for $-3 \leqq x \leqq 3$.

(c) Repeat Ex. 31b for the intervals $-3 \leqq x \leqq 0$ and $0 \leqq x \leqq 3$.

(d) Find r.m.s. for $\sin t$ over $0 \leqq t \leqq \pi/4$; $0 \leqq t \leqq \pi/2$; $0 \leqq t \leqq \pi$; $0 \leqq t \leqq 2\pi$.

32. Let $f_1 = \sin(w_1 t + s_1)$, $f_2 = \sin(w_2 t + s_2)$, where s_1 and s_2 are real constants, and w_1 and w_2 are real and rational. Find the average of the product $f_1 f_2$ over a complete period of the product $(f_1 f_2)$.

[*Ans.* Zero, if $w_1 \neq w_2$; $\frac{1}{2} \cos(s_1 - s_2)$ if $w_1 = w_2$.]

What happens when w_1 and w_2 are not commensurable?

33. Find the average of the product of $\sin t$ and $\cos t$ over a complete period of their product.

34. Prove the following:

THEOREM 14.1. *Let $f(x)$ and $g(x)$ be two single-valued functions defined and continuous over $a \leq x \leq b$, except for possibly a finite number of points. If the ratio of the functions is not constant throughout, then the average value of the product of f and g is numerically less than the product of their r.m.s. for the same interval. If the ratio is constant throughout the interval, the average value of the product fg is equal to the product of their r.m.s. for the same interval.*

35. Prove the following:

THEOREM 14.2. *If $g(x)$ is not a constant, the average value of the function $g(x)$ is numerically less than its r.m.s. value for the same interval. If g is constant, the average value of $g(x)$ is numerically equal to its r.m.s. for the same interval.* [HINT: In Ex. 34 set $f(x) = 1$.]

36. An *even* function is one for which

$$f(-x) = f(x),$$

and an *odd* function is one for which

$$f(-x) = -f(x).$$

Prove: (a) The average of an even function over $-a \leq x \leq a$ is equal to the average over $-a \leq x \leq 0$ and to the average over $0 \leq x \leq +a$.

(b) The average of an odd function over $-a \leq x \leq a$ is zero. The average of an odd function over $-a \leq x \leq 0$ is the negative of the average over $0 \leq x \leq +a$.

(c) The r.m.s. for any even (or any odd) function is the same for each of the intervals $-a \leq x \leq 0$, $0 \leq x \leq a$, $-a \leq x \leq a$.

37. The electromotive forces for a set of three networks are given by:

(a) $e_1 = 1600 \sin(360\pi t + 31°) - 30 \cos(120\pi t - 13°)$.

(b) $e_2 = 110 \cos 60\pi t + 32 \cos(180\pi t + 69°)$.

(c) $e_3 = 100 \cos 50\pi t + 400 \sin 50\pi t - 20 \sin 150\pi t + 10 \cos 150\pi t$,

and the corresponding currents by:

(a') $i_1 = 12.52 \cos(360\pi t + 87° 20') + 0.237 \sin(120\pi t - 34° 30')$.

(b') $i_2 = 2.76 \sin(60\pi t - 22°) + 3.45 \cos(180\pi t + 13°)$.

(c') $i_3 = 12 \sin 50\pi t + 30 \cos 50\pi t + 8 \sin 150\pi t - 6 \cos 150\pi t$.

(i) Find the smallest period for each of the currents and e.m.f. given above.

(ii) Find r.m.s. value of each of the e.m.f.'s and currents for an interval large compared with the period. How will these values compare with voltmeter and ammeter indications?

(iii) The instantaneous powers of the networks above are $p_1 = e_1 i_1$, $p_2 = e_2 i_2$, $p_3 = e_3 i_3$, respectively. Find the average power of a complete period in each case. How will these values compare with wattmeter indications?

38. The current and e.m.f. for a certain line are expressed in the form

$$e = E_1 \sin (wt + \psi_1) + E_3 \sin (3wt + \psi_3) + E_5 \sin (5wt + \psi_5),$$
$$i = I_1 \sin (wt + \theta_1) + I_3 \sin (3wt + \theta_3) + I_5 \sin (5wt + \theta_5).$$

Prove that for complete period, the r.m.s. value of e.m.f. and current are

$$\bar{e} = \sqrt{\frac{E_1^2 + E_3^2 + E_5^2}{2}}, \qquad \bar{i} = \sqrt{\frac{I_1^2 + I_3^2 + I_5^2}{2}},$$

and that the average power is

$$\bar{p} = \frac{E_1 I_1 \cos (\theta_1 - \psi_1) + E_3 I_3 \cos (\theta_3 - \psi_3) + E_5 I_5 \cos (\theta_5 - \psi_5)}{2}.$$

39. Generalize the result in Ex. 38 if

$$e = \sum_{k=1}^{\infty} E_{2k-1} \cos (2k - 1)wt + \sum_{k=1}^{\infty} F_{2k-1} \sin (2k - 1) wt,$$

$$i = \sum_{k=1}^{\infty} I_{2k-1} \cos (2k - 1)wt + \sum_{k=1}^{\infty} H_{2k-1} \sin (2k - 1)wt.$$

Ans.
$$\bar{e} = \sqrt{\frac{E_1^2 + F_1^2 + E_3^2 + F_3^2 + \cdots}{2}},$$

$$\bar{p} = \frac{E_1 I_1 + F_1 H_1 + E_3 I_3 + F_3 H_3 + \cdots}{2}.$$

If the impedance of the circuit be denoted by z, then $e = zi$. Show that $\bar{p} \leq \overline{ei}$, the equality holding when the ratio $e/i = z$ is a constant, i.e., when the impedance is a pure resistance; the inequality holds when z contains non-zero reactance. In electrical engineering work, $\bar{p}/\overline{ei}$ is known as the *power factor*.

15. Line Integrals. It is readily possible to state Definition 13.2 in more general form so that definite integrals may have much wider application than has been indicated above. Let us think of f as denoting any quantity having a definite value at each point of some portion of space, i.e., as a point function; for example, f may be the intensity of an electric field at any point of space, or f may be the unit pressure at any point in the interior of a turbine, or f may be some other physical or geometrical quantity; in particular, f need not be a function of three variables, and the value of f at any point P may be determined without

reference to any coordinate system.   We shall denote the value
of f at P by $f(P)$ (see Sec. 23 of Chap. I.)

DEFINITION 15.1.   *Let f denote a real, single-valued function
defined in some region R of space*,*

*and let $\widehat{AB}$ be an arc of finite
length of a curve C lying in R.
Perform the following operations*:

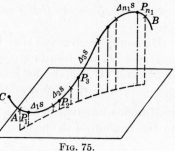

FIG. 75.

I. *Subdivide the arc $\widehat{AB}$ into an
arbitrary finite number n_1 of nonoverlapping subintervals I_1, I_2,
$\cdots$, I_{n_1} of lengths $\Delta_1 s$, $\Delta_2 s$, $\cdots$,
$\Delta_{n_1} s$ which need not be equal.   II.
In each interval I_i choose an
arbitrary point P_i.   III. Form the sum*

$$S_1 = \sum_{i=1}^{n_1} f(P_i)\,\Delta_i s$$
$$= f(P_1)\,\Delta_1 s + f(P_2)\,\Delta_2 s + \cdots + f(P_{n_1})\,\Delta_{n_1} s. \tag{1}$$

IV. *By repeated applications of steps I to III, construct an infinite
sequence*

$$S_1 = \sum_{i=1}^{n_1} f(P_i)\,\Delta_i s, \qquad S_2 = \sum_{i=1}^{n_2} f(P_i)\,\Delta_i s, \qquad \cdots ,$$

$$S_k = \sum_{i=1}^{n_k} f(P_i)\,\Delta_i s, \qquad \cdots \tag{2}$$

in any manner such that

$$\lim_{k \to \infty} \delta_k = 0, \tag{3}$$

where δ_k is the length of the longest interval in the sum S_k.   If
$\lim\limits_{k \to \infty} S_k$ *exists and has the same value for every possible construction
of the sequence (2) meeting condition (3), then this limit is denoted
by†* $S_A^B f(P)\, ds$, *i.e.,*

---

* It is possible to give a purely algebraic interpretation to the content of
this section by regarding "space" as the set of all number triples (x, y, z).

† *A* and *B* are not numbers but merely letters denoting the end points of *C*.

$$S_A^B f(P)\ ds = \lim_{k \to \infty} S_k. \tag{4}$$

We call $S_A^B f(P)\ ds$ *the line integral of* f *with respect to* s *along the arc* $\widehat{AB}$, *and we say that* f *is summable along* $\widehat{AB}$ *if* $S_A^B f(P)\ ds$ *exists.*

It should be observed that Definition 15.1 involves no specific reference to any coordinate system. A physical interpretation of (1) and (4) is given by Example 4 of Sec. 14. We shall now give a geometric interpretation of (1). Suppose $f(x,\ y)$ is a continuous function of x and y, $\widehat{AB}$ is an arc of a curve C lying in the domain of definition of $f(x,\ y)$, S is the cylindric surface

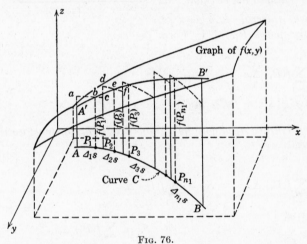

Fig. 76.

through C with elements parallel to the z-axis, $A'B'$ is the curve of intersection of S with the graph of $f(x,\ y)$, and P_i denotes $(x_i,\ y_i)$. Then $f(P_i)\ \Delta_i s$ represents the area of a cylindric rectangle of height $f(P_i)$ and base $\Delta_i s$, and the sum (1) represents an approximation to the cylindric area $ABB'A'$. (In Fig. 76 the dotted lines abc, def, $\cdots$ represent the sections of S cut by planes parallel to the xy-plane through b, e, $\cdots$.) It may be shown, as in Sec. 13, that $S_A^B f(P)\ ds$ represents exactly the area $ABB'A'$ (see Ex. XI, 3).

Example 1. An approximate value of $S_{0,0,0}^{2,1,-2} (x^2 - yz)\ ds$ along the line $x = 2y = -z$ is obtained by subdividing the interval from $(0,\ 0,\ 0)$ to

$(2, 1, -2)$ into five equal parts of length, $\frac{3}{5}$ and taking P_i for each subinterval as the end point nearest the origin. Then

$$P_1 = (0, 0, 0), P_2 = (0.4, 0.2, -0.4), \cdots, P_5 = (1.6, 0.8, -1.6),$$

and by (1) we have

$$S_1 = [0^2 - (0)(0)](\tfrac{3}{5}) + [(0.4)^2 - (0.2)(-0.4)](\tfrac{3}{5}) + \cdots$$
$$+ [(1.6)^2 - (0.8)(-1.6)](\tfrac{3}{5}) = 4.32.$$

We leave it to the student to show that S_1 is a lower bound for the value of the given integral, and to find an upper bound for this value.

As in the case of a total derivative [see Chap. I, Sec. 18, paragraph (a)], it is implied in the notation $\mathop{\mathrm{S}}\nolimits_A^B f(P)\, ds$ that f is always to be evaluated along that curve C whose arc length is measured by s. To compute $\mathop{\mathrm{S}}\nolimits_A^B f(P)\, ds$ it is customary to represent $f(P)$ along C by that function $\bar{f}(s)$ such that $f(P) \equiv \bar{f}(s)$ when P and s denote the same point on C. It is evident that $\mathop{\mathrm{S}}\nolimits_A^B f(P)\, ds = \mathop{\mathrm{S}}\nolimits_{s_A}^{s_B} \bar{f}(s)\, ds$, where $s = s_A$ at A and $s = s_B$ at B, and by Theorem 13.1 it follows that, if f is integrable,

$$\mathop{\mathrm{S}}\nolimits_A^B f(P)\, ds = \int_{s_A}^{s_B} \bar{f}(s)\, ds. \tag{5}$$

If f is represented by a function $f(x, y, z)$ of the rectangular coordinates x, y, and z in space, and if C is represented by the parametric equations

$$x = p(s), \qquad y = q(s), \qquad z = r(s), \tag{6}$$

then $\bar{f}(s) = f[p(s), q(s), r(s)]$. By (5) and the remark following Definition 11.2,

$$\mathop{\mathrm{S}}\nolimits_A^B f(P)\, ds = \mathop{\mathrm{S}}\nolimits_A^B f(x, y, z)\, ds = \int_{s_A}^{s_B} f(x, y, z)\, ds, \tag{7}$$

where in the right member of (7) x, y, and z are determined by (6). Formulas similar to (7) may be obtained when f and C are represented in other coordinate systems.

Thus, in Example 1, the parametric equations of the path of integration are $x = \frac{2}{3}s$, $y = \frac{1}{3}s$, $z = -\frac{2}{3}s$, where s denotes arc length from the origin, and the given integral is equal to $\int_0^3 \frac{2}{3}s^2\, ds = 6$.

Definition 15.1 may be modified in many ways. For example, let $\Delta_i x$ denote the length of the projection of the interval I_i on the x-axis. If in Definition 15.1 we replace $\Delta_i s$ everywhere by $\Delta_i x$, we arrive at the quantity

$$S_A^B f(x,\, y,\, z)\, dx = \lim_{k \to \infty} \sum_{i=1}^{n_k} f(P_i)\, \Delta_i x, \tag{8}$$

where P moves along C. If the equations of C are

$$y = q(x), \qquad z = r(x), \tag{9}$$

then it may be shown that

$$S_A^B f(x,\, y,\, z)\, dx = \int_{x_A}^{x_B} f(x,\, y,\, z)\, dx, \tag{10}$$

where in the right member of (10) y and z are determined by (9).

Example 2. Evaluate $S_{0,-5}^{0,5}\, y\, dx$ along the right-hand half of the circle $x^2 + y^2 = 25$.

To represent y as a single-valued function of x along the path C of integration, we must break up C into two parts, C_1 and C_2, extending from $(0, -5)$ to $(5, 0)$ and from $(5, 0)$ to $(0, 5)$, respectively. Then $y = -\sqrt{25 - x^2}$ along C_1 and $y = \sqrt{25 - x^2}$ along C_2. Hence

$$S_{0,-5}^{0,5}\, y\, dx = S_{0,-5}^{5,0}\, y\, dx + S_{5,0}^{0,5}\, y\, dx$$

$$= \int_0^5 -\sqrt{25 - x^2}\, dx + \int_5^0 \sqrt{25 - x^2}\, dx = -\frac{25\pi}{2}.$$

Observe that the limits in the integrals correspond to the direction of motion along C_1 and C_2.

Fig. 77.

Example 3. Evaluate $S_{0,-5}^{0,5}\, y\, dx$ along the line $x = 0$.

The line segment from $(0, -5)$ to $(0, 5)$ has a projection on the x-axis of length 0 (i.e., $dx = 0$), and the value of the given integral is 0. However, if we try to evaluate the given integral by the method of Example 2, we find that we cannot express y as a function of x along the path of integration. This example illustrates the common situation in which $S_A^B f(P)\, dx$ cannot be represented as in (10).

In Definition 15.1 let $\Delta_i t$ be the time required for P to pass over the interval I_i. If $\Delta_i s$ is everywhere replaced by $\Delta_i t$, we are led to the quantity

$$S_A^B f(x,\, y,\, z)\, dt = \lim_{k \to \infty} \sum_{i=1}^{n_k} f(P_i)\, \Delta_i t. \tag{11}$$

If the equations of C are

$$x = p(t), \qquad y = q(t), \qquad z = r(t), \tag{12}$$

then

$$S_A^B f(x, y, z) \, dt = \int_{t_A}^{t_B} f(x, y, z) \, dt. \tag{13}$$

Formula (11) may be modified so as to define a *Stieltjes* integral. Let u be a parameter along C and let $\varphi(u)$ be a function defined for $u_A \leqq u \leqq u_B$. If u_{i-1} and u_i are the values of u at the end points of I_i, if $\Delta_i\varphi = \varphi(u_i) - \varphi(u_{i-1})$, and if in Definition 15.1, $\Delta_i s$ is everywhere replaced by $\Delta_i\varphi$, then we are led to the quantity

$$S_A^B f(P) \, d\varphi(u) = \lim_{k \to \infty} \sum_{i=1}^{n_k} f(P_i) \, \Delta_i\varphi \tag{14}$$

which is called the *Stieltjes integral* of f with respect to φ along C. This integral has many applications in modern mathematics, and is of particular interest when φ is discontinuous so that the differential $d\varphi(u)$ does not exist.

All of the integrals discussed above are referred to generally as line integrals.

EXERCISES XI

1. Using (1), find approximate values of the following integrals. Choose the points P_i so as to obtain *upper* and *lower bounds* of the values of these integrals as in Example 1. Use only a small number of intervals, say 3, 4, or 5. Also, evaluate the integrals directly by (7), (10), or the like.

(a) $S_{0,1}^{2,3} (x^2 + 2y) \, ds$, $S_{0,1}^{2,3} (x^2 + 2y) \, dx$, and $S_{0,1}^{2,3} (x^2 + 2y) \, dy$ along the line $y = x + 1$.

(b) $S_{0,5}^{5,0} (x^2 - xy) \, ds$ and $S_{0,5}^{5,0} (x^2 - xy) \, dx + (x^2 + xy) \, dy$ along the short arc of the circle $x^2 + y^2 = 25$.

(c) $S_{0,0}^{9,18} \dfrac{y}{x+1} \, ds$ and $S_{0,0}^{9,18} \dfrac{y^2}{x+1} \, dx + \dfrac{1}{x^3+1} \, dy$ along the curve $9y^2 = 4x^3$.

(d) $S_{2,1,-2}^{10,5,-10} (x + yz^2) \, ds$ and $S_{2,1,-2}^{10,5,-10} (x + yz^2) \, dx + xyz \, dy$ along the line $x = 2y = -z$.

(e) $S_{0,1,0}^{3,10,9} \dfrac{yz}{x^2+1} \, ds$ and $S_{0,1,0}^{3,10,9} \dfrac{yz}{x^2+1} \, dx + \dfrac{yz}{x^2+1} \, dz$ along the curve $y = x^2 + 1$, $z = x^3/3$.

(f) $S_A^B \dfrac{x-y}{z} \, ds$, $S_A^B \dfrac{x-y}{z} \, dt$, and $S_A^B \dfrac{x-y}{z} \, dx$ along the curve $x = t - 3$, $y = \dfrac{2\sqrt{2}}{3}t^{3/2}$, $z = \dfrac{1}{2}t^2 + 1$, where A is at $t = 0$ and B is at $t = 4$.

(g) $S_A^B \log (x^2 + y^2 + z^2) \, ds$ and $S_A^B \log (x^2 + y^2 + z^2) \, dx$ along the helix $x = a \cos \theta$, $y = a \sin \theta$, $z = a\theta$, where A is at $\theta = 0$ and B is at $\theta = \pi$.

2. Evaluate the following integrals:

(a) $S_{1,-1}^{4,2} y \, dx$ along the curve $x = y^2$. (Two ways.)

(b) $S_{5,-4}^{5,4} xy \, dx$ along the hyperbola $x^2 - y^2 = 9$. (Two ways.)

(c) $S_{0,0}^{\pi,0} x\,dy$ along the curve $y = \sin x$.

(d) $S_C xy^2\,dy$, where C is the circle $x^2 + y^2 = 1$, and where the subscript C indicates that the integral is to be taken all the way around the curve C in the counterclockwise direction. [Start at the point $(0, 1)$ and break up C into two parts.]

(e) $S_C (2x^2 - y^2)\,dx$, where C is the closed path consisting of the lines $y = 0$, $x = 1$, and $y = x$.

(f) $\displaystyle S_C \frac{x + y}{xy + 100}\,dy$, where C is the square consisting of the lines $x = \pm 5$, $y = \pm 5$.

(g) $S_{0,0}^{2,0} (x + y)\,dx + x\,dy$ when C is the curve $y = 2x - x^2$ and also when C is the line $y = 0$.

(h) $S_C (x + y)\,dx + x\,dy$ around various closed curves. Why is the result always 0?

(i) $S_C (x - y)\,dx + x^2\,dy$ when: (1) C is the ellipse $16x^2 + 9y^2 = 144$. (2) C consists of the parabola $y = x^2$ and the line $y = 2$. (3) C is the square with sides on the lines $y = 0$, $y = 3$, $x = 0$, $x = 3$. (4) C is the closed curve consisting of the line $x = 1$ and the curve $y^2 = x^3$. (5) C is the closed curve consisting of $y = x$ and $x = y^2$.

(j) $S_{1,1,1}^{2,4,\frac{1}{4}} (x^2 + y^2)\,dx + z\,dy + xy\,dz$ along the curve $x^2 = y = 1/z$.

(k) $S_C x\,dx + (x - z)\,dy + y^2\,dz$ when: (1) C is the curve of intersection of $z = x^2 + y^2$ and $z = 1$. (2) C is the curve of intersection of $z = x^2 + y^2$ and $x + z = 1$. (3) C is the curve $y = x + 1$, $z = x^2$ from $(1, 2, 1)$ to $(-1, 0, 1)$. (4) C is the curve of intersection of $x^2 + y^2 = z^2$ and $x^2 + z^2 = 1$.

(l) $S_C z\,dx + 2y\,dy + x\,dz$ around various closed curves in space. Why is the result always 0?

3. With reference to Fig. 76, show that $S_A^B f(P)\,ds$ represents the area $ABB'A'$, and that $S_A^B f(x, y)\,dx$ and $S_A^B f(x, y)\,dy$ represent the areas of the projections of the figure $ABB'A'$ upon the xz- and yz-planes, respectively [cf. the proof of (5) in Sec. 13].

4. Show that

$$S_A^B f(P)\,ds = S_A^B f(P) \sec \alpha\,dx = S_A^B f(P) \sec \beta\,dy = S_A^B f(P) \sec \gamma\,dz,$$

where α, β, γ are the direction angles of the path C of integration at any point on C, and where $\sec \alpha = \dfrac{ds}{dx} = \sqrt{1 + \left(\dfrac{dy}{dx}\right)^2 + \left(\dfrac{dz}{dx}\right)^2}$ when the equations of C are in the form $y = q(x)$, $z = r(x)$, $\sec \beta$ and $\sec \gamma$ being expressed in a similar manner. Also, show that $S_A^B f(P) \cos \alpha\,ds = S_A^B f(P)\,dx$, etc. Evaluate $S_{0,0,0}^{1,3,1} xy\,ds$ along the curve $y = 3x$, $z = x^2$.

5. Define the symbol $\int_a^b f(u)\,d\varphi(u)$. When does

$$S_a^b f(u)\,d\varphi(u) = \int_a^b f(u)\,d\varphi(u)? \tag{15}$$

Evaluate $S_0^2 f(u)\,d\varphi(u)$ when $f(u) = e^u$ and $\varphi(u)$ is given by the formulas $\varphi(u) = -3$ when $0 \leqq u < 1$ and $\varphi(u) = 5u$ when $1 \leqq u \leqq 2$. Can this integral be evaluated by (15)?　　　　　　　*Ans.* $5e^2 + 3e$.

16. Applications of Line Integrals. In this section we shall give a few typical applications of line integrals.

Work. Let C be a curve in space with arc length s along which a point particle is moving, and let α, β, γ be the direction angles of C at any point on C. Suppose that at each point P on C this particle is acted on by a force of magnitude $F(P)$ along the line with direction angles $\alpha_F, \beta_F, \gamma_F$ (which vary with P). Let

Fig. 78.

θ be the angle between the direction of the force and the direction of C at any point P. Then the component of the force in the direction of C is $F(P) \cos \theta$, and it may be shown (as in Example 4 of Sec. 14) that the work done on the particle by the force in going from A to B is

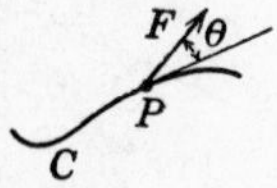

$$W = \mathop{S}\nolimits_A^B F(P) \cos \theta \, ds. \tag{1}$$

To evaluate this integral let us represent the x, y, and z-components of F by $X(x, y, z)$, $Y(x, y, z)$, and $Z(x, y, z)$. Then

$$F(P) \cos \alpha_F = X(x, y, z), \qquad F(P) \cos \beta_F = Y(x, y, z),$$
$$F(P) \cos \gamma_F = Z(x, y, z). \tag{2}$$

If in (1) we write

$$\cos \theta = \cos \alpha_F \cos \alpha + \cos \beta_F \cos \beta + \cos \gamma_F \cos \gamma$$
$$= \cos \alpha_F \frac{dx}{ds} + \cos \beta_F \frac{dy}{ds} + \cos \gamma_F \frac{dz}{ds}$$

(see Chap. I, Ex. XIX, 37), it follows by (2) that

$$W = \int_A^B X(x, y, z) \frac{dx}{ds} \, ds + \int_A^B Y(x, y, z) \frac{dy}{ds} \, ds$$
$$+ \int_A^B Z(x, y, z) \frac{dz}{ds} \, ds,$$

and hence that

$$W = \int_A^B X(x, y, z) \, dx + Y(x, y, z) \, dy + Z(x, y, z) \, dz, \tag{3}$$

where x, y, and z are determined as functions of each other by the equations of the path of the moving particle. We leave it to the student to state the requisite hypotheses and restrictions in order that this result may be valid. It follows from Ex. VIII,

14, that W is independent of the path C joining A and B when and only when $X\,dx + Y\,dy + Z\,dz$ is exact. If C lies in the xy-plane, then $\cos \gamma = 0$, X and Y may be represented along C as functions of x and y alone, and the work done is

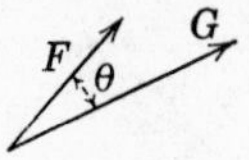

$$W = \int_A^B X(x, y)\,dx + Y(x, y)\,dy, \qquad (3')$$

Fig. 79.　W being independent of the path when and only when

$$X\,dx + Y\,dy$$

is exact.

It is often advantageous to write (1) in vector notation.

Definition 16.1. *If $\mathbf{F}$ and $\mathbf{G}$ are two vectors of lengths F and G, then the symbol $\mathbf{F} \cdot \mathbf{G}$, called the scalar product of $\mathbf{F}$ and $\mathbf{G}$, is defined by the formula*

$$\mathbf{F} \cdot \mathbf{G} = FG \cos \theta = length\ of\ \mathbf{F} \times length\ of\ \mathbf{G} \times \cos \theta, \qquad (4)$$

where θ is the angle between $\mathbf{F}$ and $\mathbf{G}$ (Fig. 79).

In constructing the integral (1), we take the limit of the sum

$$S_k = F(P_1) \cos \theta_1 \Delta_1 s + F(P_2) \cos \theta_2 \Delta_2 s + \cdots$$
$$+ F(P_{n_k}) \cos \theta_{n_k} \Delta_{n_k} s. \qquad (5)$$

Let $\Delta_i \mathbf{r}$ be the vector joining the end-points of the interval I_i, let $\mathbf{F}_i$ be the vector representing the actual force acting at P_i, and using the same intervals I_i and points P_i as in (5), let us form the sum

$$\bar{S}_k = \mathbf{F}_1 \cdot \Delta_1 \mathbf{r} + \mathbf{F}_2 \cdot \Delta_2 \mathbf{r} + \cdots$$
$$+ \mathbf{F}_{n_k} \cdot \Delta_{n_k} \mathbf{r}. \qquad (6)$$

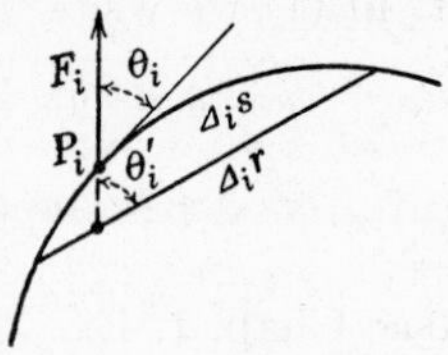

If θ_i' is the angle between $\mathbf{F}_i$ and $\Delta_i \mathbf{r}$, then by (4)

Fig. 80.

$$\mathbf{F}_i \cdot \Delta_i \mathbf{r} = F(P_i) \cos \theta_i'(\Delta_i c), \qquad (7)$$

where $\Delta_i c$ is the length of $\Delta_i \mathbf{r}$. Suppose $\mathbf{F}$ and C to be such that, for any positive number ϵ, we can take all the intervals $\Delta_i s$ sufficiently small that*

---

* It is insufficient to assume merely that $\lim\limits_{\Delta_i s \to 0} \dfrac{\Delta_i c \cos \theta_i'}{\Delta_i s \cos \theta_i} = 1$ at each point P_i. To illustrate this point, let $y = 1/x$, so that $dy = -(1/x^2)\,\Delta x$. Although $\lim\limits_{\Delta x \to 0} \Delta y / dy = 1$ when Δy and dy are computed from any fixed point $x = x_0$, yet $\Delta y / dy$ becomes infinite when computed with the values $x = 1/2^n$, $\Delta x = (1/2^{2n}) - (1/2^n)$ $(n = 1, 2, \cdots)$ even though $\Delta x \to 0$. Without condition (8) we might be able to choose P_1 (for example) for successive

$$1 - \epsilon < \frac{(\Delta_i c) \cos \theta_i'}{(\Delta_i s) \cos \theta_i} < 1 + \epsilon \tag{8}$$

for every value of i from 1 to n_k and for every position of P_i in I_i. Then

$$(1 - \epsilon)S_k < \bar{S}_k < (1 + \epsilon)S_k, \tag{9}$$

and as ϵ can be taken arbitrarily small, (5) and (6) have the same limit as $k \to \infty$. If we denote the limit of (6) by $S_A^B \mathbf{F} \cdot d\mathbf{r}$, then

$$W = \mathbf{S}_A^B \mathbf{F} \cdot d\mathbf{r} = \mathbf{S}_A^B F(P) \cos \theta \, ds$$
$$= \mathbf{S}_A^B X \, dx + Y \, dy + Z \, dz. \tag{10}$$

Fluid Flow. Suppose a liquid of unit depth is flowing over the horizontal xy-plane in such a manner that the vector velocity **V** of the liquid is everywhere horizontal and independent of the depth of the point at which it is meas-
ured. Let C be an arbitrary curve in the xy-plane, let A and B be two points on C, and let S be the cylindric surface through C with elements parallel to the z-axis. We wish to compute the volume Q of liquid flowing per unit of time across the arc $\widehat{AB}$ (i.e., through S between the ordinates at A and B). We shall give here only an intuitive derivation of Q, and shall postpone to Sec. 20 the rigorous derivation

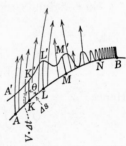

Fig. 81.

of Q. The region occupied by the liquid flowing across a short interval of arc Δs during a sufficiently short interval of time Δt is a cylinder of unit height whose base $KLL'K'$ (see Fig. 81) is approximately a parallelogram* with edges of lengths Δs and $V \cdot \Delta t$ (approximately, V varying along the path of flow and perhaps also varying with the time at each point). Hence the volume R of this region is approximately

$$R = (V \cdot \Delta t)(\Delta s) \sin \theta \ (1),$$

---

values of k so that the ratio of the first terms in (5) and (6) behaved in this same manner. It will be seen in Part C that (8) involves the idea of uniform continuity.

* Can this be said of the liquid flowing across the interval $\widehat{LM}$, or across the last interval $\widehat{NB}$, however small Δs and Δt may be? [See Chap. I, Ex. II, 1(e), (f), for other possible illustrations of the curve $A'K'L'M' \cdots$.]

where θ is the angle between **V** and the direction of C. The volume of flow per unit of time across Δs is then $R/\Delta t = V \sin \theta \, \Delta s$ approximately, and an approximate value of the total flow Q is $\sum_{i=1}^{n} V_i \sin \theta_i \, \Delta_i s$. We shall show in Sec. 20 that

$$Q = \mathbf{S}_{A}^{B} V \sin \theta \, ds. \tag{11}$$

To evaluate this integral let us represent the x- and y-components of **V** by $V_x(x, y)$ and $V_y(x, y)$. Then, α and β being the inclinations of C and **V** to the x-axis (see Fig. 82),

$$V \cos \beta = V_x(x, y), \qquad V \sin \beta = V_y(x, y),$$

and

$$\sin \theta = \sin \beta \cos \alpha - \cos \beta \sin \alpha = \sin \beta \frac{dx}{ds} - \cos \beta \frac{dy}{ds}, \tag{12}$$

so that*

$$Q = \int_{A}^{B} V_y(x, y) \frac{dx}{ds} \, ds - \int_{A}^{B} V_x(x, y) \frac{dy}{ds} \, ds. \tag{13}$$

Hence

$$Q = \int_{A}^{B} V_y(x, y) \, dx - V_x(x, y) \, dy, \tag{14}$$

where x and y are determined as functions of each other by the

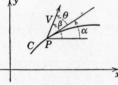

FIG. 82.

equation of C, Q being independent of the curve C joining A and B when and only when $V_y \, dx - V_x \, dy$ is exact (see Theorem 12.4).

It should be observed that (1) and (11) have not only the physical interpretations already given them, but may be used to represent the "total amount" of any vector quantity along or across a curve C. Thus, (11) represents the total magnetic flux across C when **V** represents the flux density in direction and magnitude. Again, (1) represents the "circulation" of a fluid along C when **F** is the vector velocity of the fluid and C is a closed curve. It should also be observed in (11) that Q is regarded as

---

* Throughout this book it must be remembered that we are quoting Theorem 13.1 every time we change from $\mathbf{S}_A^B$ to $\int_A^B$.

negative when θ is negative; however, the sign of θ is immaterial in (1).

Thermodynamics. It will be shown in Ex. XVI, 4, that, if p and v are the unit pressure and volume of a certain quantity of gas, the (external) work done by the gas when expanding in a container of arbitrary shape is*

$$W = \int_{v_1}^{v_2} p \, dv \tag{15}$$

when p is expressed as a function of v alone. If p varies with v as indicated in Fig. 83, then W is represented by the shaded

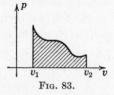

Fig. 83.

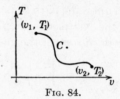

Fig. 84.

area. However, if p is represented as a function of v and the temperature T, i.e., $p = p(v, T)$, then the integral in (15) is meaningless until T has been determined as a function of v. Suppose T is given by the relation $T = \varphi(v)$ whose graph C is shown in Fig. 84. Then successive points on C represent the successive states of the gas as v varies from v_1 to v_2. It follows by (15) that

$$W = \int_{v_1}^{v_2} p(v, T) \, dv \tag{16}$$

represents the (external) work done by the gas when the function p is evaluated along C.

It is sometimes the case that we may represent the internal energy U of the gas as a function of v and T, i.e., $U = U(v, T)$. This being the case, we may write

$$U + k = \int \frac{\partial U}{\partial T}\Big)_v dT + \frac{\partial U}{\partial v}\Big)_T dv,$$

where k is a constant, when v and T are related by the equation $T = \varphi(v)$. Hence the change in U in going from state

$$S_1 = (v_1, T_1)$$

* We assume throughout that all the requisite conditions of thermodynamic equilibrium are satisfied.

to state $S_2 = (v_2,\ T_2)$ is

$$\int_{S_1}^{S_2} \frac{\partial U}{\partial T}\Big)_v dT + \frac{\partial U}{\partial v}\Big)_T dv. \qquad (17)$$

Since the total heat Q that must be added to the gas in going from S_1 to S_2 is the gain in U plus the external work done, it follows by (16) and (17) that

$$Q = \int_{S_1}^{S_2} \frac{\partial U}{\partial T}\Big)_v dT + \left[\frac{\partial U}{\partial v}\Big)_T + p\right] dv. \qquad (18)$$

Since $\partial p/\partial T \not\equiv 0$, the integral (18) is not exact, and Q and W depend upon the path C, i.e., upon the succession of states through which the gas passes in going from S_1 to S_2. If we define the change in *entropy* of the gas in going from S_1 to S_2 by the formula

$$E = \int_{S_1}^{S_2} \frac{1}{T}\frac{\partial U}{\partial T}\Big)_v dT + \frac{1}{T}\left[\frac{\partial U}{\partial v}\Big)_T + p\right] dv, \qquad (19)$$

then E is independent of the path C if and only if

$$\frac{1}{T}\frac{\partial^2 U}{\partial v\,\partial T} \equiv \frac{1}{T}\left[\frac{\partial^2 U}{\partial T\,\partial v} + \frac{\partial p}{\partial T}\right] - \frac{1}{T^2}\left[\frac{\partial U}{\partial v} + p\right],$$

i.e., when

$$T\frac{\partial p}{\partial T} - p - \frac{\partial U}{\partial v} \equiv 0. \qquad (20)$$

If the gas is such that

$$pv = RT, \qquad (21)$$

where R is a constant, then $p = RT/v$, $\partial p/\partial T = R/v$, and the left member of (20) reduces to merely $-\partial U/\partial v$. But $\partial U/\partial v \equiv 0$ if and only if U is independent of v. Hence we have the following result: *The change E in the entropy of a gas due to the change from state S_1 to state S_2 is independent of the manner in which this change of state takes place when and only when the internal energy U is independent of v.* It is found experimentally that condition (21) and this latter condition are often met (at least approximately).

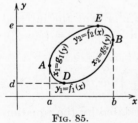

Fig. 85.

Areas. Suppose an area K in the xy-plane is such that the upper and lower parts of its boundary C may be represented by the equations $y_2 = f_2(x)$ and $y_1 = f_1(x)$ as indicated in Fig. 85, and also that the right and left parts of its boundary may be represented by the equations $x_2 = g_2(y)$ and $x_1 = g_1(y)$. It is evident that

$$K = \int_a^b y_2\,dx - \int_a^b y_1\,dx = -\left[\int_a^b y_1\,dx + \int_b^a y_2\,dx\right]$$

$$= -\int_C y\,dx, \qquad (22)$$

where in the last integral $y = y_1$ along ADB and $y = y_2$ along BEA, and where the subscript C has the significance indicated in Ex. XI, 2d. Likewise,

$$K = \int_d^e x_2\,dy - \int_d^e x_1\,dy = \int_d^e x_2\,dy + \int_e^d x_1\,dy = \int_C x\,dy, \qquad (23)$$

where in the last integral $x = x_2$ along DBE and $x = x_1$ along EAD. If we add (22) and (23), we find that

$$K = \tfrac{1}{2}\int_C x\,dy - y\,dx. \qquad (24)$$

EXERCISES XII

1. If the components of a force $\mathbf{F}$ are $X = y - z$, $Y = x + z$, $Z = y - x$, find the work done in going from $(0, 0, 0)$ to $(1, 2, 3)$. Does the result depend on the path chosen?

2. If the components of a force $\mathbf{F}$ are $X = 5x^2$, $Y = yz$, $Z = x^2 - z^2$ find the work done in going from $(1, 2, 1)$ to $(3, 4, 9)$ along the path $y = x + 1$, $z = x^2$. Does the result depend upon the path chosen?

3. If the components of a force $\mathbf{F}$ are $X = y^2$, $Y = x^4$, find the work done in going once around the circle $x^2 + y^2 = 1$.

4. According to Newton's laws, the motion of a body is determined by the equations

$$m\frac{d^2x}{dt^2} = X, \qquad m\frac{d^2y}{dt^2} = Y, \qquad m\frac{d^2z}{dt^2} = Z,$$

where X, Y, and Z are the rectangular components of the force $\mathbf{F}$ acting on the body. Multiply these equations respectively by dx/dt, dy/dt, dz/dt and integrate from t_0 to t_1 to show that the gain in kinetic energy of the body is equal to the work done on it by $\mathbf{F}$.

5. Fluid of unit depth is flowing over the xy-plane. Find the rate of flow over the curve $y = x^2$ from $x = -1$ to $x = 2$ if $V_x = x^2 - y^2$ and $V_y = xy$.

6. Fluid of unit depth is flowing over the xy-plane. Find the rate of flow over the circle $x^2 + y^2 = 1$ if $V_x = y - x^2$ and $V_y = 2xy - x$.

7. Find the rate of flow of fluid of unit depth across the path $x = u^2$, $y = 2u + 1$ from $u = 0$ to $u = 2$ when $V_x = xy$, $V_y = 1/(x + y)$.

8. Find the work done by a quantity of gas expanding from $v = 1$ to $v = 5$ if it obeys the gas law (21) and (a) $T = T_0$; (b) $p = p_0$; (c) $T = k/v^2$.

9. Find the change in entropy of a gas going from the state $p = 100$, $v = 5$ to the state $p = 10, v = 20$ if it obeys the law (21) and if it be assumed that $U = kT^2$.

10. Solve Ex. IX, 4a, c, d, e by formula (24).

11. Derive formula (3) of Sec. 14 from formula (24).

17. Surface Integrals and Volume Integrals. The concept of a line integral, as given in Definition 15.1, may be greatly extended by carrying out the process of repeated subdivision and summation, not merely for a curve C, but for a surface

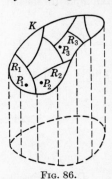

S or a volume V in space. We shall give this extension in detail for a surface S, but shall leave it as an exercise for the student to write out this extension for a volume V. The process of constructing integrals may be carried even further, but we shall not undertake to do this at the present time.

DEFINITION 17.1. *Let f denote a real single-valued function defined in some region R of space, let S be a surface lying in R, and let K be a por-*

FIG. 86.

tion of S having a finite area. Perform the following operations: I. Subdivide the area K into an arbitrary finite number n_1 of nonoverlapping* regions $R_1, R_2, \cdots, R_{n_1}$ of areas $\Delta_1 A$, $\Delta_2 A, \cdots \Delta_{n_1} A$ which need not be equal. II. In each region R_i choose an arbitrary point P_i. III. Form the sum

$$S_1 = \sum_{i=1}^{n_1} f(P_i)\, \Delta_i A$$

$$= f(P_1)\, \Delta_1 A + f(P_2)\, \Delta_2 A + \cdots + f(P_{n_1})\, \Delta_{n_1} A. \quad (1)$$

IV. *By repeated applications of steps I–III, construct an infinite sequence*

$$S_1 = \sum_{i=1}^{n_1} f(P_i)\, \Delta_i A, \qquad S_2 = \sum_{i=1}^{n_2} f(P_i)\, \Delta_i A, \qquad \cdots,$$

$$S_k = \sum_{i=1}^{n_k} f(P_i)\, \Delta_i A, \qquad \cdots \quad (2)$$

---

* The common boundary of two regions R_i and R_j may be included in both, either, or neither of these regions.

in any manner such that

$$\lim_{k \to \infty} \delta_k = 0, \qquad (3)$$

where δ_k is the diameter of the smallest sphere which can be circumscribed about each of the regions R_i in the sum S_k. If $\lim_{k \to \infty} S_k$ exists and has the same value for every possible construction of the sequence (2) meeting condition (3), then this limit is denoted by $S_K f(P)\, dA$, i.e.,

$$S_{K} f(P)\, dA = \lim_{k \to \infty} S_k. \qquad (4)$$

We call $S_K f(P)\, dA$ the surface integral of f with respect to A over the region K, and we say that f is summable over K if $S_K f(P)\, dA$ exists.

The notation in (2) should be interpreted as indicated in Definition 13.2. It should be observed that it is insufficient to suppose in the sequence (2) merely that the largest of the areas $\Delta_i A$ in the successive sums approaches zero, for the regions R_i may take the form of strips going clear across K which in successive sums become narrower without becoming shorter; while the areas of such strips all approach zero, it is possible in one sequence (2) to choose all the points P_i at the "tops" of the strips, and in another construction of (2) to choose all the points P_i at the "bottoms" of the strips, with the result that the sequence (2) would have two different limits for the two constructions. Condition (3) avoids this difficulty, for under it no two points of any one region R_i can remain a finite distance apart, however small.

Example 1. Let K be the rectangle in the xy-plane with vertices at $(0,\ 0)$, $(4,\ 0)$, $(0,\ 3)$, $(4,\ 3)$, and let $f(P) = f(x, y) = x^2 - xy$. If we subdivide K into regions R_i by drawing the lines $x = 1$ and $y = 1$, then an approximate value of $S_K f(P)\, dA$ is

$$f(\tfrac{1}{2}, \tfrac{1}{2})(1) + f(3, \tfrac{1}{2})(3) + f(\tfrac{1}{2}, 2)(2)$$
$$+ f(2, 2)(6) = 21.$$

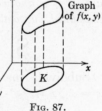

FIG. 87.

The definition of $S_K f(P)\, dA$ involves no specific reference to any coordinate system. Physical interpretations of $S_K f(P)\, dA$ will be given below; in the particular case where $f(P)$ is representable in the form $f(x, y)$ and the surface S is the xy-plane, then it may be shown in the usual way (see Sec. 14) that $S_K f(x, y)\, dA$ *represents the volume of the cylinder indicated in Fig. 87.* Formula (7) of Sec. 15 has no direct analogue in the present instance, for the symbol $\int f(x, y, z)\, dA$ is meaningless; however, $S_K f(x, y, z)\, dA$ may be evaluated by methods to be given below.

Definition 17.1 may be varied in many ways as was Definition 15.1. For example, if $\Delta_i A'$ is the area of the projection on the xy-plane of the region R_i, and if in Definition 17.1 $\Delta_i A$ is everywhere replaced by $\Delta_i A'$, then we arrive at the quantity $S_K f(P)\, dA'$. The quantities $S_K f(P)\, dA''$ and $S_K f(P)\, dA'''$ may be similarly obtained, where $''$ and $'''$ indicate projection on the xz- and yz-planes. Even though $S_K f(P)\, dA$ and each of these latter integrals involves only a single limit, they are all referred to as *double* or *surface* integrals inasmuch as the integra-

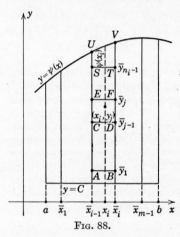

FIG. 88.

tion is over a two-dimensional region.

We now take up the problem of evaluating double integrals and we begin with a very simple special case. For clarity of notation, we shall always denote regions and areas in the xy-plane by K' and A', regions and areas in the xz-plane by K'' and A'', and regions and areas in the yz-plane by K''' and A'''.

THEOREM 17.1. *Let K' be the portion of the xy-plane bounded by the curves $x = a$, $x = b$, $y = c$, and $y = \psi(x)$, where $a < b$, where $c \leqq \psi(x)$ for values of x in the interval $a \leqq x \leqq b$, and where ψ is continuous and single-valued. If $f(x, y)$ is defined, summable, and continuous over K', then*

$$S_{K'} f(x, y)\, dA' = \int_a^b \int_c^{\psi(x)} f(x, y)\, \partial y\, dx.$$

Subdivide the region K' into m strips by the lines $x = a$, $x = \bar{x}_1$, $x = \bar{x}_2$, $\cdots$, $x = \bar{x}_{m-1}$, and $x = b$, where

$$a < \bar{x}_1 < \cdots < \bar{x}_{m-1} < b.$$

Let $\Delta_i x = \bar{x}_i - \bar{x}_{i-1}$. By Theorem 13.2, there exists a value x_i of x, $\bar{x}_{i-1} < x_i < \bar{x}_i$, such that the area of the ith strip is $[\psi(x_i) - c]\, \Delta_i x$. Subdivide the interval $c \leqq y \leqq \psi(x_i)$ along the line $x = x_i$ into n_i subintervals having c, $\bar{y}_1$, $\bar{y}_2$, $\cdots$, $\bar{y}_{n_i-1}$,

$\psi(x_i)$ as successive end points with the restriction that $\bar{y}_{n_i-1}$ is not to be greater than the smallest value of ψ in the ith strip. Draw the lines AB, $\cdots$, ST as in Fig. 88. Let $\Delta_j y = \bar{y}_j - \bar{y}_{j-1}$. By Theorems 13.2 and 13.1, wherein $f(x)$ is to be taken as the continuous function of y denoted by $f(x_i, y)$, there exists a value y_j of y, $\bar{y}_{j-1} < y_j < \bar{y}_j$, such that

$$f(x_i, y_j)\, \Delta_j y = \int_{\bar{y}_{j-1}}^{\bar{y}_j} f(x_i, y)\, \partial y. \tag{5}$$

Let us now construct the sum (1) taking as the regions R_i the small figures $\cdots$, $CDEF$, $\cdots$, into which K' has been divided, and taking as the points P_i the various points (x_i, y_j). Because of the manner in which x_i was determined, the area of the region $STVU$ is $\Delta_i x\, \Delta_{n_i} y$. Hence the sum (1) may be written in the form

$$\sum_{i=1}^{m} \left[\sum_{j=1}^{n_i} f(x_i, y_j)\, \Delta_j y \right] \Delta_i x$$

$$= \sum_{j=1}^{n_1} f(x_1, y_j)\, \Delta_j y\, \Delta_1 x + \cdots + \sum_{j=1}^{n_m} f(x_m, y_j)\, \Delta_j y\, \Delta_m x, \tag{6}$$

where each term in the right member represents the sum of all the terms $f(x, y)\, \Delta A'$ for one vertical strip, and where the outer summation in the left member represents the addition of totals for all the strips. By (5) we may write the ith term of the right member of (6) in the form

$$\left[\sum_{j=1}^{n_i} f(x_i, y_j)\, \Delta_j y \right] \Delta_i x = \left[\sum_{j=1}^{n_i} \int_{\bar{y}_{j-1}}^{\bar{y}_j} f(x_i, y)\, \partial y \right] \Delta_i x$$

$$= \left[\int_c^{\psi(x_i)} f(x_i, y)\, \partial y \right] \Delta_i x,$$

and (6) may be written as

$$\sum_{i=1}^{m} \left[\sum_{j=1}^{n_i} f(x_i, y_j)\, \Delta_j y \right] \Delta_i x = \sum_{i=1}^{m} \left[\int_c^{\psi(x_i)} f(x_i, y)\, \partial y \right] \Delta_i x. \tag{7}$$

It is evident that all of the quantities $\Delta_i x$ and $\Delta_j y$ may be taken arbitrarily small except for the quantities $\Delta_{n_i} y$, i.e., the last interval of each strip. (Recall the restriction on $\bar{y}_{n_i-1}$.) However, ψ is continuous, and by Theorem 8.7 of Chap. IX, $\Delta_{n_i}y$, and even the maximum height of each region $STVU$, can be made arbitrarily small by taking $\Delta_i x$ sufficiently small. Hence this method of choosing regions R_i' allows us to construct the sequence (2) in such a manner that (3) holds. By hypothesis,

$$\lim_{\delta\to 0}\sum_{i=1}^{m}\left[\sum_{j=1}^{n_i}f(x_i, y_j)\,\Delta_j y\right]\Delta_i x \text{ exists and equals } \mathbf{S}_{K'}f(x, y)\,dA', \quad (8)$$

where δ is defined as in Definition 17.1 and where the condition $\delta \to 0$ implies that the largest of all the numbers $\Delta_j y$ and $\Delta_i x$ approaches 0. On the other hand, $\int_c^{\psi(x)} f(x, y)\,\partial y$ is a continuous* function of x alone, and $\lim_{\delta\to 0}\sum_{i=1}^{m}[\int_c^{\psi(x_i)} f(x_i, y)\,\partial y]\,\Delta_i x$ exists and is denoted by $\mathbf{S}_a^b \int_c^{\psi(x)} f(x, y)\,\partial y\,dx$. By Theorem 13.1, this latter quantity is equal to $\int_a^b \int_c^{\psi(x)} f(x, y)\,\partial y\,dx$. Hence

$$\lim_{\delta\to 0}\sum_{i=1}^{m}\left[\int_c^{\psi(x_i)} f(x_i, y)\,\partial y\right]\Delta_i x = \int_a^b \int_c^{\psi(x)} f(x, y)\,\partial y\,dx. \quad (9)$$

The theorem follows at once from (7), (8), and (9).

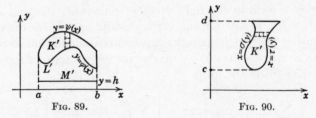

FIG. 89.   FIG. 90.

With reference to Fig. 89 it is seen that

$$\mathbf{S}_{K'} f(x, y)\,dA' = \int_a^b \int_{\varphi(x)}^{\psi(x)} f(x, y)\,\partial y\,dx, \quad (10)$$

for†

$$\mathbf{S}_{K'} f(x, y)\,dA' = \mathbf{S}_{L'} f(x, y)\,dA' - \mathbf{S}_{M'} f(x, y)\,dA'$$

$$= \int_a^b \int_h^{\psi(x)} f(x, y)\,\partial y\,dx - \int_a^b \int_h^{\varphi(x)} f(x, y)\,\partial y\,dx.$$

* See Theorem 29.1.

† If $f(x, y)$ is not already defined over all of $L' = K' + M'$, then its definition may be extended in any convenient manner to include L'.

Hence

$$\mathbf{S}_{K'} f(x, y)\, dA' = \int_a^b \Big[\int_h^{\psi(x)} f(x, y)\, \partial y - \int_h^{\varphi(x)} f(x, y)\, \partial y \Big]\, dx$$

$$= \int_a^b \int_{\varphi(x)}^{\psi(x)} f(x, y)\, \partial y\, dx.$$

With reference to Fig. 90 it may likewise be shown that

$$\mathbf{S}_{K'} f(x, y)\, dA' = \int_c^d \int_{\sigma(y)}^{\tau(y)} f(x, y)\, \partial x\, dy. \qquad (11)$$

In the event that the region K' is such that both (10) and (11) hold, then the right members of (10) and (11) are equal, and we have

THEOREM 17.2. *Let K' be such a portion of the xy-plane that its boundary may be broken up into two parts $y = \varphi(x)$ and $y = \psi(x)$ extending from $x = a$ to $x = b$, and also into two parts $x = \sigma(y)$ and $x = \tau(y)$ extending from $y = c$ to $y = d$, where φ, ψ, σ, and τ are continuous and single-valued with $\varphi(x) \leqq \psi(x)$ and $\sigma(y) \leqq \tau(y)$. If $f(x, y)$ is defined, summable, and continuous over K', then*

$$\int_a^b \int_{\varphi(x)}^{\psi(x)} f(x, y)\, \partial y\, dx = \int_c^d \int_{\sigma(y)}^{\tau(y)} f(x, y)\, \partial x\, dy.$$

It should be observed that K' in the preceding theorem is an axial region (see Sec. 11), and that this theorem may be extended to more general regions K' by breaking up K' into axial regions.

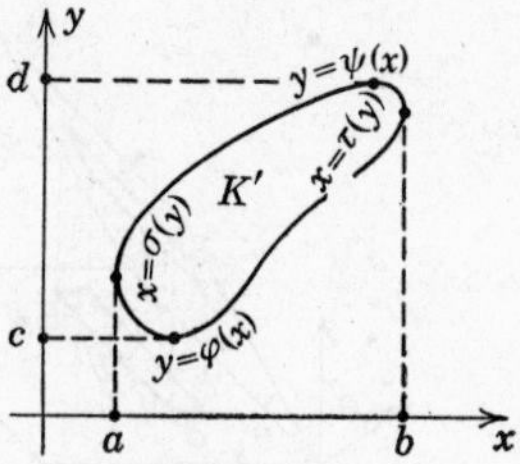

We now wish to extend the preceding results to the case where the integrand is a function $f(x, y, z)$. Suppose the surface S in Definition 17.1 is represented by the equation

FIG. 91.

$$z = r(x, y), \qquad (12)$$

where z is single-valued and continuous, and suppose the region K on S is such that its projection on the xy-plane is a region K' for which (10) holds. Since $f(x, y, z) \equiv f[x, y, r(x, y,)]$ when the point (x, y, z) is in the region K,

$$\mathbf{S}_K f(x, y, z)\, dA' = \mathbf{S}_{K'} f[x, y, r(x, y)]\, dA', \qquad (13)$$

for if K is subdivided into regions R_i, then the projections R_i' of R_i constitute a suitable set of subdivisions of K', and $\Delta_i A'$ is the same with reference to both R_i and R'_i; moreover, if (x_i, y_i, z_i) is a point in R_i, then (x_i, y_i) is in R'_i, and by (12),

$$f(x_i, y_i, z_i) \, \Delta_i A' = f[x_i, y_i, r(x_i, y_i)] \, \Delta_i A',$$

so that (13) follows at once. But by (10),

$$\mathbf{S}_{K'} f[x, y, r(x, y)] \, dA' = \int_a^b \int_{\varphi(x)}^{\psi(x)} f[x, y, r(x, y)] \, \partial y \, dx. \quad (14)$$

Hence, by (13) and (14),

$$\mathbf{S}_K f(x, y, z) \, dA' = \int_a^b \int_{\varphi(x)}^{\psi(x)} f(x, y, z) \, \partial y \, dx, \quad (15)$$

where in the right member $z = r(x, y)$, and where $\varphi(x)$ and $\psi(x)$ represent the boundary of the projection K' of K on the xy-plane. If the region K' is such that (11) holds, then

$$\mathbf{S}_K f(x, y, z) \, dA' = \int_c^d \int_{\sigma(y)}^{\tau(y)} f(x, y, z) \, \partial x \, dy. \quad (16)$$

Similar formulas may be derived for $\mathbf{S}_K f(x, y, z) \, dA''$ and $\mathbf{S}_K f(x, y, z) \, dA'''$.

It remains to evaluate $\mathbf{S}_K f(x, y, z) \, dA$. Let M and H be two planes intersecting in the line l at an angle θ. Then θ is also the

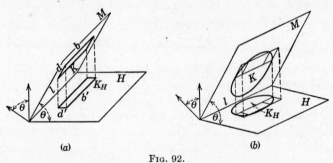

(a)   (b)

FIG. 92.

angle between normals to M and H. Let A be the area of a region K in M, and let A_H be the area of the projection K_H of K upon H. Then

$$A_H = A \cos \theta, \quad \text{or} \quad A = A_H \sec \theta. \quad (17)$$

This result is evident when K is a rectangle with two edges parallel to l, for K_H is also a rectangle and (see Fig. 92a) $b' = b$, $d' = d \cos \theta$. It may be shown that (17) holds for a general region K by approximating K by rectangles in the usual way (see Sec. 14 and Fig. 92b).

In Definition 17.1 let S be represented by (12), and suppose that there exists a tangent plane at each point of S. Let $\Delta_i A_T$ be the area of the projection of R_i upon the tangent plane T_i at P_i, the operation of projection being parallel to the z-axis. Suppose S is such that, if ϵ is an arbitrarily small positive number, the regions R_i may all be taken sufficiently small that

$$1 - \epsilon < \frac{\Delta_i A_T}{\Delta_i A} < 1 + \epsilon$$

for each value of i. Then [cf. the derivation of (10) in Sec. 16]

$$\mathsf{S}_K f(P) \, dA = \mathsf{S}_K f(P) \, dA_T. \tag{18}$$

But by (17),

$$f(P_i) \, \Delta_i A_T = f(P_i) \sec \gamma_i \, \Delta_i A',$$

where γ_i is the smaller angle made by a normal upon T_i with the z-axis. Hence

$$\mathsf{S}_K f(P) \, dA_T = \mathsf{S}_K f(P) \sec \gamma \, dA'. \tag{19}$$

Since* $\sec \gamma = \sqrt{1 + z_x^2 + z_y^2}$, it follows by (18) and (19) that, if $f(P) \equiv f(x, y, z)$, then

$$\mathsf{S}_K f(P) \, dA = \mathsf{S}_K f(P) \sec \gamma \, dA'$$
$$= \mathsf{S}_K f(x, y, z) \sqrt{1 + z_x^2 + z_y^2} \, dA', \tag{20}$$

where γ is the smaller direction angle with the z-axis of any normal to K, where $z = r(x, y)$, and where the last integral may be evaluated by (15) or (16). [In the last integral it is immaterial whether we write K or K' because of (13).] It may be shown in a similar manner that

$$\mathsf{S}_K f(P) \, dA = \mathsf{S}_K f(P) \sec \beta \, dA'' = \mathsf{S}_K f(P) \sec \alpha \, dA''', \tag{21}$$

where α and β are the smaller direction angles with the x- and y-axes of any normal to K. If in (20) and (21) we take $f(P) \equiv 1$ and let A denote the area of K, then†

---

* The student should verify this. See Chap. VII, Ex. II, 1, 2.

† For a further discussion of surface area, see Sec. 15, Chap. VI.

$$A = \mathbf{S}_K \, dA = \iint_{K'} \sec \gamma \; \partial y \; dx = \iint_{K''} \sec \beta \; \partial z \; dx$$
$$= \iint_{K'''} \sec \alpha \; \partial z \; dy. \tag{21'}$$

If in (20) we write $g(P) = f(P) \sec \gamma$, then $f(P) = g(P) \cos \gamma$, and (20) assumes the form

$$\mathbf{S}_K \, g(P) \cos \gamma \, dA = \mathbf{S}_K \, g(P) \, dA'. \tag{22}$$

Formulas (21) may be modified in a similar manner.

We now give a few examples to illustrate the meaning and use of surface integrals.

The *moment* M of a point mass m about a line l is rm, where r is the distance from m to l. If we consider a plane area K as having unit mass per unit of area, then the moment $\Delta_i M$ of a subregion R_i of K about a line l in the plane of K is such that

$$r_i' \, \Delta_i A \leqq \Delta_i M \leqq r_i \, \Delta_i A,$$

where r_i' and r_i are the smallest and largest distances from l to any point of R_i. It is seen that the moment M_l of K about l is

$$M_l = \mathbf{S}_K \, r \, dA, \tag{23}$$

where r is the (directed) distance from l to the point P of K. In particular, if K' lies in the xy-plane, the moments of K' about the lines $y = k$ and $x = h$ are

$$\mathbf{S}_{K'} \, (y - k) \, dA' \qquad \text{and} \qquad \mathbf{S}_{K'} \, (x - h) \, dA'$$

respectively, these integrals being evaluated by (10) or (11). It follows in the same way that, *the moment of inertia I of a point mass m about a line l being $r^2 m$*, the moment of inertia I_l about l of an area K on an arbitrary surface S is

$$I_l = \mathbf{S}_K \, r^2 \, dA, \tag{24}$$

where r is the distance from l to any point (x, y, z) of K. In particular, the moment of inertia about the x-axis is

$$I_x = \mathbf{S}_K \, (y^2 + z^2) \, dA,$$

and if K' lies in the xy-plane, $I_x = \mathbf{S}_{K'} \, y^2 \, dA'$. If r is the distance from the origin O to any point (x, y, z), then the moment of inertia of K about the origin is

$$I_0 = S_K \, r^2 \, dA = S_K \, (x^2 + y^2 + z^2) \, dA. \qquad (25)$$

The integrals in (24) and (25) may be evaluated by (20) or (21).

We give another example relating to fluid flow. If fluid is flowing in such a manner that it has everywhere the same constant velocity $\mathbf{V}$, then the fluid flowing across (through) a plane area A in one unit of time forms a cylinder with base A, slant height V, and altitude $V \cos \theta$, where θ is the inclination of $\mathbf{V}$ to a normal upon A. The volume of this cylinder, $AV \cos \theta$, is numerically the rate of flow of fluid across A. Since $V \cos \theta$ is the magnitude V_n of the component of $\mathbf{V}$ normal to A, the rate of flow of fluid across A is AV_n. Now suppose fluid is flowing in an arbitrary manner across a region K of a surface S. Let the velocity of the

Fig. 93.

fluid at any point be represented by the vector $\mathbf{V}$, and let θ be the angle between $\mathbf{V}$ and the normal to K at any point P of K. Then (see Sec. 20) the rate of flow of fluid across K is

$$Q = S_K \, V \cos \theta \, dA = S_K \, V_n \, dA, \qquad (26)$$

where V is the magnitude of $\mathbf{V}$, and V_n is the component of $\mathbf{V}$ normal to K at any point P of K. (This may be seen intuitively by breaking up K into small regions ΔA.) It is seen that the sign of $\cos \theta$, and hence the sign of Q, depends upon the choice of θ as between the two angles from $\mathbf{V}$ to the normal. To settle this question of sign it is customary to erect a unit vector $\mathbf{n}$, called the *unit normal*, along the normal to K at each point P of K; θ is then the angle between $\mathbf{V}$ and $\mathbf{n}$. The vector $\mathbf{n}$ may be taken in either direction along the normal at P, and the effect of introducing $\mathbf{n}$ is essentially that of determining a "positive" and "negative" side of K. If we define the vector $\Delta_i \mathbf{A}_T$ to be a vector in the direction of $\mathbf{n}$ and of length $\Delta_i A_T$ [see paragraph below (17)] then by (18) and Definition 16.1, we may write (26) in the form

$$Q = S_K \, \mathbf{V} \cdot d\mathbf{A}. \qquad (27)$$

Formulas (26) and (27) may evidently be used in connection with any quantity whose value and direction at any point P may be represented by a vector **V**; the set of all vectors **V** corresponding to the points P of our space is called a *vector field*, and (26) and (27) give the flux of this field across K. Thus, if **V** represents the direction and intensity of a magnetic field, then (26) and (27) represent the total magnetic flux across K.

In order that (27) be meaningful, it has been assumed that **n** varies continuously from point to point over the surface S

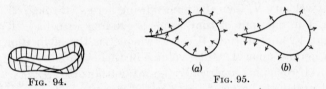

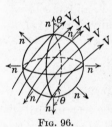

Fig. 94.   (a)   (b)
                          Fig. 95.

without, for example, sudden changes in sign or direction. It is not always possible to determine **n** in this manner even though S has a tangent plane at each point. Thus, consider the *Moebius strip* formed by a long narrow piece of paper one end of which is given a half twist before the two ends are brought together. In going once around the strip and returning to the starting point, the vector **n** must experience a discontinuous change of direction. Again, if a surface is creased (like a cusp), it may be necessary to deform the surface slightly by rounding off the crease before **n** may be everywhere continuous. We say that a surface S is *orientable* if (after any necessary "slight" deformation) it is possible to construct a vector **n** at each point of S so that **n** is continuous at *every* point of S. We shall assume throughout this discussion that we deal only with orientable surfaces.

Fig. 96.

If S is a closed surface (e.g., a sphere), and if **V** is a vector field across S (e.g., a magnetic field), then by properly choosing **n** at each point of S (e.g., in the "outward" direction), the sign of **V** $\cdot d\mathbf{A}$ determines whether Q is *inward* or *outward* at any point P of S, and (27) represents the *net* flow across S, that is, the net flow out of, or into, the region bounded by S (see Fig. 96).

The process of orienting a surface has other applications. For example,

$$V = \mathbf{S}_{K'} \, [f_2(x, y) - f_1(x, y)] \, dA' \qquad (28)$$

represents the volume of the region R bounded by the surfaces K_1 and K_2 with equations $z = f_1(x, y)$ and $z = f_2(x, y)$, where K' is the projection of R on the xy-plane.   By (22),

$$V = \mathbf{S}_{K_2} f_2(x, y) \cos \gamma \, dA - \mathbf{S}_{K_1} f_1(x, y) \cos \gamma \, dA. \quad (29)$$

By taking **n** "outward," so that $\cos \gamma$ is positive over K_2 and negative over K_1, we may write

$$V = \mathbf{S}_{S} z \cos \gamma \, dA, \quad\quad (30)$$

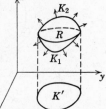

where S is the entire surface of R and where z is determined as in (29).   Formula (30) can be extended to more complicated regions.

With these conventions in mind it is possible to express (26) and (27) in a form more convenient for computational purposes.

Fig. 97.

Let α, β, γ be the direction angles of **n**, let α_V, β_V, γ_V be the direction angles of **V**, and let X, Y, and Z be the components of **V** parallel to the axes.   Then, as indicated in (22) and (15),

$$Q = \mathbf{S}_{K} V \cos \theta \, dA$$

$$= \mathbf{S}_{K} V(\cos \alpha_V \cos \alpha + \cos \beta_V \cos \beta + \cos \gamma_V \cos \gamma) \, dA$$

$$= \mathbf{S}_{K} (X \cos \alpha + Y \cos \beta + Z \cos \gamma) \, dA \quad\quad (31)$$

$$= \mathbf{S}_{K'''} (\pm X) \, dA''' + \mathbf{S}_{K''} (\pm Y) \, dA'' + \mathbf{S}_{K'} (\pm Z) \, dA' \quad (32)$$

$$= \iint_{K'''} (\pm X) \, \partial z \, dy + \iint_{K''} (\pm Y) \, \partial z \, dx$$

$$+ \iint_{K'} (\pm Z) \, \partial y \, dx, \quad (33)$$

where in each double sign we take the sign of $\cos \alpha$, $\cos \beta$, and $\cos \gamma$, respectively, as determined at the point where X, Y, Z are evaluated.   If x, y, or z is multiple-valued on K, then the first, second, or third integrals in (32) and (33) must be broken up into parts as in (29) and (28).   In particular, if K is a convex closed surface, and if **n** is the "outward" normal, the last integral in (33) is evaluated by integrating $+Z$ over the upper part of K, integrating $-Z$ over the lower part of K, and adding the results; the other integrals in (33) are evaluated similarly by using $+$ over the right or front part of K and $-$ over the left or back part of K.

It should be observed that (31) to (33) are general formulas for any integral $S_K\ V\cos\theta\ dA$, where V is any vector with rectangular components X, Y, Z.

We leave it to the student to write out in complete detail the definition of a *volume* or *triple* integral:

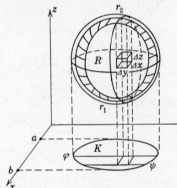

FIG. 98.

$$S_R f\,(x,\,y,\,z)\ dV$$

$$= \lim_{\delta_k \to 0} \sum_{i=1}^{n_k} f(x_i,\,y_i,\,z_i)\ \Delta_i V, \quad (34)$$

where R is a region in space. We also leave it to him to prove the following formula, where r_1, r_2, φ, ψ, a, and b have the significance indicated in Fig. 98, and to give five other forms of this formula obtained by changing the order of integrations:

$$S_R f\,(x,\,y,\,z)\ dV = \int_a^b \int_{\varphi(x)}^{\psi(x)} \int_{r_1(x,y)}^{r_2(x,y)} f(x,\,y,\,z)\ \partial z\ \partial y\ dx. \quad (35)$$

EXERCISES XIII

1. Find A, M_x, M_y, I_x, I_y, and I_0 for the areas bounded by:
(a) $x^2 + y^2 = a^2$.
(b) $y = x^2$, $y = 1$. Also find I about $y = 1$.
(c) $4x^2 = 4 - y$, $x^2 = 1 - y$. Also find I about $x = 1$.
(d) One arch of the cycloid $x = a(\theta - \sin\ \theta)$, $y = a(1 - \cos\ \theta)$, and $y = 0$.
(e) The coordinates $\bar{x}$ and $\bar{y}$ of the *center of gravity* of an area in the xy-plane are defined by the relations

$$A\bar{x} = M_y, \qquad A\bar{y} = M_x.$$

Find the center of gravity of the areas in parts (b), (c), and (d).

2. Find A, I_x, I_y, I_z, and I_0 for the following surfaces:
(a) $x/a + y/b + z/c = 1$ and in the first octant.
(b) $z = x^2$ cut off by $y + z = 1$ and $y = 0$.
(c) $z = x^2 + 2y^2$ below $z = 1$.

3. Let S be the surface of revolution obtained by rotating the curve $y = f(x)$ about the line $y = k$. Derive the formula

$$A = \int_a^b 2\pi(y - k)\sqrt{1 + (D_xy)^2}\ dx, \quad (36)$$

using tangent cones instead of tangent planes. Also, derive (36) directly from (21). [Note (11) of Sec. 19.] Find the areas of the surfaces obtained by rotating the following curves in the manner indicated:

(a) $x^2 + y^2 = a^2$ about $y = 0$.

(b) $y = \sin x$ from $x = 0$ to $x = \pi$ about $y = 2$.

(c) $y^2 = x^3$ from $x = 0$ to $x = 1$ about $x = 1$.

(d) One arch of the cycloid $x = a(\theta - \sin \theta)$, $y = a(1 - \cos \theta)$ about $y = 0$.

4. Evaluate the integral (31) in the following cases, **n** being the outward normal:

(a) $X = x^2y^2$, $Y = xz$, $Z = y^2 - z^2$, K is the entire sphere

$$x^2 + y^2 + z^2 = a^2.$$

(b) $X = x - y$, $Y = y^2 + z^2$, $Z = 1$, K is the entire cube of edge $2a$ with center at $(0, 0, 0)$ and with faces parallel to the coordinate planes.

(c) $X = Y = Z = x^2 + y^2 - z^2$, K is the entire cylindric surface $x^2 + y^2 = a^2$, $z = 0$, $z = 1$, including its bases.

(d) $X = x$, $Y = xy$, $Z = xyz$, K is the surface of the region bounded by $z = x^2 + y^2$ and $z = 1$.

5. Find the volume V, the moments M_{xy}, M_{xz}, M_{yz} about the coordinate planes, and the moments of inertia I_x, I_y, I_z, I_0 of the solids bounded by:

(a) $x^2 + y^2 + z^2 = a^2$ above $z = 0$.

(b) $x^2 + y^2 = 1 - z$ above $z = 0$.

(c) $z = 1 - x^2$, $z = 0$, $y = 0$, $x + y = 1$.

(d) $x^2 + z^2 = a^2$, $y^2 + z^2 = a^2$.

(e) $z = x^2 + y^2$, $z = y^2$, $z = 1 - y^2$, $z = 0$.

(f) The coordinates $\bar{x}$, $\bar{y}$, $\bar{z}$ of the *center of gravity* of a solid are defined by the relations

$$V\bar{x} = M_{yz}, \qquad V\bar{y} = M_{xz}, \qquad V\bar{z} = M_{xy}.$$

Find the centers of gravity of the above solids.

6. Give in complete detail the definition in (34).

7. Prove (35).

8. Prove the following *theorems of Pappus:*

(a) If a plane area A be rotated about a line l in the plane of A and not cutting A, the volume of the solid generated is equal to the product of A and the distance traveled by the center of gravity of A.

(b) If a plane curve C be rotated about a line l in the plane of C and not cutting C, the area of the surface generated is equal to the product of the length of C and the distance traveled by the center of gravity of C.

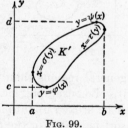

Fig. 99.

18. Green's Theorem. There exist many close relations among line, surface, and volume integrals, and in this section we shall develop a few of these relations. Let K be a region in the xy-plane of the sort described in Theorem 17.2. (In this section we shall drop our convention regarding the use of primes.) Let $M(x, y)$, $N(x, y)$, M_y, and N_x be defined and continuous over K. By (10) of Sec. 17, we have, in the notation of Theorem 17.2,

$$\begin{aligned}
S_K \frac{\partial M(x, y)}{\partial y}\, dA &= \int_a^b \int_{\varphi(x)}^{\psi(x)} \frac{\partial M}{\partial y}\, \partial y\, dx = \int_a^b \left\{ [M(x, y)]_{\varphi(x)}^{\psi(x)} \right\} dx \\
&= \int_a^b M[x, \psi(x)]\, dx - \int_a^b M[x, \varphi(x)]\, dx \\
&= -\left\{ \int_b^a M[x, \psi(x)]\, dx + \int_a^b M[x, \varphi(x)]\, dx \right\} \\
&= -\int_C M(x, y)\, dx, \qquad (1)
\end{aligned}$$

where C denotes the boundary of K, where $y = \varphi(x)$ along the lower part of C and $y = \psi(x)$ along the upper part of C, and where the point (x, y) traces out C in the *positive* (counterclockwise) direction. It follows in the same manner that

$$\begin{aligned}
S_K \frac{\partial N(x, y)}{\partial x}\, dA &= \int_c^d \int_{\sigma(y)}^{\tau(y)} \frac{\partial N}{\partial x}\, \partial x\, dy = \int_c^d \left\{ [N(x, y)]_{\sigma(y)}^{\tau(y)} \right\} dy \\
&= \int_C N(x, y)\, dy, \qquad (2)
\end{aligned}$$

where $x = \sigma(y)$ along the left part of C and $x = \tau(y)$ along the right part. If we subtract (2) from (1), we obtain

THEOREM 18.1 (*Green's Theorem*). *If K is the region described in Theorem 17.2, and if M, N, M_y, and N_x are defined and continuous over K (including the boundary C), then*

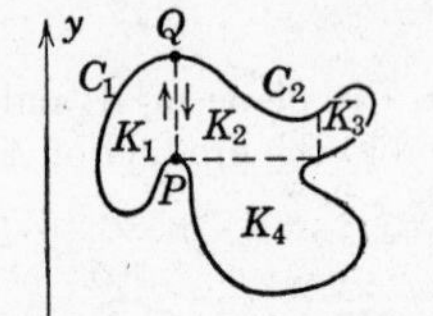

$$S_K \left(\frac{\partial M}{\partial y} - \frac{\partial N}{\partial x} \right) dA = -\int_C M(x, y)\, dx + N(x, y)\, dy, \quad (3)$$

where C is traced out by the point (x, y) in the positive direction.

FIG. 100.

Green's theorem is valid for much more general regions than is indicated in the preceding statement of it. For example, let K be the region shown in Fig. 100, and let K be broken up into a finite number of parts K_1, K_2, $\cdots$ of the sort indicated in the theorem. Then the theorem holds for each part. But in computing the line integral along the boundaries C_1 and C_2 of K_1 and K_2, the integral along the common part PQ of these boundaries cancels out because PQ is traced in opposite directions in the two cases.   Hence

$$\mathbf{S}_{K_1+K_2} (M_y - N_x)\, dA = -\int_\gamma M\, dx + N\, dy,$$

where γ is merely the (exterior) boundary of the combined region $K_1 + K_2$.   This process may be extended to the remaining parts of K to show that (3) holds for the entire region K.   We leave it to the student to develop for himself as general a statement as possible of Green's theorem, and, in particular, to consider the case where K consists of several disconnected parts as indicated by the shading in Fig. 101 (a).   [To determine the direction in

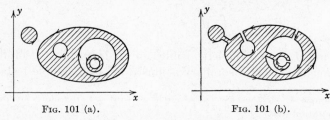

Fig. 101 (a).   Fig. 101 (b).

which the various parts of the boundary must be traced out, connect the various parts of the boundary as indicated in Fig. 101 (b), where the connecting lines are regarded as coincident so that the integrals along them have the sum zero.]   In the applications we shall make of Green's theorem we shall always explicitly assume that K denotes a region for which Green's theorem is valid.

Green's theorem enables us to compute a double integral by a line integral, or conversely, to compute a line integral by a double integral.

Example 1.   Evaluate $\int_C (3x^2 - y^2)\, dx - 2xy\, dy$, where C is the entire circle $x^2 + y^2 = 1$.

Solution.   By (3), the given integral is equal to

$$-\mathbf{S}_K (-2y + 2y)\, dA = 0.$$

It must be emphasized that this method for evaluating a line integral is available *only* when C is a closed curve, as otherwise C does not bound a region K.

Example 2.   Evaluate $\mathbf{S}_K (2y - 6x)\, dA = \int_{-2}^{2} \int_{-\sqrt{4-x^2}}^{\sqrt{4-x^2}} (2y - 6x)\, \partial y\, dx$,

where K is bounded by the circle $x^2 + y^2 = 4$.

Solution. Let $M_y = 2y$. Then we can take $M = y^2 + x^2$. Again, $N_x = 6x$, and $N = 3(x^2 + y^2)$. By (3), the given integral is equal to

$$-\int_C (x^2 + y^2)\, dx + 3(x^2 + y^2)\, dy = -\int_C 4\, dx + 12\, dy = 0,$$

where C is the boundary of K.

Example 3. By Green's theorem, $-\frac{1}{2}\int_C y\, dx - x\, dy = S_K (1)\, dA = A$. This result is consistent with (24) of Sec. 16.

We list a few corollaries of Green's theorem:

Corollary 18.11. *If $M_y(x, y) \equiv N_x(x, y)$, and if C is any closed curve in the xy-plane such that M, N, M_y, and N_x are defined and continuous over the region K bounded by C, then*

$$\int_C M\, dx + N\, dy = 0.$$

Since $M_y \equiv N_x$, the left member of (3) is 0, and the corollary is immediate. This corollary is illustrated by Example 1 above.

Example 4. If C is the entire circle $x^2 + y^2 = 1$, it follows by direct computation that

$$\int_C \frac{-y}{x^2 + y^2}\, dx + \frac{x}{x^2 + y^2}\, dy = 2\pi, \tag{4}$$

for the differential is exact, $\int \dfrac{-y}{x^2 + y^2}\, dx + \dfrac{x}{x^2 + y^2}\, dy = \tan^{-1}\dfrac{y}{x} + \text{const.}$, and as the point (x, y) moves positively around C once, $\tan^{-1}(y/x)$ increases in value by 2π. We cannot quote Green's theorem to conclude that the given integral is 0 because M, N, M_y, and N_x in this case are discontinuous at the point $(0, 0)$ within C. This example illustrates once again the fact that the hypotheses of a theorem must be fully met or the theorem cannot be applied in a given case. It is evident that the given integral is 0 for any closed path C which does not contain $(0, 0)$.

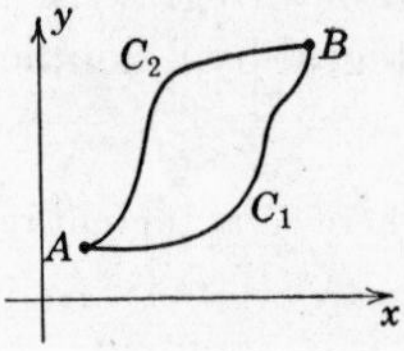

Fig. 102.

Corollary 18.12. *Let $M(x, y)$ and $N(x, y)$ be given functions, let A and B be two points in the xy-plane, and let C_1 and C_2 be any two curves joining A and B such that M, N, M_y, and N_x are defined and continuous over the region K bounded by, and including, C_1 and C_2. If $M_y \equiv N_x$, then*

$$\int_{C_1} M\, dx + N\, dy = \int_{C_2} M\, dx + N\, dy. \tag{5}$$

Let C denote the closed curve from A around to A consisting of C_1 and C_2. By Corollary 18.11,

$$0 = \int_C M \, dx + N \, dy$$
$$= \int_{C_1} M \, dx + N \, dy - \int_{C_2} M \, dx + N \, dy, \tag{6}$$

where $\int_{C_1}$ and $\int_{C_2}$ are each taken from A to B, the minus sign arising from the fact that the part of $\int_C$ along C_2 is taken from B to A. Equation (5) follows at once from (6).

While Corollary 18.12 is merely a restatement of Theorem 12.4, the preceding proof gives further insight into this important result.

Example 5. Evaluate $\int_{0,0}^{1,2} (3x^2 - y^2) \, dx - 2xy \, dy$ along the curve $\sin(\pi xy/2) + \log(2x - y + 1) = 0$.

Solution. Since the condition $M_y \equiv N_x$ is met, along with all continuity requirements, we may choose any path we please from $(0, 0)$ to $(1, 2)$ instead of the given path. If we take the path $y = 2x$, then the given integral equals

$$\int_0^1 - x^2 \, dx - \int_0^2 y^2 \, dy = -3.$$

If we choose the path consisting of the line segment l_1 from $(0, 0)$ to $(1, 0)$ and the line segment l_2 from $(1, 0)$ to $(1, 2)$, then we evaluate the given integral along l_1 and l_2 separately and add the results, where $y = 0$ and $dy = 0$ along l_1, and $x = 1$ and $dx = 0$ along l_2:

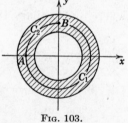

FIG. 103.

$$\left(\int_0^1 3x^2 \, dx - 0 \right) + \left(0 - \int_0^2 2y \, dy \right) = -3.$$

Corollary 18.12 is sometimes misstated as follows: Let M, N, M_y, and N_x be defined and continuous over a region K, and let A and B be two points of K. If $M_y \equiv N_x$, then $\int_C M \, dx + N \, dy$ has the same value along all curves C joining A and B and lying in K. That this statement is false is seen by taking K as the shaded ring shown in Fig. 103. The curves C_1 and C_2 lie in K, but the integral in Example 4 has the value $3\pi/2$ along C_1 and the value $-\pi/2$ along C_2. While M, N, M_y and N_x, are defined and continuous in K, the difficulty is that C_1 and C_2 bound a region L which does not lie in K; in particular, the point $(0, 0)$ is in L, though not in K. The above statement of

Corollary 18.12 is valid if we restrict K to be "simply connected" in the sense that, if C is any closed curve in K, the region bounded by C is in K.

It follows from Corollary 18.12 that if $M_y \equiv N_x$, then

$$\int_{a,b}^{x_0,y_0} M(x, y)\, dx + N(x, y)\, dy, \tag{7}$$

being independent of the curve C along which it is taken, has exactly one value for each point $(x_0,\ y_0)$ when $(a,\ b)$ is fixed. Thus the quantity (7) is a function of the point $(x_0,\ y_0)$. If we denote this function by $f(x,\ y)$, then

$$f(x_0,\ y_0) = \int_{a,b}^{x_0,y_0} M(x, y)\, dx + N(x, y)\, dy. \tag{8}$$

With this notation in mind we may state

COROLLARY 18.13. *Let M, N, M_y, N_x be defined and continuous over a simply connected region K. If $M_y \equiv N_x$, and if $f(x,\ y)$ is the function defined over K by (8), then $\partial f/\partial x \equiv M(x,\ y)$ and $\partial f/\partial y \equiv N(x,\ y)$.*

By Definition 16.1 of Chap. I,

$$f_x(x_0,\ y_0) = \lim_{\Delta x \to 0} \frac{f(x_0 + \Delta x,\ y_0) - f(x_0,\ y_0)}{\Delta x}$$

$$= \lim_{\Delta x \to 0} \frac{1}{\Delta x}\left[\int_{a,b}^{x_0+\Delta x, y_0} M\, dx + N\, dy - \int_{a,b}^{x_0,y_0} M\, dx + N\, dy \right], \tag{9}$$

where by Corollary 18.12 we may choose the path of integration as we please within K. Let C_1 be any arc in K joining $(a,\ b)$ with $(x_0,\ y_0)$, let l be the straight line $y = y_0$, and let C be the curve consisting of C_1 and l. Then (9) may be written in the form

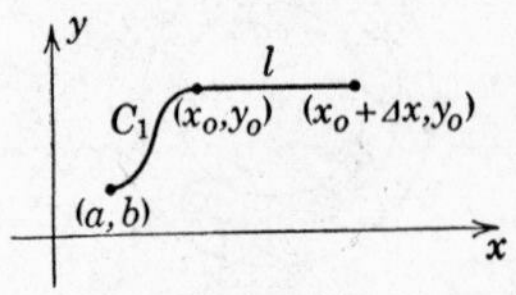

FIG. 104.

$$f_x(x_0,\ y_0) = \lim_{\Delta x \to 0} \frac{1}{\Delta x} \int_{x_0,y_0}^{x_0+\Delta x, y_0} M(x,\ y_0)\, dx + N(x,\ y_0)\, dy \tag{10}$$

since the path of integration is l. But $dy = 0$ along l and $\int_l N\, dy = 0$. By Theorem 13.2 there exists a number θ, $0 < \theta < 1$, such that

$$M(x_0 + \theta \cdot \Delta x,\ y_0) = \frac{1}{\Delta x} \int_{x_0,y_0}^{x_0+\Delta x, y_0} M(x,\ y_0)\, dx. \tag{11}$$

Since M is continuous, it follows by (10) and (11) that

$$f_x(x_0, y_0) = \lim_{\Delta x \to 0} M(x_0 + \theta \cdot \Delta x, y_0) = M(x_0, y_0).$$

The second part of the theorem is proved in a similar manner. As an immediate consequence of Corollary 18.13 we have

COROLLARY 18.14. *If M and N meet the conditions of Corollary 18.13, and if $M_y \equiv N_x$, then $\int M(x, y)\, dx + N(x, y)\, dy$ exists and is given by the formula*

$$\int M(x, y)\, dx + N(x, y)\, dy = f(x, y) + C,$$

where $f(x, y)$ is the function given by (8).

While Corollary 18.14 is merely a restatement of Theorem 12.2, yet the preceding discussion gives further insight into this important result.

EXERCISES XIV

1. Show that $\int_{0,0}^{1,2} (3x^2y - y^2)\, dx + (x^3 - 2xy)\, dy$ is independent of C. Check this result by evaluating this integral along three different paths.

2. Find $\int_C (x - y)\, dx$ around the circle $x^2 + y^2 = 1$. Carry out this evaluation by direct substitution and also by Green's theorem.

3. If $V_x = 4x/(x^2 + y^2)$ and $V_y = 4y/(x^2 + y^2)$, find the rate of flow of fluid across

(a) The unit circle with center at $(0, 0)$.

(b) Any simple closed curve not enclosing $(0, 0)$.

Account for the fact that Green's theorem is applicable in one case but not the other. What physical interpretation may be given to explain the difference between the two results in (a) and (b)?

4. Evaluate $\int_C (x^2 - y^2)\, dx + (xy)\, dy$ around the figure bounded by $y = 4 - x^2$ and $y = 0$. Use Green's Theorem and also some other method.

5. Find the work done on a particle moving along the path $y = 1 - x^2$, $z = 2x - 3$ from $(0, 1, -1)$ to $(2, -1, 1)$ when

$$X(x, y, z) = xy, \qquad Y(x, y, z) = z, \qquad Z(x, y, z) = x - z.$$

6. Using three different paths, find the work done on a particle in going from $(0, 0)$ to $(1, 2)$ when $X(x, y) = x/\sqrt{x^2 + y^2}$, $Y(x, y) = y/\sqrt{x^2 + y^2}$.

7. Solve Exs. XII, 3 and 6 by Green's theorem.

8. Find the work done on a particle going from $(0, 0, 0)$ to $(1, 2, 3)$ when $X(x, y, z) = 2x$, $Y(x, y, z) = z$, $Z(x, y, z) = y$. Use three different paths.

9. Prove the converse of Corollary 18.11, i.e., that if M, N, M_y, and N_x are defined and continuous over a simply connected region K, and if

$$\int_C M\, dx + N\, dy = 0$$

for every closed curve C in K, then $M_y \equiv N_x$.

HINT: Suppose at some point (x_0, y_0) it were the case that

$$M_y(x_0, y_0) - N_x(x_0, y_0) > 0.$$

By continuity, $M_y - N_x > 0$ over some region R about (x_0, y_0). Thus the left member of (3) is not 0 for the region R.

10. Let $f(x, y)$ and $g(x, y)$ have continuous second derivatives. By taking $M \equiv f \cdot (\partial g/\partial y)$, $N \equiv -f \cdot (\partial g/\partial x)$ in (3), show that

$$\mathop{\mathrm{S}}_K (f \, \Delta g + f_x g_x + f_y g_y) \, dA = \int_C f \frac{dg}{dn} \, ds, \tag{12}$$

and hence that

$$\mathop{\mathrm{S}}_K (f \, \Delta g - g \, \Delta f) \, dA = \int_C \left(f \frac{dg}{dn} - g \frac{df}{dn} \right) ds, \tag{13}$$

where $\Delta g \equiv (\partial^2 g/\partial x^2) + (\partial^2 g/\partial y^2)$, s denotes arc length along the boundary C of the region K, and dg/dn denotes the directional derivative of g in the direction normal to C at any point on C. To what form does (13) reduce when $g \equiv 1$? To what form does (12) reduce when $f(x, y) \equiv g(x, y)$ and $\Delta f = 0$?

11. Show that the area A bounded by the lines $\theta = \alpha$, $\theta = \beta$, and the curve $r = f(\theta)$ is given by

$$A = \tfrac{1}{2} \int_C x \, dy - y \, dx = \tfrac{1}{2} \int_\alpha^\beta r^2 \, d\theta.$$

HINT: $x = r \cos \theta$, $y = r \sin \theta$.

12. Using both integrals in Ex. 11, find the smaller area bounded by $x^2 + y^2 = 25$ and $x = 3$.

19. Transformation of Double Integrals.

In this section we shall apply Green's theorem to evaluate a double integral $\mathop{\mathrm{S}}_K f(x, y) \, dA = \int\int_K f(x, y) \, \partial y \, dx$ by introducing a new (u, v) coordinate system over the region K. [Cf. (3) in Sec. 10.] Let $N(x, y)$ be such that $f(x, y) = \partial N(x, y)/\partial x$. By (2) of Sec. 18,

$$\mathop{\mathrm{S}}_K f(x, y) \, dA = \mathop{\mathrm{S}}_K \frac{\partial N}{\partial x} \, dA = \int_C N(x, y) \, dy, \tag{1}$$

where C is the boundary of K. Let C be represented by the equations

$$x = \varphi(t), \qquad y = \psi(t), \tag{2}$$

where t varies from t_0 to t_1 as (x, y) goes around C once from some point P_0. Then

$$\int_C N(x, y)\, dy = \int_{t_0}^{t_1} N(x, y)\frac{dy}{dt}\, dt. \tag{3}$$

Let us introduce a new coordinate system by the relations

$$x = p(u, v), \qquad y = q(u, v). \tag{4}$$

As the point (u, v) moves along C, u and v are functions of t, and

$$\int_{t_0}^{t_1} N(x, y)\frac{dy}{dt}\, dt = \int_{t_0}^{t_1} N(x, y)\left(\frac{\partial y}{\partial u}\frac{du}{dt} + \frac{\partial y}{\partial v}\frac{dv}{dt}\right)dt$$

$$= \int_C N(x, y)\frac{\partial y}{\partial u}\, du + N(x, y)\frac{\partial y}{\partial v}\, dv, \tag{5}$$

where the last integral is evaluated by transforming the xy equations of C into uv equations with the aid of (2) and (4). By Green's theorem,

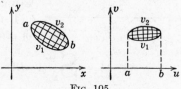

FIG. 105.

$$\int_C N(x, y)\frac{\partial y}{\partial u}\, du + N(x, y)\frac{\partial y}{\partial v}\, dv$$

$$= -\int\int_K \left[\frac{\partial}{\partial v}\left(N\frac{\partial y}{\partial u}\right) - \frac{\partial}{\partial u}\left(N\frac{\partial y}{\partial v}\right)\right]\partial v\, du$$

$$= \int\int_K \left(\frac{\partial N}{\partial u}\frac{\partial y}{\partial v} - \frac{\partial N}{\partial v}\frac{\partial y}{\partial u}\right)\partial v\, du$$

$$= \int\int_K \frac{\partial N}{\partial x}\left(\frac{\partial x}{\partial u}\frac{\partial y}{\partial v} - \frac{\partial x}{\partial v}\frac{\partial y}{\partial u}\right)\partial v\, du, \tag{6}$$

where the limits for the double integrals are given by the uv equations of C in the usual manner.* It follows by (1), (3), (5), and

* To see this more clearly, regard u and v as rectangular coordinates in a uv-plane. Then the uv equations of C represent a closed curve C_{uv} in the uv-plane. Since u and v vary in exactly the same manner along C and C_{uv}, as do also the values of N, $\partial y/\partial u$, and $\partial y/\partial v$ (see Fig. 105),

$$\mathrm{S}_C\ N\frac{\partial y}{\partial u}\, du + N\frac{\partial y}{\partial v}\, dv = \mathrm{S}_{C_{uv}}\ N\frac{\partial y}{\partial u}\, du + N\frac{\partial y}{\partial v}\, dv,$$

there being no difference whatever between the two integrals except their geometric representation. As indicated in (6),

$$\mathrm{S}_{C_{uv}}\ N\frac{\partial y}{\partial u}\, du + N\frac{\partial y}{\partial v}\, dv = \int\int_{K_{uv}} \frac{\partial N}{\partial x}\left(\frac{\partial x}{\partial u}\frac{\partial y}{\partial v} - \frac{\partial x}{\partial v}\frac{\partial y}{\partial u}\right)\partial v\, du, \tag{7}$$

where K_{uv} is the region bounded by C_{uv}, and where the limits for $\int\int_{K_{uv}}$ are determined in the usual way. Since the range of variation of u and v

(6) that

$$\iint_K f(x, y)\, \partial y\, dx = \iint_K f(x, y)\frac{\partial(x, y)}{\partial(u, v)}\, \partial v\, du, \qquad (8)$$

where $\partial(x, y)/\partial(u, v)$ denotes the Jacobian of x and y (see Sec. 20

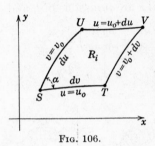

FIG. 106.

of Chap. I), and where $f(x, y)$ is expressed as a function of u and v by (4). In the preceding proof we leave it to the student to state explicitly all conditions regarding continuity, ranges of values, etc., that have been implicitly assumed.

If $f(x, y) \equiv 1$ in (8), then the area A of a region K is given by

$$A = \mathbf{S}_K (1)\, dA = \iint_K \left|\frac{\partial(x, y)}{\partial(u, v)}\right|\, \partial v\, du, \qquad (9)$$

where the absolute value is introduced because the Jacobian may be negative. To give an intuitive derivation of (9), suppose the region K is subdivided into small curvilinear parallelograms R_i as indicated in Fig. 106, where the equations of ST, for example, are $x = p(u_0, v)$, $y = q(u_0, v)$, or in uv coordinates, $u = u_0$. If u and v represent arc-lengths along the boundaries of R, then the area of R_i is approximately $du\, dv \sin \alpha$, where α is the angle between the curves $u = u_0$ and $v = v_0$. But it was pointed out in Sec. 20 of Chap. I that $\sin \alpha = \partial(x, y)/\partial(u, v)$ when u and v represent arc lengths. Hence the area of R_i is approximately $|\partial(x, y)/\partial(u, v)|\, du\, dv$, and (9) follows by the usual summation process.

Example 1. In polar coordinates (4) assumes the form

$$x = r \cos \theta, \qquad y = r \sin \theta,$$

and as $\partial(x, y)/\partial(r, \theta) = r$, (8) becomes the formula for volume in polar coordinates:

$$V = \iint_K z\, \partial y\, dx = \iint_K zr\, \partial r\, d\theta = \iint_K zr\, \partial\theta\, dr. \qquad (10)$$

If $z = f(r)$, a function of r alone, and if K is the ring bounded by $r = a$ and $r = b$, then

is exactly the same over K_{uv} and K, the last integrals in (6) and (7) are exactly the same, only the geometric representations being different.

$$\underset{K}{S} z \, dA = \int_a^b \int_0^{2\pi} r f(r) \, \partial\theta \, dr = \int_a^b 2\pi r f(r) \, dr. \qquad (11)$$

If $z \equiv 1$, (10) gives the area bounded by a plane curve:

$$A = \int\int_K r \, \partial r \, d\theta. \qquad (12)$$

In particular, the area bounded by $r = a(1 - \cos\theta)$ is

$$A = \int_0^{2\pi} \int_0^{a(1-\cos\theta)} r \, \partial r \, d\theta = \tfrac{3}{2}\pi a^2.$$

Example 2. In parabolic coordinates (4) assumes the form

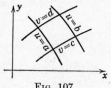

FIG. 107.

$$x = \tfrac{1}{2}(u - v), \qquad y = \sqrt{uv},$$

and as $\partial(x, y)/\partial(u, v) = \tfrac{1}{4}(u + v)/\sqrt{uv}$, (8) becomes

$$\int\int_K f(x, y) \, \partial y \, dx = \int\int_K f\left[\frac{1}{2}(u - v), \sqrt{uv}\right] \frac{1}{4} \frac{u + v}{\sqrt{uv}} \, \partial v \, du. \qquad (13)$$

In particular, the moment about the x-axis of the area bounded by the parabolas $u = a$, $u = b$, $v = c$, $v = d$ is

$$\underset{K}{S} y \, dA = \int_a^b \int_c^d y\frac{1}{4} \frac{u + v}{\sqrt{uv}} \, \partial v \, du = \frac{1}{4}\int_a^b \int_c^d (u + v) \, \partial v \, du.$$

In Sec. 15 of Chap. VI we shall show how (9) may be used to *define* the area of a warped surface (a concept we have so far taken for granted).

EXERCISES XV

Show that

1. $\underset{K}{S} f(x, y) \, dA = 2\int_c^d \int_a^b f(u + v, u - v) \, \partial v \, du$ when

$$x = u - v, \qquad y = u + v,$$

where K is the region bounded by

$$y - x = 2a, \qquad y - x = 2b, \qquad y + x = 2c, \qquad y + x = 2d.$$

2. $\int_0^3 \int_0^{4x} f(x, y) \, \partial y \, dx$

$$= \int_0^2 \int_0^{6(u+1)} f\left[\frac{v}{2(u + 1)}, \frac{uv}{u + 1}\right]\frac{-v}{2(u + 1)^2} \, \partial v \, du$$

$$= \int_0^6 \int_0^2 (f)\frac{-v}{2(u + 1)^2} \, \partial u \, dv + \int_6^{18} \int_{\frac{v}{6}-1}^2 (f)\frac{-v}{2(u + 1)^2} \, \partial u \, dv$$

when $x = \tfrac{1}{2}v/(u + 1)$, $y = uv/(u + 1)$ (see Fig. 108).

Hint: draw the parametric curves $u = u_0$ and $v = v_0$ by writing the equations of transformation in the form $u = y/2x$, $v = 2x + y$, and plotting the graphs of these equations for various values of u and v. Determine the uv equations of the bounding curves. Interpret the various integrations as a process of "adding up" little quadrilaterals by rows in one direction or the other.

3. $\int_{x_0}^{1} \int_{1/x}^{x^2+3} f(x, y) \, \partial y \, dx = \int_1^4 \int_{v-1}^3 fJ \, \partial u \, dv = \int_0^3 \int_1^{u+1} fJ \, \partial v \, du$ when

$$u = y - x^2, \qquad v = xy,$$

where x_0 is the solution of the equation $x^3 + 3x - 1 = 0$.

4. $\int_0^1 \int_0^x f(x, y) \, \partial y \, dx = \int_0^1 \int_{\sqrt{v}}^{1+\sqrt{1-v}} fJ \, \partial u \, dv$

$$= \int_0^1 \int_0^{u^2} fJ \, \partial v \, du + \int_1^2 \int_0^{2u-u^2} fJ \, \partial v \, du$$

when $u = x + y$, $v = x^2 - y^2$.

20. Green's Theorem in Space.

Theorem 18.1 relates a double integral over a plane area to a line integral around the

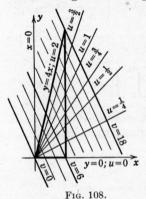

Fig. 108.

boundary of this area. This theorem may be extended (1) to relate a volume integral to a surface integral taken over the boundary of the volume, and (2) to relate a double integral over a warped area to a line integral taken around the boundary of this area. In this section we take up (1), and in the next section we discuss (2).

Let R be an axial region whose bounding surface S can be broken up into upper and lower parts K_2 and K_1 with equations $z = r_2(x, y)$ and $z = r_1(x, y)$. Let $Z(x, y, z)$ and $\partial Z/\partial z$ be defined and continuous in R. By (35) of Sec. 17,

$$\underset{R}{\mathbf{S}} \frac{\partial Z(x, y, z)}{\partial z} \, dV = \underset{K'}{\mathbf{S}} \left[\int_{r_1(x,y)}^{r_2(x,y)} \frac{\partial Z}{\partial z} \, \partial z \right] dA'$$

$$= \underset{K'}{\mathbf{S}} \{ Z[x, y, r_2(x, y)] - Z[x, y, r_1(x, y)] \} \, dA'$$

$$= \underset{S}{\mathbf{S}} Z(x, y, z) \cos \gamma \, dA, \tag{1}$$

where γ is the direction angle with the z-axis of the outward normal $\mathbf{n}$ at any point of S, and where K' is the projection of R

on the xy-plane.   It follows in a similar manner that

$$\mathbf{S}_R \frac{\partial X(x, y, z)}{\partial x}\, dV = \mathbf{S}_S X \cos \alpha\, dA,$$
$$\mathbf{S}_R \frac{\partial Y(x, y, z)}{\partial y}\, dV = \mathbf{S}_S Y \cos \beta\, dA,$$

(2)

where α and β are the direction angles of $\mathbf{n}$ with the x- and y-axes. If we add the results in (1) and (2) we obtain *Green's theorem in space:*

$$\mathbf{S}_R \left(\frac{\partial X}{\partial x} + \frac{\partial Y}{\partial y} + \frac{\partial Z}{\partial z} \right) dV$$
$$= \mathbf{S}_S (X \cos \alpha + Y \cos \beta + Z \cos \gamma)\, dA,\quad (3)$$

where each term may be evaluated as indicated for (1).   The region R may be generalized in the manner indicated in Sec. 18.

If X, Y, and Z are the rectangular components of a vector $\mathbf{V}$, we define the *divergence* of $\mathbf{V}$, div $\mathbf{V}$, by the formula

$$\operatorname{div} \mathbf{V} \equiv \frac{\partial X}{\partial x} + \frac{\partial Y}{\partial y} + \frac{\partial Z}{\partial z}.$$

(4)

By (26), (27), and (31) of Sec. 17, (3) assumes the form

$$\mathbf{S}_R \operatorname{div} \mathbf{V}\, dV = \mathbf{S}_S V_n\, dA = \mathbf{S}_S \mathbf{V} \cdot d\mathbf{A}.$$

(5)

It may be shown by (3) that

$$\iiint_R f(x, y, z)\, \partial z\, \partial y\, dx$$
$$= \iiint_R f(x, y, z) \frac{\partial(x, y, z)}{\partial(u, v, w)}\, \partial w\, \partial v\, du.\quad (6)$$

[See (22″) of Sec. 20 in Chap. I; also, see Osgood, "Advanced Calculus," p. 271.]

We shall now give a physical interpretation to div $\mathbf{V}$; we shall do this in a simple intuitive manner and then in an accurate mathematical manner.   Consider the fluid in a small volume with edges dx, dy, dz. Let A and A' be the centers of the faces of this volume parallel to the yz-plane, and let X and $X + dX$ be the x-components of the velocity $\mathbf{V}$ of the

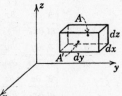

Fig. 109.

fluid at A and A'; let Y, $Y + dY$, Z, $Z + dZ$ be the other components of $\mathbf{V}$ at the centers of the other faces. Then $(dy\ dz)\ (dX)\ (dt)$ is the increase in volume V due to dX in time dt, and $dx\ dz\ dY\ dt$ and $dx\ dy\ dZ\ dt$ are the increases in V due to dY and dZ in time dt. Hence the total rate of increase in V is

$$\frac{dV}{dt} = dy\ dz\ dX + dx\ dz\ dY + dx\ dy\ dZ,$$

and the *rate of increase of V per unit of volume is*

$$\lim_{V \to 0} \frac{1}{V} \frac{dV}{dt} = \frac{\partial X}{\partial x} + \frac{\partial Y}{\partial y} + \frac{\partial Z}{\partial z} = \operatorname{div} \mathbf{V}, \tag{7}$$

where we write, for example, $\lim dX/dx = \partial X/\partial x$ because y and z are constant.

To give a rigorous derivation of (7), consider an arbitrary particle P of fluid flowing in space. If (x, y, z) is the position of P at time t, then x, y, z depend upon t and the position (x_0, y_0, z_0) of P at some fixed instant t_0, i.e.,

$$x = p(x_0, y_0, z_0, t), \qquad y = q(x_0, y_0, z_0, t), \qquad z = r(x_0, y_0, z_0, t). \tag{8}$$

Let R_0 be the region occupied by a certain portion of fluid at time t_0, and let R be the region occupied by this same portion of fluid at time t. By (8), we may regard (x_0, y_0, z_0) as a set of parametric coordinates of R, and by (6) with $f(x, y, z) \equiv 1$, the volume V of R is

$$V = \iiint_R J\left(\frac{x,\ y,\ z}{x_0,\ y_0,\ z_0}\right) \partial z_0\ \partial y_0\ dx_0, \tag{9}$$

where the subscript 0 serves merely to distinguish the variables x_0, y_0, z_0 from the variables x, y, z. By a direct extension of Sec. 33 below, we may write

$$\frac{dV}{dt} = \iiint_R \frac{\partial}{\partial t} J\left(\frac{x,\ y,\ z}{x_0,\ y_0,\ z_0}\right) \partial z_0\ \partial y_0\ dx_0. \tag{10}$$

Now

$$\frac{\partial}{\partial t} J = \begin{vmatrix} \dfrac{\partial}{\partial t}\dfrac{\partial x}{\partial x_0} & \dfrac{\partial x}{\partial y_0} & \dfrac{\partial x}{\partial z_0} \\[8pt] \dfrac{\partial}{\partial t}\dfrac{\partial y}{\partial x_0} & \dfrac{\partial y}{\partial y_0} & \dfrac{\partial y}{\partial z_0} \\[8pt] \dfrac{\partial}{\partial t}\dfrac{\partial z}{\partial x_0} & \dfrac{\partial z}{\partial y_0} & \dfrac{\partial z}{\partial z_0} \end{vmatrix} + \begin{vmatrix} \dfrac{\partial x}{\partial x_0} & \dfrac{\partial}{\partial t}\dfrac{\partial x}{\partial y_0} & \dfrac{\partial x}{\partial z_0} \\[8pt] \dfrac{\partial y}{\partial x_0} & \dfrac{\partial}{\partial t}\dfrac{\partial y}{\partial y_0} & \dfrac{\partial y}{\partial z_0} \\[8pt] \dfrac{\partial z}{\partial x_0} & \dfrac{\partial}{\partial t}\dfrac{\partial z}{\partial y_0} & \dfrac{\partial z}{\partial z_0} \end{vmatrix} + \begin{vmatrix} \dfrac{\partial x}{\partial x_0} & \dfrac{\partial x}{\partial y_0} & \dfrac{\partial}{\partial t}\dfrac{\partial x}{\partial z_0} \\[8pt] \dfrac{\partial y}{\partial x_0} & \dfrac{\partial y}{\partial y_0} & \dfrac{\partial}{\partial t}\dfrac{\partial y}{\partial z_0} \\[8pt] \dfrac{\partial z}{\partial x_0} & \dfrac{\partial z}{\partial y_0} & \dfrac{\partial}{\partial t}\dfrac{\partial z}{\partial z_0} \end{vmatrix},$$

for the first determinant represents the result of differentiating the first factor of every term in the expansion of J, and the second and third determinants arise when all the second factors and then all the third factors are differentiated. Now at $t = t_0$, x and x_0 mean the same thing, i.e., $x \equiv x_0$; likewise, $y \equiv y_0$, $z \equiv z_0$. Hence

$$\text{At } t = t_0, \quad \frac{\partial x}{\partial y_0} = \frac{\partial x}{\partial z_0} = \frac{\partial y}{\partial x_0} = \frac{\partial y}{\partial z_0} = \frac{\partial z}{\partial x_0} = \frac{\partial z}{\partial y_0} = 0, \quad \frac{\partial x}{\partial x_0} = \frac{\partial y}{\partial y_0} = \frac{\partial z}{\partial z_0} = 1.$$

On the other hand, the components of velocity of a particular particle P are

$$X = \frac{\partial x}{\partial t}, \qquad Y = \frac{\partial y}{\partial t}, \qquad Z = \frac{\partial z}{\partial t}, \tag{11}$$

since x_0, y_0, z_0 are fixed for any one particle. Hence

$$\frac{\partial}{\partial t}\frac{\partial x}{\partial x_0} = \frac{\partial}{\partial x_0}\frac{\partial x}{\partial t} = \frac{\partial X}{\partial x_0}, \qquad \frac{\partial}{\partial t}\frac{\partial y}{\partial y_0} = \frac{\partial Y}{\partial y_0}, \qquad \frac{\partial}{\partial t}\frac{\partial z}{\partial z_0} = \frac{\partial Z}{\partial z_0},$$

$$\left[\frac{\partial}{\partial t}J\!\left(\frac{x, y, z}{x_0, y_0, z_0}\right)\right]_{t_0} = \left(\frac{\partial X}{\partial x_0} + \frac{\partial Y}{\partial y_0} + \frac{\partial Z}{\partial z_0}\right)_{t_0} = (\text{div } \mathbf{V})_{t_0},$$

and by (10)

$$\left(\frac{dV}{dt}\right)_{t_0} = \int\!\!\int\!\!\int_{R_0} (\text{div } \mathbf{V})_{t_0} \, \partial z_0 \, \partial y_0 \, dx_0. \tag{12}$$

Since x, y, z are not involved in this result, we may drop all the subscripts. By an extension of Theorem 28.1 below,

$$\int\!\!\int\!\!\int_R \text{div } \mathbf{V} \, dV = [\text{div } \mathbf{V}]_{P_1}(V),$$

so that by (12),

$$\frac{1}{V}\frac{dV}{dt} = [\text{div } \mathbf{V}]_{P_1},$$

where P_1 is some point in R. If we let R shrink to any given point P_0 in R, then $P_1 \to P_0$, and

$$\lim_{V \to P_0} \frac{1}{V}\frac{dV}{dt} = [\text{div } \mathbf{V}]_{P_0},$$

as in (7). Because $\lim_{V \to P_0} (1/V)(dV/dt)$ is invariant for all coordinate systems based on the same unit of length, it follows that div $\mathbf{V}$ is also an invariant.

Because dV/dt represents the rate Q at which fluid is flowing across the surface S bounding a region R, it follows by (12) and (5) that (26) and (27) of Sec. 17 hold under general conditions.

It is seen, moreover, that (13) of Sec. 16 is merely a special case of (26) in Sec. 17 since in (13), $V \sin \theta = V_n$.

If ρ is the density of a fluid at any point P, and if M is the total mass of the fluid in a region R, then $M = S_R \rho \, dV$, and

$$\frac{dM}{dt} = S_R \frac{\partial \rho}{\partial t} \, dV. \tag{13}$$

But by (26) of Sec. 17 and (5), the rate of increase of M due to the flow of fluid into R across its boundary S is

$$-S_S \rho V_n \, dA = -S_R [\text{div} \, (\rho \mathbf{V})] \, dV. \tag{14}$$

Again, if matter is being created or destroyed (as by radioactive processes) at any point P at the rate $\lambda \rho$, λ being the "growth factor," then the rate of increase of M due to these "sources" or "sinks" is

$$S_R \lambda \rho \, dV. \tag{15}$$

Since the sum of (14) and (15) is dM/dt, it follows by (13) that

$$S_R \left[\frac{\partial \rho}{\partial t} + \text{div} \, (\rho \mathbf{V}) - \lambda \rho \right] dV = 0. \tag{16}$$

Since (16) holds for *every* region R,

$$\frac{\partial \rho}{\partial t} + \text{div} \, (\rho \mathbf{V}) - \lambda \rho = 0, \tag{17}$$

for if the integrand of (16) were (say) positive at some point P_0, then by continuity considerations the integrand would remain positive throughout some region R about P_0 and the left member of (16) would be positive for this region R. In the function $\rho(x, y, z, t)$ let x, y, z be given by (8). Then the point (x, y, z) represents a particle P as it moves along its path, and $d\rho/dt$ represents the rate of change of density of the fluid at the moving particle P. If we expand $d\rho/dt$ and div $(\rho \mathbf{V})$ completely, then, by (17), we have the *equation of continuity:*

$$\text{div} \, \mathbf{V} = \lambda - \frac{1}{\rho} \frac{d\rho}{dt} \tag{18}$$

where $d\rho/dt$ is computed at a moving particle P. As a particular case, if matter is neither created nor destroyed, so that $\lambda = 0$, and if the material is incompressible, so that $d\rho/dt = 0$, then we obtain the equation governing the flow of an incompressible liquid:

$$\text{div } \mathbf{V} = 0. \tag{19}$$

As another particular case, let us regard ρ as the quantity of heat in a substance per unit of volume. Then $\rho = CT$, where (for normal ranges of temperature T) C is a constant called the *specific heat* of the substance. Again, if $\mathbf{V}$ denotes the velocity of a "particle" of heat, then $\rho\mathbf{V}$ represents the rate of transfer of heat at any point. Moreover, it is known by experiment that this rate is $-K \text{ grad } T$, where K is the *specific conductivity* of heat for the substance, where the magnitude of $\mathbf{grad} \ T$ is dT/dn, and where the components of $\mathbf{grad} \ T$ are $X = \partial T/\partial x$, $Y = \partial T/\partial y$, $Z = \partial T/\partial z$ (see Sec. 22 of Chap. I). By (4),

$$\text{div } (\rho\mathbf{V}) = \text{div } (-K \text{ grad } T) = -K\left(\frac{\partial^2 T}{\partial x^2} + \frac{\partial^2 T}{\partial y^2} + \frac{\partial^2 T}{\partial z^2}\right).$$

Substitution of these results in (17) leads to the *heat equation:*

$$\text{div } \mathbf{grad} \ T \equiv \frac{\partial^2 T}{\partial x^2} + \frac{\partial^2 T}{\partial y^2} + \frac{\partial^2 T}{\partial z^2} = c^2\frac{\partial T}{\partial t} - k\lambda T, \tag{20}$$

where $c^2 = C/K$, and where λ represents sources or sinks of heat. In particular, if the flow of heat is *steady*, so that $\partial T/\partial t = 0$, and if $\lambda = 0$, then (20) assumes the form

$$\frac{\partial^2 T}{\partial x^2} + \frac{\partial^2 T}{\partial y^2} + \frac{\partial^2 T}{\partial z^2} = 0. \tag{21}$$

EXERCISES XVI

1. Extend the results of Ex. XIV, 10, to the case where f and g are functions of x, y, z.

2. Develop the analogues of Corollaries 18.11 to 18.14 for surface integrals, with the condition div $\mathbf{V} = 0$ taking the role played by the condition $M_y \equiv N_x$.

3. Show that $S_S F(P) dA = S_R (\mathbf{grad} \ F) dV$, where S is the bounding surface of R, and $d\mathbf{A}$ is a vector of length dA in the direction of the surface normal $\mathbf{n}$.

4. Show that the work done by an expanding gas is $W = \int p \ dv$ regardless of the shape of the container (cf. Ex. X, 16).

5. Find the force of attraction between a circular disk having electric charge ρ per unit area and a point charge e on the axis of the disk and distant a from the disk.

6. Show that the force of attraction between a particle P of mass m and a homogeneous sphere S of mass M and radius a is $F = kMm/d^2$, where $d \geqq a$ and d is the distance from P to the center of S. Show that there is no force acting on a particle inside a homogeneous spherical shell of any finite thickness. Use these results to discuss the variation in the weight of a body as it moves from a point outside the earth to the center of the earth.

7. (a) A force field is *solenoidal* if the total flux is zero across every closed surface S containing no point of discontinuity of the field (i.e., if there is no mass, charge, etc., within S). Show that the inverse square law gives a solenoidal field of force.

(b) Show that, for a solenoidal field, the flux across each end of a *tube of force* is the same; also, show that the intensity of the field within a (small) tube varies inversely with the cross-sectional area of the tube.

(c) Show that the total gravitational flux through a spherical shell of any radius with a particle of mass m at the center is $-4\pi m$. (The flux density at any point is equal to the force acting on a particle of unit mass at that point). Extend this result by (a) to an arbitrary shell containing a particle of mass m.

8. Use Green's theorem to solve Ex. XIII, 4.

21. Stokes's Theorem. We now take up the second extension of Green's theorem mentioned in the preceding section. Let S be a surface which may be represented in both of the forms

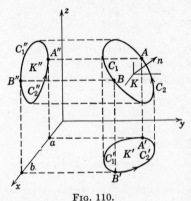

FIG. 110.

$$z = r(x, y), \qquad (1a)$$
$$y = q(x, z), \qquad (1b)$$

where r and q are continuous and single-valued. Let S be oriented by erecting a (continuous) unit vector $\mathbf{n}$ at each point of S. Let C be a simple closed curve on S bounding a region K. We say that a point P traces out C *positively* when P moves around K in that direction which would cause a right-hand screw to progress in the positive direction along any vector $\mathbf{n}$ of K. Now suppose K to be such that its projections K' and K'' on the xy- and xz-planes are bounded by the curves C' and C'' with equations

$$y = C_1'(x), \qquad y = C_2'(x), \qquad (2a)$$
$$z = C_1''(x), \qquad z = C_2''(x). \qquad (2b)$$

Since C is represented by the pair of equations (1a) and (2a),

$$\mathbf{S}_C X(x, y, z)\, dx = \mathbf{S}_{C'} X[x, y, r(x, y)]\, dx, \tag{3}$$

the integral $\mathbf{S}_C$ being taken around C in the positive direction relative to $\mathbf{n}$. By (1) of Sec. 18,

$$\mathbf{S}_{C'} X[x, y, r(x, y)]\, dx = \mp \int_a^b \int_{C_1'}^{C_2'} \frac{\partial X[x, y, r(x, y)]}{\partial y}\, \partial y\, dx$$

$$= \mp \int_a^b \int_{C_1'}^{C_2'} \left(X_y + X_z \frac{\partial z}{\partial y} \right) \partial y\, dx, \tag{4}$$

where $X_y = \dfrac{\partial X(x, y, z)}{\partial y}\Big)_{x,z}$, $X_z = \dfrac{\partial X}{\partial z}\Big)_{x,y}$, $z = r(x, y)$, and the

choice of sign depends on the choice of $\mathbf{n}$. By Ex. VII, 10,

$$\int_a^b \int_{C_1'}^{C_2'} X_z \frac{\partial z}{\partial y}\, \partial y\, dx = \int_a^b \int_{C_1''}^{C_2''} X_z\, \partial z\, dx, \tag{5}$$

for C_1'' and C_2'' result by eliminating y from (1b) and (2a). By (3), (4), (5),

$$\mathbf{S}_C X\, dx = \mp \int_a^b \int_{C_1'}^{C_2'} X_y\, \partial y\, dx \pm \int_a^b \int_{C_2''}^{C_1''} X_z\, \partial z\, dx$$

$$= \mathbf{S}_K (X_z \cos \beta - X_y \cos \gamma)\, dA, \tag{6}$$

where β and γ refer to $\mathbf{n}$. It follows in a similar manner that

$$\mathbf{S}_C Y\, dy = \mathbf{S}_K (Y_x \cos \gamma - Y_z \cos \alpha)\, dA,$$
$$\mathbf{S}_C Z\, dz = \mathbf{S}_K (Z_y \cos \alpha - Z_x \cos \beta)\, dA. \tag{7}$$

Upon adding (6) and (7), we obtain *Stokes's theorem:*

$$\mathbf{S}_C X\, dx + Y\, dy + Z\, dz = \mathbf{S}_K [(Z_y - Y_z) \cos \alpha$$

$$+ (X_z - Z_x) \cos \beta + (Y_x - X_y) \cos \gamma]\, dA. \tag{8}$$

As in (10) of Sec. 16, we may write

$$\mathbf{S}_C X\, dx + Y\, dy + Z\, dz = \mathbf{S}_C \mathbf{V} \cdot d\mathbf{r},$$

where X, Y, and Z are the components of a vector $\mathbf{V}$. If we define **curl V** to be the vector whose components are $(Z_y - Y_z)$,

$(X_z - Z_x)$, $(Y_x - X_y)$, then, as in (31) and (27) of Sec. 17, we have as the vector representation of (8),

$$S_C \mathbf{V} \cdot d\mathbf{r} = S_K \operatorname{curl} \mathbf{V} \cdot d\mathbf{A}. \tag{9}$$

Let $(\operatorname{curl} \mathbf{V})_n$ denote the component of **curl V** normal to K at any point of K. By the theorem of the mean, we may express the right member of (9) in the form

$$S_K (\operatorname{curl} \mathbf{V})_n \, dA = (\operatorname{curl} \mathbf{V})_n]_{P_1} A, \tag{10}$$

where A is the area of K. As in (7) of Sec. 20, we have by (9) and (10),

$$(\operatorname{curl} \mathbf{V})_n]_{P_0} = \lim_{A \to P_0} \frac{1}{A} S_C \mathbf{V} \cdot d\mathbf{r}. \tag{11}$$

As a consequence of (8), Corollaries 18.11 to 18.14 extend at once to functions of three variables; in particular, we have

THEOREM 21.1. *If X, Y, Z and their partial derivatives are defined and continuous over a simply connected region R, and if $Z_y \equiv Y_z$, $X_z \equiv Z_x$, $Y_x \equiv X_y$, then $S_A^B X \, dx + Y \, dy + Z \, dz$ is independent of the path (in R) from A to B.*

THEOREM 21.2. *If X, Y, Z and their partial derivatives are defined and continuous over a simply connected region R, and if $Z_y \equiv Y_z$, $X_z \equiv Z_x$, $Y_x \equiv X_y$, then $\int X \, dx + Y \, dy + Z \, dz$ exists and is given by the formula*

$$\int X \, dx + Y \, dy + Z \, dz = f(x, y, z) + C,$$

where $f(x, y, z)$ is the function such that

$$f(x_0, y_0, z_0) = S_{a,b,c}^{x_0, y_0, z_0} X \, dx + Y \, dy + Z \, dz,$$

and where the path of integration is arbitrary within R.

EXERCISES XVII

1. Prove Theorems 21.1 and 21.2.

2. (a) Show that $S_S \operatorname{curl} \mathbf{F} \cdot d\mathbf{A} = 0$, where S is a closed surface.

HINT: Let C be a closed curve on S dividing S into two parts. Note that the left member of (9) has opposite signs when C is traced out in opposite directions.

(b) Show that $S_R \operatorname{div} \operatorname{curl} \mathbf{F} \, dV = 0$ for all regions R, and hence that $\operatorname{div} \operatorname{curl} \mathbf{F} \equiv 0$.

3. Rewrite Theorems 21.1 and 21.2 in vector language, making use of the curl.

4. Give examples of functions to show that Theorems 21.1 and 21.2 may be false if X, Y, Z and their derivatives are not continuous everywhere in R, or if R is not simply connected.

5. Let X, Y, Z be the rectangular components of a force field $\mathbf{F}$, and let these components and their derivatives be defined and continuous in a simply connected region R. $\mathbf{F}$ is said to be conservative if $\int_A^P X\,dx + Y\,dy + Z\,dz$ is independent of the path C from A to P (C being in R). We define the *potential* $U(x, y, z)$ of a conservative field $\mathbf{F}$ relative to the point A by the formula $U(x, y, z) = \int_A^{(x,y,z)} X\,dx + Y\,dy + Z\,dz$, $U(x, y, z)$ being the work done by $\mathbf{F}$ in going from A to (x, y, z) along any path in R. Show that the component of $\mathbf{F}$ in any direction is dU/ds taken in that direction, s being arc-length. Conversely, show that if there exists a function $W(x, y, z)$ such that the rectangular components of $\mathbf{F}$ are given by $X = \partial W/\partial x$, $Y = \partial W/\partial y$, $Z = \partial W/\partial z$, then $\mathbf{F}$ is conservative. Find the potential function for the field around a point charge or point mass, using the usual inverse square law of attraction.

6. Let X, Y, Z be the rectangular components of the velocity $\mathbf{V}$ of a fluid at any point P. Interpret $\int_C X\,dx + Y\,dy + Z\,dz$ as the *circulation* or *rotation* around a closed curve C. The field $\mathbf{V}$ is called *irrotational* (vortex-free) if $\int_C X\,dx + Y\,dy + Z\,dz = 0$ around all closed curves C. If $\mathbf{V}$ is irrotational, show that $\int_A^P X\,dx + Y\,dy + Z\,dz$ is independent of the path from A to P. (Consider the closed curve formed by any two paths from A to P.) Define *velocity potential* for irrotational flow. Discuss analogies between quantities in this and the preceding exercise.

PART C. RIEMANN THEORY OF INTEGRATION

22. Introduction. The concept of the definite integral of a function $f(x)$ as the limit of a sum originated from the idea that the function $f(x)$ may be represented by a "curve," and that this limit is the area between the curve, the x-axis, and the two bounding ordinates (see Sec. 13).

However, the definite integral of a function may exist when the function is discontinuous, so that the graph of the function does not bound an area. Moreover, $S_a^b f(x)\,dx$ may exist when $\int_a^b f(x)\,dx$ does not exist. Hence it is necessary to investigate the properties of the symbol $S_a^b f(x)\,dx$ without reference to any geometric representation and without assuming the existence of $\int_a^b f(x)\,dx$ (as was done in Ex. IX, 3). The first rigorous arithmetical treatment of the definite integral was given by Riemann in 1854. We shall adopt Riemann's definition in the sections to follow. It will be seen that $S_a^b f(x)\,dx$, as defined by Riemann, exists only when $f(x)$ meets certain conditions.

Very recently, there have been advanced by Lebesgue (1916), de la Vallée Poussin, W. H. Young, Bliss, Hildebrandt, and others, general definitions of the definite integral, in each case the purpose of the newer definition being to remove the limitations placed on the integrand as required in Riemann's treatment. We shall not concern ourselves with a study of these later theories of integration.

23. S and s. We* shall assume that $f(x)$ is a function bounded in the interval $[a, b]$, i.e., the interval $a \leq x \leq b$. (See Ex. IX, 11, and p. 818.) Let us form a partition $\mathcal{P}$ of $[a, b]$ by subdividing $[a, b]$ into n subintervals:

$$\mathcal{P}: \qquad [x_0, x_1], [x_1, x_2], \cdots, [x_{n-1}, x_n],$$

where

$$a = x_0 < x_1 < x_2 < \cdots < x_{n-1} < x_n = b.$$

Let M denote the least upper bound† and m the greatest lower bound of $f(x)$ in $[a, b]$. Likewise, we use M_r, m_r to denote those bounds in the interval $[x_{r-1}, x_r]$. Let

$$S = \sum_{j=1}^{n} M_j(x_j - x_{j-1}), \qquad s = \sum_{j=1}^{n} m_j(x_j - x_{j-1}).$$

We leave to the reader the proof of

THEOREM 23.1. *To every partition $\mathcal{P}$ of $[a, b]$ into subintervals, there corresponds a sum S and a sum s, and $s \leq S$.*

Since $s \leq M(b - a)$ and $S \geq m(b - a)$, *s has an upper bound and S has a lower bound.* We shall denote the greatest lower bound of the sums S by J and the least upper bound of the sums s by I. (The existence of J and I is proved in Chap. IX.)

We shall now prove

THEOREM 23.2. *$I \leq J$.*

Let S and s be the sums corresponding to the partition $\mathcal{P}_1$ of $[a, b]$. Subdivide some or all of the subintervals of $\mathcal{P}_1$ into smaller intervals and denote the resulting partition of $[a, b]$ by $\mathcal{P}_{12}$, where the end points of the intervals of $\mathcal{P}_{12}$ are a, y_1, y_2, $\cdots$, y_{k-1}, x_1, y_k, y_{k+1}, $\cdots$, y_{l-1}, x_2, y_l, $\cdots$, b. We shall say that $\mathcal{P}_{12}$ is *consecutive* to $\mathcal{P}_1$.

---

* See Goursat, "Cours d'analyse," Tome I, 3d ed., pp. 171*ff*.

† The least upper bound of $f(x)$ in $[a, b]$ is the smallest number M such that $f(x) \leq M$ for all x in $[a, b]$. The existence of M is proved in Chap. IX. The greatest lower bound is defined in a similar manner.

Denote the sums corresponding to S and s for the new partition $\mathcal{P}_{12}$ by Σ and σ. Let $M_1^{(1)}, m_1^{(1)}; M_2^{(1)}, m_2^{(1)}, \cdots$ be the least upper bound and the greatest lower bound of $f(x)$ in $[a, y_1]$; $[y_1, y_2]; \cdots$, respectively. Then that part of Σ for $[a, x_1]$ is equal to

$$M_1^{(1)}(y_1 - a) + M_2^{(1)}(y_2 - y_1) + \cdots + M_k^{(1)}(x_1 - y_{k-1}),$$

which is not greater than $M_1(x_1 - a)$, for the numbers $M_1^{(1)}$, $M_2^{(1)}, \cdots$, $M_k^{(1)}$ can not exceed M_1. Similarly, we can show that the part of Σ for $[x_1, x_2]$ is not greater than $M_2(x_2 - x_1)$, and so on. Consequently, the sum Σ for $[a, b]$ can not exceed S.

Likewise, we can show that σ for $[a, b]$ is not less than s.

Suppose

$$\mathcal{P}_\xi: \qquad\qquad a, \xi_1, \xi_2, \cdots, \xi_{n-1}, b,$$

with sums S_ξ and s_ξ, and

$$\mathcal{P}_\eta: \qquad\qquad a, \eta_1, \eta_2, \cdots, \eta_{m-1}, b,$$

with sums S_η and s_η, are any two partitions of $[a, b]$. If we superimpose $\mathcal{P}_\xi$ and $\mathcal{P}_\eta$ we obtain a third partition $\mathcal{P}_{\xi+\eta}$ of $[a, b]$ which is *consecutive* to $\mathcal{P}_\xi$ as well as to $\mathcal{P}_\eta$.

Let the sums for $\mathcal{P}_{\xi+\eta}$ be denoted by $\Sigma_{\xi+\eta}$ and $\sigma_{\xi+\eta}$. Since $\mathcal{P}_{\xi+\eta}$ is consecutive to $\mathcal{P}_\xi$,

$$S_\xi \geqq \Sigma_{\xi+\eta} \qquad \text{and} \qquad \sigma_{\xi+\eta} \geqq s_\xi;$$

and since $\mathcal{P}_{\xi+\eta}$ is also consecutive to $\mathcal{P}_\eta$,

$$S_\eta \geqq \Sigma_{\xi+\eta} \qquad \text{and} \qquad \sigma_{\xi+\eta} \geqq s_\eta.$$

From Theorem 23.1, $\Sigma_{\xi+\eta} \geqq \sigma_{\xi+\eta}$. Therefore,

$$S_\xi \geqq s_\eta \qquad \text{and} \qquad S_\eta \geqq s_\xi.$$

We have now shown that *the sum S arising from any mode of partition of $[a, b]$ is not less than the sum s arising from the same partition, or any other partition, of $[a, b]$*.

Since J is the greatest lower bound of the sums S, and I is the least upper bound of the sums s, we can find a sum S as close to J as we please, and a sum s as close to I as we please (from some mode of partition, though not necessarily the same partition). If $I > J$, then there would exist an s and an S for which $s > S$, which contradicts one of the relations proved above. Hence $I \leqq J$.

24. Darboux's Theorem. A theorem of fundamental importance is

THEOREM 24.1. (*Darboux's Theorem*). *If ϵ is any preassigned positive number, there exists a positive number η, dependent on ϵ, such that the sum S exceeds J by less than ϵ, and the sum s is smaller than I by less than ϵ, for all partitions $\mathcal{P}$ of $[a, b]$ for which each partial interval (bounded by consecutive points of $\mathcal{P}$) is less than or equal to η in length.*

Proof. Let $\epsilon > 0$. Since the greatest lower bound of the sum S is J, there exists a subdivision of $[a, b]$,

$$a, a_1, a_2, \cdots, a_{p-1}, b, \tag{1}$$

with sums S_1 and s_1 for which $S_1 < J + (\epsilon/2)$. Let η be a positive number smaller than all the partial intervals in (1).

Next, consider any subdivision of $[a, b]$,

$$a = x_0, \quad x_1, \quad \cdots, \quad x_{n-1}, \quad x_n = b, \tag{2}$$

with sums S_2 and s_2, such that $(x_r - x_{r-1}) \leqq \eta, r = 1, 2, \cdots, n$. The subdivision

$$a, x_1, x_2, a_1, x_3, a_2, \cdots, x_{n-1}, b, \tag{3}$$

obtained by superposing (1) and (2) is *consecutive* to (1) and (2) with sums S_3 and s_3.

From Sec. 23, $S_1 \geqq S_3$. Since $S_1 < J + (\epsilon/2)$, we have $S_3 < J + (\epsilon/2)$. Moreover,

$$S_2 - S_3 = \Sigma[M(x_{r-1}, x_r)(x_r - x_{r-1}) - M(x_{r-1}, a_k)(a_k - x_{r-1}) - M(a_k, x_r)(x_r - a_k)], \tag{4}$$

where $M(\alpha, \beta)$ denotes the upper bound of $f(x)$ in the interval $[\alpha, \beta]$, and where the summation is extended to all the intervals in (2) which have as an interval point one of the points

$$a_1, a_2, \cdots, a_{p-1}.$$

Since each interval in (1) exceeds η, while each interval in (2) is less than η, we conclude that no two a's can lie between two consecutive x's in (2).

The number of terms in the sum (4) cannot exceed $(p - 1)$. Denote by T the upper bound of $|f(x)|$ in $[a, b]$. Consider

$$S_2 - S_3 = \Sigma[\{M(x_{r-1}, x_r) - M(x_{r-1}, a_k)\}(a_k - x_{r-1}) + \{M(x_{r-1}, x_r) - M(a_k, x_r)\}(x_r - a_k)]. \tag{5}$$

Each of the two terms in braces in (5) is nonnegative, and neither can exceed $2T$. Hence $S_2 - S_3 \leqq 2T\Sigma(x_r - x_{r-1})$, where the summation has at most $(p - 1)$ terms, and where $(x_r - x_{r-1})$ never exceeds η. Consequently, $S_2 - S_3 \leqq 2(p - 1)T\eta$, and since $S_3 < J + (\epsilon/2)$, we see that $S_2 < J + (\epsilon/2) + 2(p - 1)T\eta$.

Next, further decrease η, if necessary, so that $\eta < \dfrac{\epsilon}{4(p - 1)T}$.

Then $S_2 < J + \epsilon$.

This shows that S exceeds J by less than ϵ for any subdivision of $[a, b]$ for which the greatest of the partial intervals does not exceed a certain positive number η dependent on ϵ.

A similar argument may be made relative to s and I. By selecting for η the smaller of the two η's for S and s, we are led to Theorem 24.1.

25. Definition of the Riemann Definite Integral of a Bounded Function. A bounded function $f(x)$, defined in the (finite) interval $[a, b]$, is said to be *integrable* (Riemann) in that interval when the greatest lower bound J of the sums S and the least upper bound I of the sums s in Sec. 23 are equal. J is frequently termed the *upper Riemann integral of $f(x)$ over* $[a, b]$, and I the *lower Riemann integral*. We define their common value $I = J$ to be the (Riemann) *definite integral* of $f(x)$ over $[a, b]$, and we shall write this definite integral as

$$\mathbf{S}_a^b f(x)\,dx.$$

Evidently, we have

THEOREM 25.1. $s \leqq \mathbf{S}_a^b f(x)\,dx \leqq S$ *for any partition.*

We shall now prove

THEOREM 25.2. *If $\xi_1, \xi_2, \cdots, \xi_r, \cdots, \xi_n$ be any values of x (including possibly the end points) in the partial intervals $[a, x_1]$, $[x_1, x_2], \cdots, [x_{r-1}, x_r], \cdots, [x_{n-1}, b]$, respectively, and if $f(x)$ be integrable over $[a, b]$, then the sum*

$$Z = f(\xi_1)(x_1 - a) + f(\xi_2)(x_2 - x_1) + \cdots + f(\xi_n)(b - x_{n-1}) \tag{1}$$

has the value of the definite integral $\mathbf{S}_a^b f(x)\,dx$ for its limit when the number n of points of division increases indefinitely in such a way that the lengths of the partial intervals all tend to zero.

Evidently, $s \leqq Z \leqq S$, for $m_r \leqq f(\xi_r) \leqq M_r$ in each partial interval, $r = 1, \cdots, n$. From Theorem 24.1, as $n \to +\infty$ in such a way that the lengths of each partial interval tends to zero, the sums S and s tend toward J and I, respectively. Since $f(x)$ is integrable, $J = I = S_a^b f(x)\, dx$. Therefore the sum (1) has the same limit.

26. Integrability Conditions. In this section we shall be concerned with necessary and sufficient conditions for the Riemann integrability of a bounded function over the interval $[a, b]$.

THEOREM 26.1. *A necessary and sufficient condition that a bounded real function $f(x)$ be integrable* in $[a, b]$ is that for any preassigned positive number ϵ, there shall exist a positive number η such that $S - s < \epsilon$ for every partition of $[a, b]$ in which all the partial intervals are less than or equal to η in length.*

Sufficiency. Suppose that for a given ϵ, as stated in the theorem, there exists an η for which $S - s < \epsilon$. Now $S \geqq J$ and $s \leqq I$, so that $J - I < \epsilon$. Consequently $I = J$.

Necessity. Suppose $I = J$. Then by Theorem 24.1, for a given positive number ϵ there exists a positive number η such that for every partition of $[a, b]$ in which all the partial intervals are less than or equal to η in length,

$$S - J < \frac{\epsilon}{2} \quad \text{and} \quad I - s < \frac{\epsilon}{2}.$$

But since $I = J$,

$$S - s = (S - J) + (I - s).$$

Hence

$$S - s < \frac{\epsilon}{2} + \frac{\epsilon}{2} = \epsilon.$$

THEOREM 26.2. *A necessary and sufficient condition that $f(x)$ be integrable Riemann is that for any preassigned positive number ϵ, there shall exist a partition of $[a, b]$ for which $S - s < \epsilon$.*

We shall leave the proof of this theorem as an exercise for the reader.

THEOREM 26.3. *If $f(x)$ is continuous in $[a, b]$ closed, it is integrable in $[a, b]$.*

Since $f(x)$ is continuous in $[a, b]$ closed, it is bounded in $[a, b]$. (See Theorem 8.3 of Chap. IX). By Theorem 8.7 of Chap. IX, we know that for every preassigned positive number $\epsilon/(b - a)$

---

* In this chapter whenever we use the term *integrable*, we shall mean *integrable Riemann*.

there exists 'a positive number η such that the oscillation* of $f(x)$ is less than $\epsilon/(b - a)$ in all partial intervals less than or equal to η in length. Let $\mathcal{P}$ be a partition of this character. Then the sums for this $\mathcal{P}$ are such that

$$S - s < (b - a)\frac{\epsilon}{(b - a)} = \epsilon.$$

Consequently $f(x)$ is integrable in $[a, b]$ by Theorem 26.2.

THEOREM 26.4. *If $f(x)$ is monotone† in $[a, b]$ closed, it is integrable in $[a, b]$.*

Since $f(x)$ is *monotone* in $[a, b]$ closed, it is bounded. (See Ex. III, 6, of Chap. IX.). Suppose $f(x)$ is a monotonic increasing function. Then for a partition $\mathcal{P}: a = x_0, x_1, x_2, \cdots, x_{n-1}, x_n = b$ of $[a, b]$,

$$f(a) \leqq f(x_1) \leqq f(x_2) \leqq \cdots \leqq f(x_{n-1}) \leqq f(b).$$

Then

$$S = \sum_{j=1}^{n} f(x_j)(x_j - x_{j-1}),$$

$$s = \sum_{j=1}^{n} f(x_{j-1})(x_j - x_{j-1}).$$

Let $\mathcal{P}$ be such that all the partial intervals $(x_i - x_{i-1})$ are less than or equal to η in length. Then

$$S - s = \sum_{j=1}^{n} [f(x_j) - f(x_{j-1})](x_j - x_{j-1}) < \eta[f(x_n) - f(x_0)]$$
$$= \eta[f(b) - f(a)].$$

Now select $\eta < \dfrac{\epsilon}{f(b) - f(a)}$. Then $S - s < \epsilon$. Hence $f(x)$ is integrable in $[a, b]$. A similar proof may be given for the case when $f(x)$ is monotonic decreasing.

---

* By the *oscillation* of a function $f(x)$ for any interval δ, we mean $M - m$, where M is the least upper bound of $f(x)$ over δ and m is the greatest lower bound over δ. See Chap. IX, Sec. 7 for definitions of closed (and open) intervals.

† A function $f(x)$ is *monotonic increasing* on $[a, b]$ if $f(x_1) \leqq f(x_2)$ for any two numbers x_1 and x_2 in $[a, b]$ with $x_1 < x_2$; $f(x)$ is *monotonic decreasing* if $f(x_1) \geqq f(x_2)$ when $x_1 < x_2$; $f(x)$ is monotone on $[a, b]$ if it is either monotonic increasing or monotonic decreasing.

Theorem 26.5. *If $f(x)$ is bounded in $[a, b]$ closed and if all its points of discontinuity can be enclosed in a finite number (or denumerably infinite* number) of intervals, the sum of the lengths of which is less than any preassigned positive number, then $f(x)$ is integrable in $[a, b]$.*

Suppose the number of discontinuities is finite. Let ϵ be any preassigned positive number and let M denote the (finite) least upper bound of $|f(x)|$ in $[a, b]$. Let $\mathcal{P}$ be a partition of $[a, b]$ which includes partial intervals $\mathcal{R}$ which enclose all the points of discontinuity of $f(x)$ in a finite number of intervals, the sum of the lengths of which is less than $\epsilon/4M$. Consider the difference $S - s$ for $\mathcal{P}$. Then the part of $S - s$ coming from $\mathcal{R}$ cannot exceed $(2M)(\epsilon/4M) = \epsilon/2$. Since $f(x)$ is continuous for the closed partial intervals Q of $\mathcal{P}$ not in $\mathcal{R}$, we can partition Q into a finite number of partial intervals for which the corresponding portion of $S - s < \frac{1}{2}\epsilon$. Thus for $\mathcal{P}$, as a whole,

$$S - s < \frac{\epsilon}{2} + \frac{\epsilon}{2} = \epsilon.$$

Hence $f(x)$ is integrable in $[a, b]$.

A slight revision of this proof can be made to take care of the case when the number of discontinuities is denumerably infinite. This is left as an exercise for the student.

In a similar manner a short demonstration yields Theorems 26.6, 26.7, 26.8.

Theorem 26.6. *If $f(x)$ is bounded and integrable on the closed intervals $[a, a_1], [a_1, a_2], \cdots, [a_{p-1}, b]$, it is integrable in $[a, b]$.*

Theorem 26.7. *If $f(x)$ is bounded in $[a, b]$ and is such that the interval $[a, b]$ can be partitioned into a finite number of open partial intervals, in each of which $f(x)$ is monotonic or continuous, it is integrable in $[a, b]$.*

Theorem 26.8. *If $f(x)$ is bounded and integrable in $[a, b]$ closed, then $|f(x)|$ is also integrable in $[a, b]$.*

EXERCISES XVIII

1. Prove Theorem 25.2 with $f(\xi_1), f(\xi_2), \cdots, f(\xi_n)$ replaced by any values $\mu_1, \mu_2, \cdots, \mu_n$ intermediate between $(m_1, M_1), (m_2, M_2), \cdots, (m_n, M_n)$, respectively.

---

* A set of elements is *denumerably infinite* if it can be put into one-to-one correspondence with the set of all positive integers.

2. Prove Theorem 26.2.

3. Complete the proof of Theorem 26.4.

4. Complete the proof of Theorem 26.5.

5. Prove Theorem 26.6.

6. Prove Theorem 26.7. Is the converse of Theorem 26.7 true?

7. Prove Theorem 26.8.

8. Construct a function on [0, 1] for which the oscillation is 4 in any interval arbitrarily small.

9. Prove: If $f(x)$ is bounded and integrable on $[a, b]$, there exists an infinite number of points in any partial interval of $[a, b]$ at which $f(x)$ is continuous.

10. Prove Theorem 26.5 for the case where the number of discontinuities is denumerably infinite.

27. Properties of the Definite Integral. In this section we shall exhibit several properties of the definite integral $S_a^b f(x) \, dx$, where $f(x)$ is bounded and integrable in $[a, b]$.

THEOREM 27.1. *If $f(x)$ is bounded and integrable in $[a, b]$, it is also integrable in any subinterval $[\alpha, \beta]$ of $[a, b]$.*

Let ϵ be any arbitrary positive number. Then there exists a positive number η such that $S - s < \epsilon$ for every partition $\mathcal{P}$ of $[a, b]$ in which all the partial intervals are less than or equal to η in length.

Pick a partition $\mathcal{P}_1$ of this type having α and β as two points of division. Let Σ and σ be the sums for $\mathcal{P}_1$ over $[\alpha, \beta]$. Evidently,

$$s \leqq \sigma \leqq \Sigma \leqq S.$$

Since $S - s < \epsilon$, $0 \leqq \Sigma - \sigma \leqq S - s < \epsilon$. Hence $f(x)$ is integrable in $[\alpha, \beta]$.

THEOREM 27.2. *If $f(x)$, a bounded integrable function on $[a, b]$, is altered at a finite number of points of $[a, b]$, then $\psi(x)$ so obtained is integrable on $[a, b]$ and*

$$\mathbf{S}_a^b f(x) \, dx = \mathbf{S}_a^b \psi(x) \, dx.$$

The proof of the first part of this theorem is quite similar to that of Theorem 26.5, the second to that of Theorem 25.2. The details are left to the student.

THEOREM 27.3. *If $f(x)$ is integrable in $[a, b]$, so also is $C[f(x)]$, where C is any constant.*

This theorem is an immediate consequence of the definition of the definite integral.

THEOREM 27.4. *If $f_1(x)$ and $f_2(x)$ are integrable on $[a, b]$, then their sum and product are also integrable.*

Proof for Sum. Let S, s; S', s' be the sums corresponding to the partition $\mathcal{P}$ of $[a, b]$ for $f_1(x)$ and $f_2(x)$, respectively. Denote by Σ and σ the corresponding sums for $f_1(x) + f_2(x)$ on $\mathcal{P}$. Then

$$\Sigma - \sigma \leqq (S - s) + (S' - s'),$$

from which the theorem follows.

We shall leave the remaining portion of the proof to the student.

We have as an immediate consequence of Theorem 27.4,

Theorem 27.5. *If $f_1(x)$, $f_2(x)$, $\cdots$, $f_n(x)$ are a finite number of functions integrable on $[a, b]$, then every polynomial in $f_1(x)$, $f_2(x)$, $\cdots$, $f_n(x)$ is integrable on $[a, b]$.*

Theorem 27.6. *If $f(x)$ is bounded and integrable over $[a, b]$, then*

$$\mathbf{S}_a^b f(x)\, dx = -\mathbf{S}_b^a f(x)\, dx.$$

It was directly assumed in Sec. 25 that $a < b$ in $[a, b]$. However, the definition given in Sec. 25 automatically generalizes for $a > b$. In this case the new sum S for $a > b$ is the negative of the old sum S for the case where $a < b$, provided the partition $\mathcal{P}$ (for $a < b$) is a, x_1, x_2, $\cdots$, x_{n-1}, b and the partition $\mathcal{P}'$ (for $a > b$) is b, x_{n-1}, x_{n-2}, $\cdots$, x_1, a. A repetition of the argument given in Sec. 25 leads to Theorem 27.6.

We shall hereafter use this extension of the definition of the definite integral. It is evident that the preceding theorems of Secs. 25 to 27 still hold with at most slight modifications.

Theorem 27.7. *If $f(x)$ is bounded and integrable on $[a, b]$ and if c is any point in $[a, b]$, then*

$$\mathbf{S}_a^b f(x)\, dx = \mathbf{S}_a^c f(x)\, dx + \mathbf{S}_c^b f(x)\, dx.$$

Let $\mathcal{P}$ be a subdivision of $[a, b]$ not having c for a point of subdivision. The addition to $\mathcal{P}$ of c as a point of subdivision does not increase S. The sum S_1 for $[a, c]$ and S_2 for $[c, b]$ given by this subdivision are not less than $\mathbf{S}_a^c f(x)\, dx$ and $\mathbf{S}_c^b f(x)\, dx$, respectively. Hence, every subdivision of $[a, b]$ gives a sum S not less than $\mathbf{S}_a^c f(x)\, dx + \mathbf{S}_c^b f(x)\, dx$. Thus

$$\mathbf{S}_a^b f(x)\, dx \geqq \mathbf{S}_a^c f(x)\, dx + \mathbf{S}_c^b f(x)\, dx. \tag{1}$$

The superposition of the subdivisions of $[a, c]$ and $[c, b]$ together form a subdivision of $[a, b]$. Since subdivisions of $[a, c]$ and $[c, b]$ can be made so that the sums S_1 and S_2 differ from $S_a^c f(x) \, dx$ and $S_c^b f(x) \, dx$, respectively, by an arbitrarily small amount, it follows that we cannot have the inequality in (1).

Suppose $g(x) \geqq f(x)$ on $[a, b]$; then

$$\phi(x) \equiv g(x) - f(x) \geqq 0.$$

If $g(x)$ and $f(x)$ are integrable on $[a, b]$, then so is $\phi(x)$. Evidently all the sums s are $\geqq 0$. Hence $S_a^b \phi(x) \, dx \geqq 0$. Consequently,

THEOREM 27.8. *If $f(x)$ and $g(x)$ are integrable on $[a, b]$ and if $g(x) \geqq f(x)$, then $S_a^b g(x) \, dx \geqq S_a^b f(x) \, dx$.*

The student should prove the following theorems which are an immediate consequence of Theorem 27.8.

THEOREM 27.9. *If $f(x)$ is integrable on $[a, b]$, then*

$$\left| \mathbf{S}_a^b f(x) \, dx \right| \leqq \mathbf{S}_a^b |f(x)| \, dx.$$

THEOREM 27.10. *If $f(x)$ is nonnegative and integrable in $[a, b]$, and if $f(x)$ is continuous at $x = c$ in $[a, b]$, with $f(c) > 0$, then*

$$\mathbf{S}_a^b f(x) \, dx > 0.$$

THEOREM 27.11. *If $f(x) > g(x)$, and $f(x)$ and $g(x)$ are integrable on $[a, b]$, then*

$$\mathbf{S}_a^b f(x) \, dx > \mathbf{S}_a^b g(x) \, dx.$$

28. First Theorem of the Mean. Suppose $\varphi(x)$ and $\psi(x)$ are two bounded functions of x, integrable on $[a, b]$, with $\psi(x) \geqq 0$ on $[a, b]$. Let M and m denote the least upper bound and greatest lower bound of $\varphi(x)$ on $[a, b]$. Then for all x's in $[a, b]$,

$$m \leqq \varphi(x) \leqq M.$$

Since $\psi(x) \geqq 0$ in $[a, b]$, we have

$$m\psi(x) \leqq \varphi(x) \, \psi(x) \leqq M\psi(x).$$

From Theorems 27.8 and 27.4, we find that

$$m\mathbf{S}_a^b \psi(x) \, dx \leqq \mathbf{S}_a^b \varphi(x) \, \psi(x) \, dx \leqq M\mathbf{S}_a^b \psi(x) \, dx. \qquad (1)$$

We have now shown that there exists a number μ such that

$$\mathbf{S}_a^b \varphi(x)\,\psi(x)\,dx = \mu\mathbf{S}_a^b \psi(x)\,dx, \qquad m \leqq \mu \leqq M. \qquad (2)$$

A similar argument may be given for the case when $\psi(x) \leqq 0$ on $[a, b]$.

From Theorem 8.5 of Chap. IX we know that if $\varphi(x)$ is continuous on $[a, b]$ closed, that it takes the value μ for some value ξ of x on $[a, b]$. We have now proved

THEOREM 28.1. *Let $\varphi(x)$ and $\psi(x)$ be two bounded functions, both integrable on $[a, b]$ closed. If $\varphi(x)$ is continuous and $\psi(x)$ retains the same sign throughout $[a, b]$, then there exists a definite value ξ of x on $[a, b]$, for which*

$$\mathbf{S}_a^b \varphi(x)\,\psi(x)\,dx = \varphi(\xi)\,\mathbf{S}_a^b \psi(x)\,dx. \qquad (3)$$

The particular case of Theorem 28.1 where $\psi(x) \equiv 1$ leads to the ordinary theorem of the mean given in Theorem 13.2,

$$\mathbf{S}_a^b \varphi(x)\,dx = (b - a)\varphi(\xi), \qquad a \leqq \xi \leqq b. \qquad (4)$$

EXERCISES XIX

1. Prove Theorem 27.2.
2. Prove Theorem 27.3.
3. Complete the proof of the first part of Theorem 27.4.
4. Prove the second part of Theorem 27.4.
5. Prove Theorem 27.5.
6. Prove Theorem 27.5 with the phrase "every polynomial" replaced by the phrase "any continuous function."
7. Complete the proof of Theorem 27.6.
8. Prove Theorem 27.9. (HINT: Use Theorem 26.8 and Theorem 27.8.)
9. Prove Theorem 27.10. (HINT: Use Ex. XVIII, 9.)
10. Prove Theorem 27.11. (HINT: Use Theorem 27.10.)
11. State a theorem similar to Theorem 28.1 for the case where $\varphi(x)$ is not continuous on $[a, b]$. [HINT: Use Eq. (2).]

29. The Definite Integral as a Function of Its Upper Limit. We shall consider the definite integral

$$F(x) = \mathbf{S}_a^x f(t)\,dt \qquad (1)$$

of a function $f(x)$, where $f(x)$ is bounded and integrable on $[a, b]$ closed, and where x is any point on $[a, b]$.

If $(x + \Delta x)$ is in $[a, b]$, then from Theorem 27.7,

$$F(x + \Delta x) - F(x) = \mathbf{S}_a^{x+\Delta x} f(t) \, dt - \mathbf{S}_a^x f(t) \, dt$$

$$= \mathbf{S}_x^{x+\Delta x} f(t) \, dt. \tag{2}$$

Hence if M and m are the upper and lower bounds of $f(x)$ on $[x, x + \Delta x]$, there is a number μ such that

$$F(x + \Delta x) - F(x) = \mu(\Delta x), \qquad m \leqq \mu \leqq M. \tag{3}$$

From (3), we have

THEOREM 29.1.   *The definite integral* (1) *of a function* $f(x)$, *bounded and integrable on* $[a, b]$ *closed, is a continuous function of* x *on* $[a, b]$.

If $f(x)$ is continuous on $[a, b]$, then from (4) of Sec. 28,

$$F(x + \Delta x) - F(x) = \Delta x \cdot f(\xi), \qquad x \lesseqgtr \xi \lesseqgtr x + \Delta x. \tag{4}$$

Since $\lim_{\Delta x \to 0} f(\xi) = f(x)$, we have

$$\lim_{\Delta x \to 0} \frac{F(x + \Delta x) - F(x)}{\Delta x} = f(x). \tag{5}$$

This proves

THEOREM 29.2.   *If* $f(x)$ *is continuous on* $[a, b]$ *closed, and* x *is any point on* $[a, b]$, *then*

$$\frac{d}{dx} \mathbf{S}_a^x f(t) \, dt = f(x).$$

30. Second Theorem of the Mean.   We shall now state a very useful theorem, whose proof we leave to the reader.

THEOREM 30.1.   *If, in* $[a, b]$ *closed,* $\varphi(x)$ *is monotonic,* $\psi(x)$ *is bounded and integrable, and does not change signs more than a finite number of times in* $[a, b]$, *then:*

$$\mathbf{S}_a^b \varphi(x)\psi(x) \, dx = \varphi(a)\mathbf{S}_a^{\xi_1} \psi(x) \, dx + \varphi(b)\mathbf{S}_{\xi_1}^b \psi(x) \, dx, \quad \text{(I)}$$

for some definite value ξ_1 *of* x *on* $[a, b]$ *closed.*

$$\mathbf{S}_a^b \varphi(x)\psi(x) \, dx$$
$$= \varphi(a + 0)\mathbf{S}_a^{\xi_2} \psi(x) \, dx + \varphi(b - 0)\mathbf{S}_{\xi_2}^b \psi(x) \, dx, \quad \text{(II)}$$

for some definite value ξ_2 *of* x *on* $[a, b]$ *closed.*

$$\mathbf{S}_a^b \varphi(x)\psi(x) \, dx = A\mathbf{S}_a^{\xi_3} \psi(x) \, dx + B\mathbf{S}_{\xi_3}^b \psi(x) \, dx, \quad \text{(III)}$$

for some definite value ξ_3 *of* x *on* $[a, b]$ *closed, where* $A \leqq \varphi(a + 0)$
and $B \geqq \varphi(b - 0)$ *if* $\varphi(x)$ *is monotonic increasing, and where*
$A \geqq \varphi(a + 0)$, $B \leqq \varphi(b - 0)$ *if* $\varphi(x)$ *is monotonic decreasing.*

$$\mathrm{S}_a^b \, \varphi(x)\psi(x) \, dx = \varphi(b)\mathrm{S}_{\xi_4}^b \, \psi(x) \, dx, \qquad \text{(IV)}$$

for some definite value ξ_4 *of* x, $a \leqq \xi_4 \leqq b$, *when* $\varphi(x) \geqq 0$ *and is
monotonic increasing in* $[a, b]$.

$$\mathrm{S}_a^b \, \varphi(x)\psi(x) \, dx = \varphi(a)\mathrm{S}_a^{\xi_5} \, \psi(x) \, dx, \qquad \text{(V)}$$

for some definite value ξ_5 *of* x, $a \leqq \xi_5 \leqq b$, *when* $\varphi(x) \geqq 0$ *and is
monotonic decreasing in* $[a, b]$.*

PART D.   IMPROPER INTEGRALS

31. Interval Infinite but Integrand Bounded.   There is a very
close correspondence between the theory of improper integrals
and the theory of infinite series whose terms are functions of one
variable.   A development of the theory of improper integrals
would thus follow the theory given in Part D of Chap. IV.   It
is suggested that Chap. IV be studied before commencing the
present section.   Because of this close analogy we shall confine
ourselves to only a few typical instances of this theory.   In this
section we shall extend the definition of a definite integral to
include cases in which the interval is not finite and in which the
integral has a finite number (or denumerable infinity) of
discontinuities.

We shall assume that $f(x)$ is bounded and integrable in every
finite interval $[a, t]$, where a is fixed and $t \geqq a$.   Let

$$F(t) \equiv \int_a^t f(x) \, dx.$$

We define $\int_a^{+\infty} f(x) \, dx$ by the relation

$$I = \int_a^{+\infty} f(x) \, dx = \lim_{t \to +\infty} F(t) = \lim_{t \to +\infty} \int_a^t f(x) \, dx,$$

when this limit exists, and we speak of $\int_a^{+\infty} f(x) \, dx$ as an *improper*
or *infinite* integral.   If $\lim\limits_{t \to +\infty} F(t)$ exists, we say that I *converges;*
if $\lim\limits_{t \to +\infty} F(t)$ does not exist, we say that I *diverges;* if $\lim\limits_{t \to +\infty} F(t) \to +\infty$

* Here $\varphi(a + 0)$ denotes the right-hand limit of $\varphi(x)$ as $x \to a$; $\varphi(b - 0)$
denotes the left-hand limit of $\varphi(x)$ as $x \to b$.

(or $-\infty$), we say that I *definitely diverges to* $+\infty$ (or $-\infty$); if $F(t)$ neither converges nor definitely diverges to $+\infty$ or $-\infty$, we say that the integral is *indefinitely divergent*.

Example 1. Since $\int_0^{+\infty} e^{-x} dx = \lim_{t \to +\infty} \int_0^t e^{-x} dx = \lim_{t \to +\infty} (1 - e^{-t}) = 1$, the integral is convergent to the value 1.

Example 2. $\displaystyle\int_1^{+\infty} \frac{dx}{\sqrt{x}} = \lim_{t \to +\infty} \int_1^t \frac{dx}{\sqrt{x}} = +\infty$, that is, the integral definitely diverges to $+\infty$.

Example 3. $\int_1^{+\infty} \log (1/x) dx$ definitely diverges to $-\infty$.

Example 4. $\int_\pi^{+\infty} \sin x \, dx$ is indefinitely divergent.

In a similar manner, we define $\int_{-\infty}^b f(x) \, dx$ to be $\lim_{t \to -\infty} \int_t^b f(x) \, dx$, when this limit exists. We define $\int_{-\infty}^{+\infty} f(x) \, dx$ to be

$$\int_{-\infty}^a f(x) \, dx + \int_a^{+\infty} f(x) \, dx$$

when both of the latter integrals converge. Here a is any real value of x. It is readily seen that the value of $\int_{-\infty}^{+\infty} f(x) \, dx$, if it exists, is independent of the value a of x selected.

EXERCISES XX

Evaluate:

1. $\int_1^{+\infty} x^{-3/2} dx$. *Ans.* 2.
2. $\int_1^{+\infty} x \sin x \, dx$. (Ind. div.)
3. $\int_1^{+\infty} e^{2x} dx$. (Def. div. to $+\infty$.)
4. $\int_{-\infty}^0 e^{-2x} dx$.

5. $\int_{-\infty}^0 \cos x \, dx$.
6. $\int_{-\infty}^0 x \sin 2x \, dx$. (Ind. div.)
7. $\int_{-\infty}^0 \sinh x \, dx$. (Div. to $-\infty$.)
8. $\int_{-\infty}^0 e^{5x} dx$.

We shall now develop necessary and sufficient conditions for the convergence of $\int_a^{+\infty} f(x) \, dx$.

Consider $F(t) = \int_a^t f(x) \, dx$, where $f(x)$ is assumed to be bounded and integrable on $[a, t]$ for all $t \geq a$. The infinite integral $\int_a^{+\infty} f(x) \, dx$ converges if and only if the function $F(t)$ has a limit as $t \to +\infty$. From the definition of a limit, we have

THEOREM 31.1. *If for every positive number ϵ there exists a positive number t_0 so that, for all $t \geq t_0$, $|I - \int_a^t f(x) \, dx| < \epsilon$, then the integral $\int_a^{+\infty} f(x) \, dx$ converges to the value I.*

As an analogue of Theorem 8.1 of Chap. IV, we have

THEOREM 31.2. *A necessary and sufficient condition for the convergence of $\int_a^{+\infty} f(x) \, dx$ is that, for any preassigned positive number ϵ, there exist a positive number t_0 such that $|\int_{t'}^{t''} f(x) \, dx| < \epsilon$ for all values t' and t'' for which $t'' > t' \geq t_0$.*

Similar theorems can be stated for the infinite integral $\int_{-\infty}^{b} f(x)\, dx$.

If $f(x) \geqq 0$ for all $x > a$, then the function $F(t) = \int_{a}^{t} f(x)\, dx$ is a monotonic increasing function of t. Hence we have

THEOREM 31.3. *If $f(x) \geqq 0$ for every $x > a$, if*

$$F(t) = \int_{a}^{t} f(x)\, dx,$$

and if there exists a positive number A such that $F(t) < A$ for every $t > a$, then $\int_{a}^{+\infty} f(x)\, dx$ converges to a value $\leqq A$.

The following theorem is quite useful as a comparison test for the convergence of integrals whose integrands are positive.

THEOREM 31.4. *Let $f(x)$ and $g(x)$ be two positive, bounded, and integrable functions of x in the interval $[a,\, t]$ for all $t \geqq a$:*

(1) *If $g(x) \leqq f(x)$ when $x \geqq a$, and if $\int_{a}^{+\infty} f(x)\, dx$ is convergent, then $\int_{a}^{+\infty} g(x)\, dx$ is convergent and $\int_{a}^{+\infty} g(x)\, dx \leqq \int_{a}^{+\infty} f(x)\, dx$.*

(2) *If $g(x) \geqq f(x)$ for $x \geqq a$, and if $\int_{a}^{+\infty} f(x)\, dx$ diverges to $+\infty$, then so does $\int_{a}^{+\infty} g(x)\, dx$.*

By Theorem 27.8, $\int_{a}^{t} g(x)\, dx \leqq \int_{a}^{t} f(x)\, dx$ for $t > a$. Therefore $\int_{a}^{t} g(x)\, dx < \int_{a}^{+\infty} f(x)\, dx$. So $\int_{a}^{+\infty} g(x)\, dx \leqq \int_{a}^{+\infty} f(x)\, dx$. The proof of (2) is left to the reader.

Example 5. Examine $\displaystyle\int_{a}^{+\infty} \frac{dx}{x^n}$ for convergence, $a > 0$.

It is evident that

$$\int_{a}^{t} \frac{dx}{x^n} = \frac{1}{1-n}\left(t^{1-n} - a^{1-n}\right) \qquad \text{if} \qquad n \neq 1,$$

$$\int_{a}^{t} \frac{dx}{x^n} = \log t - \log a \qquad \text{if} \qquad n = 1.$$

If $n > 1$, $\qquad \displaystyle\lim_{t \to +\infty} \int_{a}^{t} \frac{dx}{x^n} \equiv \int_{a}^{+\infty} \frac{dx}{x^n} = \frac{a^{1-n}}{n-1}.$

If $n \leqq 1$, $\displaystyle\lim_{t \to +\infty} \int_{a}^{t} \frac{dx}{x^n} \to +\infty$, so that $\displaystyle\int_{a}^{+\infty} \frac{dx}{x^n}$ diverges.

The results of this example are quite useful, in conjunction with Theorem 31.4, when examining certain types of integrals for convergence.

Example 6. Examine $\displaystyle\int_{a}^{+\infty} \frac{dx}{x \cdot \sqrt{1 + x^2}}$ for convergence, $a > 0$.

Since $\dfrac{1}{x\sqrt{1 + x^2}} < \dfrac{1}{x^2}$ for $x \geqq a > 0$, and since $\displaystyle\int_{a}^{+\infty} \frac{dx}{x^2}$ is convergent, it follows from Theorem 31.4 that $\displaystyle\int_a^{+\infty} \frac{dx}{x\sqrt{1+x^2}}$ converges.

Example 7. Examine $\displaystyle\int_3^{+\infty} \frac{dx}{\sqrt{x^2-2}}$ for convergence.

This integral is divergent since $\dfrac{1}{\sqrt{x^2-2}} > \dfrac{1}{x}$ for $x \geqq 3$.

The integral $\int_a^{+\infty} f(x)\ dx$ is said to be *absolutely convergent* if $f(x)$ is bounded and integrable in every interval $[a, t]$ for $t \geqq a$, and if $\int_a^{+\infty} |f(x)|\ dx$ is convergent.

Theorem 31.5. *If* $\int_a^{+\infty} |f(x)|\ dx$ *converges, then so does* $\int_a^{+\infty} f(x)\ dx$.

From Theorem 27.9

$$\left|\int_{x_1}^{x_2} f(x)\ dx\right| \leqq \int_{x_1}^{x_2} |f(x)|\ dx \qquad \text{for} \qquad x_2 > x_1 \geqq a.$$

By Theorem 31.2, if $\int_a^{+\infty} |f(x)|\ dx$ converges, then so does $\int_a^{+\infty} f(x)\ dx$.

The converse of this theorem is not true, that is, an infinite integral of the type under consideration may converge, and yet may not converge absolutely.   A well-known example of this is given by the integral $\displaystyle\int_0^{+\infty} \frac{\sin x}{x}\ dx$ which is equal to $\dfrac{\pi}{2}$, but which is not absolutely convergent since $\displaystyle\int_0^{+\infty} \frac{|\sin x|}{x}\ dx$ diverges.

The following theorems are often useful in testing for the convergence of infinite integrals.

Theorem 31.6. *Let* $f(x)$ *be bounded and integrable in every interval* $[a, t]$, *where* $a > 0$ *and* $t \geqq a$.

1. *If there exists a number* $\nu > 1$ *such that* $x^\nu f(x)$ *is bounded when* $x \geqq a$, *then* $\int_a^{+\infty} f(x)\ dx$ *converges absolutely.*

2. *If there exists a number* $\nu \leqq 1$ *such that* $x^\nu f(x)$ *has a positive lower bound when* $x \geqq a$, *then* $\int_a^{+\infty} f(x)\ dx$ *diverges definitely to* $+\infty$.

3. *If there exists a number* $\nu \leqq 1$ *such that* $x^\nu f(x)$ *has a negative upper bound when* $x \geqq a$, *then* $\int_a^{+\infty} f(x)\ dx$ *diverges definitely to* $-\infty$.

Proof of (1).   By hypothesis there exists a positive number A such that $|x^\nu f(x)| < A$, and hence $|f(x)| < (A/x^\nu)$, for $x \geqq a$. Since $\int_a^{+\infty} (dx/x^\nu)$ converges when $\nu > 1$, it follows that

$\int_a^{+\infty} |f(x)|\ dx$ converges. From Theorem 31.5 we conclude that $\int_a^{+\infty} f(x)\ dx$ is convergent.

Proof of (2). As before, $x^\nu f(x) \geqq A > 0$, so that $(A/x^\nu) \leqq f(x)$, for $x \geqq a$. Since $\int_a^{+\infty} (dx/x^\nu)$ diverges definitely to $+\infty$ when $\nu \leqq 1$, it follows that $\int_a^{+\infty} f(x)\ dx$ diverges to $+\infty$.

The proof of part (3) of this theorem is left to the reader.

Let $f(x)$ be bounded for $x \geqq a$. If $\lim_{x \to +\infty} [x^\nu f(x)]$ exists, it follows that $x^\nu f(x)$ is bounded in $[a, +\infty]$. If this limit is positive, $x^\nu f(x)$ will have a positive lower bound, while if this limit is negative, $x^\nu f(x)$ will have a negative upper bound when a is sufficiently large.

We then conclude from Theorem 31.6

THEOREM 31.7. *Let $f(x)$ be bounded and integrable in every interval $[a, t]$, where $t \geqq a > 0$.*

1. *If there exists a number $\nu > 1$ for which* $\lim_{x \to +\infty} [x^\nu f(x)]$ *exists, then $\int_a^{+\infty} f(x)\ dx$ converges;*

2. *If there exists a number $\nu \leqq 1$ for which* $\lim_{x \to +\infty} [x^\nu f(x)]$ *exists and is not zero, then $\int_a^{+\infty} f(x)\ dx$ diverges.*

3. *If there exists a number $\nu \leqq 1$ for which $x^\nu f(x)$ diverges definitely as $x \to +\infty$, then $\int_a^{+\infty} f(x)\ dx$ diverges.*

The essential thing in these last two theorems is that we are comparing the integral $\int_a^{+\infty} f(x)\ dx$ with the integral $\int_a^{+\infty} (dx/x^\nu)$, and determining the convergence or divergence of the first integral from that of the second.

Example 8. Examine $\displaystyle\int_0^{+\infty} \frac{x^2}{(9 + x^2)^2}\ dx$ for convergence.

Since $\lim_{x \to +\infty} x^2 \left[\dfrac{x^2}{(9 + x^2)^2} \right] = 1$, it follows from Theorem 31.7 that

$$\int_0^{+\infty} \frac{x^2}{(9 + x^2)^2}\ dx \text{ converges.}$$

Example 9. Examine $\displaystyle\int_5^{+\infty} \frac{4x^3}{(x^2 - 9)^2}\ dx$ for convergence.

Since $\lim_{x \to +\infty} x[4x^3/(x^2 - 9)^2] = 4$, we know from Theorem 31.7 that $\displaystyle\int_5^{+\infty} \frac{4x^3}{(x^2 - 9)^2}\ dx$ diverges.

Theorem 31.8. *If $\varphi(x)$ is bounded and integrable in every interval $[a, t]$ for $t \geqq a$, and if $\int_a^{+\infty} \psi(x)\, dx$ converges absolutely, then $\int_a^{+\infty} \varphi(x)\psi(x)\, dx$ is absolutely convergent.*

Since $\varphi(x)$ is bounded, there exists a positive number A such that $|\varphi(x)| < A$ for $x \geqq a$. Evidently, for $x_2 > x_1 > a$,

$$\int_{x_1}^{x_2} |\varphi(x)| \cdot |\psi(x)|\, dx < A \int_{x_1}^{x_2} |\psi(x)|\, dx.$$

By hypothesis, the right-hand integral converges as $x_2 \to +\infty$, and the theorem follows immediately.

Theorem 31.9. *Let $\varphi(x)$ be monotone and bounded for $x \geqq a$, and suppose that $\psi(x)$ is bounded and integrable in every interval $[a, t]$ for $t \geqq a$, and not changing sign more than a finite number of times for $x > a$.*

1. *If $\int_a^{+\infty} \psi(x)\, dx$ converges, so does $\int_a^{+\infty} \varphi(x)\psi(x)\, dx$.*

2. *If $\lim\limits_{x \to +\infty} \varphi(x) = 0$, and if $\int_a^t \psi(x)\, dx$ is bounded for $t > a$, then $\int_a^{+\infty} \varphi(x)\psi(x)\, dx$ is convergent.*

Proof of (1). By the second theorem of the mean, for $a < x_1 \leqq \xi \leqq x_2$,

$$\int_{x_1}^{x_2} \varphi(x)\psi(x)\, dx = \varphi(x_1) \int_{x_1}^{\xi} \psi(x)\, dx + \varphi(x_2) \int_{\xi}^{x_2} \psi(x)\, dx. \quad (1)$$

By hypothesis, there exists a positive number A such that $|\varphi(x_1)| < A$ and $|\varphi(x_2)| < A$. Also, for every positive number ϵ, there exists an x sufficiently large, say X, such that when $X \leqq x_1 < x_2$,

$$\left| \int_{x_1}^{\xi} \psi(x)\, dx \right| < \frac{\epsilon}{2A} \quad \text{and} \quad \left| \int_{\xi}^{x_2} \psi(x)\, dx \right| < \frac{\epsilon}{2A}.$$

Hence,

$$\left| \int_{x_1}^{x_2} \varphi(x)\psi(x)\, dx \right| < \epsilon \quad \text{for} \quad X \leqq x_1 < x_2,$$

so that the given integral converges.

Proof of (2). Since $\int_a^t \psi(x)\, dx$ is bounded, there exists a positive number A such that $|\int_a^t \psi(x)\, dx| < A$. Returning to (1), we have

$$\left| \int_{x_1}^{\xi} \psi(x)\, dx \right| \leqq \left| \int_a^{\xi} \psi(x)\, dx \right| + \left| \int_a^{x_1} \psi(x)\, dx \right| < 2A$$

and

$$\left| \int_{\xi}^{x_2} \psi(x) \, dx \right| < 2A.$$

Since $\lim_{x \to +\infty} \varphi(x) = 0$, if ϵ is any positive number, there exists a positive number X, such that for $x \geqq X$,

$$|\varphi(x)| < \frac{\epsilon}{4A}.$$

From (1), we then conclude that for $X \leqq x_1 < x_2$,

$$\left| \int_{x_1}^{x_2} \varphi(x)\psi(x) \, dx \right| < \epsilon.$$

Hence $\int_{a}^{+\infty} \varphi(x)\psi(x) \, dx$ converges.

EXERCISES XXI

1. Examine $\displaystyle \int_{a}^{+\infty} \frac{\sin^2 3x}{x^2} \, dx$ for convergence, $a > 0$.   (Hint: Compare $\dfrac{\sin^2 3x}{x^2}$ with $\dfrac{1}{x^2}$.)

2. Examine $\displaystyle \int_{5}^{+\infty} \frac{x^{3/2}}{25x^2 + 36} \, dx$ for convergence.   *Ans.* Divergent.

3. Prove: If n and a are positive, $\displaystyle \int_{a}^{+\infty} \frac{\cos x}{x^{n+1}} \, dx$ and $\displaystyle \int_{a}^{+\infty} \frac{\sin x}{x^{n+1}} \, dx$ converge absolutely.

4. Show that if $a > 0$, $\int_{a}^{+\infty} e^{-ax} \cos bx \, dx$ converges absolutely.

5. Show that $\displaystyle \int_{a}^{+\infty} \frac{\cos mx}{a^2 + x^2} \, dx$ converges absolutely.

6. Show that

(a) $\displaystyle \int_{0}^{+\infty} e^{-x} \frac{\sin x}{x} \, dx$ converges.

(b) $\displaystyle \int_{2}^{+\infty} (1 - e^{-x}) \frac{\cos x}{x} \, dx$ converges.

7. Show that, if n and a are positive,

(a) $\displaystyle \int_{a}^{+\infty} \frac{\sin x}{x^n} \, dx$ converges.

(b) $\displaystyle \int_{a}^{+\infty} \frac{\cos x}{x^n} \, dx$ converges.

8. Show that $\displaystyle \int_{1}^{+\infty} \frac{5x}{1 + x^2} \sin x \, dx$ converges.

9. Prove the first theorem of the mean for infinite integrals:

$$\int_a^{+\infty} \varphi(x)\psi(x)\, dx = \mu \int_a^{+\infty} \psi(x)\, dx,$$

where $m \leqq \mu \leqq M$. Be sure to state all the hypotheses needed.

10. Prove the second theorem of the mean for infinite integrals:

$$\int_a^{+\infty} \varphi(x)\psi(x)\, dx = \varphi(a+0) \int_a^{\xi} \psi(x)\, dx + \lim_{x \to +\infty} \varphi(x) \int_{\xi}^{+\infty} \psi(x)\, dx,$$

where $a \leqq \xi < +\infty$.

32. Infinite Integrals, Integrand Unbounded.

In this section we shall extend the definition of the Riemann integral to include the case where $f(x)$ is unbounded in the neighborhood of a finite number of points in the interval of integration.*

Suppose $f(x)$ is bounded and integrable in every interval $[a + \xi, b]$, where $a < a + \xi < b$, and suppose that a is the only point in the neighborhood of which $f(x)$ is unbounded. If $\lim_{\xi \to +0} \int_{a+\xi}^b f(x)\, dx$ exists, *we define the infinite integral $\int_a^b f(x)\, dx$ to be* $\lim_{\xi \to +0} \int_{a+\xi}^b f(x)\, dx$.

Similarly, if $f(x)$ is bounded and integrable in the arbitrary interval $[a, b - \xi]$, where $a < b - \xi < b$, and if b is the only point in the neighborhood of which $f(x)$ is unbounded, we define the infinite integral $\int_a^b f(x)\, dx$ to be $\lim_{\xi \to +0} \int_a^{b-\xi} f(x)\, dx$, when this limit exists.

If a and b are the only points in $[a, b]$ in the neighborhood of which $f(x)$ is unbounded, and if $f(x)$ is bounded and integrable in $[a + \xi, b - \xi]$, we define the infinite integral $\int_a^b f(x)\, dx$ to be $\int_a^c f(x)\, dx + \int_c^b f(x)\, dx$, where it is understood that these integrals exist according to the definitions given above, c being an arbitrary point on $[a, b]$. The sum as defined is independent of the position of c in $[a, b]$. (Why?)

If $f(x)$ is unbounded in the neighborhood of a finite number of points $x_1, x_2, \cdots, x_n$ in $[a, b]$, with

$$a \leqq x_1 < x_2 < \cdots < x_n \leqq b,$$

we define the infinite integral $\int_a^b f(x)\, dx$ to be

---

* Further extensions of the concept of a Riemann integral will not be made here, for such generalizations are of no importance in view of the more modern treatments of integrals, such as the one due to Lebesgue.

$$\int_a^b f(x) \, dx =$$

$$\int_a^{x_1} f(x) \, dx + \int_{x_1}^{x_2} f(x) \, dx + \int_{x_2}^{x_3} f(x) \, dx + \cdots + \int_{x_n}^b f(x) \, dx,$$

when each of the integrals on the right-hand side exists as defined above.

It is implied in the preceding definition that $f(x)$ is bounded in any partial interval of $[a, \; b]$ which contains no point $x_1, x_2, \cdots, x_n$.

We shall use the terms convergent and divergent in the same sense as in Sec. 31.

If $f(x)$ is unbounded in the neighborhood of only the points $x_1, x_2, \cdots, x_n$, then if $\int_c^{+\infty} f(x) \, dx$ converges, where $c > x_n$, we define the infinite integral $\int_a^{+\infty} f(x) \, dx$ to be the sum

$$\int_a^{+\infty} f(x) \, dx = \int_a^{x_1} f(x) \, dx + \int_{x_1}^{x_2} f(x) \, dx + \cdots$$
$$+ \int_{x_n}^c f(x) \, dx + \int_c^{+\infty} f(x) \, dx.$$

This definition is evidently independent of the value of c.

We shall leave it to the reader to formulate the definitions of $\int_{-\infty}^b f(x) \, dx$ and $\int_{-\infty}^{+\infty} f(x) \, dx$.

We shall now develop certain theorems which give us tests for the convergence of $\int_a^b f(x) \, dx$. It is evident that we need consider only the case where there is but one point in the neighborhood of which $f(x)$ is unbounded, and this point is at an end of the interval of integration.

THEOREM 32.1. *If for every positive number ϵ, there exists a positive number δ such that $|I - \int_{a+\xi}^b f(x) \, dx| < \epsilon$ for every ξ for which $0 < \xi \leq \delta$, then the integral $\int_a^b f(x) \, dx$ is convergent.*

This theorem follows immediately from the definition of a limit.

The infinite integral $\int_a^b f(x) \, dx$ is said to be *absolutely convergent* if $f(x)$ is bounded and integrable in every interval $[a + \xi, \; b]$, where $a < a + \xi < b$, and if $\int_a^b |f(x)| \, dx$ converges.

Since

$$\int_{a+\xi}^b \frac{dx}{(x-a)^n} = \frac{1}{1-n}[(b-a)^{1-n} - \xi^{1-n}], \qquad n \neq 1,$$

it follows that

$$\int_a^b \frac{dx}{(x-a)^n} = \lim_{\xi \to +0} \int_{a+\xi}^b \frac{dx}{(x-a)^n} = \frac{(b-a)^{1-n}}{1-n}$$

converges when $0 < n < 1$. The integral diverges if $n \geq 1$.

In a manner quite like that followed in Sec. 31, we can prove

THEOREM 32.2. *Let $f(x)$ be bounded and integrable in every interval $[a + \xi, b]$, where $0 < \xi < (b - a)$:*

1. *If there exists a number ν, $0 < \nu < 1$, such that $(x - a)^\nu f(x)$ is bounded for $a < x \leqq b$, then $\int_a^b f(x)\, dx$ is absolutely convergent.*

2. *If there exists a number $\nu \geqq 1$ such that $(x - a)^\nu f(x)$ has a positive lower bound (or a negative lower bound) for $a < x \leqq b$, then $\int_a^b f(x)\, dx$ diverges to $+\infty$ (or to $-\infty$).*

3. *If there exists a number ν, $0 < \nu < 1$, such that*

$$\lim_{x \to a+0} (x - a)^\nu f(x)$$

exists, then $\int_a^b f(x)\, dx$ is absolutely convergent.

4. *If there exists a number $\nu \geqq 1$ such that $\lim_{x \to a+0} (x - a)^\nu f(x)$ exists and does not vanish, then $\int_a^b f(x)\, dx$ diverges; if*

$$(x - a)^\nu f(x) \to +\infty,$$

or $-\infty$, as $x \to a + 0$, then $\int_a^b f(x)\, dx$ diverges.

THEOREM 32.3. *If $\varphi(x)$ is bounded and integrable in $[a, b]$, and if $\int_a^b \psi(x)\, dx$ converges absolutely, then $\int_a^b \varphi(x)\psi(x)\, dx$ converges absolutely.*

Example 1. Show that $\displaystyle\int_0^1 \frac{dx}{x(3 + x)}$ diverges.

Let $f(x) = \dfrac{1}{x(3 + x)}$. Since $\lim\limits_{x \to +0} x f(x) = \dfrac{1}{3}$, by Theorem 32.2, the given integral diverges.

Example 2. Examine $\displaystyle\int_0^1 \frac{dx}{(3 + x)\sqrt{x}}$ for convergence.

Let $f(x) = \dfrac{1}{(3 + x)\sqrt{x}}$. Since $\lim\limits_{x \to +0} [x^{1/2} f(x)] = \dfrac{1}{3}$, by Theorem 32.2, the given integral converges.

Example 3. Examine $\displaystyle\int_0^3 \frac{dx}{\sqrt{x(3 - x)}}$ for convergence.

The integrand $f(x) = 1/\sqrt{x(3 - x)}$ is undefined at $x = 0$ and $x = 3$. Now $\displaystyle\int_0^3 \frac{dx}{\sqrt{x(3 - x)}} = \int_0^a \frac{dx}{\sqrt{x(3 - x)}} + \int_0^3 \frac{dx}{\sqrt{x(3 - x)}}$, where a is any number between 0 and 3. Since $\lim\limits_{x \to +0}\left[x^{1/2}\dfrac{1}{\sqrt{x(3 - x)}} \right] = 1$, we see from Theorem 32.2 that $\displaystyle\int_a^a \frac{dx}{\sqrt{x(3 - x)}}$ converges. Since

$$\lim_{x \to 3-0} \left[(3-x)^{\frac{1}{2}} \frac{1}{\sqrt{x(3-x)}} \right] = 1,$$

it follows that $\int_a^3 \dfrac{dx}{\sqrt{x(3-x)}}$ converges. Hence the given integral converges.

EXERCISES XXII

1. Show that $\int_0^1 \dfrac{\sin (1/x)}{x} dx$ is convergent but not absolutely convergent. (HINT: Replace x by $1/y$.)

2. Show that $\int_0^{\pi/2} \dfrac{\sin x}{x^{n+1}} dx$ converges for $0 < n < 1$.

3. Discuss the convergence of $\int_0^{+\infty} e^{-x} x^{n-1} dx$. (Hint: consider the three cases $n \geqq 1$, $0 < n < 1$, $n \leqq 0$.)

4. Prove that $\int_0^{\pi/2} \log \sin x \, dx = -(\pi/2) \log 2$.

5. Evaluate $\int_0^\pi \log (1 - \cos x) \, dx$.

6. Evaluate $\int_0^\pi \log (1 + \cos x) \, dx$.

7. Examine each of the following integrals for convergence, and evaluate if possible:

(a) $\displaystyle\int_0^{+\infty} \dfrac{8a^3 \, dx}{x^2 + 4a^2}.$ *Ans.* $2\pi a^2.$ (e) $\displaystyle\int_1^{+\infty} \dfrac{x \, dx}{(ax + x^2)^{\frac{3}{2}}}.$ (Convergent.)

(b) $\displaystyle\int_1^{+\infty} \dfrac{dx}{x}.$ *Ans.* $\to + \infty.$ (f) $\displaystyle\int_0^1 \dfrac{dx}{\sqrt{1 - x^4}}.$ (Convergent.)

(c) $\displaystyle\int_0^{+\infty} \cos x \, dx.$ (Oscillates.) (g) $\displaystyle\int_0^2 \dfrac{dx}{(2x - x^2)^{\frac{3}{2}}}.$ (Divergent.)

(d) $\displaystyle\int_0^{+\infty} \dfrac{e^{-x} \, dx}{\sqrt{x^3} \log x}.$ (h) $\displaystyle\int_0^{2a} \dfrac{x^{\frac{3}{2}} \, dx}{\sqrt{2a - x}}.$ *Ans.* $3\pi a^2.$

8. Examine each of the following for convergence:

(a) $\displaystyle\int_0^{+\infty} \dfrac{dx}{\sqrt{(1 - x^2)(1 - k^2 x^2)}}.$ (f) $\displaystyle\int_3^{+\infty} \dfrac{dx}{\sqrt{x^3 - 8}}.$

(b) $\displaystyle\int_0^{+\infty} e^{-x^2} \, dx.$ (g) $\displaystyle\int_0^{+\infty} \dfrac{\sin^2 x}{x^2} \, dx.$

(c) $\displaystyle\int_1^{+\infty} \dfrac{dx}{x\sqrt{4 + x^2}}.$ (h) $\displaystyle\int_0^{+\infty} \cos x^2 \, dx.$

(d) $\displaystyle\int_3^{+\infty} \dfrac{x^4 \, dx}{(9 + x^2)^{\frac{5}{2}}}.$ (i) $\displaystyle\int_1^{+\infty} \dfrac{x^2 \, dx}{(a^2 + x^2)^2}.$

(e) $\displaystyle\int_0^{+\infty} e^{-a^2 x^2} \cos bx \, dx.$

9. Examine for convergence:

(a) $\displaystyle\int_0^5 \frac{dx}{\sqrt{25 - x^2}}$.   *Ans.* $\pi/2$.

(b) $\displaystyle\int_a^b \frac{dx}{(b - x)^n}$.   *Ans.*   Convergent if $n < 1$;
            divergent   if $n \geqq 1$.

10. Prove: If $\int_a^b f(x)\, dx$ can be written in the form

$$\int_a^b \frac{\varphi(x)\, dx}{(b - x)^n}, \qquad a < b,$$

and if there exists a positive number A, such that for values of x sufficiently
close to b, $\varphi(x)$ is less in absolute value than A, and if $n < 1$, then the given
integral converges; but if for values of x sufficiently close to b, $\varphi(x)$ is greater
in absolute value than a positive number A, and $n \geqq 1$, then the given
integral diverges.

11. Use Ex. 10 to show that

(a) $\displaystyle\int_0^1 \frac{dx}{\sqrt{(1 - x^2)(1 - k^2 x^2)}}$ converges.

(b) $\displaystyle\int_0^a \frac{dx}{(x - a)\sqrt{(1 - x^2)(1 - k^2 x^2)}}$ diverges.

12. Examine for convergence:

(a) $\displaystyle\int_0^1 \frac{\log x}{1 - x^2}\, dx$.   *Ans.*   Convergent.

(b) $\displaystyle\int_0^1 (\log x)^n\, dx$.   *Ans.*   Convergent.

(c) $\displaystyle\int_0^c \frac{x^{n-1}}{x - 1}\, dx$, $0 < c < 1$.   (d) $\displaystyle\int_0^{+\infty} \frac{x^{n-1}}{x - 1}\, dx$.

(e) $\displaystyle\int_0^c \frac{x^{n-1}}{x + 1}\, dx$, $0 < c < 1$.   (f) $\displaystyle\int_0^{+\infty} \frac{x^{n-1}}{x + 1}\, dx$.

(g) $\displaystyle\int_0^1 \frac{x\, dx}{(1 - x^4)^{1/3}}$.

(h) $\displaystyle\int_0^1 \frac{\log x}{1 + x}\, dx$.   *Ans.*   Convergent.

(i) $\displaystyle\int_0^1 x^{m-1}(\log x)^n\, dx$.   (Converges if $m > 0$, $n > -1$.)

(Hint: set $x = e^{-u}$.)

(j) $\displaystyle\int_1^{+\infty} x^{m-1}(\log x)^n\, dx$.   (Converges if $m < 0$, $n > -1$.)

(k) $\displaystyle\int_0^5 x^{\alpha-1}(1-x)^{\beta-1}\,dx.$ (l) $\displaystyle\int_0^1 x^{\alpha-1}(1-x)^{\beta-1}\,dx.$

(m) $\displaystyle\int_0^1 \sqrt{\frac{1-k^2x^2}{1-x^2}}\,dx, \ k<1.$ (n) $\displaystyle\int_0^1 \left(\log\frac{1}{x}\right)^n dx.$

(o) $\displaystyle\int_0^{+\infty} e^{-a^2x^2}\cosh bx\,dx.$ (p) $\displaystyle\int_0^{+\infty} e^{-\left(x-\frac{a}{x}\right)^2} dx.$

13. (a) Show that $\int_1^{+\infty}\cos x\log x\,dx$ diverges indefinitely.

(b) Show that $\int_0^1 \cos x\log x\,dx$ converges.

14. Show that, if $\int_a^b f(x)\,dx$ is absolutely convergent, then it is convergent. Is the converse of this statement true? Illustrate.

15. Show that each of the following are absolutely convergent:

(a) $\displaystyle\int_0^b x^{-\frac{1}{2}}\sin(1/x)\,dx.$ (b) $\displaystyle\int_0^{+\infty} e^{-a^2x^2}\cos bx\,dx.$

(c) $\displaystyle\int_1^{+\infty}\frac{\cos x\,dx}{a^2+x^2}$ $\left(\text{Hint: Compare with } \displaystyle\int_1^{+\infty}\frac{dx}{a^2+x^2}.\right)$

(d) $\displaystyle\int_\pi^{+\infty}\frac{x\cos x\,dx}{a^2+x^2}$

Hint: $\displaystyle\int_\pi^{x_1}\frac{x\cos x\,dx}{a^2+x^2}=\frac{x_1\sin x_1}{a^2+x_1^2}-\int_\pi^{x_1}\frac{x^2-a^2}{(x^2+a^2)^2}\cos x\,dx.$

Compare the last integral with $\displaystyle\int_\pi^{x_1}\frac{dx}{x^2}$ and then let $x_1\to+\infty$.

(e) $\displaystyle\int_1^{+\infty}\frac{\sin x}{x^n}\,dx.$ (f) $\displaystyle\int_0^{+\infty}\frac{\cos x}{\sqrt{x}}\,dx.$ (g) $\displaystyle\int_0^{+\infty}\frac{\sin x\cos ax}{x}\,dx.$

16. Define $\int_{-\infty}^b f(x)\,dx$ and $\int_{-\infty}^{+\infty} f(x)\,dx$ when $f(x)$ is unbounded in the neighborhood of a finite number of points.

PART E. INTEGRALS CONTAINING A PARAMETER

33. Derivative of a Definite Integral. We shall consider the function $\varphi(\alpha)$ defined by means of the definite integral

$$\varphi(\alpha)\equiv\int_{x=a(\alpha)}^{x=b(\alpha)} f(x,\,\alpha)\,\partial x, \tag{1}$$

where both $a(\alpha)$ and $b(\alpha)$ are continuous and differentiable functions of the parameter α within the region $c\leqq\alpha\leqq d$, and where $f(x,\,\alpha)$ is assumed to be a continuous function of the independent variables x and α in the region $a(\alpha)\leqq x\leqq b(\alpha)$, $c\leqq\alpha\leqq d$.

Since $f(x, \alpha)$ is a continuous function of x and α, it follows that $f(x, \alpha)$ is also a continuous function of x and a continuous function of α. It then follows that $f(x, \alpha)$ is integrable with respect to x over $a \leqq x \leqq b$.

Let Δa, Δb and $\Delta \varphi$ denote the increments of a, b, and φ, respectively, when α is increased by $\Delta \alpha$. Then

$$\varphi(\alpha + \Delta \alpha) = \int_{a+\Delta a}^{b+\Delta b} f(x, \alpha + \Delta \alpha)\, \partial x = \int_{a+\Delta a}^{a} f(x, \alpha + \Delta \alpha)\, \partial x$$
$$+ \int_{a}^{b} f(x, \alpha + \Delta \alpha)\, \partial x + \int_{b}^{b+\Delta b} f(x, \alpha + \Delta \alpha)\, \partial x. \quad (2)$$

From (1), we find that

$$\Delta \varphi = \varphi(\alpha + \Delta \alpha) - \varphi(\alpha)$$
$$= \int_{a+\Delta a}^{a} f(x, \alpha + \Delta \alpha)\, \partial x + \int_{a}^{b} [f(x, \alpha + \Delta \alpha) - f(x, \alpha)]\, \partial x$$
$$+ \int_{b}^{b+\Delta b} f(x, \alpha + \Delta \alpha)\, \partial x. \quad (3)$$

By the theorem of the mean,

$$\int_{a+\Delta a}^{a} f(x, \alpha + \Delta \alpha)\, \partial x = -(\Delta a)\, f(\xi_1, \alpha + \Delta \alpha),$$
$$a + \Delta a \lessgtr \xi_1 \lessgtr a,$$
$$\int_{b}^{b+\Delta b} f(x, \alpha + \Delta \alpha)\, \partial x = +(\Delta b)\, f(\xi_2, \alpha + \Delta \alpha),$$
$$b \lessgtr \xi_2 \lessgtr b + \Delta b.$$
$$(4)$$

We shall assume that $\dfrac{\partial f}{\partial \alpha} = \lim\limits_{\Delta \alpha \to 0} \dfrac{f(x, \alpha + \Delta \alpha) - f(x, \alpha)}{\Delta \alpha}$ exists and is continuous. Then, by the theorem of the mean,

$$\int_{a}^{b} [f(x, \alpha + \Delta \alpha) - f(x, \alpha)]\, \partial x = \Delta \alpha \int_{a}^{b} f_\alpha(x, \alpha + \theta \cdot \Delta \alpha)\, \partial x, \quad (5)$$

where $0 < \theta < 1$ and $f_\alpha \equiv \partial f / \partial \alpha$. Substituting the values found in (4) and (5) in equation (3), dividing by $\Delta \alpha$, letting $\Delta \alpha \to 0$, and noting that $\xi_1 \to a$, $\xi_2 \to b$, we find that

$$\frac{d\varphi}{d\alpha} = -f(a, \alpha) \frac{da}{d\alpha} + \int_{a}^{b} \frac{\partial f(x, \alpha)}{\partial \alpha}\, \partial x + f(b, \alpha) \frac{db}{d\alpha}. \quad (6)$$

If b and a are both independent of α, (5) reduces to

$$\frac{d\varphi}{d\alpha} = \int_{a}^{b} \frac{\partial f(x, \alpha)}{\partial \alpha}\, \partial x. \quad (7)$$

A simple graphical picture of the various quantities involved here may be easily obtained. The

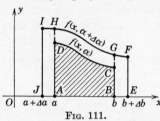

Fig. 111.

functions $f(x, \alpha)$ and $f(x, \alpha + \Delta\alpha)$ are represented by the curves DC and IF, respectively. $\varphi(\alpha)$ is represented by the shaded portion of the area, and $\Delta\varphi$ by the unshaded portion of the area $EFIJ$. The three integrals appearing in (3) give the areas of the strips $JAHI$, $DCGH$, and $BEFG$, respectively.

It is an immediate consequence of (7) that $\varphi(\alpha)$ is a continuous function of α in the region considered.

Example 1. Find $d\varphi/d\alpha$ if $\varphi(\alpha) = \int_{x=\cos 2\alpha}^{x=\alpha^3} [x^2\alpha^6 - \sin (2\alpha e^{3x})]\partial x.$

$$\frac{d\varphi}{d\alpha} = -[(\cos^2 2\alpha)\alpha^6 - \sin 2\alpha e^{3\cos 2\alpha}](-2 \sin 2\alpha)$$

$$+ \int_{\cos 2\alpha}^{\alpha^3} [6x^2\alpha^5 - 2e^{3x} \cos (2\alpha e^{3x})] \, \partial x + [\alpha^{12} - \sin (2\alpha e^{3\alpha^3})](3\alpha^2).$$

EXERCISES XXIII

1. Find the derivative with respect to α of each of the following integrals

(a) $\int_0^{\sqrt[5]{\alpha}} x^3 \, \partial x.$　　　　　　　　(b) $\int_{\sin \alpha}^1 e^{\alpha + x} \, \partial x.$

(c) $\int_{-\alpha^3}^{\log \alpha} \sin (x + \alpha) \, \partial x.$

2. By means of (6), find the derivatives with respect to α of each of the following integrals. Check your results by first integrating and then differentiating with respect to α:

(a) $\int_\alpha^{e^\alpha} x \, \partial x.$　　　　　　　　(b) $\int_0^{\alpha x} \tan (t + \alpha) \, \partial t.$

(c) $\int_0^{x^2} \sin^{-1} \alpha t \, \partial t.$　　　　　(d) $\int_{\alpha^2}^{\alpha^5} \log (x + \alpha) \, \partial x.$

34. Integral of a Definite Integral. In the previous section we found a way to compute $(d/d\alpha) \int_a^b f(x, \alpha) \, \partial x.$ The integral

$$\int_{\alpha_0}^\beta \left[\int_a^b f(x, \alpha) \, \partial x \right] d\alpha$$

may be computed in a similar manner. In fact,

$$\int_{\alpha_0}^\beta \int_a^b f(x, \alpha) \, \partial x \, d\alpha = \int_a^b \int_{\alpha_0}^\beta f(x, \alpha) \, \partial \alpha \, dx \tag{1}$$

when a and b are constants.

Example 1. Consider

$$\int_0^1 x \cos \alpha x \ \partial x = \frac{\sin \alpha}{\alpha} - \frac{1 - \cos \alpha}{\alpha^2}.$$

Apply (1) to this result. The left member of (1) gives

$$\int_{\alpha_0}^{\beta} \int_0^1 x \cos \alpha x \ \partial x \ d\alpha = \int_{\alpha_0}^{\beta} \left(\frac{\sin \alpha}{\alpha} - \frac{1 - \cos \alpha}{\alpha^2} \right) d\alpha,$$

and the right member of (1) gives

$$\int_0^1 \int_{\alpha_0}^{\beta} x \cos \alpha x \ \partial \alpha \ dx = \int_0^1 (\sin \beta x - \sin \alpha_0 x) \ dx$$

$$= \frac{1 - \cos \beta}{\beta} - \frac{1 - \cos \alpha_0}{\alpha_0}.$$

Hence $\displaystyle \int_{\alpha_0}^{\beta} \left(\frac{\sin \alpha}{\alpha} - \frac{1 - \cos \alpha}{\alpha^2} \right) d\alpha = \frac{1 - \cos \beta}{\beta} - \frac{1 - \cos \alpha_0}{\alpha_0}.$

EXERCISES XXIV

1. By integrating $\varphi(\alpha) = \int_0^1 x^\alpha \ dx = 1/(\alpha + 1)$, show that

$$\int_0^1 \frac{x^m - x^n}{\log x} \ dx = \log \frac{m + 1}{n + 1}.$$

2. Construct an illustration of (1) in which the left member of (1) is not easily evaluated by direct methods.

35. Uniform Convergence of Infinite Integrals. In general, the theorems and properties discussed in Secs. 33 and 34 do not hold for infinite integrals like $\int_a^{+\infty} f(x, \alpha) \ \partial x$. Hence we must determine the conditions under which these theorems and properties are valid. As in the case with infinite series, we are led to the concept of uniform convergence of infinite integrals.

We first consider the infinite integral $\int_a^{+\infty} f(x, \alpha) \ \partial x$, where $f(x, \alpha)$ is bounded throughout the region $a \leqq x \leqq a'$, $b \leqq \alpha \leqq b'$ for all values of $a' \geqq a$. The integral $\int_a^{+\infty} f(x, \alpha) \ \partial x$ is said to converge uniformly to its value $\varphi(\alpha)$ in $b \leqq \alpha \leqq b'$, if for every positive number ϵ there exists a positive number X such that for every α in $b \leqq \alpha \leqq b'$,

$$\left| \varphi(\alpha) - \int_a^{x_1} f(x, \alpha) \ \partial x \right| < \epsilon, \qquad \text{for} \qquad x_1 \geqq X.$$

From this definition many theorems may be proved. We shall state a few of them below. We shall omit the proofs of these theorems since they so closely parallel the theorems given Chap. IV.

Theorem 35.1. *A necessary and sufficient condition that $\int_a^{+\infty} f(x, \alpha)\, \partial x$ converge uniformly in $b \leqq \alpha \leqq b'$, is that for every positive number ϵ there exist a positive number X, such that for every α in $b \leqq \alpha \leqq b'$, $\left| \int_{x_1}^{x_2} f(x, \alpha)\, \partial x \right| < \epsilon$ when $x_2 > x_1 \geqq X$.*

Theorem 35.2. *If $\int_a^{+\infty} f(x, \alpha)\, \partial x$ converges uniformly in $b \leqq \alpha \leqq b'$, then for every positive number ϵ there corresponds a positive number X such that for every α in $b \leqq \alpha \leqq b'$,*

$$\left| \int_{x_1}^{+\infty} f(x, \alpha)\, \partial x \right| < \epsilon,$$

when $x_1 \geqq X$.

Theorem 35.3. *Let $f(x, \alpha) = \lambda(x, \alpha)\mu(x)$, where $\lambda(x, \alpha)$ is a continuous function of (x, α) in $a \leqq x \leqq a'$, $b \leqq \alpha \leqq b'$, for all $a' \geqq a$, and where $\mu(x)$ is bounded and integrable in the interval $[a, a']$. If $\int_a^{+\infty} f(x, \alpha)\, \partial x$ converges uniformly to $\varphi(\alpha)$ in $[b, b']$, then $\varphi(\alpha)$ is a continuous function of α in $[b, b']$.*

Theorem 35.4. *If $f(x, \alpha)$ satisfies the conditions of Theorem 35.3, then if α and α_0 are any two points in $[b, b']$,*

$$\int_{\alpha_0}^{\beta} \int_a^{+\infty} f(x, \alpha)\, \partial x\, d\alpha = \int_a^{+\infty} \int_{\alpha_0}^{\beta} f(x, \alpha)\, \partial \alpha\, dx.$$

Theorem 35.5. *Let $f(x, \alpha)$ and $(\partial f/\partial \alpha)_x$ have the properties stated in Theorem 35.3. If $\int_a^{+\infty} f(x, \alpha)\, \partial x$ converges to $\varphi(\alpha)$ and*

$$\int_a^{+\infty} \left(\frac{\partial f}{\partial \alpha} \right)_x \partial x$$

converges uniformly in $[b, b']$, then $\varphi(\alpha)$ has a derivative at every point in $[b, b']$, and $\varphi'(\alpha) = \displaystyle\int_a^{+\infty} \left(\frac{\partial f}{\partial \alpha} \right)_x \partial x$.

We shall now consider the convergent integral $\int_a^{a'} f(x, \alpha)\, \partial x$, where $f(x, \alpha)$ is unbounded in the neighborhood of points on $x = a'$, and is bounded for $a \leqq x \leqq a' - \xi$, $b \leqq \alpha \leqq b'$, when $a < a' - \xi < a'$.

The integral $\int_a^{a'} f(x, \alpha)\, \partial x$ is said to be *uniformly convergent* to $\psi(\alpha)$ in $b \leqq \alpha \leqq b'$, if for every positive number ϵ there exists a positive number δ such that when $0 < \xi \leqq \delta$,

$$\left| \psi(\alpha) - \int_a^{a' - \xi} f(x, \alpha)\, \partial x \right| < \epsilon$$

for every α in $b \leqq \alpha \leqq b'$.

It should be emphasized that the same number δ must serve for every α in $[b, b']$.

THEOREM 35.6. *A necessary and sufficient condition for the uniform convergence of $\int_a^{a'} f(x, \alpha) \, \partial x$ to $\psi(\alpha)$ in $b \leqq \alpha \leqq b'$ is that for any preassigned positive number ϵ, there shall exist a positive number δ, such that for every α in $[b, b']$,*

$$\left| \int_{a'-\xi'}^{a'-\xi''} f(x, \alpha) \, \partial x \right| < \epsilon \qquad when \qquad 0 < \xi'' < \xi' \leqq \delta.$$

THEOREM 35.7. *If $\int_a^{a'} f(x, \alpha) \, \partial x$ is uniformly convergent in $[b, b']$, then for any positive number ϵ there exists a positive number δ, such that for every α in $[b, b']$, $\left| \int_{a'-\xi}^{a'} f(x, \alpha) \, \partial x \right| < \epsilon$ when $0 < \xi \leqq \delta$.*

Various modifications of these results must be made when f is unbounded in the neighborhood of certain points on $x = a$, or more generally, on $x = a_1, a_2, \cdots, a_n$.

THEOREM 35.8. *Let $f(x, \alpha) = \lambda(x, \alpha)\mu(x)$, where $\lambda(x, \alpha)$ is a continuous function of (x, α) in $a \leqq x \leqq a'$, $b \leqq \alpha \leqq b'$, and where $\mu(x)$ is bounded and integrable over $[a, a']$ except in the neighborhood of certain points on $x = a_1, \cdots, a_n$. (I) If $\int_a^{a'} f(x, \alpha) \, \partial x$ is uniformly convergent to $\psi(\alpha)$ in $[b, b']$, then $\psi(\alpha)$ is a continuous function of α in $[b, b']$. (II) Also*

$$\int_{\alpha_0}^{\beta} \int_a^{a'} f(x, \alpha) \, \partial x \, d\alpha = \int_a^{a'} \int_{\alpha_0}^{\beta} f(x, \alpha) \, \partial\alpha \, dx,$$

where α_0 and β are any two points in $[b, b']$. (III) If $(\partial f/\partial \alpha)_x$ satisfies the same conditions as $f(x, \alpha)$, if $\psi(\alpha)$ converges, and if $\int_a^{a'} \left(\dfrac{\partial f}{\partial \alpha} \right)_x \partial x$ converges uniformly in $[b, b']$, then $\psi'(\alpha)$ exists in $[b, b']$ and equals $\int_a^{a'} \left(\dfrac{\partial f}{\partial \alpha} \right)_x \partial x$.

Example 1. Prove $\int_0^{+\infty} \dfrac{\sin x}{x} \, dx = \dfrac{\pi}{2}$.

Consider the integral $I \equiv \int_0^{+\infty} e^{-\alpha x} \dfrac{\sin x}{x} \, dx$, $\alpha \geqq 0$. Evidently, $e^{-\alpha x}/x$ is monotonic in x when $x > 0$. By the second theorem of the mean, when $0 < x_1 \leqq \xi \leqq x_2$,

$$\int_{x_1}^{x_2} \frac{e^{-\alpha}}{x} \sin x \, dx = \frac{e^{-\alpha x}}{x_1} \int_{x_1}^{\xi} \sin x \, dx + \frac{e^{-\alpha x_2}}{x_2} \int_{\xi}^{x_2} \sin x \, dx. \qquad (1)$$

Hence

$$\left| \int_{x_1}^{x_2} \frac{e^{-\alpha x}}{x} \sin x \, dx \right| \leq \frac{e^{-\alpha x_1}}{x_1} \left| \int_{x_1}^{\xi} \sin x \, dx \right| + \frac{e^{-\alpha x_2}}{x_2} \left| \int_{\xi}^{x_2} \sin x \, dx \right|. \quad (2)$$

Since $|\int_r^s \sin x \, dx| \leq 2$ for all values of r and s, and $\alpha \geq 0$,

$$\left| \int_{x_1}^{x_2} \frac{e^{-\alpha x}}{x} \sin x \, dx \right| < 4\frac{e^{-\alpha x_1}}{x_1} < \frac{4}{x_1}. \quad (3)$$

If $x_2 > x_1 \geq x_0$ and if $x_0 > 4/\epsilon$, then for every $\alpha \geq 0$, the left member of (3) is less than ϵ. This shows that the integral I is uniformly convergent to $\varphi(\alpha)$. By Theorems 35.3 and 35.8 we know that $\varphi(\alpha)$ is continuous for $\alpha \geq 0$. Hence,

$$\varphi(0) = \int_0^{+\infty} \frac{\sin x}{x} \, dx = \lim_{\alpha \to +0} \int_0^{+\infty} e^{-\alpha x} \frac{\sin x}{x} \, dx.$$

From Theorems 35.5 and 35.8, for $\alpha > 0$,

$$\varphi'(\alpha) = \int_0^{+\infty} \frac{\partial}{\partial \alpha}\left(e^{-\alpha x} \frac{\sin x}{x} \right) dx = - \int_0^{+\infty} e^{-\alpha x} \sin x \, dx. \quad (4)$$

The latter integral may be shown to converge uniformly for $\alpha \geq \alpha_0 > 0$. Since $(d/dx)e^{-\alpha x} (\cos x + \alpha \sin x) = -(\alpha^2 + 1)e^{-\alpha x} \sin x$, we have

$$\int_0^{+\infty} e^{-\alpha x} \sin x \, dx = \frac{1}{1 + \alpha^2},$$

so that $\varphi'(\alpha) = -1/(1 + \alpha^2)$, and $\varphi(\alpha) = -\tan^{-1} \alpha + C$, where C is a constant. Since $\lim_{\alpha \to +\infty} \varphi(\alpha) = 0$, $C = \pi/2$. Hence

$$\varphi(\alpha) \equiv \int_0^{+\infty} e^{-\alpha x} \frac{\sin x}{x} \, dx = \frac{\pi}{2} - \tan^{-1} \alpha. \quad (5)$$

By (4), we have

$$\int_0^{+\infty} \frac{\sin x}{x} \, dx = \frac{\pi}{2}. \quad (6)$$

Example 2. Prove $\int_0^{+\infty} e^{-x^2} \, dx = \sqrt{\pi}/2$.

Since $0 < e^{-x^2} < e^{-x}$ when $x \geq 0$, it follows by Example 1 and Theorem 31.4 of Sec. 31 that the given integral is convergent. Let

$$\varphi(t) = \int_0^t e^{-x^2} \, dx = \int_0^t e^{-v^2} \, dy.$$

Then, by (10) of Sec. 19,

$$[\varphi(t)]^2 = \left(\int_0^t e^{-x^2} \, dx \right)\left(\int_0^t e^{-v^2} \, dy \right) = \int_0^t \int_0^t e^{-x^2 - v^2} \, \partial y \, dx$$

$$= \iint_K e^{-r^2} r \, \partial \theta \, dr,$$

where K is the region bounded by the lines $x = y = 0$, $x = y = t$. Since K contains the first quadrant of the circle $x^2 + y^2 = t^2$ and is contained in the first quadrant of the circle $x^2 + y^2 = 2t^2$, and since $re^{-r^2} > 0$ when $r > 0$,

$$\int_0^t \int_0^{\pi/2} re^{-r^2}\, \partial\theta\, dr \leqq [\varphi(t)]^2 \leqq \int_0^{t\sqrt{2}} \int_0^{\pi/2} re^{-r^2}\, \partial\theta\, dr,$$

that is,

$$\frac{\pi}{4}(1 - e^{-t^2}) \leqq [\varphi(t)]^2 \leqq \frac{\pi}{4}(1 - e^{-2t^2}).$$

Therefore

$$\int_0^{+\infty} e^{-x^2}\, dx = \lim_{t \to +\infty} \varphi(t) = \frac{\sqrt{\pi}}{2}.$$

Example 3. Since $\int_0^{t/\alpha} e^{-\alpha^2 x^2}\, dx = \frac{1}{\alpha} \int_0^t e^{-v^2}\, dy$, it follows at once from Example 2 that

$$\int_0^{+\infty} e^{-\alpha^2 x^2}\, dx = \frac{\sqrt{\pi}}{2\alpha}.$$

Example 4. Show that $\int_0^{+\infty} \cos(x^2)\, dx = \int_0^{+\infty} \sin(x^2)\, dx = \frac{1}{2}\sqrt{\pi/2}$.

We shall evaluate these integrals without justifying the operations used. By Sec. 7 of Chap. V, $e^{-ix^2} = \cos x^2 - i \sin x^2$, where $i^2 = -1$. Hence, by Example 3,

$$\int_0^{+\infty} e^{-ix^2}\, dx = \int_0^{+\infty} \cos x^2\, dx - i \int_0^{+\infty} \sin x^2\, dx = \frac{\sqrt{\pi}}{2\sqrt{i}}.$$

Since $\sqrt{\pi}/2\sqrt{i} = \frac{1}{2}\sqrt{\pi/2}(1 - i)$, we find by equating real and imaginary parts the results stated in the example.

EXERCISES XXV

1. Show that $\int_0^{+\infty} e^{-\alpha x}\, dx$ converges uniformly in $\alpha \geqq \alpha_0 > 0$.
2. Show that $\int_1^{+\infty} x^{-(1+\alpha)}\, dx$ converges uniformly in $\alpha \geqq \alpha_0 > 0$.
3. Determine an interval in which $\int_0^{+\infty} e^{-x/\alpha}\, dx$ converges uniformly.
4. Determine an interval in which $\displaystyle\int_1^{+\infty} \frac{\sin \alpha x}{x^{1+n}}\, dx$ converges uniformly.
5. Determine an interval in which $\displaystyle\int_0^{+\infty} \frac{\cos \alpha x}{1 + x^2}\, dx$ converges uniformly.
6. Prove that if $f(x, \alpha)$ is bounded and integrable in $a \leqq x \leqq a'$, $b \leqq \alpha \leqq b'$ for all $a' \geqq a$, then $\int_a^{+\infty} f(x, \alpha)\, dx$ converges uniformly in $[b, b']$, provided there exists a function $\lambda(x)$, independent of α, such that (I) $\lambda(x) \geqq 0$

when $x \geqq a$; (II) $|f(x, \alpha)| \leqq \lambda(x)$ when $x \geqq a$ and $b \leqq \alpha \leqq b'$; and (III) $\int_a^{+\infty} \lambda(x)\, dx$ exists.

7. Show that $\displaystyle\int_1^{+\infty} e^{-\alpha x}\, \frac{\cos x}{x}\, dx$ converges uniformly for $\alpha \geqq 0$.

8. Show that $\int_0^{+\infty} e^{-\alpha x} \cos x\, dx$ converges uniformly for $\alpha \geqq \alpha_0 > 0$.

9. Show that $\displaystyle\int_0^{+\infty} \frac{\sin \alpha x}{x}\, dx$ converges uniformly for $\alpha \geqq \alpha_0 > 0$.

10. Show that $\int_0^1 x^{\alpha-1}\, dx$ converges uniformly for $0 < \alpha_0 \leqq \alpha \leqq 1$.

11. Show that $\int_0^1 x^{\alpha-1} e^{-x}\, dx$ converges uniformly for $0 < \alpha_0 \leqq \alpha \leqq 1$.

12. Prove: If $B(x, \alpha)$ is bounded in $x \geqq a$, $b \leqq \alpha \leqq b'$, and for every α in $[b, b']$ is a monotone function of x, if $\psi(x)$ is bounded and does not change sign more than a finite number of times in $[a, a']$ for any $a' \geqq a$, and if $\int_a^{+\infty} \psi(x)\, dx$ exists, then $\int_a^{+\infty} B(x, \alpha)\psi(x)\, \partial x$ is uniformly convergent in $[b, b']$.

Evaluate the following integrals by differentiating with respect to k. Show that the operations involved are permissible.

13. $\displaystyle\int_0^1 \frac{x^k - 1}{\log x}\, dx.$

14. Prove $\displaystyle\int_0^{+\infty} \frac{\sin kx}{x(1 + x^2)}\, dx = \frac{\pi}{2}(1 - e^{-k}),\ k \geqq 0.$

15. $\int_0^{+\infty} e^{-kx^2}\, dx = \frac{1}{2}\sqrt{\pi/k}.$

16. $\displaystyle\int_0^{+\infty} x^{2n} e^{-kx^2}\, dx = \frac{\sqrt{\pi}}{2}\, \frac{1 \cdot 3 \cdots (2n - 1)}{2^n k^{n+\frac{1}{2}}}.$

17. From (16) prove $\int_0^1 x^n(-\log x)^m\, dx = m!/(n + 1)^{m+1}.$

18. $\displaystyle\int_0^{+\infty} \frac{x^k}{1 + x^2}\, dx = \frac{\pi}{2 \cos (k\pi/2)},\ 0 < k < 1.$

19. From (18) prove $\displaystyle\int_0^{+\infty} \frac{x^k \log x}{1 + x^2}\, dx = \frac{\pi^2}{4} \sec \frac{k\pi}{2} \tan \frac{k\pi}{2}.$

20. $\int_0^\pi \log (1 + k \cos x)\, dx.$

21. $\int_0^1 x^k\, dx = 1/(k + 1),\ k > -1.$

22. Prove that $\displaystyle\int_0^\pi \frac{dx}{k - \cos x} = \frac{\pi}{\sqrt{k^2 - 1}},\ k > 1.$

23. Prove that $\int_0^{+\infty} e^{-kx}\, dx = 1/k.$

24. Prove that $\displaystyle\int_0^{+\infty} \frac{dx}{x^2 + k} = \frac{\pi}{2\sqrt{k}}.$

25. From Ex. 22 show that $\displaystyle\int_0^\pi \log \frac{b - \cos x}{a - \cos x}\, dx = \pi \log \frac{b + \sqrt{b^2 - 1}}{a + \sqrt{a^2 - 1}}.$

26. From Ex. 23 show that $\int_0^{+\infty} x^n e^{-kx}\, dx = n!/k^{n+1}.$

27. From Ex. 24 show that $\displaystyle\int_0^{+\infty} \frac{dx}{(x^2 + k)^{n+1}} = \frac{\pi}{2}\, \frac{1 \cdot 3 \cdots (2n - 1)}{2 \cdot 4 \cdots 2nk^{n+\frac{1}{2}}}.$

28. $\int_0^{+\infty} e^{-kx} \cos mx\, dx = k/(k^2 + m^2),\qquad k > 0.$

29. Obtain by integration from Ex. 28 the relation

$$\int_0^{+\infty} \frac{e^{-kx} - e^{-ux}}{x \sec mx}\, dx = \frac{1}{2} \log \frac{u^2 + m^2}{k^2 + m^2}.$$

30. $\int_0^{+\infty} e^{-kx} \sin mx\, dx = m/(k^2 + m^2),\qquad k > 0.$

31. From Ex. 30 obtain by integration

$$\int_0^{+\infty} \frac{e^{-kx} - e^{-ux}}{x \csc mx}\, dx = \tan^{-1} \frac{u}{m} - \tan^{-1} \frac{k}{m}.$$

32. From Exs. 28 and 30 find the values of

$$\int_0^{+\infty} xe^{-kx} \cos mx\, dx,\ \int_0^{+\infty} x^2 e^{-kx} \sin mx\, dx.$$

33. From Ex. 23 show that $\displaystyle\int_0^{+\infty} \frac{e^{-ux} - e^{-kx}}{x}\, dx = \log \frac{k}{u}.$

34. From Example 3 show that

$$\int_0^{+\infty} \frac{e^{-k^2 x^2} - e^{-u^2 x^2}}{x^2}\, dx = (u - k)\sqrt{\pi}.$$

35. By differentiating, prove

$$\int_0^{\pi} \log (1 - 2\alpha \cos x + \alpha^2)\, dx = \begin{cases} \pi \log \alpha^2, & \alpha^2 \geqq 1, \\ 0, & \alpha^2 \leqq 1. \end{cases}$$

PART F. SPECIAL FUNCTIONS DEFINED BY MEANS OF DEFINITE INTEGRALS

36. Gamma Function. We here consider the integral $\int_0^{+\infty} x^{n-1} e^{-x}\, dx$. By the methods given in Sec. 31, it is easy to show that this integral converges, and hence defines a function of n, for all positive real values of n. This function is called the *Gamma* function:

$$\Gamma(n) \equiv \int_0^{+\infty} x^{n-1} e^{-x}\, dx. \quad (0 < n < +\infty) \quad (1)$$

In particular,

$$\Gamma(1) = 1. \tag{2}$$

An important property of the Gamma function is given by the equation

$$\Gamma(n + 1) = n\Gamma(n), \tag{3}$$

the proof of which is obtained by integrating by parts:

$$\Gamma(n) = \int_0^{+\infty} x^{n-1}e^{-x}\,dx = \frac{1}{n}x^n e^{-x}\Big]_0^{+\infty} + \frac{1}{n}\int_0^{+\infty} x^n e^{-x}\,dx$$

$$= \frac{1}{n}\Gamma(n+1).$$

From (3) and (2), we find upon setting

$$n = 1, 2, 3, \cdots, n+1,$$

successively,

$$\Gamma(2) = 1 \cdot \Gamma(1) = 1 \cdot 1 = 1, \qquad \Gamma(3) = 2 \cdot \Gamma(2) = 2 \cdot 1 = 2!,$$

$$\Gamma(4) = 3 \cdot \Gamma(3) = 3!, \qquad \cdots, \qquad \Gamma(n+1) = n!. \qquad (4)$$

In view of property (4), $\Gamma(n+1)$ is sometimes called the *factorial function*, and is in fact one generalization of $n!$ to the case where n is not a positive integer.

Relation (3) also shows that the values of the function may be determined for all $n > 0$ if it is determined for all values of n over a unit interval. For this reason, in constructing tables of $\Gamma(n)$, it is sufficient to construct such a table for values of n from 1 to 2.

When $n < 0$, the integral (1) diverges and hence fails to define a function. However, we can extend the definition of $\Gamma(n)$ by means of equation (3). Let $-1 < n < 0$. Then $\Gamma(n+1)$ is defined by (1), since $(n+1)$ is positive. We define $\Gamma(n)$ for $-1 < n < 0$ by means of the relation

$$\Gamma(n) = \frac{\Gamma(n+1)}{n}. \qquad (5)$$

Let $-2 < n < -1$. We again define $\Gamma(n)$ by means of (5), since in the right-hand side of (5), $\Gamma(n+1)$ is now known. This process of extension of the definition of $\Gamma(n)$ can be carried on to include all negative real numbers n, except the negative integers and zero. (Why?)

From (3) it is easy to see that if k is a positive integer,

$$\Gamma(n+1) = n(n-1) \cdots (n-k)\Gamma(n-k), \qquad (6)$$

and

$$\Gamma(n+k) = (n+k-1) \cdots (n+1)n\Gamma(n). \qquad (7)$$

By means of various transformations the integral (1) may be reduced to other forms. For example, the transformation $x = ay$ reduces (1) to

$$\Gamma(n) = a^n \int_0^{+\infty} y^{n-1} e^{-ay}\, dy; \qquad (8)$$

the transformation $x = y^2$ reduces (1) to

$$\Gamma(n) = 2 \int_0^{+\infty} y^{2n-1} e^{-y^2}\, dy, \qquad (9)$$

and $x = -(m+1) \log y$ reduces (1) to

$$\Gamma(n) = (m+1)^n \int_0^1 y^m \left(\log \frac{1}{y}\right)^{n-1} dy. \quad (-1 < m,\ \ 0 < n) \quad (10)$$

From (9) with $n = \frac{1}{2}$, we find by Example 2 of Sec. 35 that

$$\Gamma\left(\frac{1}{2}\right) = 2 \int_0^{+\infty} e^{-y^2}\, dy = 2\left(\frac{\sqrt{\pi}}{2}\right) = \sqrt{\pi}. \qquad (11)$$

Many other similar forms of (1) are given in the exercises below.

By the methods of Sec. 35, it is possible to show that (1) is uniformly convergent for all values of $n \geq N$, where N is any positive number. From Theorem 35.3 we can then conclude that $\Gamma(n)$ is continuous for all positive values of n.

By Theorem 35.5 the integral

$$\Gamma(n) = \int_0^{+\infty} x^{n-1} e^{-x}\, dx, \qquad (n > 0) \qquad$$

may be differentiated with respect to n under the integral sign, giving

$$\Gamma'(n) = \int_0^{+\infty} x^{n-1} e^{-x} \log x\, dx. \qquad (12)$$

From Ex. XXV, 33, we know that

$$\log x = \int_0^{+\infty} \frac{e^{-\alpha} - e^{-\alpha x}}{\alpha}\, \partial x. \qquad (13)$$

Substituting (13) in (12) we have

$$\Gamma'(n) = \int_0^{+\infty} \int_0^{+\infty} x^{n-1} e^{-x} \frac{e^{-\alpha} - e^{-\alpha x}}{\alpha}\, \partial\alpha\, dx. \qquad (14)$$

By Theorem 35.4 the order of integration in (14) may be interchanged, giving

$$\Gamma'(n) = \int_0^{+\infty} \int_0^{+\infty} \frac{e^{-\alpha} - e^{-\alpha x}}{\alpha} \, x^{n-1} e^{-x} \, \partial x \, d\alpha$$

$$= \int_0^{+\infty} \int_0^{+\infty} x^{n-1} e^{-x} \frac{e^{-\alpha}}{\alpha} \, \partial x \, d\alpha$$

$$- \int_0^{+\infty} \int_0^{+\infty} x^{n-1} e^{-(\alpha+1)x} \frac{1}{\alpha} \, \partial x \, d\alpha. \quad (15)$$

Using relationships (1) and (8), we see that

$$\Gamma'(n) = \Gamma(n) \int_0^{+\infty} \frac{1}{\alpha} \left[e^{-\alpha} - \frac{1}{(1 + \alpha)^n} \right] d\alpha. \quad (16)$$

The *Gamma* function was defined by Weierstrass by the equation

$$\frac{1}{\Gamma(z)} = z e^{\gamma z} \prod_{n=1}^{\infty} \left[\left(1 + \frac{z}{n} \right) e^{-z/n} \right],$$

where z is a complex number, and $\gamma = 0.5772 \cdots$ is Euler's constant. Euler showed that

$$\Gamma(z) = \frac{1}{z} \prod_{n=1}^{\infty} \left[\left(1 + \frac{1}{n} \right)^z \left(1 + \frac{z}{n} \right)^{-1} \right]$$

EXERCISES XXVI

1. Prove that (1) converges. (Hint: Prove that $\int_0^1 x^{n-1} e^{-x} \, dx$ converges for $0 < n < 1$, and $\int_1^{+\infty} x^{n-1} e^{-x} \, dx$ converges for all real values of n.)

2. Prove (2), (6), and (7).

3. Prove $\Gamma(n) \to +\infty$ as $n \to +0$.

4. Make a table of values of $\Gamma(n)$ for every half integer and graph your results.

5. Verify the reduction of (1) to forms (8), (9), (10), and (11).

6. Prove that (1) is uniformly convergent for all $n \geq N > 0$.

7. (a) From (16) show $\Gamma'(1) = \int_0^{+\infty} \left(e^{-\alpha} - \frac{1}{1 + \alpha} \right) \frac{1}{\alpha} \, d\alpha.$

(b) From this relation and (16), prove

$$\frac{\Gamma'(n)}{\Gamma(n)} = \Gamma'(1) + \int_0^{+\infty} \left[\frac{1}{1 + \alpha} - \frac{1}{(1 + \alpha)^n} \right] \frac{1}{\alpha} \, d\alpha.$$

(c) From the expression for $\Gamma'(n)/\Gamma(n)$ found in (b), show that when n is an integer greater than one,

$$\frac{\Gamma'(n)}{\Gamma(n)} = \int_1^{+\infty} [t^{-2} + t^{-3} + \cdots + t^{-n}]\,dt = 1 + \frac{1}{2} + \cdots + \frac{1}{n-1}.$$

HINT: In (b) set $t = 1 + \alpha$.

Remark. The value of the constant $\Gamma'(1)$ is known as Euler's constant. It is denoted by $+\gamma$, where $\gamma = 0.5772157 \cdots$.

(d) From the results of (b) and (c), prove that

$$\frac{\Gamma'(n)}{\Gamma(n)} = -\gamma + 1 + \frac{1}{2} + \frac{1}{3} + \cdots + \frac{1}{n-1}.$$

8. (a) From the fact that $\displaystyle\int_0^{+\infty} \frac{y^{n-1}}{1+y}\,dy = \frac{\pi}{\sin n\pi}$, show that

$$\Gamma(n) \cdot \Gamma(1-n) = \frac{\pi}{\sin n\pi}.$$

(b) From (a) prove

$$\Gamma\!\left(\frac{1}{n}\right)\Gamma\!\left(\frac{2}{n}\right) \cdots \Gamma\!\left(\frac{n-1}{n}\right) = \frac{(2\pi)^{(n-1)/2}}{\sqrt{n}}.$$

(c) From (b) show that

$$\sum_{k=1}^{n} \log \Gamma\!\left(\frac{k}{n}\right) \cdot \frac{1}{n} = \left(\frac{1}{2} - \frac{1}{2n}\right)\log 2\pi - \frac{1}{2}\frac{\log n}{n}.$$

(d) From (c) show $\int_0^1 \log \Gamma(x)\,dx = \log \sqrt{2\pi}$.
HINT: In (d) let $1/n = \Delta_n x$. Then let $n \to +\infty$.

37. Beta Function. The integral

$$\int_0^1 x^{m-1}(1-x)^{n-1}\,dx \tag{1}$$

converges for m and n positive and so defines a function of m and n called the *Beta function:*

$$B(m, n) = \int_0^1 x^{m-1}(1-x)^{n-1}\,dx. \quad (m > 0, n > 0) \tag{2}$$

Evidently $B(m, n)$ is symmetric in m and n, that is,

$$B(m, n) = B(n, m), \tag{3}$$

for the transformation $x = 1 - y$ reduces (2) to

$$B(m, n) = \int_0^1 (1-y)^{m-1} y^{n-1}\,dy = \int_0^1 (1-x)^{m-1} x^{n-1}\,dx \tag{4}$$
$$= B(n, m).$$

As in the case of the Gamma function, various forms of the Beta function may be derived by a change of variable. Thus, if in (2) we set $x = y/a$, where a is a constant, then

$$B(m, n) = \frac{1}{a^{m+n-1}} \int_0^a y^{m-1}(a - y)^{n-1} \, dy; \tag{5}$$

if in (2) we place $x = \sin^2 \psi$, we have

$$B(m, n) = 2 \int_0^{\pi/2} \sin^{2m-1} \psi \cos^{2n-1} \psi \, d\psi; \tag{6}$$

if we set $x = y/(y + 1)$, we find that

$$B(m, n) = \int_0^{+\infty} \frac{y^{m-1}}{(1 + y)^{m+n}} \, dy. \tag{7}$$

38. Relations between Gamma and Beta Functions. From (9) of Sec. 36, we have

$$\Gamma(m)\Gamma(n) = 4 \int_0^{+\infty} x^{2n-1} e^{-x^2} \, dx \int_0^{+\infty} y^{2m-1} e^{-y^2} \, dy$$

$$= 4 \int_0^{+\infty} \int_0^{+\infty} x^{2n-1} y^{2m-1} e^{-x^2-y^2} \, \partial x \, dy. \tag{1}$$

This double integral is to be taken over the first quadrant of the xy-plane. With polar coordinates, (1) may be written

$$\Gamma(m)\Gamma(n) = 4 \int_0^{\pi/2} \int_0^{+\infty} r^{2(m+n-1)} e^{-r^2} \sin^{2m-1} \theta \cos^{2n-1} \theta \, r \, \partial r \, d\theta$$

$$= 4 \int_0^{\pi/2} \int_0^{+\infty} r^{2(m+n)-1} e^{-r^2} \sin^{2m-1} \theta \cos^{2n-1} \theta \, \partial r \, d\theta. \tag{2}$$

From (9) and (6), we find

$$\Gamma(m)\Gamma(n) = B(m, n)\Gamma(m + n). \tag{3}$$

Hence

$$B(m, n) = \frac{\Gamma(m)\Gamma(n)}{\Gamma(m + n)}. \tag{4}$$

Example 1. $\int_0^1 5(1 - x)^{\frac{1}{2}} x^3 \, dx = 5B(\tfrac{3}{2}, 4) = \dfrac{5\Gamma(\frac{3}{2})\Gamma(4)}{\Gamma(\frac{11}{2})}.$

Since $\Gamma(\tfrac{3}{2}) = \tfrac{1}{2}\Gamma(\tfrac{1}{2})$, $\Gamma(\tfrac{1}{2}) = \sqrt{\pi}$, $\Gamma(4) = 3!$,

$$\Gamma(\tfrac{11}{2}) = \tfrac{9}{2} \cdot \tfrac{7}{2} \cdot \tfrac{5}{2} \cdot \tfrac{3}{2} \cdot \tfrac{1}{2}\sqrt{\pi},$$

we find

$$\int_0^1 5(1 - x)^{\frac{1}{2}} x^3 \, dx = \tfrac{32}{63}.$$

Example 2.   Evaluate the Dirichlet integral

$$I = \iiint_R x^{l-1}y^{m-1}z^{n-1}\, \partial x\, \partial y\, dz \tag{5}$$

over that portion of the first octant which is bounded by the ellipsoid $(x^2/a^2) + (y^2/b^2) + (z^2/c^2) = 1$ and the coordinate planes.

To simplify matters, we shall let $x^2 = a^2\xi$, $y^2 = b^2\eta$, $z^2 = c^2\zeta$. Then our problem is to evaluate

$$I = \frac{a^l b^m c^n}{8} \iiint_R \xi^{\frac{l}{2}-1}\, \eta^{\frac{m}{2}-1}\, \zeta^{\frac{n}{2}-1}\, \partial \xi\, \partial \eta\, d\zeta$$

over the octant bounded by the coordinate planes and $\xi + \eta + \zeta = 1$. Putting in the limits and integrating, we have

$$I = \frac{a^l b^m c^n}{8} \int_0^1 \int_0^{1-\xi} \int_0^{1-\xi-\eta} \xi^{\frac{l}{2}-1}\, \eta^{\frac{m}{2}-1}\, \zeta^{\frac{n}{2}-1}\, \partial \zeta\, \partial \eta\, d\xi$$

$$= \frac{2a^l b^m c^n}{8n} \int_0^1 \int_0^{1-\xi} \xi^{\frac{l}{2}-1}\, \eta^{\frac{m}{2}-1}\, (1 - \xi - \eta)^{\frac{n}{2}}\, \partial \eta\, d\xi.$$

By (5) of Sec. 37 this can be written

$$I = \frac{a^l b^m c^n}{4n} \int_0^1 \xi^{\frac{l}{2}-1}\, (1 - \xi)^{\frac{m+n}{2}}\, B\!\left(\frac{m}{2}, \frac{n}{2} + 1\right) d\xi.$$

By (2) of Sec. 37 and (4), this is equal to

$$I = \frac{a^l b^m c^n}{4n} B\!\left(\frac{l}{2}, \frac{m+n}{2} + 1\right) B\!\left(\frac{m}{2}, \frac{n}{2} + 1\right)$$

$$= \frac{a^l b^m c^n}{8} \frac{\Gamma(l/2)\Gamma(m/2)\Gamma(n/2)}{\Gamma\!\left(\dfrac{l + m + n}{2} + 1\right)}. \tag{6}$$

If $l = 1$, $m = 1$, $n = 1$, the integral (5) gives the volume of an octant of the above ellipsoid:

$$V = \frac{abc}{8} \frac{\Gamma(\tfrac{1}{2})\Gamma(\tfrac{1}{2})\Gamma(\tfrac{1}{2})}{\Gamma(\tfrac{5}{2})} = \frac{\pi abc}{6}.$$

If $l = 3$, $m = 1$, $n = 1$, (5) gives the moment of inertia of this volume with respect to the yz-plane:

$$I_{yz} = \iiint_R x^2\, \partial x\, \partial y\, dz = \frac{a^3 bc}{8} \frac{\Gamma(\tfrac{3}{2})\Gamma(\tfrac{1}{2})\Gamma(\tfrac{1}{2})}{\Gamma(\tfrac{7}{2})} = \frac{\pi a^3 bc}{30}.$$

EXERCISES XXVII

1. Verify (5) of Sec. 37.

2. Prove that if integral (5) be taken over the octant bounded by a portion of the surface

$$\left(\frac{x}{a}\right)^p + \left(\frac{y}{b}\right)^q + \left(\frac{z}{c}\right)^r = 1$$

and the three coordinate planes, then (5) is

$$I = \frac{a^l b^m c^n}{pqr} \frac{\Gamma(l/p)\Gamma(m/q)\Gamma(n/r)}{\Gamma\left(\dfrac{l}{p} + \dfrac{m}{q} + \dfrac{n}{r} + 1\right)}. \tag{7}$$

3. Prove

(a) $\displaystyle\int\int_R x^{l-1} y^{m-1}\, \partial x\, dy = a^l b^m h^{l+m} \frac{\Gamma(l)\Gamma(m)}{\Gamma(l+m+1)},$ over $\dfrac{x}{a} + \dfrac{y}{b} \leqq h.$

(b) $\displaystyle\int\int_R x^{l-1} y^{m-1}\, \partial x\, dy = \frac{a^l b^m}{pq} \frac{\Gamma(l/p)\Gamma(m/q)}{\Gamma\left(\dfrac{l}{p} + \dfrac{m}{q} + 1\right)} h^{\frac{l}{p}+\frac{m}{q}},$

$$\text{over } \left(\frac{x}{a}\right)^p + \left(\frac{y}{b}\right)^q \leqq h.$$

PART G.   NUMERICAL INTEGRATION

39. Numerical Integration. By Theorem 13.1, the evaluation of $S_a^b f(x)\, dx$ depends upon the determination of an explicit representation of the function $\int f(x)\, dx$. It often happens that it is inconvenient or impossible to obtain such a representation of $\int f(x)\, dx$; for example, $f(x)$ may be given by a complicated formula or merely by a table of values for certain values of x. In such a case it is necessary to rely on certain formulas which give an accurate approximation to $S_a^b f(x)\, dx$. We shall now derive some of the most useful of these formulas.

It is evident that

$$\int_{-l/2}^{l/2} f(c + x)\, dx = \int_{-l/2}^{0} f(c + x)\, dx + \int_{0}^{l/2} f(c + x)\, dx.$$

Replace x by $x' - (l/2)$ in the second integral and by $(l/2) - x'$ in the third. Then

$$\int_{-l/2}^{l/2} f(c + x)\, dx$$
$$= \int_{0}^{l/2} \left[f\left(c + \frac{l}{2} - x\right) + f\left(c - \frac{l}{2} + x\right) \right] dx. \tag{1}$$

We define $\varphi(x)$ and $\varphi_k(x)$ by the relations

$$\varphi(x) = f\left(c + \frac{l}{2} - x\right) + f\left(c - \frac{l}{2} + x\right);$$

$$\varphi_k(x) = (-1)^k \frac{d^k\varphi(x)}{dx^k}$$

$$= f^{(k)}\left(c + \frac{l}{2} - x\right) + (-1)^k f^{(k)}\left(c - \frac{l}{2} + x\right),$$

where $k = 1, 2, 3, \cdots$. If we evaluate the second integral in (1) by repeated integration by parts, we find that

$$\int_{-l/2}^{l/2} f(c + x) \, dx = [(x + B_1 l)\varphi(x)]_0^{l/2} + \int_0^{l/2} (x + B_1 l)\varphi_1(x) \, dx$$

$$= [(x + B_1 l)\varphi(x)]_0^{l/2} + \frac{1}{2!}[(x^2 + 2B_1 lx + B_2 l^2)\varphi_1(x)]_0^{l/2}$$

$$+ \frac{1}{3!}[(x^3 + 3B_1 lx^2 + 3B_2 l^2 x + B_3 l^3)\varphi_2(x)]_0^{l/2} + \cdots , \quad (2)$$

where the B's are arbitrary constants.

To obtain formulas useful for computational purposes, we shall require the B's to be such that upon making the substitution $x = l/2$ in (2), the coefficient of $\varphi_k(l/2)$ is 0 for every even k, $\varphi_k(l/2)$ itself being 0 for every odd k. We are thus led to the conditions

$$\tfrac{1}{2} + B_1 = 0, \qquad \tfrac{1}{8} + \tfrac{3}{4}B_1 + \tfrac{3}{2}B_2 + B_3 = 0,$$
$$\tfrac{1}{32} + \tfrac{5}{16}B_1 + \tfrac{10}{8}B_2 + \tfrac{10}{4}B_3 + \tfrac{5}{2}B_4 + B_5 = 0, \qquad \cdots , \qquad (3)$$

and under these conditions (2) reduces to the form

$$\int_{-l/2}^{l/2} f(c + x) \, dx = -\left[B_1 l\varphi(0) + \frac{B_2 l^2}{2!}\varphi_1(0) + \frac{B_3 l^3}{3!}\varphi_2(0) \right.$$
$$\left. + \frac{B_4 l^4}{4!}\varphi_3(0) + \cdots \right]. \quad (4)$$

Let $\psi(r) = f(c + rl) + f(c - rl)$. Then

$$\frac{d^k\psi(r)}{dr^k}\bigg]_{r = -\frac{1}{2}} = (-l)^k\varphi_k(0).$$

If we expand $\psi(r)$ by Taylor's series about $r = -\frac{1}{2}$, we find that

$$\psi(r) = \varphi(0) - Rl\varphi_1(0) + \frac{R^2 l^2}{2!}\varphi_2(0) - \frac{R^3 l^3}{3!}\varphi_3(0) + \cdots , \quad (5.1)$$

where $R = r + \frac{1}{2}$. Likewise, if $S = s + \frac{1}{2}$, $T = t + \frac{1}{2}$, $\cdots$, then

$$\psi(s) = \varphi(0) - Sl\varphi_1(0) + \frac{S^2l^2}{2!}\varphi_2(0) - \cdots, \qquad (5.2)$$

$$\psi(t) = \varphi(0) - Tl\varphi_1(0) + \frac{T^2l^2}{2!}\varphi_2(0) - \cdots, \qquad (5.3)$$

and so on. If we multiply (5.1) by $-Kl/2$, (5.2) by $-Ll/2$, (5.3) by $-Ml/2$, $\cdots$, and add the results to (4), we obtain the formula

$$\int_{-l/2}^{l/2} f(c + x)\, dx = \frac{l}{2}[K\psi(r) + L\psi(s) + M\psi(t) + \cdots]$$

$$- \left[l\left(B_1 + \frac{A_0}{2}\right)\varphi(0) + l^2\left(\frac{B_2}{2!} - \frac{A_1}{2}\right)\varphi_1(0) \qquad (6) \right.$$

$$\left. + l^3\left(\frac{B_3}{3!} + \frac{A_2}{2\cdot 2!}\right)\varphi_2(0) + l^4\left(\frac{B_4}{4!} - \frac{A_3}{2\cdot 3!}\right)\varphi_3(0) + \cdots \right]$$

$$= \frac{l}{2}\{K\psi(r) + L\psi(s) + \cdots\}$$

$$- [b_0\varphi(0) + b_1\varphi_1(0) + b_2\varphi_2(0) + \cdots], \qquad (7)$$

where

$$A_0 = K + L + M + \cdots,$$
$$A_1 = KR + LS + MT + \cdots, \qquad (8)$$
$$A_2 = KR^2 + LS^2 + MT^2 + \cdots, \qquad \cdots$$

We impose the additional requirement on the B's, $K, L, M, \cdots$ that

$$b_0 = b_2 = b_4 = b_6 = b_8 = \cdots = 0. \qquad (9)$$

It follows from (3) and (9) that

$$
\begin{array}{ll}
1 + 2B_1 = 0, & B_1 = -\tfrac{1}{2}A_0, \\
B_1 + 3B_2 + 2B_3 = 0, & B_3 = -\tfrac{3}{2}A_2, \\
B_2 + 4B_3 + 5B_4 + 2B_5 = 0, & B_5 = -\tfrac{5}{2}A_4, \qquad (10) \\
B_3 + 5B_4 + 9B_5 + 7B_6 + 2B_7 = 0, & B_7 = -\tfrac{7}{2}A_6,
\end{array}
$$

$\cdots\cdots\cdots\cdots\cdots\cdots\cdots\cdots\cdots\cdots\cdots\cdots\cdots$

Hence

$$B_2 = A_2 + \tfrac{1}{6}A_0, \qquad B_4 = A_4 + A_2 - \tfrac{1}{30}A_0,$$
$$B_6 = A_6 + \tfrac{5}{2}A_4 - \tfrac{1}{2}A_2 + \tfrac{1}{42}A_0, \qquad \cdots. \qquad (11)$$

Let $\beta_k(x)$ denote the kth Bernoulli polynomial,* i.e.,

$$\beta_0(x) = 1, \qquad\qquad\qquad \beta_4(x) = x^4 - 2x^3 + x^2 - \tfrac{1}{30},$$
$$\beta_1(x) = x - \tfrac{1}{2}, \qquad\qquad \beta_5(x) = x^5 - \tfrac{5}{2}x^4 + \tfrac{5}{3}x^3 - \tfrac{1}{6}x,$$
$$\beta_2(x) = x^2 - x + \tfrac{1}{6}, \qquad \beta_6(x) = x^6 - 3x^5 + \tfrac{5}{2}x^4 - \tfrac{1}{2}x^2 + \tfrac{1}{42},$$
$$\beta_3(x) = x^3 - \tfrac{3}{2}x^2 + \tfrac{1}{2}x, \qquad \cdots \cdots \cdots \cdots \cdots \cdots \cdots \cdots$$

Then by (6) and (7)

$$b_k = \beta_{k+1}(A)\frac{l^{k+1}}{(k+1)!}, \qquad (k \text{ odd}) \quad (12)$$

where $\beta_{k+1}(A)$ denotes the result of substituting A_i for x^i in the $(k+1)$th Bernoulli polynomial $\beta_{k+1}(x)$; e.g.,

$$\beta_2(A) = A_2 - A_1 + \tfrac{1}{6}A_0.$$

Thus (6) reduces to

$$\int_{-l/2}^{l/2} f(c+x)\, dx = \frac{l}{2}\{K\psi(r) + L\psi(s) + \cdots\}$$
$$- \sum_{\text{odd } k}\beta_{k+1}(A)\frac{l^{k+1}}{(k+1)!}\varphi_k(0). \quad (13)$$

If we let $\gamma_{k+1}(x) = \beta_{k+1}(x + \tfrac{1}{2})$, so that

$$\gamma_0(x) = 1,$$
$$\gamma_2(x) = x^2 - \tfrac{1}{12},$$
$$\gamma_4(x) = x^4 - \tfrac{1}{2}x^2 + \tfrac{7}{240},$$
$$\gamma_6(x) = x^6 - \tfrac{5}{4}x^4 + \tfrac{7}{16}x^2 - \tfrac{31}{1344},$$
$$\gamma_8(x) = x^8 - \tfrac{7}{3}x^6 + \tfrac{49}{24}x^4 - \tfrac{31}{48}x^2 + \tfrac{127}{3840},$$
$$\cdots \cdots \cdots \cdots \cdots \cdots \cdots \cdots \cdots \cdots$$

then

$$\beta_{k+1}(A) = K\beta_{k+1}(R) + L\beta_{k+1}(S) + \cdots$$
$$= K\gamma_{k+1}(r) + L\gamma_{k+1}(s) + \cdots, \qquad (14)$$

and (13) may be written in the form

$$\int_{-l/2}^{l/2} f(c+x)\, dx = \frac{l}{2}\{K\psi(r) + L\psi(s) + \cdots\}$$
$$- \sum_{\text{odd } k}\frac{l^{k+1}}{(k+1)!}\{K\gamma_{k+1}(r) + L\gamma_{k+1}(s) + \cdots\}\varphi_k(0), \quad (15)$$

* See Steffensen, "Interpolation," Sec. 13.

where, by the first equations in (10), the only condition on $K, L, M, \cdots$ is that

$$A_0 \equiv K + L + M + \cdots + P = 1. \tag{16}$$

If there are ν constants $K, L, \cdots, P$, there remain $\nu - 1$ conditions to impose on $K, L, \cdots, P$. Let

$$b_1 = b_3 = b_5 = \cdots = b_{2\nu-3} = 0. \tag{17}$$

By (15),

$$K\gamma_2(r) + L\gamma_2(s) + \cdots + P\gamma_2(w) = 0,$$
$$K\gamma_4(r) + L\gamma_4(s) + \cdots + P\gamma_4(w) = 0,$$
$$\cdots \cdots \cdots \cdots \cdots \cdots \cdots \cdots \cdots \cdots$$
$$K\gamma_{2\nu-2}(r) + L\gamma_{2\nu-2}(s) + \cdots + P\gamma_{2\nu-2}(w) = 0. \tag{18}$$

By (16) and (18), $K = \Delta_1/\Delta$, where*

$$\Delta = \begin{vmatrix} 1 & 1 & \ldots & 1 \\ \gamma_2(r) & \gamma_2(s) & \ldots & \gamma_2(w) \\ \gamma_4(r) & \gamma_4(s) & \ldots & \gamma_4(w) \\ \cdots & \cdots & \cdots & \cdots \\ \gamma_{2\nu-2}(r) & \gamma_{2\nu-2}(s) & \ldots & \gamma_{2\nu-2}(w) \end{vmatrix},$$

$$\Delta_1 = \begin{vmatrix} 1 & 1 & 1 \\ 0 & \gamma_2(s) & \ldots & \gamma_2(w) \\ 0 & \gamma_4(s) & \ldots & \gamma_4(w) \\ \cdots & \cdots & \cdots \\ 0 & \gamma_{2\nu-2}(s) & \ldots & \gamma_{2\nu-2}(w) \end{vmatrix}. \tag{19}$$

Because each polynomial $\gamma_{2m}(x)$ contains terms of only even degree, the first term being x^{2m}, Δ and Δ_1 reduce to

$$\Delta = \begin{vmatrix} 1 & 1 & \ldots & 1 \\ r^2 & s^2 & \ldots & w^2 \\ \cdots & \cdots & \cdots \\ r^{2\nu-2} & s^{2\nu-2} & \ldots & w^{2\nu-2} \end{vmatrix},$$

$$\Delta_1 = \begin{vmatrix} s^2 - a_2 & t^2 - a_2 & \cdots & w^2 - a_2 \\ s^4 - a_4 & t^4 - a_4 & \cdots & w^4 - a_4 \\ \cdots & \cdots & \cdots & \cdots \\ s^{2\nu-2} - a_{2\nu-2} & t^{2\nu-2} - a_{2\nu-2} & \cdots & w^{2\nu-2} - a_{2\nu-2} \end{vmatrix}, \tag{20}$$

where $a_2 = \dfrac{1}{2^2 \cdot 3}$, $a_4 = \dfrac{1}{2^4 \cdot 5}$, $\cdots$, $a_{2m} = \dfrac{1}{2^{2m}(2m+1)}$,

* See Sec. 4 of Chap. VI.

In particular, we have

$$
\begin{cases} \nu = 1, \\ K = 1, \end{cases} \quad
\begin{cases} \nu = 2, \\ K = \dfrac{s^2 - a_2}{s^2 - r^2}, \end{cases} \quad
\begin{cases} \nu = 3, \\ K = \dfrac{s^2 t^2 - a_2(s^2 + t^2) + a_4}{(s^2 - r^2)(t^2 - r^2)}, \end{cases}
$$

$$
\begin{cases} \nu = 4, \\ K = \dfrac{s^2 t^2 u^2 - a_2(s^2 t^2 + s^2 u^2 + t^2 u^2) + a_4(s^2 + t^2 + u^2) - a_6}{(s^2 - r^2)(t^2 - r^2)(u^2 - r^2)}. \end{cases}
$$

The other coefficients, L, M, $\cdots$ result from suitable permutations of r, s, t, $\cdots$.

So far, r, s, t, $\cdots$ have been arbitrary. By specializing them we obtain all the well-known Newton-Cotes, Steffensen, and Gauss quadrature formulas. For example, if we take $\nu = 1$, $r = \frac{1}{2}$, we obtain from (15) the Euler-Maclaurin formula:

$$
\int_{-l/2}^{l/2} f(c + x)\, dx = \frac{l}{2}\left[f\left(c + \frac{l}{2}\right) + f\left(c - \frac{l}{2}\right) \right]
$$
$$
- \sum_{\text{odd } k} \frac{l^{k+1} B_{k+1}}{(k+1)!}\left[f^{(k)}\left(c + \frac{l}{2}\right) - f^{(k)}\left(c - \frac{l}{2}\right) \right], \quad (21)
$$

where the first term is called the trapezoidal rule, and where the B's are the Bernoulli numbers:

$$
B_2 = \gamma_2(\tfrac{1}{2}) = \beta_2(1) = \tfrac{1}{6}, \qquad B_4 = -\tfrac{1}{30}, \qquad B_6 = \tfrac{1}{42}, \qquad \cdots.
$$

If we write $c - \dfrac{l}{2} = x_0, c + \dfrac{l}{2} = x_1, f\left(c - \dfrac{l}{2}\right) = y_0, f\left(c + \right)\dfrac{l}{2} = y_1,$

$\cdots$ and apply (21) to successive intervals $[x_0, x_1]$, $[x_1, x_2]$, $\cdots$, $[x_{n-1}, x_n]$, and add the results, we find that

$$
\int_a^b f(x)\, dx = \frac{h}{2}(y_0 + 2y_1 + 2y_2 + \cdots + 2y_{n-1} + y_n)
$$
$$
- \sum_{\text{odd } k} \frac{h^{k+1} B_{k+1}}{(k+1)!}[y_n^{(k)} - y_0^{(k)}], \quad (22)
$$

where h is the common interval length $x_1 - x_0$. If we take $\nu = 2$, $r = \frac{1}{2}$, $s = 0$, we obtain from (15) Uspenski's formula:

$$
\int_{-l/2}^{l/2} f(c + x)\, dx = \frac{l}{6}(y_0 + 4y_1 + y_2)
$$
$$
- \sum_{\text{odd } k > 1} \frac{l^{k+1}}{(k+1)!}\left[\frac{1}{3}\gamma_{k+1}\left(\frac{1}{2}\right) + \frac{2}{3}\gamma_{k+1}(0) \right][y_2^{(k)} - y_0^{(k)}], \quad (23)
$$

where the first term is called Simpson's rule. It is seen that $\gamma_{2m}(0) = \left(1 - \dfrac{1}{2^{2m-1}}\right)B_{2m}$. If we apply (23) to successive intervals, $[x_0, x_2], [x_2, x_4], \cdots, [x_{2n-2}, x_{2n}]$, and add the results, we find that

$$\int_a^b f(x)\ dx = \frac{h}{3}(y_0 + 4y_1 + 2y_2 + 4y_3 + 2y_4 + \cdots$$
$$+ 2y_{2n-2} + 4y_{2n-1} + y_{2n})$$
$$- \sum_{\text{odd } k>1} \frac{(2h)^{k+1}}{(k+1)!}\left(1 - \frac{1}{3 \cdot 2^{k-1}}\right)B_{k+1}(y_{2n}^{(k)} - y_0^{(k)}), \quad (24)$$

where h is the common interval length $x_1 - x_0$. A formula to be used in Chap. III is obtained by taking $\nu = 2$, $r = \frac{1}{4}$, $s = 0$ in (15). Omitting the remainder, we have

$$\int_{x_0}^{x_4} f(x)\ dx = \frac{4h}{3}(2y_1 - y_2 + 2y_3), \quad (25)$$

where h is the common interval length $x_1 - x_0$. Gauss's formulas are obtained from (15) by specializing $r, s, t, \cdots$ so that additional b's are zero.

It should be observed that (15) is a perfectly general formula for the case where the ordinates y_i are spaced symmetrically about the mid-point of the interval $[-l/2, l/2]$. For further special cases of (15) see: Steffensen, "Interpolation," Sec. 16; Whittaker and Robinson, "Calculus of Observations." Questions relating to the convergence of the series in (15) may be dealt with by including the remainder term in (2) and (5).

Asymmetric formulas may be obtained by forming linear combinations of (15). For example,

$$2\int_{x_0}^{x_1} f(x)\ dx = \int_{x_0}^{x_2} f(x)\ dx - \int_{x_1}^{x_2} f(x)\ dx + \int_{x_0}^{x_1} f(x)\ dx. \quad (26)$$

By (21) and (23), we have (omitting remainder terms)

$$\int_{x_0}^{x_1} f(x)\ dx = \frac{1}{2}\left[\frac{h}{3}(y_0 + 4y_1 + y_2) - \frac{h}{2}(y_1 + y_2) + \frac{h}{2}(y_0 + y_1)\right]$$
$$= \frac{h}{12}(5y_0 + 8y_1 - y_2). \quad (27)$$

This formula is more accurate than the first term of (21) and avoids the necessity of introducing extra points of division, such as $x_{\frac{1}{2}}$. [While (21) was used in deriving (27), much of the error attendant upon omitting the remainder in (21) is made up because (26) involves the *difference* between the last two terms in it.]

EXERCISES XXVIII

In the following exercises use both (22) and (24). Take two different values of n, say $n = 3$ or 4 and $n = 10$, and use sufficiently many remainder terms to attain the required accuracy. Compare the amounts of labor involved in each computation.

1. Evaluate $\mathrm{S}_1^{10} \dfrac{1}{x} \, dx$ to compute $\log_e 10 = 2.30258509.$

2. Evaluate $\mathrm{S}_0^1 \dfrac{1}{1 + x^2} \, dx$ to compute $\tan^{-1} 1 = \dfrac{\pi}{4} = 0.78539816.$

3. Evaluate $2/\sqrt{\pi} \, \mathrm{S}_0^1 \, e^{-x^2} \, dx.$ *Ans.* 0.84270080.

4. Evaluate each of the following to eight decimals:

(a) $\mathrm{S}_0^2 \sqrt{4 + x^3} \, dx.$ (b) $\mathrm{S}_0^{\pi/4} \log_{10} \cos x \, dx.$ (c) $\mathrm{S}_0^{\pi/2} \sqrt{\sin x} \, dx.$

5. Use a mean-value theorem for integrals to show that

(a) $\displaystyle \int_{x_0}^{x_1} f(x) \, dx = \dfrac{h}{2}(y_0 + y_1) - \dfrac{h^3}{12} f''(\xi), \qquad x_0 < \xi < x_1.$

(b) $\displaystyle \int_{x_0}^{x_2} f(x) \, dx = \dfrac{h}{3}(y_0 + 4y_1 + y_2) - \dfrac{h^5}{90} f^{(4)}(\xi), \qquad x_0 < \xi < x_2.$

6. Find expressions, similar to those in Ex. 5, for the remainder after m terms of the summation in (22) and (24).

CHAPTER III

ORDINARY DIFFERENTIAL EQUATIONS

PART A. ELEMENTARY TYPES

1. Introduction. In many branches of mathematics, mechanics, physics, and chemistry, there arise equations involving derivatives or differentials. Such equations are called *differential equations*. The following are typical differential equations:

$$\frac{dy}{dt} = ky. \tag{1}$$

$$\frac{d^2y}{dt^2} + p^2y = C. \tag{2}$$

$$L\frac{d^2y}{dt^2} + R\frac{dy}{dt} + Dy = E \sin pt. \tag{3}$$

$$\frac{\partial^2 y}{\partial t^2} = a^2\frac{\partial^2 y}{\partial x^2}. \tag{4}$$

$$\frac{\partial^2 T}{\partial x^2} + \frac{\partial^2 T}{\partial y^2} = 0. \tag{5}$$

$$\frac{\partial^2 v}{\partial x^2} + \frac{\partial^2 v}{\partial y^2} + \frac{\partial^2 v}{\partial z^2} = k\frac{\partial v}{\partial t}. \tag{6}$$

Equation (1) appears in the study of the disintegration of radioactive substances and in various problems of growth; equation (2) is involved in the study of simple harmonic motion; (3) occurs in the study of oscillating mechanical and electrical systems; (4) represents the transverse vibrations of a stretched string; (5) is used to obtain the lines of force and lines of constant potential in electrostatics and hydrodynamics; and (6) is the equation for the conduction of heat through an isotropic medium.

In this chapter we shall give a few elementary methods for solving equations which involve only ordinary derivatives, and in Chap. VII we shall take up the question of solving equations containing partial derivatives. Many physical applications of differential equations will be given in the exercises.

2. Definitions.　Differential equations which involve but one independent variable are called *ordinary*. For example, equations (1), (2), and (3) are ordinary. Differential equations which involve two or more independent variables, such as (4), (5), and (6), are called *partial*.

A differential equation is said to be of *order n* if it involves* a derivative of order n and no derivative of higher order. The *degree* of a differential equation is the degree to which the highest order derivative enters into the equation after the equation has been made rational and integral in all of its derivatives.

A function $y = p(x)$ is said to be a *solution* of the differential equation

$$f(x, y, y') = 0 \tag{1}$$

if, upon substituting $p(x)$ and $p'(x)$ for y and y' in (1), f is transformed into a function of x which is identically zero for all values of x, i.e., if

$$f(x, p(x), p'(x)) \equiv 0. \tag{2}$$

This definition can be readily extended to differential equations of higher order. Thus,

$$y = 3e^{-x} + x - 2 \tag{3}$$

is a solution of

$$y'' + 2y' + y = x, \tag{4}$$

for when

$$y' = -3e^{-x} + 1 \quad \text{and} \quad y'' = 3e^{-x}$$

are substituted in (4), we obtain the identity

$$3e^{-x} + 2(-3e^{-x} + 1) + (3e^{-x} + x - 2) \equiv x.$$

Again, the equation†

$$y^3 + y - x = 0, \tag{5}$$

which defines y as a function of x, $y = p(x)$, determines $y = p(x)$ as a solution of

$$(3x - 2y)y' = y, \tag{6}$$

---

* For example, we do not consider the equation $0\dfrac{d^3y}{dx^3} + y\dfrac{dy}{dx} = 1$ as involving $\dfrac{d^3y}{dx^3}$.

† Equations in x and y are usually regarded as defining y as a function of x. For a rigorous statement, see Sec. 20 of Chap. I.

for when y' is obtained from (5) as a function of x and y, say $y' = q(x, y)$, and y' then substituted in (6) with y replaced by $p(x)$, then (6) reduces by means of (5) to an identity in x. In general we shall say that the equation $F(x, y) = 0$ *furnishes a solution* of $f(x, y, y') = 0$ when $F(x, y) = 0$ defines y as a function of x, $y = p(x)$, such that $y = p(x)$ is a solution of $f(x, y, y') = 0$. In such a case it is often convenient to call *the equation* $F(x, y) = 0$ a solution of $f(x, y, y') = 0$, though actually what we mean is that $F(x, y) = 0$ defines y as a function $p(x)$ which is really the solution of $f(x, y, y') = 0$.

The question is of considerable importance as to whether or not a given differential equation has a solution. But we shall have to postpone consideration of this question with the bare statement that the existence of solutions to many general types of differential equations has been established.

EXERCISES I

1. State the order and degree of each of the following:
(a) Each of the equations in Sec. 1.

(b) $d^2y/dx^2 = y\sqrt{3 + (dy/dx)^4}$.   (c) $y\left(\dfrac{dy}{dx}\right)^2 = 3x\dfrac{dy}{dx}$.

(d) $\dfrac{dy}{dx} + 3y + \left[\dfrac{3}{d^2y/dx^2}\right] = 0$.   (e) $10^{y^2} - yy' = 0$.

2. Construct a differential equation of the second degree and third order. Construct a differential equation to which the idea of degree is inapplicable.

3. Show that the following differential equations have the solutions indicated:
(a) $y'' - 7y' + 10y = 0$; $y = e^{5x}$.
(b) $4y(y')^2 - 2xy + y = 0$; $y^2 - x + 1 = 0$.

(c) $x^2\dfrac{\partial z}{\partial x} + y\dfrac{\partial z}{\partial y} = 2y^2$; $z = y^2 + 2ye^{1/x}$.

(d) $\dfrac{\partial^2 T}{\partial x^2} + \dfrac{\partial^2 T}{\partial y^2} = 0$; $T = \log{(x^2 + y^2)} + \mathrm{Tan}^{-1}\dfrac{y}{x}$.

(e) $\dfrac{\partial^2 w}{\partial x^2} + \dfrac{\partial^2 w}{\partial y^2} = 0$; $w = \varphi(x + iy) + \psi(x - iy)$, where $i^2 = -1$, and where φ and ψ are arbitrary differentiable functions.

4. When is the function $y = p(x)$ a solution of the nth order differential equation $f(x, y, y', y'', \cdots, y^{(n)}) = 0$?

5. Define a solution $z = p(x, y)$ of the partial differential equation

$$f(x, y, z, z_x, z_y, z_{xx}, z_{xy}, \cdots) = 0.$$

Extend this definition to a more general type of differential equation.

6. Let

$$\varphi(x, y, t, \dot{x}, \dot{y}) = 0,$$
$$\psi(x, y, t, \dot{x}, \dot{y}) = 0,$$

be a system of first order differential equations with t the independent variable. (The symbols $\dot{x}$ and $\ddot{x}$ are frequently used in dynamics for dx/dt and d^2x/dt^2.) Define the term solution for this system. Extend this definition to a more general system of differential equations.

7. In the study of the steady-state flow of heat in a sphere, the Fourier equation (6) of Sec. 1 reduces to

$$\frac{d}{dr}\left(r^2 \frac{dT}{dr}\right) = 0, \tag{7}$$

where T is the temperature at any point in the sphere at distance r from the center and is independent of the time. Show that $T = A + \dfrac{B}{r}$ is a solution of (7), where A and B are arbitrary constants.

8. Show that $x = (w^2/a) \log \cosh (at/w)$ is a solution of the differential equation

$$m\ddot{x} = ma - mk(\dot{x})^2, \tag{8}$$

where a, k, m, and $w = \sqrt{a/k}$ are constants.

Equation (8) represents the motion of a particle of constant mass m along a straight line when it is acted on by a constant force and is subject to resistance proportional to the square of the velocity. In this equation x is the distance of the particle from a fixed point on the line of motion, $\dot{x}$ and $\ddot{x}$ denote dx/dt and d^2x/dt^2, ma represents the constant force acting on the particle which would produce the uniform acceleration a, $mk(\dot{x})^2$ is the force of the resistance opposing the motion of the particle and acts in the direction opposite to that of the force ma, and $m\ddot{x}$ is the resultant of the forces ma and $mk(\dot{x})^2$. What is k?

9. (a) State the differential equation for the motion of a particle of mass m if it moves along a straight line under the action of a constant force ma and is subject to a force of resistance proportional to the velocity. Show that $x = \dfrac{a(e^{-kt} + kt - 1)}{k^2}$ is a solution of this equation. Find a formula for the speed and acceleration at any time t.

(b) State the differential equation for the motion of the particle in part (a) when it is subject to no resistance. Find a solution of this equation.

10. Show that

$$x = (u \cos \alpha)\frac{1 - e^{-kt}}{k}, \qquad y = -\frac{gt}{k} + (ku \sin \alpha + g)\frac{1 - e^{-kt}}{k^2}$$

is a solution of the system

$$m\ddot{x} = -km\dot{x}, \qquad m\ddot{y} = -km\dot{y} - gm, \tag{9}$$

where k, g, and u are constants.

This system of differential equations represents the motion of a projectile fired with initial velocity u in a vertical plane at an angle α with the horizontal x-axis. The student should give the physical interpretation of each term in (9).

11. The system of differential equations

$$\frac{\partial^2 \xi}{\partial t^2} = -g\frac{\partial \eta}{\partial x}, \qquad \eta = -h\frac{\partial \xi}{\partial x} \tag{10}$$

occurs in the study of tidal waves and of wave motion in a canal. In these equations t denotes time, g is the acceleration due to gravity, h is the original depth of the water, and ξ and η are the horizontal and vertical displacements of a particle on the surface of the water which was originally at position x From (10) show that

$$\frac{\partial^2 \xi}{\partial t^2} = gh\frac{\partial^2 \xi}{\partial x^2}. \tag{11}$$

Show that

$$\xi = \varphi(ct + x) + \psi(ct - x) \tag{12}$$

is a solution of (11), where $c^2 = gh$, and where φ and ψ are arbitrary differentiable functions. Show that $\xi = 2\lambda \sin (nwx/l) \cos (nwct/l)$ is a solution of (11), where λ, c, n, w, and l are constants, and show that this solution may be expressed in the form (12). Give at least three other solutions of (11).

3. Primitives. If we differentiate the function

$$y = x^2 + ax + b \tag{1}$$

twice, we obtain the result

$$y'' = 2. \tag{2}$$

Thus we eliminate a and b from (1) by differentiating it twice. Again, if

$$y = A \sin (px - q), \tag{3}$$

then

$$\frac{dy}{dx} = Ap \cos (px - q), \qquad \frac{d^2y}{dx^2} = -Ap^2 \sin (px - q),$$
$$\frac{d^3y}{dx^3} = -Ap^3 \cos (px - q). \tag{4}$$

Hence

$$\frac{d^2y}{dx^2} = -p^2y, \qquad \frac{d^3y}{dx^3} = -p^2\frac{dy}{dx},$$

and elimination of p^2 leads to the result

$$\frac{d^3y}{dx^3} = \frac{1}{y}\frac{dy}{dx}\frac{d^2y}{dx^2}. \tag{5}$$

Thus we may eliminate the three constants from (3) by differentiating it three times.   In general, if

$$f(x, y, c) = 0 \tag{6}$$

is a relation defining y as a function of x and involving an arbitrary constant c, and if we differentiate (6) with respect to x, obtaining

$$f_1(x, y, c) \equiv \frac{\partial f(x, y, c)}{\partial x} + \frac{\partial f(x, y, c)}{\partial y} \frac{dy}{dx} = 0, \tag{7}$$

then we may (generally) eliminate c from (6) and (7) to obtain a relation

$$\varphi(x, y, y') = 0 \tag{8}$$

not involving c.   More generally, if we differentiate the relation

$$f(x, y, c_1, c_2, \cdots, c_n) = 0 \tag{9}$$

n times, and if (9) defines y as a function of x, then we may (see Sec. 20 of Chap. I) eliminate the arbitrary constants $c_1, \cdots, c_n$ from the resulting equations to obtain a relation

$$\varphi(x, y, y', y'', \cdots, y^{(n)}) = 0 \tag{10}$$

not involving these constants.

We say that (9) is the *primitive* of (10).   Thus, in particular, (1) is the primitive of (2) and (3) is the primitive of (5).   We say that the arbitrary constants $c_1, \cdots, c_n$ in (9) are *dependent*[*] if it is possible to write an equation

$$g(x, y, b_1, \cdots, b_m) = 0 \tag{11}$$

with arbitrary constants $b_1, \cdots, b_m$ such that $m < n$ and such that any function y of x obtainable from (9) by assigning values to the c's is obtainable from (11) by assigning values to the b's. For example, the equation $y = c_1 \log x^{c_2}$ can be reduced to $y = b \log x$ by the substitution $b = c_1 c_2$. We say that the c's in (9) are *independent* if they are not dependent.

It is seen that a primitive involving n independent constants leads, in general, to an nth order differential equation, and such a primitive is always a solution of the differential equation constructed from it, provided of course that the primitive defines y as a function of x.   Conversely, it can be shown that, in general,

---

[*] This meaning of dependent must be distinguished from that intended in the sentence "y is dependent upon x."

any nth order differential equation has a solution involving n independent constants; such a solution is called a *complete primitive* or *general solution* of the given differential equation. Any solution derived from a complete primitive by assigning particular values to the constants in it is called a *particular integral*.

Thus, a complete primitive of $y = xy' + \dfrac{1}{y'}$ is $y = cx + \dfrac{1}{c}$, and $y = 2x + \frac{1}{2}$ and $y = x + 1$ are examples of particular integrals.

Sometimes a differential equation has solutions which are not included in a complete primitive. Such solutions are sometimes called *singular* and will be considered later. We mention in passing that the problem of determining all solutions of a given differential equation requires great care. For example, a general solution of the equation $y' = 2y/x$ is $y = cx^2$. Yet the equation $y' = 2y/x$ has many solutions which are not included in the formula $y = cx^2$, one such solution being $y = f(x)$, where $f(x) = 3x^2$ when $x \geqq 0$ and $f(x) = -2x^2$ when $x < 0$. The reader should have no difficulty in constructing other such solutions. This example illustrates the fact that a general solution of a differential equation need not include all particular integrals of the equation. Moreover, a differential equation may sometimes have two or more different general solutions which represent different sets of particular integrals. It is seen that one must not attribute too much significance to the term general solution.

In physical, geometrical, and other problems which require the solving of a differential equation, *initial* or *boundary* conditions are imposed on the solution of the equation so as to obtain a particular integral which represents the specific physical, geometrical, or other conditions of the problem. For example, in Ex. I, 7, suppose the temperature is maintained at $T = T_1$ deg. over the shell $r = r_1$ and at $T = T_2$ deg. over the shell $r = r_2$. Substitution of these values in the solution $T = A + \dfrac{B}{r}$ determines numerical values $\bar{A}$ and $\bar{B}$ of the constants A and B, where

$$\bar{A} = \frac{T_2 r_2 - T_1 r_1}{r_2 - r_1}, \qquad \bar{B} = \frac{T_1 - T_2}{r_2 - r_1} r_1 r_2.$$

It follows that the particular integral $T = \bar{A} + \dfrac{\bar{B}}{r}$ represents the temperature in the sphere under the particular boundary conditions that T have the values T_1 and T_2 at r_1 and r_2. Again, the differential equation

$$\frac{d^2s}{dt^2} = g \tag{12}$$

represents the motion of a body falling freely under the action of gravity alone and has

$$s = \tfrac{1}{2}gt^2 + at + b \tag{13}$$

for a solution, where a and b are arbitrary constants, and g is the acceleration due to gravity. Suppose the body moves so that $s = s_0$ and the velocity $v = v_0$ at $t = t_0$. The particular integral of (12) representing the motion determined by these initial conditions is found by making the substitutions

$$s_0 = \tfrac{1}{2}gt_0^2 + at_0 + b, \qquad v_0 = gt_0 + a,$$

and solving for a and b. It is found that $a = v_0 - gt_0$ and $b = s_0 - \tfrac{3}{2}gt_0^2 - v_0t_0$. Hence the particular integral of (12) representing this particular motion is

$$s = \tfrac{1}{2}gt^2 + (v_0 - gt_0)t + (s_0 - \tfrac{3}{2}gt_0^2 - v_0t_0).$$

Again, the particular integral of $y' = 2y/x$ whose graph passes through the point (1,3) is found by substituting $x = 1$, $y = 3$ in the general solution $y = cx^2$. It is seen that $c = 3$, so that the particular integral determined by this boundary condition is $y = 3x^2$. In Ex. I, 11, a particular integral ξ is determined by the initial conditions of the wave motion, that is, the functions φ and ψ are determined by the initial configuration and velocity of the water. (The method for finding φ and ψ will be taken up later.)

Fig. 112.

Two types of constants sometimes appear in the solution of a differential equation: Constants of integration, which may be determined by initial conditions as illustrated above; and given constants of the problem. To illustrate this point, consider the following problem in the theory of electric circuits: A resistance of R ohms and a coil with a self-inductance of L henries are connected in series with a source of E volts e.m.f. It is known by experiment that the drop in potential across the coil is the coefficient of self-inductance L times the time rate of change of the current i flowing through the coil, and that the drop in potential across the resistance is the product of the resistance R and the current i. By Kirchhoff's law, the algebraic sum of all the potential drops around the entire circuit is zero. Hence

$$L\frac{di}{dt} + Ri = E \tag{14}$$

is the differential equation for the circuit. Suppose E, R, and L are constants. Then the current i at any time is given by the primitive

$$i = ce^{-Rt/L} + \frac{E}{R}, \tag{15}$$

where c is an *arbitrary* constant of integration, but where E, R, and L are determined by the physical objects composing the given electric circuit. Since there is only one arbitrary constant in (15), it requires only one initial condition to determine a particular integral of (14). If $i = i_0$ when $t = 0$, then c is determined by the relation $i_0 = c(1) + \frac{E}{R}$, and the particular integral determined by this condition is

$$i = \left(i_0 - \frac{E}{R}\right)e^{-Rt/L} + \frac{E}{R}.$$

No further initial condition can be imposed since E, R, and L are known beforehand.

EXERCISES II

1. Form differential equations having the following as primitives, A, B, a, k, and p being arbitrary constants:

(a) $y = Ae^{2x} + Be^{-2x}$. \qquad (b) $z = A \sin 5x + B \cos 5x$.
(c) $y = 10 \sin (pt - 30°)$. \qquad (d) $x^2 + y^2 = a^2$.

(e) The family of all parabolas whose axis is the x-axis.
(f) The family of tangents to the family of parabolas in (e).
(g) The family of all lines through the origin.
(h) The family of all circles whose centers are on the curve $y = 3x^2$.
(i) The family of all ellipses with foci at $(a, 0)$ and $(-a, 0)$.

2. Find a differential equation which may be interpreted as representing the geometric properties common to the family of parabolas $y = cx^2$. Plot a few curves of this family, say for $c = -3, -2, \cdots, 3$. Interpret geometrically the differential equation representing this family, and illustrate with the curves you have just plotted. What is the difference in

significance between the differential equation you have found and the equation $y' = 2cx$?

3. Form a first-order differential equation having $mx = \frac{1}{2}mgt^2$ as a primitive, where m and g are constants. Does this result contradict the general statement that n differentiations are needed to eliminate n constants from a primitive? Explain.

4. (a) Verify that $y = cx + \dfrac{1}{c}$ is a complete primitive of $y = xy' + \dfrac{1}{y'}$.

(b) Verify that $y^2 = 4x$ is a solution of $y = xy' + \dfrac{1}{y'}$.

(c) Plot the singular solution in (b) and several particular integrals in (a). What geometric relation does the singular solution have to these other solutions?

(d) Find the particular integral in (a) which passes through the point $(-\frac{5}{2}, 1)$.

5. Show that a general solution of $4(dy/dx)^2 = 9x$ is $(y + c)^2 = x^3$. Plot a few particular integrals, say for $c = -3, -2, \cdots, 3$. Show that $x = 0$ is an integral and plot. Discuss the relation between this integral and the other integrals. Find the integral curves which pass through the point $(3, 1)$.

6. Show that $y^2 + (x + c)^2 = 100$ is a solution of $y^2[1 + (dy/dx)^2] = 100$. Find the particular integrals which pass through $(6, 8)$. Plot a few integrals of this equation. Show that $y = \pm 10$ are solutions, plot, and discuss their relation to the other solutions.

7. Determine the number of independent parameters in the following families:

(a) $y = c_1 + x^2 - c_2$.   (b) $y = c_1 e^{x + c_2}$.

(c) $y = \log (c_1 x^2) + c_2$.   (d) $y = c_1 e^{3x}(c_2 \cos 2x + c_3 \sin 2x)$.

8. Find partial differential equations of lowest possible order having the following for primitives, c_1 and c_2 being arbitrary independent constants:

(a) $z = c_1 x + c_2 xy$.   (b) $z = c_1 \log (x^2 + y^2) + c_1 x^2 + c_2 y^2$.

9. (a) State the differential equation representing curves having the property that the slope at (x, y) is proportional to the square of the abscissa and inversely proportional to the ordinate. The order of this differential equation is one. How many initial conditions may be imposed on the general solution of this differential equation? Distinguish between the two types of constants appearing in this solution.

(b) Solve the differential equation in (a) and find the particular integral curve passing through $(1, 3)$ with slope 5.

10. (a) The acceleration of a certain particle moving in a straight line is proportional to the cube of the velocity. State the differential equation representing the motion, using the velocity v as the dependent variable. Solve this equation. Distinguish between the constants appearing in the solution. How many initial conditions may be imposed on this solution?

(b) Experiment shows that when the particle has a velocity of 2 ft. per second, the acceleration is 16 ft. per second per second in a direction opposed to the velocity. Find a formula for the velocity at any time t if $v = 3$ when $t = 1$.

(c) Using the result of part (b), find a formula for the distance traveled at any time t, given that this distance is 0 at $t = 1$.

11. Show that $s = A \cos bt$ is a solution of the differential equation $s'' + b^2 s = 0$ which represents simple harmonic motion. Determine the particular integral representing the motion when the maximum value attained by s is 3, this maximum value being attained at $t = 1$.

12. In connection with equation (14), suppose that $E = 100$, $R = 10$, and $L = 1$. If $i = 30$ at $t = 0$, what is the value of i at $t = 1$?

4. Equations of the First Order and First Degree. The problem of finding the solutions of a given differential equation is often very difficult. It is frequently impossible to obtain a solution in terms of a finite number of elementary functions. However, certain types of differential equations can be solved by ordinary integration. Perhaps the simplest of these types are equations of the form

$$M + N\frac{dy}{dx} = 0, \tag{1}$$

where $M \equiv M(x, y)$ and $N \equiv N(x, y)$ are functions of x and y. Since the two members of (1) are identical when $y = f(x)$ is a solution of (1), it follows that their integrals with respect to x are identical, i.e.,

$$\int \left(M + N\frac{dy}{dx} \right) dx = \int 0 \, dx = C'. \tag{2}$$

By Theorem 11.2 of Chap. II, (2) may be written as

$$\int M \, dx + N \, dy = C'. \tag{3}$$

[Because of the form of (3), it is sometimes convenient to write (1) in the form

$$M \, dx + N \, dy = 0, \tag{4}$$

it being understood that, while (3) is formally obtained from (4) by "integrating both sides," the rigorous justification for writing (3) is as indicated above]. If we can find a function $F(x, y)$ such that

$$\int M \, dx + N \, dy = F(x, y) + C'', \tag{5}$$

then a solution of (1) is given by the equation

$$F(x, y) = C, \qquad (C = C' - C'') \tag{6}$$

provided, of course, (6) defines y as a function of x. In the succeeding sections we describe methods for determining $F(x, y)$ in (6).

5. Exact Differential Equations. By Theorem 12.2 of Chap. II, there exists a function $F(x, y)$ satisfying (5) of the preceding section when and only when $M \, dx + N \, dy$ is exact, i.e., when and only when

$$\frac{\partial M(x, y)}{\partial y} \equiv \frac{\partial N(x, y)}{\partial x}. \tag{1}$$

A method is given in Sec. 12 of Chap. II for determining $F(x, y)$ when (1) holds.

Example.   Solve the equation $(2x - y) \, dx + (3y^2 - x) \, dy = 0$.
It is seen that this differential is exact. As indicated in Sec. 12 of Chap. II,

$$\int (2x - y) \, dx + (3y^2 - x) \, dy = x^2 - xy + y^3 + C'.$$

Hence a solution of the given differential equation is given by

$$x^2 - xy + y^3 = C.$$

EXERCISES III

Show that the following differential equations are exact, and solve:
1. $(12x + 5y - 9) \, dx + (5x + 2y - 4) \, dy = 0$.
2. $(e^y + 1) \cos x \, dx + e^y \sin x \, dy = 0$.
3. $2 \sin 2x \cos y \, dx + \cos 2x \sin y \, dy = 0$.

4. $\dfrac{y}{x} \, dx + (y^2 + \log x) \, dy = 0$.

5. $\dfrac{2xt + 1}{t} \, dx + \dfrac{t - x}{t^2} \, dt = 0$.

6. $\dfrac{1 + v^2}{u^3} \, du - \dfrac{v(u^2 + 1)}{u^2} \, dv = 0$.

7. $\dfrac{dx}{\sqrt{x^2 + y^2}} + \dfrac{dy}{y} = \dfrac{x \, dy}{y \sqrt{x^2 + y^2}}$.

8. When one obtains (3) from (4) in Sec. 4 by "integrating both sides," is one integrating with respect to x or y, or both x and y at once?   Explain.

9. In what sense can we say that $F(x, y)$ is an integral of $M \, dx + N \, dy$ in (5) of Sec. 4?   (See Sec. 12 of Chap. II.)   Does the validity of (5) depend

on the fact that y is being determined as a function of x by (1)?   Define exactly what is meant by a solution of (3).   Explain fully why (6) gives a solution of (1).

6. Variables Separable.   *In the event that*

$$M\,dx + N\,dy = 0 \tag{1}$$

is not exact, then it is usually necessary to rewrite (1) *in such a form that it becomes exact.*   The simplest procedure is to multiply or divide both sides of (1) by such a function $\mu(x, y)$ (if it exists) that the coefficients of dx and dy become functions of x and y alone respectively, i.e., to reduce (1) to the form

$$f(x)\,dx + g(y)\,dy = 0. \tag{2}$$

It is seen that (2) is always exact, and hence is always integrable. (Cf. Ex. VIII, 10 of Chapter II.)   If (1) can be reduced to the form (2) by the above procedure, then we say that the variables are *separable* in (1).

Example.   Solve the equation $x^3 y^2\,dx - dy = 0$.
Upon dividing by y^2, we have

$$x^3\,dx - \frac{dy}{y^2} = 0.$$

Upon integrating we find that

$$\frac{x^4}{4} + \frac{1}{y} = C.$$

EXERCISES IV

1. Solve the following differential equations:

(a) $\dfrac{1}{x} - \tan y \dfrac{dy}{dx} = 0.$ (b) $y' = 2xy.$

(c) $x\sqrt{1 - y^2}\,dx + y\sqrt{1 - x^2}\,dy = 0.$

(d) $xy^2 + y\dfrac{dy}{dx} = x.$ (e) $x^3\,dy - 3(1 + x)y^2\,dx = 0.$

(f) $\cos x \sin^2 y\,dx + \sin^2 x\,dy = 0.$

2. Find those curves which have the property that the tangent to any curve of the family at (x_0, y_0), the line joining the origin and (x_0, y_0), and the x-axis together form an isoceles triangle.

3. The rate of decomposition of radium is proportional to the amount A of radium present.   If $\frac{1}{3}$ the original quantity A_0 disappears in 1600 years, what percentage disappears in 200 years?

4. The sum of $500 is deposited at 2 per cent interest, the interest being compounded each instant. How long will it take the deposit to amount to $1000?

5. Find an expression for the position s and the velocity v of a particle falling vertically under the action of gravity and subject to resistance proportional to the velocity. Determine the constants of integration to meet the initial conditions that $s = 0$ and $v = 0$ at $t = 0$. Find the limiting velocity that the particle can attain when allowed to fall a great distance.

6. Solve Ex. 5 when the resistance is proportional to the square of the velocity, given that the resisting force is 3 lb. per unit of mass of the particle when $v = 100$ ft. per second.

7. A tank contains 500 gal. of brine having 250 lb. of salt in solution. Pure water is running into the tank at the rate of 15 gal. per minute, and the mixture runs out at the same rate. How much salt is in the tank at the end of 3 hr.? (Assume that the water and solution are kept perfectly stirred.)

8. The rate at which a certain substance S dissolves is proportional to the amount A of undissolved S present, and also is proportional to the difference between the actual concentration c of S in the solvent and the saturated concentration y of S in the solvent.

(a) State the differential equation which represents the process of dissolving.

(b) A certain inert material contains 12 g. of sulphur which is to be removed by dissolving in benzol. It is known that $\frac{1}{3}$ of the sulphur can be extracted in 40 min. when 300 g. of benzol are used, and that this amount of benzol is saturated by 13 g. of sulphur. How much of the sulphur would be removed in 7 hr.? (In the above notation, $y = \frac{13}{300}$.)

7. Homogeneous Equations.

A function $f(x, y, z, \cdots, t)$ of any finite number of variables is called *homogeneous* in

$$x, y, z, \cdots, t$$

if the substitution of $\lambda x, \lambda y, \lambda z, \cdots, \lambda t$, respectively, for $x, y, z, \cdots, t$ multiplies the function by λ^n, that is, if

$$f(\lambda x, \lambda y, \lambda z, \cdots, \lambda t) \equiv \lambda^n \cdot f(x, y, z, \cdots, t), \qquad (1)$$

where λ ranges over all real numbers. The power n of λ in (1) is called the *order of homogeneity* of the function f. For example, $2xe^{y/z} - (y^3/x^2)$ is a homogeneous function of order 1, $\text{Tan}^{-1}(y/x)$ is homogeneous of order 0, and $(x^2 + y^2 + z^2)^{-3/2}$ is homogeneous of order -3. If in the equation

$$M(x, y) + N(x, y)\frac{dy}{dx} = 0, \qquad (2)$$

M and N are homogeneous of the same order, then equation (2) is called *homogeneous*.   Let us write (2) in the form

$$\frac{dy}{dx} = -\frac{M(x, y)}{N(x, y)}. \tag{3}$$

If M and N are homogeneous of the same degree, then (3) reduces* to the form

$$v + x\frac{dv}{dx} = \varphi(v) \tag{4}$$

upon substituting $y = vx$.   We may separate the variables in (4), obtaining

$$\frac{dv}{\varphi(v) - v} = \frac{dx}{x}, \tag{5}$$

from which we may obtain the solution immediately by integration.   Thus we have reduced the problem of solving a homogeneous equation to the case where the variables are separable.

Sometimes the substitution $x = vy$ is more convenient than the substitution $y = vx$; in this case we take the reciprocal of (3) before making the substitution $x = vy$.

Example.   Solve the equation $2x^2\, dy = (x^2 + y^2)\, dx$.

This equation is homogeneous of order 2.   If we let $y = vx$, we find that

$$\frac{2dv}{(v - 1)^2} = \frac{dx}{x},$$

whence

$$-\frac{2}{v - 1} = \log cx, \qquad \text{and} \qquad \frac{2x}{x - y} = \log cx.$$

8. Equations Reducible to Homogeneous Form.   Sometimes a differential equation may be reduced to homogeneous form by

---

* Since $M(u, v)$ and $N(u, v)$ are homogeneous of the same order,

$$-\frac{M(xu, xv)}{N(xu, xv)} = -\frac{x^n M(u, v)}{x^n N(u, v)} = -\frac{M(u, v)}{N(u, v)}.$$

Now set $u = 1$.   The left member of this equation becomes

$$-\frac{M(x, y)}{N(x, y)}$$

upon writing $y = vx$, and the right member becomes $- M(1, v)/N(1, v)$, which is a function φ of v alone.

changing the variables.   For example, if

$$\frac{dy}{dx} = \frac{a_1x + b_1y + c_1}{a_2x + b_2y + c_2}, \tag{1}$$

then the substitution $x = x_0 + u$, $y = y_0 + v$ reduces (1) to

$$\frac{dv}{du} = \frac{a_1u + b_1v + a_1x_0 + b_1y_0 + c_1}{a_2u + b_2v + a_2x_0 + b_2y_0 + c_2}. \tag{2}$$

If x_0 and y_0 are determined so that

$$a_1x_0 + b_1y_0 + c_1 = 0, \qquad a_2x_0 + b_2y_0 + c_2 = 0, \tag{3}$$

then (2) becomes

$$\frac{dv}{du} = \frac{a_1u + b_1v}{a_2u + b_2v}. \tag{4}$$

This equation is homogeneous and may be solved by the methods of the preceding section.

It should be noted that x_0 and y_0 are determined by (3) when and only when $a_1b_2 - a_2b_1 \neq 0$.   If $a_1b_2 - a_2b_1 = 0$, then $a_2/a_1 = b_2/b_1 = k$ (say).   Let $w = a_1x + b_1y$.   Then

$$\frac{dw}{dx} = a_1 + b_1\frac{w + c_1}{kw + c_2}. \tag{5}$$

This equation is evidently separable.   The substitution

$$w = a_2x + b_2y$$

is sometimes more convenient.

EXERCISES V

1. Which of the following functions are homogeneous in x and y?   State the order of homogeneity whenever possible.

(a) $2x^2y - xy\sqrt{x^2 - 4y^2}$.

(b) $3x^2y^3 + 2y^3\sqrt{x^2 - 1}$.

(c) $\frac{x^2}{y} + y(\log y - \log x)$.

(d) $\sqrt{3x}\ \mathrm{Tan}^{-1}(2y/x)$.

(e) $5(3x^2 - 4y^2)^{-\frac{1}{2}}$.

(f) $\frac{x}{y}e^{-3x^2/y^2}$.

2. Solve the following differential equations by the method of Sec. 7:

(a) $(xy - y^2)\,dx + x^2\,dy = 0$.

(b) $x^3\,dy = y^3\,dx$.

(c) $(x - 2\sqrt{xy})\dfrac{dy}{dx} - y = 0$.

(d) $\dfrac{dy}{dx} = \dfrac{x + y}{x - y}$.

(e) $xy\dfrac{dy}{dx} = x^2 + y^2$.

(f) $ye^{x/y} + x = y\dfrac{dx}{dy}$.

(g) $x(1 + e^{y/x}) \, dy + e^{y/x}(x - y) \, dx = 0.$

(h) $x \, dy = y \, dx + \sqrt{x^2 + y^2} \, dx.$

(i) $\left[x\left(\cos \dfrac{x}{y} \right) + y \right] dy = y\left(\cos \dfrac{x}{y} \right) dx.$

(j) $y\left(\dfrac{dy}{dx} \right)^2 + 2x\dfrac{dy}{dx} - y = 0.$

3. Solve the following differential equations by the method of Sec. 8:

(a) $\dfrac{dy}{dx} = \dfrac{x - y + 3}{x + y - 5}.$

(b) $\dfrac{dy}{dx} = \dfrac{6x - 2y - 7}{2x + 3y - 6}.$

(c) $\dfrac{dy}{dx} = \dfrac{x + y}{x + y + 1}.$

(d) $\dfrac{dy}{dx} = \dfrac{12x - 4y - 7}{3x - y + 4}.$

(e) $2\dfrac{dy}{dx} = \dfrac{y^2}{x^2} + \dfrac{y}{x}.$

4. If Equation (2) of Sec. 7 is homogeneous, show that it may be reduced to the case of variables separable by means of the substitutions $x = r \cos \theta$, $y = r \sin \theta$. Use this method to solve Ex. 2a, b, e.

5. (a) Find a substitution which will separate the variables in the equation

$$y\phi(xy) \, dx + x\psi(xy) \, dy = 0,$$

where ϕ and ψ are functions of the product xy.

(b) Use the method developed in part (a) to solve

$$(x^2y^3 + 2xy^2 - y) \, dx + 2x^2y \, dy = 0.$$

6. Develop a method for solving the equation

$$\frac{dy}{dx} = \varphi\left(\frac{a_1x + b_1y + c_1}{a_2x + b_2y + c_2} \right),$$

where φ is a function of the quantity indicated. Use this method to solve

$$\frac{dy}{dx} = \left(\frac{x + y - 1}{2x + 2y + 1} \right)^2.$$

7. (a) Prove the following theorem concerning the integral curves of a homogeneous differential equation $M \, dx + N \, dy = 0$:

If the points of the xy-plane are subjected to the transformation $x = kX$, $y = kY$, then each integral curve is carried into an integral curve.

(b) State and prove a theorem converse to the preceding theorem.

(c) Interpret geometrically the transformation $x = kX$, $y = kY$.

9. Linear Equations. An equation of the form

$$\frac{dy}{dx} + P(x)y = Q(x), \tag{1}$$

where P and Q are functions of x alone or are constants, is called a *linear* equation of the first order. To solve (1), we make (1) exact by multiplying both sides by $e^{\int P\,dx}$, obtaining

$$e^{\int P\,dx}\frac{dy}{dx} + e^{\int P\,dx}Py = e^{\int P\,dx}Q. \tag{2}$$

But the left member of (2) is itself exact, and

$$\int (e^{\int P\,dx}\,dy + e^{\int P\,dx}Py\,dx) = \int Qe^{\int P\,dx}\,dx. \tag{3}$$

Evaluation of the left member (see Sec. 5) leads to the result

$$ye^{\int P\,dx} = \int Qe^{\int P\,dx}\,dx + C, \tag{4}$$

so that

$$y = e^{-\int P\,dx}\int Qe^{\int P\,dx}\,dx + Ce^{-\int P\,dx}. \tag{5}$$

Example. Solve the equation $(dy/dx) + (y/x) = x^3$.
Here $P = 1/x$ and $Q = x^3$. If we multiply both sides by

$$e^{\int P\,dx} = e^{\log x} = x,$$

we obtain

$$x\frac{dy}{dx} + y \equiv \frac{d}{dx}(xy) = x^4.$$

Hence

$$xy = \int x^4\,dx + C' = \frac{x^5}{5} + C, \quad \text{and} \quad y = \frac{x^4}{5} + \frac{C}{x}.$$

10. Bernoulli's Equation. An equation of the form

$$\frac{dy}{dx} + P(x)y = Q(x)y^n, \tag{1}$$

where P and Q are functions of x alone, is known as a *Bernoulli equation*. To solve (1), let $z = y^{1-n}$. Then

$$\frac{dz}{dx} = (1 - n)y^{-n}\frac{dy}{dx}. \tag{2}$$

If we solve (2) for dy/dx and substitute in (1) we obtain

$$\frac{y^n}{1 - n}\frac{dz}{dx} + Py = Qy^n. \tag{3}$$

If we multiply both sides by $(1 - n)y^{-n}$ and substitute $z = y^{1-n}$, the result is

$$\frac{dz}{dx} + (1 - n)Pz = (1 - n)Q. \tag{4}$$

This equation is linear and may be solved by the method of Sec. 9.

Example. Solve the equation $x(dy/dx) + y = x^3y^3$.

Divide by x to put the equation in Bernoulli's form. Let $z = y^{-2}$. Since $dz/dx = -2y^{-3}(dy/dx)$, the given equation may be written in the form

$$\frac{dz}{dx} - \frac{2}{x}z = -2x^2.$$

Hence

$$z = -2x^3 + Cx^2.$$

Since $z = y^{-2}$, it follows that

$$-2x^3y^2 + Cx^2y^2 = 1.$$

EXERCISES VI

1. Solve the following equations by the methods of Secs. 9 and 10:

(a) $\dfrac{dy}{dx} + y \operatorname{ctn} x = \csc^2 x.$

(b) $(x - 2)\dfrac{dy}{dx} - 3y = (x - 2)^5.$

(c) $\dfrac{dy}{dx} + \dfrac{x}{1 + x^2}y = \dfrac{1}{x(1 + x^2)}.$

(d) $x \log x \, dy = (2 \log x - y) \, dx.$

(e) $(y + 2x^3)\dfrac{dx}{dy} = x.$

(f) $\dfrac{dy}{dx} + \dfrac{y}{x} - y^2 = 0.$

(g) $xy = \dfrac{dy}{dx} + y^3e^{-x^2}.$

(h) $xy' - 5y = x + 1.$

(i) $xy' = y \pm \sqrt{x^2 + y^2}.$

(j) $x \, dy + dx = e^{-y} \sec^2 y \, dy.$

(k) $\dfrac{dx}{dy} + \dfrac{2x}{y} = \dfrac{x^3}{y^3}.$

2. In the discussion of Sec. 9 and in the example following, no constant of integration was used in evaluating $\int P \, dx$. Justify this omission.

3. Develop a method for solving (a) $(dx/dy) + p(y)x = q(y)$, and (b) $(dx/dy) + \varphi(y)x = \psi(y)x^n$.

4. Show that Bernoulli's equation may be solved by means of the substitution $y = ve^{-\int P \, dx}$ inasmuch as this substitution separates the variables. Use this method to solve $(x^3y^2 + xy) \, dx = dy$.

5. An electric circuit consists of a constant resistance of R ohms and a coil of constant inductance of L henries in series with an electromotive force of E volts. In each of the following cases state and solve the differ-

ential equation for this circuit under the condition that the current $i = i_0$ amp. at time $t = t_0$ sec.

(a) $E = 0$.   (b) $E = E_0$.   (c) $E = E_0 \sin \omega t$, where E_0 and ω are constants.

Case (c) arises in the study of alternating currents; in this case $2\pi/\omega$ is the *period*, and E_0 the maximum value, of the electromotive force E.

Give the physical interpretation of your solution in each of the above cases.

6. A condenser of capacity C farads and a resistance of R ohms are connected in series with an electromotive force of E volts. It is known by experiment that the potential drop across the condenser is q/C volts, where q is the charge (measured in coulombs) on the condenser; it is also known that the current is the time rate of change of the charge q. State and solve the differential equation for this circuit to determine the charge and current under the condition that the charge $q = q_0$ coulombs at time $t = t_0$ sec. and (a) $E = 0$; (b) $E = E_0$; (c) $E = E_0 \sin \omega t$. Give the physical interpretation of each of your solutions.

11. Integrating Factors. We pointed out in Sec. 5 that the equation

$$M(x, y)\, dx + N(x, y)\, dy = 0 \tag{1}$$

may be integrated immediately if it is exact. In Secs. 6 and 9 we showed that, if (1) was not originally exact, then (1) could sometimes be made exact by multiplying by a suitable function $\mu(x, y)$; in Sec. 6 we chose $\mu(x, y)$ so as to separate the variables, and in Sec. 9 we took μ as $e^{\int P\, dx}$. This raises the question, can (1) always be made exact by multiplying by a suitable function $\mu(x, y)$? The answer is that, not only does there always exist a multiplier $\mu(x, y)$ which makes (1) exact, but there exist infinitely many such multipliers. However, we shall not prove this fundamental fact.

A multiplier $\mu(x, y)$ which makes (1) exact, i.e., which is such that $(\mu M)\, dx + (\mu N)\, dy$ is an exact differential, is called an *integrating factor*. While the existence of integrating factors is established, it is seldom easy to find them. However, experience has shown that it is well worth the trouble to try to determine such a factor by trial, for when one is found, the integration is relatively simple. Sometimes a change of variable will aid in effecting a solution.

Example. The factor $1/y^2$ makes

$$(3x^2 y^2 e^{x^3} + y)\, dx - x\, dy = 0 \tag{2}$$

exact, for application of this factor enables us to write (2) in the form

$$\frac{y\,dx - x\,dy}{y^2} = -3x^2 e^{x^3}\,dx.$$

Integration of this equation leads immediately to the result

$$\frac{x}{y} = -e^{x^3} + C.$$

Many rules have been devised for finding integrating factors. A few of the more common ones are included in the following exercises.

EXERCISES VII

1. Determine integrating factors for the following and integrate:
   (a) $(4x^2 y - 3y^2)\,dx + (x^3 - 3xy)\,dy = 0$.
   (b) $(x^4 e^x - 4xy^2)\,dx + 4x^2 y\,dy = 0$.

   (c) $(x + y)\,dx + (y - x)\,dy = 0$.   (d) $2x\,dx + (x^2 + y^2 + 2y)\,dy = 0$.

   (e) $(\sqrt{xy} - 1)x\,dy - (\sqrt{xy} + 1)y\,dx = 0$.
   (f) $(2x^2 + 3xy)\,dy + (3y^2 + 6xy + 3x^2)\,dx = 0$.

2. (a) Show that $1/u^2$, $1/v^2$, $1/(u^2 + v^2)$, $1/(u^2 - v^2)$, $1/uv$, $1/(u - v)^2$, $1/(u + v)^2$ are integrating factors of $v\,du - u\,dv = 0$.

   (b) Solve the equation $v\,du - u\,dv = 0$ using the seven integrating factors in (a). (The student is advised to keep a careful record of the results of this problem.)

3. Subject to certain mild restrictions on M and N, equation (1) is known to have a solution of the form $\varphi(x, y, c) = 0$, where c is an arbitrary constant. By Theorem 20.1 of Chap. I, the equation $\varphi(x, y, c) = 0$ defines c as a function of x and y, i.e., $c = \psi(x, y)$. By comparing equation (1) with the equation $d\psi = 0$, show the existence of an integrating factor $\mu(x, y)$ for (1).

4. (a) Show that if μ is an integrating factor of (1), then $k\mu$ is also an integrating factor, where k is any real number other than zero.

   (b) Show that if μ is an integrating factor of (1) leading to the solution $\psi(x, y) = c$, then $\mu g(\psi)$ is also an integrating factor of (1), where $g(\psi)$ is any single-valued continuous function of ψ.

   It follows from this result that, if (1) has an integrating factor, then (1) has infinitely many integrating factors.

5. If μ is an integrating factor of (1), show by the criterion for exactness that μ must satisfy the differential equation

$$M\frac{\partial u}{\partial y} - N\frac{\partial u}{\partial x} = \mu\left(\frac{\partial N}{\partial x} - \frac{\partial M}{\partial y}\right). \tag{3}$$

While μ might be found in some cases by solving (3), it is usually easier to solve (1) than (3).

6. Prove the following statements, including qualifying conditions where necessary:

(a) If (1) is homogeneous, then $1/(Mx + Ny)$ is an integrating factor for (1).

(b) The function $y^{-n}e^{(1-n)\int P\,dx}$ is an integrating factor of the Bernoulli equation $(dy/dx) + P(x)y = Q(x)y^n$, where P and Q are functions of x alone.

(c) The function $1/(Mx - Ny)$ is an integrating factor of (1) if $M = yg(xy)$ and $N = xh(xy)$, where g and h are functions of the product xy.

(d) The function $e^{\int\phi(x)\,dx}$ is an integrating factor of (1) when

$$\frac{1}{N}\left(\frac{\partial M}{\partial y} - \frac{\partial N}{\partial x}\right) \equiv \phi(x).$$

(e) State a theorem similar to (d), but in y instead of x.

(f) The function $x^{km-1-\alpha}y^{kn-1-\beta}$ is an integrating factor of

$$x^\alpha y^\beta(my\,dx + nx\,dy) = 0,$$

where k is arbitrary.   Determine k so that this function is an integrating factor of

$$x^{\alpha_1}y^{\beta_1}(m_1y\,dx + n_1x\,dy) + x^{\alpha_2}y^{\beta_2}(m_2y\,dx + n_2x\,dy) = 0.$$

7. Prove the following theorems, including any additional assumptions needed to insure the validity of these theorems:

(a) If a solution of (1) is known, then an integrating factor for (1) may be found.   State and prove the converse of this theorem.

(b) Let $f(x, y) = C$ and $g(x, y) = C$ be two solutions of (1).   Show that $g = \phi(f)$ or $f = \psi(g)$.   (Hint: Form the Jacobian of f and g.)   Show that any function of g, say $H(g)$, is also a solution of (1).   Would $H(f)$ be a solution?   Illustrate these results, using the equation $y\,dx - x\,dy = 0$. (See Ex. 2.)

(c) Let $f(x, y) = C$ be a solution of (1) obtained by means of the integrating factor $\mu(x, y)$.   Show that the normal derivative df/dn equals

$$\mu\sqrt{M^2 + N^2}.$$

(d) Show that, if μ and ν are any two integrating factors of (1), then either $\mu/\nu = C$ is a solution of (1) or μ/ν is identically a constant.

Hint: divide (3) by μ, and then write (3) in the form

$$M\frac{\partial\log\mu}{\partial y} - N\frac{\partial\log\mu}{\partial x} = \frac{\partial N}{\partial x} - \frac{\partial M}{\partial y}.$$

Repeat this operation with ν, and obtain the equation

$$M\frac{\partial\log\dfrac{\mu}{\nu}}{\partial y} - N\frac{\partial\log\dfrac{\mu}{\nu}}{\partial x} = 0.$$

Show that $F(x, y) = C$ is a solution of (1) when $MF_y - NF_x = 0$.   Prove the theorem from these results.

12. Equations of the First Order and nth Degree. The general first-order differential equation of arbitrary degree may be written in the form

$$F(x, y, p) = 0, \tag{1}$$

where we let p denote dy/dx, $p^2 = (dy/dx)^2$, etc. We give two methods for solving equations of this type.

Method I. If (1) can be factored in the form

$$[p - f_1(x, y)][p - f_2(x, y)] \cdots [p - f_n(x, y)] = 0, \tag{2}$$

then the solutions of the various equations

$$p - f_1(x, y) = 0, \quad \cdots, \quad p - f_n(x, y) = 0 \tag{3}$$

are solutions of (1). Methods for solving (3) have already been given in the preceding sections.

Example 1. Solve the equation $p^2 - 2xp + 2yp - 4xy = 0$.

This equation may be written in the form $(p - 2x)(p + 2y) = 0$. Upon integrating the equations

$$p - 2x = 0, \qquad p + 2y = 0,$$

we obtain as solutions of the given equation

$$y = x^2 + C, \qquad \log Cy = -2x.$$

Method II. In this method we eliminate p from (1) by a process somewhat similar to that indicated in Sec. 3. Suppose (1) is solvable for y in the form

$$y = g(x, p). \tag{4}$$

Differentiation of (4) with respect to x eliminates y and gives an equation

$$p = \frac{dg}{dx} = \frac{\partial g}{\partial x} + \frac{\partial g}{\partial p} \frac{dp}{dx} \tag{5}$$

of the first order in p and x. Suppose a solution of (5) is

$$G(x, p, C) = 0. \tag{6}$$

Elimination of p from (1) and (6) leads to an equation

$$\varphi(x, y, C) = 0 \tag{7}$$

which may be a solution of (1). It is necessary in every case to test (7) by substitution in (1) because the above process of elimination may introduce extraneous factors.

Example 2. Solve the equation $py - 2p^4 + 2 = 0$.

If we solve for y and differentiate with respect to x, we obtain

$$y = -2p^{-1} + 2p^3, \qquad p = (2p^{-2} + 6p^2)\frac{dp}{dx}. \tag{8}$$

If in the latter equation we separate the variables and integrate, we find that

$$x = 3p^2 - p^{-2} + C. \tag{9}$$

Elimination of p from this equation and the first equation (8) gives the desired solution. However, the following device is sometimes useful. In (9) and the first part of (8) let us formally substitute an arbitrary parameter u instead of p:

$$x = 3u^2 - u^{-2} + C, \qquad y = 2u^3 - 2u^{-1}. \tag{10}$$

Elimination of u from (10) leads to the same solution as obtained above. But (10) may be regarded as a parametric representation of this solution. Hence the equations

$$x = 3p^2 - p^{-2} + C, \qquad y = 2p^3 - 2p^{-1}, \tag{11}$$

in which p is regarded merely as an ordinary parameter, represent a solution of the given differential equation. In testing this solution by substitution in the given equation, we may utilize the fact that p is not only a parameter, but also denotes dy/dx.

If (1) is not solvable for y, it may be possible to differentiate (1) as it stands with respect to x, obtaining an equation

$$\Phi\left(x, y, p, \frac{dp}{dx}\right) = 0, \tag{12}$$

and to eliminate y from (1) and (12), obtaining an equation analogous to (5) in p and x alone.

A special case of (4) is *Clairaut's* equation

$$y = px + f(p). \tag{13}$$

Upon differentiating (13) with respect to x, we find that

$$[x + f'(p)]\frac{dp}{dx} = 0. \tag{14}$$

If we set $dp/dx = 0$, then $p = c$, and a solution of (13) is

$$y = cx + f(c). \tag{15}$$

Another solution of (13) is given by the parametric equations

$$x = -f'(p), \qquad y = -pf'(p) + f(p).$$

It is sometimes possible to eliminate x, instead of y, from (1) by differentiating with respect to y.

Example 3.   Solve the equation $p^2 + py - x = 0$.
If we solve for x and differentiate with respect to y, we find that

$$x = py + p^2, \qquad \frac{dx}{dy} \equiv \frac{1}{p} = p + y\frac{dp}{dy} + 2p\frac{dp}{dy}.$$

Hence

$$\left(\frac{1}{p} - p\right)\frac{dy}{dp} - y = 2p.$$

This is a linear equation of the first order, the solution of which we leave to the reader (see Sec. 9).

EXERCISES VIII

1. Solve the following differential equations by the methods of Sec. 12.

(a) $\left(\dfrac{dy}{dx}\right)^2 - \dfrac{dy}{dx} - 6 = 0.$ (b) $\left(\dfrac{dy}{dx}\right)^2 + 2x\dfrac{dy}{dx} = 3x^2.$

(c) $\left(\dfrac{dy}{dx}\right)^2 + (x+y)\dfrac{dy}{dx} + xy = 0.$ (d) $x\left(\dfrac{dy}{dx}\right)^2 + 2y\dfrac{dy}{dx} - x = 0.$

(e) $(dy/dx)^3 = 6x^4.$ (f) $x = yp + 4p^2.$

(g) $x - y\dfrac{dy}{dx}\left[2\left(\dfrac{dy}{dx}\right)^2 + 3\right] = 0.$ (h) $2px + y + \log p = 0.$

(i) $y^2 = 4(1 + p^2).$ (j) $x - y = 9 \log p.$

(k) $y - (1 + p)x = p^2.$ (l) $p = x^2 - 2xy + y^2.$

(m) $y = px + \operatorname{Sin}^{-1} p.$

2. A particle of mass m moves around a horizontal circle of radius a.   If its initial speed is V, and if it is resisted by the air with a force proportional to the square of the speed, then the motion of the particle is found by solving the differential equation $m\dfrac{d^2\theta}{dt^2} + \dfrac{ka}{m}\left(\dfrac{d\theta}{dt}\right)^2 = 0$, where θ is the angle of rotation of the radius vector through the particle.   Show that a solution of this equation is $\theta = \dfrac{m}{ka} \log\left[m + \dfrac{kVt}{m} \right].$

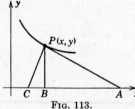

FIG. 113.

3. Show that (a) the length of the tangent $\overline{PA}$ to the curve $y = f(x)$ from the point of tangency $P(x, y)$ to the intersection A with the x-axis is $y\sqrt{1 + (dx/dy)^2}$.   (b) The length of the normal $\overline{PC}$ from P to the x-axis is $y\sqrt{1 + (dy/dx)^2}$.   (c) The length of the subtangent $\overline{AB}$ is $y\,dx/dy$.   (d) The length of the subnormal $\overline{BC}$ is $y\,dy/dx$.

4. Using the results of the preceding exercise, determine the curves C having the following properties:

(a) The subtangent at any point P on C is n times the abscissa of P. Find the particular curve of this family passing through the point (3, 4).

(b) The area of the right triangle formed by the tangent at P, the normal at P, and the x-axis, is inversely proportional to the slope of C at P.

(c) The area bounded by C, the x-axis, and any two ordinates, is equal to the length of C between these ordinates.

(d) The angle α between the radius vector and the tangent at the point (r, θ) is constant. $\left[\text{Hint: } \alpha = \tan^{-1}\left(r\frac{d\theta}{dr}\right). \right]$

(e) The polar subnormal at (r, θ) is proportional to sin θ.

(f) The subnormal is constant.

(g) The x-intercept of the tangent at (x, y) is kx.

(h) The length of the tangent is constant and equal to a. (This curve is called a *tractrix*, and represents the path of P when P pursues A with the same speed as A.)

PART B. LINEAR EQUATIONS

13. Linear Equations. A differential equation of order n is said to be *linear* if it is of the first degree in y and each of its derivatives. Such an equation can be written in the form

$$\frac{d^n y}{dx^n} + X_1\frac{d^{n-1}y}{dx^{n-1}} + \cdots + X_{n-1}\frac{dy}{dx} + X_n y = X, \qquad (A)$$

where $X_1, X_2, \cdots, X_n$ and X are functions of x alone or are constants. We shall denote the left member of (A) by $P(D)y$. If X is replaced by 0 in (A), the result

$$P(D)y \equiv \frac{d^n y}{dx^n} + X_1\frac{d^{n-1}y}{dx^{n-1}} + \cdots + X_{n-1}\frac{dy}{dx} + X_n y = 0 \quad (B)$$

is known as the *auxiliary* or *reduced* equation corresponding to the *complete* equation (A). We first state several theorems about the solutions of (A) and (B). It will appear that the solutions of (B) are intimately related to the solutions of (A).

Theorem 13.1. *If $y_1, y_2, \cdots, y_n$ are solutions of (B), so that $P(D)y_1 = 0, \cdots, P(D)y_n = 0$, then*

$$y = c_1 y_1 + c_2 y_2 + \cdots + c_n y_n \qquad (C)$$

is also a solution of (B), where $c_1, \cdots, c_n$ are arbitrary constants.

Since

$$\frac{d^k}{dx^k}(c_1 y_1 + \cdots + c_n y_n) = c_1\frac{d^k y_1}{dx^k} + \cdots + c_n\frac{d^k y_n}{dx^k},$$

it follows that

$$P(D)[c_1y_1 + \cdots + c_ny_n] = c_1P(D)y_1 + \cdots + c_nP(D)y_n. \quad (1)$$

By hypothesis, each term in the right member of (1) is 0. Hence the left member of (1) equals 0 and y is a solution of (B).

We say that $y_1, \cdots, y_n$ are *linearly independent* if there exists no set of numbers $c_1, \cdots, c_n$, not all zero, such that

$$c_1y_1 + c_2y_2 + \cdots + c_ny_n \equiv 0. \quad (2)$$

It follows that, if the y's in (C) are linearly independent, then the number of c's in (C) cannot be reduced without loss of generality. It can be shown that, if $X_1, \cdots, X_n$ in (B) are continuous over an interval I of the x-axis, then (B) has n, but not more than n, linearly independent solutions in this interval. It is for this reason that, the y's in (C) being linearly independent, we speak of these y's as a *fundamental set* of solutions, and we call (C) a *general solution* of (B); incidentally, we also speak of (C) as a *complementary function* for (A). A criterion that the y's in (C) be linearly independent is given by

THEOREM 13.2.   *A set of functions $y_1, \cdots, y_n$ of x are linearly independent when and only when the Wronskian*

$$\begin{vmatrix} y_1 & y_2 & \cdots & y_n \\ y_1' & y_2' & \cdots & y_n' \\ \cdot & \cdot & & \cdot \\ \cdot & \cdot & & \cdot \\ y_1^{(n-1)} & y_2^{(n-1)} & \cdots & y_n^{(n-1)} \end{vmatrix} \neq 0.$$

This theorem is an immediate consequence of a well-known theorem concerning homogeneous linear equations.   (See Chap. VI, Sec. 4.)

THEOREM 13.3.   *If $y_1, \cdots, y_n$ are linearly independent solutions of (B), and if Y is any particular solution of (A), then a general solution of (A) is*

$$y = c_1y_1 + \cdots + c_ny_n + Y. \quad (D)$$

Since $P(D)[c_1y_1 + \cdots + c_ny_n] = 0$ and $P(D)Y = X$, it follows that $P(D)y = X$.

14. Linear Equations with Constant Coefficients and X = 0. We shall here consider equations of the form (A) with the X's all constants and with $X = 0$, i.e., equations of the form

$$\frac{d^n y}{dx^n} + a_1 \frac{d^{n-1} y}{dx^{n-1}} + \cdots + a_{n-1} \frac{dy}{dx} + a_n y = 0. \tag{E}$$

Equations of this type occur very frequently, especially in the study of acoustical, mechanical, and electrical vibrations.

The case $n = 1$ has already been studied in Sec. 9; it is found by the methods of this section that the solution of the equation $(dy/dx) + a_1 y = 0$ is $y = ce^{-a_1 x}$. Let us next consider the case $n = 2$:

$$\frac{d^2 y}{dx^2} + a_1 \frac{dy}{dx} + a_2 y = 0. \tag{1}$$

The solution of the case $n = 1$ suggests the possibility that (1) has a solution of the form

$$y = ce^{mx}, \tag{2}$$

where c and m are constants. Substitution of (2) in (1) leads to the equation

$$ce^{mx}(m^2 + a_1 m + a_2) = 0. \tag{3}$$

It is seen that (2) is a solution of (1) when c is arbitrary and m is a root of

$$m^2 + a_1 m + a_2 = 0. \tag{4}$$

If m_1 and m_2 denote the roots of (4), and if c_1 and c_2 are arbitrary constants, then

$$y_1 = c_1 e^{m_1 x} \qquad \text{and} \qquad y_2 = c_2 e^{m_2 x} \tag{5}$$

are solutions of (1). By Theorem 13.1,

$$y = c_1 e^{m_1 x} + c_2 e^{m_2 x} \tag{6}$$

is a solution of (1). By Theorem 13.2, the solutions (5) are linearly independent if $m_1 \neq m_2$. Hence if $m_1 \neq m_2$, (6) is a general solution of (1). Equation (4) is called the *characteristic equation* of (1).

If $m_1 = m_2$, the solutions (5) are not linearly independent. To obtain a solution independent of (5), let $y = zy_1$, where $y_1 = c_1 e^{m_1 x}$ is one of the solutions (5). Since

$$\frac{dy}{dx} = y_1 \frac{dz}{dx} + z \frac{dy_1}{dx}, \qquad \frac{d^2 y}{dx^2} = y_1 \frac{d^2 z}{dx^2} + 2 \frac{dy_1}{dx} \frac{dz}{dx} + z \frac{d^2 y_1}{dx^2},$$

equation (1) may be written in the form

$$y_1 \frac{du}{dx} + \left(2\frac{dy_1}{dx} + a_1 y_1\right)u = 0, \tag{7}$$

where $u = dz/dx$ and where it is remembered that y_1 is a solution of (1). If we substitute $y_1 = c_1 e^{m_1 x}$ in (7) and divide by $c_1 e^{m_1 x}$, we find that

$$\frac{du}{dx} + (2m_1 + a_1) = 0.$$

Since $m_1 = m_2$, it follows by (4) that $m_1 = -\frac{1}{2}a_1$. Hence $du/dx = 0$, and $u = C_2$. But $u = dz/dx$, so that $z = C_2 x + C_3$. Therefore

$$y = zy_1 = (C_2 x + C_3)e^{m_1 x} \tag{8}$$

is a solution of (1). It follows by Theorem 13.2 that this solution is linearly independent of the solution $y_1 = c_1 e^{m_1 x}$. If we add these two solutions (and combine c_1 and C_3), then by Theorem 13.1,

$$y = (C_1 + C_2 x)e^{m_1 x} \tag{9}$$

is a general solution of (1) when the roots of (4) are equal.

With reference to the general equation (E), it is seen that

$$y = c_1 e^{m_1 x} + \cdots + c_n e^{m_n x} \tag{F}$$

is a solution of (E), where $m_1, \cdots, m_n$ are the roots of the characteristic equation

$$m^n + a_1 m^{n-1} + \cdots + a_n = 0 \tag{G}$$

of (E). If the roots of (G) are all distinct, then (F) is a general solution of (E). However, if (G) factors into the form

$$(m - m_1)^\alpha (m - m_2)^\beta \cdots (m - m_r)^\rho = 0,$$

so that $m_1, m_2, \cdots, m_r$ are roots of (G) of multiplicities α, $\beta, \cdots, \rho$, then a general solution of (E) is

$$y = (a_1 + a_2 x + \cdots + a_\alpha x^{\alpha-1})e^{m_1 x}$$
$$+ \cdots + (p_1 + p_2 x + \cdots + p_\rho x^{\rho-1})e^{m_r x}, \tag{H}$$

where $a_1, a_2, \cdots, a_\alpha; \cdots ; p_1, p_2, \cdots, p_\rho$ are arbitrary constants.

EXERCISES IX

1. Solve the following equations:

(a) $\dfrac{d^2y}{dx^2} - \dfrac{dy}{dx} - 6y = 0.$ *Ans.* $y = c_1e^{3x} + c_2e^{-2x}.$

(b) $\dfrac{d^2y}{dx^2} - 6\dfrac{dy}{dx} + 9y = 0.$ *Ans.* $y = (c_1 + c_2x)e^{3x}.$

(c) $\dfrac{d^3y}{dx^3} - 4\dfrac{dy}{dx} = 0.$

(d) $\dfrac{d^2y}{dx^2} - 4\dfrac{dy}{dx} + 13y = 0.$ *Ans.* $y = e^{2x}(c_1e^{3ix} + c_2e^{-3ix}).$

To change the form of this solution, write $e^{i\theta} = \cos\,\theta + i\,\sin\,\theta$ (see Chap. II, Sec. 5). Then the preceding solution may be written in the form

$$y = e^{2x}(A\cos 3x + B\sin 3x). \qquad (10)$$

But $A\cos\theta + B\sin\theta = \sqrt{A^2 + B^2}\left(\dfrac{A}{\sqrt{A^2 + B^2}}\cos\theta + \dfrac{B}{\sqrt{A^2 + B^2}}\sin\theta\right)$

$$= \lambda(\sin\,\psi\,\cos\,\theta + \cos\,\psi\,\sin\,\theta) = \lambda\,\sin\,(\psi + \theta),$$

where $\lambda = \sqrt{A^2 + B^2}$ and $\psi = \tan^{-1}(A/B).$ Hence (10) may be written as

$$y = \lambda e^{2x}\sin(3x + \psi), \qquad (11)$$

where λ and ψ are arbitrary constants.

(e) $\dfrac{d^2y}{dx^2} + 2\dfrac{dy}{dx} + 5y = 0.$ *Ans.* $y = \lambda e^{-x}\sin(2x + \psi).$

(f) $\dfrac{d^2y}{dx^2} + k^2y = 0.$

(g) $\dfrac{d^2y}{dx^2} - k^2y = 0.$

Ans. $y = \lambda\cosh(kx + \psi).$ (See Chap. II, Sec. 5, (2) and Ex. II, 7.)

(h) $\dfrac{d^3y}{dx^3} - \dfrac{d^2y}{dx^2} - \dfrac{dy}{dx} - y = 0.$ (i) $\dfrac{d^4y}{dx^4} + 4\dfrac{d^2y}{dx^2} + 4y = 0.$

(j) $\dfrac{d^3y}{dx^3} + \dfrac{d^2y}{dx^2} + \dfrac{dy}{dx} = 0.$ (k) $\dfrac{d^3y}{dx^3} + y = 0.$

(l) $\dfrac{d^4y}{dx^4} - 4\dfrac{d^3y}{dx^3} + 6\dfrac{d^2y}{dx^2} - 4\dfrac{dy}{dx} + y = 0.$

15. The Particular Integral.   Method of Undetermined Coefficients.

We now consider equations of the form

$$\frac{d^ny}{dx^n} + a_1\frac{d^{n-1}y}{dx^{n-1}} + \cdots + a_{n-1}\frac{dy}{dx} + a_ny = X, \qquad (\mathrm{I})$$

where X is a function of x alone. Since (E) is the reduced equation for (I), it follows that (F) or (H) is the complementary function for (I). By Theorem 13.3, a general solution of (I) is $y = y_c + Y$, where y_c denotes the function (F) or (H), and Y is a particular integral of (I). Thus, to solve (I), it remains merely to develop a method for finding Y. In Sec. 17 we shall outline a general procedure for determining Y; but in this section we shall give a much shorter method which may be used when the general form of Y is known beforehand. We begin with a simple numerical example.

The discussion of Sec. 17 below leads us to suspect that a particular integral of

$$\frac{d^2y}{dx^2} - 2\frac{dy}{dx} - 3y = e^{2x} + 3x \tag{1}$$

is a function of the form $Y = Ae^{2x} + Bx + C$. We wish to determine, if possible, the values of A, B, and C so that Y may satisfy (1). Since $dY/dx = 2Ae^{2x} + B$ and $d^2Y/dx^2 = 4Ae^{2x}$, we find upon substitution in (1) that the following identity must hold if Y is to be a solution of (1):

$$(-3A)e^{2x} + (-3B)x + (-2B - 3C) \equiv e^{2x} + 3x.$$

This will be an identity if

$$-3A = 1, \qquad -3B = 3, \qquad -2B - 3C = 0.$$

Hence $A = -\frac{1}{3}$, $B = -1$, $C = -\frac{2}{3}$, and a particular integral of (1) is

$$Y = -\tfrac{1}{3}e^{2x} - x - \tfrac{2}{3}.$$

Since the complementary function for (1) is $y_c = c_1e^{-x} + c_2e^{3x}$, a general solution of (1) is

$$y = c_1e^{-x} + c_2e^{3x} - \tfrac{1}{3}e^{2x} - x - \tfrac{2}{3}.$$

This example illustrates the method of *undetermined coefficients* for finding a particular integral of (I). In this method we construct a function $Y(x)$ whose form depends upon the form of X, and which involves coefficients A, B, $\cdots$. We then substitute Y in (I), and evaluate the coefficients A, B, $\cdots$ so that the result is an identity. The following table gives a few rules for constructing Y in certain cases.

I. If $X = b_0x^m + b_1x^{m-1} + \cdots + b_m$, and if the characteristic equation (G) has $m = 0$ as a root of multiplicity k, then

$$Y = x^k(A_0x^m + A_1x^{m-1} + \cdots + A_m).$$

(If, as is usually the case, $m = 0$ is not a root of (G), then we say that $m = 0$ is a root of multiplicity 0 (i.e., $k = 0$), $x^k = x^0 = 1$, and

$$Y = A_0x^m + A_1x^{m-1} + \cdots + A_m.)$$

II. If $Y = be^{ax}$, and if (G) has $m = a$ as a root of multiplicity k, then

$$Y = Ax^ke^{ax}.$$

III. If $X = b \sin ax$ or if $X = b \cos ax$, and if $(m^2 + a^2)$ is a factor of (G) of multiplicity k, then

$$Y = x^k(A \sin ax + B \cos ax).$$

IV. If $X = e^{ax}\psi(x)$, where ψ is some function of x, let $y = ze^{ax}$, divide by e^{ax}, and solve for z.

V. If $X = u_1(x) + \cdots + u_m(x)$, then Y is the sum of the functions constructed for the respective terms $u_1(x), \cdots, u_m(x)$.

EXERCISES X

1. Find the complementary, particular, and general solutions of the following equations:

(a) $\dfrac{d^2y}{dx^2} + 6\dfrac{dy}{dx} + 5y = e^{3x}$.   *Ans.* $y = c_1e^{-x} + c_2e^{-5x} + \dfrac{1}{32}e^{3x}$.

(b) $\dfrac{d^2y}{dx^2} - 2\dfrac{dy}{dx} - 8y = 4 \cos 2x$.

Ans. $y = c_1e^{4x} + c_2e^{-2x} - \tfrac{3}{10} \cos 2x - \tfrac{1}{10} \sin 2x$.

(c) $\dfrac{d^2y}{dx^2} - 6\dfrac{dy}{dx} + 5y = 5x^2 + 1$.

Ans. $y = c_1e^x + c_2e^{5x} + x^2 + \tfrac{12}{5}x + \tfrac{62}{5}$.

(d) $\dfrac{d^2y}{dx^2} + 3\dfrac{dy}{dx} = 4x^3 - 2$.

(e) $\dfrac{d^2y}{dx^2} - 4\dfrac{dy}{dx} + 4y = 3e^{2x}$.   (f) $\dfrac{d^2y}{dx^2} + 9y = 5 \sin 2x + 3 \cos 2x$.

(g) $\dfrac{d^2y}{dx^2} + 16y = x + 5 \cos 4x$.   (h) $\dfrac{d^2y}{dx^2} - 5\dfrac{dy}{dx} + 6y = x^2e^x$.

(i) $\dfrac{d^2y}{dx^2} + 3\dfrac{dy}{dx} = \sin^2 x$.   (j) $\dfrac{d^2y}{dx^2} + 6\dfrac{dy}{dx} + 9y = e^{3x} \sin 2x$.

2. In many practical problems, linear equations occur whose right-hand members are sines and cosines.   In such cases it is frequently convenient to regard these right-hand members as the real or imaginary components of complex exponentials (see Chap. V).   For example, to solve the equation

$$\frac{d^2y}{dx^2} - \frac{dy}{dx} - 2y = 3 \sin 2x, \tag{2}$$

write the equation

$$\frac{d^2u}{dx^2} - \frac{du}{dx} - 2u = 3 \cos 2x, \tag{3}$$

and after multiplying (2) by i and changing y to v, add (2) and (3), obtaining

$$\left(\frac{d^2u}{dx^2} - \frac{du}{dx} - 2u\right) + i\left(\frac{d^2v}{dx^2} - \frac{dv}{dx} - 2v\right) = 3(\cos 2x + i \sin 2x). \tag{4}$$

If we recall that $e^{i(2x)} = \cos 2x + i \sin 2x$, and if we let $w = u + iv$, then (4) may be written in the form

$$\frac{d^2w}{dx^2} - \frac{dw}{dx} - 2w = 3e^{2ix}. \tag{5}$$

A particular integral of (5) is found in the usual manner to be

$$w = -\frac{3e^{2ix}}{6 + 2i} = -\frac{3(3 - i)}{20}e^{2ix} = -\frac{3(3 - i)}{20}(\cos 2x + i \sin 2x)$$

$$= \frac{-9 \cos 2x - 3 \sin 2x}{20} + i\frac{3 \cos 2x - 9 \sin 2x}{20}.$$

Since $w = u + iv$ and since $y = v$, a particular integral of (2) is given by

$$Y = \frac{3 \cos 2x - 9 \sin 2x}{20}.$$

A general solution of (2) is $y = c_1e^{-x} + c_2e^{2x} + \dfrac{3 \cos 2x - 9 \sin 2x}{20}.$

Solve the following equations by the method illustrated above:

(a) $\dfrac{d^2y}{dx^2} - \dfrac{dy}{dx} - 2y = 3 \cos 2x.$

(b) $\dfrac{d^2y}{dx^2} + y = 5 \cos 3x + 7 \sin 2x.$

(c) $\dfrac{d^2y}{dx^2} + 4y = 4 \cos 10x.$

(d) $\dfrac{d^2y}{dx^2} + 5\dfrac{dy}{dx} + 7y = 4.$ (Hint: $4 = 4e^{0x}$.)

(e) $\dfrac{dy}{dx} + 5y = 7e^{2x} \sin 3x.$ (The right member is the imaginary component of $7e^{(2+3i)x}$.)

(f) $\dfrac{d^2y}{dx^2} + 8y = x \sin 3x.$ (The right member is the imaginary component of xe^{3ix}.)

16. Elastic Vibrations. Before we develop more general methods for solving linear equations, we give a few applications of these equations. The simplest application is in connection with

Simple Harmonic Motion. A variable x is said to vary in simple harmonic motion if it changes in such a manner that its acceleration is always proportional and opposite in sign to its instantaneous value. Simple harmonic motion is the simplest type of oscillatory motion about a position of equilibrium and is typical (at least to a first approximation) of the great majority of physical systems having one degree of freedom.

Simple harmonic motion may be represented by the differential equation

$$\frac{d^2x}{dt^2} = -\omega^2 x, \tag{1}$$

where $\omega^2 > 0$. A general solution of (1) is

$$x = A \cos \omega t + B \sin \omega t, \tag{2}$$

where A and B are arbitrary constants. This solution may be written in the form

$$x = C \cos (\omega t - \alpha), \tag{2'}$$

where

$$C = \sqrt{A^2 + B^2}, \qquad \alpha = \tan^{-1} \frac{B}{A}.$$

(Cf. Ex. IX, 1(d).)   Solution (2') shows that any given value of x occurs *periodically*, for consider the value of x at the following instants: t_0, $t_0 + \dfrac{2\pi}{\omega}$, $t_0 + \dfrac{4\pi}{\omega}$, $\cdots$, $t_0 + \dfrac{2k\pi}{\omega}$, $\cdots$, where k is any integer. It is seen that x has the same value at each of these instants since

$$C \cos \left[\omega \left(t_0 + \frac{2k\pi}{\omega} \right) - \alpha \right] = C \cos (\omega t_0 - \alpha)$$

for every integer value of k. The common interval of time $2\pi/\omega$ between these successive equal values of x is called the *period* of x. The constant C is called the *amplitude* of the motion, and α is the *phase* angle.

Damped Simple Harmonic Motion.   Suppose the variable x of
the preceding paragraph is subjected to some form of resistance
(mechanical, electrical, or otherwise) proportional to the velocity
and acting in the direction opposite that of the motion at any
instant.   This resistance may be represented by $-2\rho(dx/dt)$,
where $\rho > 0$, and the equation of motion may be reduced to the
form

$$\frac{d^2x}{dt^2} + 2\rho\frac{dx}{dt} + \omega^2 x = 0. \tag{3}$$

The coefficient 2ρ is known as the *coefficient of resistance.*   As an
example of a physical situation representable by (3) let us con-

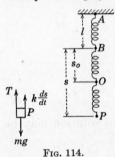

FIG. 114.

sider an elastic wire or spring of negligible
mass whose upper end is fixed at A and to
whose lower end P is attached a point particle
of mass m.   Let the natural length of the
spring be $l = \overline{AB}$, let $s_0 = \overline{BO}$ be the amount
the spring extends when supporting m while
at rest, and let $s = \overline{BP}$ be an arbitrary extension of the spring.   If the tension T in the
spring is proportional to the extension s,
then $T = \lambda s/l$, and in particular, $mg = \lambda s_0/l$.
Let P be displaced slightly from its position of equilibrium and
then released.   If f is a force of resistance proportional to the
velocity of P and acting in the direction opposite the motion of
P, then $f = -k\,ds/dt$, and the resultant force F acting on m is

$$F = mg - T - k\frac{ds}{dt}.$$

By Newton's second law of motion, $F = m\,d^2s/dt^2$.   Hence

$$m\frac{d^2s}{dt^2} = mg - T - k\frac{ds}{dt}. \tag{4}$$

But $mg - T = -(\lambda/l)(s - s_0) = -(\lambda/l)x$, where $x = s - s_0$.
Since $ds/dt = dx/dt$ and $d^2s/dt^2 = d^2x/dt^2$, (4) may be written
in the form

$$m\frac{d^2x}{dt^2} = -\frac{\lambda}{l}x - k\frac{dx}{dt}. \tag{5}$$

This reduces to (3) when we write $\omega^2 = \lambda/ml$, $2\rho = k/m$.

By Sec. 14 a solution of (3) is found to be

$$x = Ae^{(-\rho+\sqrt{\rho^2-\omega^2})t} + Be^{(-\rho-\sqrt{\rho^2-\omega^2})t}$$
$$= \bar{A}e^{-\rho t} \cosh(\sqrt{\rho^2-\omega^2}\,t + \bar{B}), \tag{6}$$

when $\rho^2 - \omega^2 \neq 0$, and

$$x = (A + Bt)e^{-\rho t} \tag{7}$$

when $\rho^2 - \omega^2 = 0$. The values of A and B, or of $\bar{A}$ and $\bar{B}$, are determined by the initial values of x and $v = dx/dt$. To discuss the variation of x with t we consider three cases:

(a) $\rho^2 > \omega^2$. In this case $\sqrt{\rho^2 - \omega^2}$ in (6) is real and not zero. If A and B are both positive, then x is always positive; moreover, $-\rho + \sqrt{\rho^2 - \omega^2}$ and $-\rho - \sqrt{\rho^2 - \omega^2}$ being both

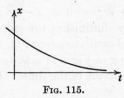

Fig. 115. 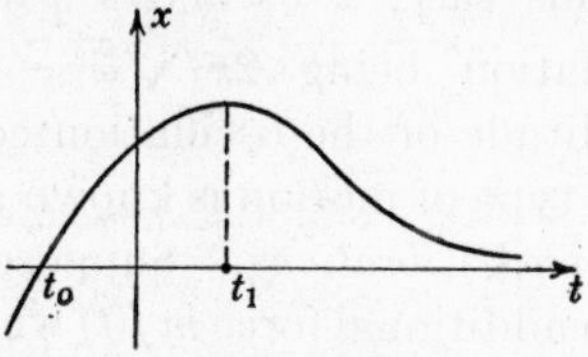   Fig. 116.

negative, $v = dx/dt$ is always negative. It is seen that $x \to 0$ as $t \to \infty$ as indicated in Fig. 115. A similar situation occurs when A and B are both negative. If A and B have opposite signs, then $x = 0$ only once, i.e., at $t_0 = \dfrac{1}{2\sqrt{\rho^2-\omega^2}} \log\left(-\dfrac{B}{A}\right)$;

moreover, $v = 0$ only once, i.e., at

$$t_1 = \frac{1}{2\sqrt{\rho^2-\omega^2}} \log\left(-\frac{B(\rho+\sqrt{\rho^2-\omega^2})}{A(\rho-\sqrt{\rho^2-\omega^2})}\right),$$

t_1 being later than t_0. When $t > t_1$, x and dx/dt have opposite signs, and $x \to 0$ as $t \to \infty$ as indicated in Fig. 116. This type of motion is known as *overdamped*, the retarding force being so great that no vibration can occur.

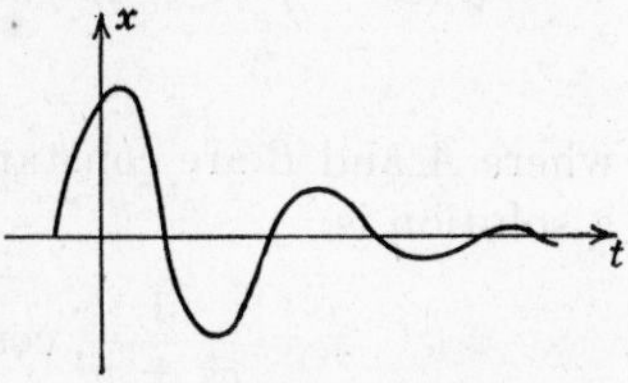

(b) $\rho^2 = \omega^2$. Regardless of the signs of A and B, the motion in this case [see (7)] is similar to that in the preceding case when A and B have

Fig. 117.

opposite signs. This type of motion is known as *critically damped*, for [as indicated in case (c)] the motion becomes oscillatory with an arbitrarily small decrease in the retarding force (Fig. 116).

(c) $\rho^2 < \omega^2$. Let us write (6) in the form

$$x = e^{-\rho t}(A e^{i\sqrt{\omega^2 - \rho^2}\,t} + B e^{-i\sqrt{\omega^2 - \rho^2}\,t}). \quad (i^2 = -1) \quad (8)$$

This may also be written in the forms

$$x = e^{-\rho t}(C \cos \sqrt{\omega^2 - \rho^2}\,t + D \sin \sqrt{\omega^2 - \rho^2}\,t), \quad (9)$$
$$x = e^{-\rho t}[\bar{C} \cos (\sqrt{\omega^2 - \rho^2}\,t - \gamma)],$$

where

$$\bar{C} = \sqrt{C^2 + D^2}, \qquad \gamma = \tan^{-1}\frac{D}{C}. \quad (10)$$

In this case, x oscillates with alternating sign, the period of oscillation being $2\pi/\sqrt{\omega^2 - \rho^2}$; since $e^{-\rho t} \to 0$ as $t \to \infty$, the amplitude of the oscillation continually diminishes toward zero. This type of motion is known as *damped oscillatory* (see Fig. 117).

Forced Vibrations. Suppose the spring of Fig. 114 is subjected to an additional force $m f(t)$ which is a function of the time. Then (3) assumes the form

$$m\frac{d^2x}{dt^2} = -\frac{\lambda}{l}x - k\frac{dx}{dt} + mf(t), \quad (11)$$

or

$$\frac{d^2x}{dt^2} + 2\rho\frac{dx}{dt} + \omega^2 x = f(t). \quad (12)$$

This is known as the *equation of motion* for a *forced vibration*. If the applied force is periodic, say $f(t) = L \cos pt$, and if $\rho^2 \neq \omega^2$, then a solution of (12) is

$$x = \frac{L}{\sqrt{(\omega^2 - p^2)^2 + 4\rho^2 p^2}} \cos (pt - \beta)$$
$$+ e^{-\rho t}[A e^{\sqrt{\rho^2 - \omega^2}\,t} + B e^{-\sqrt{\rho^2 - \omega^2}\,t}], \quad (13)$$

where A and B are constants of integration; but if $\rho^2 = \omega^2$, then a solution is

$$x = \frac{1}{\rho^2 + p^2} \cos (pt - \beta) + (A + Bt)e^{-\rho t}. \quad (14)$$

When the impressed frequency p is such that the amplitude of vibration [in (13)] has a maximum value, *resonance* is said to occur. Thus the maximum extension of the spring may become so great as to produce rupture.   Equation (12) is of great importance in many cases of forced vibrations encountered in the theory of electricity, sound, and mechanics.   The first term in the right member of (13) is called the *steady-state* solution, and the second term is called the *transient* solution; the significance of these names is evident when we consider the relative magnitudes of these two terms for small and large values of t.

EXERCISES XI

1. Solve Eq. (3) under the condition that $x = x_0$ and $v = 0$ at $t = 0$. Consider each of the three cases. Solve Eq. (12) under these same conditions.

2. Suppose the mass m of a simple pendulum to be concentrated at a point P distant l from the fulcrum.   (a) Find the equation of motion when there is no friction.   (b) If the angular displacement θ is small and is measured in radians, then $\sin \theta$ may be approximated by θ since $\lim\limits_{\theta \to 0} \dfrac{\sin \theta}{\theta} = 1$.

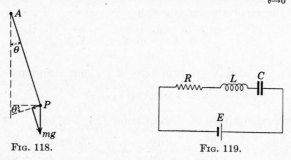

FIG. 118.   FIG. 119.

Using this approximation, solve the equation of motion under the condition that $\theta = \theta_0$ and $d\theta/dt = 0$ at $t = 0$.

3. An electric circuit consists of a constant resistance of R ohms, a coil of constant inductance of L henries, and a condenser of constant capacity of C farads in series with an e.m.f. of E volts.   It is seen by Sec. 3 and Ex. VI, 6, that

$$L\frac{di}{dt} + Ri + \frac{q}{C} = E,$$

and hence that

$$L\frac{d^2q}{dt^2} + R\frac{dq}{dt} + \frac{q}{C} = E. \tag{15}$$

For each of the following cases solve (15) to determine the charge q and the current i as functions of the time t under the condition that $q = 0$ and $i = 0$ when $t = 0$:

(a) $E = 0$.   (b) $E = E_0$.   (c) $E = E_0 \cos pt$.   (d) $E = E_0 e^{-\omega t} \sin pt$,

where E_0, p, and ω are constants.   (e) Show that if R is small and p is close to $1/\sqrt{LC}$, then the amplitude of the oscillation is large.

4. Find the steady-state current in the circuit of Ex. 3 when $R = 60$ ohms, $L = 8$ henries, $C = 3$ mf. $= 3 \cdot 10^{-6}$ farad, and $E = 100 \sin 120\pi t$.

5. A condenser of 5 mf. has a charge of 0.004 coulomb.   Find the transient current when this condenser is discharged through a resistance of 2 ohms and an inductance of 14 henries connected in series.

6. Set up the differential equation for the motion of a simple pendulum when there is a resisting force proportional to the angular velocity.

17. Method of Variation of Constants.   In this section we return to the general linear equation (A) of Sec. 13 and we shall show how the general solution of (A) may be found when the complementary function (C) is known for (A).   It will be seen that this method is merely an extension of the method described in Sec. 15.   For the sake of simplicity, we shall base our explanations on the second order equation

$$\frac{d^2y}{dx^2} + X_1\frac{dy}{dx} + X_2y = X, \qquad (1)$$

where X_1, X_2, and X are functions of x alone.   Suppose

$$y = c_1y_1(x) + c_2y_2(x) \qquad (2)$$

is the general solution of the equation

$$\frac{d^2y}{dx^2} + X_1\frac{dy}{dx} + X_2y = 0, \qquad (3)$$

so that (2) is the complementary function for (1).   In (2) replace c_1 and c_2 by functions $C_1(x)$ and $C_2(x)$, and write

$$Y = C_1(x)y_1 + C_2(x)y_2. \qquad (4)$$

We wish to determine $C_1(x)$ and $C_2(x)$ so that (4) is a solution of (1).   Now

$$\frac{dY}{dx} = C_1(x)\frac{dy_1}{dx} + C_2(x)\frac{dy_2}{dx} + C_1'(x)y_1 + C_2'(x)y_2. \qquad (5)$$

Since the *two* unknown functions in (4) are not completely determined by the *single* condition that (4) satisfy (1), we may arbitrarily impose a further condition on $C_1(x)$ and $C_2(x)$.   It is convenient to require $C_1(x)$ and $C_2(x)$ to be such that

$$C_1'(x)y_1 + C_2'(x)y_2 \equiv 0. \tag{6}$$

Upon differentiating (5) after substituting (6), we find that

$$\frac{d^2Y}{dx^2} = C_1(x)\frac{d^2y_1}{dx^2} + C_2(x)\frac{d^2y_2}{dx^2} + C_1'(x)\frac{dy_1}{dx} + C_2'(x)\frac{dy_2}{dx}. \tag{7}$$

When we substitute (4), (5), (6), and (7) in (1), and remember that y_1 and y_2 are solutions of (3), we obtain the equation

$$C_1'(x)\frac{dy_1}{dx} + C_2'(x)\frac{dy_2}{dx} = X. \tag{8}$$

If we solve (6) and (8) simultaneously for $C_1'(x)$ and $C_2'(x)$, we find that

$$C_1'(x) = \frac{-y_2X}{y_1y_2' - y_1'y_2}, \qquad C_2'(x) = \frac{y_1X}{y_1y_2' - y_1'y_2}, \tag{9}$$

where $y_1y_2' - y_1'y_2 \neq 0$ since we supposed y_1 and y_2 to be linearly independent (see Theorem 13.2 and the paragraph preceding this theorem).   Hence

$$C_1(x) = -\int \frac{y_2X}{y_1y_2' - y_1'y_2}\,dx, \qquad C_2(x) = \int \frac{y_1X}{y_1y_2' - y_1'y_2}\,dx. \tag{10}$$

Substitution of these results in (4) gives a particular integral of (1).   By (2) and (4) the general solution of (1) is

$$y = \{c_1 + C_1(x)\}y_1(x) + \{c_2 + C_2(x)\}y_2(x), \tag{11}$$

where $C_1(x)$ and $C_2(x)$ are given by (10).

Example 1.   Solve the equation $(d^3y/dx^3) - (dy/dx) = x^2$.
The complementary function for this equation is

$$Y = C_1 + C_2e^x + C_3e^{-x}. \tag{12}$$

Considering the C_i's as functions of x, we find that

$$\frac{dY}{dx} = C_2e^x - C_3e^{-x} \tag{13}$$

when we impose the restriction that

$$C_1' + C_2'e^x + C_3'e^{-x} \equiv 0. \tag{14}$$

Furthermore,

$$\frac{d^2Y}{dx^2} = C_2e^x + C_3e^{-x}, \tag{15}$$

when we impose the additional restriction that

$$C_2'e^x - C_3'e^{-x} \equiv 0. \tag{16}$$

Finally,

$$\frac{d^3Y}{dx^3} = C_2e^x - C_3e^{-x} + C_2'e^x + C_3'e^{-x}. \tag{17}$$

Substitution of conditions (12) to (17) in the given equation leads to the result

$$C_2'e^x + C_3'e^{-x} = x^2. \tag{18}$$

Solving (14), (16), and (18) for C_1', C_2', and C_3', we find that

$$C_1' = -x^2, \qquad C_2' = \tfrac{1}{2}x^2e^{-x}, \qquad C_3' = \tfrac{1}{2}x^2e^x.$$

Hence*

$$C_1 = -\tfrac{1}{3}x^3, \quad C_2 = -\tfrac{1}{2}x^2e^{-x} - xe^{-x} + e^{-x}, \quad C_3 = \tfrac{1}{2}x^2e^x - xe^x + e^x. \tag{19}$$

By (12), a particular integral of the given equation is

$$Y = -\tfrac{1}{3}x^3 + (-\tfrac{1}{2}x^2e^{-x} - xe^{-x} + e^{-x})e^x + (\tfrac{1}{2}x^2e^x - xe^x + e^x)e^{-x}$$
$$= -\tfrac{1}{3}x^3 - 2x + 2,$$

and the complete integral is

$$y = c_1 + c_2e^x + c_3e^{-x} - \tfrac{1}{3}x^3 - 2x + 2. \tag{20}$$

While the method of variation of constants is far-reaching, it is inferior in practical value because it requires a knowledge of the complete complementary function and this in general frequently requires a great deal of laborious computation.

EXERCISES XII

1. Solve by the method of variation of constants.

(a) $\dfrac{d^2y}{dx^2} + y = \tan x.$
   (b) $\dfrac{dy}{dx} + \dfrac{1}{x}y = x^3.$

(c) $\dfrac{d^2y}{dx^2} - y = \sin x.$
   (d) $\dfrac{d^2y}{dx^2} + 4y = 4\tan 2x.$

(e) $\dfrac{d^2y}{dx^2} - 4y = \log x.$
   (f) $\dfrac{dy}{dx} + P(x)\,y = Q(x).$

(g) $(1 - x)^2\left(\dfrac{d^3y}{dx^3} - 1\right) - x^2\dfrac{d^2y}{dx^2} + 2x\dfrac{dy}{dx} = y + 1.$

* It is unnecessary to add arbitrary constants in (19) because they would merely combine with the constants in (20).

(h) $\dfrac{d^2y}{dx^2} - 2\dfrac{dy}{dx} + y - e^x(1 - x)^{-2} = 0.$

(i) $\dfrac{d^3y}{dx^3} + X_1\dfrac{d^2y}{dx^2} + X_2\dfrac{dy}{dx} + X_3y \quad X$

2. Prove rules I to V in Sec. 15.

3. If a solution $y = y_1$ is known for Eq. (A) in Sec. 13, show that this solution may be used to transform (A) into an equation of order $n - 1$ (see Sec. 14).

18. Linear Equations of the Second Order. Because of their importance in physical applications, we shall consider linear second order equations of the type

$$\frac{d^2y}{dx^2} + P\frac{dy}{dx} + Qy = X, \tag{1}$$

where P, Q, and X are functions of x only.

We have already considered in Secs. 14 to 17 (a) the case where P and Q are constants; and (b) the case where (1) is exact.

If a particular integral y of (1) with $X = 0$ is known, or can be found by inspection, the substitution $y = y_1w$ will reduce (1) to a linear equation of the first order in dw/dx, which can be solved by the methods of Secs. 5 to 12.

If none of these methods seem applicable, try substituting $y = uw$ in (1). This yields the equation

$$\frac{d^2w}{dx^2} + \left(\frac{2}{u}\frac{du}{dx} + P\right)\frac{dw}{dx} + \frac{1}{u}\left(\frac{d^2u}{dx^2} + P\frac{du}{dx} + Qu\right)w = \frac{X}{u}. \tag{2}$$

If u can be selected so that the coefficient of dw/dx is zero, then

$$u = e^{-\frac{1}{2}\int P\,dx}$$

and

$$\frac{d^2w}{dx^2} + \left(Q - \frac{1}{2}\frac{dP}{dx} - \frac{1}{4}P^2\right)w = Xe^{\frac{1}{2}\int P\,dx}. \tag{3}$$

If the coefficient of w in (3) is a constant, the new equation (3) can be integrated by the methods of Sec. 14; if the coefficient of w in (3) is equal to a constant divided by x^2, the equation (3) may be integrated by the method indicated for (32) of Sec. 19.

Sometimes replacing the independent variable x by w, where $w = \varphi(x)$ is an arbitrary function of x, will lead to a solution to (1). The first and second derivatives of y with respect to x are

$$\frac{dy}{dx} = \frac{dy}{dw}\frac{dw}{dx}, \qquad \frac{d^2y}{dx^2} = \left(\frac{dw}{dx}\right)^2\frac{d^2y}{dw^2} + \frac{d^2w}{dx^2}\frac{dy}{dw},$$

so that (1) is transformed into

$$\frac{d^2y}{dw^2} + \left[\frac{\frac{d^2w}{dx^2} + P\frac{dw}{dt}}{\left(\frac{dw}{dx}\right)^2}\right]\frac{dy}{dw} + \frac{Q}{\left(\frac{dw}{dx}\right)^2}\,y = \frac{X}{\left(\frac{dw}{dx}\right)^2}. \qquad (4)$$

If w can be so selected that the coefficients of y and dy/dw are constants, the equation can be integrated by the methods of Sec. 14.

It frequently happens that all the methods mentioned above fail to solve equations met in certain applications. Such cases may be treated by assuming a solution in the form of an infinite series. The series arising from such an equation often defines a new function, which must then be studied. This was the situation which led to the Bessel functions, Legendre functions, and others. However, we shall postpone this subject until a later section.

EXERCISES XIII

1. Show that when $Q = dP/dx$, equation (1) may be integrated to yield $(dy/dx) + Py = \int X\,dx + C$, a case considered in Sec. 9.

2. Solve: $\dfrac{d^2y}{dx^2} - x^2\dfrac{dy}{dx} + xy = x$.   *Ans.* $y = 1 + c_1x + c_2x\int x^{-2}\,e^{x^3/3}\,dx$.

3. Solve: $(1 + x^2)\dfrac{d^2y}{dx^2} - 2x\dfrac{dy}{dx} + 2y = 0$.

4. Solve: $(1 + x)\dfrac{d^2y}{dx^2} + (1 - x)\dfrac{dy}{dx} - y = e^x$.

Hint: e^x is a particular solution.

5. Solve: $9\left(\dfrac{d^2y}{dx^2}\right)^2 - 1 = \left(\dfrac{dy}{dx}\right)^2$.   *Ans.* $y = 3\cosh\left(\dfrac{x + c_1}{3}\right) + c_2$.

Hint: Let $dy/dx = p$, $d^2y/dx^2 = dp/dx$.

6. Solve: $\dfrac{d^2y}{dx^2} + \dfrac{2}{x}\dfrac{dy}{dx} + \dfrac{9}{x^4}y = 0$.

Hint: Let $z = \dfrac{-3}{x}$.   *Ans.* $y = c_1\cos\left(\dfrac{3}{x}\right) + c_2\sin\left(\dfrac{3}{x}\right)$.

7. Solve: $\dfrac{d^2y}{dx^2} + x^{-\frac{1}{3}}\dfrac{dy}{dx} + \left[(8x)^{-\frac{2}{3}} - \dfrac{1}{6}(x)^{-\frac{4}{3}} - 6x^{-2}\right]y = 0$.

$$\text{\textit{Ans.} } \quad y = e^{-\frac{3}{2}x^{\frac{2}{3}}}\left(\frac{c_1}{x^2} + c_2x^3\right).$$

8. Prove that if y_1 is a known integral of (1), then the general solution of (1) is

$$y = c_1 y_1 + c_2 y_1 \int \frac{e^{-\int P\,dx}}{y_1^2}\,dx + y_1 \int \frac{1}{y_1^2} e^{-\int P\,dx} \int y_1 e^{\int P\,dx} X\,dx\,dx.$$

9. Solve: $x\dfrac{d^2y}{dx^2} - \dfrac{dy}{dx} + 4x^3 y - x^5 = 0.$

10. Solve the differential equation $dy/dx = x^2 + y$ by assuming the solution to be an infinite series of the form

$$y = a_0 + a_1 x + a_2 x^2 + a_3 x^3 + \cdots + a_n x^n + a_{n+1} x^{n+1} + \cdots$$

and determining the coefficients $a_1,\ a_2,\ \cdots$.
Solution.

$$\frac{dy}{dx} = a_1 + 2a_2 x + 3a_3 x^2 + \cdots + n a_n x^{n-1} + (n+1)a_{n+1}x^n + \cdots.$$

Substituting in the given equation, we must have

$$a_1 + 2a_2 x + 3a_3 x^2 + \cdots + (n+1)a_{n+1}x^n + \cdots$$
$$\equiv x^2 + a_0 + a_1 x + a_2 x^2 + \cdots + a_n x^n + \cdots.$$

Equating the coefficients of like powers of x in this identity, we have

$$a_1 = a_0,\ 2a_2 = a_1,\ 3a_3 = 1 + a_2,\ 4a_4 = a_3,\ \cdots,\ (n+1)a_{n+1} = a_n,\ \cdots$$

Hence, if we consider a_0 to be the constant of integration, we find that

$$a_1 = a_0, \qquad a_2 = \frac{a_0}{2}, \qquad a_3 = \frac{1}{3} + \frac{a_0}{6}, \qquad a_4 = \frac{1}{4}\left(\frac{1}{3} + \frac{a_0}{6}\right), \ \cdots,$$

so that the solution is

$$y = a_0 + a_0 x + \frac{a_0}{2}x^2 + \frac{1}{3}\left(1 + \frac{a_0}{2}\right)x^3 + \frac{1}{3\cdot 4}\left(1 + \frac{a_0}{2}\right)x^4 + \cdots.$$

11. Solve each of the following equations by the method of series:

(a) $\dfrac{dy}{dx} = x^2 + y^2.$ (b) $\dfrac{dy}{dx} = y^2 + 2x.$

(c) $\dfrac{dy}{dx} = xy.$ (d) $\dfrac{d^2y}{dx^2} + k^2 y = 0.$

(e) $\dfrac{d^2y}{dx^2} + \lambda xy = 0.$

12. Solve: $(x^2 + 1)\dfrac{d^2y}{dx^2} + \left(\dfrac{dy}{dx}\right)^2 + 1 = 0.$ $\left(\text{Hint: Let } p = \dfrac{dy}{dx}.\right)$

13. Solve: $\left[\dfrac{d^2y}{dx^2} - x\dfrac{d^3y}{dx^3}\right]^2 = \left(\dfrac{d^3y}{dx^3}\right)^2 + 1.$ $\left(\text{Hint: Let } w = \dfrac{d^2y}{dx^2}.\right)$

14. Solve: $y\dfrac{d^2y}{dx^2} = \left(\dfrac{dy}{dx}\right)^2 + y^2\dfrac{dy}{dx}.$ $\left(\text{Hint: Let } p = \dfrac{dy}{dx},\; p\dfrac{dp}{dy} = \dfrac{d^2y}{dx^2}.\right)$

15. Solve: $(x^2 - x)\dfrac{d^2y}{dx^2} + (4x + 2)\dfrac{dy}{dx} + 2y = 0.$

16. Solve: $\cos x\dfrac{d^2y}{dx^2} - 2\sin x\dfrac{dy}{dx} = 10(\cos x)y.$

17. Solve: $x^4\dfrac{d^2y}{dx^2} + 2x^3\dfrac{dy}{dx} + 9y = 0.$

18. Solve: $3\dfrac{d^2y}{dx^2} - e^y = 0.$

19. Operator Methods. In this section we shall develop another method for solving the equation

$$\frac{d^ny}{dx^n} + a_1\frac{d^{n-1}y}{dx^{n-1}} + \cdots + a_ny = X, \tag{I}$$

where the coefficients a_i are constants and X is a function of x alone. Let D, D^2, D^3, $\cdots$ denote the symbols d/dx, d^2/dx^2, d^3/dx^3, $\cdots$, respectively. Thus $2D^2y + 11Dy - 6y$, or written more briefly as $(2D^2 + 11D - 6)y$, denotes

$$2\frac{d^2y}{dx^2} + 11\frac{dy}{dx} - 6y.$$

If $f(x)$ and $g(x)$ are differentiable functions of x, then

$$\frac{d}{dx}[f(x) + g(x)] = \frac{df(x)}{dx} + \frac{dg(x)}{dx}.$$

Hence the operator D obeys the *distributive* law

$$D[f(x) + g(x)] = Df(x) + Dg(x). \tag{1}$$

It may be shown in a similar manner that

$$D[cg(x)] = c[Dg(x)] \tag{2}$$

when c is a constant but not when c is a variable. If m and n are positive integers,

$$D^m[D^nf(x)] = D^n[D^mf(x)] = D^{m+n}f(x). \tag{3}$$

Thus D satisfies certain of the fundamental laws of elementary algebra.

Equation (I) may be written in the form

$$P(D)y = X, \tag{I'}$$

where

$$P(D) \equiv D^n + a_1 D^{n-1} + \cdots + a_n.$$

The expression $P(D)$ is called an *operator*, and we say that we operate on a function $f(x)$ with $P(D)$ when we carry out the indicated operations of differentiation, multiplication, and addition. By virtue of (1), (2), and (3), it is possible to "factor" an operator $P(D)$. For example,

$$
\begin{aligned}
(2D^2 + 11D - 6y) &= (2D^2 + 12D)y - (D + 6)y \\
&= 2[D(Dy) + D(6y)] - (D + 6)y \\
&= 2D[(D + 6)y] - [(D + 6)y] \tag{4} \\
&= (2D - 1)[(D + 6)y] \\
&= (2D - 1)(D + 6)y, \tag{5}
\end{aligned}
$$

(4) following by (1). It may be shown in a similar manner that

$$(2D^2 + 11D - 6)y = (D + 6)(2D - 1)y. \tag{6}$$

It is seen by (5) and (6) that the factors of an operator $P(D)$ may be written in arbitrary order. If $y = x^3 - \sin x$, then by (5),

$$
\begin{aligned}
(2D^2 + 11D - 6)(x^3 - \sin x) &= (2D - 1)[(D + 6)(x^3 - \sin x)] \\
&= (2D - 1)[(3x^2 - \cos x) + 6(x^3 - \sin x)] \\
&= (12x + 2 \sin x + 36x^2 - 12 \cos x) \\
&\quad - (3x^2 - \cos x + 6x^3 - 6 \sin x), \tag{7}
\end{aligned}
$$

and by (6),

$$
\begin{aligned}
(2D^2 + 11D - 6)(x^3 - \sin x) &= (D + 6)[(2D - 1)(x^3 - \sin x)] \\
&= (D + 6)[(6x^2 - 2 \cos x) - (x^3 - \sin x)] \\
&= (12x + 2 \sin x - 3x^2 + \cos x) \\
&\quad + (36x^2 - 12 \cos x - 6x^3 + 6 \sin x). \tag{8}
\end{aligned}
$$

It is evident that (7) and (8) are identically equal.

If ω is a constant, then $De^{\omega x} = \omega e^{\omega x}$, $D^2 e^{\omega x} = \omega^2 e^{\omega x}, \cdots$, and

$$P(D)e^{\omega x} = P(\omega)e^{\omega x}, \tag{9}$$

for

$$
\begin{aligned}
P(D)e^{\omega x} &= (D^n + a_1 D^{n-1} + \cdots + a_{n-1}D + a_n)e^{\omega x} \\
&= (\omega^n + a_1\omega^{n-1} + \cdots + a_{n-1}\omega + a_n)e^{\omega x} = P(\omega)e^{\omega x}.
\end{aligned}
$$

Again, $D^2 \cos \omega x = -\omega^2 \cos \omega x$,

$$D^4 \cos \omega x = (-\omega^2)^2 \cos \omega x, \cdots,$$

and

$$P(D^2) \cos \omega x = P(-\omega^2) \cos \omega x, \tag{10}$$

for

$$P(D^2) \cos \omega x = (D^{2n} + a_1 D^{2n-2} + \cdots + a_{n-1} D^2 + a_n) \cos \omega x$$
$$= [(-\omega^2)^n + a_1(-\omega^2)^{n-1} + \cdots + a_{n-1}(-\omega^2) + a_n] \cos \omega x$$
$$= P(-\omega^2) \cos \omega x.$$

It follows in a similar manner that

$$P(D^2) \sin \omega x = P(-\omega^2) \sin \omega x. \tag{11}$$

It is readily possible to derive many other formulas of this sort. For example,

$$D[e^{\omega x} f(x)] = e^{\omega x}(D + \omega) f(x),$$
$$D^2[e^{\omega x} f(x)] = D\{e^{\omega x}[(D + \omega) f(x)]\} = e^{\omega x}\{(D + \omega)[(D + \omega) f(x)]\}$$
$$= e^{\omega x}(D + \omega)^2 f(x), \cdots,$$

and

$$P(D)[e^{\omega x} f(x)] = e^{\omega x} P(D + \omega) f(x). \tag{12}$$

Thus,

$$(D^2 - 5D + 6)e^{3x} y = e^{3x}[(D + 3)^2 - 5(D + 3) + 6]y$$
$$= e^{3x}(D^2 + D)y = e^{3x}\left(\frac{d^2 y}{dx^2} + \frac{dy}{dx}\right).$$

Complementary Functions. It follows by (9) that the characteristic equation [see (G) of Sec. 14] of the equation

$$P(D)y = 0 \tag{13}$$

is $P(m) = 0$. Hence if $P(D)$ is factored in the form

$$P(D) = (D - r_1)(D - r_2) \cdots (D - r_n),$$

then

$$P(m) = (m - r_1)(m - r_2) \cdots (m - r_n),$$

the roots of the equation $P(m) = 0$ are $r_1, r_2, \cdots, r_n$, and if the r's are all distinct, the general solution of (13) is

$$y = c_1 e^{r_1 x} + \cdots + c_n e^{r_n x}.$$

We wish to show how the general solution of (13) may be obtained with the aid of operators when some of the r's are equal.

It follows from the preceding discussion that the equation

$$(D - r)^p y = 0 \tag{14}$$

has $y_1 = e^{rx}$ for a solution. Let $y = e^{rx}f(x)$, where $f(x)$ is to be determined so that y is a solution of (14). If we substitute y in (14) it follows by (12) that

$$(D - r)^p[e^{rx}f(x)] = e^{rx}[(D + r) - r]^p f(x) = e^{rx}D^p f(x) = 0.$$

Hence $D^p f(x) = 0$ since e^{rx} is never zero. If we integrate p times we find that $f(x) = C_1 + C_2 x + C_3 x^2 + \cdots + C_p x^{p-1}$. Thus the general solution of (14) is

$$y = (C_1 + C_2 x + \cdots + C_p x^{p-1})e^{rx}. \tag{15}$$

Now suppose (13) factors into the form

$$(D - r_1)^{p_1}(D - r_2)^{p_2} \cdots (D - r_k)^{p_k} y = 0. \tag{16}$$

It is evident that any solution of the equation

$$(D - r_k)^{p_k} y = 0 \tag{17}$$

is a solution of (16). By reordering the factors in (16) it is seen that the solutions of each of the equations

$$(D - r_1)^{p_1} y = 0, \qquad (D - r_2)^{p_2} y = 0, \cdots \tag{18}$$

are solutions of (16). If all these solutions, each of the form given in (15), are added, the result is the general solution of (16) [see (H) of Sec. 14].

Example 1. Solve the equation $\dfrac{d^4 y}{dx^4} - 18\dfrac{d^2 y}{dx^2} + 81y = 0$.

We may write the equation in the form

$$(D^4 - 18D^2 + 81)y = (D^2 - 9)^2 y = 0.$$

The characteristic equation is $(D^2 - 9)^2 = 0$, where we write D instead of m, and the roots are -3, -3, 3, 3. Hence the general solution is

$$y = (C_1 + C_2 x)e^{3x} + (C_3 + C_4 x)e^{-3x}.$$

Example 2. Solve the equation $(D^2 + 9)^2 y = 0$.
The characteristic roots are $-3i$, $-3i$, $3i$, $3i$, and the solution is

$$y = (c_1 + c_2 x)e^{3ix} + (c_3 + c_4 x)e^{-3ix},$$

or

$$y = (C_1 + C_2 x)\cos 3x + (C_3 + C_4 x)\sin 3x.$$

Particular Integral.   To obtain a particular integral of equation
(I), let us first consider the equation

$$(D - r)y = X(x),$$ (19)

which, by Sec. 9, has the solution

$$y = e^{rx} \int e^{-rx} X(x)\, dx + Ce^{rx}.$$ (20)

Let us formally write (19) in the form

$$y = \frac{1}{D - r} X(x),$$ (21)

where the symbol $1/(D - r)$ is as yet undefined.   Comparison
of (20) and (21) shows that (21) determines the solution of (19)
if we interpret the symbol $1/(D - r)$ as an operator which, when
acting on the function $X(x)$, gives the right member of (20),
i.e., if we define the operator $1/(D - r)$ by the formula

$$\frac{1}{D - r} X(x) = e^{rx} \int e^{-rx} X(x)\, dx + Ce^{rx}.$$ (22)

It is seen that the term Ce^{rx} in (22) is the complementary function
for (19) and that the term $e^{rx}\int e^{-rx} X(x)\, dx$ is the particular
integral.   It is also seen that if $r = 0$ in (22), then $1/D$ means
the same thing as $\int$, i.e., that $1/D$ is the inverse operation of D;
in the same sense, $1/(D - r)$ is the inverse of $D - r$, i.e.,

$$(D - r)\left[\frac{1}{D - r} X(x) \right] = X(x).$$

Let us next consider the equation

$$(D - r_1)(D - r_2)y = X(x).$$ (23)

To solve this equation, let $z = (D - r_2)y$.   Then (23) assumes
the form

$$(D - r_1)z = X(x),$$ (24)

and by (21) and (22) a solution of this equation is

$$z = \frac{1}{D - r_1} X(x) = e^{r_1 x} \int e^{-r_1 x} X(x)\, dx + C_1' e^{r_1 x}.$$

If we now replace z by $(D - r_2)y$ and solve the resulting equation
we find that

$$y = \frac{1}{D - r_2}\left[e^{r_1 x} \int e^{-r_1 x} X(x)\ dx + C_1' e^{r_1 x}\right]$$

$$= e^{r_2 x} \int e^{-r_2 x}\left[e^{r_1 x} \int e^{-r_1 x} X(x)\ dx + C_1' e^{r_1 x}\right] dx + C_2 e^{r_2 x} \quad (25)$$

$$= e^{r_2 x} \int e^{(r_1 - r_2) x} \int e^{-r_1 x} X(x)\ dx\ dx + C_1 e^{r_1 x} + C_2 e^{r_2 x}, \quad (26)$$

if $r_1 \neq r_2$. However, if $r_1 = r_2$, then (25) reduces to

$$y = e^{r_1 x} \int \left[\int e^{-r_1 x} X(x)\ dx + C_1' \right] dx + C_2 e^{r_1 x}$$

$$= e^{r_1 x} \int \int e^{-r_1 x} X(x)\ dx\ dx + (C_1' x + C_2) e^{r_1 x}. \quad (26')$$

If we evaluate the integral in (26) by integrating by parts (integrating $e^{(r_1 - r_2) x}$ and differentiating $\int e^{-r_1 x} X(x)\ dx$), then (26) assumes the form

$$y = e^{r_2 x}\left[\frac{e^{(r_1 - r_2) x}}{r_1 - r_2} \int e^{-r_1 x} X(x)\ dx - \int \frac{e^{(r_1 - r_2) x}}{r_1 - r_2} e^{-r_1 x} X(x)\ dx \right]$$
$$+ C_1 e^{r_1 x} + C_2 e^{r_2 x}$$

$$= \left(\frac{1}{(r_1 - r_2)(D - r_1)} + \frac{1}{(r_2 - r_1)(D - r_2)} \right) X(x). \quad (27)$$

By (24) and 21) we may write (23) in the form

$$y = \frac{1}{D - r_2} \cdot \frac{1}{D - r_1} \cdot X(x) = \frac{1}{(D - r_2)(D - r_1)} X(x). \quad (27')$$

It is readily verified that (27) results from (27') when the operator $\frac{1}{(D - r_2)(D - r_1)}$ is treated like an ordinary fraction and resolved into partial fractions. Formula (26') may be reduced in a similar manner to the form

$$y = x \frac{1}{D - r_1} X(x) - \frac{1}{D - r_1}[x\ X(x)]. \quad (28)$$

An immediate extension of the preceding discussion shows that the general solution of the equation

$$(D - r_1)(D - r_2) \cdots (D - r_n) y = X(x) \quad (29)$$

is

$$y = e^{r_n x} \int e^{(r_{n-1} - r_n) x} \int \cdots \int e^{(r_1 - r_2) x} \int e^{-r_1 x} X(x)\ dx\ dx \cdots dx$$
$$+ C_1 e^{r_1 x} + C_2 e^{r_2 x} + \cdots + C_n e^{r_n x}, \quad (30)$$

where the integrations are carried out by beginning at the extreme right and working to the left, and where all the r's are distinct. However, if some of the r's are equal, then (30) must be suitably modified [see (15), and (H) of Sec. 14]. We may write the solution of (29) formally as

$$y = \frac{1}{D - r_n} \cdot \frac{1}{D - r_{n-1}} \cdot \cdot \cdot \cdot \frac{1}{D - r_1} X(x)$$

$$= \frac{1}{(D - r_n)(D - r_{n-1}) \cdot \cdot \cdot (D - r_1)} X(x). \qquad (31)$$

If the r's are all distinct, we may resolve the operator

$$\frac{1}{(D - r_n) \cdot \cdot \cdot (D - r_1)}$$

into "partial fractions" in the usual way [see (27) and Ex. 7 below]. If we define $\frac{1}{P(D)}$ to mean $\frac{1}{D - r_n} \cdot \cdot \cdot \cdot \frac{1}{D - r_1}$, where $P(D) \equiv (D - r_1)(D - r_2) \cdot \cdot \cdot (D - r_n)$, then we may write the solution of the equation $P(D)y = X(x)$ in the form $y = \frac{1}{P(D)} X(x)$. It should be observed that $\frac{1}{P(D)}$ is the inverse of $P(D)$ in the same sense that $1/D$ is the inverse of D.

Example 3. Solve the equation $(D^3 - 9D)y = x$.
Considering only the particular integral, we have

$$y = \frac{1}{D} \cdot \frac{1}{D - 3} \cdot \frac{1}{D + 3} x = \frac{1}{D} \cdot \frac{1}{D - 3} \left(e^{-3x} \int e^{+3x} x \, dx \right)$$

$$= \frac{1}{D} \cdot \frac{1}{D - 3} \left[e^{-3x} \left(+ \frac{1}{3} x e^{3x} - \frac{1}{9} e^{3x} \right) \right] = \frac{1}{D} \cdot \frac{1}{D - 3} \left(+ \frac{x}{3} - \frac{1}{9} \right)$$

$$= \frac{1}{D} \left[e^{3x} \int e^{-3x} \left(+ \frac{x}{3} - \frac{1}{9} \right) dx \right] = \frac{1}{D} \left(- \frac{x}{9} \right)$$

$$= e^{0x} \int e^{-0x} \left(- \frac{x}{9} \right) dx = - \frac{x^2}{18}.$$

Hence the general solution is

$$y = C_1 + C_2 e^{-3x} + C_3 e^{3x} - \frac{x^2}{18}.$$

It is sometimes possible to simplify (30) and (31) considerably.

Example 4. Solve the equation $P(D)y = e^{\omega x}$.

Let $P(D) = (D - r_1) \cdots (D - r_n)$ and suppose that ω is distinct from the r's. It is readily verified by direct computation that

$$\frac{1}{P(D)} e^{\omega x} = \frac{1}{P(\omega)} e^{\omega x},$$

where $P(\omega) \neq 0$ and where we consider only the particular integral. Another way to arrive at this result is as follows: The operator $\dfrac{1}{P(D)}$ is the inverse of $P(D)$. But $P(D)$, when applied to $\dfrac{1}{P(\omega)} e^{\omega x}$, gives the function $e^{\omega x}$ [see (9)]. Hence $\dfrac{1}{P(D)}$, when applied to $e^{\omega x}$, brings us back to $\dfrac{1}{P(\omega)} e^{\omega x}$. Thus a particular solution of the given equation is $y = \dfrac{1}{P(\omega)} e^{\omega x}$ when $P(\omega) \neq 0$. Again, if $P(D) = (D - \omega)^p$, then it may be directly verified that $\dfrac{1}{(D - \omega)^p} e^{\omega x} = e^{\omega x} \dfrac{x^p}{p!}$. {By (12), $\dfrac{1}{(D - \omega)^p}[e^{\omega x} D^p f(x)] = e^{\omega x} f(x)$. In the present instance, $D^p f(x) = 1$, so that $f(x) = x^p/p!$.} Finally, if the given equation is of the form

$$\phi(D) \cdot (D - \omega)^p y = e^{\omega x},$$

where $\phi(D)$ does not contain the factor $(D - \omega)$, then a particular solution is

$$y = \frac{1}{(D - \omega)^p} \cdot \frac{1}{\phi(D)} e^{\omega x} = \frac{1}{(D - \omega)^p} \frac{e^{\omega x}}{\phi(\omega)} = \frac{e^{\omega x}}{\phi(\omega)} \frac{x^p}{p!}.$$

The complementary function is obtained in the usual way.

Example 5. Solve the equation $P(D^2)y = \cos \omega x$.

By (10), $P(D^2)\left[\dfrac{1}{P(-\omega^2)} \cos \omega x\right] = \cos \omega x$. Hence

$$\frac{1}{P(D^2)} \cos \omega x = \frac{1}{P(-\omega^2)} \cos \omega x,$$

and a particular integral of the given equation is $y = \dfrac{1}{P(-\omega^2)} \cos \omega x$, provided that $P(-\omega^2) \neq 0$. The case where $P(-\omega^2) = 0$ is left to the student.

Example 6. Solve the equation $(D^2 + 3D + 2)y = \cos 4x$.

It is apparent that a particular integral of this equation is of the form $y = A \cos 4x + B \sin 4x$. By (10) and (11) we may write

$$(D^2 + 3D + 2)y = (-16 + 3D + 2)y = \cos 4x.$$

Hence

$$y = \frac{1}{D^2 + 3D + 2} \cos 4x = \frac{1}{-16 + 3D + 2} \cos 4x.$$

$$= \frac{1}{3D - 14} \cos 4x = \frac{1}{9D^2 - (14)^2}[(3D + 14) \cos 4x]$$

$$= \frac{1}{9(-16) - (14)^2}[(3D + 14) \cos 4x] = -\frac{1}{340}(-12 \sin 4x + 14 \cos 4x).$$

An equation of the form

$$x^n D^n y + a_1 x^{n-1} D^{n-1} y + \cdots + a_{n-1} x D y + a_n y = X(x), \quad (32)$$

where $a_1, \cdots, a_n$ are constants, is known as a *homogeneous linear* equation. To solve this equation, let $x = e^t$. Then

$$\frac{dy}{dx} = \frac{dy}{dt}\frac{dt}{dx} = e^{-t}\frac{dy}{dt},$$

$$\frac{d^2y}{dx^2} = \frac{d}{dt}\left(e^{-t}\frac{dy}{dt}\right)\frac{dt}{dx} = e^{-2t}\frac{d^2y}{dt^2} - e^{-2t}\frac{dy}{dt},$$

$$\frac{d^3y}{dx^3} = e^{-3t}\frac{d^3y}{dt^3} - 3e^{-3t}\frac{d^2y}{dt^2} + 2e^{-3t}\frac{dy}{dt},$$

and so on. Hence

$$x\frac{dy}{dx} = Dy,$$

$$x^2\frac{d^2y}{dx^2} = (D^2 - D)y,$$

$$x^3\frac{d^3y}{dx^3} = (D^3 - 3D^2 + 2D)y,$$

and so on, where D denotes d/dt. Substitution of these results in (32) leads to a linear equation with constant coefficients which can be dealt with in the manner indicated above.

Example 7. Solve the equation $x^2\dfrac{d^2y}{dx^2} - 6x\dfrac{dy}{dx} + 6y = x^2$.

If we let $x = e^t$ and make the above substitutions, we obtain the equation

$$(D^2 - 7D + 6)y = e^{2t}$$

whose solution is

$$y = c_1 e^t + c_2 e^{6t} - \tfrac{1}{4}e^{2t}.$$

Hence the given equation has for its solution

$$y = c_1 x + c_2 x^6 - \tfrac{1}{4}x^2.$$

The operator $1/P(D)$ may be written in many convenient and useful forms by skillful algebraic manipulations. For example, if $X(x)$ in equation (I) is a polynomial in x, then a formal solution may be obtained by expanding $1/P(D)$ in a power series in D. Thus, the solution of

$$(D^2 + 1)y = x^3 - 7x + 1$$

is

$$y = \frac{1}{1 + D^2}(x^3 - 7x + 1)$$
$$= (1 - D^2 + D^4 - D^6 + \cdots)(x^3 - 7x + 1)$$
$$= (x^3 - 7x + 1) - (6x) = x^3 - 13x + 1.$$

EXERCISES XIV

1. Solve the following equations:

(a) $(D^4 + 6D^3 + 9D^2)y = 0.$ (b) $(D^6 + 3D^4 + 3D^2 + 1)y = 0.$
(c) $(4D^5 + 7D^3 - 2D^2)y = 0.$

2. Solve the following equations by formula (30) or by the method of Example 4:

(a) $D^p y = 1.$

(b) $(D^2 + 1)y = \sin x.$ $\left(\text{HINT: } \sin x = \dfrac{e^{ix} - e^{-ix}}{2i}. \right)$

(c) $(D - 3)^5 y = 0.$ (d) $(D^2 + D + 1)y = x^2.$
(e) $(D + 3)^2 y = 100e^{2x}.$ (f) $(D^2 - 16)y = 27e^{4x}.$
(g) $(D^3 - D)y = e^x + 3e^{-x}.$

3. Solve the following equations by the method of Example 6:

(a) $(D - 1)y = 9 \sin 2x.$ (b) $(D^2 + 8D + 25)y = 48 \sin x - 16 \cos x.$

4. Solve the following equations by resolving $\dfrac{1}{P(D)}$ into partial fractions:

(a) $(D^2 - 1)y = 5 + 7x.$ (b) $(D^2 - 2D + 1)y = 3e^{2x}.$
(c) $(D^3 + 1)y = 5 + e^{-x} + 4e^{2x}.$ (d) $(D^3 - 3D^2 - D + 3)y = x^2.$
(e) $(D^2 - 3D + 2)y = xe^x.$

5. Solve the following equations:

(a) $(D^2 - 4D + 2)y = x.$ (b) $(D^2 + D + 1)y = xe^x.$
(c) $(D^2 + 4)y = \cos 2x.$

[HINT: Solve $(D^2 + 4)y = e^{2ix}$ and use the real part of your answer.]

(d) $(D^2 + 4)y = \sin 2x.$ (e) $(D - 1)^3 y = \sin x.$
(f) $(D^4 - 1)^3 y = 0.$ (g) $(D^4 - 81)y = x^4.$
(h) $(D^3 + 1)y = 3 + e^{-x} + 7e^{2x}.$ (i) $(D^2 - 2D)y = e^{2x} + 7.$
(j) $(D^2 - 2D + 4)y = e^x \cos x.$ (k) $(D^2 + 16)y = \sin^2 x.$

(l) $x^3\dfrac{d^3y}{dx^3} + 3x^2\dfrac{d^2y}{dx^2} + x\dfrac{dy}{dx} = 24x^2.$ (m) $x^3\dfrac{d^3y}{dx^3} + 5x^2\dfrac{d^2y}{dx^2} + 3x\dfrac{dy}{dx} = x^2.$

(n) $x^2\dfrac{d^2y}{dx^2} + 9x\dfrac{dy}{dx} + 25y = 50.$ (o) $(x^3D^3 + xD - 1)y = 2x \log x.$

(p) $(1 + 2x)^2\dfrac{d^2y}{dx^2} + (1 + x)\dfrac{dy}{dx} + y = 4 \cos \log (1 + x).$

[HINT: Let $1 + 2x = e^t$.]

(q) $(x + 1)^2\dfrac{d^2y}{dx^2} - 4(x + 1)\dfrac{dy}{dx} + 6y = x.$

6. Show that

$$P(D^2)(\text{A} \cosh \omega x + \text{B} \sinh \omega x) = P(\omega^2)(\text{A} \cosh \omega x + \text{B} \sinh \omega x).$$

7. Show that

$$\frac{1}{(D - a)(D - b)(D - c)}X = \left[\frac{1}{(a - b)(a - c)} \cdot \frac{1}{D - a}\right.$$
$$\left. + \frac{1}{(b - a)(b - c)} \cdot \frac{1}{D - b} + \frac{1}{(c - a)(c - b)} \frac{1}{D - c}\right]X,$$

when a, b, and c are distinct.   Generalize this result.

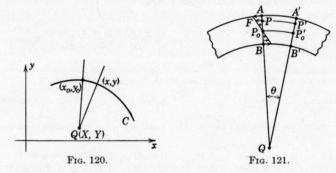

FIG. 120.   FIG. 121.

8. In Fig. 120 the equations of the normals to the curve C at the fixed point (x_0, y_0) and at the variable point (x, y) are

$$Y - y_0 = -\frac{1}{(y')_0}(X - x_0), \qquad Y - y = -\frac{1}{y'}(X - x).$$

Solve these equations simultaneously for the coordinates (X, Y) of the point Q of intersection of these normals, use the results to compute

$$r = \sqrt{(X - x_0)^2 + (Y - y_0)^2},$$

and evaluate $\lim\limits_{x \to x_0} r$ by L'Hôpital's rule (Theorem 11.2, Chap. I) to show that $\lim\limits_{x \to x_0} r$ is the radius of curvature ρ of the curve C at (x_0, y_0).

9. Let AB and $A'B'$ be neighboring normal sections of a beam. Suppose that, after the beam is bent, these sections remain plane and intersect at Q. Owing to the bending of the beam, a tensile force F acts across the outer part of AB and a compressive force F acts across the inner part of AB. Let P_0 be the point of AB where this internal force F is 0, let P be any other point of AB, let $QP_0 = r_0$, $QP = r$, $P_0P = r - r_0 = y$, and let ρ be the radius of curvature of P_0P_0' at P_0. The value of F at P (in pounds per square inch) is $E\delta$, where E is the modulus of elasticity of the material in the beam and δ is the elongation (or compression) per unit of length along PP'. Now

$$\delta = \lim_{P_0' \to P_0} \frac{PP' - P_0P_0'}{P_0P_0'} = \lim_{\theta \to 0} \frac{\theta r - \theta r_0}{\theta r_0} = \frac{1}{\rho} y = Ky,$$

for, as indicated above, $\lim\limits_{P_0' \to P_0} r_0$ is the radius of curvature ρ of the curve P_0P_0' at P_0 and $K = 1/\rho$, where K is the curvature of P_0P_0' at P_0. Hence

$$F = EKy,$$

and the total moment of all the forces F about P_0 is

$$M = \int_{y_B}^{y_A} Fy\, b(y)\, dy = EK \int_{y_B}^{y_A} y^2\, b(y)\, dy = EKI, \qquad \text{(i)}$$

where $b(y)$ is the breadth of the beam at height y and I is the moment of inertia of the section AB about the axis through P_0 perpendicular to the plane of QP_0 and P_0P_0'. Show that this axis is the gravity axis of the section AB.

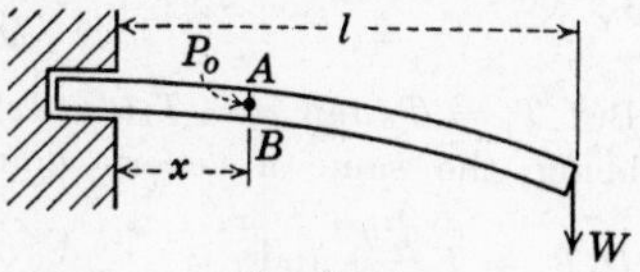

In Fig. 122 it is seen that the moment M in (i) at any section AB is induced by, and exactly balances, the moment of the impressed force W about the point P_0 in AB. Hence

Fig. 122.

$$EIK = W(l - x). \qquad \text{(ii)}$$

But $K = y''/(1 + y'^2)^{3/2}$. If the bending of the beam is small so that y'^2 is negligible, then (ii) may be written in the approximate form

$$EI \frac{d^2y}{dx^2} = -W(l - x), \qquad \text{(iii)}$$

where we write $-W$ because y'' is negative (the beam being concave downward). Solve this equation, determining the constants of integration suitably, and find the deflection of the beam at its end. The solution of (iii) is called the *elastic curve* of the beam.

10. Show that the following equations represent the elastic curves of the beams loaded as indicated, where shading over the beam represents a uniform load (including the weight of the beam) of w lb. per foot of length. Solve these equations and find the maximum deflections.

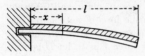

(a) $EI\dfrac{d^2y}{dx^2} = wlx - \dfrac{w}{2}(l^2 + x^2)$.

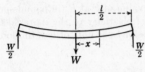

(b) $EI\dfrac{d^2y}{dx^2} = \dfrac{W}{2}\left(\dfrac{l}{2} - x\right)$.

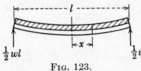

(c) $EI\dfrac{d^2y}{dx^2} = \dfrac{w}{2}\left(\dfrac{l^2}{4} - x\right)$.

Fig. 123.

(d) Show that if a concentrated load W and a uniform load w per foot are combined, the deflection is the sum of the deflections for the separate loads.

11. Let there be suspended from two points A and B a flexible, inextensible cable of weight w per foot of length. Let T_0 be the tension at the bottom point P_0, let T_v be the vertical component of the tension at any point P, and let W be the total weight of the cable to the left of P. Then

$$D_x T_v = D_x W.$$

But $T_v = T_0 \tan \alpha = T_0(dy/dx)$, the horizontal component of the tension being the same at every point P as at P_0,

$$D_x T_v = T_0\dfrac{d^2y}{dx^2},\text{ and}$$

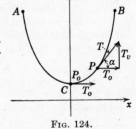

$$D_x W = D_s W D_x s = w \cos \alpha = w\sqrt{1 + (dy/dx)^2}.$$

Hence

$$\dfrac{d^2y}{dx^2} = \dfrac{1}{c}\sqrt{1 + \left(\dfrac{dy}{dx}\right)^2},$$

Fig. 124.

where $c = T_0/w$. Solve this equation.

Hint: Let $p = dy/dx$ and show that a first integral is

$$\sqrt{1 + p^2} + p = e^{x/c}.$$

Taking reciprocals and rationalizing, we have $\sqrt{1 + p^2} - p = e^{-x/c}$. Find the difference between these two last equations and integrate, determining the constant of integration so that $y = c$ where $x = 0$.

Show that $D_x s = y/c$ and hence that the tension T at any point P is $T = T_0 \sec \alpha = T_0 D_x s = wy$.

12. In the preceding exercise, suppose the cable is of negligible weight, but that a horizontal roadbed of weight w per foot is suspended from the cable. Find the equation of the curve along which the cable hangs.

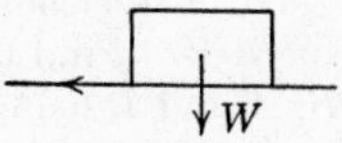

13. In the preceding exercises, state the differential equation representing the curve along which the cable hangs when the weight of the cable, supporting rods (supposed infinitely close together), and roadbed are all taken into account.

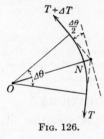

Fig. 125.

14. If a weight W is pulled (at constant velocity) along a horizontal surface and if the motion is opposed by a force of friction F, we say that the coefficient of friction between W and the surface is $\mu = F/W$. We may extend this idea of coefficient of friction to the case where we have a cord wound around a (circular) drum: We define the coefficient of friction μ between the cord and drum by the formula

$$\mu = \lim_{\Delta\theta\to 0} \frac{(\Delta T) \cos (\Delta\theta/2)}{(2T + \Delta T) \sin (\Delta\theta/2)}, \qquad \text{(iv)}$$

where $(\Delta T) \cos (\Delta\theta/2)$ represents the resultant force normal to ON and $(2T + \Delta T) \sin (\Delta\theta/2)$ represents the resultant force along ON. Since we may write (iv) in the form

$$\mu = \lim_{\Delta\theta\to 0} \left[\frac{\cos (\Delta\theta/2)}{T + (\Delta T/2)} \cdot \frac{\Delta\theta/2}{\sin (\Delta\theta/2)} \cdot \frac{\Delta T}{\Delta\theta} \right] = \frac{1}{T}(1) \frac{dT}{d\theta},$$

Fig. 126.

it follows that

$$\frac{dT}{d\theta} = \mu T.$$

If $T = T_0$ at $\theta = 0$, show that the tension T at any point is

$$T = T_0 e^{\mu\theta}.$$

Show that if a brake band $(\mu = \frac{1}{2})$ is increased from a half circumference to a whole circumference, its effectiveness is increased about fivefold.

15. Suppose that the bottom surface of a solid stone bridge is in the shape of an arch, the roadway being level. Show that the equation

$$\frac{d}{dx} \frac{p}{\sqrt{1 + p^2}} = \frac{y}{c^2}, \qquad p = \frac{dy}{dx},$$

represents the arch when there is no tendency to bend at any point and when the weight of the bridge is supported by the arch alone.

16. A particle P is dragged slowly over the horizontal xy-plane by a line PA of constant length l, A moving along the x-axis. The path of P is called a *tractrix*. Show that this path is represented by

$$\frac{p}{\sqrt{1 + p^2}} = -\frac{y}{l}, \qquad p = \frac{dy}{dx},$$

and solve this equation.

17. A river flows with speed v and a boat sails (relative to the water) with speed V. Find the path of the boat when it sails across the river from A to B, A and B being directly opposite and the boat always pointing to B.

18. The point $P(x, y)$ moves with speed v and Q moves along OX away from O with speed V. If P always moves toward Q, show that the path of P is represented by

$$y\frac{d^2x}{dy^2} = c\sqrt{1 + \left(\frac{dx}{dy}\right)^2}, \qquad c = \frac{V}{v}$$

and solve this equation.

19. A particle moves in the xy-plane subject to forces attracting it toward the axes and proportional to its distance from the axes. Find and solve the equations representing the motion.

20. A mass m is attracted to a fixed point Q by a force inversely proportional to the square of the distance from m to Q. Find the path of m. Also find the path of m when the force is directly proportional to the distance; also when the force is proportional to the square of the distance.

PART C.　SYSTEMS OF DIFFERENTIAL EQUATIONS

20. Total Differential Equations. A differential equation of the form

$$P(x, y, z)\, dx + Q(x, y, z)\, dy + R(x, y, z)\, dz = 0 \qquad (1)$$

is called a *total differential equation* in three variables. Suppose a solution of (1) can be written in the form

$$\varphi(x, y, z) = C. \qquad (2)$$

Differentiating (2), we obtain the equation

$$\frac{\partial \varphi}{\partial x}\, dx + \frac{\partial \varphi}{\partial y}\, dy + \frac{\partial \varphi}{\partial z}\, dz = 0. \qquad (3)$$

The left member of (3) is either (a) identically the left member of (1), or (b) the left member of (3) differs from the left member of (1) by a factor $\mu(x, y, z)$, so that

$$\frac{\partial \varphi}{\partial x} = \mu P, \qquad \frac{\partial \varphi}{\partial y} = \mu Q, \qquad \frac{\partial \varphi}{\partial z} = \mu R, \qquad (4)$$

with $\mu = 1$ in case (a). Thus in case (b), $\mu \neq 1$ is an integrating factor for (1).

We now seek an answer to the question: *Given an equation of the form* (1), *does it always have a solution of the form* (2)? If (1) has such a solution, then P, Q, and R must satisfy equations (4), leading to cases (a) and (b). A third case (c) to consider is the one where (1) does not have an integrating factor.

Case (a), $\mu \equiv 1$. In this case the left member of (1) is exact and the solution to (1) can be found by the method of Sec. 12, Chap. II. The method given below for case (b) may also be used to solve (1).

Case (b), $\mu \not\equiv 1$. In this case the left member of (1) has an integrating factor $\mu \neq 0$, so that

$$\mu P \, dx + \mu Q \, dy + \mu R \, dz = 0 \tag{5}$$

is exact. From Sec. 12, Chap. II, we then have (subject to the proper assumptions as to the existence and continuity of the derivatives of μP, μQ, and μR)

$$\frac{\partial(\mu P)}{\partial y} = \frac{\partial(\mu Q)}{\partial x}, \qquad \frac{\partial(\mu Q)}{\partial z} = \frac{\partial(\mu R)}{\partial y}, \qquad \frac{\partial(\mu R)}{\partial x} = \frac{\partial(\mu P)}{\partial z}. \tag{6}$$

Multiplying the equations in (6) by R, P, and Q, respectively, and adding we find, upon simplifying the result, that

$$P\left(\frac{\partial Q}{\partial z} - \frac{\partial R}{\partial y}\right) + Q\left(\frac{\partial R}{\partial x} - \frac{\partial P}{\partial z}\right) + R\left(\frac{\partial P}{\partial y} - \frac{\partial Q}{\partial x}\right) = 0. \tag{7}$$

Equation (7) is often written in the operator form

$$\begin{vmatrix} P & Q & R \\ \dfrac{\partial}{\partial x} & \dfrac{\partial}{\partial y} & \dfrac{\partial}{\partial z} \\ P & Q & R \end{vmatrix} = 0. \tag{7'}$$

Thus, Eq. (7) is *a necessary condition that* (1) *have an integrating factor*.

We shall now show that *relation* (7) *is also sufficient* by indicating a method for obtaining a solution for (1) when (7) is satisfied.

Assume that the coefficients in (1) satisfy relations (7). Hold z constant. Then (1) becomes

$$P \, dx + Q \, dy = 0 \tag{8}$$

which (under the proper restrictions on P and Q) has a solution of the form

$$f(x, y, z) = C(z), \tag{9}$$

where of course the constant C of integration may be a function of z.

We now determine C so that (9) is a solution of (1). From (9),

$$f_z \, dx + f_y \, dy + (f_z - C') \, dz = 0. \tag{10}$$

Hence, as before, if (9) is an integral of (1), then there exists a nonzero factor λ such that

$$f_x = \lambda P, \qquad f_y = \lambda Q, \qquad f_z - C' = \lambda R. \tag{11}$$

From (11),

$$f_z - \lambda R = C'(z). \tag{12}$$

Suppose (9) defines y as a function of x, z, and C, say

$$y = \varphi(x, z, C). \tag{13}$$

Substitute (13) in (12). In order that the left-hand side of the resulting equation be independent of x, it is necessary and sufficient that

$$\left[\frac{\partial}{\partial x}(f_z - \lambda R) \right]_{z,c} = 0. \tag{14}$$

But

$$\left[\frac{\partial(f_z - \lambda R)}{\partial x} \right] = \left(f_{zx} - \lambda \frac{\partial R}{\partial x} - R \frac{\partial \lambda}{\partial x} \right) + \left(f_{zy} - \lambda \frac{\partial R}{\partial y} - R \frac{\partial \lambda}{\partial y} \right) \left(\frac{\partial y}{\partial x} \right)_{z,c} . \tag{15}$$

From (10), with $C' \, dz = dC$, we have $(\partial y / \partial x)_{z,c} = -f_x / f_y$, and from (11), $(\partial y / \partial x)_{z,c} = -P/Q$. [We shall suppose that $Q \neq 0$, for if $Q = 0$, (1) is reducible to an equation free of y.]

Equation (15) may now be put into the form

$$Q \left[\frac{\partial(f_z - \lambda R)}{\partial x} \right]_{z,c} = Q f_{zx} - P f_{zy} + R \left(P \frac{\partial \lambda}{\partial y} - Q \frac{\partial \lambda}{\partial x} \right) + \lambda \left(P \frac{\partial R}{\partial y} - Q \frac{\partial R}{\partial x} \right). \tag{16}$$

From (11), it is easy to show that

$$f_{zx} = \frac{\partial}{\partial z}(\lambda P), \qquad f_{zy} = \frac{\partial}{\partial z}(\lambda Q), \qquad \frac{\partial(\lambda P)}{\partial y} = \frac{\partial(\lambda Q)}{\partial x},$$
$$P \frac{\partial \lambda}{\partial y} - Q \frac{\partial \lambda}{\partial x} = \lambda \left(\frac{\partial Q}{\partial x} - \frac{\partial P}{\partial y} \right), \tag{17}$$

so that (16) may be written as

$$Q\left[\frac{\partial}{\partial x}(f_z - \lambda R)\right]_{z,c} = \lambda \begin{vmatrix} P & Q & R \\ \dfrac{\partial}{\partial x} & \dfrac{\partial}{\partial y} & \dfrac{\partial}{\partial z} \\ P & Q & R \end{vmatrix}. \tag{18}$$

We now see that if (7) holds, then so does (14); consequently (12) can be expressed as an equation in C, C', and z, and solved for C. Equation (9) is then of the form

$$\Psi(x, y, z, C) = 0, \tag{19}$$

which is a solution of (1).

If (7) is violated, our method of solution fails, for (7) is a necessary condition for the solution of (1). If (1) is exact, (7) holds. Thus we have proved

THEOREM 20.1. *A necessary and sufficient condition that* $P\,dx + Q\,dy + R\,dz = 0$ *have a solution of the form*

$$\Psi(x, y, z, C) = 0$$

is that

$$\begin{vmatrix} P & Q & R \\ \dfrac{\partial}{\partial x} & \dfrac{\partial}{\partial y} & \dfrac{\partial}{\partial z} \\ P & Q & R \end{vmatrix} = 0.$$

Example 1. Solve $zy\,dx - zx\,dy - y^2\,dz = 0$.
Evidently,

$$\begin{vmatrix} zy & -zx & -y^2 \\ \dfrac{\partial}{\partial x} & \dfrac{\partial}{\partial y} & \dfrac{\partial}{\partial z} \\ zy & -zx & -y^2 \end{vmatrix} = zy(-2y + x) + zx(0 - y) - y^2(-z - z) = 0.$$

Let z be a constant. Then we have $zy\,dx - zx\,dy = 0$. Integrating, we find that

$$\frac{x}{y} = C.$$

Differentiating, we have

$$\frac{y\,dx - x\,dy}{y^2} = dC,$$

and combining with the given differential equation, we find

$$y^2 \, dz = y^2 z \, dC,$$

which has for a solution $\log z = C + C_2$, where C_2 is a constant. Thus the solution of the given equation is

$$\log z = \frac{x}{y} + C_2.$$

EXERCISES XV

1. Solve: $y^2 \, dx + z \, dy - y \, dz = 0.$ *Ans.* $yx - z + cy = 0.$

2. Solve: $yz^2 \, dx + (y^2 z - xz^2) \, dy = y^3 \, dz.$ *Ans.* $\dfrac{x}{y} + \dfrac{y}{z} = c.$

3. Solve: $(ye^{xy} + z) \, dx + (xe^{xy}) \, dy + x \, dz = 0.$

4. Solve: $(y + z - \beta - \gamma) \, dx + (x + z - \gamma - \alpha) \, dy$
$$+ (x + y - \alpha - \beta) \, dz = 0.$$

5. Solve: $x \, dx + y \, dy + \sqrt{\alpha^2 - x^2 - y^2} \, dz = 0.$
            Ans. $x^2 + y^2 + (z - c)^2 = \alpha^2.$

6. Verify the relations indicated in (17) and (18).

Case (c). [*Equation* (7) *not satisfied.*] In case (7) is not satisfied, (1) is said to be *nonintegrable*, i.e., (1) has no integral of the form $f(x, y, z, c) = 0$. Since (1) is an equation in three variables, we might suspect that (1) really has infinitely many integrals. If we assume any arbitrary relation whatever between the variables x, y, z, say $g(x, y, z) = 0$, this relation $g = 0$ will then (with suitable restrictions) determine any one of the variables in terms of the other two, say, $z = h(x, y)$. Substituting h for z in (1), we then obtain a new differential equation in the two variables x and y. The resulting equation may have an integral $w(x, y, c) = 0$. The general solution of (1) for the nonintegrable case then consists of an arbitrarily chosen relation $g(x, y, z) = 0$ together with a second relation $w(x, y, c) = 0$ containing an arbitrary constant.

Example 2. Find a solution of $x \, dx + y \, dy - xz^3 \, dz = 0$. This equation is nonintegrable for relation (7) does not hold,

$$\begin{vmatrix} x & y & -xz^3 \\ \dfrac{\partial}{\partial x} & \dfrac{\partial}{\partial y} & \dfrac{\partial}{\partial z} \\ x & y & -xz^3 \end{vmatrix} = yz^3 \neq 0.$$

Suppose $g(x, y, z) = x^2 + y^2 - z^2 - a = 0$. Then $x \, dx + y \, dy - z \, dz = 0$. Subtracting this relation from the given equation we find $(xz^3 - z) \, dz = 0$, $dz = 0$, $z = c$. Hence

$$\begin{cases} x^2 + y^2 - z^2 - a = 0, \\ z = c, \end{cases}$$

is a solution of the given equation.   This solution consists of the curves cut from the hyperboloids $x^2 + y^2 - z^2 - a^2 = 0$ by the planes $z = c$.

Geometrical Interpretation.   The statement that (1) satisfies the condition (7) of integrability may be interpreted geometrically as stating that through each point (x_0, y_0, z_0) there passes one of the surfaces of a family of surfaces $\varphi(x, y, z) = c$, namely, $\varphi(x, y, z) = \varphi(x_0, y_0, z_0)$, and that the equation of the tangent plane at any point (x, y, z) of this surface is

$$P(x, y, z)(X - x) + Q(x, y, z)(Y - y) + R(x, y, z)(Z - z) = 0.$$

(Here φ is assumed to be single-valued to avoid certain difficulties.)   To find the integral of (1), then, is the problem of determining a family of surfaces such that the surface passing through any point $\mathcal{P}$ is tangent to the plane corresponding to that point $\mathcal{P}$.

If (1) is nonintegrable, that is if (7) does not hold, the assumption of a second relation $g(x, y, z) = 0$, determines in conjunction with (1) a curve $\mathcal{C}$ at each point on the assumed surface $g(x, y, z) = 0$, i.e.,

$$\begin{cases} P(X - x) + Q(Y - y) + R(Z - z) = 0, \\ \dfrac{\partial g}{\partial x}(X - x) + \dfrac{\partial g}{\partial y}(Y - y) + \dfrac{\partial g}{\partial z}(Z - z) = 0. \end{cases}$$

Thus, the problem of finding the integrals of (1) is that of determining a family of curves such that the curve passing through any point $\mathcal{P}$ is tangent to the curve $\mathcal{C}$ corresponding to that point $\mathcal{P}$.   In other words, finding the integrals of (1) is the problem of finding that family of curves on any arbitrarily selected surface S whose tangent at any point of the surface S lies in the plane determined by the given differential equation at that point $\mathcal{P}$.

The differential equation (1) may be interpreted as a statement that two vectors having direction cosines proportional to $P:Q:R$ and $dx:dy:dz$, respectively, are perpendicular to each other. To solve (1) is to determine geometric loci which satisfy the property of perpendicularity mentioned above.   If (1) is integrable, the loci corresponding to the solution of (1) consist of surfaces which are orthogonal to the direction $P:Q:R$ at each point $\mathcal{P}$.   Clearly then any ordinary curve drawn on the surface has this orthogonal property at each of its points. If (1) is nonintegrable, there exists no such family of surfaces. The solution to (1) then consists in finding a family of curves upon some assumed surface having the property of orthogonality to a vector of direction $P:Q:R$.

Example 3. Consider the nonintegrable equation

$$2xy\, dx + 4y\, dy + z\, dz = 0. \tag{20}$$

Here $P = 2xy$, $Q = 4y$, $R = z$. There exists no family of surfaces perpendicular at each point (x, y, z) to the direction $P:Q:R$. However, we shall find a family of curves upon some surface, say,

$$x^2 + y^2 - z^2 = 9, \tag{21}$$

which has the property of being perpendicular to the direction $2xy:4y:z$. From (21),

$$x\, dx + y\, dy - z\, dz = 0. \tag{22}$$

Adding (22) to (20) we have

$$(2xy + x)\, dx + 5y\, dy = 0, \tag{23}$$

whose solution is

$$\frac{x^2}{5} + y - \frac{1}{2} \log (2y + 1) = c_2. \tag{24}$$

Hence, in a certain sense, the curves cut by (24) from (21) satisfy (20). Other solutions of (20) may be found by assuming various other surfaces instead of (21).

EXERCISES XVI

1. Given: $y\, dx + x\, dy = (x + y + z)\, dz$.
  (a) Find solution on $x + y + z = 1$.   *Ans.* $xy = z$.

  (b) Find solution on $x + y = 1$.   *Ans.* $xy = z + \dfrac{z^2}{2} + c$.

  (c) Find solution on some other surface.

2. Given: $xz\, dx + y\, dy + z\, dz = 0$.
  (a) Find solution on sphere $x^2 + y^2 + z^2 = 100$.   *Ans.* $x = c$.

  (b) Find solution on $y = xz$.   *Ans.* $(1 + z)\sqrt{1 + x^2} = c$.

  (c) Find solution on some other surface.

If P, Q, and R are all homogeneous and of the same degree, then the variables are separable by means of transformations such as, $x = uz$, $y = vz$, $\cdots$. Use this method to solve:

3. $(y^2 - yz)\, dx + (z^2 - xz)\, dy + (xy - y^2)\, dz = 0$. *Ans.* $\dfrac{y(x - z)}{y - z} = c$.

4. $(y^2 - yz + z^2) - (z^2 + xz + x^2) \, dy + (x^2 - xy + y^2) \, dz = 0.$

5. $t(y - z) \, dx + t(y - z + 1) \, dy - t \, dz + (z - y) \, dt = 0.$

$$Ans. \quad (y - z)e^{x+y} = ct.$$

6. Interpret geometrically the solutions in Exs. 1 and 2.

21. Simultaneous Linear Equations with Constant Coefficients.
Operators may be used advantageously in solving a system of
η linear equations with constant coefficients in η dependent
variables and one independent variable.   When $\eta = 2$ we may
represent such a system in the form

$$(a_0 D^s + a_1 D^{s-1} + \cdots + a_s)x$$
$$+ (b_0 D^m + b_1 D^{m-1} + \cdots + b_m)y = X_1(t),$$
$$(c_0 D^p + c_1 D^{p-1} + \cdots + c_p)x \tag{1}$$
$$+ (d_0 D^q + d_1 D^{q-1} + \cdots + d_q)y = X_2(t),$$

where the a's, b's, c's, and d's are constants, t is the independent
variable, $D = d/dt$, and x and y are the dependent variables to
be determined as functions of t.   For convenience we shall write
(1) in the form

$$A_{11}(D)x + A_{12}(D)y = X_1(t), \}$$
$$A_{21}(D)x + A_{22}(D)y = X_2(t). \} \tag{2}$$

To solve for x and y we may resort to the usual algebraic processes, since the symbols D, $A_{11}(D)$, $A_{12}(D)$, $A_{21}(D)$, $A_{22}(D)$ obey
the necessary algebraic laws.   If we apply the operator $A_{22}(D)$
to the first equation (2), $A_{12}(D)$ to the second, and subtract,
we find that

$$[A_{11}(D)A_{22}(D) - A_{21}(D)A_{12}(D)]x$$
$$= A_{22}(D)X_1(t) - A_{12}(D)X_2(t). \tag{3}$$

Hence

$$x = \frac{1}{A_{11}(D)A_{22}(D) - A_{21}(D)A_{12}(D)}[A_{22}(D)X_1(t)$$
$$- A_{12}(D)X_2(t)], \tag{4}$$

where the operator $\dfrac{1}{A_{11}(D)A_{22}(D) - A_{21}(D)A_{12}(D)}$ has the
significance indicated in Sec. 19.   A solution for y may be
obtained in a similar manner.   Thus the solution of (2) is

$$x = \frac{1}{\Delta}\begin{vmatrix} X_1 & A_{12}(D) \\ X_2 & A_{22}(D) \end{vmatrix} \qquad y = \frac{1}{\Delta}\begin{vmatrix} A_{11}(D) & X_1 \\ A_{21}(D) & X_2 \end{vmatrix}, \tag{5}$$

where $\Delta = \begin{vmatrix} A_{11}(D) & A_{12}(D) \\ A_{21}(D) & A_{22}(D) \end{vmatrix}$, provided of course that $\Delta \not\equiv 0$.

[The case where $\Delta \equiv 0$ will not be considered, since it implies either the inconsistency or dependence of Eqs. (2). In expanding the determinants in (5) the terms involving X_1 or X_2 should always be written with X_1 and X_2 to the right, as in (3); thus, we write $A_{22}X_1$, and not X_1A_{22}.]

To illustrate the method, we shall solve the system

$$\left. \begin{array}{c} (3D + 3)x + (2)y = e^t, \\ (4)x + (-3D + 3)y = 3t. \end{array} \right\} \tag{6}$$

By (5), we have

$$x = \frac{1}{\Delta} \begin{vmatrix} e^t & 2 \\ 3t & -3D + 3 \end{vmatrix}, \quad y = \frac{1}{\Delta} \begin{vmatrix} 3D + 3 & e^t \\ 4 & 3t \end{vmatrix}, \tag{7}$$

where

$$\Delta = \begin{vmatrix} 3D + 3 & 2 \\ 4 & (-3D + 3) \end{vmatrix} = 1 - 9D^2. \tag{8}$$

Hence

$$\left. \begin{array}{c} x = \dfrac{(-3D + 3)e^t - 6t}{1 - 9D^2} = \dfrac{-6t}{1 - 9D^2}, \\[2mm] y = \dfrac{(3D + 3)3t - 4e^t}{1 - 9D^2} = \dfrac{9 + 9t - 4e^t}{1 - 9D^2}. \end{array} \right\} \tag{9}$$

By the methods of Sec. 19, we find that

$$\left. \begin{array}{c} x = -6t + c_1 e^{t/3} + c_2 e^{-t/3}, \\ y = 9t + 9 + \frac{1}{2}e^t + c_3 e^{t/3} + c_4 e^{-t/3}. \end{array} \right\} \tag{10}$$

The constants of integration appearing in the solutions for x and y are not independent, nor are they necessarily identical. To determine the relations between these constants, we substitute (10) in one of the Eqs. (5), say the first. Upon simplifying the result, we find that

$$(4c_1 + 2c_3)e^{t/3} + (2c_2 + 2c_4)e^{-t/3} \equiv 0.$$

Since the terms $e^{t/3}$ and $e^{-t/3}$ are independent, it follows that each of the coefficients must vanish. Hence

$$4c_1 + 2c_3 = 0, \qquad 2c_2 + 2c_4 = 0,$$

so that
$$c_3 = -2c_1, \qquad c_4 = -c_2.$$
Thus the solution of (5) is
$$\left. \begin{aligned} x &= -6t + c_1 e^{t/3} + c_2 e^{-t/3}, \\ y &= 9t + 9 + \tfrac{1}{2}e^t - 2c_1 e^{t/3} - c_2 e^{-t/3}. \end{aligned} \right\} \qquad (11)$$

While the above method leading to (11) includes the complementary solution of (6), we now wish to show how the complementary solution may be obtained directly. The complementary solution of (6) is the solution of the system
$$\left. \begin{aligned} (3D + 3)x + (2)y &= 0, \\ (4)x + (-3D + 3)y &= 0. \end{aligned} \right\} \qquad (12)$$
By (5) this solution is
$$x = \frac{1}{\Delta}0 = c_1 e^{t/3} + c_2 e^{-t/3}, \qquad y = \frac{1}{\Delta}0 = c_3 e^{t/3} + c_4 e^{-t/3}, \quad (13)$$
where the c's are related as indicated above.

In the same manner, the complementary solution of (2) is
$$\left. \begin{aligned} x &= \frac{1}{\Delta}0 = c_1 e^{r_1 t} + c_2 e^{r_2 t} + \cdots + c_n e^{r_n t}, \\ y &= \frac{1}{\Delta}0 = d_1 e^{r_1 t} + d_2 e^{r_2 t} + \cdots + d_n e^{r_n t}, \end{aligned} \right\} \qquad (14)$$
where
$$\Delta = \begin{vmatrix} A_{11}(D) & A_{12}(D) \\ A_{21}(D) & A_{22}(D) \end{vmatrix},$$
and where $r_1, r_2, \cdots, r_n$ are the roots of the equation
$$\Delta = 0.$$
Here Δ is regarded as a polynomial in the variable D, so that
$$\Delta \equiv k(D - r_1)(D - r_2) \cdots (D - r_n),$$
k arising from the coefficients in (1). [Of course, (14) must be suitably modified if some of the r's are equal.] Substitution of (14) in (2), X_1 and X_2 being replaced by 0, leads to the equations
$$[c_1 A_{11}(r_1) + d_1 A_{12}(r_1)]e^{r_1 t}$$
$$+ \cdots + [c_n A_{11}(r_n) + d_n A_{12}(r_n)e^{r_n t} = 0, \quad (15)$$
$$[c_1 A_{21}(r_1) + d_1 A_{22}(r_1)]e^{r_1 t}$$
$$+ \cdots + [c_n A_{21}(r_n) + d_n A_{22}(r_n)]e^{r_n t} = 0. \quad (16)$$

The r's being all distinct, the coefficient of each factor $e^{r_i t}$ must be 0. By (15),

$$c_1 A_{11}(r_1) + d_1 A_{12}(r_1) = 0, \quad \cdots,$$
$$c_n A_{11}(r_n) + d_n A_{12}(r_n) = 0. \tag{17}$$

Since

$$\begin{vmatrix} A_{11}(r_i) & A_{12}(r_i) \\ A_{21}(r_i) & A_{22}(r_i) \end{vmatrix} = 0, \quad (i = 1, 2, \cdots, n)$$

it follows that the coefficients of $e^{r_i t}$ in (15) and (16) are linearly dependent, and (17) insures that the coefficients in (16) are all zero.

The general theory of systems of differential equations would require too great a space to present here. For a more extended treatment the reader should consult a good treatise on the subject. The exceptional cases where $\Delta = 0$ has multiple roots occur rarely in practice. In the exercises below several such special cases are encountered. The method of undetermined coefficients will be found to be quite useful at times.

The following remarks in regard to methods for finding solutions of n ordinary differential equations involving n dependent variables may be helpful. It often happens that differentiating the given equations a sufficient number of times enables one to eliminate $(n - 1)$ of the dependent variables and their derivatives, leading to a single equation containing only one dependent variable, x_1. If this equation then be integrated and the value of x_1 thus found be substituted in the other $(n - 1)$ equations there may be obtained a system of $(n - 1)$ equations in $(n - 1)$ dependent variables. By a repetition of this method a system of one equation in one dependent variable may be eventually obtained. From the solution of this latter equation the complete solution of the given system may then be obtained. Systems of n equations in n dependent variables of order higher than the first may be replaced by systems of 1st order differential equations. Thus the equation

$$\frac{d^2 y}{dx^2} + 9y = 0$$

is equivalent to the system

$$\frac{dy}{dx} = u, \qquad \frac{du}{dx} = -9y.$$

EXERCISES XVII

1. (a) Solve by (5):

$$\begin{cases} \dfrac{dx}{dt} - \dfrac{dy}{dt} + x = \cos t, \\[2mm] \dfrac{d^2x}{dt^2} - \dfrac{dy}{dt} + 3x - y = e^{2t}. \end{cases}$$

(b) Find the complementary solution by (14).

Ans. $x = \dfrac{c_1}{2}e^t + \left(\dfrac{c_2}{2} - \dfrac{c_3}{2} + \dfrac{3}{4}\right)\sin t + \left(\dfrac{c_2}{2} + \dfrac{c_3}{2} + \dfrac{1}{4}\right)\cos t$

$$+ \dfrac{2}{5}e^{2t} + \dfrac{t}{2}\cos t,$$

$y = c_1 e^t + c_2 \sin t + c_3 \cos t + \tfrac{1}{5}e^{2t} + \tfrac{1}{2}t(\sin t + \cos t).$

Solve each of the following systems:

2. $\begin{cases} 2\dfrac{d^2x}{dt^2} - \dfrac{dy}{dt} - 4x = 2t, \\[2mm] 2\dfrac{dx}{dt} + 4\dfrac{dy}{dt} - 3y = 0. \end{cases}$

$$Ans. \quad \begin{cases} x = (c_1 + c_2 t)e^t + c_3 e^{-3t/2} - \dfrac{t}{2}. \\[2mm] y = (6c_2 - 2c_1 - 2c_2 t)e^t - \tfrac{1}{3}c_3 e^{-3t/2} - \tfrac{1}{3}. \end{cases}$$

3. $\begin{cases} \dfrac{dy}{dt} - 17y + 2\dfrac{dz}{dt} - 8z = 0, \\[2mm] 13\dfrac{dy}{dt} = 53y + 2z. \end{cases}$

4. $\begin{cases} \dfrac{dx}{dt} = 3y, \\[2mm] \dfrac{dy}{dt} = 3z, \\[2mm] \dfrac{dz}{dt} = 3x. \end{cases}$ *Ans.* $\begin{cases} x = c_1 e^{2t} + c_2 e^{-t}\cos(\sqrt{3}t - \alpha), \\[2mm] y = c_1 e^{2t} + c_2 e^{-t}\cos\left(\sqrt{3}t - \alpha + \dfrac{2\pi}{3}\right), \\[2mm] z = c_1 e^{2t} + c_2 e^{-t}\cos\left(\sqrt{3}t - \alpha + \dfrac{4\pi}{3}\right). \end{cases}$

5. $\begin{cases} t\dfrac{dx}{dt} + y = 0, \\[2mm] t\dfrac{dy}{dt} + x = 0. \end{cases}$ *Ans.* $\begin{cases} x = c_1 t + c_2 t^{-1}, \\[2mm] y = c_2 t^{-1} - c_1 t. \end{cases}$

6. $\begin{cases} \dfrac{dx}{dt} + 2\dfrac{dy}{dt} - 4x - 2y = e^{2t} + 5e^{3t}, \\[2mm] \dfrac{dx}{dt} + \dfrac{dy}{dt} - 3x - y = 0. \end{cases}$

7. The differential equations of the transformer circuit indicated in the figure are

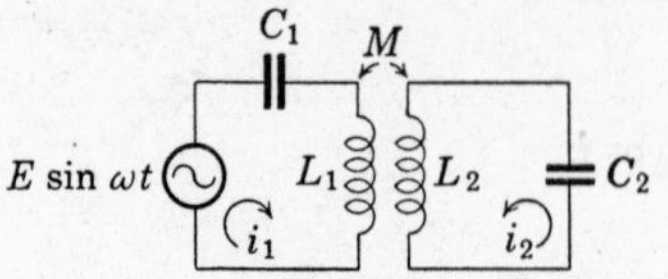

FIG. 127.

$$\begin{cases} L_1\dfrac{di_1}{dt} + \dfrac{q_1}{C_1} + M\dfrac{di_2}{dt} = E\sin wt, \\[2mm] M\dfrac{di_1}{dt} + L_2\dfrac{di_2}{dt} + \dfrac{q_2}{C_2} = 0, \end{cases}$$

where the e.m.f. impressed in the first mesh is $E\sin wt$, i_1 and q_1 are the current and charge, respectively, in mesh one, and i_2 and q_2 are the current and charge, respectively, in mesh two.

(a) Recalling that $dq_1/dt = i_1$ and $dq_2/dt = i_2$, write these equations entirely in i's.   (HINT: Differentiate.)

(b) Solve the resulting system for the currents i_1 and i_2.

(c) State the transient (complementary) solution.

(d) State the steady-state (particular integral) solution.

(e) Find the solution to this problem if at $t = 0$,

$$i_1 = 0, \qquad i_2 = 0, \qquad q_1 = 0, \qquad \text{and} \qquad q_2 = 0.$$

8. The equations of motion of a particle of mass m in pounds are

$$m\frac{d^2x}{dt^2} = gX, \qquad m\frac{d^2y}{dt^2} = gY, \qquad m\frac{d^2z}{dt^2} = gZ,$$

where x, y, and z are measured in feet and where X, Y, and Z are the x, y, and z components, respectively, of the force acting on the particle, measured in pounds weight.

(a) Find the equation of the path of a projectile shot into the air with a given initial velocity v_0 in a direction making an angle α_0 with horizontal plane.   (Assume flight to be in a vertical plane.)

(b) Solve (a) if the air exerts a resistance proportional to the velocity and directed along the path.

9. A particle moves in the xy-plane under an attractive force proportional to its distance from the origin.   (a) State the equations of motion of the particle.   (b) Show that the path followed by the particle is an ellipse. (c) State the period.

10. Solve Ex. 9 if the particle is subject to a resisting force proportional to the velocity and directed along the path.

11. A particle A moves about a particle S which exerts an attracting force inversely proportional to the square of the distance between A and S.

(a) Show that the equations of motion are $d^2x/dt^2 = -Kx/r^3$, $d^2y/dt^2 = -Ky/r^3$, where K is a constant and $r^2 = x^2 + y^2$, if the particle S is located at the origin.   (This is the case of the motion of a planet about a central sun.)

(b) Show that the radius vector $\overrightarrow{SA}$ sweeps out equal areas in equal times.

HINT: By substituting $x = r \cos \theta$, $y = r \sin \theta$, rewrite the equations of motion in polar coordinates and integrate, obtaining the integral $r^2 \dfrac{d\theta}{dt} = h$.

$$Ans. \quad \frac{d^2r}{dt^2} - r\left(\frac{d\theta}{dt}\right)^2 = -\frac{K}{r^2}, \quad 2\frac{dr}{dt}\frac{d\theta}{dt} + r\frac{d^2\theta}{dt^2} = 0.$$

(c) Show that $r = \dfrac{h^2}{K[1 + \alpha \cos (\theta - \beta)]}$ is a solution of the equations found in (b). (This shows that the path of motion is a conic with focus at S.)

12. A particle moves under the influence of the force of gravity near the surface of the earth (taken to be plane). If the particle is projected at time $t = 0$ with an initial speed of u ft. per second at an angle α with the horizontal, determine the equation of motion of the particle. Solve this equation, assuming that at $t = 0$, the particle is at the origin of a given coordinate system. What is the time of flight of the particle if the ground is perfectly flat? What is the angle α for maximum range? What is the envelope of the family of trajectories, for fixed u? What is the physical significance of this envelope? How many trajectories touch this envelope at a given point? How many trajectories reach a point on the interior of the envelope? Above the envelope? If the ground slopes at an angle β with the horizontal, find the range. Find the maximum range.

13. By Newton's law of gravitation, the force of attraction exerted by the earth on a body is given by $F = -\gamma mM/r^2$, where m is the mass of body, M the mass of the earth, r the distance between the bodies and

$$\gamma = 6.65(10)^{-8} \text{ g.}^{-1} \text{ cm.}^3 \text{ sec}^{-2}.$$

What is the differential equation of motion of a body falling to the earth from a great distance? Solve this equation for the velocity, assuming that at $t = 0$, $r = r_0$ and $v = 0$, and that if a is the radius of the earth, $F = -mg$ and $M = \dfrac{a^2g}{\gamma}$. $\qquad$ *Ans.* $v^2 = 2a^2g\left(\dfrac{1}{r} - \dfrac{1}{r_0}\right).$

If the body starts at a very great distance from the earth what is v at the surface? Neglect the resistance of the air. $\qquad$ *Ans.* 7 miles per second.

22. Simultaneous Total Differential Equations.
We shall consider the following special system which is of considerable importance:

$$\left.\begin{array}{l} P_1 \, dx + Q_1 \, dy + R_1 \, dz = 0, \\ P_2 \, dx + Q_2 \, dy + R_2 \, dz = 0, \end{array}\right\} \tag{1}$$

where P_1, Q_1, R_1, P_2, $\cdots$ are functions of x, y, and z. Equations (1) may be written

$$\frac{dx}{P} = \frac{dy}{Q} = \frac{dz}{R}, \tag{2}$$

where

$$P = \begin{vmatrix} Q_1 & R_1 \\ Q_2 & R_2 \end{vmatrix}, \qquad Q = \begin{vmatrix} R_1 & P_1 \\ R_2 & P_2 \end{vmatrix}, \qquad R = \begin{vmatrix} P_1 & Q_1 \\ P_2 & Q_2 \end{vmatrix}.$$

It can be shown that the general solution of (2) consists of two relations involving two arbitrary constants:

$$\left.\begin{array}{c} \varphi_1(x, y, z, c_1) = 0, \\ \varphi_2(x, y, z, c_2) = 0. \end{array}\right\} \tag{3}$$

Equations (3) may be interpreted as representing a family of curves whose direction at (x, y, z) is given by $dx:dy:dz$ in (2), curves whose tangent at (x, y, z) have direction cosines proportional to $P:Q:R$.

We shall indicate certain methods of obtaining solutions to (2).

Method 1.   It is sometimes possible to deduce from (2) two equations each of which contains only two variables and their differentials.

Example 1.   Consider

$$\frac{dx}{yz} = \frac{dy}{zx} = \frac{dz}{xy}, \tag{4}$$

Evidently

$$\frac{dx}{z} = \frac{dz}{x}, \qquad \frac{dy}{z} = \frac{dz}{y}, \tag{5}$$

which have the solutions

$$x^2 = z^2 + c_1, \qquad y^2 = z^2 + c_2. \tag{6}$$

Equations (6) are solutions of (4).

Method 2.   It may happen that but one equation containing only two variables and their differentials is readily obtained. In this case the solution of this equation may often be used to obtain another equation in two variables.

Example 2.   Consider

$$\frac{dx}{y} = \frac{dy}{x + z} = \frac{dz}{y}. \tag{7}$$

From the first and third members of (7) we find

$$x = z + c_1. \tag{8}$$

Substituting (8) in (7), we find

$$\frac{dy}{2z + c_1} = \frac{dz}{y,} \tag{9}$$

whose solution is

$$\frac{y^2}{2} = z^2 + c_1 z + c_2. \tag{10}$$

The solution of (7) consists of (8) and (10) taken together.

Method 3.   Each of the fractions in (2) is equal to

$$\frac{l\,dx + m\,dy + n\,dz}{lP + mQ + nR},$$

where l, m, and n are arbitrary multipliers not necessarily constants. This fact may sometimes be used advantageously to obtain a zero denominator and a numerator that is an exact differential, or to obtain a nonzero denominator for which the numerator is the differential.

Example 3.   Consider

$$\frac{dx}{y + z} = \frac{dy}{z + x} = \frac{dz}{x + y}. \tag{11}$$

Evidently

$$\frac{dx - dy}{y - x} = \frac{dy - dz}{z - y} = \frac{dx - dz}{z - x},$$

from which we find

$$y - x = c_1(z - y), \qquad z - y = c_2(z - x). \tag{12}$$

Example 4.   Consider

$$\frac{dx}{y + 2z} = \frac{dy}{x + y + 2z} = \frac{2dz}{-x}. \tag{13}$$

Then

$$\frac{dx}{y + 2z} = \frac{dy}{x + y + 2z} = \frac{2dz}{-x} = \frac{dx - dy - 2dz}{(y + 2z) - (x + y + 2z) - (-x)}$$

$$= \frac{dx - dy - 2dz}{0}.$$

Hence

$$dx - dy - 2dz = 0,$$

so that

$$x - y - 2z = c_1. \tag{14}$$

Substituting (14) in the first fraction of (13), we find

$$\frac{dx}{x - c_1} = \frac{2dz}{-x},$$

whose solution is

$$c_2(x - c_1) = \frac{1}{x^2}, \tag{15}$$

The solution of (13) is (14) and (15) taken together.

The relation of (2) and the equation

$$P\, dx + Q\, dy + R\, dz = 0 \tag{16}$$

is of some geometric interest.

Equations (2) define a family of curves whose direction vector **V** at each point (x, y, z) has direction cosines proportional to $P:Q:R$. If (16) is integrable, its solution consists of a family of surfaces everywhere orthogonal to the direction vector **V** and normal to the curves (3) defined by (2). While (2) always has a solution, (4) does not in the nonintegrable case. This means that if a family of curves is given, it is sometimes impossible to find a family of surfaces orthogonal to them. On the contrary, for a given family of surfaces, P, Q, R are defined, so that equations (2) may be solved. This means that to a given family of surfaces a family of curves orthogonal to the surfaces can always be constructed.

EXERCISES XVIII

Solve, check, and interpret geometrically each solution:

1. $dx/1 = dy/1 = dz/1.$ *Ans.* $\begin{cases} x - z = c_1, \\ y - z = c_2. \end{cases}$

2. $dx/x = dy/xyze^x = dz/z.$ *Ans.* $\begin{cases} z = c_1 x, \\ c_1(x - 1)e^x = \log c_2 y. \end{cases}$

3. $dx/y = dy/-x = dz/0.$ *Ans.* $x^2 + z^2 = c_1,\ y = c_2.$

4. $\dfrac{dx}{z(x + y)} = \dfrac{dy}{z(x - y)} = \dfrac{dz}{x^2 + y^2}.$ *Ans.* $\begin{cases} x^2 - y^2 - z^2 = c_1, \\ 2xy - z^2 = c_2. \end{cases}$

5. $\dfrac{dx}{y + 1} = \dfrac{dy}{x + 1} = \dfrac{dz}{z}.$ *Ans.* $z = c_1(2 + x + y) = \dfrac{c_2}{x - y}.$

6. $\dfrac{dx}{x} = \dfrac{dy}{x+y} = \dfrac{dz}{z+x}.$ *Ans.* $\begin{cases} x = c_1(y-x), \\ \log(y-z) = c_2 + \dfrac{y}{c_1(y-x)}. \end{cases}$

7. $\dfrac{dx}{bz-cy} = \dfrac{dy}{cx-az} = \dfrac{dz}{ay-bz}.$ *Ans.* $\begin{cases} ax + by + cz = c_1, \\ x^2 + y^2 + z^2 = c_2. \end{cases}$

8. $dx/yz = dy/zx = dz/xy.$

9. $\dfrac{dx}{1} = \dfrac{dy}{3x^2 \sin(2x+z)} = \dfrac{dz}{-2}.$ *Ans.* $\begin{cases} z + 2x = c_1, \\ y = x^3 \sin c_1 + c_2. \end{cases}$

10. In Ex. 7 determine the circle which passes through $(0, -c, b)$.

11. Find curves of Ex. 9 which intersect the circle $x^2 + y^2 = 1$, $z = 0$. Find and name the surface generated by these curves.

12. Show that the lines of the system in Ex. 1 meet the curve $x^2 + y^2 = 4$, $z = 0$, to form the surface $(x-z)^2 + (y-z)^2 = 4$; also the curve

$$\varphi(x, y) = 0, \qquad z = 0$$

to form the surface $\varphi(x-z, y-z) = 0$.

13. Show that a general integral of $\dfrac{dx}{1+\sqrt{z-x-y}} = dy = \dfrac{dz}{2}$ is $\varphi(2y - z, y + 2\sqrt{z-x-y}) = 0$, when φ is arbitrary.

14. Discuss from a geometrical standpoint the solution of

$$dx + dy + dz = 0$$

and the solutions of Ex. 1.

15. Find a set of surfaces orthogonal to the set of curves given by

$$\frac{dx}{yz} = \frac{dy}{2zx} = \frac{dz}{-3xy}.$$ *Ans.* $xy^2 = cz^3$.

16. Show that there exists no set of surfaces orthogonal to the curves whose differential equation is $dx/z = dy/(x+y) = dz/1$.

17. Find a set of surfaces orthogonal to the set of curves given by

$$\frac{dx}{x} = \frac{dy}{z} = \frac{dz}{y+2z}.$$ *Ans.* $x^2 + 2yz + 2z^2 = c_1^2$.

18. Find a set of curves orthogonal to the surfaces represented by $zy\,dx - zx\,dy - y^2\,dz = 0$.

19. Find the set of curves orthogonal to the family of surfaces $xyz = c^3$.

Ans. See Ex. 9.

20. Show that the problem of finding the orthogonal trajectories of a family of surfaces whose equation is $f(x, y, z) = c$ necessitates solving the system

$$\frac{dx}{\partial f/\partial x} = \frac{dy}{\partial f/\partial y} = \frac{dz}{\partial f/\partial z}.$$

Illustrate this by finding the orthogonal trajectories of the family of surfaces $xz = cy$; $a^2x^2 + b^2y^2 + c^2z^2 = c$; $y = x \tan(z + c)$.

21. Solve $\dfrac{dx}{x^2 + y^2} = \dfrac{dy}{2xy} = \dfrac{dz}{xz + yz}$.

22. Solve $\dfrac{dx}{y - z} = \dfrac{dy}{x + y + t} = \dfrac{dz}{x + z + t} = dt$.

PART D.   SINGULAR SOLUTIONS

23. Singular Solutions.   Suppose that a general solution of the equation

$$F(x, y, p) = 0 \tag{1}$$

is

$$\phi(x, y, c) = 0, \tag{2}$$

where $p = dy/dx$. It sometimes happens that (1) has one or more solutions which cannot be obtained by assigning a value to c in (2); such solutions are frequently called *singular*. In this section we shall illustrate the way singular solutions may sometimes be found; because an accurate treatment of singular

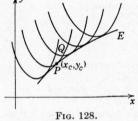

Fig. 128.

solutions is very difficult, we shall rely largely on geometric intuition.

If the family $\mathfrak{F}$ of curves (2) are all tangent to a fixed curve E, then E is called an *envelope* of the family $\mathfrak{F}$. At each point P of E, x, y, and p have the same values for E as for the particular curve (2) passing through P. Hence E represents a solution of (1).

To determine the equation of E, let (x_c, y_c) be the point of tangency of E and the curve (2) for any particular value of c. Thus x_c and y_c are functions* of c, i.e., $x_c = x(c)$, $y_c = y(c)$. Since the point (x_c, y_c) is on the curve (2) for each value of c,

$$\phi(x_c, y_c, c) \equiv \phi[x(c), y(c), c] \equiv 0$$

for every value of c.   Hence

$$\frac{d\phi[x(c), y(c), c]}{dc} = \phi_x \frac{dx}{dc} + \phi_y \frac{dy}{dc} + \phi_c$$

$$= \left(\phi_x + \phi_y \frac{dy}{dx} \right) \frac{dx}{dc} + \phi_c = 0, \tag{3}$$

* We pass over various difficulties in this discussion, such as the possibility that x and y are multiple-valued functions of c.

when ϕ_x, ϕ_y, ϕ_c are evaluated at points (x, y) on E.   On the other hand, if we regard c as constant in (2), then

$$\frac{d\phi(x, y, c)}{dx} = \phi_x + \phi_y\frac{dy}{dx} = 0, \tag{4}$$

where (4) holds at any point (x, y) on any curve (2).   Hence, when (x, y) is on E, both (3) and (4) hold simultaneously, and

$$\phi_c(x, y, c) = 0. \tag{5}$$

Thus, as (x, y) ranges along E, c varying correspondingly, (2)

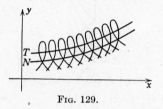

Fig. 129.

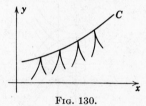

Fig. 130.

and (5) hold simultaneously, and the equation of E may be obtained by eliminating c from these equations, i.e., from

$$\phi(x, y, c) = 0, \qquad \phi_c(x, y, c) = 0. \tag{6}$$

We call the result of eliminating c from (6) the *c-discriminant* of (2).   It turns out that the c-discriminant may include other loci besides E, but we shall not try to analyze these other loci except to mention in passing that they may involve nodal loci N (see Fig. 129) or cusp loci C (see Fig. 130), and that these other loci are seldom solutions of (1).

Example 1.   A general solution of the equation

$$4p^2x = (3x - 1)^2 \tag{7}$$

is

$$(y + c)^2 - x(x - 1)^2 = 0 \tag{8}$$

Here the left member of (8) is ϕ and $\phi_c = 2(y + c)$.   Eliminating c between $\phi = 0$ and $\phi_c = 0$, we find the c-discriminant of this solution to be

$$x(x - 1)^2 = 0.$$

The line $x = 0$ is the envelope E of (8) and the line $x = 1$ is the *nodal locus* N in Fig. 131.

Example 2. A general solution of the equation

$$4p^2 = 9x$$

is

$$(y + c)^2 = x^3,$$

and the c-discriminant of this solution is

$$x^3 = 0.$$

The line $x = 0$ is a cusp locus C, and there is no envelope (Fig. 132).

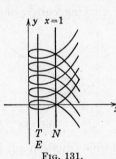
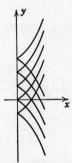

FIG. 131.   FIG. 132.

It should be observed that if (2) is solved for c, so that it is of the form $c - \psi(x, y) = 0$. then the second equation (6) reduces to the absurdity $1 = 0$, and the above procedure fails. Thus the applicability of this procedure depends upon the form in which (2) is written. This illustrates the need of carefully analyzing the preceding discussion in order to render it exact.

The equation of an envelope E may sometimes be obtained directly from the differential equation (1) without first obtaining the solution (2). Suppose that neighboring curves of (2) intersect at points Q near E (see Fig. 128), and suppose it were the case that, for some point (x_1, y_1) on E, $F_p(x_1, y_1, p_1) \neq 0$. Then $F_p \neq 0$ throughout some region about (x_1, y_1), and in particular at a point Q near (x_1, y_1). By Theorem 20.1 of Chap. I, Eq. (1) would determine p as a single-valued function of x and y near (x_1, y_1). But p is obviously not a single-valued function of x and y at points Q near (x_1, y_1). Hence, for each point (x, y) on E,

$$F_p(x, y, p) = 0. \tag{9}$$

Since (1) and (9) hold simultaneously for each point (x, y) on

E, the equation of E may be obtained by eliminating p from (1) and (9).   The expression resulting from this elimination is called the *p-discriminant*.   It turns out that the *p-discriminant* may include other loci besides E, such as a *taclocus* T or a cusp locus C, and that these other loci are seldom solutions of (1).

Example 3.   In Example 1, $F(x,\ y,\ p) \equiv 4p^2x - (3x - 1)^2$.   Hence, $F_p(x, y, p) = 8px$.   If we eliminate p from $F = 0$ and $F_p = 0$, we find the *p*-discriminant of (7) to be

$$x(3x - 1)^2 = 0.$$

In Fig. 131 we see that the line $x = 0$ is the envelope E and that the line $x = \frac{1}{3}$ is a taclocus T.

The *p*-discriminant method for obtaining the envelope is subject to the same difficulties as the *c*-discriminant method (see paragraph following Example 2).   Thus, the equation $p = 3y^{\frac{2}{3}}$ has no *p*-discriminant, while the equation $p^3 = 3y^2$ has the *p*-discriminant $y = 0$; moreover, $y = 0$ is the envelope of solutions of $p^3 = 3y^2$.

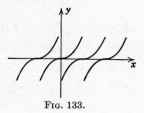

Fig. 133.

EXERCISES XIX

Find the singular solutions of each of the following equations.   Use two methods where possible, and verify that the solution obtained actually satisfies the differential equation.

1. $y = xp - (1/p)$.
   Ans. $y^2 = -4x$.
2. $xp^2 - 2yp - x = 0$.
   Ans. $x^2 + y^2 = 0$.
3. $4p^2 = 9x$.
4. $(1 + x^2)p^2 = 1$.
5. $p^2 + 2xp = y$.
6. $p^3 - 4xyp + 8y^2 = 0$.   Ans. $y = 0, 27y = 4x^3$.

Find the envelopes of the following families of curves:

7. $y = 2cx + c^4$.
8. $y^2 = cx - c^2$.
9. $(y - c)^2 = x(x - 1)$

24. Evolute and Involute.   Consider the curve C whose equation is $y = f(x)$ and let (a, b) be a point P on C.   Then $b = f(a)$ and the equation of the normal to C at (a, b) is

$$y - f(a) = -\frac{1}{f'(a)}(x - a).$$

The envelope of these normals to C is called the *evolute* E of C.

By the method of Sec. 23, we find the parametric equations of the evolute E of C to be

$$x = a - \frac{1 + [f'(a)]^2}{f''(a)} f'(a), \\ y = f(a) + \frac{1 + [f'(a)]^2}{f''(a)} \Bigg\} \tag{1}$$

In these equations (x, y) are the coordinates of the point T on E corresponding to the point P on C, i.e., the normal at P is tangent to E at (x, y). By (1), the square of the line segment $\overline{PT}$ is equal to

$$(x - a)^2 + [y - f(a)]^2 = \frac{\{1 + [f'(a)]^2\}^3}{[f''(a)]^2},$$

which is the square of the radius of curvature ρ of the curve C at $(a. b)$. Consequently T is the center of curvature of the curve C for the point P. This proves that *the evolute of a curve C is the locus of the centers of curvature of C.*

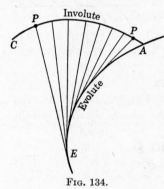

Fig. 134.

It is quite easy to show that the length of the line segment $\overline{PT}$ is equal to the length of the curve E measured from some fixed point A.

Now regard E as a given curve. Draw the tangent line τ to E at a point $P = A$, and thinking of P as fixed on τ with A fixed on E, let τ roll around E without sliding. The locus of P is called an *involute* of E. It is seen that, at any later position of τ,

$$\overline{TP} = \widehat{TA},$$

where T is the point of tangency of τ with E. It follows from the preceding paragraph that E is the evolute of the locus of P.

EXERCISES XX

1. Find the evolutes of the following curves:

(a) $y^2 = 4ax$.

(b) $\dfrac{x^2}{a^2} + \dfrac{y^2}{b^2} = 1$.

(c) $x^{2/3} + y^{2/3} = a^{2/3}$.

2. Find involutes of the following curves:

(a) $x^2 + y^2 = a^2$.

(b) $y^2 = 4ax$.

PART E.   ELECTRICAL NETWORKS

25. Linear Networks.*   Electric-circuit theory is a branch of general electromagnetic theory and deals with electrical oscillations in electrical networks.   An electrical network is a connected set of circuits or meshes (forming closed paths) each of which can be regarded as made up of circuit parameters called resistance, capacitance, and inductance elements.   In a *linear* network, the circuit parameters are assumed to be constants (independent of current strength).   A *passive* network is one which has no internal source of power, and an *active* network is one which has one or more internal sources of power.   Ordinary network theory proceeds from the assumption that the network is linear and passive.

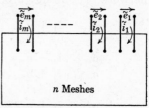

n Meshes

Fig. 135.

Two laws of great importance in the theory of such networks are Kirchhoff's laws (see Ex. XI, 3 for the relations connecting R, L, C, i, and e):

(a) *The total impressed e.m.f. around any closed loop or circuit in the network is equal to the potential drop due to resistance, capacitance, and inductance.   This total must include applied e.m.fs. as well as voltage drops due to the effects of self-parameters and induced couplings with neighboring circuits.*

(b) *The algebraic sum of currents flowing into a branch (or junction) point is zero.*

Consider the m-terminal pair n-mesh linear electrical network containing (lumped) resistances, inductances, and capacitances. Let $\tilde{e}_1, \cdots, \tilde{e}_m$ be the (real) e.m.fs. impressed on terminal pairs 1, 2, $\cdots$, m, respectively: $\tilde{q}_s$ and $\tilde{i}_s$, be the instantaneous (real) charges and (real) current, respectively, in mesh s; R_{st}, L_{st}, D_{st}, $s \neq t$, (real numbers) be the (lumped) circuit parameters

---

* GUILLEMIN, "Communication Networks," Vols. I, II.

BURINGTON, R. S., Matrices in Electric Circuit Theory, *Jour. Math. Physics*, Vol. XIV, No. 4, December, 1935.

(resistance, inductance, and elastance*, respectively) mutual to meshes s and t; and R_{ss}, L_{ss}, D_{ss}, the total circuit (real) parameters of mesh s, that is, the total resistance, inductance, and elastance of mesh s (s, $t = 1$, $\cdots$, n). The meshes are so chosen that mesh s ($s = 1$, $\cdots$, m) is the only one which passes through the terminal pairs s.

By Kirchhoff's laws, an equation for each circuit of the network may be written. The complete differential equations for the network of n meshes are:

$$\left.\begin{aligned}
a_{11}\quad &\tilde{\imath}_1 + a_{12}\quad \tilde{\imath}_2 + \cdots + a_{1n}\quad \tilde{\imath}_n = \tilde{e}_1, \\
&\cdots\cdots\cdots\cdots\cdots\cdots\cdots\cdots\cdots\cdots \\
a_{m,1}\quad &\tilde{\imath}_1 + a_{m,2}\quad \tilde{\imath}_2 + \cdots + a_{mn}\quad \tilde{\imath}_n = \tilde{e}_m, \\
a_{m+1,1}\,&\tilde{\imath}_1 + a_{m+1,2}\,\tilde{\imath}_2 + \cdots + a_{m+1,n}\tilde{\imath}_n = 0, \\
&\cdots\cdots\cdots\cdots\cdots\cdots\cdots\cdots\cdots\cdots \\
a_{n1}\quad &\tilde{\imath}_1 + a_{n2}\quad \tilde{\imath}_2 + \cdots + a_{n,n}\quad \tilde{\imath}_n = 0,
\end{aligned}\right\} \tag{1}$$

where

$$a_{st} = R_{st} + L_{st}p + D_{st}p^{-1}, \qquad p = \frac{d}{dt},$$

p being the usual derivative operator and p^{-1} its inverse.† These equations, together with a description of the initial conditions of the network, completely specify the network performance.

If the row by column rule for multiplying matrices‡ be used, Eqs. (1) may be written

$$\left\|\begin{matrix} a_{11} & \cdots & a_{1n} \\ \cdot & & \cdot \\ \cdot & & \cdot \\ \cdot & & \cdot \\ a_{n1} & \cdots & a_{nn} \end{matrix}\right\| \left\{\begin{matrix} \tilde{\imath}_1 \\ \cdot \\ \cdot \\ \cdot \\ \tilde{\imath}_n \end{matrix}\right\} = \left\{\begin{matrix} \tilde{e}_1 \\ \cdot \\ \tilde{e}_m \\ 0 \\ 0 \end{matrix}\right\}, \quad \text{or} \quad \mathbf{A}\{\tilde{\imath}\} = \{\tilde{e}\},$$

where $\mathbf{A} = (a_{rs})$ is a *network matrix* for the given network.

We shall assume that the mutual impedances are (bilateral) reciprocal, that is, $a_{rs} = a_{sr}$, and hence $R_{rs} = R_{sr}$, $L_{rs} = L_{sr}$, $C_{rs} = C_{sr}$, $D_{rs} = D_{sr}$. In other words, $\mathbf{A}$ is a symmetric matrix.

---

* By definition the *elastance* is $D_{st} = 1/C_{st}$ where C_{st} is the capacity common to meshes s and t.

† $dq_s/dt = i_s$, $q_s = \int_{t=t_0}^{t=t} i_s\, dt = p^{-1}i_s$.

‡ See Chap. VI, Part A.

It is important to note that the network matrix $\mathbf{A}$ is dependent not only upon the circuit parameters a_{rs}, but also upon the particular agreement made upon the selection of the circuits of paths forming the meshes, the numbering of these meshes and the directions which the currents in these meshes are assumed to take.

26. Steady-state Solution of $\mathbf{A}\{\bar{\imath}\} = \{\bar{e}\}$. The solution of (1) in the preceding section is divided into two parts, the particular or *steady-state* solution and the complementary or *transient* solution. The general solution of (1) is the sum of the particular and the complementary solutions.

Let the driving force e.m.fs. for the terminal pair in mesh μ be*

$$\left.\begin{array}{llll} e_\mu = E_\mu \epsilon^{j\omega t}, & \text{for} & \mu = 1, \cdots, m, & j^2 = -1, \\ e_\mu = 0, & \text{for} & \mu = m + 1, \cdots, n, \end{array}\right\} \quad (1)$$

or more briefly,

$$\{e\} = \{E\}\epsilon^{j\omega t},$$

where e_μ is the *complex e.m.f.* impressed in mesh μ, and where E_μ is the *complex voltage* for terminal pair μ. The real part of e_μ is the actual e.m.f., $\bar{e}_\mu$ i.e., $\bar{e}_\mu = \mathfrak{R}(e_\mu)$. Since phase relations are to be taken into account, the E_μ, being complex numbers, may be made to take care of the situation. Thus, if the actual e.m.f. in mesh 1 is $100 \cos (\omega t + \alpha)$, the complex e.m.f. is $e_1 \equiv E_1\epsilon^{j\omega t}$, where $E_1 = 100e^{j\alpha}$, and where

$$\mathfrak{R}(e_1) = 100 \cos (\omega t + \alpha).$$

Suppose that

$$\{i\} = \{I\}\epsilon^{j\omega t}, \quad (2)$$

that is,

$$i_\mu = I_\mu \epsilon^{j\omega t}, \quad \mu = 1, \cdots, n,$$

is a solution of (1), Sec. 25. (i_μ is called the *complex current* in mesh μ, the actual current $\bar{\imath}_\mu$ being the real part of i_μ.) Then

$$\mathbf{A}\{i\} = \mathbf{A}\{I\}\epsilon^{j\omega t} = \{E\}\epsilon^{j\omega t},$$

* In order to avoid confusion, we shall use $j = \sqrt{-1}$, $\epsilon = 2.71828 \cdots$, instead of the symbols i and e, usually used by mathematicians. Here α, ω are measured in radians.

hence

$$\mathbf{B}\{\mathbf{I}\} = \{\mathbf{E}\}, \tag{3}$$

where $\{\mathbf{I}\}$ and $\{\mathbf{E}\}$ are column arrays and $\mathbf{B} \equiv (b_{st})$,

$$b_{st} = b_{ts} = R_{st} + L_{st}\lambda + D_{st}\lambda^{-1}, \qquad \lambda = j\omega, \qquad j^2 = -1.$$

If $d(\mathbf{B}) \neq 0$, from (3)

$$\mathbf{B}^{-1}\mathbf{B}\{\mathbf{I}\} = \mathbf{B}^{-1}\{\mathbf{E}\},$$

and

$$\{\mathbf{I}\} = \mathbf{B}^{-1}\{\mathbf{E}\}, \tag{4}$$

or in the usual notation,

$$I_k = \sum_{\mu=1}^{m} \frac{E_\mu B_{\mu k}}{d(B)} = \sum_{\mu=1}^{m} \frac{E_\mu}{Z_{\mu k}}, \qquad (k = 1, \cdots, n)$$

where $B_{\mu k}$ is the cofactor of $b_{\mu k}$ and $Z_{\mu k} = d(B)/B_{\mu k}$ is the *generalized network impedance*, being a *transfer impedance* if $\mu \neq k$ and a *driving-point impedance* if $\mu = k$.

The steady-state solution of equation (1), Sec. 25 is (2), where $\{\mathbf{I}\}$ is given by (4). From (4) follows the

Superposition Principle. The result of m voltages of the same frequency simultaneously impressed in the various meshes is a linear superposition of the individual responses in mesh k for the voltages $\tilde{e}_1, \cdots, \tilde{e}_m$ *impressed successively in meshes* 1, 2, $\cdots$, m, *respectively.*

If all the e.m.fs. are zero except at terminal pair μ, then

$$\frac{I_k}{I_s} = \frac{B_{\mu k}}{B_{\mu s}} = \frac{b_{\mu s}}{b_{\mu k}}. \tag{5}$$

Now it is known that $B_{\mu k} = B_{k\mu}$. Hence if $I_k = E_\mu/b_{\mu k}$ and $I_\mu = E_k/b_{k\mu}$, then $I_\mu = I_k$ if $E_\mu = E_k$. Thus, the reciprocal

Theorem 26.1. *Let an e.m.f., $\tilde{e}_\mu$ be impressed in mesh μ and the current $\tilde{\imath}_k$ be measured in mesh k. If the same e.m.f. be placed in mesh k instead of μ, and the resulting current $\tilde{\imath}_\mu$ measured in mesh μ, then the currents $\tilde{\imath}_\mu$ and $\tilde{\imath}_k$ are exactly the same, both in magnitude and relative phases, as before; i.e., $\tilde{\imath}_\mu = \tilde{\imath}_k$.*

For simplicity of notation, we shall frequently omit the factor $\epsilon^{j\omega t}$ from notations for currents and e.m.fs., and shall speak of the actual currents and e.m.fs., in terms of their complex representations I and E.

Theorem 26.2. *If a set $\{E'\}$ of e.m.fs. all of the same frequency acting in the m branches of an invariable network, produce a current distribution $\{I'\}$, and a second set $\{E''\}$ of the same frequency produce a second current distribution $\{I''\}$, then*

$$(E')\{I''\} = (E'')\{I'\},$$

i.e., $\displaystyle\sum_{j=1}^{m} E_j' I_j'' = \sum_{j=1}^{m} E_j'' I_j'.$

Proof. By (4) $\{I'\} = B^{-1}\{E'\}$ and $\{I''\} = B^{-1}\{E''\}$ or $(I'') = (E'')(B^{-1})^T$. [(I) is a row vector $(I_1, \cdots, I_m)$]. Multiply by the transpose (E'') of $\{E''\}$. Then

$$(E'')\{I'\} = (E'')B^{-1}\{E'\} = (I'')\{E'\},$$

for $(I'') = (E'')B^{-1}$, $(B^{-1})^T = B^{-1}$, since B is symmetric.

If several different e.m.fs. of different frequencies ω_s are simultaneously impressed, each of the type $e_{r,s} = E_{r,s}\epsilon^{j\omega_s t}$, $e_{r,s}$ being the e.m.f. impressed in mesh r of frequency ω_s, then

$$\{i\} = (I_{r,s})\{\epsilon^{j\omega_s t}\} \equiv \left\{ \sum_{s=1}^{\mu} I_{r,s}\epsilon^{j\omega_s t} \right\} \tag{6}$$

is the steady-state solution, where $(I_{r,s})$ is a rectangular array and $I_{r,s}$ is the current amplitude in response to frequency ω_s in mesh r, $i_{r,s} = I_{r,s}\epsilon^{j\omega_s t}$.

In connection with (1) of Sec. 25 and its solution, it may happen that (3) are insufficient to yield a unique solution due to the fact that all the independent relationships that can be expressed by Kirchhoff's laws have not been utilized, or some of the equations may be linearly dependent upon certain others, i.e., a linear dependence relation may exist between the e's, etc. Such situations arise in the theory of ideal transformers. The rank r of B is the number of equations determining uniquely r of the currents $\{I\}$ as linear functions of the remaining $(n - r)$ I's, and $(n - r)$ is the number of linear independent mesh currents.

27. Transient Solution. In this section the complementary or transient solution of $A\{i\} = \{e\}$ is considered, that is, the solution of

$$A\{i\} = \{0\}, \tag{1}$$

where $\{0\}$ is a column array all of whose elements are zero.

Let a solution of (1) be

$$i_\mu = J_\mu^{(\nu)} \epsilon^{p_\nu t}, \quad \text{i.e.,} \quad \{i\} = \{J^{(\nu)}\} \epsilon^{p_\nu t}, \quad (\mu = 1, \cdots, n) \quad (2)$$

Then

$$A\{i\} = A\{J^{(\nu)}\} \epsilon^{p_\nu t} = \{0\},$$

hence

$$C^{(\nu)}\{J^{(\nu)}\} = \{0\}, \tag{3}$$

where

$$C^{(\nu)} \equiv (c_{jk}^{(\nu)}), \quad c_{jk}^{(\nu)} = R_{jk} + L_{jk}p_\nu + D_{jk}p_\nu^{-1}.$$

If (2) is valid, then (3) must hold. For each *mode* p_ν of the system there is a set of equations (3).

A trivial solution of (3) is $\{J^{(\nu)}\} = \{0\}$. This means that the natural behavior of the system may be to remain at rest. However, nontrivial solutions are desired. In (2), the p_ν are as yet undetermined. By Corollary 4.5 of Chap. VI, a necessary condition that (3) have a nontrivial solution is that

$$d(C^{(\nu)}) = D(p_\nu) = 0. \tag{4}$$

This polynomial equation is of degree $\tau \leqq 2n$ and is known as the *determinantal equation.* Let $p_1, p_2, \cdots, p_\tau$ be the solutions of (4).

The number of independent solutions of (3) is $(n - \rho)$, while every other solution is linearly dependent upon them, ρ being the rank of $C^{(\nu)}$.

A solution X of the matric equation $C^{(\nu)}X = 0$ of rank ρ, where ρ is the rank of $C^{(\nu)}$, is called a *complete solution.* Let $\{x\} = \{x_1 \cdots, x_n\}$ be arbitrary. Then it is known that if $\beta^{(\nu)}$ is a complete solution of $C^{(\nu)}\beta = 0$, then

$$\{J^{(\nu)}\} = \beta^{(\nu)}\{x\} \tag{5}$$

is a general solution of (3).

The solution of (1) for p_ν is

$$\{i\} = \{J^{(\nu)}\} \epsilon^{p_\nu t} = \beta^{(\nu)}\{x\} \epsilon^{p_\nu t}. \tag{6}$$

If all the natural modes p_ν are distinct, the transient mesh (complex) currents are

$$i_k = \sum_{\nu=1}^{\tau} J_k^{(\nu)} \cdot \epsilon^{p_\nu t}, \qquad (k = 1, \cdots, n)$$

or

$$\{i\} = J\{\epsilon^{pt}\}, \tag{7}$$

$J = (J_k^{(\nu)})$ being a rectangular array.

The following theorem concerning the determinantal equation is well known:

THEOREM 27.1. *The $\tau \leq 2n$ roots of (4) are the natural modes $p_1, \cdots, p_\tau$ of the network. If the network is passive, i.e., the matrices R, L, D are positive semidefinite, the real modes are negative, and the complex roots always occur in conjugate pairs with their real parts negative.*

The individual terms $J_k^{(\nu)}\epsilon^{p_\nu t}$ of (7) are known as *natural* or *normal* functions; τ is the number of *normal meshes,* "fictitious meshes" having one natural frequency and one rate of decay. $J_k^{(\nu)}$ is the transient current amplitude in mesh k of mode ν. If p_1, p_2 are conjugate complex numbers, then $J_k^{(1)}$ and $J_k^{(2)}$ are conjugates.   For $p_1 = -\alpha + jg$, α real and positive, then

$$J_k^{(1)}\epsilon^{p_1 t} + J_k^{(2)}\epsilon^{p_2 t} = 2|J_k^{(1)}|\epsilon^{-\alpha t}[\cos (gt + \phi_k^{(1)})],$$

where g is the natural frequency in radians per second, α is the decrement per second, $2|J_k^{(1)}| = 2|J_k^{(2)}|$ is the initial amplitude in amperes, and $\phi_k^{(1)}$ is the phase angle in radians.

The number n of *degrees of freedom* of a network is the number of linearly independent mesh currents; i.e., the least number of meshes by which a network may be specified.

THEOREM 27.2. *The maximum number of modes that a network may contain is twice the number of independent meshes. The degree τ of $D(p) = 0$ is $\leq 2n$. τ is the number of independent integration constants of (1), the maximum number of initial conditions that can be specified for the network, the number of independent modes of the system and the number of transient current amplitudes for a given mesh current.*

While (7) contains $2n^2$ amplitudes $J_k^{(\nu)}$, only the amplitudes for one mesh current need be considered as the integration constants of the system (1).

In electrical networks the rank of C is either n or $(n - 1)$. Then from (3), for the νth mode and any $i = 1, \cdots, n$,

$$J_k^{(\nu)} = \Gamma_{ik}^{(\nu)} G^{(\nu)}, (k = 1, 2, \cdots, n; r = 1, 2, \cdots, 2n) \tag{8}$$

where

$$\Gamma_{ik}^{(\nu)} = \text{cofactor of } c_{ik}^{(\nu)}$$

and the $G^{(\nu)}$ are arbitrary constants.

Since **C** is symmetric, $\Gamma^{(\nu)} \equiv (\Gamma_{ik}^{(\nu)})$ is the adjoint matrix of $\mathbf{C}^{(\nu)}$, and for arbitrary i and s,

$$J_k^{(\nu)} = \Gamma_{ik}^{(\nu)} \frac{J_s^{(\nu)}}{\Gamma_{is}^{(\nu)}}. \qquad (k = 1, \cdots, n; \nu = 1, \cdots, 2n). \quad (9)$$

Thus, all the J's are expressible in terms of those for the sth mesh and may be considered the true integration constants of (1).

If certain of the modes are coincident, instead of (7) the transient mesh current solution will be of the form

$$\{i\} = \mathbf{J}\{\gamma \epsilon^{pt}\}, \quad (10)$$

where $\{\gamma \epsilon^{pt}\}$ is a column array with elements

$$\epsilon^{p_1 t}, \ \epsilon^{p_2 t}, \ \cdots, \ \epsilon^{p_\mu t}, \ t \epsilon^{p_\mu t}, \ \cdots, \ t^{q-1} \epsilon^{p_\mu t}, \ \cdots,$$

p_μ being a representative q coincident mode, and p_1 a representative distinct mode.

The general solution $\{i\}_g$ of (2), Sec. 25 is the sum of the steady-state solution $\{i\}_s$ and the transient solution $\{i\}_t$ of (1),

$$\{i\}_g = \{i\}_s + \{i\}_t. \quad (11)$$

If it is required to find the charges q_k, recall that

$$\{q\} = \mathbf{p}^{-1}\{i\}. \quad (12)$$

Equations (1), Sec. 25, may be replaced by a similar set in $\{q\}$. The solution for $\{q\}_g$ could then be carried out in a manner entirely analogous to that given here for $\{i\}_g$.

It should be emphasized here that the actual currents (and charges) are given by the real part of $\{i\}_g$ and $\{q\}_g$, written $\Re\{i\}$ and $\Re\{q\}$.

The use of elementary divisors in the transient solution of (1), Sec. 25 is well known* in the theory of differential equations. This method will not be discussed here.

28. Energy Relationships. If both sides of equation (1), Sec. 25 be multiplied on the left by the transpose of $\{\bar{\imath}\}$,

$$\{\bar{\imath}\}^{\mathrm{T}} \equiv (\bar{\imath}),$$

* Moulton, J. R., "Differential Equations."

a one-rowed array, then we have the expression

$$\mathcal{P} \equiv (\tilde{\imath})\mathbf{A}\{\tilde{\imath}\} = (\tilde{\imath})\{\tilde{\mathbf{e}}\} \equiv \sum_{j=1}^{n} \tilde{\imath}_j \tilde{e}_j, \tag{1}$$

which is the rate at which the applied e.m.fs. are supplying energy to the network. $\mathcal{P}$ is known as the *instantaneous power*.

The left-hand side of (1) is evidently equal to

$$\sum_{k=1}^{n} \sum_{j=1}^{n} \tilde{\imath}_j a_{jk} \tilde{\imath}_k. \tag{2}$$

Since $a_{jk} = R_{jk} + L_{jk}p + D_{jk}p^{-1}$, we may express $\mathcal{P}$ in the form

$$\mathcal{P} \equiv (\tilde{\imath})\mathbf{R}\{\tilde{\imath}\} + \frac{p(\tilde{\imath})\mathbf{L}\{\tilde{\imath}\}}{2} + \frac{p(\tilde{\mathbf{q}})\mathbf{D}\{\tilde{\mathbf{q}}\}}{2}, \tag{3}$$

where $\mathbf{R} \equiv (R_{jk})$ is the *resistance matrix*, $\mathbf{L} \equiv (L_{jk})$ the *inductance matrix*, and $\mathbf{D} \equiv (D_{jk})$ the *elastance matrix*.

The rate at which energy is being converted into heat, the *total instantaneous power loss*, is

$$\mathcal{R} \equiv (\tilde{\imath})\mathbf{R}\{\tilde{\imath}\} = \sum_{j=1}^{n} \sum_{k=1}^{n} R_{jk} \tilde{\imath}_j \tilde{\imath}_k,$$

the rate of increase of magnetic energy, the *total instantaneous magnetic energy*, is

$$\mathcal{L} \equiv \frac{p(\tilde{\imath})\mathbf{L}\{\tilde{\imath}\}}{2} = \frac{p}{2} \sum_{j=1}^{n} \sum_{k=1}^{n} L_{jk} \tilde{\imath}_j \tilde{\imath}_k;$$

and the rate of increase in electric energy, the *total instantaneous electrostatic energy*, is

$$\mathcal{D} \equiv \frac{p(\tilde{\mathbf{q}})\mathbf{D}\{\tilde{\mathbf{q}}\}}{2} = \frac{p}{2} \sum_{j=1}^{n} \sum_{k=1}^{n} D_{jk} \tilde{\imath}_j \tilde{\imath}_k.$$

It is important to note that the network matrix $\mathbf{A}$ is actually the matrix of the instantaneous power, $\mathbf{A} = \mathbf{R} + p\mathbf{L} + p^{-1}\mathbf{D}$.

In applying matrix theory we should emphasize the fact that the network matrix **A** can be written down quite readily from the wiring diagram of the network, once an agreement has been made as to the numbering and path of the mesh currents. It is merely a step then to state the differential equations $\mathbf{A}\{\bar{\imath}\} = \{\bar{e}\}$ of the network, and the relation for power.

29. Equivalent Networks. Let $\mathbf{Y} \equiv (\mathbf{Y}_{st})$ be $\mathbf{B}^{-1}$ with all but the first m rows and columns deleted. Then from (4), Sec. 26, we have

$$\left\{\begin{matrix} I_1 \\ \cdot \\ \cdot \\ \cdot \\ I_m \end{matrix}\right\} = \left\|\begin{matrix} Y_{11} \ldots Y_{1m} \\ \cdot \qquad \cdot \\ \cdot \qquad \cdot \\ \cdot \qquad \cdot \\ Y_{m1} \ldots Y_{mm} \end{matrix}\right\| \left\{\begin{matrix} E_1 \\ \cdot \\ \cdot \\ \cdot \\ E_m \end{matrix}\right\},$$

or

$$\{\mathbf{I}\}_m = \mathbf{Y}\{\mathbf{E}\}_m. \tag{1}$$

The matrix **Y** is called a *characteristic (admittance) coefficient matrix* of the network N.

Two m-terminal-pair networks, N_1 and N_2, are said to be *equivalent* if, for all frequencies $(\omega = -\lambda j)$, they have equal characteristic coefficient matrices **Y**; i.e., for all ω they have equal electrical characteristics.

The element Y_{st}, $s \neq t$, of Y is the *short-circuit transfer admittance* between terminal pairs s and t, and the element Y_{ss} is the *short-circuit driving-point admittance* between terminal pair s, $(s = 1, \cdot \cdot \cdot, m)$.

Assuming that $I_1, \cdot \cdot \cdot, I_m$ are linearly independent, we know that Y is of rank m, and that (1) gives

$$\left\{\begin{matrix} E_1 \\ \cdot \\ \cdot \\ \cdot \\ E_m \end{matrix}\right\} = \left\|\begin{matrix} Z_{11} \ldots Z_{1m} \\ \cdot \qquad \cdot \\ \cdot \qquad \cdot \\ \cdot \qquad \cdot \\ Z_{m1} \ldots Z_{mm} \end{matrix}\right\| \left\{\begin{matrix} I_1 \\ \cdot \\ \cdot \\ \cdot \\ I_m \end{matrix}\right\},$$

or

$$\{\mathbf{E}\}_m = \mathbf{Z}\{\mathbf{I}\}_m, \tag{2}$$

where

$$Z \equiv (Z_{st}) = Y^{-1}. \qquad (s, t = 1, \cdot \cdot \cdot, m) \qquad (3)$$

The matrix Z is known as a *characteristic (impedance) coefficient matrix* of the network.

The element Z_{st}, $s \neq t$, of Z is the *open-circuit transfer impedance* between terminal pairs s and t, and the element Z_{ss} is the *open-circuit driving-point impedance* between terminal pair s, $(s = 1, \cdot \cdot \cdot, m)$.

The admittance Y_{st} may be shown to be equal, save for sign, to the ratio of the determinant of B_t^s, where B_t^s is B with row t and column s deleted, to the determinant of B as given in (3), Sec. 26, that is,

$$Y_{st} = (\pm)\frac{d(B_t^s)}{d(B)}, \qquad (s, t = 1, \cdot \cdot \cdot, m) \qquad (4)$$

where $(+)$ is used if $(s + t)$ is even, $(-)$ if $(s + t)$ is odd.

Equation (2) may also be obtained from (1) of Sec. 25 by eliminating the inner currents $i_{m+1}, \cdot \cdot \cdot, i_n$, provided, of course, that the matrix $A_{1 \cdots m}^{1 \cdots m}$ obtained from A by eliminating the first m rows and columns, is nonsingular.

The rate at which energy is being supplied to the network (1), Sec. 25, *the instantaneous power*, is (dropping the symbol $\sim$ from above $\tilde{i}$ and $\tilde{e}$)

$$\mathcal{P} = i_1 e_1 + \cdot \cdot \cdot + i_m e_m = \sum_{s,t=1}^{n} i_s R_{st} i_t + \frac{p}{2}\sum_{s,t=1}^{n} i_s L_{st} i_t$$

$$+ \frac{p}{2}\sum_{s,t=1}^{n} q_s D_{st} q_t \qquad (5)$$

or in the language of matrices

$$\mathcal{P} = (i)\{e\} = (i)A\{i\} = (i)R\{i\} + \frac{p}{2}(i)L\{i\} + \frac{p}{2}(q)D\{q\}. \qquad (6)$$

Suppose we fix the impressed e.m.fs., $e_1, \cdot \cdot \cdot, e_m$, but let the currents and charges in the quadratic form $\mathcal{P}$ be subjected to the real cogredient nonsingular linear transformation T,

$$
\begin{Bmatrix} i_1 \\ \cdot \\ \cdot \\ \cdot \\ i_m \\ i_{m+1} \\ \cdot \\ \cdot \\ \cdot \\ i_n \end{Bmatrix}
=
\left\|
\begin{array}{cccc|cccc}
1 & 0 & \cdots & 0 & 0 & \cdots & \cdot & 0 \\
0 & 1 & & \cdot & & & & \cdot \\
\cdot & & \cdot & & & & & \\
\cdot & & & \cdot & & & & \\
\cdot & & 1 & 0 & \cdot & & & \\
0 & \cdots & 0 & 1 & 0 & \cdots & \cdot & 0 \\ \hline
t_{m+1,1} & & \cdots & & & \cdots & & t_{m+1,n} \\
\cdot & & & & & & & \\
\cdot & & & & & & & \\
t_{n,1} & & \cdots & & & \cdots & & t_{n,n}
\end{array}
\right\|
\begin{Bmatrix} \bar{\imath}_1 \\ \cdot \\ \cdot \\ \cdot \\ \bar{\imath}_m \\ \bar{\imath}_{m+1} \\ \cdot \\ \cdot \\ \cdot \\ \bar{\imath}_n \end{Bmatrix}
$$

$$
\begin{Bmatrix} q_1 \\ \cdot \\ \cdot \\ \cdot \\ q_m \\ q_{m+1} \\ \cdot \\ \cdot \\ \cdot \\ q_n \end{Bmatrix}
=
\left\|
\begin{array}{cccc|cccc}
1 & 0 & \cdots & 0 & 0 & \cdots & \cdot & 0 \\
0 & 1 & & \cdot & & & & \cdot \\
\cdot & & \cdot & & & & & \\
\cdot & & & \cdot & & & & \\
\cdot & & 1 & 0 & \cdot & & & \\
0 & \cdots & 0 & 1 & 0 & \cdots & \cdot & 0 \\ \hline
t_{m+1,1} & & \cdots & & & \cdots & & t_{m+1,n} \\
\cdot & & & & & & & \\
\cdot & & & & & & & \\
t_{n,1} & & \cdots & & & \cdots & & t_{n,n}
\end{array}
\right\|
\begin{Bmatrix} \bar{q}_1 \\ \cdot \\ \cdot \\ \cdot \\ \bar{q}_m \\ \bar{q}_{m+1} \\ \cdot \\ \cdot \\ \cdot \\ \bar{q}_n \end{Bmatrix}
\tag{7}
$$

or more briefly,

$$
\{\mathbf{i}\} = \mathbf{T}\{\bar{\mathbf{\imath}}\}, \qquad \text{and} \qquad \{\mathbf{q}\} = \mathbf{T}\{\bar{\mathbf{q}}\}.
\tag{7'}
$$

where

$$
\mathbf{T} =
\left\|
\begin{array}{cccc|cccc}
1 & 0 & \cdots & 0 & 0 & \cdots & \cdot & 0 \\
0 & 1 & & \cdot & & & & \cdot \\
\cdot & & \cdot & & & & & \\
\cdot & & & \cdot & & & & \\
\cdot & & 1 & 0 & \cdot & & & \\
0 & \cdots & 0 & 1 & 0 & \cdots & \cdot & 0 \\ \hline
t_{m+1,1} & & \cdots & & & \cdots & & t_{m+1,n} \\
\cdot & & & & & & & \\
\cdot & & & & & & & \\
t_{n,1} & & \cdots & & & \cdots & & t_{n,n}
\end{array}
\right\|
$$

Then $\mathcal{P}$ becomes

$$\mathcal{P} = \bar{\imath}_1 e_1 + \cdots + \bar{\imath}_m e_m = i_1 e_1 + \cdots + i_m e_m = \sum_{s,t=1}^{n} \bar{\imath}_s \bar{a}_{st} \bar{\imath}_t,$$

or, more briefly,

$$\mathcal{P} = (\mathrm{i})\{\mathbf{e}\} = (\bar{\imath})\{\mathbf{e}\} = (\bar{\imath})\bar{\mathbf{A}}\{\bar{\imath}\}, \tag{8}$$

where

$$\bar{\mathbf{A}} = \mathbf{T}^\mathrm{T}\mathbf{A}\mathbf{T}, \qquad \bar{\mathbf{A}} \equiv (\bar{a}_{st}). \tag{9}$$

Hence the matrix corresponding to $\mathbf{B}$ in (3) of Sec. 26, becomes

$$\bar{\mathbf{B}} = \mathbf{T}^\mathrm{T}\mathbf{B}\mathbf{T}, \tag{10}$$

or

$$\bar{\mathbf{B}} \equiv \begin{Vmatrix} \bar{b}_{11} & \cdots & \bar{b}_{1n} \\ & & \\ & & \\ \bar{b}_{n1} & \cdots & \bar{b}_{nn} \end{Vmatrix}$$

$$= \begin{Vmatrix} 1 & \cdots & 0 & t_{m+1,1} & \cdots & t_{n,1} \\ & & & & & \\ & & & & & \\ 0 & \cdots & 1 & & & \\ \hline 0 & \cdots & 0 & & & \\ & & & & & \\ 0 & \cdots & 0 & t_{m+1,n} & \cdots & t_{n,n} \end{Vmatrix} \begin{Vmatrix} b_{11} & \cdots & b_{1n} \\ & & \\ & & \\ & & \\ b_{n1} & \cdots & b_{nn} \end{Vmatrix} \begin{Vmatrix} 1 & \cdots & 0 & 0 & \cdots & 0 \\ & & & & & \\ & & & & & \\ 0 & \cdots & 1 & 0 & \cdots & 0 \\ \hline t_{m+1,1} & \cdots & & t_{m+1,n} \\ & & & & & \\ t_{n,1} & \cdots & & & t_{n,n} \end{Vmatrix}$$

where

$$\bar{\mathbf{B}} = \bar{\mathbf{R}} + \bar{\mathbf{L}}\lambda + \bar{\mathbf{D}}\lambda^{-1}, \qquad \lambda = j\omega. \tag{11}$$

Hence

$$\bar{\mathbf{R}} = \mathbf{T}^\mathrm{T}\mathbf{R}\mathbf{T}, \qquad \bar{\mathbf{L}} = \mathbf{T}^\mathrm{T}\mathbf{L}\mathbf{T}, \qquad \bar{\mathbf{D}} = \mathbf{T}^\mathrm{T}\mathbf{D}\mathbf{T}. \tag{12}$$

It can be shown that the elements of $\mathbf{Y}$ as given in (1) are absolutely invariant under nonsingular m-affine transformations $\mathbf{T}$ operating upon $\mathbf{A}$ as given in (7).* Hence $\mathbf{Y}$ *is an absolutely*

* That is, $\mathbf{A}$ and $\bar{\mathbf{A}}$ have the same characteristic coefficient matrices $\mathbf{Y}$.

invariant matrix of **A** *under* **T**. **Z** *is likewise absolutely invariant
under* **T**. We thus conclude that *any m-terminal pair network
having the network matrix* $\bar{\mathbf{B}}$ *is electrically equivalent to the network
of matrix* **B**. Moreover, if the network of matrix **B** is passive
then the networks (if any) of matrix $\bar{\mathbf{B}}$ are all passive.

Inspection of the transformation **T** clearly shows that the
currents passing through the terminal pairs 1, $\cdots$, m are
left absolutely invariant under **T**. Consequently, if the e.m.fs.
$e_1, \cdots, e_m$ are kept fixed, the instantaneous power

$$\mathcal{P} = \sum_{j=1}^{m} i_j e_j = \sum_{j=1}^{m} \bar{\imath}_j \bar{e}_j$$

is absolutely invariant under the transformation **T**. In fact, if
the matrix **Z** in (2) is fixed, then under transformation **T**, $\{e\}$
remains absolutely invariant.

EXERCISES XXI

1. Solve Ex. XVII, 1 to 7, by matrix methods.

2. In each of the following circuits: (a) Set up the equations of the network
in matrix form; (b) find (or indicate) the steady state solution; (c) find (or
indicate) the transient solution if at $t = 0$, $i_s = q_s = 0$ in all meshes; (d) find
instantaneous power; (e) find the driving point and transfer impedances.

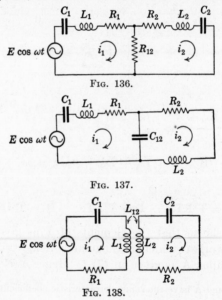

Fig. 136.

Fig. 137.

Fig. 138.

3. Show that the following networks are equivalent:

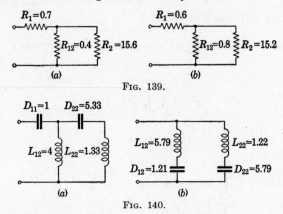

Fig. 139.

Fig. 140.

PART F.   NUMERICAL SOLUTION OF DIFFERENTIAL EQUATIONS

30. Numerical Solution of Differential Equations.

When the equation

$$\frac{dy}{dx} = f(x, y) \tag{1}$$

cannot be solved by any direct method, we may sometimes find a numerical approximation to a solution y under the condition that $y = y_0$ when $x = x_0$. Let us write (1) in the form

$$y = y_0 + \int_{x_0}^{x} f(x, y) \, dx, \tag{2}$$

where y is to be determined as a function of x. Evidently this equation determines y as y_0 when the upper limit x is x_0. As a first approximation to the solution y in (1) and (2), let*

$$y^{(1)}(x) \equiv y_0, \tag{3}$$

and for succeeding approximations, let

$$y^{(2)}(x) = y_0 + \int_{x_0}^{x} f[x, y^{(1)}] \, dx,$$

$$y^{(3)}(x) = y_0 + \int_{x_0}^{x} f[x, y^{(2)}] \, dx, \tag{4}$$

$$\cdots\cdots\cdots\cdots\cdots\cdots\cdots$$

$$y^{(n)}(x) = y_0 + \int_{x_0}^{x} f[x, y^{(n-1)}] \, dx,$$

$$\cdots\cdots\cdots\cdots\cdots\cdots\cdots$$

* The figure 1 in $y^{(1)}(x)$ is merely a superscript, and not an exponent or a symbol indicating differentiation.

It can be shown that, under certain conditions, $\lim\limits_{n \to \infty} y^{(n)}(x)$ is the desired solution y of (1).

Example 1. Solve $dy/dx = x - y$ under the condition that $y = 1$ when $x = 0$.

Write

$$y = 1 + \int_0^x (x - y)\, dx.$$

By (3) and (4),

$$y^{(1)}(x) \equiv 1,$$

$$y^{(2)}(x) = 1 + \int_0^x (x - 1)\, dx = 1 - x + \frac{x^2}{2},$$

$$y^{(3)}(x) = 1 + \int_0^x \left[x - \left(1 - x + \frac{x^2}{2}\right) \right] dx = 1 - x + x^2 - \frac{x^3}{6},$$

$$y^{(4)}(x) = 1 + \int_0^x \left[x - \left(1 - x + x^2 - \frac{x^3}{6}\right) \right] dx$$

$$= 1 - x + x^2 - \frac{x^3}{3} + \frac{x^4}{24},$$

and so on. It is readily verified that $y = 2e^{-x} + x - 1$ is a solution of the given equation, and that $y^{(4)}(x)$ contains the first four terms of the Maclaurin series for y.

It may happen that the integrals in (4) cannot be computed directly. In this event we approximate a solution y of (1) by a procedure consisting essentially of two steps:

Step I. Evaluate the integrals in (4) by some numerical method so that accurate numerical values of y in (1) are determined at a few values of x near x_0, say x_1, x_2, x_3, these x's being equally spaced at a distance h apart. (The computational labor makes it impractical to extend this procedure to very many values of x.)

Step II. Extend the tabulation of values of y for later values of x (say x_4, x_5, $\cdots$) by a step-by-step process using values of y already obtained.

To describe step I in detail, write

$$y^{(2)}(x_0) = y_0^{(2)},\ y^{(2)}(x_1) = y_1^{(2)},\ \cdots,\ y^{(3)}(x_0) = y_0^{(3)},\ \cdots.$$

Then by (3) and (4),

$$y_0^{(2)} = y_0, \qquad y_1^{(2)} = y^{(2)}(x_1) = y_0 + \int_{x_0}^{x_1} f(x, y_0)\, dx,$$

$$y_2^{(2)} = y_0 + \int_{x_0}^{x_2} f(x, y_0)\, dx, \qquad y_3^{(2)} = y_0 + \int_{x_0}^{x_3} f(x, y_0)\, dx, \tag{5}$$

y_0 being a known number. We evaluate $y_1^{(2)}$ and $y_2^{(2)}$ by (27) and (23) of Sec. 39 Chap. II, and we find $y_3^{(2)}$ from the relation

$$y_3^{(2)} = y_0 + \int_{x_0}^{x_3} f(x, y_0)\, dx = y_0 + \int_{x_0}^{x_1} f(x, y_0)\, dx + \int_{x_1}^{x_3} f(x, y_0)\, dx$$

$$= y_1^{(2)} + \int_{x_1}^{x_3} f(x, y_0)\, dx,$$

the last integral being evaluated in the same manner as $y_2^{(2)}$. By (4),

$$y_0^{(3)} = y_0, \qquad y_1^{(3)} = y_0 + \int_{x_0}^{x_1} f(x, y^{(2)})\, dx,$$

$$y_2^{(3)} = y_0 + \int_{x_0}^{x_2} f(x, y^{(2)})\, dx, \qquad y_3^{(3)} = y_0 + \int_{x_0}^{x_3} f(x, y^{(2)})\, dx,$$

where the values of $y^{(2)}$, and hence the values of $f(x, y^{(2)})$, are known at x_0, x_1, x_2, x_3 by (5). This process is continued until $y_1^{(n)}$, $y_2^{(n)}$, $y_3^{(n)}$ remain constant (to within the desired accuracy) as n increases. If we denote the values of y in (1) at x_1, x_2, x_3 by y_1, y_2, y_3, then

$$y_1 = y_1^{(n)}, \qquad y_2 = y_2^{(n)}, \qquad y_3 = y_3^{(n)}, \tag{6}$$

when n is sufficiently large.

Step II is now readily carried out. By (2),

$$y_4 = y_0 + \int_{x_0}^{x_4} f(x, y)\, dx,$$

where y is evaluated by (6). This integral may be evaluated by formula (25) of Sec. 39, Chap. II. Again,

$$y_5 = y_0 + \int_{x_0}^{x_5} f(x, y)\, dx = y_0 + \int_{x_0}^{x_1} f(x, y)\, dx + \int_{x_1}^{x_5} f(x, y)\, dx$$

$$= y_1 + \int_{x_1}^{x_5} f(x, y)\, dx,$$

where the last integral may be evaluated in the same manner as y_4. Since we may write

$$y_k = y_0 + \int_{x_0}^{x_k} f(x, y)\, dx = y_0 + \int_{x_0}^{x_{k-4}} f(x, y)\, dx + \int_{x_{k-4}}^{x_k} f(x, y)\, dx$$

$$= y_{k-4} + \int_{x_{k-4}}^{x_k} f(x, y)\, dx,$$

this process may be continued as long as desired.

To guard against errors, either accidental or arising from the approximations involved, it should be verified for each k that

$$y_k = y_0 + \int_{x_0}^{x_k} f(x, y)\, dx \tag{7}$$

by computing the integral by Simpson's rule, using the values of y given by the preceding formula, or by some other more accurate formula involving y_k (as previously estimated by the above method). If this check is carried out simultaneously with the above computation, it may be possible at each step to eliminate small discrepancies in the last computed number y_k by adjusting y_k by trial and error so that (7) is accurately verified. Extreme care must be taken to avoid small errors in y_1, y_2, y_3; to this end h may have to be very small.

Sometimes the integrals (4) may be computed directly, but the successive functions $y^{(n)}(x)$ converge slowly (or not at all) to y except in the immediate neighborhood of x_0. In such a case it may be possible to use $y^{(n)}(x)$ (for sufficiently large n) to evaluate y_1, y_2, y_3 directly (thus shortening step I), and then to find y_4, y_5, $\cdots$ by step II.

The above method may be readily extended to higher order equations, and to systems of equations, but we shall not give these extensions here. Many other methods have been devised for approximating a solution y of (1), but in most cases the gist of these methods is to replace y in (1) or (2) by its Taylor series and then to manipulate this series in some convenient fashion. We shall give an example to illustrate the manner in which this manipulation may be effected. Let us consider the *wave equation*

$$\frac{d^2y}{dx^2} + \rho(x)y = 0 \tag{8}$$

which occurs in connection with many forms of wave motion. If $y = f(x)$, we have

. . . .

$$y_2 = f(x_0 + 2h) = f(x_0) + 2hf'(x_0) + 4h^2\frac{f''(x_0)}{2!} + 8h^3\frac{f'''(x_0)}{3!}$$
$$+ 16h^4\frac{f^{(4)}(x_0)}{4!} + \cdots,$$

$$y_1 = f(x_0 + h) = f(x_0) + hf'(x_0) + h^2\frac{f''(x_0)}{2!} + h^3\frac{f'''(x_0)}{3!}$$
$$+ h^4\frac{f^{(4)}(x_0)}{4!} + \cdots, \quad (9)$$

$$y_0 = f(x_0),$$

$$y_{-1} = f(x_0 - h) = f(x_0) - hf'(x_0) + h^2\frac{f''(x_0)}{2!} - h^3\frac{f'''(x_0)}{3!}$$
$$+ h^4\frac{f^{(4)}(x_0)}{4!} - \cdots,$$

. . . .

Let us introduce the notation

$$\Delta_0 y = y_1 - y_0 = f(x_0 + h) - f(x_0),$$
$$\Delta_1 y = y_2 - y_1, \quad \Delta_2 y = y_3 - y_2, \cdots,$$
$$\Delta_0^2 y = \Delta_1 y - \Delta_0 y = y_2 - 2y_1 + y_0,$$
$$\Delta_1^2 y = \Delta_2 y - \Delta_1 y, \cdots,$$
$$\Delta_0^3 y = \Delta_1^2 y - \Delta_0^2 y = y_3 - 3y_2 + 3y_1 - y_0,$$
$$\Delta_1^3 y = \Delta_2^2 y - \Delta_1^2 y, \cdots,$$

and so on. It is readily verified from (9) that

$$\frac{1}{2!}\Delta_{-1}^2 y = h^2\frac{f''(x_0)}{2!} + h^4\frac{f^{(4)}(x_0)}{4!} + h^6\frac{f^{(6)}(x_0)}{6!} + \cdots, \quad (10.1)$$

$$\frac{1}{4!}\Delta_{-2}^4 y = h^4\frac{f^{(4)}(x_0)}{4!} + 5h^6\frac{f^{(6)}(x_0)}{6!} + \cdots, \quad (10.2)$$

$$\frac{1}{6!}\Delta_{-3}^6 y = h^6\frac{f^{(6)}(x_0)}{6!} + \cdots. \quad (10.3)$$

If we neglect terms of order higher than the sixth, it follows by (10) that

$$h^6\frac{f^{(6)}(x_0)}{6!} = \frac{1}{6!}\Delta_{-3}^6 y,$$

$$h^4\frac{f^{(4)}(x_0)}{4!} = \frac{1}{4!}\Delta_{-2}^4 y - 5\frac{1}{6!}\Delta_{-3}^6 y, \quad (11)$$

$$h^2\frac{f''(x_0)}{2!} = \frac{1}{2!}\Delta_{-1}^2 y - \frac{1}{4!}\Delta_{-2}^4 y + 4\frac{1}{6!}\Delta_{-3}^6 y.$$

Let $\varphi(x) = -\rho(x)y = -\rho(x)\,f(x)$. By (8),

$$y'' \equiv \varphi(x), \qquad y''' \equiv \varphi'(x), \cdot$$

Hence, by (10.1),

$$\frac{1}{2!}\Delta^2_{-1}y = h^2\frac{\varphi(x_0)}{2!} + h^4\frac{\varphi''(x_0)}{4!} + h^6\frac{\varphi^{(4)}(x_0)}{6!} + h^8\frac{\varphi^{(6)}(x_0)}{8!} + \cdots$$

$$= h^2\left[\frac{\varphi(x_0)}{2!} + \frac{1}{12}\left\{h^2\frac{\varphi''(x_0)}{2!}\right\} + \frac{1}{30}\left\{h^4\frac{\varphi^{(4)}(x_0)}{4!}\right\}\right.$$

$$\left. + \frac{1}{56}\left\{h^6\frac{\varphi^{(6)}(x_0)}{6!}\right\} + \cdots\right]. \quad (12)$$

Since (11) holds for an arbitrary function f, we may replace f and y in (11) by φ and substitute the results in (12). We find that

$$\Delta^2_{-1}y = h^2\left[\varphi(x_0) + \frac{1}{12}\Delta^2_{-1}\varphi - \frac{1}{240}\Delta^4_{-2}\varphi\right.$$

$$\left. + \frac{31}{60,480}\Delta^6_{-3}\varphi - \cdots\right]. \quad (13)$$

Now suppose the values $y_0, y_1, y_2, \cdots, y_n$ of a particular solution y of (8) have been determined in some way [as by a power series solution of (8)] at the values $x_0, x_1, \cdots, x_n$ of x, and suppose the following table has been constructed (neglecting $\Delta^6\varphi$ and higher differences) as far down as the line:

1	2	3	4	5	6	7	8	9	10
φ_0									y_0
φ_1	$\Delta_0\varphi$							$\Delta_0 y$	y_1
φ_2	$\Delta_1\varphi$	$\Delta^2_0\varphi$	$\frac{1}{12}\Delta^2_0\varphi$				$\Delta^2_0 y$	$\Delta_1 y$	y_2
φ_3	$\Delta_2\varphi$	$\Delta^2_1\varphi$	$\frac{1}{12}\Delta^2_1\varphi$	$\Delta^3_0\varphi$			$\Delta^2_1 y$	$\Delta_2 y$	y_3
φ_4	$\Delta_3\varphi$	$\Delta^2_2\varphi$	$\frac{1}{12}\Delta^2_2\varphi$	$\Delta^3_1\varphi$	$\Delta^4_0\varphi$	$-\frac{1}{240}\Delta^4_0\varphi$	$\Delta^2_2 y$	$\Delta_3 y$	y_4
φ_5	$\Delta_4\varphi$	$\Delta^2_3\varphi$	$\frac{1}{12}\Delta^2_3\varphi$	$\Delta^3_2\varphi$	$\Delta^4_1\varphi$	$-\frac{1}{240}\Delta^4_1\varphi$	$\Delta^2_3 y$	$\Delta_4 y$	y_5
. . . .									
φ_n	$\Delta_{n-1}\varphi$	$\Delta^2_{n-2}\varphi$	$\frac{1}{12}\Delta^2_{n-2}\varphi$	$\Delta^3_{n-3}\varphi$	$\Delta^4_{n-4}\varphi$	$-\frac{1}{240}\Delta^4_{n-4}\varphi$	$\Delta^2_{n-2}y$	$\Delta_{n-1}y$	y_n
		$\Delta^2_{n-1}\varphi$					$\Delta^2_{n-1}y$		
					$\Delta^4_{n-2}\varphi$				

Make preliminary estimates of $\Delta^4_{n-2}\varphi$ and $\Delta^2_{n-1}\varphi$. This is a simple matter when $\Delta^4\varphi$ varies slowly; but if $\Delta^4\varphi$ does not vary slowly, then a smaller value of h should be used or $\Delta^6\varphi$ should be included. These estimates need not be strictly accurate because of the small coefficients $h^2/12$ and $h^2/240$ applied to these quantities in (13). By (13) we may compute $\Delta_{n-1}^2 y$, x_0 in (13) now being replaced by x_n with n added to the subscript of each Δ. The entries $\Delta_n y$, y_{n+1}, φ_{n+1}, $\Delta_n \varphi$, $\Delta_{n-1}^2 \varphi$, $\cdots$ in the next line of the table may now be computed in the order named. If the computed value of $\Delta_{n-1}^2 \varphi$ agrees with the value previously estimated, the computation is correct and the process may be repeated for the next line; but if there is a discrepancy, the computed value of $\Delta_{n-1}^2 \varphi$ should be used as a new estimate and the computation done over. If the discrepancy is small, there will (probably) be no change in column 4, and hence no further change in this computation. The preliminary estimates of $\Delta^4 \varphi$ should be checked in a similar manner, it being unnecessary to repeat any computation so long as the discrepancies cause no alteration in column 7.

With regard to the early values of y in the table, y_0 and y_1 are determined by the "initial conditions" on the solution y of (8). If $\Delta^4 \varphi$ is almost constant, it is sometimes possible to follow the above procedure right at the start by guessing y_2, y_3, and y_4 adroitly; however, great care must be exercised because the only check on the accuracy of these values is the uniformity of variation of $\Delta^4 \varphi$.

Other formulas like (13) may be obtained by combining formulas (9) in different ways to express the derivatives in terms of differences.

EXERCISES XXII

Solve by numerical methods:

1. $dy/dx = x + y^2$, with $y = 0$ at $x = 0$.
2. $dy/dx = 2y - 2x^2$ with $y = 1$ at $x = 0$.
3. $dy/dx = (y - x)/(y + x)$ with $y = 1$ at $x = 0$.
4. $dy/dx = 1 - (y/x)$ with $y = 1$ at $x = 1$.
5. Extend the methods described above to solve the system

$$\frac{dy}{dx} = z, \qquad \frac{dz}{dx} = x^3(y + z)$$

with $y = 1$ and $z = \frac{1}{2}$ at $x = 0$.

6. Solve $(d^2y/dx^2) + (\sqrt{x + 1})y = 0$ under the set of conditions $y = 0$ at $x = 0$, $y = 0.2$ at $x = 0.1$.

7. Solve $(d^2y/dx^2) + y \sin x = 0$ under the set of conditions $y = 1$ at $x = 0$, $y = 0.95$ at $x = 0.1$.

PART G. LEGENDRE'S AND BESSEL'S EQUATIONS

31. The Linear Differential Equations of Mathematical Physics. It has been shown that all the linear differential equations of certain branches of classical mathematical physics are special cases of the *generalized Lamé equation:*

$$\frac{d^2u}{dW^2} + \left(\sum_{r=1}^{4} \frac{\frac{1}{2} - 2\alpha_r}{W - a_r} \right) \frac{du}{dW} + \left[\sum_{r=1}^{4} \frac{\alpha_r(\alpha_r + \frac{1}{2})}{(W - a_r)^2} \right.$$

$$\left. + \frac{AW^2 + 2BW + C}{\displaystyle\prod_{r=1}^{4}(W - a_r)} \right] u = 0, \quad (1)$$

where

$$A = \left(\sum_{r=1}^{4} \alpha_r \right)^2 - \sum_{r=1}^{4} \alpha_r^2 - \tfrac{3}{2} \sum_{r=1}^{4} \alpha_r + \tfrac{3}{16},$$

and where u, w, and z are complex variables.

By suitable selection of the constants in (1), a number of the important equations of physics are obtained, among which we list:

Lamé's equation:

$$\frac{d^2u}{dW^2} + \left[\sum_{r=1}^{3} \frac{\frac{1}{2}}{(W - a_r)} \right] \frac{du}{dW} - \frac{[n(n + 1)W + h]u}{4\displaystyle\prod_{r=1}^{3}(W - a_r)} = 0, \quad (2)$$

where h and n are constants.

Mathieu's equation:

$$\frac{d^2u}{dz^2} + (a + 16q \cos 2z)u = 0, \quad (3)$$

where a and q are constants.

Legendre's equation:

$$(1 - z^2) \frac{d^2u}{dz^2} - 2z\frac{du}{dz} + \left[n(n + 1) - \frac{m^2}{1 - z^2} \right]u = 0. \quad (4)$$

(The case where $m = 0$ is also called Legendre's equation.)

Bessel's (cylinder) equation:

$$z^2 \frac{d^2u}{dz^2} + z\frac{du}{dz} + (z^2 - n^2)u = 0. \tag{5}$$

Weber's (Hermite's) equation:

$$\frac{d^2u}{dz^2} + \left(n + \frac{1}{2} - \frac{1}{4}z^2\right)u = 0. \tag{6}$$

Stoke's equation:

$$z^2 \frac{d^2u}{dz^2} + z\frac{du}{dz} + \left(z^2 - \frac{1}{9}\right)u = 0. \tag{7}$$

Gauss's equation:

$$z(1 - z)\frac{d^2u}{dz^2} + [\gamma - (\alpha + \beta + 1)z]\frac{du}{dz} - \alpha\beta u = 0. \tag{8}$$

Hermite's equation:

$$\frac{d^2u}{dz^2} - 2z\frac{du}{dz} + 2nu = 0. \tag{9}$$

Laguerre equation:

$$z\frac{d^2u}{dz^2} + (1 - z)\frac{du}{dz} + nu = 0. \tag{10}$$

We shall not have space to undertake a detailed study of these important equations. However, we will make a sufficiently detailed study of the Legendre and Bessel equations so as to acquaint the student with many of the properties and methods relating to functions defined by such differential equations.

In most of these cases, the equations—such as Bessel's equation —cannot be solved in terms of the so called elementary functions. Such equations define a new class of functions.

We shall begin our study of these equations by considering the Legendre's equations for real variables.

32. Legendre's Equation. We consider the equation

$$(1 - x^2)\frac{d^2y}{dx^2} - 2x\frac{dy}{dx} + n(n + 1)y = 0, \tag{1}$$

where n is a real constant, and x and y are real variables.

We shall solve this equation by assuming a series solution of the form

$$y = a_0x^m + a_1x^{m+1} + \cdots + a_kx^{m+k} + \cdots = \sum_{k=0}^{\infty} a_kx^{m+k}. \quad (2)$$

Differentiating, we have

$$\frac{dy}{dx} = \sum_{k=0}^{\infty} (m + k)a_kx^{m+k-1},$$

$$\frac{d^2y}{dx^2} = \sum_{k=0}^{\infty} (m + k)(m + k - 1)a_kx^{m+k-2}. \quad (3)$$

Substituting (2) and (3) in the left hand member of (1), we find

$$m(m - 1)a_0x^{m-2} + (m + 1)ma_1x^{m-1} + \sum_{k=0}^{\infty} \lambda_kx^{m+k}, \quad (4)$$

where

$$\lambda_k \equiv (m + k + 2)(m + k + 1)a_{k+2} - (m + k)(m + k - 1)a_k$$
$$- 2(m + k)a_k + n(n + 1)a_k.$$

If (2) is a solution of (1), the expression (4) must vanish identically. Hence

$$m(m - 1)a_0 = 0, \quad (5)$$
$$(m + 1)ma_1 = 0, \quad (6)$$
$$\lambda_0 \equiv (m + 2)(m + 1)a_2 - (m - n)(m + n + 1)a_0 = 0, \quad (7)$$
$$\lambda_k \equiv (m + k + 2)(m + k + 1)a_{k+2}$$
$$+ (n - m - k)(n + m + k + 1)a_k = 0. \ (k = 1, 2, \cdots). \quad (8)$$

From (5), we see that $m = 0$ or $m = 1$ if a_0 is assumed to be an arbitrary constant; by (6), a_1 is arbitrary if $m = 0$ or -1.

Case $m = 0$. Substituting $m = 0$ in (8), we have

$$a_{k+2} = \frac{-(n - k)(n + k + 1)a_k}{(k + 2)(k + 1)}, \quad (9)$$

from which we can determine all the coefficients of (1) in terms of a_0 and a_1. The solution of (1) is then

$$y = a_0 \left[1 - \frac{n(n+1)}{2!} x^2 + \frac{n(n-2)(n+1)(n+3)}{4!} x^4 - \cdots \right]$$

$$+ a_1 \left[x - \frac{(n-1)(n+2)}{3!} x^3 \right.$$

$$\left. + \frac{(n-1)(n-3)(n+2)(n+4)}{5!} x^5 - \cdots \right] \quad (10)$$

By the ratio test, Theorem 7.6, Chap. IV, this series may be shown to converge for $-1 < x < 1$. In fact by Ex. XXIII, 8, Chap. IV, the series is uniformly convergent in any subinterval of $[-1, 1]$, which justifies the operation of differentiation carried out in (3).

Since a_0 and a_1 are arbitrary, (10) is the general solution of (1).

Case $m = 1$. Substituting $m = 1$ in (8), we find the corresponding solution of (1) to be the second series in (10), so that we arrive at nothing essentially different from the solution found for $m = 0$.

When n is an even integer, the first series of (10) reduces to a polynomial. Similarly, if n is an odd integer, the second series of (10) is a polynomial.

Selecting $a_0 = 0$, $a_1 \neq 0$ when n is an odd integer, and $a_0 \neq 0$, $a_1 = 0$ when n is even, we find the following particular solutions of (1):

$$P_0(x) \equiv 1,$$
$$P_1(x) \equiv x,$$
$$P_2(x) \equiv \tfrac{3}{2}x^2 - \tfrac{1}{2},$$
$$P_3(x) \equiv \tfrac{5}{2}x^3 - \tfrac{3}{2}x,$$
$$P_4(x) \equiv \frac{7 \cdot 5}{4 \cdot 2}x^4 - 2\frac{5 \cdot 3}{4 \cdot 2}x^2 + \frac{3 \cdot 1}{4 \cdot 2}, \quad (11)$$
$$P_5(x) \equiv \frac{9 \cdot 7}{4 \cdot 2}x^5 - 2\frac{7 \cdot 5}{4 \cdot 2}x^3 + \frac{5 \cdot 3}{4 \cdot 2}x, \cdots,$$

where a_1, or a_0, are so determined that $P_n(1) = 1$.

These solutions $P_n(x)$ are called *Legendre polynomials*, each satisfying a Legendre differential equation in which n has the value indicated in the subscript.

The general value for $P_n(x)$ is given by

$$P_n(x) = \sum_{\nu=0}^{[n/2]} (-1)^\nu \frac{1 \cdot 3 \cdot 5 \cdot \cdots \cdot (2n - 2\nu - 1)}{2^\nu \nu!(n - 2\nu)!} x^{n-2\nu}, \quad (12)$$

where $[n/2] = n/2$ if n is even and $[n/2] = (n - 1)/2$ if n is odd. From (12) it is possible to show that $P_n(x)$ satisfies the following recursion formulas:

$$(1 - x^2)P_n' = (n + 1)(xP_n - P_{n+1}), \quad (13)$$
$$P_{n+1}' = xP_n' + (n + 1)P_n, \quad (14)$$
$$(2n + 1)xP_n = (n + 1)P_{n+1} + nP_{n-1}, \quad (15)$$
$$(2n + 1)P_n = P_{n+1}' - P_{n-1}'. \quad (16)$$

If the function

$$\Phi = (1 - 2xh + h^2)^{-\frac{1}{2}}, \quad (17)$$

be expanded in the form

$$\Phi = \sum_{n=0}^{n=\infty} a_n h^n, \quad (18)$$

it will be found that the coefficient a_n of h^n is identically equal to the Legendre polynomial $P_n(x)$.

Zeros of $P_n(x)$. We shall have need of the following theorem:

Theorem 32.1. *If y is any solution of the linear differential equation*

$$a(x)y'' + b(x)y' + c(x)y = 0, \quad (19)$$

where x is the independent variable, and a, b, c are continuous functions of x having continuous derivatives, then the function y cannot have any repeated zeros except (possibly) for those values of x which satisfy $a(x) = 0$.

If $y(x)$ has a repeated root at x_0 then $y'(x_0) = 0$; so from (19) if $a(x_0) \neq 0$, $y''(x_0) = 0$. Differentiating (19) with respect to x and evaluating the resulting expression at x_0, we see that $y'''(x_0) = 0$.

Repeating this process we find that

$$0 = y^{\mathrm{IV}}(x_0) = \cdots = y^{(n)}(x_0) = \cdots .$$

If $y(x)$ is expandible into a Taylor's series, we then see that $y(x)$ vanishes identically at x_0.

Thus the Legendre polynomials $P_n(x)$ being solutions of Legendre's equation, an equation of the type in Theorem 32.1 in which $a(x) \equiv 1 - x^2$, has no repeated zero between -1 and $+1$.

It can be shown that the n zeros of $P_n(x)$ are all real and lie between -1 and $+1$.

Associated Legendre Polynomials. If one differentiates equation (1) m times with respect to x and then replaces $d^m y / dx^m$ by u, one finds that

$$(1 - x^2) \frac{d^2 u}{dx^2} - 2x(m + 1) \frac{du}{dx}$$
$$+ (n - m)(n + m + 1)u = 0. \quad (20)$$

The polynomial

$$u = \frac{d^m P_n(x)}{dx^m}, \quad (21)$$

evidently satisfies Eq. (20).

If we let $w = u(1 - x^2)^{m/2}$, we find from (20) that

$$(1 - x^2) \frac{d^2 w}{dx^2} - 2x \frac{dw}{dx} + \left[n(n + 1) - \frac{m^2}{1 - x^2} \right] w = 0, \quad (22)$$

which is known as the *associated Legendre equation*. This equation has for a solution,

$$w = (1 - x^2)^{m/2} \frac{d^m}{dx^m} P_n(x), \quad (23)$$

where w is usually denoted by $P_n^m(x)$ and is called an *associated Legendre polynomial*. When $m > n$, $P_n^m(x) = 0$.

EXERCISES XXIII

1. Verify the formulas (14) through (17).

2. Prove that the coefficient a_n in (18) is equal to the Legendre polynomial $P_n(x)$.

3. Show that $P_n(x) = \dfrac{1}{2^n n!} \dfrac{d^n}{dx^n} (x^2 - 1)^n$.

4. Prove that $\int_{-1}^{+1} P_n(x) P_m(x) \, dx = 0$, $m < n$,

$$\int_{-1}^{+1} P_n^2(x) \, dx = \frac{2}{2n + 1}.$$

5. The *Laguerre polynomials* $L_k(x)$ in a variable x, $0 \leqq x < \infty$, may be defined as the coefficient of u^k in the identity

$$\sum_{k=0}^{\infty} \frac{L_k(x)}{k!} u^k \equiv \frac{e^{-\frac{xu}{1-u}}}{1-u}.$$

Prove that:

(a) $L_n(x) = e^x \frac{d^n}{dx^n}(x^n e^{-x}).$

$$= \sum_{k=0}^{n} (-1)^{n-k} \frac{[n(n-1) \cdots (n-k+1)]^2}{k!} x^{n-k}.$$

(b) $L_{n+1}(x) - (2n+1-x)L_n(x) + n^2 L_{n-1}(x) = 0$, $n \geqq 1$.
(c) $L_n(x)$ is a solution of $xy'' + (1-x)y' + ny = 0$.
(d) $\int_0^\infty e^{-x} L_n L_m \, dx = 0$, $n > m$.

6. The *Hermite polynomials* $H_n(x)$ may be defined as the coefficient of u^k in the identity

$$e^{x^2-(u-x)^2} \equiv \sum_{n=0}^{\infty} \frac{H_n(x)u^k}{n!}.$$

Prove that:

(a) $H_n(x) = (-1)^n e^{x^2} \frac{d^n e^{-x^2}}{dx^n}.$

(b) $H_{n+1}(x) - 2xH_n(x) + 2nH_{n-1}(x) = 0$, $n \geqq 1$.
(c) $H_n(x)$ is a solution of $y'' - 2xy' + 2ny = 0$, $n \geqq 0$.
(d) $\int_{-\infty}^{+\infty} H_m H_n e^{-x^2} \, dx = 0$.

7. Develop the theory of Sec. 32 for the case $m = -1$.

33. Bessel's Equation.

We shall now solve *Bessel's equation*

$$x^2 \frac{d^2y}{dx^2} + x \frac{dy}{dx} + (x^2 - n^2)y = 0, \tag{1}$$

where n is a real constant, and x and y are real variables. We shall use a method similar to that given in Sec. 32. Let

$$y = x^m \sum_{k=0}^{\infty} a_k x^k. \tag{2}$$

Upon twice differentiating (2) and substituting the result in (1), we find that the left member of (1) becomes

$$(m^2 - n^2)a_0x^m + [(m + 1)^2 - n^2]a_1x^{m+1}$$
$$+ \sum_{k2=}^{\infty} \{[(m + k)^2 - n^2]a_k + a_{k-2}\}x^{m+k}. \quad (3)$$

In order that (2) may be a solution of (1), (3) must vanish identically. This can happen only when the coefficient of each power of x is zero, i.e., only if

$$(m^2 - n^2)a_0 = 0, \quad (4)$$
$$[(m + 1)^2 - n^2]a_1 = 0, \quad (5)$$
$$[(m + 2)^2 - n^2]a_2 + a_0 = 0, \quad (6)$$
$$[(m + k)^2 - n^2]a_k + a_{k-2} = 0. \quad (k = 2, 3, \cdots) \quad (7)$$

Equation (4) is called the *indicial equation* for (1), and a value of m satisfying (4) is called an *index* for (1). If we consider a_0 to be arbitrary, then (4) shows that $m = \pm n$.

Case $m = n$. If $m = n$, then by (5), (6), and (7),

$$a_1 = 0, \qquad a_2 = -\frac{a_0}{2(2n + 2)}, \qquad \cdots,$$
$$a_k = -\frac{a_{k-2}}{k(2n + k)}, \qquad \cdots . \quad (8)$$

Substitution of these coefficients in (2) leads to the result that

$$y_1 = a_0x^n\left[1 - \frac{x^2}{2(2n + 2)}\right.$$
$$\left. + \frac{x^4}{2 \cdot 4(2n + 2)(2n + 4)} - \cdots \right], \quad (9)$$

provided that n is not a negative integer.

Case $m = -n$. If $m = -n$, then

$$a_1 = 0, \qquad a_2 = \frac{1}{2(2n - 2)}, \qquad \cdots,$$
$$a_k = \frac{a_{k-2}}{k(2n - k)}, \qquad \cdots, \quad (10)$$

so that (2) assumes the form

$$y_2 = a_0x^{-n}\left[1 + \frac{x^2}{2(2n - 2)}\right.$$
$$\left. + \frac{x^4}{2 \cdot 4(2n - 2)(2n - 4)} + \cdots \right], \quad (11)$$

provided that n is not a positive integer.

If $n = 0$, then (9) and (11) are identical.

It can be shown that, if n is not an integer, (9) and (11) are independent solutions of (1), so that the general solution of (1) is

$$y = c_1 y_1 + c_2 y_2. \tag{12}$$

34. Bessel Functions of the First Kind. Formula (9) of the preceding section may be written in more convenient form when we let*

$$a_0 = \frac{1}{2^n \Gamma(n + 1)}, \tag{1}$$

where $\Gamma(n + 1) = n!$ when n is a positive integer. The particular function (9) resulting from this determination of a_0 is known as the *Bessel function of the first kind of order n* and is denoted by $J_n(x)$. It follows at once that

$$J_n(x) = \sum_{k=0}^{\infty} \frac{(-1)^k}{k! \Gamma(n + k + 1)} \left(\frac{x}{2}\right)^{n+2k}.$$

$$(n \text{ not a negative integer}) \quad (2)$$

It can be shown that the series (2) is absolutely convergent for all values of x. We shall show below how $J_n(x)$ may be defined for negative integer values of n.

The Bessel functions are related to each other in many ways. To derive a few of these relations, let us construct the product,

$$x^n J_n(x) = \sum_{k=0}^{\infty} \frac{(-1)^k}{k! \Gamma(n + k + 1) 2^{n+2k}} x^{2n+2k}, \tag{3}$$

and differentiate† it with respect to x. We find that

$$\frac{d}{dx}[x^n J_n(x)] = \sum_{k=0}^{\infty} \frac{(-1)^k}{k! \Gamma(n + k) 2^{n+2k-1}} x^{2n+2k-1}. \tag{4}$$

---

* See Sec. 36, Chap. II.

† All of the series in these sections may be shown to be uniformly convergent over any finite interval; hence they may be differentiated and integrated term by term, and they may be multiplied and divided.

But the right member of (4) is merely $x^n J_{n-1}(x)$. Hence

$$\frac{d}{dx}[x^n J_n(x)] = x^n J_{n-1}(x), \tag{5}$$

where n is not a negative integer or zero. However,

$$\frac{d}{dx}[x^n J_n(x)] = x^n \frac{d}{dx} J_n(x) + n x^{n-1} J_n(x).$$

If we equate this result with the right member of (5), we find that

$$\frac{dJ_n(x)}{dx} = J_{n-1}(x) - \frac{n}{x} J_n(x). \tag{6}$$

We may obtain the relation

$$\frac{d}{dx}[x^{-n} J_n(x)] = -x^{-n} J_{n+1}(x) \tag{7}$$

by the method used to derive (5), and also the relation

$$\frac{dJ_n(x)}{dx} = \frac{n}{x} J_n(x) - J_{n+1}(x) \tag{8}$$

in the same way that we derived (6). If we add and subtract (6) and (8), we see that

$$J_{n-1}(x) - J_{n+1}(x) = 2\frac{dJ_n(x)}{dx}, \tag{9}$$

$$J_{n-1}(x) + J_{n+1}(x) = \frac{2n}{x} J_n(x), \tag{10}$$

where n is not a negative integer or zero.

We now *define* $J_n(x)$ inductively when n is a negative integer. We first define $J_{-1}(x)$ by (10) with $n = 0$, i.e.,

$$J_{-1}(x) = -J_1(x). \tag{11}$$

Next we define $J_{-2}(x)$ by (10) with $n = -1$; the resulting formula reduces to

$$J_{-2}(x) = J_2(x) \tag{12}$$

by means of (11) and (10) with $n = 1$. In general,

$$J_{-n}(x) = (-1)^n J_n(x). \tag{13}$$

It follows from (13) that formulas (5) and (10) hold for negative integer values of n and $n = 0$.   In (11) of Sec. 33 we let

$$a_0 = \frac{1}{2^{-n}\Gamma(-n+1)},$$

then $y_2 = J_{-n}(x)$, for (9) in Sec. 33 reduces to (11) upon substituting $-n$ for n.   By (12) of Sec. 33, the general solution of Bessel's equation is

$$y = c_1 J_n(x) + c_2 J_{-n}(x) \tag{14}$$

when n is not an integer.

It is possible to express certain Bessel functions in terms of $\sin x$ and $\cos x$.   By (2),

$$
\begin{aligned}
J_{1/2}(x) &= \sum_{k=0}^{\infty} \frac{(-1)^k}{k!\Gamma(k+\frac{3}{2})} \left(\frac{x}{2}\right)^{\frac{1}{2}+2k} \\
&= \sqrt{\frac{2}{x}} \sum_{k=0}^{\infty} \frac{(-1)^k x^{2k+1}}{k!\Gamma(k+\frac{3}{2}) 2^{2k+1}}.
\end{aligned}
\tag{15}
$$

But

$$
\begin{aligned}
\Gamma\left(k+\frac{3}{2}\right) &= \left(k+\frac{1}{2}\right)\left(k-\frac{1}{2}\right)\cdots\left(\frac{1}{2}\right)\Gamma\left(\frac{1}{2}\right) \\
&= \frac{(2k+1)(2k-1)\cdots(1)}{2^{k+1}}\sqrt{\pi}, \\
k!\Gamma\left(k+\frac{3}{2}\right) &= \frac{(2k)\cdot 2(k-1)\cdot 2(k-2)\cdots 2(1)}{2^k}\Gamma\left(k+\frac{3}{2}\right) \\
&= \frac{(2k+1)!}{2^{2k+1}}\sqrt{\pi},
\end{aligned}
$$

and (15) reduces to

$$J_{1/2}(x) = \sqrt{\frac{2}{\pi x}} \sum_{k=0}^{\infty} \frac{(-1)^k x^{2k+1}}{(2k+1)!} = \sqrt{\frac{2}{\pi x}} \sin x, \tag{16}$$

since the summation is merely the Maclaurin series for $\sin x$. It may be shown in a similar manner that

$$J_{-1/2}(x) = \sqrt{\frac{2}{\pi x}} \cos x. \tag{17}$$

It follows by repeated applications of (11) that $J_{k+\frac{1}{2}}(x)$ may be expressed in the form

$$J_{k+\frac{1}{2}}(x) = P_k \sin x + Q_k \cos x, \tag{18}$$

where k is an integer, and P_k and Q_k are polynomials in $x^{-\frac{1}{2}}$.

35. Bessel Functions of the Second Kind. If n is an integer, then $J_{-n}(x) = (-1)^n J_n(x)$, and $J_n(x)$ and $J_{-n}(x)$ are not linearly independent. We shall now obtain a solution of Bessel's equation which is linearly independent of $J_n(x)$. Let

$$y = uJ_n(x), \tag{1}$$

let $J_n'(x)$ denote $\dfrac{d}{dx}[J_n(x)]$, and let $p = \dfrac{du}{dx}$. If we differentiate (1) twice and substitute the result in Bessel's equation, we find that

$$\frac{dp}{dx} + \left(\frac{2J_n'(x)}{J_n(x)} + \frac{1}{x}\right)p = 0. \tag{2}$$

Since a solution of this equation is

$$p = \frac{C_1}{x[J_n(x)]^2}, \tag{3}$$

we have the result that

$$u = \int p \, dx = C_1 \int \frac{dx}{x[J_n(x)]^2} + C_2. \tag{4}$$

We shall now represent u by a power series in the case where n *is a positive integer.* If we express $J_n(x)$ by (2) of Sec. 34, then

$$x[J_n(x)]^2 = b_1 x^{2n+1} + b_2 x^{2n+3} + b_3 x^{2n+5} + \cdots,$$

$$\frac{1}{x[J_n(x)]^2} = c_{-n}x^{-2n-1} + c_{-n+1}x^{-2n+1} + \cdots + c_{-1}x^{-3}$$
$$+ c_0 x^{-1} + c_1 x^1 + \cdots,$$

where the b's and c's denote certain numerical coefficients, and where the term $c_0 x^{-1}$ occurs because n is a positive integer. If we integrate this last series term by term, we find that

$$u = d_{-n}x^{-2n} + d_{-n+1}x^{-2n+2} + \cdots + d_{-1}x^{-2} + d_0 \log x$$
$$+ d_1 x^2 + \cdots + C_2.$$

Choose C_1 in (4) so that $d_0 = 1$. Then by (1),

$$y = J_n(x) \log x + L(x), \tag{5}$$

where

$$L(x) = a_0 x^{-n} + a_2 x^{-n+2} + a_4 x^{-n+4}$$
$$+ \cdots + a_{2\nu} x^{-n+2\nu} + \cdots . \quad (6)$$

To determine the a's we substitute (5) in Bessel's equation and follow the procedure of Sec. 33; we find that

$$x^2 L''(x) + x L'(x) + (x^2 - n^2) L(x) + 2x J_n'(x) = 0. \quad (7)$$

Substitution of (6) in (7) leads to the expression

$$\sum_{\nu=1}^{\infty} [4\nu(-n + \nu) a_{2\nu} + a_{2\nu-2}] x^{-n+2\nu}$$

$$+ \sum_{k=0}^{\infty} \frac{2(n + 2k)(-1)^k}{k! \Gamma(n + k + 1) 2^{n+2k}} x^{n+2k} = 0. \quad (8)$$

Since the terms of the first sum for which $\nu < n$ do not combine with any term of the second sum, it is convenient to group these terms by themselves; let us renumber the remaining terms of the first sum (beginning with $\nu = n$) by writing $\nu = n + k$, where $k = 0, 1, \cdots$. If we combine these latter terms with the corresponding terms of the second sum, then (8) assumes the form

$$\sum_{\nu=1}^{n-1} \{ 4\nu(\nu - n) a_{2\nu} + a_{2\nu-2} \} x^{-n+2\nu} + \sum_{k=0}^{\infty} \Big\{ 4k(n + k) a_{2n+2k}$$

$$+ a_{2n+2k-2} + \frac{2(n + 2k)(-1)^k}{k!(n + k)! 2^{n+2k}} \Big\} x^{n+2k} = 0. \quad (9)$$

With reference to the first sum we see that, each coefficient being 0,

$$a_{2\nu} = \frac{a_{2\nu-2}}{4\nu(n - \nu)}. \quad (\nu < n) \quad (10)$$

Taking $\nu = 1, 2, \cdots$, we find that

$$a_2 = \frac{a_0}{2^2(n - 1)}, \quad \cdots ,$$

$$a_{2\nu} = \frac{a_0}{2^{2\nu} \nu!(n - 1)(n - 2) \cdots (n - \nu)}. \quad (\nu < n) \quad (11)$$

Because the first term ($k = 0$) of the second sum in (9) involves only one of the a's, this coefficient is determined explicitly when this term is set equal to zero; it turns out that

$$a_{2n-2} = -\frac{2_n}{n!2^n}.$$ (12)

Substitution of this value in (11) with $\nu = n - 1$ shows that

$$a_0 = -\frac{(n-1)!}{2^{-n+1}}.$$ (13)

Hence, substituting back in (11),

$$a_{2\nu} = -\frac{1}{2}\frac{(n-\nu-1)!}{\nu!2^{-n+2\nu}}. \qquad (\nu < n) \quad (14)$$

To determine the remaining a's, let us set

$$N_k = \frac{(-1)^k}{k!(n+k)!2^{n+2k}}.$$ (15)

Upon equating to zero each coefficient in the second sum of (9), where $k > 0$, we find that

$$-2\frac{a_{2n+2k}}{N_k} = \frac{a_{2n+2k-2}}{2k(n+k)N_k} + \frac{1}{k} + \frac{1}{n+k}.$$ (16)

It follows from (15) that

$$2k(n+k)N_k = -\tfrac{1}{2}N_{k-1}.$$ (17)

Substitution of this result in (16) shows that

$$-2\frac{a_{2n+2k}}{N_k} = -2\frac{a_{2n+2k-2}}{N_{k-1}} + \frac{1}{k} + \frac{1}{n+k}.$$ (18)

The coefficient a_{2n} is as yet undetermined; for certain applications it is convenient to choose a_{2n} so that

$$-2\frac{a_{2n}}{N_0} = 1 + \frac{1}{2} + \frac{1}{3} + \cdots + \frac{1}{n}.$$ (19)

Taking $k = 1, 2, \cdots$ in (18), we find that

$$a_{2n+2k} = -\frac{N_k}{2}\left[\left(1 + \frac{1}{2} + \cdots + \frac{1}{k}\right) + \left(1 + \frac{1}{2} + \cdots + \frac{1}{n+k}\right)\right].$$ (20)

All the a's are now determined, and (5) may be written in the form

$$K_n(x) = J_n(x) \log x - \frac{1}{2} \sum_{\nu=0}^{n-1} \frac{(n - \nu - 1)!}{\nu!} \left(\frac{x}{2}\right)^{-n+2\nu}$$

$$- \frac{1}{2} \sum_{k=0}^{\infty} \frac{(-1)^k}{k!(n+k)!} \left[\left(1 + \frac{1}{2} + \cdots + \frac{1}{k}\right)\right. \tag{21}$$

$$\left. + \left(1 + \frac{1}{2} + \cdots + \frac{1}{n+k}\right)\right]\left(\frac{x}{2}\right)^{n+2k}$$

where $1 + \dfrac{1}{2} + \cdots + \dfrac{1}{k}$ is to be taken as 0 when $k = 0$. The function $K_n(x)$ is called *Neumann's Bessel function of the second kind of order n*. The series (21) may be shown to converge uniformly for all values of x. It is possible to show that relations (6) to (11) of Sec. 34 hold for $K_n(x)$ as well as $J_n(x)$. The general solution of the Bessel equation is

$$y = c_1 J_n(x) + c_2 K_n(x) \tag{22}$$

when n is a positive integer.

Other solutions of the second kind have been constructed, but they may all be obtained by assigning proper values to the c's in (22).

A modified Bessel function is defined as follows:

$$I_n(x) = i^{-n} J_n(ix), \qquad i^2 = -1. \tag{23}$$

It may be shown that $I_n(x)$ satisfies the equation

$$x^2 \frac{d^2y}{dx^2} + x \frac{dy}{dx} - (x^2 + n^2)y = 0. \tag{24}$$

and relations similar to (6) to (11) in Sec. 34.

36. Representation of Bessel Functions by Definite Integrals.

If we expand the function $e^{\frac{x}{2}\left(t - \frac{1}{t}\right)}$ by Maclaurin's series, treating x as constant and t as variable, we find that*

---

* Expand e^u and set $u = \dfrac{x}{2}t$ or $u = -\dfrac{x}{2}\dfrac{1}{t}$.

$$e^{\frac{x}{2}\left(t-\frac{1}{t}\right)} = e^{\frac{x}{2}t}e^{-\frac{x}{2}\frac{1}{t}} = \left(\sum_{k=0}^{\infty}\frac{x^k}{2^k k!}t^k\right)\left(\sum_{\nu=0}^{\infty}\frac{(-1)^\nu x^\nu}{2^\nu \nu!}\frac{1}{t^\nu}\right)$$

$$= \sum_{n=-\infty}^{\infty}\left[\sum_{\mu=0}^{\infty}\frac{(-1)^\mu x^{n+2\mu}}{2^{n+2\mu}\mu!(n+\mu)!}\right]t^n = \sum_{n=-\infty}^{\infty}J_n(x)t^n$$

$$= J_0(x) + \sum_{k=1}^{\infty}J_k(x)\left[t^k + \frac{(-1)^k}{t^k}\right]. \tag{1}$$

[Cf. (2) and (14) of Sec. 34.]   In (1) set $t = e^{i\phi}$, where $i^2 = -1$. Since $t - (1/t) = e^{i\phi} - e^{-i\phi} = 2i \sin \phi$, the left member of (1) is

$$e^{\frac{x}{2}\left(t-\frac{1}{t}\right)} = e^{ix\sin\phi} = \cos (x \sin \phi) + i \sin (x \sin \phi). \tag{2}$$

Since $t^{2k} + (1/t^{2k}) = e^{i2k\phi} + e^{-i2k\phi} = 2 \cos 2k\phi$, and

$$t^{2k-1} - \frac{1}{t^{2k-1}} = 2i \sin (2k - 1)\phi,$$

the last member of (1) may be written in the form

$$J_0(x) + 2\sum_{k=1}^{\infty}J_{2k}(x) \cos 2k\phi + i2\sum_{k=1}^{\infty}J_{2k-1}(x) \sin (2k - 1)\phi. \tag{3}$$

Since (3) and the right member of (2) are equal, we may equate their real and imaginary parts:

$$\cos (x \sin \phi) = J_0(x) + 2\sum_{k=1}^{\infty}J_{2k}(x) \cos 2k\phi, \tag{4}$$

$$\sin (x \sin \phi) = 2\sum_{k=1}^{\infty}J_{2k-1}(x) \sin (2k - 1)\phi. \tag{5}$$

Let us multiply both sides of (4) by $\cos n\phi$, both sides of (5) by $\sin n\phi$, and integrate from 0 to π, noting that

$$\int_0^\pi \cos k\phi \cos n\phi \, d\phi = \int_0^\pi \sin k\phi \sin n\phi \, d\phi = \begin{cases} \dfrac{\pi}{2} & \text{if} \quad k = n, \\ 0 & \text{if} \quad k \neq n. \end{cases}$$

We find that

$$\frac{1}{\pi}\int_0^\pi \cos(x\sin\phi)\cos n\phi\, d\phi = \begin{cases} J_n(x) \text{ if } n \text{ is even (or zero)}, \\ 0 \text{ if } n \text{ is odd.} \end{cases}$$

$$\frac{1}{\pi}\int_0^\pi \sin(x\sin\phi)\sin n\phi\, d\phi = \begin{cases} J_n(x) \text{ if } n \text{ is odd}, \\ 0 \text{ if } n \text{ is even.} \end{cases} \tag{6}$$

Hence, for any integer n (even or odd),

$$J_n(x) = \frac{1}{\pi}\int_0^\pi [\cos(x\sin\phi)\cos n\phi + \sin(x\sin\phi)\sin n\phi]\, d\phi.$$

Consequently,

$$J_n(x) = \frac{1}{\pi}\int_0^\pi \cos(n\phi - x\sin\phi)\, d\phi. \quad (n \text{ any integer}) \tag{7}$$

Bessel functions may be represented by integrals in many other ways. For example,

$$J_n(x) = \frac{x^n}{1\cdot 3\,\cdots\,(2n-1)\pi}\int_{-1}^{+1} e^{ixt}(1-t^2)^{n-\frac{1}{2}}\, dt, \tag{8}$$

where n is any real number.

37. The Zeros of the Bessel Functions. Properties relating to the zeros of the Bessel functions have many important applications.

Theorem 37.1. *Every zero of the Bessel function $J_n(x)$ is a simple zero, except possibly $x = 0$.*

This is a direct consequence of Theorem 32.1 since the Bessel equation is of the type discussed in this theorem.

Theorem 37.2. *Two linearly independent solutions $P(x)$ and $Q(x)$ of Bessel's equation can have no common zero except possibly $x = 0$.*

By Ex. 30 below, $PQ' - P'Q \equiv C/x$, where C is a constant. Suppose that both P and Q vanish at $x = x_0$ ($x_0 \neq 0$). Then $C = 0$ and $P'/P = Q'/Q$. Hence the Wronskian of P and Q is zero. But this is impossible, for P and Q are linearly independent.

It follows from this theorem that $J_n(x)$ and $K_n(x)$ have no common zero except possibly at $x = 0$.

Theorem 37.3. *$J_n(x)$ and $J_{n+1}(x)$ have no common zero except possibly $x = 0$.*

If $J_n(x_0) = J_{n+1}(x_0) = 0$, then by (9) of Sec. 34,

$$J_n(x_0) = J_n'(x_0) = 0.$$

But by Theorem 37.1, J_n and J_n' can have no common zero except possibly $x = 0$.

THEOREM 37.4. *Between any two consecutive (real) zeros of* $x^{-n}J_n(x)$ *there lies exactly one zero of* $x^{-n}J_{n+1}(x)$, *and between any two consecutive zeros of* $J_n(x)$ *where n is an integer, there lies exactly one zero of* $J_{n+1}(x)$.

It follows by Rolle's theorem that, between two consecutive zeros of $x^{-n}J_n(x)$ there lies at least one zero of

$$\frac{d}{dx}[x^{-n}J_n(x)] = -x^{-n}J_{n+1}(x)$$

[see (8) of Sec. 34]. Let $y = x^{-n}J_n(x)$. Then

$$\frac{d^2y}{dx^2} + \frac{1 + 2n}{x}\frac{dy}{dx} + y = 0. \tag{1}$$

Now y and y' can have no common zero x_0, for if

$$y(x_0) = y'(x_0) = 0,$$

then by (1), $y''(x_0) = 0$. Moreover, successive differentiations of (1) show that $y'''(x_0) = y^{IV}(x_0) = \cdots = 0$. Hence y

FIG. 141.

would be a constant. By Rolle's theorem, between two zeros of $x^{n+1}J_{n+1}(x)$ there lies at least one zero of $x^{n+1}J_n(x)$ [see (7) of Sec. 34 with n replaced by $n + 1$]. This proves the theorem except for the numerically smallest zeros $\pm\lambda$ of $x^{-n}J_n(x)$. But $x = 0$ is a zero of $x^{-n}J_{n+1}(x)$. There can be no other zero of $x^{-n}J_{n+1}(x)$ numerically less than λ, as otherwise $x^{n+1}J_n(x)$ would have another zero numerically less than λ.

We omit the proofs of the following theorems:

THEOREM 37.5. *If* $n \geq 0$, *there lies exactly one zero of* $J_n'(x)$ *between consecutive zeros of* $J_n(x)$.

THEOREM 37.6. *The function* $J_n(x)$ *has infinitely many real zeros.*

Theorem 37.7. *Between any two consecutive positive or negative zeros of any real Bessel function of order n there lies exactly one zero of any other real Bessel function of order n.*

EXERCISES XXIV

1. Show by the ratio test that series (9) and (11) of Sec. 33 converge for suitable values of n.

2. Show that series (2) of Sec. 34 is absolutely convergent for all values of x.

3. Show by direct computation with (2) of Sec. 34 that $\dfrac{dJ_0(x)}{dx} = -J_1(x)$.

4. Prove (8) and (9) of Sec. 34.

5. Verify (14) of Sec. 34.

6. Find expressions for $J_{k+\frac{1}{2}}(x)$ in terms of $\sin x$ and $\cos x$.

7. Prove: $J_2(x) - J_0(x) = 2J_0''(x)$.
$$J_2(x) = J_0''(x) - x^{-1}J_0'(x).$$
$$J_3(x) + 3J_0'(x) + 4J_0'''(x) = 0.$$

8. Show that: $I_n(x) = \displaystyle\sum_{k=0}^{\infty} \frac{1}{k!\,\Gamma(n+k+1)}\left(\frac{x}{2}\right)^{n+2k}$.

$$\frac{d}{dx}[x^n I_n(x)] = x^n I_{n-1}(x), \qquad \frac{d}{dx}[x^{-n} I_n(x)] = x^{-n} I_{n+1}(x).$$

$$I_{n-1}(x) - I_{n+1}(x) = \frac{2n}{x} I_n(x), \qquad I_{n-1}(x) + I_{n+1}(x) = 2\frac{d}{dx}[I_n(x)].$$

9. Prove: $\dfrac{d}{dx}[J_n^2(x) + J_{n+1}^2(x)] = 2\left[\dfrac{n}{x}J_n^2(x) - \dfrac{n+1}{x}J_{n+1}^2(x)\right]$.

$$\frac{d}{dx}[xJ_n(x)J_{n+1}(x)] = x[J_n^2(x) - J_{n+1}^2(x)].$$

10. By Ex. 9 show that

$$1 = J_0^2(x) + 2J_1^2(x) + \cdots + 2J_n^2(x) + \cdots.$$
$$x = 2J_0(x)J_1(x) + 6J_1(x)J_2(x) + \cdots + 2(2n+1)J_n(x)J_{n+1}(x) + \cdots.$$

11. Show that $J_{-\frac{1}{2}}(x) = \sqrt{2/\pi x}\,\cos x$.

12. From the theory of the Beta functions it is known that

$$\frac{1}{(n+k)!} = \frac{2^{n+k}}{1 \cdot 3 \cdots (2n-1) \cdot 1 \cdot 3 \cdots (2k-1)\pi} \int_0^\pi \sin^{2n}\phi \cos^{2k}\phi\, d\phi.$$

Substitute this expression for $(n+k)!$ in (2) of Sec. 34 with n an integer, and from the resulting expression show that

$$J_n(x) = \frac{x^n}{1 \cdot 3 \cdots (2n-1)\pi} \int_0^\pi \sin^{2n} \phi \cos(x \cos \phi) \, d\phi.$$

HINT: $\cos(x \cos \phi) = \sum_{k=0}^\infty (-1)^k \frac{(x \cos \phi)^{2k}}{(2k)!}$.

13. In the result of Ex. 12 set $t = \cos \phi$ and show that

$$J_n(x) = \frac{x^n}{1 \cdot 3 \cdots (2n-1)\pi} \int_{-1}^{+1} (1-t^2)^{n-\frac{1}{2}} \cos(xt) \, dt.$$

To this expression add $0 = \int_{-1}^{+1} (1-t^2)^{n-\frac{1}{2}} \sin(xt) \, dt$, and prove (8) of Sec. 36.

14. Show that the following functions are solutions of the equations indicated:

(a) $x^{-n}J_n(x)$ of $y'' + \left(\frac{1+2n}{x}\right)y' + y = 0$.

(b) $x^n J_n(x)$ of $y'' + \left(\frac{1-2n}{x}\right)y' + y = 0$.

(c) $x^{-n/2}J_n(2\sqrt{x})$ of $xy'' + (1+n)y' + y = 0$.

(d) $x^{n/2}J_n(2\sqrt{x})$ of $xy'' + (1-n)y' + y = 0$.

(e) $\sqrt{x}J_n(bx)$ of $y'' + \left(b^2 - \frac{4n^2-1}{4x^2}\right)y = 0$.

15. From (1) of Sec. 36 show that $\sum_{n=-\infty}^\infty t^n J_n(u+v) = \sum_{r=-\infty}^\infty t^r J_r(u) \sum_{s=-\infty}^\infty t^s J_s(v)$.

16. Show that

$$J_n(u+v) = \sum_{k=-\infty}^\infty J_k(u)J_{n-k}(v)$$

$$= \sum_{r=0}^n J_r(u)J_{n-r}(v) + \sum_{r=1}^\infty (-1)^r[J_r(u)J_{n+r}(v) + J_r(v)J_{n+r}(u)],$$

where n is an integer.

17. Neumann's Addition Formula for $J_0(x)$. Show that

$$J_0\left(\sqrt{b^2 + c^2 - 2bc \cos \alpha}\right) = \sum_{n=-\infty}^\infty e^{in(\pi-\alpha)} J_n(b)J_{-n}(c)$$

$$= J_0(b)J_0(c) + 2\sum_{n=1}^\infty J_n(b)J_n(c) \cos n\alpha.$$

Hint: Show that

$$\sum_{m=-\infty}^{\infty} e^{im\beta} J_m(b) t^m \sum_{n=-\infty}^{\infty} e^{-in\gamma} J_n(c) t^n - e^{\frac{i}{t}(b\sin\beta - c\sin\gamma)} \sum_{m=-\infty}^{\infty} J_m(be^{i\beta}) t^m \sum_{n=-\infty}^{\infty} J_n(ce^{-i\gamma}) t^n$$

$$= e^{\frac{i}{t}(b\sin\beta - c\sin\gamma)} \sum_{n=-\infty}^{\infty} J_n(be^{i\beta} + ce^{-i\gamma}) t^n.$$

Then let $a = be^{i\beta} + ce^{-i\gamma}$, $b\sin\beta - c\sin\gamma = 0$, $\alpha = \pi - \beta - \gamma$, so that $a^2 = b^2 + c^2 - 2bc\cos\alpha$. Finally, equate terms independent of t in the above identity.

18. Develop relations similar to (6) to (11) of Sec. 34 valid for $K_n(x)$.

19. Show that (7) of Sec. 36 satisfies the equation

$$x^2 y'' + xy' + (x^2 - n^2)y = \frac{\sin n\pi}{\pi}(x - n).$$

20. Show that $J_0(x) = \dfrac{1}{\pi} \displaystyle\int_0^\pi \cos(x\cos\phi)\, d\phi.$

21. Show that $J_n(x) \to 0$ as $n \to \infty$.

22. Show that $J_{-(n+\epsilon)}(x) \to (-1)^n J_n(x)$ as $\epsilon \to 0$ if n is an integer.

23. Show by (11) of Sec. 34 that

$$J_{n-1}(x) = \frac{2}{x}\left[\sum_{k=0}^{\infty}(-1)^k(n+2k)J_{n+2k}(x)\right].$$

24. By Ex. 23 show that

$$J_n'(x) = \frac{2}{x}\left[\frac{n}{2}J_n(x) + \sum_{k=1}^{\infty}(-1)^k(n+2k)J_{n+2k}(x)\right].$$

25. Show that, if n is any constant, $\cos n\theta\, J_n(r)$ and $\sin n\theta\, J_n(r)$ are solutions of $\dfrac{\partial^2 v}{\partial r^2} + \dfrac{1}{r}\dfrac{\partial v}{\partial r} + \dfrac{1}{r^2}\dfrac{\partial^2 v}{\partial \theta^2} + v = 0.$

26. Show that $e^{\pm kz}\cos n\phi\, J_n(kr)$ and $e^{\pm kz}\sin n\phi\, J_n(kr)$ are solutions of

$$\frac{\partial^2 v}{\partial r^2} + \frac{1}{r^2}\frac{\partial^2 v}{\partial \phi^2} + \frac{\partial^2 v}{\partial z^2} + \frac{1}{r}\frac{\partial v}{\partial r} = 0.$$

Is $e^{\pm kz + in\phi} J_n(kr)$ a solution?

27. Show that, if n is a positive integer or zero,

$$x^n = 2^n \sum_{r=0}^{\infty} \frac{(n+2r)(n-r-1)!}{r!} J_{n+2r}(x).$$

28. If $G_n(x) = \dfrac{\pi}{2 \sin n\pi}[J_{-n}(x) - e^{-in\pi}J_n(x)]$, show that

$$G_n(x) = -K_n(x) + J_n(x)(\log 2 - \gamma + \tfrac{1}{2}i\pi),$$

where $\gamma = 0.5772 \cdot \cdot \cdot$ is Euler's constant.

29. Show that $xG_n'(x) = -nG_n(x) + xG_{n-1}(x)$.

30. Let $P(x)$ and $Q(x)$ be any two Bessel functions, i.e., functions obtainable from (22) of Sec. 35. Show that

$$P(x)Q'(x) - P'(x)Q(x) = \frac{C}{x},$$

where C is a constant.

31. In Ex. 30, let $P(x) = J_n(x)$ and $Q(x) = J_{-n}(x)$. Show that

$$\lim_{x \to 0} [x(J_n(x)J_{-n}'(x) - J_n'(x)J_{-n}(x))] = -\frac{2}{\pi} \sin n\pi.$$

32. Show that $e^{-k\lambda^2 t}J_n(\lambda r)(A \cos n\theta + B \sin n\theta)$ is a solution of

$$\frac{\partial v}{\partial t} = k\left(\frac{\partial^2 v}{\partial r^2} + \frac{1}{r}\frac{\partial v}{\partial r} + \frac{1}{r^2}\frac{\partial^2 v}{\partial \theta^2}\right).$$

33. Show that $J_n(x)$ and $J_n'(x)$ have no common zero except possibly $x = 0$.

34. Show that $J_n'(x)$ and $AxJ_n'(x) + BJ_n(x)$ have no repeated zero except possibly $x = 0$.

35. Prove Theorems 37.3, 37.5, 37.6, and 37.7 by methods similar to that given for Theorem 37.4.

CHAPTER IV

INFINITE SEQUENCES AND SERIES

PART A. SEQUENCES

1. ^{cv}Sequences of Numbers. If to each positive integer n, $n = 1, 2, \cdots$, there corresponds a definite number s_n, then the ordered set $\{s_n\}$ of numbers

$$s_1, s_2, \cdots, s_n, \cdots$$

is called a *sequence*.

A sequence $\{s_n\}$ is said to be *bounded* if a real constant K exists such that $|s_n| \leq K$ for every positive integer n. If no such constant K exists, the sequence is said to be *unbounded*. Thus the sequence $\{s_n\} \equiv \left\{1 - \dfrac{1}{n^2}\right\}$ is bounded, while the sequence $\{s_n\} \equiv \{2n\}$ is unbounded.

A sequence $\{s_n\}$ is said to *converge* to the number ξ, or to be *convergent* with the *limit* ξ, if for any preassigned positive number ϵ there exists a number N, which may be dependent on ϵ, such that for every $n > N$, $|s_n - \xi| < \epsilon$. We shall indicate that $\{s_n\}$ converges to ξ by writing $s_n \to \xi$ as $n \to +\infty$, or $\lim\limits_{n \to +\infty} s_n = \xi$.

If $\xi = 0$, then $\{s_n\}$ is said to be a *null sequence*. Thus $1, \frac{1}{2}, \frac{1}{3}, \cdots, 1/n, \cdots$ is a null sequence, for if ϵ be any preassigned positive number, then $1/n < \epsilon$ for every $n > N$, where $N > 1/\epsilon$.

A sequence* which is not convergent is said to be *divergent*. Thus, $1, 2, 3, 4, \cdots, n, \cdots$ is divergent.

If the sequence $\{s_n\}$ is such that for any arbitrary positive number G a number N exists such that for all $n > N$, $s_n > G$, then we shall say that $\{s_n\}$ *definitely diverges positively*, or increases without bound, and we then shall write $s_n \to +\infty$ as $n \to +\infty$; if $\{s_n\}$ is such that for any arbitrary negative number $-G$, there

---

* By a sequence we shall hereafter mean a real sequence unless otherwise stated. The notation ^{c} preceding a definition, theorem, or section, indicates that the statements involved hold, with at most slight modifications, for complex numbers. The notation ^{v} indicates a similar extension for vectors.

446

exists a number N such that for all $n > N$, $s_n < -G$, then we shall say that $\{s_n\}$ *definitely diverges negatively*, or decreases without bound, and shall write $s_n \to -\infty$ as $n \to +\infty$. Thus, if $s_n = n^2$, $s_n \to +\infty$, while if $\sigma_n = (-1)^{n-1}(n)$, σ_n does not diverge definitely, either positively or negatively.

A divergent sequence $\{s_n\}$ which is not definitely divergent is said to be *indefinitely divergent*. Thus the sequence $\{\sigma_n\}$ mentioned above is indefinitely divergent, as is also the sequence 0, 1, 0, 2, 0, 3, 0, 4, 0, 5, $\cdots$.

If two sequences $\{s_n\}$ and $\{\sigma_n\}$, neither necessarily convergent, are so related to one another that the quotient s_n/σ_n tends, as $n \to +\infty$, to a definite finite limit K different from zero, then we shall say that $\{s_n\}$ and $\{\sigma_n\}$ are *asymptotically proportional*, and we write $s_n \sim \sigma_n$. If $K = 1$, we shall say that the two sequences $\{s_n\}$ and $\{\sigma_n\}$ are *asymptotically equal*, and we write $s_n \cong \sigma_n$. Thus, for instance, $\sqrt{n^2 + 1} \cong n$, since $\sqrt{n^2 + 1}/n \to 1$ as $n \to +\infty$; $\sqrt{n + 1} - \sqrt{n} \sim 1/\sqrt{n}$, since

$$\left[\frac{\sqrt{n + 1} - \sqrt{n}}{1/\sqrt{n}} \right] \to \frac{1}{2}.$$

EXERCISES I

1. Examine each of the following sequences for convergence, or type of divergence:

(a) $\{n + 1\}$.

(b) $\{n^2 - n\}$.

(c) $\{\log n\}$.

(d) $\{(-1)^{n-1}2n\}$.

(e) $\{(-1)^n/n\}$.

(f) $\{(-1)^n\}$.

(g) $\{(-3)^n\}$.

(h) $\{3^n + (-2)^n\}$.

(i) $\{n^2 + (-1)^n n\}$.

2. Prove:

(a) $1 + 2 + \cdots + n \sim n^2$.

(b) $1^2 + 2^2 + \cdots + n^2 \cong \frac{1}{3}n^3$.

(c) $\log (7n^9 + 17) \sim \log n$.

3. If $a > 1$, prove that $\sqrt[n]{a} \to 1$ as $n \to +\infty$.   (HINT: Let

$$x_n = \sqrt[n]{a} - 1,$$

show $a = (1 + x_n)^n > 1 + nx_n > nx_n$, and finally prove

$$x_n \to 0 \text{ as } n \to +\infty.)$$

4. Prove the theorem stated in Ex. 3 for the case where $0 < a \leqq 1$.

5. Prove that $\sqrt[n]{n} \to 1$ as $n \to +\infty$.   (HINT: Follow the method used in Ex. 3.)

2. Convergent Sequences.   The following theorems indicate a few of the elementary properties of convergent sequences:

^{cv}THEOREM 2.1.   *A convergent sequence $\{s_n\}$ has a unique limit.*

We base our proof on the fact that if a number α is such that $|\alpha| < \epsilon$ for every positive number ϵ, then certainly $\alpha = 0$. Suppose $s_n \to \xi$ and $s_n \to \xi'$. Then for any arbitrary positive number ϵ there exists a number N such that for $n > N$, $|s_n - \xi| < \epsilon/2$ and $|s_n - \xi'| < \epsilon/2$. Now

$$|\xi - \xi'| = |(s_n - \xi) - (s_n - \xi')| \leqq |s_n - \xi| + |\xi' - s_n|$$
$$< \frac{\epsilon}{2} + \frac{\epsilon}{2} = \epsilon.$$

By the preceding remark, $\xi' = \xi$.

^{cv}THEOREM 2.2.   *If a sequence $\{s_n\}$ is convergent, it is bounded; and if $|s_n| \leqq K$, where K is a finite number, then the limit ξ of the sequence is such that $|\xi| \leqq K$.*

If $s_n \to \xi$, then for any given positive number ϵ there exists a number N such that for every $n > N$, $\xi - \epsilon < s_n < \xi + \epsilon$. Hence, if K is a number greater than the N values $|s_1|, |s_2|, \cdots, |s_N|$, and greater than $|\xi| + \epsilon$, then $|s_n| < K$ for every n.

We shall leave to the reader the proof that $|\xi| \leqq K$.

^{cv}THEOREM 2.3.   *If $s_n \to \xi$, then $|s_n| \to |\xi|$.*

Since $||s_n| - |\xi|| \leqq |s_n - \xi|$, it is clear that $(|s_n| - |\xi|) \to 0$ when $(s_n - \xi) \to 0$.

^{c}THEOREM 2.4.   *If $\{s_n\}$ is a convergent sequence all of whose terms are different from zero, and if $\lim_{n \to +\infty} s_n = \xi \neq 0$, then the sequence $\{1/s_n\}$ is bounded.*

There exists an integer N such that for every $n > N$, $|s_n - \xi| < \frac{1}{2}|\xi|$, and consequently $|s_n| > \frac{1}{2}|\xi|$. Let γ be the smallest of the positive numbers $|s_1|, |s_2|, \cdots, |s_N|, \frac{1}{2}|\xi|$. Then $\gamma > 0$ and for every n, $|s_n| \geqq \gamma$, so that $|1/s_n| \leqq K = 1/\gamma$.

If $\{s_n\}$ is a given sequence and if

$$k_1 < k_2 < k_3 < \cdots < k_n < \cdots$$

is any increasing sequence of positive integers, then the numbers $s'_n = s_{k_n}$, $n = 1, 2, \cdots$, are said to form a *subsequence* of the given sequence.

^{cv}THEOREM 2.5.   *Let $\{s'_n\}$ be any subsequence of $\{s_n\}$. If $s_n \to \xi$, then $s'_n \to \xi$.*

Using N and ϵ with the significance given in Sec. 1, we see that for every $n > N$, $|s_n - \xi| < \epsilon$. Hence for any $n > N$,

$$|s_n' - \xi| = |s_{k_n} - \xi| < \epsilon,$$

since $k_n > N$ when $n > N$.

*cv*THEOREM 2.6.   *If the sequence $\{s_n\}$ can be subdivided into a finite number p of subsequences, each of which converges to ξ, then $\{s_n\}$ itself converges to ξ.*

We shall prove the theorem for the case where $p = 2$. Let ϵ be any arbitrary positive number. By hypothesis there exist numbers n' and n'' such that for every $n > n'$, $|s_n' - \xi| < \epsilon$, and for every $n > n''$, $|s_n'' - \xi| < \epsilon$. The terms s_n' and s_n'' have definite positions in the original sequence $\{s_n\}$. Hence there exists an N sufficiently large in $\{s_n\}$ such that for every $n > N$, $|s_n - \xi| < \epsilon$.

Let $K_1, K_2, \cdots, K_n, \cdots$ be a sequence of positive integers such that every positive integer occurs once and only once in the sequence; the sequence $\{s_n'\}$ formed from the sequence $\{s_n\}$ by letting $s_n' = s_{K_n}$ is said to be a *rearrangement* of the given sequence.

*cv*THEOREM 2.7.   *Let $\{s_n'\}$ be an arbitrary rearrangement of $\{s_n\}$. If $s_n \to \xi$ then $s_n' \to \xi$.*

For every $n > N$, $|s_n - \xi| < \epsilon$. Let n' be the largest of the indices belonging to the finite number of places which the terms $s_1, s_2, \cdots, s_n$ occupy in $\{s_n'\}$. Then for every $n > n'$, $|s_n' - \xi| < \epsilon$.

Consider any sequence $\{s_n\}$. If we alter this sequence $\{s_n\}$ by omitting, or inserting, or changing a finite number of terms, or by doing all or a part of these things at once, and then renumber the resulting sequence $\{s_n'\}$, then we shall say that $\{s_n'\}$ is obtained from $\{s_n\}$ *by a finite number of alterations.*

*cv*THEOREM 2.8.   *Let $\{s_n'\}$ be derived from $\{s_n\}$ by a finite number of alterations. If $s_n \to \xi$ then $s_n' \to \xi$.*

The proof of this theorem rests on the fact that for a suitable integer p and a sufficiently large number N, $s_n' = s_{n+p}$ for $n > N$.

*cv*THEOREM 2.9.   *If $s_n' \to \xi$ and $s_n'' \to \xi$, and if for a sufficiently large m, the sequence $\{s_n\}$ is such that*

$$s_n' \leqq s_n \leqq s_n'', \qquad n > m,$$

then $s_n \to \xi$.

We shall leave the proof of this theorem to the reader.

*c*THEOREM 2.10. *If* $s_n \to \xi$ *and* $\sigma_n \to \eta$, *then*

(a) $(s_n + \sigma_n) \to (\xi + \eta)$; (b) $(s_n - \sigma_n) \to (\xi - \eta)$; (c) $s_n \sigma_n \to \xi \eta$; (d) *if every* $s_n \neq 0$ *and* $\xi \neq 0$, $\sigma_n/s_n \to \eta/\xi$.

The proofs of the various parts of this theorem are very similar to the proof of Theorem 3.2, Chap. I.

*cv*COROLLARY 2.101. *If* $s_n \to \xi$ *and* c *is any constant, then* $cs_n \to c\xi$.

By repeated application of the above theorems, we have

*c*THEOREM 2.11. *Let* $(s_n^{(1)})$, $(s_n^{(2)})$, $\cdots$, $(s_n^{(p)})$ *be* p *given sequences converging respectively to* $\xi^{(1)}$, $\xi^{(2)}$, $\cdots$, $\xi^{(p)}$. *If* $R_n = R(s_n^{(1)}, s_n^{(2)}, \cdots, s_n^{(p)})$ *is any rational function of the* p *variables* $s_n^{(1)}, \cdots, s_n^{(p)}$, *with numerical coefficients, then the sequence* $R_n \to R(\xi^{(1)}, \xi^{(2)}, \cdots, \xi^{(p)})$, *provided division by zero is not required either in the evaluation of the terms* R_n, *or in that of the number* $R(\xi^{(1)}, \cdots, \xi^{(p)})$.

The symbols $O(z)$ *and* $o(z)$. Let $\{\zeta_n\}$ and $\{z_n\}$ be two sequences. Then the sequence $\{\zeta_n\}$ is said to be *of the order of the sequence* $\{z_n\}$ if there exists a positive constant k, and a value N of n such that, for every $n > N$, $|\zeta_n/z_n| < k \neq 0$, and we write

$$\zeta_n = O(z_n).$$

If $\lim_{n \to \infty} (\zeta_n/z_n) = 0$, we write $\zeta_n = o(z_n)$.

Example 1. $\dfrac{7n + 19}{1 + n^3} = O\left(\dfrac{1}{n^2}\right)$. Since $\dfrac{\zeta_n}{z_n} \equiv \dfrac{7n + 19}{1 + n^3} \div \dfrac{1}{n^2} \to 7$, it follows that for n sufficiently large, $|\zeta_n/z_n| < k$, where k is a real number greater than 7.

Example 2. $\dfrac{1}{n^3} = o\left(\dfrac{7n + 19}{1 + n^3}\right)$. (Why?)

EXERCISES II

1. Complete the proof of Theorem 2.2.
2. Complete the proof of Theorem 2.6.
3. Prove the statement given in Theorem 2.3 that

$$\big||s_n| - |\xi|\big| \leq |s_n - \xi|.$$

4. Prove that if $\{s_n\}$ is a null sequence and $\{a_n\}$ is any bounded sequence, then the numbers $\sigma_n = a_n s_n$ also form a null sequence.

5. Prove Theorems 2.8; 2.9.

6. Prove Theorems 2.10; 2.11.

7. If $\{\rho_n\} \to 0$, show that $s_n = a^{\rho_n} - 1 \to 0$, $a > 0$.

8. If $a > 0$ and $s_n \to \xi$, then $a^{s_n} \to a^\xi$.

HINT: Show that $a^{s_n} - a^\xi = a^\xi(a^{s_n - \xi} - 1)$ is a null sequence. Use Ex. 7.

9. Let $\{s_n\}$ be a null sequence all of whose terms are greater than -1. Prove that $\log (1 + s_n)$ is a null sequence.

10. If $s_n > 0$ for every n, $\xi > 0$, and if $s_n \to \xi$, then

$$\log s_n \to \log \xi.$$

HINT: $\log s_n - \log \xi = \log \dfrac{s_n}{\xi} = \log \left(1 + \dfrac{s_n - \xi}{\xi} \right)$. Demonstrate that $\log \left(1 + \dfrac{s_n - \xi}{\xi} \right)$ is a null sequence. Use Ex. 9.

11. If $\{s_n\}$ is a null sequence all of whose terms are greater than -1, then $z_n = (1 + s_n)^\rho - 1$ is a null sequence. Here ρ denotes any real number.

HINT: Show that $\rho_n = \rho \log (1 + s_n) \to 0$. Next show $z_n \to 0$.

12. If $s_n > 0$ for every n, and if $s_n \to \xi > 0$, then $s_n^\rho \to \xi^\rho$, where ρ denotes an arbitrary real number.

HINT: By Ex. 11 show that $s_n^\rho - \xi^\rho = \xi^\rho \left[\left(1 + \dfrac{s_n - \xi}{\xi} \right)^\rho - 1 \right] \to 0$.

3. Cauchy's Theorem and Its Generalizations.   We shall now prove certain theorems of great importance.

^{cv}THEOREM 3.1 (*Cauchy's Theorem*). *If* $s_n \to \xi$, *then the arithmetic means*

$$s_n' = \frac{s_1 + s_2 + \cdots + s_n}{n}, \qquad n = 1, 2, \cdots$$

also approach ξ.

Let $\epsilon > 0$. Then there exists an m such that for every $n > m$, $|s_n - \xi| < \epsilon/2$. Then for $n > m$,

$$|s_n' - \xi| < \frac{|(s_1 - \xi) + \cdots + (s_m - \xi)|}{n} + \frac{\epsilon(n - m)}{2n}.$$

The numerator of the first fraction on the right-hand side contains a fixed number m of terms of $\{s_n\}$, so that we can determine an $N \geqq m$ so that for every $n > N$, that fraction remains less than $\epsilon/2$. Consequently, for $n > N$, $|s_n' - \xi| < \epsilon$.

^{c}THEOREM 3.2. *If* $s_n \to \xi$, *where each* $s_n > 0$ *and* $\xi > 0$, *then the sequence of geometric means*

$$\sigma_n = \sqrt[n]{s_1 s_2 \cdots s_n} \to \xi.$$

Since $s_n \to \xi$, $x_n = \log s_n \to X = \log \xi$ (by Exs. II, 9 and 10). By Theorem 3.1,

$$x'_n = \frac{x_1 + x_2 + \cdots + x_n}{n} = \log \sqrt[n]{s_1 s_2 \cdots s_n}$$

$$= \log \sigma_n \to \log \xi.$$

The theorem follows at once from Ex. 8 and the fact that $e^{\log \sigma} = \sigma$.

EXERCISES III

Prove:

1. $\dfrac{1 + (1/2) + \cdots + (1/n)}{n} \to 0$, as $n \to +\infty$.

2. $\sqrt[n]{n} = \sqrt[n]{1 \cdot \dfrac{2}{1} \cdot \dfrac{3}{2} \cdots \dfrac{n}{n-1}} \to 1$, as $n \to +\infty$.

3. $\dfrac{1 + \sqrt{2} + \sqrt[3]{3} + \cdots + \sqrt[n]{n}}{n} \to 1$, as $n \to +\infty$.

4. $\sqrt[n]{\left(\dfrac{2}{1}\right)^1 \cdot \left(\dfrac{3}{2}\right)^2 \cdot \left(\dfrac{4}{3}\right)^3 \cdots \left(\dfrac{n+1}{n}\right)^n} = \sqrt[n]{\dfrac{(n+1)^n}{n!}} \to e.$

HINT: Recall $\left(1 + \dfrac{1}{n}\right)^n \to e$.

5. Prove $\sqrt[n]{n!} \cong n/e$. (Use Ex. 4.)

Many generalizations of Cauchy's theorem have been given. The following theorem (due to O. Toeplitz, 1911) is perhaps one of the most important and far-reaching of these generalizations. Consider the system M of real numbers a_{rs},

$$M \equiv \begin{pmatrix} a_{00} & 0 & 0 & \cdots & 0 & \cdots \\ a_{10} & a_{11} & 0 & \cdots & 0 & \cdots \\ \cdot & \cdot & \cdot & & \cdot & \cdots \\ \cdot & \cdot & \cdot & & \cdot & \cdots \\ a_{n0} & a_{n1} & a_{n2} & \cdots & a_{nn} & \cdots \\ \cdot & \cdot & \cdot & \cdots & \cdot & \cdots \end{pmatrix},$$

where M is subject to one or more of the following conditions:

(a) Every column of M is a null sequence; i.e., for any fixed $p \geqq 0$, $a_{np} \to 0$ as $n \to +\infty$.

(b) There exists a positive constant K such that for every n,

$$\sum_{j=0}^{n} |a_{nj}| < K.$$

(c) If $A_n \equiv \sum\limits_{j=0}^{n} a_{nj}$, then $A_n \to 1$ as $n \to +\infty$.

(d) For any fixed $p \geqq 0$, $a_{n,n-p} \to 0$ when $n \to +\infty$.

[cv]THEOREM 3.3.   *If $x_0, x_1, \cdots$ is a null sequence and if M is subject to conditions* (a) *and* (b), *then the sequence* $\{x_n'\}$ *formed by the numbers* $x_n' = \sum\limits_{j=0}^{n} a_{nj}x_j$ *is also a null sequence.*

Let ϵ be any positive number.   Select an integer m such that for every $n > m$, $|x_n| < \epsilon/2K$.   Then for $n > m$,

$$|x_n'| \leqq |a_{n0}x_0 + \cdots + a_{nm}x_m| + |a_{n,m+1}x_{m+1} + \cdots + a_{nn}x_n|$$

$$< |a_{n0}x_0 + \cdots + a_{nm}x_m| + \sum_{j=m+1}^{n} |a_{nj}|\frac{\epsilon}{2K}$$

$$< |a_{n0}x_0 + \cdots + a_{nm}x_m| + K\frac{\epsilon}{2K}.$$

By (a) there exists an $N > m$ so that for every $n > N$,

$$\left| \sum_{j=0}^{m} a_{nj}x_j \right| < \frac{\epsilon}{2}.$$

Hence

$$|x_n'| < \frac{\epsilon}{2} + \frac{\epsilon}{2} = \epsilon.$$

[cv]THEOREM 3.4.   *If $x_n \to \xi$, and M is subject to conditions* (a), (b), *and* (c), *then the sequence* $x_n' = \sum\limits_{j=0}^{n} a_{nj}x_j \to \xi$.

Evidently,

$$x_n' = A_n\xi + \sum_{q=0}^{n} a_{nq}(x_q - \xi).$$

Theorem 3.4 now follows as an immediate consequence of Theorem 3.3 and condition (c).

[c]THEOREM 3.5.   *Suppose M satisfies conditions* (a), (b), (c), (d); *then if $x_n \to \xi$ and $y_n \to \eta$, the sequence* $z_n = \sum\limits_{p=0}^{n} a_{np}x_p y_{n-p} \to \xi\eta$.

Write

$$x_p y_{n-p} = (x_p - \xi)y_{n-p} + \xi y_{n-p}.$$

Then

$$z_n = \sum_{p=0}^{n} a_{np} y_{n-p}(x_p - \xi) + \xi \sum_{p=0}^{n} a_{np} y_{n-p}.$$

Since $(x_p - \xi) \to 0$ and the y_{n-p} are all bounded, it follows from Theorem 3.3 and Ex. IV, 1 that the first sum in z_n tends to zero. From Theorem 3.4 and condition (d), it follows that the sum

$$\xi \sum_{p=0}^{n} a_{np} y_{n-p} \equiv \xi \sum_{p=0}^{n} a_{n,n-p} y_p$$

tends to $\xi\eta$.   Consequently $z_n \to \xi\eta$.

EXERCISES IV

1. Prove: (*Corollary to Theorem* 3.3.)   *If in Theorem* 3.3, *the* a_{rs} *are replaced by* $\alpha_{rs} \equiv a_{rs}\lambda_{rs}$, *where* $|\lambda_{rs}|$ *are all less than or equal to a fixed constant* Γ, *then* $\{\beta_n\}$ *is a null sequence, where* $\beta_n = \sum_{j=0}^{n} \alpha_{nj} x_j$.

2. By setting $a_{n0} = a_{n1} = \cdots = a_{nn} = 1/(n+1)$ in Theorem 3.3, $n = 0, 1, 2, \cdots$, prove Theorem 3.1 with $\xi = 0$.

3. Prove Theorem 3.1 from Theorem 3.4.

4. Let $p_0, p_1, \cdots$ be any positive numbers such that

$$\sigma_n \equiv \sum_{j=0}^{n} p_j \to +\infty.$$

Prove that if $x_n \to \xi$, then so does $x_n' \to \xi$, where $x_n' = \left(\sum_{j=0}^{n} p_j x_j \right) \Big/ \sigma_n$.

Hint: In Theorem 3.4, set

$$a_{nk} = p_k/\sigma_n; n = 0, 1, 2, \cdots; \qquad k = 0, 1, \cdots, n.$$

5. From Ex. 4, prove Theorem 3.1.

6. Prove Theorem 3.1 is true for $\xi = +\infty$ and for $\xi = -\infty$.

7. Prove Theorem 3.4 is true for $\xi = +\infty$ and for $\xi = -\infty$, provided $a_{pq} \geqq 0$.

8. Prove Ex. 4 assuming, instead of the positiveness of the p_j, that $\sum_{j=0}^{n} |p_j| \to +\infty$, and the existence of a constant G such that

$$\sum_{j=0}^{n} |p_j| \leq G \left| \sum_{j=0}^{n} p_j \right|.$$

9. Prove that if $y_n/p_n \to \xi$, then $\sum_{j=0}^{n} y_j \Big/ \sum_{j=0}^{n} p_j \to \xi$ provided the proper restrictions are placed upon the p_j. (HINT: In Ex. 4 or 6, set $p_n x_n = y_n$.) What are these restrictions?

10. Let $Y_n = \sum_{j=0}^{n} y_j$, $P_n = \sum_{j=0}^{n} p_j$, and suppose that

$$p_n = A_n - A_{n-1} \ (n \geq 1, \ p_0 = A_0)$$

satisfy the restrictions given in Ex. 4 or 8.   Prove that if

$$\frac{Y_n - Y_{n-1}}{A_n - A_{n-1}} \to \xi, \qquad \text{then} \qquad \frac{Y_n}{A_n} \to \xi.$$

11. From Ex. 10, show that

(a) $\lim_{n \to \infty} \dfrac{\displaystyle\sum_{k=1}^{n} k}{n^2} = \lim_{n \to \infty} \dfrac{n}{n^2 - (n-1)^2} = \dfrac{1}{2}$,

(b) $\lim_{n \to \infty} \dfrac{\displaystyle\sum_{k=1}^{n} k^2}{n^3} = \lim_{n \to \infty} \dfrac{n^2}{n^3 - (n-1)^3} = \dfrac{1}{3}$,

(c) $\lim_{n \to \infty} \dfrac{\displaystyle\sum_{k=1}^{n} k^p}{n^{p+1}} = \lim_{n \to \infty} \dfrac{n^p}{n^{p+1} - (n-1)^{p+1}} = \dfrac{1}{p+1}$,

where p is a positive integer.

12. Prove: If $x_n \to \xi$ and $y_n \to \eta$, then $\left(\displaystyle\sum_{j=0}^{n} x_j y_{n-j} \right) \Big/ (n+1) \to \xi\eta$.

13. Prove: If $x_n \to 0$, and $y_n \to 0$, and for every n, $\displaystyle\sum_{j=0}^{n} |y_j| < K$, where K is fixed, then $z_n \equiv \displaystyle\sum_{j=0}^{n} x_j y_{n-j} \to 0$.   (HINT: Use Theorem 3.3.)

14. Show $\left[\dfrac{\displaystyle\sum_{k=1}^{m} \log k}{m \log m} \right] \to 1$.   This shows that $\log m! \cong \log m^m$.

4. Criteria for Convergence. In examining a sequence $\{s_n\}$ two important questions present themselves: (1) Is the sequence $\{s_n\}$ convergent, definitely divergent, or indefinitely divergent? (2) If the sequence $\{s_n\}$ converges, what is its limit? In general, (2) is by far the more difficult.

We now state what is sometimes termed the *first principal criterion for convergence.*

THEOREM 4.1. *Every bounded monotone sequence is convergent, and every unbounded monotone sequence is definitely divergent.*

This theorem is proved in Chap. IX, Ex. III, 5. (A monotone sequence is defined in the same manner as a monotone function. See footnote to Theorem 26.4 of Chap. II.)

A second criterion of convergence is given by

^{cv}THEOREM 4.2. *Let $\{s_n\}$ be an arbitrary sequence of real numbers, and let ϵ be any preassigned positive number. A necessary and sufficient condition that $\{s_n\}$ be convergent is that there exists a number $N = N(\epsilon)$ such that for every $n > N$ and every $k \geqq 1$, $|s_{n+k} - s_n| < \epsilon$.*

Necessity. If $s_n \to \xi$, then for a given $\epsilon > 0$, there exists an N such that for $n > N$, $|s_n - \xi| < \epsilon/2$, and for any $n' > N$, $|s_{n'} - \xi| < \epsilon/2$. Hence

$$|s_n - s_{n'}| = |(s_n - \xi) - (s_{n'} - \xi)|$$

$$\leqq |s_n - \xi| + |s_{n'} - \xi| < \frac{\epsilon}{2} + \frac{\epsilon}{2} = \epsilon.$$

Sufficiency. The sufficiency proof for this theorem will be deferred to Chap. IX, Ex. III, 5.

Let $\{s_n\}$ be a given sequence, let $v_1, v_2, \cdots, v_n, \cdots$ be any sequence of positive integers (equal or unequal, monotone or not monotone) which diverges to $+\infty$, and let $k_1, k_2, \cdots, k_n, \cdots$ be any positive integers (unrestricted); then we call the sequence $\{d_n\}$, where

$$d_n = s_{v_n+k_n} - s_{v_n},$$

a *difference sequence* of $\{s_n\}$.

^{cv}THEOREM 4.3. *A necessary and sufficient condition for the convergence of a sequence $\{s_n\}$ is that every one of its difference sequences be a null sequence.*

The proof of this theorem follows quite easily from Theorem 4.2.

EXERCISES V

1. Let $s_n = \dfrac{1}{n+1} + \dfrac{1}{n+2} + \cdots + \dfrac{1}{2n}$. Prove $\{s_n\}$ is convergent. Estimate its limit.

2. Let $s_n = 1 + \dfrac{1}{2} + \cdots + \dfrac{1}{n}$. Is $\{s_n\}$ convergent or divergent? (Hint: Prove $\{s_n\}$ is unbounded.)

3. Prove: If $s_n = 1 - \dfrac{1}{3} + \dfrac{1}{5} - \dfrac{1}{7} + \cdots + \dfrac{(-1)^{n-1}}{2n-1}$, the sequence $\{s_n\}$ converges. (Use Theorem 4.2.)

4. Let $s_n = \left(1 + \dfrac{1}{n}\right)^n$, $\sigma_n = \left(1 + \dfrac{1}{n}\right)^{n+1}$. Prove
   (a) that $\{\sigma_n\}$ is monotone decreasing and bounded;
   (b) that $\{s_n\}$ is monotone increasing and bounded;
   (c) that $\{s_n\}$ and $\{\sigma_n\}$ converge to the same limit.
   (d) What is this limit called?

5. Prove Theorem 4.3.

5. Limiting Points of a Sequence. In this section we shall introduce certain general concepts which will be of considerable importance for our later work.

If $s_n \to \xi$, then every neighborhood of ξ contains all but at most a finite number of terms of the sequence. Since every neighborhood of ξ contains an infinite number of terms of the sequence, ξ is sometimes called a *point of accumulation* or *limiting point* of the given sequence. However, divergent sequences may also have such points of accumulation, as for example the divergent sequence $1, 2, \tfrac{1}{2}, 2, \tfrac{1}{3}, 2, \tfrac{1}{4}, 2, \tfrac{1}{5}, 2, \cdots$, which has 0 and 2 as points of accumulation.

*cv*DEFINITION 5.1. *A number ξ is called a point of accumulation of a given sequence $\{s_n\}$ if every neighborhood of ξ contains an infinite number of terms of the sequence.*

Perhaps the most fundamental theorem here is that due to Bolzano (1817):

*cv*THEOREM 5.1. *Every bounded sequence possesses at least one point of accumulation.*

This theorem is proved in Chap. IX, Ex. III, 5, but owing to its importance we are including it here. Theorem 4.1 is a special case of this theorem.

A particularly interesting theorem which brings out the relationship between the limit point and a limiting point of a sequence is the following:

^{cv}**Theorem 5.2.** *Every accumulation point of a sequence* $\{s_n\}$ *is the unique accumulation point of some subsequence of* $\{s_n\}$.

Let ξ denote a point of accumulation of $\{s_n\}$. For every $\epsilon > 0$, there exists an infinite number of indices n for which $|s_n - \xi| < \epsilon$. We can pick a suitable $n = p_1$ for which

$$|s_{p_1} - \xi| < 1;$$

a suitable $n = p_2 > p_1$ for which $|s_{p_2} - \xi| < \tfrac{1}{2}; \cdots$; an $n = p_v > p_{v-1}$ for which $|s_{p_v} - \xi| < 1/v, \; v = 2, \; 3, \; 4, \; \cdots$. The subsequence $\{s_{p_v}\} = \{s_n'\}$ thus selected converges to ξ.

From Theorem 5.2, we may prove that every bounded sequence has a least accumulation point m as well as a greatest accumulation point M. (See Chap. IX, Ex. III, 2.)

The least accumulation point m of a (bounded) sequence $\{s_n\}$ is frequently called its *lower limit* or *inferior limit*, and is often indicated by

$$\underset{n \to +\infty}{\lim} s_n = m, \qquad \text{or} \qquad \underset{n \to +\infty}{\lim \inf} \; s_n = m.$$

Likewise, the greatest point of accumulation M is called the *upper limit* or *superior limit* of the sequence $\{s_n\}$, and is indicated by

$$\underset{n \to +\infty}{\overline{\lim}} \; s_n = M, \qquad \text{or} \qquad \underset{n \to +\infty}{\lim \sup} \; s_n = M.$$

Evidently, $m \leqq M$.

If a sequence has no lower bound, we shall write $\underset{n \to +\infty}{\underline{\lim}} \; s_n = -\infty$;

if it has no upper bound, $\underset{n \to +\infty}{\overline{\lim}} \; s_n = +\infty$.

For example, if $\{x_n\} = a, b, c, a, b, c, a, b, c, \cdots, a < b < c$, then $\underset{n \to +\infty}{\overline{\lim}} \; x_n = c$, $\underset{n \to +\infty}{\underline{\lim}} \; x_n = a$. If $\{x_n\} \equiv 5 - 1, \; 5 - \tfrac{1}{2}, \; 5 - 3$,

$5 - \tfrac{1}{4}, \; \cdots$, $\underset{n \to +\infty}{\underline{\lim}} \; x_n = -\infty$, $\underset{n \to +\infty}{\overline{\lim}} \; x_n = 5$.

EXERCISES VI

1. Distinguish between the definition of limit as given in Sec. 1 and point of accumulation as given in Sec. 5.

2. Find the points of accumulation of $\{s_n\}$, where

(a) $s_n = \tfrac{1}{2}[1 - (-1)^n]$.
(c) $s_n = (n + 1)/n$.

(b) $s_n = 2^n$.
(d) $s_n = (n - 1)/n$.

3. Construct a sequence of rational numbers having every real number as a point of accumulation.

4. Do the accumulation points of a sequence necessarily belong to the sequence? Illustrate.

5. In each of the following sequences determine $\liminf\limits_{n \to +\infty} s_n$ and $\limsup\limits_{n \to +\infty} s_n$ (if they exist):

(a) $s_n = n \equiv 1, 2, 3, 4, \cdots$.

(b) $s_n = 3 - n^{(-1)^n}$.

(c) $s_n = -n$.

(d) $s_n = (-1)^n n$.

(e) $3, 5, 3, 5, 3, 5, \cdots, 3, 5, \cdots$.

(f) $s_n = 5 + \dfrac{(-1)^n}{n}$.

(g) $s_n = 7 + n^{n \sin \pi n}$.

6. Prove the following theorems:

(a) A sequence $\{s_n\}$ is convergent if and only if its upper and lower limits M and m are equal and finite.

(b) A sequence $\{s_n\}$ is indefinitely divergent if and only if its upper and lower limits are distinct.

(c) State and prove a theorem similar to (a) and (b) for the case where $\{s_n\}$ is definitely divergent.

7. Let $\overline{\lim\limits_{n \to +\infty}} x_n = \mu$, $\mu \neq \pm \infty$. Prove:

(a) The limit S of every convergent subsequence $\{x'_n\}$ of $\{x_n\}$ is always $\leq \mu$.

(b) There exists at least one subsequence of $\{x_n\}$ whose limit is μ. State a similar theorem for the lower limit.

PART B.   SERIES

6. Infinite Series, Products, and Continued Fractions.* In the application of sequences to mathematics and applied fields, the sequences to be examined do not as a rule present themselves directly. Sequences appear indirectly in a number of common types, the most common of which are (1) infinite series, (2) infinite products, and (3) continued fractions. We shall first consider infinite series.

^{cv}DEFINITION 6.1.   *An infinite series*

$$a_1 + a_2 + a_3 + \cdots, \qquad or \qquad \sum_{k=1}^{\infty} a_k,$$

is a symbol for the sequence $\{s_n\}$, *where*

$$s_1 = a_1, \qquad s_2 = a_1 + a_2, \qquad \cdots, \qquad s_n = \sum_{k=1}^{n} a_k, \qquad \cdots.$$

* See the excellent treatise, by K. Knopp, "Theory and Application of Infinite Series."

An infinite series $\sum\limits_{k=1}^{\infty} a_k$ *is said to be convergent, definitely divergent, or indefinitely divergent, according as the sequence* $\{s_n\}$ *of its partial sums* s_n *exhibits the behavior indicated by those names. If the sequence* $\{s_n\}$ *converges to* s, *that is, if* $s_n \rightarrow s$, *then we say that* s *is the value or the sum of the convergent infinite series* $\sum\limits_{k=1}^{\infty} a_k$, *and we then shall write* $\sum\limits_{k=1}^{\infty} a_k = s$. *If* $\{s_n\}$ *is definitely divergent, we shall say that the series* $\sum\limits_{k=1}^{\infty} a_k$ *is definitely divergent to* $+\infty$ *or* $-\infty$, *according as* $s_n \rightarrow +\infty$ *or* $-\infty$. *If* $\{s_n\}$ *diverges indefinitely, and* M *and* m *are the upper and lower limits of the sequence, then we shall say that the series* $\sum\limits_{k=1}^{\infty} a_k$ *is indefinitely divergent and oscillates between the upper and lower limits* M *and* m.

The term *sum* as used here is not a sum in the ordinary sense, but really the limit of an infinite sequence of finite partial sums.

We shall now briefly mention the second and third common types of sequences. An *infinite product* $u_1 u_2 u_3 \cdots u_n \cdots$, or $\prod\limits_{n=1}^{\infty} u_n$, is simply a symbol for the sequence of partial products

$$p_1 = u_1, \qquad p_2 = u_1 u_2, \qquad p_3 = u_1 u_2 u_3, \cdots,$$
$$p_n = u_1 u_2 \cdots u_n, \qquad \cdots$$

For example, the sequence of numbers

$$p_1 = \frac{2^2}{3 \cdot 5}, \qquad p_2 = \frac{2^2}{3 \cdot 5} \cdot \frac{3^2}{4 \cdot 6}, \qquad p_3 = \frac{2^2}{3 \cdot 5} \cdot \frac{3^2}{4 \cdot 6} \cdot \frac{4^2}{5 \cdot 7}, \cdots$$

may be represented by the infinite product

$$\prod_{n=1}^{\infty} \frac{(n+1)^2}{(n+2)(n+4)}.$$

The theory of infinite products parallels the development of the theory of infinite series, except for a few particular conventions due to the peculiar part the number zero plays in multiplication.

Let a_1, a_2, $\cdots$ and b_0, b_1, b_2, $\cdots$ be any two sequences of numbers with $b_n \neq 0$ for $n > 0$. Form the sequence $\{s_n\}$ as follows:

$$s_0 = b_0, \qquad s_1 = b_0 + \frac{a_1}{b_1}, \qquad s_2 = b_0 + \cfrac{a_1}{b_1 + \cfrac{a_2}{b_2}},$$

$$s_3 = b_0 + \cfrac{a_1}{b_1 + \cfrac{a_2}{b_2 + (a_3/b_3)}}, \quad \cdots,$$

the term s_n being deduced from s_{n-1} by replacing the last denominator b_{n-1} of s_{n-1} by the value $b_{n-1} + (a_n/b_n)$, and so on. We shall use $b_0 + \overset{\infty}{\underset{n=1}{\mathrm{K}}} (a_n/b_n)$ as a symbol for an *infinite continued fraction*.

We shall not concern ourselves with the theory of continued fractions any further at this point. However, it is worth remarking that considerable use of infinite continued fractions is made in the study of certain phases of electrical network theory and design.*

We shall concern ourselves principally with problem (1) mentioned in Sec. 4, since it is the simpler of the two problems and lends itself to a systematic solution.

While Theorem 2.1 shows that a convergent sequence $\sum\limits_{k=1}^{\infty} a_k$ completely determines its limit S, we are faced with the difficulty that this representation of S is frequently of an unusual form. Thus to calculate S we must find a familiar representation for it, e.g., as a decimal fraction. For example, it is not at all evident that

$$1 - \tfrac{1}{3} + \tfrac{1}{5} - \tfrac{1}{7} + \tfrac{1}{9} - \cdots$$

and

$$\frac{7}{10} + \frac{8}{100} + \frac{5}{1000} + \frac{3}{10,000} + \cdots = 0.7853 \cdots$$

represent the same number $\pi/4$.

* See T. C. Fry, *Bull. Amer. Math. Soc.*, July–August, 1929, pp. 463–498.

Considering the representation of a real number by a sequence, we may state question (2) in Sec. 4 as follows: Given two convergent sequences $s_n \to \xi$ and $\sigma_n \to \eta$. How can we determine if ξ is equal to η, or if ξ and η are in a simple relation one to the other? For example, if

$$s_n = \left(\frac{n+1}{n}\right)^n \to \xi \text{ and } \sigma_n = \left(\frac{n+3}{n}\right)^n \to \eta,$$

it is not at all evident that $\eta = \xi^3$; nor is it evident that $1, \frac{3}{2}$, $\frac{7}{5}, \frac{17}{12}, \cdots$ and $1.414213563 \cdots$ both converge to $\sqrt{2}$.

EXERCISES VII

1. Does $\displaystyle\sum_{n=0}^{\infty} (-1)^n = (1-1) + (1-1) + \cdots + (1-1) + \cdots$?

$$= 1 - (1-1) - (1-1) - (1-1) - \cdots \text{ ?}$$

2. Prove:

(a) $\displaystyle\sum_{n=0}^{\infty} \frac{1}{2^n} = 2.$

(b) $\displaystyle\sum_{n=0}^{\infty} \frac{1}{(n+1)(n+2)} = 1.$

(c) $\displaystyle\sum_{n=0}^{\infty} \frac{1}{(x+n)(x+n+1)} = \frac{1}{x}$, where x is real and

$$x \neq 0, -1, -2, \cdots.$$

3. Test for convergence. If the series diverges, does it diverge definitely or indefinitely?

(a) $\displaystyle\sum_{n=1}^{\infty} n.$

(b) $\displaystyle\sum_{n=1}^{\infty} \frac{(-1)^n}{n+1}.$

(c) $\displaystyle\sum_{n=1}^{\infty} (-1)^n(2n+1).$

(d) $\displaystyle\sum_{n=1}^{\infty} (-1)^n.$

4. Prove:
(a) If λ be fixed, $0 < \lambda < 1$, $\quad s_n = (n+1)^\lambda - n^\lambda \to 0.$

(b) $s_n = \displaystyle\sum_{k=1}^{n} \frac{k}{n^2} \to \frac{1}{2}.$

(c) $s_n = \displaystyle\sum_{k=1}^{n} \frac{1}{\sqrt{n^2+k}} \to 1.$

(d) $s_n = \displaystyle\sum_{k=1}^{n} \frac{n}{n^2+k^2} \to \frac{\pi}{4}.$

5. Let $s_n = \dfrac{a_1 + a_2 + \cdots + a_n}{b_1 + b_2 + \cdots + b_n}$. Prove that if $\dfrac{a_n}{b_n}$ is monotone and $b_n > 0$, then s_n is also monotone.

7. Series of Positive Terms.

We shall now concern ourselves exclusively with series all of whose terms are real and nonnegative numbers.

If $\displaystyle\sum_{n=0}^{\infty} a_n$, (all $a_n \geqq 0$), denotes such a series of positive terms, then the sequence $\{s_n\}$ of partial sums is monotone increasing since

$$s_n = s_{n-1} + a_n \geqq s_{n-1}.$$

It is easy to see (from Theorem 4.1) that

THEOREM 7.1.   *A series of positive terms converges if and only if its partial sums are bounded; otherwise it diverges to $+\infty$.*

THEOREM 7.2.   *The two series $\displaystyle\sum_{n=0}^{\infty} a_n$ and $\displaystyle\sum_{n=p}^{\infty} a_n$, p being any positive integer, converge or diverge together.*

THEOREM 7.3.   *If each λ_n satisfies the inequality*

$$0 < \lambda' \leqq \lambda_n \leqq \lambda'',$$

where λ' and λ'' are fixed finite real positive numbers, then the two series of positive terms $\displaystyle\sum_{n=0}^{\infty} a_n$ and $\displaystyle\sum_{n=0}^{\infty} \lambda_n a_n$ converge or diverge together.

Proof.   If Σa_n converges,* then the partial sums of Σa_n are all less than some fixed number K, and the factors λ_n are $\leqq \lambda''$, so that the partial sums of $\Sigma \lambda_n a_n$ are all $\leqq \lambda'' K$, whence $\Sigma \lambda_n a_n$ converges.

A similar argument may be given for the case where Σa_n diverges.

THEOREM 7.4 *(Comparison Test).*   *Let Σc_n and Σd_n be two series of positive terms, the first of which is known to be convergent, the second, divergent.   Let Σa_n be a given series of positive terms.*

---

* We shall often use the symbol $\displaystyle\sum a_n$ for $\displaystyle\sum_{n=0}^{\infty} a_n$ where no confusion will result.

I. *If there exists a positive integer m such that for every $n > m$,*

$$a_n \leqq c_n, \text{ then } \Sigma a_n \text{ is convergent;} \tag{A.1}$$

and if for every $n > m$,

$$a_n \geqq d_n, \text{ then } \Sigma a_n \text{ is divergent.} \tag{A.2}$$

II. *If there exists a positive integer m such that for every $n > m$,*

$$\frac{a_{n+1}}{a_n} \leqq \frac{c_{n+1}}{c_n}, \text{ then } \Sigma a_n \text{ is convergent;} \tag{B.1}$$

and if for every $n \geqq m$,

$$\frac{a_{n+1}}{a_n} \geqq \frac{d_{n+1}}{d_n}, \text{ then } \Sigma a_n \text{ is divergent.} \tag{B.2}$$

Case A.1. The hypothesis permits us to write $a_n = \gamma_n c_n$, $\gamma_n \leqq 1$ for every $n > m$. Consequently, by Theorems 7.2 and 7.3, Σa_n and Σc_n converge together.

A similar proof may be given for *case A*.2.

Case B.1. Consider the sequence $\{g_n\}$, $g_n = a_n/c_n$. For every $n > N$, $g_{n+1} \leqq g_n$; hence there exists an N such that for $n > N$, $\{g_n\}$ is monotone decreasing, and since all of its terms are positive, is bounded. Theorem 7.3 assures the convergence of Σa_n.

Case B.2 may be proved in a similar manner by considering the sequence $\{h_n\}$, $h_n = a_n/d_n$, and applying Theorem 7.3.

In order that these comparison tests may be useful, it is necessary to have a large stock of series whose convergence or divergence is known. The exercises given in the following sections of this chapter should form a nucleus.

EXERCISES VIII

1. Prove Theorem 7.2.
2. Complete the proof of Theorem 7.3.

3. Consider the *geometric series* $\displaystyle\sum_{n=0}^{\infty} a^n$. Derive an expression for the sum (if it exists) of this series. For what values of a does this series converge? diverge?

4. Show that the partial sum s_n of $\displaystyle\sum_{n=1}^{\infty} \frac{1}{n(n+1)}$ is $\left[1 - \dfrac{1}{n+1}\right]$. Find

the sum (if it exists) of the series.

5. A series of the form $\sum_{n=1}^{\infty} \dfrac{1}{n^p}$, p real, is called a *harmonic series*. Show that if $p \leq 1$, the series diverges; if $p > 1$, the series converges.

6. Show that $\sum_{n=0}^{\infty} \dfrac{1}{n!}$ is convergent to a sum ≤ 3, where $0! = 1$.

HINT: Show that $s_n \leq 2 + \dfrac{1}{2} + \dfrac{1}{2^2} + \cdots + \dfrac{1}{2^{n-1}}$.

7. Prove Cases A.2 and B.2 of Theorem 7.4.

THEOREM 7.5. *(Cauchy's Root Test).* Let $\sum_{n=1}^{\infty} a_n$ be a series of positive terms. If for N sufficiently large, $a_n < a^n$, $n > N$ with $0 < a < 1$, that is, if $\sqrt[n]{a_n} \leq a < 1$ for all $n > N$, then the series $\sum_{n=1}^{\infty} a_n$ converges; but if for some N, $\sqrt[n]{a_n} \geq 1$ for all $n > N$, then the series $\sum_{n=1}^{\infty} a_n$ diverges.

We shall leave the proof, depending on Theorem 7.4, to the reader.

From Theorem 7.4, we see

THEOREM 7.6. *(Cauchy's Ratio Test).* If for N sufficiently large, and for all $n > N$, $a_n > 0$,

$$\frac{a_{n+1}}{a_n} \leq a < 1,$$

then $\sum_{n=1}^{\infty} a_n$ converges; but if for all $n > N$,

$$\frac{a_{n+1}}{a_n} \geq 1,$$

then $\sum_{n=1}^{\infty} a_n$ diverges.

EXERCISES IX

1. Prove Theorem 7.5.
2. Prove Theorem 7.6.

3. (a) Use Theorems 7.5 and 7.6 to test $\displaystyle\sum_{n=1}^{\infty} \frac{1}{n}$ for convergence.

(b) Why is it essential that the root $\sqrt[n]{a_n}$ and ratio a_{n+1}/a_n should not approach arbitrarily near to 1?

4. Determine whether or not the following series are convergent or divergent. In each of the examples where x appears, assume $x \geqq 0$ and determine the values of x, if any, for which the given series converges:

(a) $\displaystyle\sum_{n=0}^{\infty} \frac{x^n}{n!}$, $x \geqq 0$. $(0! = 1)$ (convergent for $x \geqq 0$)

(b) $\displaystyle\sum_{n=1}^{\infty} \frac{x^n}{n^n}$, $x \geqq 0$.   (convergent)

(c) $\displaystyle\sum_{n=1}^{\infty} n^p x^n$, $x > 0$, p arbitrary.   (convergent if $x < 1$) (divergent if $x > 1$)

(d) $\displaystyle\sum_{n=1}^{\infty} \frac{1}{\sqrt{n(n+1)}}$.   (divergent)

(e) $\displaystyle\sum_{n=1}^{\infty} \frac{1}{\sqrt{n(1+n^2)}}$.   (convergent)

(f) $\displaystyle\sum_{n=1}^{\infty} \frac{1}{1+n^2}$.   (convergent)

(g) $\displaystyle\sum_{n=2}^{\infty} \frac{1}{(\log n)^n}$.   (convergent)

(h) $\displaystyle\sum_{n=1}^{\infty} \frac{n!}{n^n}$.   (convergent)

(i) $\displaystyle\sum_{n=1}^{\infty} \frac{1}{n\sqrt[n]{n}}$.   (divergent)

(j) $\displaystyle\sum_{n=2}^{\infty} \frac{1}{(\log n)^{\log n}}.$ (convergent)

5. (a) Prove that $\displaystyle\sum_{n=1}^{\infty} \frac{1}{(2n+1)^p}$ is divergent for $p \leq 1$, convergent for $p > 1$.

(b) Show that $\displaystyle\sum_{n=1}^{\infty} \frac{1}{(an+b)^p},$ a and b being positive numbers, diverges for $p \leq 1$, and converges for $p > 1$.   [HINT: Prove $1/(an+b)^p \sim 1/n^p$.]

6. Prove that $\displaystyle\sum_{p=1}^{\infty} \frac{1}{p^k}$ is convergent if $k > 1$, where p is a prime.

7. Let $z_1, z_2, \cdots, z_n$ denote any "digits," 0, 1, 2, $\cdots$, 9.   Prove that $z_0 + \displaystyle\sum_{n=1}^{\infty} \frac{z_n}{10^n}$ converges when z_0 is any integer.

This example shows that every infinite decimal fraction may be regarded as a convergent infinite series, and therefore may be regarded as a representation of a definite real number, the sum of the infinite series.

Test each of the following series for convergence.   If the series diverges, does it diverge definitely or indefinitely?

8. $1 + \dfrac{1}{2^2} + \dfrac{1}{2^3} + \cdots + \dfrac{1}{2^n} + \cdots.$ (converges)

9. $1 + \dfrac{1}{\sqrt{2^3}} + \dfrac{1}{\sqrt{3^3}} + \cdots + \dfrac{1}{\sqrt{n^3}} + \cdots.$ (converges)

10. $1 + \dfrac{1}{\sqrt{2}} + \dfrac{1}{\sqrt{3}} + \cdots + \dfrac{1}{\sqrt{n}} + \cdots.$ (diverges definitely)

11. $\dfrac{1}{3} + \dfrac{1}{6} + \dfrac{1}{9} + \cdots + \dfrac{1}{3n} + \cdots.$ (diverges definitely)

12. $\dfrac{1}{2+1} + \dfrac{1}{4+1} + \dfrac{1}{8+1} + \cdots + \dfrac{1}{2^n+1} + \cdots.$ (converges)

13. $\dfrac{1}{1 \cdot 2} + \dfrac{1}{2 \cdot 3} + \dfrac{1}{3 \cdot 4} + \cdots + \dfrac{1}{n(n+1)} + \cdots.$ (converges)

14. $\dfrac{1}{1+1} + \dfrac{1}{4+1} + \dfrac{1}{9+1} + \cdots + \dfrac{1}{n^2+1} + \cdots.$ (converges)

15. $\dfrac{2}{2 \cdot 3 \cdot 4} + \dfrac{4}{3 \cdot 4 \cdot 5} + \dfrac{6}{4 \cdot 5 \cdot 6} + \cdots$

$$+ \dfrac{2n}{(n+1)(n+2)(n+3)} + \cdots. \qquad \text{(converges)}$$

16. $\dfrac{3}{2 \cdot 3} + \dfrac{6}{3 \cdot 4} + \dfrac{9}{4 \cdot 5} + \cdots + \dfrac{3n}{(n+1)(n+2)} + \cdots$ \qquad (diverges)

Test each of the following sequences $\{s_n\}$ for convergence, where:

17. $s_n = \displaystyle\sum_{k=1}^{n} \left(\dfrac{k}{3^k}\right).$ \quad (converges) \qquad 18. $s_n = \displaystyle\sum_{k=1}^{n} \dfrac{k}{10^{k-1}}.$ \quad (converges)

19. $s_n = \displaystyle\sum_{k=1}^{n} \dfrac{k!}{10^k}.$ \quad (diverges) \qquad 20. $s_n = \displaystyle\sum_{k=1}^{n} \dfrac{2^k}{k}.$ \quad (diverges)

21. $s_n = \displaystyle\sum_{k=1}^{n} \dfrac{k!}{3 \cdot 5 \cdot 7 \cdots (2k+1)}.$ \qquad (converges)

22. $s_n = \displaystyle\sum_{k=1}^{n} \dfrac{1 \cdot 2 \cdot 3 \cdot 4 \cdots (k)}{1 \cdot 3 \cdot 5 \cdot 7 \cdots (2k-1)}.$ \qquad (converges)

23. $s_n = \displaystyle\sum_{k=1}^{n} k\left(\dfrac{2}{3}\right)^k.$ \quad (converges) \qquad 24. $s_n = \displaystyle\sum_{k=1}^{n} \dfrac{2^k}{\sqrt{k}}.$

THEOREM 7.7. *Let* $\displaystyle\sum_{n=1}^{\infty} a_n$ *be a series whose terms form a positive monotone decreasing sequence* $\{a_n\}$, *and let* $g_0, g_1 \cdots$ *be any increasing sequence of positive integers. Then the two series*

$$\sum_{n=0}^{\infty} a_n \qquad and \qquad \sum_{k=0}^{\infty} (g_{k+1} - g_k)a_{g_k}$$

are either both convergent or both divergent, provided that there exists a positive constant M *such that for every* $k > 0$,

$$g_{k+1} - g_k \leqq M(g_k - g_{k-1}).$$

Let s_n denote the partial sums of the given series and t_k the partial sums of the second series. Let A denote the sum of the terms (if any) preceding a_{g_0}. Then for $n < g_k$,

$$s_n < s_{g_k} \leqq A + (a_{g_0} + \cdots + a_{g_1-1}) + \cdots$$
$$+ (a_{g_k} + \cdots + a_{g_{k+1}-1})$$
$$\leqq A + (g_1 - g_0)a_{g_0} + \cdots + (g_{k+1} - g_k)a_{g_k} \equiv A + t_k; \quad (1)$$

for $n > g_k$,

$$s_n > s_{g_k} > (a_{g_0+1} + \cdots + a_{g_1}) + \cdots + (a_{g_{k-1}+1} + \cdots + a_{g_k})$$
$$\geqq (g_1 - g_0)a_{g_1} + \cdots + (g_k - g_{k-1})a_{g_k} \equiv t_k - t_0.$$

Also,

$$M s_n > (g_2 - g_1)a_{g_1} + \cdots + (g_{k+1} - g_k)a_{g_k}.$$

Hence

$$M s_n > t_n - t_0. \tag{2}$$

From Eq. (1), if $\{t_n\}$ is bounded, then so is $\{s_n\}$; and from Eq. (2), if $\{s_n\}$ is bounded, so is $\{t_n\}$. Consequently $\{t_n\}$ and $\{s_n\}$ are both bounded or both unbounded, and so converge or diverge together.

THEOREM 7.8. *If* $\sum\limits_{n=1}^{\infty} a_n$, *a positive monotone decreasing series, is to converge, not only must* $a_n \to 0$ *but also* $na_n \to 0$.

If Σa_n converges, for every chosen $\epsilon > 0$, there exists an m such that for every $\mu > m$ and every $\sigma \geqq 1$, $|s_{\mu+\sigma} - s_\mu| < \epsilon/2$. Pick $n > 2m$ and μ the largest integer not greater than $n/2$.

Then $\mu \geqq m$ and $\sum\limits_{j=\mu+1}^{n} a_j < \epsilon/2$. Therefore $(n - \mu)a_n < \epsilon/2$ and $\dfrac{n}{2}a_n < \dfrac{\epsilon}{2}$. Hence, $na_n \to 0$ as $n \to +\infty$.

EXERCISES X

1. Retaining the relevant assumptions of Theorem **7.7**, prove that $\sum\limits_{n=1}^{\infty} a_n$ and $\sum\limits_{k=0}^{\infty} 2^k a_{2^k}$ converge and diverge together.

2. Show that $\sum\limits_{n=1}^{\infty} \dfrac{1}{n}$ and $\sum\limits_{k=1}^{\infty} \dfrac{2^k}{2^k}$ diverge together (use Ex. 1).

3. Show that $\sum\limits_{n=1}^{\infty} \dfrac{1}{n^p}$ and $\sum\limits_{k=1}^{\infty} \dfrac{2^k}{(2^k)^p}$ converge and diverge together, p fixed but arbitrary.

4. Show that $g_k = 3^k, 4^k, \cdots, k^2, k^3, \cdots$ are examples of particular values of g_k for which Theorem 7.7 holds.

Exercises 1 to 4 clearly show the value of Theorem 7.7, for the divergence and convergence of $\Sigma 2^k a_{2^k}$ is more easily determined than that of the series Σa_n.

5. Prove that $\Sigma(2k + 1)a_{k^2}$ and Σa_n converge and diverge together.

6. Prove that $\displaystyle\sum_{k=1}^{\infty} \frac{1}{(\log 2)k} \equiv \sum_{k=1}^{\infty} \frac{2^k}{2^k \log\,(2^k)}$ and $\displaystyle\sum_{n=2}^{\infty} \frac{1}{n \log n}$ diverge together.

7. Prove that $\displaystyle\sum_{k=2}^{\infty} \frac{1}{k \log 2 \cdot \log\,(k \log 2)} \equiv \sum_{k=2}^{\infty} \frac{2^k}{2^k \cdot \log 2^k \cdot \log\,(\log 2^k)}$

and $\displaystyle\sum_{n=3}^{\infty} \frac{1}{n \cdot \log n \cdot \log \log n}$ diverge together.

8. Generalize Ex. 7.

9. Prove that, if $b > 1$, $\displaystyle\sum_{n=2}^{\infty} \frac{1}{n \log n \, \cdots \, \log_{p-1} n \cdot (\log_p n)^b}$ converges

and diverges together with $\displaystyle\sum_{k} \frac{3^{k+1} - 3^k}{3^k(\log 3^k) \, \cdots \, (\log_p 3^k)^b}$.

10. Consider $\displaystyle\sum_{n=2}^{\infty} a_n$, where $a_n = 1/(n \log n)$. Show that $a_n \to 0$ and

$na_n \to 0$. Does $\displaystyle\sum_{n=2}^{\infty} a_n$ diverge?   (No.)

11. Investigate the behavior of $\displaystyle\sum_{n=N}^{\infty} a_n$, where for $n \geqq N$ with N sufficiently large, a_n has the following values:

(a) $n^p/n!$,   (b) $\dfrac{(n!)^2}{(2n)!}$ (c) $\dfrac{1}{n^{1+(n^{-1})}}$,

(d) $3^n(n!)/n^n$,   (e) $\sqrt{a} - 1$,   (f) $a^{\log n}$,

(g) $(\sqrt{n+1} - \sqrt{n})$, (h) $\dfrac{\sqrt{n+1} - \sqrt{n}}{n}$, (i) $\dbinom{a+n}{n}$.

12. Prove: $\dfrac{n}{2} < 1 + \dfrac{1}{2} + \dfrac{1}{3} + \cdots + \dfrac{1}{2^n - 1} < n$ for every $n > 1$.

13. Prove: The sequence $\{x_n\}$, where $x_n = 1 + \dfrac{1}{2} + \cdots + \dfrac{1}{n} - \log n$, is monotone decreasing.

14. Prove: If $\displaystyle\sum_{n=1}^{\infty} a_n$ converges, then so does $\displaystyle\sum_{n=1}^{\infty} \frac{\sqrt{a_n}}{n}$.

15. Prove: Every positive real number x is expressible uniquely in the form

$$x = a_1 + \frac{a_2}{2!} + \frac{a_3}{3!} + \cdots + \frac{a_n}{n!} + \cdots,$$

where a_n is a nonnegative integer with $a_n \leq n - 1$ for $n > 1$, and where $a_n \neq n - 1$ for every n after some definite value N of n. The series terminates if and only if x is rational.

8. Series of Arbitrary Terms.   In this section we shall assume that the terms a_n in $\displaystyle\sum_{n=0}^{\infty} a_n$ are arbitrary real numbers.

From Theorem 4.2 follows immediately

^{cv}THEOREM 8.1.   *A necessary and sufficient condition for the convergence of the series Σa_n is that for any preassigned positive number ϵ there exists a number $N = N(\epsilon)$ such that for every $n > N$ and every $k \geq 1$, $|s_{n+k} - s_n| < \epsilon$, that is, that*

$$|a_{n+1} + a_{n+2} + \cdots + a_{n+k}| < \epsilon.$$

^{cv}THEOREM 8.2.   *Let $\{\mu_n\}$ and $\{k_n\}$ be two arbitrary sequences of positive integers, the first (at least) of which tends to $+\infty$. The series Σa_n converges if and only if the sequence*

$$T_n = (a_{\mu_n+1} + a_{\mu_n+2} + \cdots + a_{\mu_n+k_n})$$

is always a null sequence.

This theorem is an immediate consequence of Theorem 4.3.

An immediate corollary to Theorem 8.1 is

^{cv}THEOREM 8.3.   *A necessary condition that Σa_n converge_ is that $a_n \to 0$.*

Is Theorem 8.3 true if the condition *necessary* is replaced by *sufficient?*

^{cv}THEOREM 8.4.   *If $\displaystyle\sum_{n=0}^{\infty} a_n$ converges, and if $r_n = \displaystyle\sum_{j=n+1}^{\infty} a_j$ denotes the "remainder" after n terms, then $r_n \to 0$ as $n \to +\infty$.*

Since $\displaystyle\sum_{n=0}^{\infty} a_n$ converges, for every $\epsilon > 0$, there exists an N such that for every $n > N$, and every $k \geq 1$,

$$|a_{n+1} + a_{n+2} + \cdots + a_{n+k}| < \epsilon.$$

Let $k \to +\infty$. Then for every $n > N$, $r_n \leqq \epsilon$.

^{cv}Theorem 8.5. *Let p_0, p_1, $\cdots$, p_n, $\cdots$ be an arbitrary monotone increasing sequence of positive numbers tending to $+\infty$.*

If $\sum\limits_{n=0}^{\infty} a_n$ is a convergent series of arbitrary terms, then as $n \to +\infty$,

$$\frac{p_0 a_0 + p_1 a_1 + \cdots + p_n a_n}{p_n} \to 0.$$

From Ex. IV, 4, if $s_n \to s$, then

$$\frac{p_1 s_0 + (p_2 - p_1)s_1 + \cdots + (p_n - p_{n-1})s_{n-1}}{p_n} \to s.$$

Now $p_0 s_0 / p_n \to 0$ and $s_n \to s$, so that

$$s_n - \frac{(p_1 - p_0)s_0 + (p_2 - p_1)s_1 + \cdots + (p_n - p_{n-1})s_{n-1}}{p_n} \to 0.$$

Since $s_n = \sum\limits_{j=0}^{n} a_j$,

$$\frac{p_0 a_0 + p_1 a_1 + \cdots + p_n a_n}{p_n} \to 0.$$

^{cv}Theorem 8.6. *Let $\sum\limits_{n=0}^{\infty} a_n$ be a given series of arbitrary terms.*

From $\sum\limits_{n=0}^{\infty} a_n$ construct a new series $\sum\limits_{n=0}^{\infty} a_n'$ by omitting a finite number of terms, prefixing a finite number of terms, or altering a finite number of terms (or by doing any or all of these things at once), and then renaming the terms of the series so constructed a_0', a_1', $\cdots$.

Then $\sum\limits_{n=0}^{\infty} a_n$ and $\sum\limits_{n=0}^{\infty} a_n'$ converge or diverge together.

By hypothesis there exists a definite integer k (positive, zero, or negative) and an integer m, such that for every $n > m$, $a_n' = a_{n+k}$. Hence, if the initial index of the one series be greater than $m + |k|$, then every portion of the one series is a portion of the other. Then from Theorem 8.1 we have Theorem 8.6.

A series whose terms are alternately positive and negative is called an *alternating series*.

Theorem 8.7. *Let* $\sum\limits_{n=0}^{\infty} a_n$ *be an alternating series. If as*

$n \to +\infty$, $|a_n| \to 0$, *then* $\sum\limits_{n=0}^{\infty} a_n$ *is convergent.*

Write $|a_n| = \alpha_n$, $\alpha_n = (-1)^{n+1} a_n$. Then

$$T_{n,k} = \pm[\alpha_{n+1} - \alpha_{n+2} + \cdots + (-1)^{k-1}\alpha_{n+k}].$$

A short argument shows that $|T_{n,k}| < \alpha_{n+1}$. Since $\alpha_n \to 0$, it follows that $T_{n,k} \to 0$. Theorem 8.7 then follows from Theorem 8.1.

EXERCISES XI

1. Show that every sequence is expressible as a series.

2. A finite part of a series $T_{\alpha\beta} = a_{\alpha+1} + a_{\alpha+2} + \cdots + a_{\alpha+\beta}$ is frequently called a *portion* of the series $\sum\limits_{n=1}^{\infty} a_n$. Prove: *A necessary and sufficient condition that* $\sum\limits_{n=1}^{\infty} a_n$ *converge is that every sequence of portions* $T_{\alpha\beta} \to 0$ *as* $\alpha \to +\infty$.

3. Prove that $\sum\limits_{n=1}^{\infty} (1/n)$ is divergent by exhibiting a sequence of "portions" which is not a null sequence.

Hint: Show $T_{n,n} \equiv \dfrac{1}{n+1} + \dfrac{1}{n+2} + \cdots + \dfrac{1}{2n} > \dfrac{1}{2}.$

4. Show that the series $\sum\limits_{n=1}^{\infty} \dfrac{1}{n^2}$ converges by demonstrating that

$$T_{\alpha\beta} \equiv \left[\frac{1}{(\alpha+1)^2} + \cdots + \frac{1}{(\alpha+\beta)^2} \right] \to 0 \text{ as } \alpha \to +\infty.$$

Hint: Prove that

$$\frac{1}{(\alpha+\beta)^2} < \frac{1}{(\alpha+\beta-1)(\alpha+\beta)} = \left(\frac{1}{\alpha+\beta-1} - \frac{1}{\alpha+\beta} \right),$$

and then consider $T_{\alpha\beta}$.

5. Prove Theorem 8.3.

6. Explain the absence of comparison tests in the case of series of arbitrary terms.

ALGEBRA OF CONVERGENT SERIES

9. Algebra of Series. We have already pointed out that the term "sum," used to designate the limit of a sequence of partial sums of a series is quite misleading, because it is apt to foster the belief that an infinite series may be manipulated by the same rules as an actual sum of a finite number of definite terms. This belief is, of course, erroneous.

In the following paragraphs we shall show to what extent the principal laws (the associative, distributive, and commutative laws) of the algebra of actual finite sums hold for infinite series.

We first consider to what extent the associative law is valid in the theory of infinite series, this law being expressed by the relation

$$a_0 + (a_1 + a_2) = (a_0 + a_1) + a_2.$$

^{cv}THEOREM 9.1.   *Let μ_1, μ_2, $\cdots$ denote any increasing sequence of distinct positive integers.   Suppose that*

$$a_0 + a_1 + a_2 + \cdots = S$$

is a convergent infinite series.   If

$$A_k = a_{\mu_k+1} + a_{\mu_k+2} + \cdots + a_{\mu_{k+1}}, \qquad k = 0, 1, 2, \cdots$$
$$(\mu_0 = -1)$$

where each A_k is considered as one term, then the series

$$A_0 + A_1 + A_2 + \cdots + A_k + \cdots$$

converges to S.

The partial sums S_k of $\displaystyle\sum_{k=1}^{\infty} A_k$ is a subsequence $s_{\mu_1}, s_{\mu_2}, \cdots,$

$s_{\mu_k}, \cdots$ of the sequence of partial sums s_n of $\displaystyle\sum_{n=0}^{\infty} a_n$. So, from Theorem 2.5, we see that S_k tends to the same limit as s_n.

Thus the convergence of $\displaystyle\sum_{n=1}^{\infty} \frac{(-1)^{n-1}}{n}$ implies that of

$$\sum_{k=1}^{\infty} \left[\frac{1}{(2k-1)} - \frac{1}{2k} \right] \equiv \sum_{k=1}^{\infty} \frac{1}{(2k-1) \cdot 2k}$$

and

$$1 - \sum_{k=2}^{\infty} \left(\frac{1}{k} - \frac{1}{k+1} \right)$$

to the same sum S.

The following example shows that, while Theorem 9.1 permits us to introduce brackets, we may not omit brackets occurring in an infinite series without special consideration.

In the convergent series $0 + 0 + 0 + \cdots + 0 + \cdots$ with sum 0, replace each 0 by $(1 - 1)$. We obtain

$$(1 - 1) + (1 - 1) + \cdots = 0.$$

However, upon omitting brackets we have the series

$$1 - 1 + 1 - 1 + 1 - 1 + \cdots$$

which is divergent.

^{cv}THEOREM 9.2. *If $\sum_{k=0}^{\infty} A_k$ is a convergent infinite series and the terms A_k are themselves actual sums, then the brackets enclosing the A_k may be removed if and only if the series $\sum_{n=0}^{\infty} a_n$ so obtained is also convergent.*

We shall leave the proof of this theorem to the reader.

^{cv}THEOREM 9.3. *If $\sum_{n=1}^{\infty} a_n = A$ and $\sum_{n=1}^{\infty} b_n = B$ are both convergent, they may be added term by term, i.e.,*

$$\sum_{n=1}^{\infty} (a_n + b_n) = A + B.$$

Also without braces,

$$a_1 + b_1 + a_2 + b_2 + \cdots + a_n + b_n + \cdots = A + B.$$

Let s_n and σ_n be the partial sums of the first two series. Then

$(s_n + \sigma_n)$ are the partial sums of the third. By Theorem 2.10 it follows that $(s_n + \sigma_n) \to (A + B)$. The proof of the remainder of the theorem is left to the reader.

Similarly, it may be shown that

*cv*THEOREM 9.4. *Two convergent series may be subtracted term by term.*

*cv*THEOREM 9.5. *If* $\displaystyle\sum_{n=1}^{\infty} a_n = s$ *converges and if c is an arbitrary constant, then the series may be multiplied by the constant c, that is,*

$\displaystyle\sum_{n=1}^{\infty} (ca_n)$ *converges to cs.*

Theorem 9.5 provides a partial extension of the *distributive law* to infinite series.

EXERCISES XII

1. Prove that S in the example following Theorem 9.1 satisfies the inequality $\frac{7}{12} < S < \frac{10}{12}$.

2. Prove that $\displaystyle\sum_{p=1}^{\infty}\left(\frac{1}{4p-3} + \frac{1}{4p-1} - \frac{1}{2p}\right)$ is convergent as well as the series resulting from it by removing the braces.

3. Show that the sum σ of the series in Ex. 2 is $\frac{3}{2}$ times the sum S of the series in Ex. 1.

4. Prove Theorem 9.2.

5. Prove Theorem 9.4.

6. Prove Theorem 9.5.

7. Prove: *The series* Σa_n *deduced from* ΣA_n *in Theorem 9.1 is convergent if the quantities*

$$\bar{A}_p = |a_{\mu_p+1}| + |a_{\mu_p+2}| + \cdots + |a_{\mu_{p+1}}|$$

form a null sequence.

8. Complete the proof of Theorem 9.3.

10. Absolute Convergence. The following definition enables us to extend further the laws of algebra to infinite series.

*cv*DEFINITION 10.1. *A convergent series* Σa_n *is said to be absolutely convergent if* $\Sigma |a_n|$ *also converges, otherwise it is said to be nonabsolutely convergent.*

For example, the convergent series

$$1 - \tfrac{1}{2} + \tfrac{1}{3} - \tfrac{1}{4} + \tfrac{1}{5} - \tfrac{1}{6} + \cdots$$

is nonabsolutely convergent, for $1 + \tfrac{1}{2} + \tfrac{1}{3} + \cdots$ is divergent,

while the convergent series $1 - \dfrac{1}{2^2} + \dfrac{1}{3^2} - \dfrac{1}{4^2} + \cdots$ is absolutely convergent since $1 + \dfrac{1}{2^2} + \dfrac{1}{3^2} + \dfrac{1}{4^2} + \cdots$ is convergent.

^{c}**THEOREM 10.1.** *If $\Sigma|a_n|$ converges, then so does Σa_n. If $\Sigma a_n = s$ and $\Sigma|a_n| = \sigma$, then $|s| \leqq \sigma$.*

Since $\left|\sum_{p=1}^{k} a_{n+p}\right| \leqq \sum_{p=1}^{k} |a_{n+p}|$, the left hand number is $< \epsilon$ if the right-hand number is. The first part of the theorem then follows from Theorem 8.1. Since $|s_n| \leqq \sum_{p=0}^{n} |a_p| < \sigma$, then by Theorem 2.2, $|s| \leqq \sigma$.

^{c}**THEOREM 10.2.** *Let Σc_n^- be a convergent series of positive terms. If, for every $n > m$, $|a_n| \leqq c_n$, then Σa_n is absolutely convergent.*

Comparison of $\Sigma|a_n|$ with Σc_n together with Theorem 10.1 makes this theorem evident.

^{c}**THEOREM 10.3.** *Let $p_1, p_2, \cdots, p_n, \cdots$ form a bounded sequence. If Σa_n is absolutely convergent, then so is $\Sigma p_n a_n$.*

The sequences $\{|p_n|\}$ and $\{p_n\}$ are both bounded. From Theorem 7.3, $\Sigma|p_n| \cdot |a_n| \equiv \Sigma|p_n a_n|$ converges with $\Sigma|a_n|$.

We shall now show that the fundamental laws of algebra for finite sums are essentially maintained in the case of absolutely convergent series, but not for nonabsolutely convergent series.

^{c}**DEFINITION 10.2.** *Let Σa_n be a given series. If $\mu_1, \mu_2, \mu_3, \cdots$ is any rearrangement of the sequence $1, 2, 3, \cdots$, then the series*
$$\sum_{n=1}^{\infty} a_n' \equiv \sum_{n=1}^{\infty} a_{\mu_n} \text{ is said to be generated from } \sum a_n \text{ by rearrangement.}$$

^{c}**DEFINITION 10.3.** *A convergent infinite series which remains convergent, without alteration in sum, under every rearrangement (i.e., obeys the commutative law) is said to be unconditionally convergent. If a convergent series is such that its convergence can be altered by rearrangement (i.e., does not obey the commutative law), the series is said to be conditionally convergent.*

For example, the series $\sum \dfrac{(-1)^{n+1}}{2^n}$ is unconditionally convergent; but the series $\sum \dfrac{(-1)^{n-1}}{n}$ is conditionally convergent.

^{c}THEOREM 10.4. *Every absolutely convergent series is unconditionally convergent.*

(a) *Case when* $\Sigma c_n = S$ *Is a Series of Positive Terms.* Let $S_n = \sum_{p=1}^{n} c_p$. Consider an arbitrary rearrangement $\sum c_n' \equiv \sum c_{p_n}$ of Σc_n. Then if S_n' be the partial sums of $\Sigma c_n'$, then $S_n' < S_N$, provided N is greater than all of p_0, p_1, $\cdots$, p_n. Since $S_N < S$, $S_n' < S$ for every $n > N$. Hence by Theorem 7.1, $\Sigma c_n'$ converges. If S' be the sum of $\Sigma c_n'$, then by Theorem 2.2, $S' \leqq S$. But Σc_n can be thought of as a rearrangement of $\Sigma c_n'$, so that as before, $S \leqq S'$. Hence $S = S'$.

(b) *Case when* Σa_n *Is an Arbitrary Absolutely Convergent Series.* Let $\Sigma a_n'$ be an arbitrary rearrangement of Σa_n. By (a), $\Sigma |a_n'|$ is convergent; so by Theorem 10.1, $\Sigma a_n'$ is also convergent. We shall now show that any rearrangement of Σa_n does not alter the sum. Let $\epsilon > 0$. From Theorem 8.1, there exists an M sufficiently large that for every $k \geqq 1$, $\sum_{p=1}^{k} |a_{m+p}| < \epsilon$. Next select an integer N_0 so large that p_0, p_1, $\cdots$, p_{N_0} contain at least all of the integers 0, 1, 2, $\cdots$, M. Only terms a_{M+1}, a_{M+2}, $\cdots$ of index $> M$ remain in the difference $S_n' - S_n$ for all $n > N_0$. Hence for $n > N_0$, $|S_n' - S| < \epsilon$. From this we infer that $S_n' = S_n + (S_n' - S_n)$ converges to the same limit as S_n, so that Σa_n and $\Sigma a_n'$ have the same sum.

^{c}THEOREM 10.5. *If* Σa_n *is nonabsolutely convergent, it is only conditionally convergent.*

To prove this we shall show that by a suitable rearrangement of Σa_n a divergent series $\Sigma a_n'$ can be obtained. Denote the terms of Σa_n which are $\geqq 0$ by p_1, p_2, $\cdots$, and the terms which are <0 by $-q_1$, $-q_2$, $\cdots$. At least one of the series of positive terms, Σp_n and Σq_n, diverges, for if they both converged, then Σa_n would be absolutely convergent. Suppose Σp_n diverges. Consider a rearrangement $\Sigma a_n'$ of Σa_n as follows:

$$p_1 + p_2 + \cdots + p_{n_1} - q_1 + p_{n_1+1} + p_{n_1+2} + \cdots + p_{n_2}$$
$$- q_2 + p_{n_2+1} + \cdots .$$

Since Σp_n diverges its partial sums are unbounded, so that we can select an integer n_1 sufficiently large that $\sum\limits_{j=1}^{n_1} p_j > 1 + q_1$, an

$n_2 > n_1$ so that $\sum\limits_{j=1}^{n_2} p_j > 2 + q_1 + q_2, \cdots$, a $\; n_t > n_{t-1}$ so that

$\sum\limits_{=1}^{n_t} p_j > t + \sum\limits_{j=1}^{} q_j$. Evidently $\sum a'_n$ diverges. A similar argument

holds when Σq_n diverges.

^{c}THEOREM 10.6. *Let* $\mu_1, \mu_2, \cdots, \mu_n, \cdots$ *be any increasing sequence of positive integers. If* Σa_n *is absolutely convergent, then so is the subseries* Σa_{μ_n}.

This theorem follows from Theorem 10.1.

Let Σa_n be any absolutely convergent series. Let Σa_{μ_n} be any subseries of Σa_n (finite or infinite). Arrange this subseries in any order and denote the resulting series by $\sum\limits_{k} a_k^{(0)} = \sigma^{(0)}$,

where $\sigma^{(0)}$ is its sum. (Why does this sum exist independently of the arrangement selected?) Pick a second subseries of Σa_n (finite or infinite), arranged in any order $\sum\limits_{k} a_k^{(1)} = \sigma^{(1)}$ with sum

$\sigma^{(1)}$. Continue this process in such a manner that each term of Σa_n appears exactly once in exactly one of the subseries. The series $\sigma^{(0)} + \sigma^{(1)} + \cdots + \sigma^{(n)} + \cdots$ is said to be a *rearrangement of* Σa_n *in the extended sense.* It can be shown that

^{c}THEOREM 10.7. *If an absolutely convergent series be rearranged in the extended sense, the series* $\sum\limits_{k} \sigma^{(k)}$ *is absolutely convergent and its sum is equal to the sum of* Σa_n.

^{c}THEOREM 10.8. *Let* $z^{(0)} = \sum\limits_{s=0}^{\infty} a_s^{(0)}, \; z^{(1)} = \sum\limits_{s=0}^{\infty} a_s^{(1)}, \cdots,$

$z^{(k)} = \sum\limits_{s=0}^{\infty} a_s^{(k)}, \cdots$ *be an infinite set of absolutely convergent series.*

If $\sum\limits_{r=0}^{\infty} \lambda^{(r)}$ *converges to* ζ, *where* $\sum\limits_{s=0}^{\infty} |a_s^{(r)}| = \lambda^{(r)}$, *then for each fixed* s,

$(s = 0, 1, 2, \cdots)$ *the series* $\sum\limits_{r=0}^{\infty} a^{(r)} = \sigma^{(s)}$ *is absolutely convergent and* $\sum_{s=0}^{\infty} \sigma^{(s)} = \sum_{r=0}^{\infty} z^{(r)}$. (*In other words, in the infinite matrix* $(a_s^{(r)})$ *the sums of the rows and the sums of the columns are both absolutely convergent to the same sum.*)

Arrange all the terms in $[a_s^{(r)}] = A$ in some simple sequence, say, $a_0, a_1, a_2, \cdots \cdot$. Now every partial sum $\sum_{j=0}^{m} |a_j| \leq \sigma$, since if we pick k large enough that $a_0, a_1, \cdots, a_m$ all occur in the first k rows of A, $\sum_{j=0}^{m} |a_j| \leq \sum_{j=0}^{k} \lambda^{(j)} \leq \sigma$. Hence $\sum a_n$ is absolutely convergent. A new rearrangement of the terms $a_s^{(r)}$ in A, $a_0', a_1', a_2', \cdots$ would produce a series $\Sigma a_n'$ which is merely a rearrangement of Σa_n, and consequently absolutely convergent to the same sum σ.

Both $\Sigma z^{(r)}$ and $\Sigma \sigma^{(s)}$ are rearrangements of $\Sigma a_n = \sigma$ in the sense of Theorem 10.7; hence these series both converge absolutely to the same sum σ.

EXERCISES XIII

1. Examine each of the following series for absolute convergence:

(a) $\sum (1/n^p)$, $p > 1$.   (b) $\sum (1/n^p)$, $p < 1$.

(c) $\sum \dfrac{(-1)^n}{n^2}$.   (d) $\sum \dfrac{(-1)^{n-1}}{n^p}$, $p > 1$.

(e) $\sum \dfrac{x^n}{n!}$, $x < 0$.

2. Prove Theorem 10.2 with the condition $|a_n| < c_n$ replaced by the condition $|a_{n+1}/a_n| \leq c_{n+1}/c_n$.

3. Prove that if Σa_n is absolutely convergent, then the series generated from it by an arbitrary alteration in the signs of its terms is absolutely convergent.

4. Prove that $\sum_{n=1}^{\infty} \dfrac{(-1)^n}{n}$ is nonabsolutely convergent. Rearrange the series to give a divergent series.

5. Prove *Riemann's theorem: The terms of a nonabsolutely convergent series can always be rearranged* (1) *so that the new series is convergent to any arbi-*

trarily given number, (2) so that the new series oscillates between arbitrarily assigned bounds, (3) so that the new series is definitely divergent.

6. Illustrate Riemann's theorem by means of the series

$$\sum_{n=0}^{\infty}\left(\frac{1}{2n+1} - \frac{1}{2n+2}\right).$$

7. Prove Theorem 10.7.

11. Multiplication of Series. The distributive law for finite sums is

$$\left(\sum_{r=0}^{l} a_r\right)\left(\sum_{s=0}^{m} b_s\right) = \sum_{\substack{r=0,\ldots,l \\ s=0,\ldots,m}} a_r b_s$$

irrespective of the order in which the products $a_r b_s$ are added.

Let $\sum_{r=0}^{\infty} a_r = A$ and $\sum_{s=0}^{\infty} b_s = B$ be two convergent series with sums A and B. Under what conditions does

$$\left(\sum_{r=0}^{\infty} a_r\right)\left(\sum_{s=0}^{\infty} b_s\right) = AB$$

independently of the order in which the products $a_r b_s$ are added? Let $p_0, p_1, p_2, \cdots$ denote the series of all the products $a_r b_s$ in any chosen order. Under what conditions does Σp_n converge? Converge to AB? These questions are partially answered by

*c*THEOREM 11.1. *If $\Sigma a_r = A$ and $\Sigma b_s = B$ are absolutely convergent, then the product series Σp_n converges absolutely to the sum AB.*

(a) Let $n > 0$. Denote by M the largest of the indices r and s in the products $a_r b_s$ which were denoted above by $p_0, p_1, \cdots$, p_n. Then $\sum_{j=1}^{n} |p_j| \leqq \left(\sum_{r=0}^{M} |a_r|\right)\left(\sum_{s=0}^{M} |b_s|\right) < \alpha\beta$, where $\sum_{n=0}^{\infty} |a_n| = \alpha$ and $\sum_{n=0}^{\infty} |b_n| = \beta$. This shows that the partial sums of $\sum |p_n|$ are bounded, so that Σp_n converges absolutely.

(b) The sum S of Σp_n can be determined quickly by the "squares arrangement," $a_0 b_0 = p_0$,

$$(a_0 + a_1)(b_0 + b_1) = p_0 + p_1 + p_2 + p_3, \cdots,$$
$$(a_0 + \cdots + a_n)(b_0 + \cdots + b_n) = p_0 + \cdots + p_{(n+1)^2 - 1}$$
$$= \sigma_n.$$

By Theorems 2.5 and 2.10, $\sigma_n \to S = AB$.

EXERCISES XIV

1. Let $\Sigma a_r = A$, $\Sigma b_s = B$ be two absolutely convergent series. Let $M = (a_r b_s)$ be the infinite matrix whose element in rth row and sth column is $a_r b_s$. Show that AB is equal to the sum of the diagonals of M,

$$a_0 b_0 + (a_0 b_1 + a_1 b_0) + (a_0 b_2 + a_1 b_1 + a_2 b_0) + \cdots.$$

This form of the product is called *Cauchy's product*. Write the product in the form indicated when squares of the main diagonal of M are used, starting from the upper left hand corner of M.

2. Let $\Sigma a_r x^r$, $\Sigma b_s x^s$ be two power series. Indicate the Cauchy's product of these two series.

3. Prove: $\left(\sum_{n=0}^{\infty} x^n \right)\left(\sum_{n=0}^{\infty} x^n \right) = \sum_{n=0}^{\infty} (n+1)x^n$, $|x| < 1$.

HINT: If $x_1 + x_2 = x_3$, prove that $\left(\sum_{n=0}^{\infty} \frac{x_1^n}{n!} \right)\left(\sum_{n=0}^{\infty} \frac{x_2^n}{n!} \right) = \sum_{n=0}^{\infty} \frac{x_3^n}{n!}.$

4. Prove that if the series $\sum \frac{(-1)^{n-1}}{n}$ be rearranged so that we have alternately r positive terms and r negative terms, that the resulting series converges. What results if the number of positive terms used is different from the number of negative terms?

5. Prove that any conditionally convergent series can be grouped together in such a manner that the resulting series is absolutely convergent.

6. Let $\sum_{n=1}^{\infty} \frac{1}{n^2} = s$. Show that $1 + \frac{1}{3^2} + \frac{1}{5^2} + \frac{1}{7^2} + \cdots = \frac{3}{4}s$; that,

$$1 - \frac{1}{2^2} - \frac{1}{4^2} + \frac{1}{5^2} + \frac{1}{7^2} - \frac{1}{8^2} - \frac{1}{10^2} + \cdots = \frac{4}{9}s.$$

7. *Abel's Partial Sum.* Let $a_0, a_1, \cdots; b_0, b_1, \cdots$ be arbitrary numbers. Show that for every $k \geq 1$, and for every $n \geq 0$,

$$\sum_{r=n+1}^{n+k} a_r b_r = \sum_{r=n+1}^{n+k} A_r(b_r - b_{r+1}) - A_n b_{n+1} + A_{n+k} b_{n+k+1},$$

where $A_n = \sum_{r=0}^{n} a_r.$

8. ^{c}*Mertens' Theorem.   Suppose that at least one of the two convergent series* $\Sigma a_n = A$ and $\Sigma b_n = B$ *converges absolutely.   Let*

$$c_n = (a_0 b_n + a_1 b_{n-1} + \cdots + a_n b_0).$$

Prove that Σc_n *converges to the sum* AB.

9. ^{c}*Abel's Theorem.   Show that if* $\Sigma a_n = A$, $\Sigma b_n = B$ *and* $\Sigma c_n = C$ *each converge, then* $AB = C$, *where* $c_n = a_0 b_n + a_1 b_{n-1} + \cdots + a_n b_0$.

PART C.   POWER SERIES

12. Power Series.   In this section we shall consider series of the type $\sum_{n=0}^{\infty} a_n x^n$, where x is assumed to be a real variable.   Such series are known as *power series* in x, and the (real) numbers a_n are called their *coefficients*.

We shall first consider the question, for what values of x is the series convergent and for what values is it divergent?

It is quite obvious that every power series $\sum_{n=0}^{\infty} a_n x^n$ is convergent for $x = 0$, no matter what the coefficients a_n may be.   However, as will be seen in Exs. XV, 1 to 5, power series exist which converge for all values of x, which converge for only certain values of x, or which converge for no values of x different from zero.   In the first case, the series is said to be *everywhere convergent* and in the last case the series is said to be *nowhere convergent* (even though convergent at 0).

The *totality* of points x for which the given series $\sum_{n=0}^{\infty} a_n x^n$ converges is known as its *region of convergence*.   (Thus the region of convergence for $\sum_{n=0}^{\infty} x^n$ is the set of all points x for which $|x| < 1$.)

^{c}**THEOREM 12.1.**   *Let* $\sum_{n=0}^{\infty} a_n x^n$ *be any power series which is neither convergent everywhere nor convergent nowhere.   Then there exists a positive number* r *such that* $\sum_{n=0}^{\infty} a_n x^n$ *converges (even absolutely) for every* $|x| < r$ *but diverges for every* $|x| > r$.

The number r in this theorem is called the *radius of convergence* and the *region of convergence* of the given power series is the interval $-r < x < r$.

It should be remarked here that the question of the convergence of the series at $x = r$ and $x = -r$ is not answered. A separate investigation must be made for the values r and $-r$ of x.

We shall base our proof of Theorem 12.1 in Chap. IX on the following two theorems:

*c*THEOREM 12.2. *Let* $\sum\limits_{n=0}^{\infty} a_n x^n$ *be a given power series convergent*

for $x = x_0$, $x_0 \neq 0$. *Then* $\sum\limits_{n=0}^{\infty} a_n x^n$ *is absolutely convergent for*

every $x = x_1$ *for which* $|x_1| < |x_0|$.

If $\sum\limits_{n=0}^{\infty} a_n x^n$ converges for x_0, then there exists a positive number K such that $|a_n x_0^n| < K$ for every n. Then

$$|a_n x_1^n| = |a_n x_0^n| \cdot \left|\frac{x_1}{x_0}\right|^n \leqq K \cdot \left|\frac{x_1}{x_0}\right|^n.$$

The theorem now follows immediately from Theorem 10.2.

*c*THEOREM 12.3. *If* $\sum\limits_{n=0}^{\infty} a_n x^n$ *diverges for* $x = x_0$, *then it diverges*

for every $x = x_1$ *for which* $|x_1| > |x_0|$.

If the series were convergent for x_1, then by Theorem 12.2, it would also converge for x_0 since $|x_0| < |x_1|$, contradictory to the hypothesis.

Theorem 12.1 merely assures the existence of the radius of convergence without giving us any information as to its magnitude. To supply this need we shall now prove

*c*THEOREM 12.4. *Let* $\sum\limits_{n=0}^{\infty} a_n x^n$ *be a given power series. Let*

$$\mu = \varlimsup_{n \to +\infty} \sqrt[n]{|a_n|}.$$

Then, (a) *if* $\mu = 0$, *the power series is everywhere convergent*,
   (b) *if* $\mu = +\infty$, *the power series is nowhere convergent*,

(c) *if* $0 < \mu < +\infty$, *the power series converges absolutely for every* $|x| < 1/\mu$, *but diverges for every* $|x| > 1/\mu$. *Thus,* $r = 1/\mu$, *is the radius of convergence of the given power series.*

(a) Let $x_0 \neq 0$ be an arbitrary real number. Then there exists an m large enough that $\sqrt[n]{|a_n|} < 1/2|x_0|$, or $|a_n x_0^n| < 1/2^n$ for $n > m$. By Theorem 10.2, $\Sigma a_n x_0^n$ converges absolutely.

(b) If $\Sigma a_n x^n$ converges for some $x_1 \neq 0$, then $\{a_n x_1^n\}$ and $\{\sqrt[n]{|a_n x_1^n|}\}$ are bounded. From this we can conclude that $\{\sqrt[n]{|a_n|}\}$ is bounded. This contradicts hypothesis (b). Hence $\Sigma a_n x^n$ cannot converge for any $x_1 \neq 0$.

(c) Suppose x_2 is any number such that $|x_2| < 1/\mu$. Select a positive ρ such that $|x_2| < \rho < 1/\mu$. Then $1/\rho > \mu$. Then for m sufficiently large, $\sqrt[n]{|a_n|} < 1/\rho$, and $\sqrt[n]{|a_n x_2^n|} < |x_2|/\rho < 1$ for $n > m$. $\Sigma a_n x_2^n$ is evidently absolutely convergent. If $|x_3| > 1/\mu$, $|1/x_3| < \mu$, and there must exist infinitely many n's such that $\sqrt[n]{|a_n|} > |1/x_3|$, or $|a_n x_3^n| > 1$. Hence the series cannot converge. (Why?)

^{c}THEOREM 12.5. *If* $\displaystyle\sum_{n=0}^{\infty} a_n x^n$ *has the radius of convergence* r,

then so has $\displaystyle\sum_{n=0}^{\infty} n a_n x^{n-1}$.

Let $n a_n = a_n'$. Then $\sqrt[n]{|a_n'|} = \sqrt[n]{a_n} \cdot \sqrt[n]{n}$. Since $\sqrt[n]{n} \to 1$, the sequences $\{\sqrt[n]{|a_n'|}\}$ and $\{\sqrt[n]{|a_n|}\}$ have the same upper limits, and the theorem follows from Theorems 12.4 and 9.5.

So far we have considered only power series of the form $\displaystyle\sum_{n=0}^{\infty} a_n x^n$. However, our results are essentially unaltered if we also consider power series of the more general type $\displaystyle\sum_{n=0}^{\infty} a_n (x - x_0)^n$.

By setting $x - x_0 = x'$, we see that the series converges absolutely for all x's such that $|x'| = |x - x_0| < r$, but diverges for $|x - x_0| > r$, where r denotes the number determined by Theorem 12.4. Evidently, the region of convergence of the series is therefore an interval (or the point x_0) the middle point of which is x_0. The interval of convergence may or may not include one or both end points. All the considerations given above for the series

$\sum\limits_{n=0}^{\infty} a_n x^n$ are valid, except for the translation of the interval of convergence.

For each value of x in the interval of convergence, the power series $\sum\limits_{n=0}^{\infty} a_n(x - x_0)^n$ has a definite sum S. In general the value of S is dependent on the value of x. To denote this dependence of S on x, we shall write

$$\sum_{n=0}^{\infty} a_n(x - x_0)^n = S(x), \qquad |x - x_0| < r,$$

and say that the power series defines, within its interval of convergence, a function of x.

EXERCISES XV

1. Prove that the geometric series $\sum\limits_{n=0}^{\infty} x^n$ is absolutely convergent for $|x| < 1$ and divergent for $|x| \geq 1$.

2. Prove that $\Sigma(x^n/n!)$ is absolutely convergent for all real x's.

3. Prove that $\Sigma(x^n/n)$ is absolutely convergent for $|x| < 1$; is divergent for $|x| > 1$; is convergent for $x = -1$; and is divergent for $x = 1$.

4. Prove that $\sum\limits_{k=1}^{\infty} (-1)^k \dfrac{x^{2k}}{(2k)!}$ is absolutely convergent for all real x's.

5. Prove that $\sum\limits_{k=1}^{\infty} \dfrac{x^k}{2^k k^2}$ is absolutely convergent for $|x| \leq 2$, and divergent for $|x| > 2$.

6. For what values of x is $\sum\limits_{n=1}^{\infty} n^n x^n$ convergent?   *Ans.* 0.

7. For what values of x is $\sum\limits_{n=1}^{\infty} \dfrac{1}{n^x}$ convergent?   *Ans.* $x > 1$.

8. Prove Theorem 12.2 if the first sentence is changed to read, "If the sequence $\{a_n x_0^n\}$ of its terms is bounded at $x = x_0$, $x_0 \neq 0$."

9. Show that $\dfrac{1}{\overline{\lim}\ \sqrt[n]{|a_n|}}$ is not necessarily equal to $\underline{\lim}\ \dfrac{1}{\sqrt[n]{|a_n|}}$.

10. If a power series is everywhere convergent, then $\sqrt[n]{|a_n|} \to 0$ as $n \to +\infty$.

11. Prove that $\sqrt[n]{1/n!} \to 0$ as $n \to +\infty$. (HINT: $\Sigma x^n/n!$ converges everywhere.)

12. Show that each of the following have the same radius of convergence as $\displaystyle\sum_{n=0}^{\infty} a_n x^n$:

$$\sum_{n=0}^{\infty} (n+1)a_{n+1}x^n; \qquad \sum_{n=0}^{\infty} na_n x^{n-1}; \qquad \sum_{n=0}^{\infty} n(n-1)a_n x^{n-2}; \qquad \cdots ;$$

$$\sum_{n=0}^{\infty} n(n-1) \cdots (n-k+1)a_n x^{n-k}, \text{ for all positive integers } k.$$

13. Show that each of the following have the same radius of convergence as $\displaystyle\sum_{n=0}^{\infty} a_n x^n$:

$$\sum_{n=0}^{\infty} \frac{a_n x^{n+1}}{n+1}; \qquad \sum_{n=0}^{\infty} \frac{a_n x^{n+2}}{(n+1)(n+2)}; \qquad \cdots ;$$

$$\sum_{n=0}^{\infty} \frac{a_n x^{n+k}}{(n+1)(n+2) \cdots (n+k)}.$$

Find for what values of x (if any) each of the following series converges:

14. $x - \dfrac{x^2}{2^2} + \dfrac{x^3}{3^2} - \dfrac{x^4}{4^2} + \cdots + (-1)^{n-1}\dfrac{x^n}{n^2} + \cdots$.

$Ans.\quad -1 \leqq x \leqq 1.$

15. $1 + x + x^2 + \cdots + x^n + \cdots$. $\qquad\qquad Ans.\quad -1 < x < 1.$

16. $1 + \dfrac{x^2}{2!} + \dfrac{x^4}{4!} + \cdots + \dfrac{x^{2n}}{(2n)!} + \cdots$. $\quad Ans.\quad -\infty < x < +\infty.$

17. $x + x^4 + x^9 + \cdots + x^{n^2} + \cdots$. $\qquad\qquad Ans.\quad -1 < x < 1.$

18. $x - \dfrac{x^2}{2} + \dfrac{x^3}{3} - \dfrac{x^4}{4} + \cdots + (-1)^{n-1}\dfrac{x^n}{n} + \cdots$.

$Ans.\quad -1 < x \leqq 1.$

19. $1 + x + \dfrac{x^2}{2!} + \cdots + \dfrac{x^n}{n!} + \cdots$. $\qquad Ans.\quad -\infty < x < +\infty.$

20. $x - \dfrac{x^3}{3!} + \dfrac{x^5}{5!} - \dfrac{x^7}{7!} + \cdots + (-1)^{n-1}\dfrac{x^{2n-1}}{(2n-1)!} + \cdots$.

$Ans.\quad -\infty < x < +\infty.$

21. $x + \dfrac{x^2}{\sqrt{2}} + \dfrac{x^3}{\sqrt{3}} + \cdots + \dfrac{x^n}{\sqrt{n}} + \cdots$

$\qquad\qquad\qquad$ *Ans.* $-\infty < x < +\infty$.

22. $\dfrac{1}{3} + \dfrac{2x}{2 \cdot 3^2} + \dfrac{3x^2}{2^2 \cdot 3^3} + \cdots + \dfrac{nx^{n-1}}{2^{n-1} \cdot 3^n} + \cdots$

$\qquad\qquad\qquad$ *Ans.* $-6 < x < +6$.

23. $1 - 2(x-1) + 3(x-1)^2 - 4(x-1)^3 + \cdots$

$\qquad\qquad + (-1)^{n-1}(n)(x-1)^{n-1} + \cdots$. $\quad$ *Ans.* $0 < x < 2$.

For what values of x, if any, does each of the following sequences $\{s_n\}$ converge, where:

24. $s_n = \displaystyle\sum_{k=1}^{n} (-1)^k kx^{k-1}$. $\qquad\qquad$ *Ans.* $-1 < x < 1$.

25. $s_n = \displaystyle\sum_{k=1}^{n} \dfrac{x^k}{k \cdot 3^k}$. $\qquad\qquad$ *Ans.* $-3 \leqq x < 3$.

26. $s_n = \displaystyle\sum_{k=1}^{n} \dfrac{2^k x^k}{k^2 + 1}$. $\qquad\qquad$ *Ans.* $-\dfrac{1}{2} \leqq x \leqq \dfrac{1}{2}$

27. $s_n = \displaystyle\sum_{k=1}^{n} \dfrac{(k+1)x^k}{k!}$. $\qquad\qquad$ *Ans.* $-\infty < x < +\infty$.

28. $s_n = \displaystyle\sum_{k=1}^{n} (-1)^{k-1}\dfrac{x^{(2k-1)}}{(2k-1)}$. $\qquad$ 29. $s_n = \displaystyle\sum_{k=1}^{n} \dfrac{x^k}{3^{1/k}}$.

30. $s_n = \displaystyle\sum_{k=1}^{n} kx^k$.

31. $s_n = \displaystyle\sum_{k=1}^{n} \dfrac{x^k}{2^{(k-1)}(k+1)}$. $\qquad$ *Ans.* $-2 \leqq x < 2$.

32. $s_n = 1 + \displaystyle\sum_{k=2}^{n} \dfrac{(x-2)^{k-1}}{(k-1)^2}$. $\qquad$ *Ans.* $1 < x < 3$.

13. Properties of Functions Represented by Power Series.

Let the power series $f(x) = \displaystyle\sum_{n=0}^{\infty} a_n(x - x_0)^n$ define a function of x

within the (open) interval $|x - x_0| < r$.   As a general rule the most important problem concerning this series is to deduce from the series the principal properties of the function represented by the series.

^{c}Theorem 13.1.   *The function $f(x)$ defined (in its interval of convergence) by the power series $\sum\limits_{n=0}^{\infty} a_n(x - x_0)^n$ is continuous at $x = x_0$ (i.e., $f(x) \to f(x_0) = a_0$ as $x \to x_0$).*

Suppose $0 < \rho < r$.   By Theorem 9.5, $\sum\limits_{n=0}^{\infty} |a_n|\rho^{n-1} = K \ (K > 0)$ and $\sum\limits_{n=0}^{\infty} |a_n|\rho^n$ converge together.   Then for every $|x - x_0| < \rho$,

$$|f(x) - a_0| = \left| (x - x_0)\sum_{n=1}^{\infty} a_n(x - x_0)^{n-1} \right| \leqq |x - x_0| \cdot K. \quad \text{Let}$$

$\epsilon > 0$.   Then if $\delta > 0$ be less than both ρ and ϵ/K, then for every $|x - x_0| < \delta$, $|f(x) - a_0| < \epsilon$.   Theorem 13.1 follows from Theorem 4.2 of Chap. I.

^{c}Theorem 13.2 (*Uniqueness Theorem*).   *Let $\sum\limits_{n=0}^{\infty} a_n x^n$ and $\sum\limits_{n=0}^{\infty} b_n x^n$ be two power series both having a radius of convergence $r \geqq \rho > 0$, where ρ is some positive number, and both having the same sum for every $|x| < \rho$.   Then, for every $n = 0, 1, 2, \cdots$, the two series are entirely identical, that is, $a_n = b_n$ for all n.*

Consider

$$a_0 + a_1 x + a_2 x^2 + \cdots = b_0 + b_1 x + b_2 x^2 + \cdots,$$
$$|x| < \rho. \quad (1)$$

Let $x \to 0$.   Then by Theorem 13.1, $a_0 = b_0$.   Subtracting $a_0 = b_0$ from (1) and then dividing by x, we find that

$$a_1 + a_2 x + a_3 x^2 + \cdots = b_1 + b_2 x + b_3 x^2 + \cdots,$$
$$(0 < |x| < \rho). \quad (2)$$

Again let $x \to 0$ and apply Theorem 13.1.   We find $a_1 = b_1$, and

$$a_2 + a_3x + a_4x^2 + \cdots = b_2 + b_3x + b_4x^2 + \cdots,$$
$$(0 < |x| < \rho).$$

By a complete induction proof, we are then led to the conclusion that $a_n = b_n$ for every n.

A corresponding statement holds for the more general series

$$\sum_{n=0}^{\infty} a_n(x - x_0)^n.$$

It should be remarked in passing that this theorem holds for series involving but a finite number of terms as well as for infinite series.

We shall now prove a number of theorems which are without doubt among the most important theorems in the theory of infinite series.

*^c*Theorem 13.3. *Let* $\sum_{n=0}^{\infty} a_n(x - x_0)^n$ *be a power series with radius of convergence* r, *representing the function* $f(x)$ *for all values*

$x_0-r \qquad x_0 \quad x \; x_1 \quad x_0+r$

Fig. 142.

of x *for which* $|x - x_0| < r$. *Then* $f(x)$ *may also be expanded in a power series with any other point* x_1 *of the interval of convergence as center; in fact,*

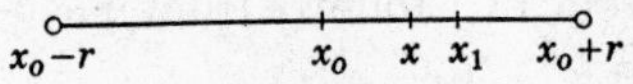

$$f(x) = \sum_{k=0}^{\infty} b_k(x - x_1)^k,$$

where

$$b_k = \sum_{n=0}^{\infty} \binom{n+k}{k} a_{n+k}(x_1 - x_0)^n,$$

and where the radius r_1 *of this new series is*

$$r_1 \leqq r - |x_1 - x_0|.$$

Suppose x_1 is such that $|x_1 - x_0| < r$. Then (see Ex. XVI, 2)

$$f(x) = \sum_{n=0}^{\infty} a_n[(x_1 - x_0) + (x - x_1)]^n$$

$$= \sum_{n=0}^{\infty} a_n\left[\sum_{k=0}^{n} \binom{n}{k}(x_1 - x_0)^{n-k}(x - x_1)^k \right], \tag{3}$$

so that

$$f(x) = \sum_{k=0}^{\infty} \sum_{n=k}^{n+k} a_n \binom{n}{k} (x_1 - x_0)^{n-k} (x - x_1)^k$$

$$= \sum_{k=1}^{\infty} \sum_{n=0}^{n} a_{n+k} \binom{n+k}{k} (x_1 - x_0)^n (x - x_1)^k \qquad (4)$$

$$\equiv \sum_{k=0}^{\infty} b_k (x - x_1)^k,$$

provided the indicated rearrangement (see Theorem 10.8) of the series is valid.   Theorem 10.8 is applicable, since the series

$$\sum_{n=0}^{\infty} |a_n|(|x_1 - x_0| + |x - x_1|)^n$$

converges if $|x_1 - x_0| + |x - x_1| < r$.   Hence, if x is closer to x_1 than either $(x_0 + r)$ or $(x_0 - r)$, the rearranged series (4) converges to $f(x)$.

Theorem 13.4.   *A function $f(x)$ represented by a power series* $\sum_{n=0}^{\infty} a_n(x - x_0)^n$ *is continuous for every value x_1 of x interior to the interval of convergence.*

From Theorem 13.3, within a certain neighborhood of x_1, we may write

$$f(x) = \sum_{n=0}^{\infty} a_n(x - x_0)^n = \sum_{n=0}^{\infty} b_n(x - x_1)^n,$$

where

$$b_0 = \sum_{n=0}^{\infty} a_n(x_1 - x_0)^n = f(x_1).$$

By Theorem 13.1, as $x \to x_1$, $f(x) \to f(x_1)$, from which the theorem follows.

*c*Theorem 13.5.   *A function $f(x)$ represented by a power series* $\sum_{n=0}^{\infty} a_n(x - x_0)^n$ *has a derivative at every point x_1 interior to the* *interval of convergence of the series, and the value of the derivative*

$f'(x_1)$ *at* x_1 *is equal to* $f'(x_1) = \sum\limits_{n=1}^{\infty} n a_n (x_1 - x_0)^{n-1}$.

Since $f(x) = \sum\limits_{n=0}^{\infty} b_n (x - x_1)^n$, then for all x's sufficiently close to x_1,

$$\frac{f(x) - f(x_1)}{x - x_1} = b_1 + b_2 (x - x_1) + \cdots .$$

Upon letting $x \to x_1$, and applying Theorem 13.1, we find that

$$f'(x_1) = b_1 = \sum\limits_{n=1}^{\infty} n a_n (x_1 - x_0)^{n-1}.$$

From Theorem 13.5, it follows that

^{c}THEOREM 13.6. *A function* $f(x)$ *represented by a power series* $\sum\limits_{n=0}^{\infty} a_n (x - x_0)^n$ *has derivatives of every order at every point* x_1 *interior to the interval of convergence, and the value of the* kth *derivative* $f^{(k)}(x_1)$ *at* x_1 *is equal to*

$$f^{(k)}(x_1) = (k!) b_k$$
$$= \sum\limits_{n=0}^{\infty} (n+1)(n+2) \cdots (n+k) a_{n+k} (x_1 - x_0)^n.$$

From Theorem 13.5, for every x in the interval of convergence,

$$f'(x) = \sum\limits_{n=0}^{\infty} (n+1) a_{n+1} (x - x_0)^n.$$

By Theorem 12.5, $f'(x)$ has the same interval of convergence as the original series. Hence we may again apply this result to $f'(x)$, yielding

$$f''(x) = \sum\limits_{n=1}^{\infty} n(n+1) a_{n+1} (x - x_0)^{n-1}$$
$$= \sum\limits_{n=0}^{\infty} (n+1)(n+2) a_{n+2} (x - x_0)^n.$$

Repeating this process, we obtain

$$f^{(k)}(x) = \sum_{n=0}^{\infty} (n+1)(n+2) \cdots (n+k)a_{n+k}(x-x_0)^n,$$

which converges for every x of the original interval of convergence for the series of $f(x)$. In particular, this relation holds for $x = x_1$.

Substituting for the coefficients b_k in the series of Theorem 13.3, the values of $\dfrac{f^{(k)}(x_1)}{k!}$ obtained in Theorem 13.6, we have

^{c}THEOREM 13.7 (*Taylor's Series*). *If $f(x)$ is a function represented by the power series $\displaystyle\sum_{n=0}^{\infty} a_n(x-x_0)^n$ for every x for which $|x - x_0| < r$, where r is the radius of convergence of the series, and if x_1 denotes any point interior to the interval of convergence, then*

$$f(x) = f(x_1) + \frac{f'(x_1)}{1!}(x - x_1) + \frac{f''(x_1)}{2!}(x - x_1)^2$$
$$+ \cdots + \frac{f^{(k)}(x_1)}{k!}(x - x_1)^k + \cdots,$$

for every x for which $|x - x_1| < r_1 = r - |x_1 - x_0|$.

^{c}THEOREM 13.8. *A function $f(x)$ represented by a power series $\displaystyle\sum_{n=0}^{\infty} a_n(x - x_0)^n$ may be integrated term by term within the interval of convergence of the series; and the definite integral from $t = x_1$ to $t = x_2$, where x_1 and x_2 are interior to the interval of convergence, is equal to*

$$\int_{x_1}^{x_2} f(t)\, dt = \sum_{n=0}^{\infty} \frac{a_n}{n+1}[(x_2 - x_0)^{n+1} - (x_1 - x_0)^{n+1}].$$

By Ex. XV, 13, the series $S(x) = \displaystyle\sum_{n=0}^{\infty} \frac{a_n}{n+1}(x - x_0)^{n+1}$ converges if $|x - x_0| < r$. From Theorem 13.5, the derivative $S'(x) = \Sigma a_n(x - x_0)^n = f(x)$. By Sec. 33 of Chap. II, the function $g(x) = \int_{x_0}^{x} f(t)\, dt$ has for its derivative, $g'(x) = f(x)$. From Theorem 2.1, Chap. II, $g(x) - S(x) = C$, a constant. But

$g(x_0) - S(x_0) = 0$, so that $C = 0$. Thus $g(x) \equiv S(x)$, and

$$\int_{x_0}^{x} f(t)\, dt = \sum_{n=0}^{\infty} \frac{a_n}{n+1} (x - x_0)^{n+1}. \quad \text{Theorem 13.8 now follows.}$$

It should be emphasized that Theorem 13.4, on the continuity of the function represented by a power series, is valid only for the open interval of convergence. In fact, we are unable to conclude directly that the function is continuous even if the series converges at one or both of the end points of the interval. However, the following theorem is of interest in this connection:

THEOREM 13.9 (*Abel's Limit Theorem.*)* *If the power series*

$$\sum_{n=0}^{\infty} a_n x^n \text{ has a radius of convergence } r \text{ and converges for } x = +r,$$

and if $f(x)$ denotes the function defined by the series, then $\lim\limits_{x \to r-0} f(x)$

exists and is equal to $\sum\limits_{n=0}^{\infty} a_n r^n$*; i.e., $f(x)$ is continuous on the left at*

$x = r$.

If $\Sigma a_n x^n$ has the radius r, then $\Sigma b_n x^n$ with $b_n = a_n r^n$ has the radius 1. We shall accordingly simplify our proof by assuming $r = 1$, and $\Sigma a_n = S$, and then show that $\lim\limits_{x \to 1-0} f(x) = S$. By Theorem 11.1, since

$$\frac{1}{1-x} \sum_{n=0}^{\infty} a_n x^n = \sum_{n=0}^{\infty} x^n \sum_{n=0}^{\infty} a_n x^n = \sum_{n=0}^{\infty} S_n x^n, \quad \text{for} \quad |x| < 1,$$

where $S_n = \sum\limits_{n=0}^{n} a_n$, it follows that $f(x) = (1-x) \sum S_n x^n$. Since $(1-x) \Sigma x^n = 1$,

$$S - f(x) = (1-x) \sum_{n=0}^{\infty} (S - S_n) x^n \equiv (1-x) \sum_{n=0}^{\infty} r_n x^n, \quad |x| < 1,$$

where $r_n \equiv S - S_n \to 0$. (Why?)

* ABEL: *Jour. reine angew. Math.*, Vol. 1, p. 311, 1826. This paper is one of the most famous in the history of infinite series. The serious student will find it well worth studying.

Select a positive number ϵ.   Then for n sufficiently large, say, $n > N$, $|r_n| < \epsilon/2$.   Then for $0 \leq x < 1$,

$$|S - f(x)| \leq \left| (1 - x) \sum_{n=0}^{N} r_n x^n \right| + \frac{\epsilon(1 - x)}{2} \sum_{n=N+1}^{\infty} x^n$$

$$\leq P(1 - x) + \frac{\epsilon(1 - x)}{2} \frac{x^{N+1}}{1 - x},$$

where $P = \sum_{k=0}^{N} |r_k|$.   Hence for $1 - \delta < x < 1$,

$$|S - f(x)| < \frac{\epsilon}{2} + \frac{\epsilon}{2} = \epsilon,$$

so that $f(x) \to S$ as $x \to 1 - 0$.

A similar theorem can be stated for the left end of the interval of convergence.

EXERCISES XVI

1. Complete the inductive proof begun in the proof of Theorem 13.2.
2. Apply the result of Theorem 13.2 to prove that

$$\binom{p}{0}\binom{p}{p} + \binom{p}{1}\binom{p}{p-1} + \cdots + \binom{p}{p}\binom{p}{0}$$

$$\equiv \binom{p}{0}^2 + \binom{p}{1}^2 + \cdots + \binom{p}{p}^2 = \binom{2p}{p}.$$

HINT: Since $(1 + x)^p(1 + x)^p = (1 + x)^{2p}$, then

$$\left[\sum_{v=0}^{p} \binom{p}{v} x^v \right] \cdot \left[\sum_{v=0}^{p} \binom{p}{v} x^v \right] = \sum_{\mu=0}^{2p} \binom{2p}{\mu} x^\mu.$$

Here $\binom{p}{v}$ is a symbol for the binomial coefficient;

$$\binom{p}{v} \equiv \frac{p(p - 1)(p - 2) \cdots (p - v + 1)}{1 \cdot 2 \cdot 3 \cdots v}, \qquad \binom{p}{0} = 1, \qquad v \leq p.$$

Thus,

$$(a + b)^p = a^p + \binom{p}{1} a^{p-1}b + \binom{p}{2} a^{p-2}b^2 + \cdots + \binom{p}{v} a^{p-v}b^v$$

$$+ \cdots + \binom{p}{p} b^p.$$

3. Let $f(x)$ be defined by a power series $\sum_{n=0}^{\infty} a_n x^n$ convergent for $|x| < r$.

(a) If $f(x)$ is an *even* function [i.e., $f(x) = f(-x)$], show that only even powers of x can have nonvanishing coefficients.

(b) Show that if $f(x)$ is an *odd* function [i.e., $f(x) = -f(-x)$] only odd powers of x can have nonvanishing coefficients.

4. Show that in Theorem 13.5, $f'(x_1) = \sum_{n=0}^{\infty} (n+1)a_{n+1}(x_1 - x_0)^n$.

5. The distinction between Taylor's series and Taylor's theorem of Chap. I should be carefully noted. State these distinctions.

6. Prove: If $\sum_{n=0}^{\infty} a_n x^n$ converges for $x = -r$, then $\lim_{x \to -r+0} f(x)$ exists and is equal to $\sum_{n=0}^{\infty} (-1)^n a_n r^n$.

7. From Theorems 13.4 and 13.9, show that $\lim_{x \to \xi} (\Sigma a_n x^n) = \Sigma a_n \xi^n$, provided the series on the right converges and $x \to \xi$ from the origin side.

8. If $\sum_{n=0}^{\infty} a_n$ is a divergent series of positive terms and $\sum_{n=0}^{\infty} a_n x^n$ has a radius of convergence 1, show that $f(x) = \sum_{n=0}^{\infty} a_n x^n \to +\infty$ as $x \to 1 - 0$.

14. The Algebra of Power Series. It follows immediately from Theorems 9.3 and 9.4 that convergent power series may be added and subtracted. From Theorem 11.1 we see that two power series may be multiplied provided, of course, that we remain within the interior of the intervals of convergence. Thus

$$\sum_{n=0}^{\infty} a_n x^n \pm \sum_{n=0}^{\infty} b_n x^n = \sum_{n=0}^{\infty} (a_n \pm b_n)x^n,$$

$$\left(\sum_{n=0}^{\infty} a_n x^n\right)\left(\sum_{n=0}^{\infty} b_n x^n\right) = \sum_{n=0}^{\infty} (a_0 b_n + a_1 b_{n-1} + \cdots + a_n b_0)x^n,$$

provided that x lies in the interior of the intervals of convergence of both series.

Since power series may be added, subtracted, and multiplied (within the interior of their common region of convergence), it is natural to suspect that, under certain conditions, one can divide by power series. That this is the case follows from

Theorem 14.1. *Let* $\sum\limits_{n=0}^{\infty} a_n x^n$ *be convergent with sum* $A(x)$ *and*

suppose $\sum\limits_{n=0}^{\infty} b_n y^n$ *is convergent with radius* R *and sum* $B(y)$. *If in*

$\sum\limits_{n=0}^{\infty} b_n y^n$, y *be replaced by* $\sum\limits_{n=0}^{\infty} a_n x^n$, *obtaining*

$$b_0 + b_1\left(\sum_{n=0}^{\infty} a_n x^n\right) + b_2\left(\sum_{n=0}^{\infty} a_n x^n\right)^2 + \cdots \equiv \sum_{n=0}^{\infty} c_n x^n,$$

then $\sum\limits_{n=0}^{\infty} c_n x^n$ *converges to the sum* $B[A(x)]$, *if* x *is such that* $\sum\limits_{n=0}^{\infty} |a_n x^n|$
converges.

This is a special case of Theorem 10.8.   Write

$$y^k = \left(\sum_{j=0}^{\infty} a_j x^j\right)^k = \sum_{j=0}^{\infty} a_j^{(k)} x^j, \qquad k = 0, 1, \cdots.$$

Then the series $b_0 = b_0\left(\sum\limits_{k=0}^{\infty} a_k^{(0)} x^k\right)$, $b_1 y = b_1\left(\sum\limits_{k=0}^{\infty} a_k^{(1)} x^k\right)$, $\cdots$ of
array $\mathfrak{a} \equiv [a_r^{(s)}]$ corresponds to the $z^{(k)}$ series of Theorem 10.8.
Next, consider the series

$$|b_0| = |b_0|\left(\sum_{k=0}^{\infty} \alpha_k^{(0)} \xi^k\right), \quad |b_1|\eta = |b_1|\left[\sum_{k=0}^{\infty} \alpha_k^{(1)} \xi^k\right], \quad \cdots$$

of array $\alpha \equiv (\alpha_r^{(s)})$, with $|x| = \xi$, $\eta = \sum\limits_{n=0}^{\infty} |a_n x^n|$.   Each element
of α is $\geqq 0$.   Since $\Sigma|b_k|\eta^k$ is convergent by assumption, Theorem
10.8 applies to α.   Since every element of $\mathfrak{a}$ is in absolute value $\leqq$
the corresponding element in α, Theorem 10.8 applies to $\mathfrak{a}$, and
Theorem 14.1 is now an immediate consequence.

EXERCISES XVII

1. (a) From $\left(\sum\limits_{r=0}^{\infty} a_r x^r\right)\left(\sum\limits_{k=0}^{\infty} x^k\right) = \sum\limits_{n=0}^{\infty} s_n x^n$, show that

$$\sum_{n=0}^{\infty} a_n x^n = (1 - x) \sum_{n=0}^{\infty} s_n x^n,$$

where $s_n = \sum_{k=0}^{n} a_k$, $|x| < 1$, $|x| < R$ where R is the radius of $\sum_{r=0}^{\infty} a_r x^r$.

(b) Consider $1/(1 - y) = \sum_{n=0}^{\infty} y^n$ which converges for $|y| < 1$. Let $\Sigma |a_n x^n|$ be convergent. Show that the resulting power series

$$1 + (\Sigma a_n x^n) + (\Sigma a_n x^n)^2 + \cdots \equiv \Sigma c_n x^n$$

converges to the sum $\dfrac{1}{1 - (\Sigma a_n x^n)} < 1$.

2. Let $\dfrac{1}{a_0 + a_1 x + a_2 x^2 + \cdots} = c_0 + c_1 x + c_2 x^2 + \cdots$. We may express the c's in terms of the a's (for, of course, the common region of convergence of Σa_n and Σc_n). Evidently, $(\Sigma a_n x^n) \cdot (\Sigma c_n x^n) \equiv 1$, from which we find

$$a_0 c_0 = 1,$$
$$a_0 c_1 + a_1 c_0 = 0,$$
$$a_0 c_2 + a_1 c_1 + a_2 c_0 = 0,$$
$$\cdots \cdots \cdots \cdots \cdots$$

From these equations, if $a_0 \neq 0$, the coefficients may be uniquely determined.

(a) Find the c's if $\sec x = \dfrac{1}{\cos x} = \dfrac{1}{1 - \dfrac{x^2}{2!} + \dfrac{x^4}{4!} - \dfrac{x^6}{6!} + \cdots} \equiv \Sigma c_n x^n$.

(b) Determine the coefficients B_0, B_1, $\cdots$ in

$$\left(1 + \frac{x}{2!} + \frac{x^2}{3!} + \cdots\right)\left(B_0 + \frac{B_1}{1!}x + \frac{B_2}{2!}x^2 + \cdots\right) \equiv 1.$$

Ans. $B_0 = 1$, $B_1 = -\frac{1}{2}$, $B_2 = \frac{1}{6}$, $B_3 = 0$, $B_4 = -\frac{1}{30}$, $B_5 = 0$, $B_6 = \frac{1}{42}$, $B_7 = 0$, $B_8 = -\frac{1}{30}$, $B_9 = 0$, $B_{10} = \frac{5}{66}$, $\cdots$.

These numbers are called *Bernoulli's numbers.*

(c) Show from your work in (a) that

$$\binom{n}{0}B_0 + \binom{n}{1}B_1 + \binom{n}{2}B_2 + \cdots + \binom{n}{n-1}B_{n-1} = 0,$$
$$n = 2, 3, \cdots.$$

(d) Show that $(B + 1)^n - B^n = 0$, where $B^k \equiv B_k$, from which the B's may be determined successively.

15. Reversion of Power Series.   Let

$$y = \sum_{n=1}^{\infty} a_n(x - x_0)^n + y_0 = f(x)$$

be convergent for $|x - x_0| < r$.   It is easy to see that if

$$\frac{\partial y}{\partial x}\bigg]_{0,0} = a_1 \neq 0,$$

(see Sec. 20 of Chap. I) the given series determines uniquely a function which may be expressed in the form of a power series

$$x = g(y) \equiv \sum_{n=1}^{\infty} b_n(y - y_0)^n + x_0,$$

which converges in a certain neighborhood of y_0.
Furthermore, $f[g(y)] \equiv y$ and $b_1 = 1/a_1$.

EXERCISES XVIII

1. Let $x_0 = y_0 = 0$.   By substituting $x = \Sigma b_n y^n$ in $y = \Sigma a_n x^n$, giving

$$y \equiv a_1(\Sigma b_n y^n) + a_2(\Sigma b_n y^n)^2 + a_3(\Sigma b_n y^n)^3 + \cdots,$$

find a set of equations from which b_1, b_2, $\cdots$ can be found in terms of a_1, a_2, $\cdots$.

2. Determine the first few terms of the series, obtained by division, for

$$\frac{1}{1 + \dfrac{x}{2} + \dfrac{x^2}{3} + \cdots}.$$

3. From

$$\left(1 - \frac{x^2}{2!} + \frac{x^4}{4!} - + \cdots\right)\left(E_0 - \frac{E_2}{2!}x^2 + \frac{E_4}{4!}x^4 - + \cdots\right) \equiv 1,$$

determine E_0, E_1, E_2, $\cdots$.   Show

$$E_{2n} + \binom{2n}{2}E_{2n-2} + \binom{2n}{4}E_{2n-4} + \cdots + E_0 = 0.$$

These numbers E_k are called *Euler's numbers*.
$$\text{Ans.}\quad E_0 = 1,\ E_1 = 0,\ E_2 = -1,\ \cdots.$$

4. Show that:

(a) $\dfrac{1}{1 - x} = \displaystyle\sum_{n=0}^{\infty} x^n.$ (b) $1/(1 - x)^2 = \displaystyle\sum_{n=0}^{\infty} (n + 1)x^n.$

(c) $\dfrac{1}{(1-x)^{k+1}} = \displaystyle\sum_{n=0}^{\infty} \binom{n+k}{k} x^n, \quad k > 0, \quad |x| < 1.$

(d) $(1+x)^p = \displaystyle\sum_{n=0}^{\infty} \binom{p}{n} x^n.$

(e) $\dfrac{x}{e^x - 1} = \displaystyle\sum_{n=0}^{\infty} \dfrac{B_n x^n}{n!}.$

(f) $x \operatorname{ctn} x = 1 - \dfrac{2^2 B_2}{2!} x^2 + \cdots + (-1)^k \dfrac{2^{2k} B_{2k} x^{2k}}{(2k)!} + \cdots.$

(g) $\tan x = \displaystyle\sum_{k=1}^{\infty} (-1)^{k-1} \dfrac{2^{2k}(2^{2k}-1)B_{2k}}{(2k)!} x^{2k-1}.$

HINT: $\tan x \equiv \operatorname{ctn} x - 2 \operatorname{ctn} 2x$; use (f).

(h) $\dfrac{x}{\sin x} = \displaystyle\sum_{k=0}^{\infty} (-1)^{k-1} \dfrac{(2^{2k}-2)B_{2k}}{(2k)!} x^{2k}.$

HINT: $1/(\sin x) \equiv \operatorname{ctn} x + \tan (x/2)$. Use (f) and (g).

5. From the series for $y = \sin x$, determine by reversion a series for (a) $x = \operatorname{Sin}^{-1} y$; (b) $\operatorname{Tan}^{-1} y$. [A simpler method for the finding series for $\operatorname{Sin}^{-1} y$ would be to integrate the series for $(d \operatorname{Sin}^{-1} x)/dx = (1 - x^2)^{-\frac{1}{2}}$.] Discuss the validity of this method.

6. Expand into power series: (a) $e^x/(e^x + 1)$, (b) $x^2/(1 - \cos x)$.

7. By integration, find series for:

(a) $\operatorname{Sin}^{-1} x.$ (b) $\log (1 + x).$

(c) $\operatorname{Tan}^{-1} x.$ (d) $\log \cos x.$

8. By differentiation, find series for:

(a) $\sec^2 x.$ (b) $\csc^2 x.$

9. By integration, find approximate values of:

(a) $\int_0^1 e^{-x^2}\, dx.$ (b) $\int_0^{\frac{1}{4}} \log (1 + \sqrt{x})\, dx.$

(c) $\int_0^1 \sqrt{2 - \cos x}\, dx.$ (d) $\int_0^1 e^{\sqrt{x}}\, dx.$

(e) $\int_0^1 \cos \sqrt{x}\, dx.$ (f) $\int_0^1 \sin x^2\, dx.$

PART D.   OTHER TOPICS

16. Euler's Transformation. In computational work it is frequently desirable to replace a given convergent series by one which converges more rapidly. Many devices for doing this are known.   One of the most useful and one which often leads to more rapidly convergent series is due to Euler (1755).

Consider any sequence $\{x_n\}$ of numbers $x_0, x_1, x_2, \cdots$.   Construct the *first differences* of $\{x_n\}$:

$$\Delta x_0 = x_0 - x_1, \quad \Delta x_1 = x_1 - x_2, \cdots, \quad \Delta x_k = x_k - x_{k+1}, \cdots.$$

Construct the *second differences* of $\{x_n\}$:

$$\Delta^2 x_0 = \Delta x_0 - \Delta x_1, \quad \Delta^2 x_1 = \Delta x_1 - \Delta x_2, \quad \cdots,$$
$$\Delta^2 x_k = \Delta x_k - \Delta x_{k+1}, \quad \cdots.$$

Continue this process, constructing the *n*th *differences* of $\{x_n\}$:

$$\Delta^n x_0 = \Delta^{n-1} x_0 - \Delta^{n-1} x_1, \quad \Delta^n x_1 = \Delta^{n-1} x_1 - \Delta^{n-1} x_2, \quad \cdots,$$
$$\Delta^n x_k = \Delta^{n-1} x_k - \Delta^{n-1} x_{k+1}, \quad \cdots,$$

and so on.

In carrying out this computation, it is quite convenient to arrange the work in a triangular array:

$$
\begin{array}{ccccc}
x_0, & x_1, & x_2, & x_3, & x_4, \cdots \\
\Delta x_0, & \Delta x_1, & \Delta x_2, & \Delta x_3, \cdots \\
\Delta^2 x_0, & \Delta^2 x_1, & \Delta^2 x_2, \cdots \\
\Delta^3 x_0, & \Delta^3 x_1, \cdots \\
\Delta^4 x_0, \cdots
\end{array}
$$

Euler's transformation of series is given by

^{c}**Theorem 16.1.**   *If* $\displaystyle\sum_{k=0}^{\infty} (-1)^k a_k$ *is an arbitrary convergent series,*

then $\displaystyle\sum_{k=0}^{\infty} (-1)^k a_k = \sum_{n=0}^{\infty} \frac{\Delta^n a_0}{2^{n+1}}.$

Example 1.   Consider $\log 2 = 1 - \frac{1}{2} + \frac{1}{3} - \frac{1}{4} + \cdots$, a slowly converging series.   Arrange the array of differences in the form

$$
\begin{array}{ccccc}
1, & \dfrac{1}{2}, & \dfrac{1}{3}, & \dfrac{1}{4}, & \dfrac{1}{5}, \cdots \\[2ex]
\dfrac{1}{1 \cdot 2}, & \dfrac{1}{2 \cdot 3}, & \dfrac{1}{3 \cdot 4}, & \dfrac{1}{4 \cdot 5}, \cdots \\[2ex]
\dfrac{1 \cdot 2}{1 \cdot 2 \cdot 3}, & \dfrac{1 \cdot 2}{2 \cdot 3 \cdot 4}, & \dfrac{1 \cdot 2}{3 \cdot 4 \cdot 5}, \cdots \\[2ex]
\dfrac{1 \cdot 2 \cdot 3}{1 \cdot 2 \cdot 3 \cdot 4}, & \dfrac{1 \cdot 2 \cdot 3}{2 \cdot 3 \cdot 4 \cdot 5}, \cdots
\end{array}
$$

In general,

$$\Delta^n a_0 = \frac{1}{n+1}, \cdots, \Delta^n a_k = \frac{n!}{(k+1)(k+2)\cdots(k+n+1)}, \cdots$$

By Euler's transformation:

$$\log 2 = \sum_{k=1}^{\infty} (-1)^{k-1}\frac{1}{k} \equiv \frac{1}{1\cdot 2} + \frac{1}{2\cdot 2^2} + \frac{1}{3\cdot 2^3} + \frac{1}{4\cdot 2^4} + \cdots,$$

this series converging more rapidly than the given one.

EXERCISES XIX

1. Show that

$$\text{Tan}^{-1} 1 \equiv \frac{\pi}{4} = 1 - \frac{1}{3} + \frac{1}{5} - \frac{1}{7} + \cdots$$

$$= \frac{1}{2}\left[1 + \frac{1}{3} + \frac{1\cdot 2}{3\cdot 5} + \frac{1\cdot 2\cdot 3}{3\cdot 5\cdot 7} + \cdots\right].$$

2. Show that for k fixed,

$$\Delta^2 x_k = x_k - 2x_{k+1} + x_{k+2}, \qquad \Delta^3 x_k = x_k - 3x_{k+1} + 3x_{k+2} - x_{k+3}, \qquad \cdots,$$

$$\Delta^n x_k = x_k - \binom{n}{1}x_{k+1} + \binom{n}{2}x_{k+2} - \cdots + (-1)^n\binom{n}{n}x_{k+n}.$$

3. Given $\sum_{n=0}^{\infty} (\frac{1}{2})^n$. Find the corresponding series generated by Euler's

transformation.   *Ans.* $\frac{1}{2}\sum_{n=0}^{\infty} (\frac{3}{4})^n$.

Which series converges the most rapidly?   *Ans.* The first.
This shows that Euler's transformation does not always lead to a more rapidly convergent series.

4. Apply Euler's transformation to

$$\sum_{n=0}^{\infty}(-1)^n\frac{1}{2^n}; \qquad \sum_{n=0}^{\infty}(-1)^n\frac{1}{3^n}; \qquad \sum_{n=0}^{\infty}(-1)^n\frac{1}{4^n}.$$

17. Infinite Products. Consider the sequence of products $p_1 = u_1$, $p_2 = u_1 u_2$, $\cdots$, $p_n = u_1 u_2 \cdots u_n$, $\cdots$. Such a sequence of products, called an *infinite product*, might be said to be convergent to the value U if the sequence of partial products $\{p_n\}$ tends to U as a limit. If this definition were used, then every product would be convergent for which a single factor was zero. Similarly, if for every $n > m$, m being a fixed integer, $|u_n| \leqq \theta < 1$, then $p_n \to 0$. However, such trivial cases are quite inconvenient, due to the part played by zero in multiplication. To exclude these special cases, we shall adopt the following definition:

DEFINITION 17.1.   *The infinite product*

$$\prod_{n=1}^{\infty} u_u \equiv u_1 u_2 u_3 \cdots ,$$

is said to be convergent (in the new and stricter sense) if for every $n > N$, N being some fixed integer, no factor vanishes, and if as $n \to +\infty$, the partial products

$$p_n = u_{N+1} u_{N+2} \cdots u_n \qquad (n > N)$$

approach a finite limit U_N different from 0. The number

$$U = u_1 u_2 \cdots u_N U_N$$

(which is independent of N) is called the value of the product.

The following elementary theorems follow immediately from the definition. (Note the analogy with similar theorems for finite products.)

*c*THEOREM 17.1.   *A convergent infinite product has the value 0 when and only when at least one of its factors is 0.*

*c*THEOREM 17.2.   *In a convergent infinite product, the sequence of factors always approaches 1.*

If $p_{n-1} \to U_N$, then so does $p_n \to U_N$. Since $U_N \neq 0$,

$$u_n = \frac{p_n}{p_{n-1}} \to 1.$$

Theorem 17.2 suggests the more convenient device of denoting the factors of an infinite product by $u_n = 1 + a_n$. The infinite products under consideration then have the form

$$\prod_{n=1}^{\infty} (1 + a_n).$$

The numbers a_n are usually called the *terms* of the product. Obviously, a necessary condition for the convergence of an infinite product is that $a_n \to 0$.

^{c}Theorem 17.3. *The product* $\prod\limits_{n=1}^{\infty} (1 + a_n)$, *with* $a_n \geqq 0$, *con-*

verges if and only if the positive series $\sum\limits_{n=1}^{\infty} a_n$ *converges.*

The product sequence $\{p_n\}$ is monotone increasing since each $a_n \geqq 0$. Since $1 + a_k \leqq e^{a_k}$, $p_n \leqq e^{s_n}$ for each n, where

$$s_n = a_1 + \cdots + a_n.$$

Moreover

$$p_n = (1 + a_1) \cdots (1 + a_n)$$
$$= 1 + a_1 + \cdots + a_n + a_1 a_2 + \cdots > s_n$$

(why?), so for each n, $s_n < p_n$. From the first inequality, we see that s_n is bounded, so that p_n is bounded. Conversely, by the second inequality, when p_n is bounded, s_n remains bounded. This completes the proof.

Remark. Theorem 17.3 answers completely the question of convergence.

^{c}Theorem 17.4. *The product* $\Pi(1 - a_n)$, *where* $a_n \geqq 0$ *for every* n, *converges if and only if* Σa_n *converges.*

In case the a_n have arbitrary signs, it can be shown that

^{c}Theorem 17.5. *The infinite product* $\Pi(1 + a_n)$ *converges if and only if, for every preassigned positive number* ϵ, *there exists a number* N *such that for every* $n > N$, *and every* $k \geqq 1$,

$$[(1 + a_{n+1})(1 + a_{n+2}) \cdots (1 + a_{n+k}) - 1] < \epsilon.$$

^{c}Definition 17.2. $\Pi(1 + a_n)$ *is said to be absolutely convergent if* $\Pi(1 + |a_n|)$ *converges.*

^{c}Theorem 17.6. *The convergence of* $\Pi(1 + |a_n|)$ *implies the convergence of* $\Pi(1 + a_n)$.

Evidently,

$$|(1 + a_{n+1})(1 + a_{n+2}) \cdots (1 + a_{n+k}) - 1|$$
$$\leqq (1 + |a_{n+1}|)(1 + |a_{n+2}|) \cdots (1 + |a_{n+k}|) - 1.$$

So if $\Pi(1 + |a_n|)$ converges, $\Pi(1 + a_n)$ must also.

As an immediate consequence of theorems 17.3 and 17.6 we can state

^{c}Theorem 17.7. $\Pi(1 + a_n)$ *is absolutely convergent if and only if* Σa_n *converges absolutely.*

The question of the convergence of products may be reduced to the corresponding problem for the convergence of series by means of

Theorem 17.8. $\prod\limits_{n=1}^{\infty} (1 + a_n)$ *converges if and only if the series*

$\sum\limits_{n=N+1}^{\infty} \log (1 + a_n)$, *with an appropriate integer N, converges.*

$\prod\limits_{n=1}^{\infty} (1 + a_n)$ *converges absolutely if and only if* $\sum\limits_{n=N+1}^{\infty} \log (1 + a_n)$

converges absolutely. If σ is the sum of $\sum\limits_{n=N+1}^{\infty} \log (1 + a_n)$, *then*

$$\prod_{n=1}^{\infty} (1 + a_n) = (1 + a_1) \cdots (1 + a_N)e^{\sigma}.$$

Definition 17.3.   *If $\Pi(1 + a_n)$ remains convergent with value unaltered, no matter how its factors are rearranged, the product is said to be unconditionally convergent.*

Theorem 17.9. $\Pi(1 + a_n)$ *is unconditionally convergent if and only if it converges absolutely.*

EXERCISES XX

1. By means of Theorem 17.3 construct several examples of convergent products $\Pi(1 + a_n)$.

2. Show that $\Pi\left(1 + \dfrac{1}{n^k}\right)$ converges if $k > 1$, diverges if $k \leqq 1$.

3. Show that $\Pi(1 + x^n)$ converges for $0 \leqq x < 1$.

4. Prove Theorem 17.4.

5. Prove: $\Pi\left(1 - \dfrac{1}{n^k}\right)$ converges if $k > 1$, diverges if $k \leqq 1$.

6. Prove: $p_n = \left(1 - \dfrac{1}{2}\right)\left(1 - \dfrac{1}{3}\right) \cdots \left(1 - \dfrac{1}{n}\right) \to 0$.   (Hint: show $p_n = 1/n$.)

7. Show that $\prod\limits_{n=2}^{\infty}\left(1 - \dfrac{1}{n}\right)$ diverges to zero. Discuss carefully the reason for divergence in the light of Definition 17.1.

Remark. An infinite product is said to be *divergent* (in the sense of our Definition 17.1.) if its partial products form a null sequence.

8. Prove Theorem 17.5.

9. Give several examples of absolutely convergent products; also non-absolutely convergent products.

10. If $\Pi(1 + |a_n|)$ is convergent, does it follow that $\Pi(1 + a_n)$ converges in the strict sense?

11. Prove Theorem 17.8.

12. Show that $\displaystyle\prod\left(1 + \frac{(-1)^{n-1}}{n}\right)$ converges to the value.

13. Prove $\displaystyle\prod\left(1 - \frac{x^2}{n^2}\right)$ is absolutely convergent for every x.

14. What is value of product in Ex. 13 when $x = 1$?

15. Examine for region of convergence $\displaystyle\prod_{n=1}^{\infty}\left(1 + \frac{x}{n}\right).$

16. Show that the symbols

$$\sum_{n=1}^{\infty}\frac{1}{2^n} \quad \text{and} \quad \frac{1}{2}\prod_{n=2}^{\infty}\left(1 + \frac{1}{2^n - 2}\right)$$

have the same meaning.

HINT: $\displaystyle\sum_{n=1}^{\infty} a_n$ is a symbol for the sequence $\{s_n\}$ of its partial sums;

$\displaystyle\prod_{n=1}^{\infty}(1 + a_n)$ is a symbol for the sequence $\{p_n\}$ of partial products

$$p_n = \prod_{\lambda=1}^{n}(1 + a_\lambda).$$

17. (a) Show that the sequence $\{p_n\}$ may also be represented by the series

$$p_1 + (p_2 - p_1) + (p_3 - p_2) + \cdots$$

$$\equiv p_1 + \sum_{n=2}^{\infty}(1 + a_1)\cdots(1 + a_{n-1})\cdot a_n.$$

(b) Show that the sequence $\{s_n\}$ with $s_n = \displaystyle\sum_{\lambda=1}^{n} a_\lambda$ may be represented by the product

$$s_1 \cdot \frac{s_2}{s_1} \cdot \frac{s_3}{s_2} \cdots \equiv s_1 \cdot \prod_{n=2}^{\infty} \frac{s_n}{s_{n-1}} = a_1 \cdot \prod_{n=2}^{\infty} \left(1 + \frac{a_n}{a_1 + a_2 + \cdots + a_{n-1}}\right),$$

provided that each $s_n \neq 0$.

This shows that every series may be written as a product and that every product may be written as a series.

18. Prove Theorem 17.9.

19. Construct unconditionally convergent infinite products; also, conditionally convergent products.

20. Prove: If $\Pi(1 + a_n)$ is not absolutely convergent and has no zero factor, then the factors may be so rearranged that the sequence of partial products has arbitrarily prescribed upper and lower bounds, subject, however, to the restriction that these bounds have the same sign as the value of the given product.

21. Illustrate Ex. 20 by constructing appropriate examples.

22. Prove: $\Pi[1 + (\frac{1}{2})^{2n}] = 2$.

23. Prove: $\displaystyle\prod_{n=2}^{\infty} \frac{1 - n^3}{1 + n^3} = \frac{2}{3}$.

18. Divergent Sequences and Series.   If a series

$$a_1 + a_2 + \cdots + a_n + \cdots$$

does not converge to a sum S, it is still often possible to associate with the sequence a "sum" indirectly.   Many such methods have been studied, the simplest of which is "summation by arithmetic means."

Let $S_n = \displaystyle\sum_{k=1}^{n} a_k$.   Construct the arithmetic means

$$\sigma_n = \frac{S_1 + S_2 + \cdots + S_n}{n}$$

of the partial sums of the series Σa_n.   If $S_n \to S$ as $n \to +\infty$, then by Theorem 3.1 so does $\sigma_n \to S$.   It sometimes happens that σ_n will tend to a limit even though S_n does not tend to a limit as $n \to +\infty$.   If σ_n tends to a limit S as $n \to +\infty$, the sequence $\{S_n\}$ is said to be *limitable* C_1, the series Σa_n is said to be *summable* C_1 to S by *arithmetic means*, or by *Cesaro's means of the first order*, or *summable* $(C, 1)$; S is called its C_1-*sum*.

Example 1.   The sequence $1, 1, 1, \cdots$ approaches the limit $S = 1$, and is also limitable C_1 to $S = 1$.

Example 2. The series $1 - 1 + 1 - 1 + 1 \cdots$ is divergent but is summable C_1 to $\frac{1}{2}$ since $\sigma_n \to \frac{1}{2}$ as $n \to + \infty$.

If σ_n does not tend to a limit, but the arithmetic means

$$\Sigma_n = \frac{\sigma_1 + \cdots + \sigma_n}{n}$$

tends to a limit S as $n \to + \infty$, then Σa_n is said to be summable C_2, or $(C, 2)$. This process is readily generalized.

EXERCISES XXI

1. Construct a series which is divergent but summable $(C, 1)$; a series not summable $(C, 1)$, but summable $(C, 2)$; $\cdots$; (C, n).

2. Show that $1 + 0 - 1 + 1 + 0 - 1 + \cdots$ is summable $(C, 1)$ to the "sum" $\frac{2}{3}$.

3. Show that $1 - 2 + 3 - 4 + \cdots$ is summable $(C, 2)$ to the "sum" $\frac{1}{4}$, but not summable $(C, 1)$.

4. Show that $1 + z + z^2 + \cdots$ is summable C_1 on the circumference $|z| = 1$ to the "sum" $\dfrac{1}{1 - z}$ except for $z = +1$. Here z is a complex number.

PART E.   SEQUENCES OF FUNCTIONS

19. Sequences of Functions.

In the following sections we shall consider series $\displaystyle\sum_{n=0}^{\infty} f_n(x)$ and sequences whose terms are arbitrary functions $f_n(x)$ of an independent variable x. We shall assume that all the functions $f_n(x)$ have at least one common interval of definition.

^{c}DEFINITION 19.1. *An interval I is said to be an interval of convergence of the series $\Sigma f_n(x)$ if, at every point of I (except possibly one or both the end points), all of the functions $f_n(x)$ are defined and the series converges.*

A very simple example of a series whose terms are functions of x is the geometric series Σx^n. This series has an interval of convergence $-1 < x < 1$, and no other interval of convergence exists. Another example is formed from the harmonic series, $\displaystyle\sum_{n=1}^{\infty} (1/n^x)$, which converges in $1 < x < + \infty$; no other interval of convergence outside of this one exists.

Since a series Σa_n is simply a symbol for a certain sequence of numbers, so the series $\Sigma f_n(x)$ is no more than a symbol for a sequence of functions, namely, the sequence of its partial sums

$$S_n(x) = f_0(x) + f_1(x) + \cdots + f_n(x).$$

Thus, it is immaterial whether the terms of the series or its partial sums are considered, since each set determines the other uniquely.

In view of this fact, we shall usually state our definitions and theorems in the language of series, and leave as exercises for the student their formulation for the case of sequences. If a given series $\Sigma f_n(x)$ is convergent in the interval I, then to every point in I there corresponds a definite value of the *sum* of the series. This sum is itself a function $S(x)$ and is defined or represented by the series.

When a series of variable terms is given, it is usually quite important to know whether properties possessed by all the functions $f_n(x)$ are also properties of its sum.

If each $f_n(x)$ is continuous it does not follow that the sum of the series $\Sigma f_n(x)$ is continuous (see Ex. XXII, 2). If each $f_n(x)$ is differentiable (or integrable) it does not follow that the sum is differentiable (or integrable), or that, if the sum is differentiable, its derivative is equal to the sum of the derivatives $f_n'(x)$.

In view of this situation, we shall be forced to investigate under what additional conditions a property of the terms $f_n(x)$ is transferred to the sum $S(x)$. The mere fact of convergence does not insure the transfer of a property of $f_n(x)$ to the sum $S(x)$. A study of a few examples will soon show that the *mode* of convergence is at the heart of the problem. This leads us to the concept of uniform convergence in an interval.

Before giving a general formulation of this concept we shall consider the following example:

Example 1.   Consider the series whose partial sums are

$$S_n(x) = \frac{nx}{1 + n^2 x^2}, \qquad n = 1, 2, 3, \cdots.$$

Since $S_n(x) = 0$ for every n when $x = 0$, since

$$0 < \left| S_n(x) \right| < \left| \frac{nx}{n^2 x^2} \right| = \left| \frac{1}{nx} \right| \tag{1}$$

when $x \neq 0$, and since $\lim\limits_{n \to +\infty} \left| \dfrac{1}{nx} \right| = 0$ for each $x \neq 0$, it follows that

$$S(x) = \lim_{n \to +\infty} S_n(x) = 0$$

for every value of x.

By (1), $S_n(x) < 1/nx \leq 1/n$ when $1 \leq x < \infty$, and in particular, when $1 \leq x \leq 2$. Hence the nth curve $S_n(x)$ of approximation to $S(x)$ lies above $S(x) = 0$ for $1 \leq x \leq 2$, but at a distance less than $1/n$ from the limiting curve $S(x) = 0$. The larger n, the smaller this distance all along the curve.

However, the situation over the interval $0 \leq x \leq 1$ is quite different, even though $S(x) = 0$ over this interval. In this case the nth approximation curve $S_n(x)$ does not lie close to the limiting curve $S(x) = 0$ throughout the

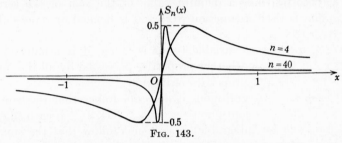

FIG. 143.

interval, for *any* n whatever. For $x = 1/n$, $S_n(x) = \frac{1}{2}$ for every n. Hence the approximation curve $S_n(x)$ in the interval $0 \leq x \leq 1$ has a hump of height $\frac{1}{2}$ for every n. The larger the n's, the closer the hump to the ordinate axis. However, it is still true that, for every *fixed* x, the ordinates of the approximation curves ultimately shrink down to a point on the x-axis, so that $\lim\limits_{n \to +\infty} S_n(x) = 0$ for *every* fixed x.

We say that the series under study *converges uniformly* in $1 \leq x \leq 2$, but not uniformly in $0 \leq x \leq 1$.

Uniform Convergence. Suppose $\Sigma f_n(x)$ is convergent for every value of x in an interval I. Write the sum of this series as $S(x) = S_n(x) + r_n(x)$, where $S_n(x)$ is the nth partial sum.

*e*DEFINITION 19.2. *A series $\Sigma f_n(x)$, convergent in I, is said to be uniformly convergent in a subinterval I' of I, if for every positive number ϵ, there exists a single number $N \equiv N(\epsilon)$, independent of x in I', such that $|r_n(x)| < \epsilon$ for every $n > N$ and for every x in I'.*

EXERCISES XXII

1. Show that the series $1 + x + x^2 + \cdots$ converges and has for its sum $\dfrac{1}{1-x}$, when $-1 < x < 1$.

2. Show that the function $S(x)$ defined as the sum of the series

$$2(\sin x - \tfrac{1}{2} \sin 2x + \tfrac{1}{3} \sin 3x - \cdots)$$

over $-\pi < x < +\pi$ is discontinuous at $x = (2r + 1)\pi$, r being an integer.

3. If $S_n(x) = \dfrac{(x^2)^n}{1 + (x^2)^n}$, show that $S_n(x) \to 0$ as $n \to +\infty$ if $|x| < 1$, $S_n \to 1$ if $|x| > 1$, and $S_n \to \tfrac{1}{2}$ if $|x| = 1$.

4. Let $S_n(x) = \lim\limits_{k \to +\infty} (\cos^2 n!\pi x)^k$. Show $S(x) \equiv \lim\limits_{n \to +\infty} S_n(x)$ is 1 for rational values of x and 0 for irrational values of x.

This function $S(x)$ was discovered by Dirichlet and is an example of a function which is everywhere discontinuous, and is consequently not integrable.

5. Show that $S_n(x) \equiv (2 \sin x)^n$ defines a series with an infinity of isolated intervals of convergence, namely,

$$-\pi/6 < x \leqq \pi/6, \qquad 5\pi/6 \leqq x < 7\pi/6, \cdots.$$

Prove that the sum of the series is 0 everywhere in the interior of these intervals, but equal to 1 at one end point of each interval.

6. Examine the series $\dfrac{x}{x + 1} + \dfrac{x}{(x + 1)(2x + 1)} + \cdots$, $x \geqq 0$, for convergence. Show that the sum $S(x)$ of the series is 1 if $x > 0$ and 0 if $x = 0$. $\left[\text{HINT: } S_n(x) = 1 - \dfrac{1}{1 + nx}\cdot\right]$ Examine the approximation curves $S_n(x) = 1 - \dfrac{1}{1 + nx}\cdot$ Plot $S(x)$, $S_1(x)$, $S_5(x)$, $S_{10}(x)$.

7. Examine the series whose partial sums are $S_n(x) = \dfrac{n^2 x}{1 + n^3 x^2}\cdot$ Plot the sum $S(x)$ and the approximation curves $S_5(x)$ and $S_{10}(x)$. Show that the sum of the series is continuous but that the approximation curves differ greatly from the curve $S(x) = 0$ in the neighborhood of the origin.

8. Show that a power series $\Sigma a_n (x - x_0)^n$ of positive radius of convergence r converges uniformly in every subinterval of the form

$$|x - x_0| \leqq \rho < r$$

of its interval of convergence.

9. Show that $\displaystyle\sum_{n=1}^{\infty} \dfrac{\sin nx}{n^2}$ is uniformly convergent in all finite intervals. $\left[\text{HINT: } r_n(x) \leqq \dfrac{1}{(n + 1)^2} + \dfrac{1}{(n + 2)^2} + \cdots\right]$

10. Prove that the geometric series Σx^n is not uniformly convergent in the whole interval $-1 < x < +1$.

11. Prove that the series $\dfrac{1}{1 + x^2} - \dfrac{1}{2 + x^2} + \dfrac{1}{3 + x^2} - \cdots$ converges uniformly in the interval $x \geqq 0$.

12. Prove that $\dfrac{x}{1 \cdot 2} + \dfrac{x}{2 \cdot 3} + \dfrac{x}{3 \cdot 4} + \cdots$ converges uniformly in any fixed interval $0 \leqq x \leqq b$ but not in the infinite interval $x \geqq 0$.

13. Consider the series

$$1 + (x - 1) + (x^2 - x) + \cdots + (x^n - x^{n-1}) + \cdots .$$

Show that this series converges in the interval $-1 < x \leqq +1$, and that in the interval $0 \leqq x \leqq 1$, the sum is $S(x) = \begin{cases} 0 \text{ for } 0 \leqq x < 1 \\ 1 \text{ for } x = 1. \end{cases}$ Prove that the convergence is not uniform in $0 \leqq x < 1$. Plot $S_n(x)$ for

$$n = 1, 2, 4, 12, 20.$$

Plot $S(x)$ also.

14. Consider the series $(1/x) + 1 + x + x^2 + \cdots$. Show that this series is uniformly convergent in $0 < x \leqq \frac{1}{2}$, even though the term $1/x$ is unbounded in this interval. $\left(\text{Hint: } |r_n(x)| = \left| \dfrac{x^n}{1 - x} \right| \leqq \dfrac{1}{2^{n-1}}. \right)$

15. *Prove*: A series $\Sigma f_n(x)$ is uniformly convergent over the interval I if for any set of positive integers $k_1, k_2, \cdots$, and any set of points $x_1, x_2, \cdots$ of I, the quantities $|f_{n+1}(x_n) + f_{n+2})(x_n) + \cdots + f_{n+k_n}(x_n)|$ always form a null sequence.

20. Properties of Uniformly Convergent Series. We first prove

Theorem 20.1. *A necessary and sufficient condition for the uniform convergence of the series $\Sigma f_n(x)$ in an interval I is that for any positive number ϵ, there shall exist a positive integer N such that, for $n \geqq N$, for every positive integer k, and for all values of x in I,*

$$|f_{n+1}(x) + f_{n+2}(x) + \cdots + f_{n+k}(x)| < \epsilon.$$

Necessity. Let ϵ be any positive number. If $\Sigma f_n(x)$ is uniformly convergent there exists an N such that for all $n \geqq N$, $|r_n(x)| < \epsilon/2$ quite independent of x on I. Then for every $n \geqq N$, for every $k = 1, 2, \cdots$, and for all values of x on I,

$$|S_{n+k}(x) - S_n(x)| \leqq |S_{n+k}(x) - S(x)| + |S(x) - S_n(x)|$$

$$< \frac{\epsilon}{2} + \frac{\epsilon}{2} = \epsilon.$$

Sufficiency. By Theorem 8.1, $\Sigma f_n(x)$ converges to a function $S(x)$. Select a positive number ϵ. By hypothesis, there exists an integer N such that for every $n \geq N$ and for every positive integer k, $|S_{n+k}(x) - S_n(x)| < \epsilon/2$, with both N and k independent of x on I. Hence

$$S_N(x) - \frac{\epsilon}{2} < S_{N+k}(x) < S_N(x) + \frac{\epsilon}{2}.$$

Since $\lim_{k \to +\infty} S_{N+k}(x) = S(x)$, we know

$$S_N(x) - \frac{\epsilon}{2} \leq S(x) \leq S_N(x) + \frac{\epsilon}{2}.$$

Since $|S_n(x) - S(x)| \leq |S_n(x) - S_N(x)| + |S_N(x) - S(x)|$, it follows that for $n \geq N$, $|S_n(x) - S(x)| < (\epsilon/2) + (\epsilon/2) = \epsilon$, and furthermore, this is true for all values of x on I.

*[c]*THEOREM 20.2. *If the k series $\Sigma f_{n1}(x)$, $\Sigma f_{n2}(x)$, $\cdots$, $\Sigma f_{nk}(x)$ are all uniformly convergent in the same interval I, the series $\Sigma f_n(x)$ in which*

$$f_n(x) = C_1 f_{n1}(x) + C_2 f_{n2}(x) + \cdots + C_k f_{nk}(x),$$

with C_1, C_2, $\cdots$, C_k constants, is also uniformly convergent in I.

This shows that uniformly convergent series may be multiplied by constant factors and then added term by term. We leave the proof of this and the following theorem as exercises.

*[c]*THEOREM 20.3. *If $\Sigma f_n(x)$ is uniformly convergent in I, so is the series $\Sigma h(x) f_n(x)$, where $h(x)$ is any function defined and bounded in the interval I, i.e., a uniformly convergent series $\Sigma f_n(x)$ may be multiplied term by term by a bounded function.*

The determination as to whether or not a series converges uniformly is frequently a difficult problem. However, the following important test is quite easy to apply.

*[c]*THEOREM 20.4 (*Weierstrass Test*). *If each of the functions $f_n(x)$ is defined and bounded in I, i.e., if*

$$|f_n(x)| \leq M_n$$

throughout I, and if the positive series ΣM_n converges, the series $\Sigma f_n(x)$ converges uniformly in I.

If $\{x_n\}$ be an arbitrary sequence on I, then

$$|f_{n+1}(x_n) + f_{n+2}(x_n) + \cdots + f_{n+k_n}(x_n)|$$
$$\leq M_{n+1} + M_{n+2} + \cdots + M_{n+k_n}.$$

By Theorem 8.1 the right-hand side $\to 0$ as $n \to +\infty$; hence, so does the left-hand member. By Ex. XXII, 15, $\Sigma f_n(x)$ is uniformly convergent in I.

While, in general, properties possessed by $f_n(x)$ are not necessarily possessed by the sum $S(x)$ of $\Sigma f_n(x)$, it will now be shown that if $\Sigma f_n(x)$ converges uniformly, many properties of $f_n(x)$ are retained by $S(x)$.

^cTHEOREM 20.5. *If $\Sigma f_n(x)$ converges uniformly in an interval I, and if its terms $f_n(x)$ are each continuous at a point x_0 of I, the function $S(x)$ represented by the series is also continuous at this point.*

Select an $\epsilon > 0$. Then there exists a $\delta \equiv \delta(\epsilon) > 0$ such that for every x for which $|x - x_0| < \delta$, $|F(x) - F(x_0)| < \epsilon$ in I. Write

$$S(x) - S(x_0) = s_n(x) - s_n(x_0) + r_n(x) - r_n(x_0).$$

Since $\Sigma f_n(x)$ converges uniformly, there exists an N so that for every x in I, $|r_N(x)| < \epsilon/3$. Hence

$$|S(x) - S(x_0)| \leqq |S_N(x) - S_N(x_0)| + \tfrac{2}{3}\epsilon.$$

Now for N, $S_N(x)$ is the sum of a fixed number of functions each of which is continuous at x_0; hence $S_N(x)$ is continuous at x_0 (see Theorem 4.3 of Chap. I). As a consequence, we can select a δ sufficiently small that $|S_N(x) - S_N(x_0)| < \epsilon/3$ for every x in I for which $|x - x_0| < \delta$. Hence, for these x's, we conclude that $|S(x) - S(x_0)| < \epsilon$.

Remark. While uniform convergence is a sufficient condition for the continuity of the sum of a series of continuous functions, it is not a necessary condition, since nonuniformly convergent series are known whose sum is continuous in the interval of nonuniform convergence. (See Example 1, Sec. 19.)

^cTHEOREM 20.6. *If each $f_n(x)$ is continuous in the closed interval $a \leqq x \leqq b$, and if the series $\Sigma f_n(x)$ converges uniformly in $a < x < b$, then it converges for $x = a$ and $x = b$, and the series is uniformly convergent in the closed interval $a \leqq x \leqq b$.*

Since the series is uniformly convergent in (a, b) open, then

$$|S_n(x) - S_N(x)| < \frac{\epsilon}{3} \qquad \text{for} \qquad n > N \geqq N_1, \qquad (1)$$

where N_1 is sufficiently large that the inequality holds for all x in (a, b) open.

Suppose n and N are fixed. Since each term in the series is continuous in (a, b) closed, then there exist positive numbers δ_1 and δ_2 such that

$$|S_n(x) - S_n(a)| < \frac{\epsilon}{3} \quad \text{for} \quad 0 \leqq |x - a| \leqq \delta_1,$$

$$|S_N(x) - S_N(a)| < \frac{\epsilon}{3} \quad \text{for} \quad 0 \leqq |x - a| \leqq \delta_2.$$

Let δ be a positive number not greater than δ_1 or δ_2 and let x be such that $0 \leqq |x - a| \leqq \delta$. Then

$$|S_n(a) - S_N(a)| \leqq |S_n(a) - S_n(x)| + |S_n(x) - S_N(x)| \\ + |S_N(x) - S_N(a)| < \epsilon \quad (2)$$

for $n > N \geqq N_1$. Similarly,

$$|S_n(b) - S_N(b)| < \epsilon \quad \text{for} \quad n > N \geqq N_1. \quad (3)$$

We conclude from (2) and (3) that the series converges for $x = a$ and for $x = b$. From (1), (2), and (3), we conclude that $\Sigma f_n(x)$ converges uniformly in (a, b) closed.

THEOREM 20.7.   Let $S(x) = \sum_{n=0}^{\infty} f_n(x)$ be uniformly convergent in $x_0 < x < x_1$, *and suppose that* $\lim_{x \to x_0} f_n(x) = a_n$ *exists when* x *approaches x_0 from the interior of the interval. Then the series* $\sum_{n=0}^{\infty} a_n$ *converges and limit $S(x)$ exists as $x \to x_0$ as specified. Furthermore,*

$$\lim_{x \to x_0} S(x) = \sum_{n=0}^{\infty} \left(\lim_{x \to x_0} f_n(x) \right),$$

that is,

$$\lim_{x \to x_0} \left[\sum_{n=0}^{\infty} f_n(x) \right] = \sum_{n=0}^{\infty} \left[\lim_{x \to x_0} f_n(x) \right].$$

Thus, in the case of uniform convergence, we may proceed to the limit term by term.

Let $\epsilon > 0$. Select an N_1 (see Theorem 20.1) such that for every $n > N_1$, for every $k \geqq 1$ and for every x in $x_0 < x < x_1$,

$|f_{n+1}(x) + \cdots + f_{n+k}(x)| < \epsilon.$ Fix n and k, and then let $x \to x_0$. By Theorem 3.2 of Chap. I, $|a_{n+1} + \cdots + a_{n+k}| \leqq \epsilon$ for every $n > N_1$ and for every $k \geqq 1$, so that Σa_n converges.

Let the partial sums of Σa_n be A_n and let the sum of Σa_n be A. We shall show that $S(x) \to A$ as $x \to x_0$. Write

$$S(x) = s_n(x) + r_n(x).$$

Let N_1 be so large that for every $n > N_1$, both $|r_n(x)| < \epsilon/3$ and $|A - A_n| < \epsilon/3$. Then if m be fixed and $m > N_1$,

$$|S(x) - A| = |[s_m(x) - A_m] - (A - A_m) + r_m(x)|$$
$$\leqq |s_m(x) - A_m| + \frac{\epsilon}{3} + \frac{\epsilon}{3}.$$

Since $s_m(x) \to A_m$ as $x \to x_0$, we can find a δ so that for every x in $x_0 < x < x_1$ such that $0 < |x - x_0| < \delta$, $|s_m(x) - A_m| < \epsilon/3$. Hence, for these same x's, $|S(x) - A| < \epsilon$.

Theorem 20.8. *If $\Sigma f_n(x) = S(x)$ is uniformly convergent in the interval I, and all the functions $f_n(x)$ are continuous throughout the closed subinterval $I' : a \leqq x \leqq b$, then the sum $S(x)$ is continuous in I' and the integral of $S(x)$ over I' may be found by term by term integration; that is,*

$$\int_a^b S(x)\, dx = \int_a^b \left[\sum f_n(x) \right] dx = \sum \left[\int_a^b f_n(x)\, dx \right],$$

i.e., the series on the right converges and has for its sum the indicated integral of $S(x)$.

Let $\epsilon > 0$. Select an N sufficiently large that for every x in (a, b), and for every $n > N$, $|r_n(x)| < \epsilon/(b - a)$. Since

$$S(x) = s_n(x) + r_n(x),$$

$\left| \int_a^b S(x)\, dx - \int_a^b s_n(x)\, dx \right| = \left| \int_a^b r_n(x)\, dx \right| < \epsilon.$ From Theorem 27.4 of Chap. II, $\left| \int_a^b S(x)\, dx - \sum_{k=0}^n \int_a^b f_k(x)\, dx \right| < \epsilon.$ But this implies the convergence of $\Sigma \int_a^b f_k(x)\, dx$ to $\int_a^b S(x)\, dx$.

Uniform convergence is not a necessary condition for term by term integration. This fact is illustrated in Ex. XXIII, 5, 6. In neither case is the convergence uniform. In the first case term by term integration leads to an incorrect result. In the second case term by term integration leads to a correct result.

Theorem 20.9. *Let* $S(x) = \sum\limits_{n=0}^{\infty} f_n(x)$ *be a series each of whose terms has derivatives in the interval* I: $a < x < b$. *If the series*

$\varphi(x) \equiv \sum\limits_{n=0}^{\infty} f_n'(x)$ *obtained from it by differentiating term by term converges uniformly in* I, *then so does the original series, provided the given series converges at least at one point* c *in* I. *If* $S(x)$ *has a derivative, then*

$$S'(x) = \sum\limits_{n=0}^{\infty} f_n'(x).$$

(a) We shall show that $\Sigma f_n(x)$ is uniformly convergent in the whole interval I and consequently represents a definite function $S(x)$ in that interval.

By the Theorem of the mean,

$$\sum\limits_{j=n+1}^{n+k} [f_j(x) - f_j(c)] = (x - c) \sum\limits_{j=n+1}^{n+k} f_j'(\xi),$$

where $x < \xi < c$. Select an $\epsilon > 0$. By hypothesis, there exists an N so that for every $n > N$, every $k \geqq 1$, and every x in I,

$$\left| \sum\limits_{j=n+1}^{n+k} f_j'(x) \right| < \frac{\epsilon}{b - a}.$$

Hence for these conditions,

$$\left| \sum\limits_{j=n+1}^{n+k} [f_j(x) - f_j(c)] \right| < \epsilon.$$

This shows that $\sum\limits_{j=0}^{\infty} [f_j(x) - f_j(c)]$, and hence $\sum f_j(x)$, is uniformly convergent throughout I.

(b) We shall next show that $S'(x_0) = \sum\limits_{n=0}^{\infty} f_n'(x_0) = \varphi(x_0)$.

Suppose x_0 is a particular point of I. Let

$$g_j(h) = \frac{f_j(x_0 + h) - f_j(x_0)}{h}, \qquad (j = 0, 1, 2, \cdots)$$

where $(x_0 + h)$ is restricted to belong to I. By the Theorem of the mean,

$$\sum_{j=n+1}^{n+k} g_j(h) = \sum_{j=n+1}^{n+k} f_j'(x_0 + \theta h), \qquad (0 < \theta < 1).$$

Following an argument similar to that given in (a) we find that $\sum_{n=0}^{\infty} g_n(h)$ converges uniformly for all the values of h permitted above. The series $\sum_{n=0}^{\infty} g_n(h)$ represents the function

$$\frac{S(x_0 + h) - S(x_0)}{h}.$$

From Theorem 20.7, letting $h \to 0$ term by term, we conclude that $S'(x_0)$ exists and $S'(x_0) = \sum_{n=0}^{\infty} \left[\lim_{h \to 0} g_n(h) \right] = \sum_{n=0}^{\infty} f_n'(x_0)$.

EXERCISES XXIII

1. Since $1 + 2\gamma + 3\gamma^2 + \cdots$ is convergent for $0 \le \gamma < 1$, show that

$$1 + 2x + 3x^2 + \cdots$$

is uniformly convergent in $-\gamma < x < \gamma$. Is it in $-\gamma \le x \le \gamma$?

2. Prove that $x \cos \alpha + x^2 \cos 2\alpha + x^3 \cos 3\alpha + \cdots$ is uniformly convergent in any interval interior to $-1 < x < 1$, where α is any real number.

3. If $f_n(x)$ are all continuous throughout I and if $\Sigma f_n(x) = S(x)$ converges uniformly in I, then $S(x)$ is continuous throughout I.

4. From the logarithmic series

$$x - \tfrac{1}{2}x^2 + \tfrac{1}{3}x^3 - \cdots \tag{i}$$

form the series

$$x + \tfrac{1}{3}x^3 - \tfrac{1}{2}x^2 + \tfrac{1}{5}x^5 + \tfrac{1}{7}x^7 - \tfrac{1}{4}x^4 + \cdots \tag{ii}$$

by taking two consecutive positive terms and then one negative term.

(a) Prove that this series is convergent for $-1 < x \le 1$, and that its sum is $\tfrac{3}{2} \log 2$ when $x = 1$.

(b) Show that the logarithmic series is absolutely convergent for $|x| < 1$. Will the sum of the logarithmic series be altered by taking the terms in another order? (No.)

(c) Show that the sum of the series (ii) is $\log (1 + x)$ when $|x| < 1$.

(d) Is the sum of (i) continuous at $x = 1$? (No.) Does the interval of uniform convergence of (i) extend to and include $x = 1$? (No.)

5. Show that the series for which $S_n(x) = nxe^{-nx^2/2}$ converges, but not uniformly, for every x. Prove that the sum is $S(x) = 0$. Is term by term integration possible? [No, for $\int_0^1 S(x)\, dx = 0$, while

$$\sum_{k=0}^{n} \int_0^1 f_k(x)\, dx = \int_0^1 S_n(x)\, dx = 1 - e^{-n/2} \to 1.]$$

6. It was shown in Example 1 of Sec. 19 that the series for which $S_n(x) = nx/(1 + n^2x^2)$ converges nonuniformly over $(0, 1)$, and that its sum is $S(x) = 0$. Show that term by term integration gives

$$\sum_{k=0}^{n} \int_0^1 f_k(x)\, dx = \int_0^1 S_n(x)\, dx \to 0 = \int_0^1 S(x)\, dx.$$

7. Prove that Theorem 20.8 holds when the continuity assumptions placed upon $f_n(x)$ are replaced by the assumption that $f_n(x)$ all be integrable.

8. Let $\Sigma a_n(x - x_0)^n$ have the radius of convergence $r > 0$. If $0 < \rho < r$, prove that the series $\Sigma na_n(x - x_0)^{n-1}$ converges uniformly whenever $|x - x_0| \leq \rho$. Is term by term differentiation permissible in the open interval $|x - x_0| < r$; in the closed interval $|x - x_0| \leq r$? Is term by term integration permissible? Discuss.

9. Show that if Σa_n converges absolutely, $\Sigma a_n \cos nx$ and $\Sigma a_n \sin nx$ converge uniformly for every x. (HINT: $|a_n \cos nx| \leq a_n$.) Are these series continuous anywhere?   *Ans.* Everywhere. Why?

10. Show that $S(x) \equiv \sum_{n=1}^{\infty} (\sin nx)/n^3$ has a derivative and that

$$S'(x) = \sum_{n=1}^{\infty} \frac{\cos nx}{n^2}.$$

11. Prove: *If the power series $S(x) = \Sigma a_n x^n$ converges for either of the ends of its interval of convergence, the interval of uniform convergence extends up to and includes that point, and the continuity of the sum $S(x)$ of the series extends up to and includes that point.*

12. Show that

$$x^2 + \frac{x^2}{(1 + x^2)} + \frac{x^2}{(1 + x^2)^2} + \cdots$$

is convergent everywhere, but is not uniformly convergent in any interval containing the origin.

13. Examine for continuity: $\sum_{n=1}^{\infty} \frac{x}{n(1 + nx^2)}$.

Ans. Finite and continuous.

For what values of x is this series uniformly convergent?

14. From $\text{Tan}^{-1} x = \displaystyle\int_0^x \frac{dx}{1 + x^2}$ show that

$$\text{Tan}^{-1} x = x - \tfrac{1}{3}x^3 + \tfrac{1}{5}x^5 - \cdots$$

What is the interval of convergence?

15. Develop a series for $\text{Sin}^{-1} x$. [HINT: $\text{Sin}^{-1} x = \int_0^x dx/\sqrt{1 - x^2}$.]

16. Evaluate $\displaystyle\int_0^x \frac{\text{Sin}^{-1} x}{x} \, dx$. (HINT: Use series for $\text{Sin}^{-1} x$.)   Justify your method.

17. Evaluate $\displaystyle\int_0^x \frac{\text{Tan}^{-1} x}{x} \, dx$.

18. Prove $\displaystyle\int_0^1 \frac{\text{Tan}^{-1} x}{x} \, dx = \sum_{n=0}^{\infty} (-1)^n \frac{1}{(2n + 1)^2}$.

19. Evaluate $\int_0^x \text{Tan}^{-1} x \, dx$ for $|x| < 1$.

20. Evaluate $\int_0^x \log (1 + x) \, dx$ for $|x| < 1$.

21. Evaluate $\displaystyle\int_0^x \frac{\log (1 + x)}{x} \, dx$ for $0 < x < 1$.   *Ans.* $\displaystyle\sum_{n=1}^{\infty} (-1)^{n-1} \frac{x^n}{n^2}$.

22. Find the derivative of $S(x) = \displaystyle\sum_{n=1}^{\infty} \frac{1}{n^3 + n^4 x^2}$.   Justify your result.

23. It is known that

$$\pi \cosh ax = 2 \sinh a\pi \left[\frac{1}{2a} - \frac{a \cos x}{1^2 + a^2} + \frac{a \cos 2x}{2^2 + a^2} - \cdots \right].$$

Find $\pi \sinh ax$.   (HINT: Differentiate.)   Justify your method rigorously.

24. Determine the interval of convergence of $e^x \sin x + e^{2x} \sin 2x + \cdots$; also the interval of uniform convergence.   Can you differentiate term by term for all values of x?

25. Evaluate $\displaystyle\int^1 \frac{x^{n-1}}{1 + x} \, dx$, $n > 0$.

26. Consider the series $S_1 = \displaystyle\sum_{n=1}^{\infty} \frac{1}{(n + x)^2}$, $x \geq 0$, and $S_2 = \displaystyle\sum_{n=1}^{\infty} \frac{1}{(n + x)^3}$,

$x \geq 0$.   Prove that term by term integration over a finite interval is permissible in each case.   Prove that the second series can be integrated term by term over the interval $(0, \infty)$, but not the first.

27. Prove Theorem 20.2.
28. Prove Theorem 20.3.
29. Construct examples of a series nonuniformly convergent in an interval I but whose sum is continuous in I.

PART F. FOURIER SERIES. ORTHOGONAL FUNCTIONS

21. Introduction. One of the most interesting and important applications of the theory of series of variable functions is provided by the theory of trigonometric series and, more particularly, by the theory of Fourier series.

By a *trigonometric series* we shall mean any series of the form

$$\frac{a_0}{2} + \sum_{n=1}^{\infty} (a_n \cos nx + b_n \sin nx),$$

where a_n and b_n are constants.

We say that 2π is the *fundamental period* of $\cos x$ and $\sin x$; the fundamental period of $\cos 2x$ and $\sin 2x$ is π, not 2π; $\cdots$; and the fundamental period of $\cos nx$ and $\sin nx$ is $2\pi/n$.

Since $\cos n(x + 2\pi) = \cos nx$ and $\sin n(x + 2\pi) = \sin nx$ for all integer values of n, we see that $\cos nx$ and $\sin nx$ have the period 2π. Evidently, any sum of a convergent series of cosines and sines of integral multiples of x will have a period 2π. By altering the coefficients in such a sum, or series, we may build up many functions of x with period 2π.

If a trigonometric series T converges in some interval of the form $-\xi \leq x < \xi + 2\pi$, then, in view of the periodicity of the trigonometric functions involved, the series T converges for *every* real x, and the series T represents *a function of period 2π defined for all values of x.*

Trigonometric series are capable of representing many of the so-called "arbitrary functions" and as a consequence constitute a far more powerful tool in higher analysis than power series.

The power of the method of Fourier series is very great indeed, but its importance is not confined to pure mathematics; in fact, perhaps the most important applications of the subject occur in physics. It is significant that Fourier series were first obtained and studied in theoretical physics.

More explicitly, Fourier series were first encountered incidentally to a serious theoretical study of periodic motions in acoustics, optics, the theory of heat, and later in electrodynamics.

The first thorough study of trigonometric series was made by Fourier in his "Théorie de la chaleur" (1811). Although Fourier did not discover any of the principal results of the theory, his paper has been of greatest importance and has led to a vast field of investigation which even today seems to be only in its youth.

22. Euler's Formula. We shall begin by asking certain questions, the complete answers to which have been the concern of investigators for many years. (I) What functions are representable by trigonometric series? (II) How can we obtain the representation of a given representable function?

To begin with, we shall suppose that $f(x)$ is a certain function of the independent variable x, represented by a trigonometric series which is convergent everywhere, namely, by a series of the form

$$f(x) = \tfrac{1}{2}a_0 + \sum_{n=1}^{\infty} (a_n \cos nx + b_n \sin nx).$$

Since the sine and cosine are periodic, $f(x)$ is evidently of period 2π. Hence, it is sufficient to consider any interval of length 2π. For convenience we shall choose (for the balance of the section on Fourier series) as this interval the particular interval $0 \leqq x \leqq 2\pi$ (where we may omit one of the end points if desirable).

Evidently, $f(x)$ is represented by a series of continuous functions. From our studies in Sec. 20, we know that $f(x)$ may or may not be continuous; although, if the series converges uniformly in $[0, 2\pi]$, $f(x)$ will be continuous.

We shall now prove the following theorem due to Euler.

THEOREM 22.1. *If the series*

$$\tfrac{1}{2}a_0 + \sum_{n=1}^{\infty} (a_n \cos nx + b_n \sin nx) \tag{1}$$

converges uniformly to the sum $f(x)$ in the interval $0 \leqq x \leqq 2\pi$, then for $n = 0, 1, 2, \cdots$,

$$a_n = \frac{1}{\pi}\int_0^{2\pi} f(x) \cos nx \, dx, \qquad b_n = \frac{1}{\pi}\int_0^{2\pi} f(x) \sin nx \, dx. \tag{E}$$

Relations (E) are known as *Euler's formulas.*

Proof. Since

$$\cos px \cdot \cos qx = \tfrac{1}{2}[\cos (p + q)x + \cos (p - q)x]$$

for any two positive integers p and q, it follows that

$$\int_0^{2\pi} \cos px \cos qx \, dx = \begin{cases} 0 & \text{for} & p \neq q, \\ \pi & \text{for} & p = q > 0, \\ 2\pi & \text{for} & p = q = 0. \end{cases} \qquad (2)$$

Similarly,

$$\int_0^{2\pi} \cos px \sin qx \, dx = 0; \qquad (3)$$

$$\int_0^{2\pi} \sin px \sin qx \, dx = \begin{cases} 0 & \text{for} & p \neq q, \text{ and } \quad p = q = 0, \\ \pi & \text{for} & p = q > 0. \end{cases} \qquad (4)$$

We shall now multiply the series (1) for $f(x)$ by $\cos nx$. Since (1) is assumed to be uniformly convergent in $[0, 2\pi]$, so is the series for $f(x) \cos nx$ uniformly convergent (see Sec. 20). In view of Theorem 20.8, we may integrate term by term from $x = 0$ to $x = 2\pi$. We then obtain

$$\int_0^{2\pi} f(x) \cos nx \, dx = \begin{cases} \tfrac{1}{2}a_0 \int_0^{2\pi} \cos nx \, dx, & \text{for } n = 0, \\ a_n \int_0^{2\pi} \cos nx \cos nx \, dx, & \text{for } n > 0, \end{cases} \qquad (5)$$

the remaining terms each being equal to zero. (The student should write out each step indicated here in detail). Hence, by (2), we find

$$a_n = \frac{1}{\pi} \int_0^{2\pi} f(x) \cos nx \, dx, \qquad n = 0, 1, 2, \cdots . \qquad (6)$$

In a similar manner, we obtain, upon multiplying equation (1) by $\sin nx$ and integrating term by term, the relations

$$b_n = \frac{1}{\pi} \int_0^{2\pi} f(x) \sin nx \, dx, \qquad n = 1, 2, 3, \cdots . \qquad (7)$$

This completes the proof of Theorem 22.1. It should be noted that, subject to the restrictions of Theorem 22.1, we have shown the *uniqueness* of the Fourier series generated from $f(x)$.

It is now clear that the representation of the constant term by $a_0/2$, rather than a_0, is a means of making the general formula for a_n applicable without change when $n = 0$.

The very restrictive assumptions in Theorem 22.1 diminish its value. Moreover, we still have no intimation as to whether or not a given function can be represented by a trigonometric series; or if the function is so representable, what the values of the coefficients of the series are in the general case.

We should note however, that Euler's formulas (E) certainly have definite values if the arbitrary function $f(x)$ is integrable Riemann over the interval $0 \leqq x \leqq 2\pi$. We shall call the numbers $a_0/2$, a_1, a_2, $\cdots$; b_1, b_2, $\cdots$ defined by Euler's formula [when $f(x)$ is integrable Riemann] the *Fourier coefficients of the function* $f(x)$, and we shall call the corresponding series

$$\frac{a_0}{2} + \sum_{n=1}^{\infty} (a_n \cos nx + b_n \sin nx)$$

the Fourier series generated by $f(x)$, or *the Fourier series of* $f(x)$; symbolically we shall express this by

$$f(x) \, \underset{\sim}{\text{L}} \, \tfrac{1}{2}a_0 + \sum_{n=1}^{\infty} (a_n \cos nx + b_n \sin nx). \tag{G}$$

We should emphasize that (G) does not imply that the series converges or not; nor does it imply that if the series converges, it converges to a sum equal to $f(x)$;—relation (G) implies only that certain constants $a_0/2$, a_1, a_2, $\cdots$; b_1, b_2, $\cdots$ have been deduced by means of (E) from a function $f(x)$ assumed to be integrable Riemann, and that the series so generated has been written down.

In general, the series (G) may not converge anywhere; and even if it does converge everywhere on $0 \leqq x \leqq 2\pi$, the sum of the series is not necessarily equal to $f(x)$.

It is usually impossible to say at sight which of the various cases mentioned occur in a particular example. This very difficult restriction makes it impossible for the theory to be entirely simple. For these reasons, mathematicians have found the subject to be very attractive for investigation.

Mathematically, the most outstanding problems that have arisen in connection with the theory of Fourier series may be listed under the following types:

(I) If $f(x)$ is integrable Riemann, is the Fourier series generated by $f(x)$ convergent for some or all values of x in $0 \leqq x \leqq 2\pi$?

(II) If the Fourier series generated from $f(x)$ converges, does it converge to a sum equal to $f(x)$?

(III) If the Fourier series generated from $f(x)$ converges everywhere on $\xi \leqq x \leqq \eta$, is the convergence uniform on this interval?

(IV) If a function is capable of expansion in a trigonometric series, is it possible for the function to possess several such expansions?

No complete answers to these questions have ever been given. The subject is a very vast one. Hence we shall confine ourselves to a beginning of the study of certain partial answers to questions I, II, and III.

23. Dirichlet's Integral. We shall now consider the first of the problems listed in Sec. 22, namely, the question of the convergence of a Fourier series.

If the Fourier series $\frac{1}{2}a_0 + \sum\limits_{n=1}^{\infty} (a_n \cos nx + b_n \sin nx)$ generated by a given integrable function $f(x)$ according to Euler's formulas (E) is to converge at the point $x = x_0$, its partial sums

$$s_n(x_0) = \tfrac{1}{2}a_0 + \sum_{p=1}^{n} (a_p \cos px_0 + b_p \sin px_0) \qquad (1)$$

must tend to a limit as $n \to +\infty$. It is frequently possible to determine whether or not this is the case by expressing $s_n(x_0)$ in the form of a definite integral. By (E), we see that

$$a_p \cos px_0 + b_p \sin px_0$$
$$= \left[\frac{1}{\pi}\int^{2\pi} f(t) \cos pt\, dt\right] \cos px_0 + \left[\frac{1}{\pi}\int^{2\pi} f(t) \sin pt\, dt\right] \sin px_0$$
$$= \frac{1}{\pi}\int_0^{2\pi} f(t) \cos p(t - x_0)\, dt. \qquad (p = 1, 2, \cdots)$$

Hence

$$s_n(x_0) = \frac{1}{\pi}\int_0^{2\pi} f(t)\left[\frac{1}{2} + \cos (t - x_0) + \cos 2(t - x_0)\right.$$
$$\left. + \cdots + \cos n(t - x_0)\right] dt. \qquad (2)$$

Thus, it appears that a necessary and sufficient condition that $s_n(x_0)$ converge at a point x_0 as $n \to +\infty$ is that the integral in (2) should tend to a (finite) limit as $n \to +\infty$.

We shall now prove the following important result:

Theorem 23.1. *A necessary and sufficient condition that the Fourier series generated by a function $f(x)$, integrable (bounded) and periodic of period 2π, converge at a point x_0, is that the Dirichlet integral*

$$\frac{2}{\pi} \int_0^{\pi/2} \frac{f(x_0 + 2t) + f(x_0 - 2t)}{2} \cdot \frac{\sin (2n + 1)t}{\sin t} \, dt \qquad (3)$$

should tend to a finite limit as $n \to +\infty$. This limit (if it exists) is the sum of the Fourier series at the point x_0.

Proof. We shall need certain identities from trigonometry.

$$\cos (\alpha + z) + \cos (\alpha + 2z) + \cdots + \cos (\alpha + mz)$$
$$\equiv \frac{\sin \left[\alpha + (2m + 1)\dfrac{z}{2} \right] - \sin \left(\alpha + \dfrac{z}{2} \right)}{2 \sin \dfrac{z}{2}}. \qquad (4)$$

$$\equiv \frac{\sin m\dfrac{z}{2} \cdot \cos \left[\alpha + (m + 1)\dfrac{z}{2} \right]}{\sin \dfrac{z}{2}}. \qquad (5)$$

$$\tfrac{1}{2} + \cos (t - x_0) + \cdots + \cos n(t - x_0)$$
$$\equiv \frac{1}{2} + \frac{\sin \left[(2n + 1)\left(\dfrac{t - x_0}{2}\right) \right] - \sin \left(\dfrac{t - x_0}{2} \right)}{2 \sin \left(\dfrac{t - x_0}{2} \right)}$$

$$\equiv \frac{\sin (2n + 1)\left(\dfrac{t - x_0}{2}\right)}{2 \sin \left(\dfrac{t - x_0}{2} \right)}. \qquad (6)$$

By (2) and (6), we see that

$$s_n(x_0) = \frac{1}{2\pi} \int_0^{2\pi} f(t) \frac{\sin \left[(2n + 1)\left(\dfrac{t - x_0}{2}\right) \right]}{\sin \left(\dfrac{t - x_0}{2} \right)} dt \equiv \frac{1}{2\pi} \int_0^{2\pi} * \, dt. \qquad (7)$$

If $f(x)$ is defined and integrable only on $[0, 2\pi]$, we extend the definition of $f(x)$ as follows:

$$f(x) = f(x - 2k\pi), \qquad 2k\pi \leqq x \leqq 2(k + 1)\pi.$$

$$(k = \pm 1, \pm 2, \cdots)$$

Now $f(x)$ is defined for all real values x and it is of period 2π.

We shall use the well known property of any periodic function $\varphi(x)$ of period 2π; namely, the fact that for every c and d,

$$\int_0^{2\pi} \varphi(t)\, dt = \int_c^{c+2\pi} \varphi(t)\, dt = \int_0^{2\pi} \varphi(d + t)\, dt, \qquad (8)$$

$$\int_\alpha^\beta \varphi(t)\, dt = \int_{\alpha+2\pi}^{\beta+2\pi} \varphi(t)\, dt. \qquad (9)$$

Applying (9) and (8) to (7), we find that

$$s_n(x_0) = \frac{1}{2\pi} \int^{2\pi} f(x_0 + t) \cdot \frac{\sin\left[(2n + 1)\dfrac{t}{2}\right]}{\sin \dfrac{t}{2}}\, dt. \qquad (10)$$

Now (7) may be written in the form

$$s_n(x_0) = \frac{1}{2\pi} \int_0^\pi * \, dt + \frac{1}{2\pi} \int_\pi^{2\pi} * \, dt. \qquad (11)$$

In the second integral, set $-t = \tau$.   The latter integral becomes

$$-\frac{1}{2\pi} \int_{-\pi}^{-2\pi} f(x_0 - \tau) \cdot \frac{\sin\left[(2n + 1)\dfrac{\tau}{2}\right]}{\sin \dfrac{\tau}{2}}\, d\tau.$$

By (9), this becomes

$$\frac{1}{2\pi} \int_0^\pi f(x_0 - \tau) \cdot \frac{\sin\left[(2n + 1)\dfrac{\tau}{2}\right]}{\sin \dfrac{\tau}{2}}\, d\tau.$$

Hence, since the letter t indicating the variable of integration may be replaced by τ and not change the value of the integral, we see from (11) that

$$s_n(x_0) = \frac{1}{\pi} \int_0^\pi \frac{f(x_0 + \tau) + f(x_0 - \tau)}{2} \cdot \frac{\sin\left[(2n + 1)\dfrac{\tau}{2}\right]}{\sin \dfrac{\tau}{2}}\, d\tau. \qquad (12)$$

Now replace τ by $2t$.   We have

$$s_n(x_0) = \frac{2}{\pi}\int_0^{\pi/2} \frac{f(x_0 + 2t) + f(x_0 - 2t)}{2} \cdot \frac{\sin (2n + 1)t}{\sin t} \, dt. \quad (13)$$

We have thus proved Theorem 23.1.

The integral (13) is known as Dirichlet's integral,* and is an expression for the partial sums $s_n(x_0)$ of the Fourier series generated by $f(x)$.

Let $\lim\limits_{n \to \infty} s_n(x_0) \equiv s(x_0)$.   We consider question II of Sec. 22, and express $s(x_0)$ in the form of a Dirichlet integral.

By Eq. (6) with $x_0 = 0$ and $t/2$ replaced by t, we have

$$\frac{2}{\pi}\int_0^{\pi/2} \frac{\sin (2n + 1)t}{\sin t} \, dt = 1. \quad (14)$$

Multiplying (14) by $s(x_0)$ and subtracting from (13), we find

$$s_n(x_0) - s(x_0) =$$

$$\frac{2}{\pi}\int_0^{\pi/2} \left[\frac{f(x_0 + 2t) + f(x_0 - 2t)}{2} - s(x_0) \right] \frac{\sin (2n + 1)t}{\sin t} \, dt. \quad (15)$$

Whence,

THEOREM 23.2.   *A necessary and sufficient condition that the Fourier series generated by a function $f(x)$, integrable of period 2π, should converge to the sum $s(x_0)$ at the point x_0, is that*

$$\lim_{n \to \infty} \left[\frac{2}{\pi}\int_0^{\pi/2} \varphi(t; x_0) \cdot \frac{\sin (2n + 1)t}{\sin t} \, dt \right] = 0, \quad (16)$$

where

$$\varphi(t; x) \equiv \left[\frac{f(x + 2t) + f(x - 2t)}{2} - s(x) \right]. \quad (17)$$

A partial answer to question III is given by the following obvious modification of Theorem 23.2.

---

* More generally, any integral of the form

$$\int_0^a \varphi(t) \cdot \frac{\sin kt}{\sin t} \, dt \quad \text{or} \quad \int_0^a \varphi(t) \cdot \frac{\sin kt}{t} \, dt$$

is known as a Dirichlet integral.

THEOREM 23.3. *If the partial sums $s_n(x)$ converge to $s(x)$ at every point of the interval $\alpha \leqq x \leqq \beta$, they will converge uniformly to this limit in the interval, if and only if, given $\epsilon > 0$, we can assign an $N \equiv N(\epsilon)$ so that*

$$\left| \frac{2}{\pi} \int_0^{\pi/2} \varphi(t; x) \frac{\sin (2n + 1)t}{\sin t} \, dt \right| < \epsilon, \tag{18}$$

for every $n > N$ and for every x in $\alpha \leqq x \leqq \beta$.

The reader should note that while questions I, II, III of Sec. 22 are only partially answered by Theorems 23.1, 23.2, and 23.3, these theorems have given us a new mode of attack for their solution.

24. Further Theorems. We shall now prove a number of theorems in preparation for our main purpose of modifying the above theorems so as to construct immediate tests of convergence for Fourier series.

THEOREM 24.1. *If $f(x)$ is integrable (bounded) over the interval $[0, 2\pi]$, the series $\sum_{n=1}^{\infty} (a_n^2 + b_n^2)$, formed by the sum of the squares of its Fourier constants, converges.*

The integral

$$I \equiv \int_0^{2\pi} \left[f(t) - \sum_{p=0}^{n} (a_p \cos pt + b_p \sin pt) \right]^2 dt, \tag{1}$$

where $b_0 = 0$ and a_0 is written instead of $a_0/2$, is nonnegative, since its integrand is never negative.   Also, by squaring, we find

$$I \equiv \int_0^{2\pi} [f(t)]^2 \, dt - 2 \sum_{p=0}^{n} \left[a_p \int_0^{2\pi} f(t) \cos pt \, dt \right]$$

$$- 2 \sum_{p=0}^{n} \left[b_p \int_0^{2\pi} f(t) \sin pt \, dt \right]$$

$$+ \int_0^{2\pi} \left[\sum_{p=0}^{n} (a_p \cos pt + b_p \sin pt) \right]^2 dt$$

$$= \int_0^{2\pi} [f(t)]^2 \, dt - 2\pi a_0^2 - \pi \sum_{p=1}^{n} (a_p^2 + b_p^2).$$

Hence, for all values of n,*

$$\frac{a_0^2}{2} + \sum_{p=1}^{n} (a_p^2 + b_p^2) \leq \frac{1}{\pi} \int_0^{2\pi} [f(t)]^2 \, dt, \tag{2}$$

where a_0 now has its usual meaning. Thus the partial sums are bounded and the series (of positive terms) is convergent, for the last integral is independent of n.

Moreover, we have proved

THEOREM 24.2. *The Fourier coefficients a_n and b_n of an integrable function form a null sequence, i.e.,*

$$\lim_{n \to +\infty} a_n = 0, \qquad \lim_{n \to +\infty} b_n = 0.$$

THEOREM 24.3 (*Riemann-Lebesgue Theorem*). *If $\Phi(t)$ is integrable in $a \leq t \leq b$, then as $n \to +\infty$,*

$$A_n = \int_a^b \Phi(t) \cos nt \, dt \to 0,$$

and

$$B_n = \int_a^b \Phi(t) \sin nt \, dt \to 0.$$

Suppose that a and b both belong to the same interval I, $2k\pi \leq t \leq 2(k+1)\pi$, where k is some fixed integer. Let $f(t)$ be a function defined as follows:

$$\begin{cases} f(t) = \Phi(t) & \text{for} \quad a \leq t < b, \\ f(t) = 0 & \text{for all other values of } t \text{ in } I, \\ f(t + 2p\pi) = f(t) & \text{for all other values of } t \text{ and for all} \\ & \qquad\qquad\qquad\qquad \text{integers } p. \end{cases} \tag{3}$$

Then

$$A_n = \int_a^b \Phi(t) \cos nt \, dt = \int_0^{2\pi} f(t) \cos nt \, dt = \pi a_n, \quad B_n = \pi b_n, \tag{4}$$

where a_n and b_n denote the Fourier coefficients of $f(t)$. By Theorem 24.2, $A_n \to 0$ and $B_n \to 0$ as $n \to +\infty$.

If a and b do not satisfy the conditions imposed above, split the interval $a \leq t \leq b$ into a finite number of subdivisions, each of which satisfies the conditions. Then A_n and B_n are expressible

---

* Relation (2) is known as *Bessel's inequality* if $<$ holds, *Parseval's equation* if $=$ holds.

as the sum of a fixed finite number of terms each of which tends to 0 as $n \to +\infty$, and hence $A_n \to 0$ and $B_n \to 0$.

Theorem 24.3 is quite important, for it enables us to simplify the problem of the convergence of Dirichlet's integral.

Let δ be any arbitrarily chosen number with $0 < \delta < \pi/2$. Then the function

$$\psi(t) \equiv \frac{\varphi(t; x_0)}{\sin t} = \frac{\frac{1}{2}[f(x_0 + 2t) + f(x_0 - 2t)] - s(x_0)}{\sin t} \qquad (5)$$

is integrable in the interval $\delta \leqq t \leqq \pi/2$. Hence, for a fixed δ, it follows from Theorem 24.3 that as $n \to +\infty$,

$$\int_\delta^{\pi/2} \psi(t) \sin (2n + 1)t \, dt \to 0. \qquad (6)$$

The Dirichlet integral (3) of Sec. 23 will therefore tend to 0 as $n \to +\infty$, if and only if (for a fixed arbitrary $\delta > 0$),

$$\lim_{n \to +\infty} \left[\frac{2}{\pi} \int_0^\delta \varphi(t; x_0) \frac{\sin (2n + 1)t}{\sin t} \, dt \right] = 0. \qquad (7)$$

The integral (7) involves only the values of $f(x_0 \pm 2t)$ in $0 \leqq t \leqq \delta$; [i.e., of $f(x)$ in $x_0 - 2\delta \leqq x \leqq x_0 + 2\delta$].

Since $\delta > 0$ may be assumed arbitrarily small, we have the very peculiar result

Theorem 24.4 [*Riemann's* (1854) *Theorem*]. *The behavior about the point x_0 of the Fourier series generated by $f(x)$ depends only on the values of $f(x)$ in the neighborhood of x_0. This neighborhood may be assumed arbitrarily small.*

As an illustration of this theorem, we note the following consequence of it: Consider the set Γ of all possible functions $f(x)$, integrable in $[0, 2\pi]$, all of which coincide at a point x_0 of the interval $[0, 2\pi]$ and in some neighborhood of this point, however small, the length of the neighborhood possibly being dependent upon the particular function. Then the Fourier series of all these functions in Γ, irrespective of how much they may differ outside the neighborhood in question, must, at x_0 itself, either all converge or all diverge; and in case they converge, all the members of Γ have the same sum $s(x_0)$, which may or may not be equal to $f(x_0)$.

We shall now restate the criterion obtained above and formulate a theorem which we shall substitute for Theorem 23.1 in the discussion to follow.

THEOREM 24.5. *A necessary and sufficient condition for the convergence of the Fourier series generated by $f(x)$ to the sum $s(x_0)$ at x_0, is that for any arbitrarily chosen positive number $0 < \delta < \pi/2$, Dirichlet's integral (7) tends to 0 as $n \to +\infty$, i.e.,*

$$\lim_{n \to +\infty} \left[\frac{2}{\pi} \int_0^\delta \varphi(t; x_0) \cdot \frac{\sin (2n + 1)t}{\sin t} \, dt \right] = 0. \qquad (8)$$

We can assert nothing as to the uniformity of convergence in this theorem, because we do not know whether the integral in (8) tends to 0 uniformly for every x of the specified interval. This is true, actually, but we shall not enter into this question here.

We shall leave it as an exercise for the student to show that

$$\lim_{n \to +\infty} \left\{ \frac{2}{\pi} \int \varphi(t; x_0) \left[\frac{1}{\sin t} - \frac{1}{t} \right] \sin (2n + 1)t \, dt \right\} = 0,$$
$$0 < \delta < \frac{\pi}{2}, \qquad (9)$$

and then prove

THEOREM 24.6. *A necessary and sufficient condition for the Fourier series generated by a function $f(x)$, periodic of period 2π, and integrable (bounded) over $[0, 2\pi]$, to converge to $s(x_0)$ at the point x_0, is that for any arbitrarily chosen positive number δ, $0 < \delta < \pi/2$, the sequence of the values of the integral*

$$\frac{2}{\pi} \int_0^\delta \varphi(t; x_0) \cdot \frac{\sin (2n + 1)t}{t} \, dt$$

forms a null sequence as $n \to +\infty$.

25. Conditions for the Convergence of a Fourier Series. We are now in a position to tackle problems I and II directly, and for convenience we shall restate these problems in the following form:

Let $\varphi(t)$ be a given function integrable in $0 \leqq t \leqq \delta$. What additional conditions must be imposed upon $\varphi(t)$ in order that the sequence of integrals

$$J_p = \frac{2}{\pi} \int_0^\delta \varphi(t) \frac{\sin pt}{t} \, dt, \qquad p = 1, 2, \cdots$$

should tend to a (finite) limit L as $p \to +\infty$; and if L exists, what is its value?

In view of Riemann's theorem and the fact that δ has a fixed arbitrarily small positive value, it follows that this question depends *only* on the behavior of $\varphi(t)$ immediately to the right of 0. We are thus led to ask the question: What properties must $\varphi(t)$ possess immediately to the right of 0 in order that L may exist?

In the attempt to answer this question many papers have been published giving sufficient conditions for the existence of L. We shall present two very general sets of sufficient conditions:

THEOREM 25.1 (*Dirichlet's Rule**). *If* $\varphi(t)$ *is monotone in some interval* $0 < t < \delta_1$, *where* $\delta_1 \leqq \delta$ *and* δ *is a fixed positive number arbitrarily small, then* $\lim\limits_{p \to +\infty} J_p$ *exists and is equal to* φ_0, *where* φ_0 *denotes the right hand limiting value* $\lim\limits_{t \to +0} \varphi(t)$.

Proof. From Chap. V, Sec. 23, Example 2, $\lim\limits_{x \to +\infty} \int^x \dfrac{\sin t}{t} \, dt = \dfrac{\pi}{2}$.

By Sec. 23, Equation (14),

$$I_n \equiv \int_0^{\pi/2} \frac{\sin (2n + 1)t}{\sin t} \, dt = \frac{\pi}{2} \qquad \text{for} \qquad n = 0, 1, 2, \cdots .$$

Hence $I_n \to \pi/2$ as $n \to +\infty$. By Theorem 24.3, as $n \to +\infty$,

$$I_n^{(1)} \equiv \int_0^{\pi/2} \left(\frac{1}{\sin t} - \frac{1}{t} \right) \sin (2n + 1)t \, dt \to 0.$$

This proves that

$$I_n^{(2)} \equiv I_n - I_n^{(1)} = \int_0^{\pi/2} \frac{\sin (2n + 1)t}{t} \, dt \to \frac{\pi}{2}.$$

But $\displaystyle \int_0^{\frac{\pi}{2}} \frac{\sin (2n + 1)t}{t} \, dt = \int^{\frac{(2n+1)\pi}{2}} \frac{\sin t}{t} \, dt.$

Evidently, a constant $K_2 > 0$ exists such that $\left| \displaystyle\int_0^x \dfrac{\sin t}{t} \, dt \right| \leqq K_2$ for every $x \geqq 0$; hence for every a and b such that $0 \leqq a \leqq b$,

$$\left| \int_a^b \frac{\sin t}{t} \, dt \right| < 2K_2 = K.$$

---

* Due to Dirichlet, Sur la convergence des séries trigonométriques, *Jour. reine angew. Math.*, Vol. 4, p. 157, 1829. The first exact condition for the convergence of a Fourier series was given in this very fundamental paper.

Let $\epsilon > 0$ be given. Select a positive number $\delta_2 < \delta_1$ so that $|\varphi(\delta_2) - \varphi_0| < \dfrac{\epsilon}{3K}.$ Let $J_p^{(1)} \equiv \dfrac{2}{\pi} \displaystyle\int_0^{\delta_2} \varphi(t)\dfrac{\sin pt}{t}\, dt.$ By Theorem 24.3, $(J_p - J_p^{(1)}) \to 0$ as $p \to +\infty.$ Hence we can select a p_1 sufficiently large that $|J_p - J_p^{(1)}| < \epsilon/3$ for every $p > p_1.$ Write

$$J_p^{(1)} = \frac{2}{\pi}\int_0^{\delta_2}[\varphi(t) - \varphi_0]\frac{\sin pt}{t}\, dt + \frac{2}{\pi}\varphi_0\int_0^{\delta_2}\frac{\sin pt}{t}\, dt.$$

Let $J_p^{(2)}$ denote the second of these quantities on the right-hand side and $J_p^{(3)}$ the third. Then $J_p^{(1)} = J_p^{(2)} + J_p^{(3)}.$ Evidently,

$$J_p^{(3)} = \frac{2}{\pi}\varphi_0\int_0^{p\delta_2}\frac{\sin t}{t}\, dt \to \frac{2}{\pi}\varphi_0\int_0^{+\infty}\frac{\sin t}{t}\, dt = \varphi_0.$$

Hence there exists a $p_0 > p_1$ such that for every $p > p_0,$ $|J_p^{(3)} - \varphi_0| < \epsilon/3.$ By Theorem 30.1, Chap. II, for an appropriate nonnegative number $\delta_3 \leqq \delta_2,$

$$J_p^{(2)} = \frac{2}{\pi}\int_0^{\delta_2}[\varphi(t) - \varphi_0]\frac{\sin pt}{t}\, dt = \frac{2}{\pi}[\varphi(\delta_2) - \varphi_0]\int_{\delta_3}^{\delta_2}\frac{\sin pt}{t}\, dt.$$

The latter integral is equal to $\displaystyle\int_{p\delta_3}^{p\delta_2}\frac{\sin t}{t}\, dt,$ and as shown above, is $< K.$ Hence $|J_p^{(2)}| \leqq \dfrac{2}{\pi}\dfrac{\epsilon}{3K}K < \dfrac{\epsilon}{3}.$ A consideration of the sum $J_p = (J_p - J_p^{(1)}) + J_p^{(2)} + J_p^{(3)}$ shows that for a given $\epsilon > 0,$ there exists a p_0 such that for every $p > p_0,$

$$|J_p - \varphi_0| \leqq |J_p - J_p^{(1)}| + |J_p^{(2)}| + |J_p^{(3)} - \varphi_0| \leqq 3\frac{\epsilon}{3} = \epsilon.$$

This completes the proof of Theorem 25.1.

THEOREM 25.2 (*Dini's Rule*). *If* $\lim\limits_{t \to +0} \varphi(t) = \varphi_0$ *exists, and if the integral*

$$\int_\sigma^\delta \frac{|\varphi(t) - \varphi_0|}{t}\, dt$$

is numerically less than some fixed positive number for each positive value of $\sigma < \delta,$ *then* $\lim\limits_{p \to +\infty} J_p$ *exists and is equal to* $\varphi_0.$

Proof. The integral

$$\int_\sigma^\delta \frac{|\varphi(t) - \varphi_0|}{t}\, dt$$

is monotonically increasing but bounded as $\sigma \to +0$, and consequently tends to a definite limit L which we shall denote by $\int_0^\delta \frac{|\varphi(t) - \varphi_0|}{t}\, dt$. Let $\epsilon > 0$. We can select a positive number $\delta_1 < \delta$ so that

$$\int_0^{\delta_1} \frac{|\varphi(t) - \varphi_0|}{t}\, dt < \frac{\epsilon}{3}.$$

Let $J_p^{(1)} = J_p^{(2)} + J_p^{(3)}$ denote the same integrals as used in the proof of Theorem 25.1. As before, we can select a p_1 so that for every $p > p_1$, $|J_p - J_p^{(1)}| < \epsilon/3$, and a $p_0 > p_1$ so that

$$|J_p^{(3)} - \varphi_0| < \epsilon/3$$

for every $p > p_0$. Now

$$|J_p^{(2)}| = \left| \frac{2}{\pi} \int_0^{\delta_2} [\varphi(t) - \varphi_0] \frac{\sin pt}{t}\, dt \right| < \int_0^{\delta_2} \frac{|\varphi(t) - \varphi_0|}{t}\, dt,$$

so for a properly selected δ_2, $|J_p^{(2)}| < \epsilon/3$. We thus conclude that for every $p > p_0$, $|J_p - \varphi_0| < \epsilon$.

THEOREM 25.3 (*Lipschitz's Rule*). *If two positive numbers A and N exist such that for every t in the interval $0 < t \leqq \delta$,*

$$|\varphi(t) - \varphi_0| < At^N,$$

then $J_p \to \varphi_0$ as $p \to +\infty$.

Since $\int_\sigma^\delta \frac{|\varphi(t) - \varphi_0|}{t}\, dt < A \int_\sigma^\delta t^{N-1}\, dt < A \frac{\delta^N}{N} = $ a fixed number for all $\sigma < \delta$, it follows from Dini's rule that $J_p \to \varphi_0$ as $p \to +\infty$.

THEOREM 25.4. *If $\varphi'(0)$ exists, then $\lim\limits_{t \to +0} \varphi(t) = \varphi_0 = \varphi(0)$ exists and $J_p \to \varphi_0$ as $p \to +\infty$.*

If $\lim\limits_{t \to +0} \dfrac{\varphi(t) - \varphi(0)}{t}$ exists, then the ratio $\dfrac{\varphi(t) - \varphi(0)}{t}$ is bounded in some interval $0 < t < \delta_1$. But this is an example of a Lipschitz condition with $N = 1$.

As a consequence of Theorems 25.1 to 25.4, we have

THEOREM 25.5. *If $\varphi(t)$ is expressible as the sum of a finite number of functions, each of which satisfies the conditions of one of the four Theorems 25.1, $\cdots$, 25.4, then $\lim\limits_{t \to +0} \varphi(t) = \varphi_0$ exists* *and the integrals J_p for the function $\varphi(t)$ tend to φ_0 as $p \to +\infty$.*

We shall now adapt Theorems 25.1 to 25.4 to the theory of the Fourier series of an integrable function $f(x)$, which we shall assume to be defined in $0 \leqq x < 2\pi$ and extended by means of the equation

$$f(x \pm 2k\pi) = f(x) \qquad (k = 1, 2, \cdots)$$

to all other real values of x.

By Theorem 24.5, in order that the Fourier series generated by $f(x)$ shall converge to a sum $s(x_0)$ at $x = x_0$, it is necessary that the integrals J_n in (7) of Sec. 24 form a null sequence.

Thus, it is clear that the properties of $f(x)$ to the right of x_0 must stand in such a relation to the properties of $f(x)$ to the left of x_0 that the function $\varphi(t)$ shall possess necessary and sufficient conditions for the existence of the limit of the Dirichlet integrals J_n for $\varphi(t)$.

What these conditions are is not known. However, we have available in the theorem given above a number of conditions *sufficient* for the convergence of the Fourier series of a function $f(x)$ at some fixed point x_0.

In the following paragraph, we summarize certain criteria for the convergence of the Fourier series of $f(x)$ at the point x_0 which follow immediately from the relations presented above.

THEOREM 25.6. *Criteria for Convergence. Let $f(x)$ be defined and integrable (bounded) in the interval $0 \leqq x < 2\pi$ with its definition extended to include all real values of x by means of the relation $f(x) = f(x + 2k\pi)$, $k = \pm 1, \pm 2, \cdots$. Let x_0 denote any fixed real arbitrary number. Suppose that*

$$\lim_{t \to +0} \tfrac{1}{2}[f(x_0 + 2t) + f(x_0 - 2t)]$$

exists and is denoted by $s(x_0)$, and that consequently

$$\varphi(t) \equiv \varphi(t; x_0) = \tfrac{1}{2}[f(x_0 + 2t) + f(x_0 - 2t)] - s(x_0)$$

has a right hand limit and $\lim_{t \to +0} \varphi(t) = 0$. Then:

1. *Dirichlet's Rule. If $\varphi(t)$ is monotone in some interval*

$$0 < t < \delta_1,$$

then the Fourier series generated from $f(x)$ converges with the sum $s(x_0)$ at x_0.

2. *Dini's Rule.* Let δ be any fixed (though arbitrary) positive number. If the integral

$$\int_\sigma^\delta \frac{|\varphi(t) - \varphi_0|}{t}\, dt$$

remains less than some fixed positive number for all σ such that $0 < \sigma < \delta$, then the Fourier series of $f(x)$ converges to $s(x_0)$ at x_0.

3. *Lipschitz's Rule.* Let δ be any fixed (though arbitrary) positive number. If two positive numbers A and N exist such that, for every t for which $0 < t < \delta$, $|\varphi(t) - \varphi_0| < At^N$, then the Fourier series of $f(x)$ converges to $s(x_0)$ at x_0.

4. If the function $\varphi(t)$ corresponding to $f(x)$ possesses a right hand derivative at 0, then the Fourier series of $f(x)$ converges to $s(x_0)$ at (x_0).

In the application of Theorem 25.6 to particular problems the following theorems will be found to be helpful.

Theorem 25.7.   If $f(x)$ is continuous except for a finite number of finite jumps in a period, if it has a finite jump for $x = x_0$, and if the right hand limit is $f(x_0 + 0)$ and the left hand limit is $f(x_0 - 0)$, and if $f(x)$ has a derivative from the right and a derivative from the left at this point, its Fourier series converges for $x = x_0$ to the value $\dfrac{f(x_0 + 0) + f(x_0 - 0)}{2}$.

Theorem 25.8 (*Weierstrass' Theorem*).   If $f(x)$ is any continuous function of period 2π, and if ϵ is any positive number arbitrarily small, it is possible to construct a trigonometric series $T_n(x)$ having a finite number of terms so that for all values of x

$$|f(x) - T_n(x)| < \epsilon.$$

Theorem 25.9.   If $f(x)$ is continuous of period 2π whose Fourier coefficients are all zero, then $f(x)$ vanishes identically.

Theorem 25.10.   If $f(x)$ has a continuous second derivative except for a finite number of corners* in a period, and if a_p, b_p are the coefficients in its Fourier series, there is a number C, independent of k, such that

$$|a_p| \leqq \frac{C}{p^2}, \qquad |b_p| \leqq \frac{C}{p^2}.$$

---

* A *corner* is a point where $f(x)$ has right and left hand first derivatives which are unequal in value.

THEOREM 25.11. *If $\varphi(x)$ is any function continuous in $[0, 2\pi]$ except for a finite number of finite jumps,*

$$\lim_{n \to +\infty} \int_0^{2\pi} \varphi(x) \sin (n + \tfrac{1}{2})x \, dx = 0.$$

THEOREM 25.12 (*Jordan's Test*). *If $f(x)$ is of bounded variation in a neighborhood of x_0, then the Fourier series generated from $f(x)$ converges to the sum $\tfrac{1}{2}[f(x_0 + 0) + f(x_0 - 0)]$.*

Proof. Since $f(x)$ is of bounded variation over an interval about x_0, the condition assures convergence over that interval. The function

$$\varphi(h) \equiv f(x + h) + f(x - h) - f(x + 0) - f(x - 0)$$

is of bounded variation (see Sec. 8, Chap. IX) in any interval to the right of $h = 0$, and as $h \to 0$, $\varphi(h) \to 0$, for $f(x)$ being of bounded variation, $f(x + 0)$ and $f(x - 0)$ exist. We can thus write

$$\varphi(h) = \varphi_1(h) - \varphi_2(h),$$

where φ_1 and φ_2 are both positive increasing functions of h. But φ_1 and φ_2 both tend to the same limit L as $h \to 0$. By subtracting L from each of the quantities φ_1 and φ_2, we can construct the limit of the two new functions to be zero in both cases.

Let $\delta > 0$ be selected small enough so that $\varphi(h)$ is of bounded variation in $[0, \delta]$. Then

$$\int_0^{\delta} \frac{\sin (n + \tfrac{1}{2})h}{h} \varphi(h) \, dh = J_1 - J_2,$$

where

$$J_1 = \int_0^{\delta} \frac{\sin (n + \tfrac{1}{2})h}{h} \varphi_1(h) \, dh - \int_0^{\delta} \frac{\sin (n + \tfrac{1}{2})h}{h} \varphi_2(h) \, dh.$$

Let $\epsilon > 0$. Select a positive number μ small enough that $\varphi_1(\mu) < \epsilon$. By Theorem 30.1 of Chap. II,

$$\int_0^{\mu} \frac{\sin (n + \tfrac{1}{2})h}{h} \varphi_1(h) \, dh = \varphi_1(\mu) \int_{\xi}^{\mu} \frac{\sin (n + \tfrac{1}{2})h}{h} \, dh \quad (0 < \xi < \mu)$$

$$= \varphi_1(\mu) \int_{(n+\frac{1}{2})\xi}^{(n+\frac{1}{2})\mu} \frac{\sin t}{t} \, dt.$$

Since for all n, ξ, μ, the last integral is bounded,

$$\left| \int_0^\mu \frac{\sin\,(n+\tfrac{1}{2})h}{h} \varphi_1(h)\,dh \right| < A\epsilon,$$

where A is some positive constant. With μ fixed we find from Theorem 24.3 for n large enough,

$$\left| \int_0^\mu \frac{\sin\,(n+\tfrac{1}{2})h}{h} \varphi_1(h)\,dh \right| < \epsilon, \qquad n > n_0.$$

This shows $J_1 \to 0$. Likewise, we can show $J_2 \to 0$.

An immediate consequence of Theorem 25.11 is

THEOREM 25.13 (*Dirichlet's Conditions*). *If $f(x)$ is continuous except for a finite number of finite discontinuities in $0 \leqq x \leqq 2\pi$ and if $f(x)$ has only a finite number of maxima and minima in the interval, then the Fourier series generated from $f(x)$ converges to $\tfrac{1}{2}[f(x+0)+f(x-0)]$ for all values of x.*

It is not very difficult to extend Theorem 25.11 to prove

THEOREM 25.14. *The Fourier series generated from $f(x)$ converges uniformly to $f(x)$ in an interval interior to an interval throughout which $f(x)$ is continuous and is of bounded variation.*

26. Application of the Convergence Criteria. From the general character of the theorems given in Sec. 25, it is clear that very general classes of functions may be represented by Fourier series.

As stated before, the function $f(x)$ to be expanded should be given in the interval $0 \leqq x < 2\pi$ and must have the period 2π; that is, $f(x \pm 2k\pi) = f(x)$. The Fourier series then generated from $f(x)$ is of the form

$$\tfrac{1}{2}a_0 + \sum_{n=1}^{\infty} (a_n \cos nx + b_n \sin nx).$$

Suppose $f(x)$ is an *even function*, that is, a function having the property that $f(x) = f(-x)$. Then since $f(x)$ is of period 2π, i.e., $f(x) = f(-x) = f(2\pi - x)$, the Fourier coefficients b_n all vanish, for

$$\pi b_n = \int_0^{2\pi} f(x) \sin nx\,dx$$

$$= \int_0^{\pi} f(x) \sin nx\,dx + \int_\pi^{2\pi} f(x) \sin nx\,dx = 0. \qquad (1)$$

Thus, if $f(x)$ is an even function* the Fourier series generated from $f(x)$ reduces to a pure cosine series.

Suppose $f(x)$ is an *odd function*, that is, a function with the property that $f(x) = -f(-x)$. Then since $f(x)$ is of period 2π, $f(-x) = f(2\pi - x) = -f(x)$, and hence the Fourier coefficients a_n all vanish, for

$$\pi a_n = \int_0^{2\pi} f(x) \cos nx \, dx = 0. \qquad (2)$$

Thus, if $f(x)$ is an odd function, the Fourier series generated from $f(x)$ reduces to a pure sine series.

We now conclude that there are three ways in which a given $F(x)$, defined and integrable over the interval $a \leqq x \leqq b$, may be prepared for the generation of a Fourier series:

I. *Case* $(b - a) \geqq 2\pi$. In this method a portion, say

$$\alpha \leqq x < \alpha + 2\pi,$$

is cut out of the interval (a, b), and the origin is then transferred to the point α. In this way we obtain a function $f(x)$ defined in $0 \leqq x < 2\pi$, $f(x)$ being defined elsewhere by the condition $f(x \pm 2k\pi) = f(x)$. When $(b - a) > 2\pi$, a portion of $F(x)$ is omitted altogether. This omission can be avoided by changing the unit of measure on the x-axis so that the interval of definition of $F(x)$ has the length 2π. This change can readily be made by replacing x by $2\pi x/(b - a)$.

Case $(b - a) < 2\pi$. In this case define $f(x)$ to be some constant $F(b)$, in $b \leqq x < a + 2\pi$ and then proceed as before. An alternate method is to make the interval of definition of $F(x)$ exactly the length 2π by changing the unit of measurement on the x-axis.

II. This method is similar to that in I, except that we define the function $f(x)$ to be $F(x)$ in $0 \leqq x \leqq \pi$, $f(x) = f(2\pi - x)$ in $\pi \leqq x \leqq 2\pi$, and define $f(x)$ elsewhere by $f(x \pm 2k\pi) = f(x)$.

III. In this method we define $f(x)$ as in II for $0 \leqq x < \pi$, set $f(\pi) = 0$, $f(x) = -f(2\pi - x)$ for $\pi < x \leqq 2\pi$, and define $f(x)$ elsewhere by $f(x \pm 2k\pi) = f(x)$.

We shall denote by $f_1(x), f_2(x), f_3(x)$, respectively, the functions obtained by methods I, II, III, respectively, from a given func-

---

* The graph of an even function is symmetric with respect to the y-axis; that of an odd function is symmetric to the origin.

tion $F(x)$.   A function of type $f_2(x)$ will always generate a pure cosine series and a function of type $f_3(x)$ will always generate a pure sine series.

We shall further modify our functions f_1, f_2, f_3, by defining

$$f(0) = f(2k\pi) = \lim_{x\to+0} \tfrac{1}{2}[f(x) + f(2\pi - x)], \qquad (3)$$

whenever this limit exists.   This additional definition is necessitated by the fact that our rules for convergence enable us to detect the convergence of a Fourier series at points x_0 for which $\lim_{t\to+0} \tfrac{1}{2}[f(x_0 + 2t) + f(x_0 - 2t)]$ exists.   In case the limit in (3) does not exist we can not discover (with our present knowledge of the subject) whether the Fourier series converges or not; consequently, in this case, we need not concern ourselves with the value of $f(2k\pi)$.

Example 1.   Given $F(x) \equiv 3$.   Expand $F(x)$ in a sine series.
We shall use method III.   Define

$$f_3(x) = \begin{cases} 0 \text{ for } x = 0 \text{ and } x = \pi, \\ 3 \text{ for } 0 < x < \pi, \\ -3 \text{ for } \pi < x < 2\pi, \end{cases} \qquad f_3(x \pm 2k\pi) = f_3(x).$$

Evidently, f_3 fulfills Dirichlet's conditions at every point including the "jump points."   Consequently, the Fourier series obtained from f_3 must converge everywhere and actually represents f_3.

By Euler's formula we find

$$b_n = \frac{1}{\pi}\int_0^{2\pi} f_3(x) \sin nx\, dx = \frac{3}{\pi}\int_0^{\pi} \sin nx\, dx - \frac{3}{\pi}\int_\pi^{2\pi} \sin nx\, dx$$

$$= \frac{6}{\pi}\int_0^{\pi} \sin nx\, dx,$$

or
$b_n = 0$ for n an even integer, $b_n = 12/n\pi$ for n an odd integer.
Hence, the Fourier series for $f_3(x)$ is

$$f_3(x) = \frac{12}{\pi}\left[\sin x + \frac{\sin 3x}{3} + \frac{\sin 5x}{5} + \cdots + \frac{\sin (2n + 1)x}{2n + 1} + \cdots \right].$$

Figure 144 indicates the function $f_3(x)$ and the partial sums of the Fourier series, S_1, S_2, S_3.

Example 2.   Expand $F(x) = x$ by method III.   We define

$$j_3(x) = \begin{cases} x & \text{for} & 0 \leqq x < \pi, \\ 0 \text{ at } 0 \text{ and at } \pi, \\ -(2\pi - x) & \text{for} & \pi < x \leqq 2\pi. \end{cases}$$

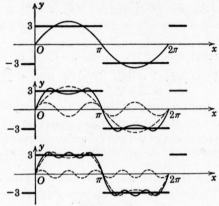

Fig. 144.

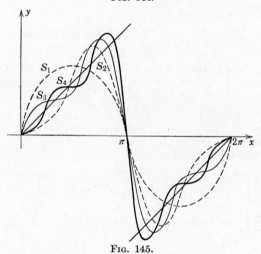

Fig. 145.

(See Fig. 145.)   From Euler's formula we readily obtain

$$2\left(\sin x - \frac{\sin 2x}{2} + \frac{\sin 3x}{3} - \frac{\sin 4x}{4} + \cdots \right),$$

which converges to $f_3(x)$ over the interval $0 \leqq x \leqq 2\pi$.

Example 3.* Expand $F(x) = x$ by method I.   Here we define

$$f_1(x) = \begin{cases} x, & 0 < x < 2\pi, \\ \pi, & \text{for } x = 0 \text{ and } x = 2\pi, \end{cases} \qquad f_1(x \pm 2k\pi) = f_1(x).$$

* For a large collection of such examples, see H. Burkhardt, Trigonometrische Reihen und Integrale bis etwa 1850, *Enzyk. math. Wiss.*, Vol. IIA, pp. 902–920.

From Euler's formula we readily obtain

$$\pi - 2\left[\, \sin x + \frac{\sin 2x}{2} + \cdots + \frac{\sin nx}{n} + \cdots \,\right],$$

which converges to $f_1(x)$ over the interval $0 \le x \le 2\pi$.

EXERCISES XXIV

1. Verify (2), (3), and (4) in Sec. 22.

2. Carry out in detail the steps leading to the proof of relations (5), (6), and (7) in Sec. 22.

3. Subject to the assumptions stated in Theorem 22.1, prove that the convergence of series (1) is uniform for every x.

4. Prove relation (2) in Sec. 23.

5. Verify formula (4) of Sec. 23. (HINT: Multiply each term of the left member by $\sin (z/2)$ and then represent each product as the difference between two sines.) Also verify (5) and (6) of Sec. 23.

6. Prove the statements given in (8) and (9) of Sec. 23.

7. Prove Theorem 24.3 without the use of Theorem 24.2.

8. Prove relation (9) in Sec. 24.

9. Prove Theorem 24.6.

10. Prove that another condition for the validity of Theorem 24.6 is: *If for every $\epsilon > 0$, we can assign a $\delta < \pi/2$, and an $N > 0$, so that for every $n > N$,*

$$\left| \frac{2}{\pi} \int_0^\delta \varphi(t; x_0) \frac{\sin (2n + 1)t}{t}\, dt \right| < \epsilon.$$

11. Find a Fourier series expression for the function $F(x)$ given in Example 1, using methods I and II.

12. Repeat Ex. 11 for $F(x) = k$, a constant, using methods I, II, and III.

13. From the results of Ex. 12, find a series for $\pi/4$, $\pi/3$.

14. Prove Theorems 25.7 to 25.13.

15. Expand $F(x) = x$ by method II (see Fig. 146).

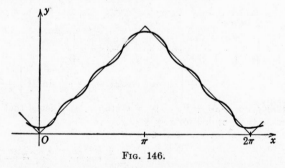

FIG. 146.

16. In each of the following exercises find a Fourier series and plot $F(x)$, S_0, S_1, S_2, $\cdots$:

(a) $F(x) = x^2$ for $0 < x < 2\pi$.

$$Ans. \quad x^2 = \frac{4}{3}\pi^2 + \sum \frac{4}{n^2} \cos nx - \sum \frac{4\pi}{n} \sin nx.$$

(b) $F(x) = \begin{cases} 4x \text{ for } 0 < x < \pi \\ 4x - 8\pi \text{ for } \pi < x < 2\pi. \end{cases}$

$$Ans. \quad F(x) = 8[\sin x - \tfrac{1}{2} \sin 2x + \tfrac{1}{3} \sin 3x - \cdots].$$

(c) $F(x) = \begin{cases} c \text{ for } 0 < x < \pi/2, \\ 0 \text{ for } \pi/2 < x < 3\pi/2, \\ -c \text{ for } 3\pi/2 < x < 2\pi. \end{cases}$

$$Ans. \quad F(x) = \frac{2c}{\pi}\left[\sin x + \frac{2}{2} \sin 2x + \frac{1}{3} \sin 3x + \frac{1}{5} \sin 5x + \cdots \right].$$

What is the value of this series at the discontinuity of $F(x)$?

(d) $F(x) = \begin{cases} x \text{ from } 0 \text{ to } \pi/2, \\ \pi - x \text{ from } \pi/2 \text{ to } \pi. \end{cases}$

$$Ans. \quad f(x) = \frac{4}{\pi}\left[\frac{\sin x}{1^2} - \frac{\sin 3x}{3^2} + \frac{\sin 5x}{5^2} - \frac{\sin 7x}{7^2} + \cdots \right].$$

(e) Same as (d) but with cosine series.

(f) $F(x) = x^2$ for $0 \leqq x \leqq \pi$.

$$Ans. \quad f(x) = \frac{2}{\pi}\left[\left(\frac{\pi^2}{1} - \frac{4}{1^3}\right) \sin x - \frac{\pi^2}{2} \sin 2x + \left(\frac{\pi^3}{3} - \frac{4}{3^3}\right) \sin 3x \right.$$
$$\left. - \frac{\pi^2}{4} \sin 4x + \left(\frac{\pi^2}{5} - \frac{4}{5^3}\right) \sin 5x + \cdots \right].$$

(g) $F(x) = \sin x$.

$$Ans. \quad f(x) = \frac{2}{\pi}\left[1 - \frac{2 \cos 2x}{1 \cdot 3} - \frac{2 \cos 4x}{3 \cdot 5} - \frac{2 \cos 6x}{5 \cdot 7} - \cdots \right].$$

(h) $F(x) = x \sin x$.

$$Ans. \quad f(x) = 1 - \frac{\cos x}{2} - \frac{2 \cos 2x}{1 \cdot 3} + \frac{2 \cos 3x}{2 \cdot 4} - \frac{2 \cos 4x}{3 \cdot 5} - \cdots .$$

(i) $F(x) = \dfrac{\pi}{2 \sinh \pi} e^x$ for $-\pi < x < \pi$.

$$Ans. \quad f(x) = \frac{1}{2} + \left[-\frac{1}{1 + 1^2} \cos x + \frac{1}{1 + 1^2} \sin x \right]$$
$$+ \left[\frac{1}{1 + 2^2} \cos 2x - \frac{2}{1 + 2^2} \sin 2x \right] + \cdots .$$

Prove that $f(-\pi + 0) + f(\pi - 0) = \pi \operatorname{ctnh} \pi$, and hence that the sum of the series is $(\pi/2) \operatorname{ctnh} \pi$ for $x = \pm\pi$.

(j) $F(x) = x + x^2$ for $-\pi < x < \pi$.

$$Ans. \quad a_n = \frac{4}{n^2} \cos n\pi, \qquad b_n = (-1)^{n-1}\frac{2}{n}.$$

Also obtain an expansion of $F(x) = x + x^2$ for $0 < x < 2\pi$.

Using this result, find $\dfrac{\pi^2}{6} = 1 + \dfrac{1}{2^2} + \dfrac{1}{3^2} + \cdots$.

(k) $F(x) = \begin{cases} 0, & -\pi < x \leqq 0, \\ \pi x/4, & 0 < x < \pi. \end{cases}$

Evaluate this Fourier series for $x = \pm\pi$. Show that

$$\frac{\pi^2}{8} = 1 + \frac{1}{3^2} + \frac{1}{5^2} + \cdots.$$

(l) $F(x) = \sin^2 x$ for $-\pi < x < \pi$.

17. Show that the Euler coefficients valid for the range $t = 0$ to $t = 2l$ are

$$a_n = \frac{1}{l}\int_0^{2l} \phi(t) \cos\frac{n\pi t}{l}\,dt, \qquad b_n = \frac{1}{l}\int_0^{2l} \phi(t) \sin\frac{n\pi t}{l}\,dt$$

where $\phi(t) = f(\pi t/l)$.

18. Using Ex. 17, expand $F(x) = \begin{cases} (l/4) - x, & 0 < x < l/2, \\ x - (3l/4), & l/2 < x < l. \end{cases}$

Ans. $f(x) = \dfrac{2l}{\pi^2}\left[\cos\dfrac{2\pi x}{l} + \dfrac{1}{9}\cos\dfrac{6\pi x}{l} + \dfrac{1}{25}\cos\dfrac{10\pi x}{l} + \cdots\right].$

27. Theorem (of Fejer) 27.1.* *If $f(x)$ is integrable in*

$$0 \leqq x \leqq 2\pi$$

and periodic of period 2π, and if at x_0 in the interval, the limits $f(x_0 + 0)$ and $f(x_0 - 0)$ exist, then the Fourier series generated from $f(x)$ is summable $(C, 1)$ at x_0 to $\frac{1}{2}[f(x_0 + 0) + f(x_0 - 0)]$.

Proof. From (13) of Sec. 23 the partial sum $s_n(x_0)$ of the Fourier series $\frac{1}{2}a_0 + \sum_{n=1}^{\infty}(a_n \cos nx_0 + b_n \sin nx_0)$ at x_0 may be written

$$s_n \equiv s_n(x_0) = \frac{2}{\pi}\int_0^{\pi/2} \frac{1}{2}[f(x_0 + 2t) + f(x_0 - 2t)]\frac{\sin (2n + 1)t}{\sin t}\,dt.$$
$$(n = 0, 1, \cdots.) \quad (1)$$

The arithmetical mean σ_{n-1} formed from the first n partial sums is

---

* This remarkable theorem was discovered by L. Fejer, Untersuchungen über die Fourierschen Reihen, *Math. Ann.*, Vol. 58, p. 51, 1903.

$$\sigma_{n-1} = \frac{s_0 + s_1 + \cdots + s_{n-1}}{n}$$

$$= \frac{2}{n\pi} \int_0^{\pi/2} \frac{1}{2}[f(x_0 + 2t) + f(x_0 - 2t)] \frac{\sum\limits_{r=1}^{n} \sin{(2r-1)t}}{\sin t} dt \quad (2)$$

But $\displaystyle\sum_{r=1}^{n} \sin{(2r-1)t} = \begin{cases} \dfrac{\sin^2 nt}{\sin t} & \text{if } t \neq k\pi, \\ 0 & \text{if } t = k\pi, \end{cases}$ since $\dfrac{\sin^2 nt}{\sin t} \to 0$ as

$t \to k\pi$. Hence (2) is equal to

$$\sigma_{n-1} = \frac{2}{n\pi} \int_0^{\pi/2} \frac{1}{2}[f(x_0 + 2t) + f(x_0 - 2t)]\left(\frac{\sin nt}{\sin t}\right)^2 dt. \quad (3)$$

This integral is called *Fejer's integral*. Comparison of (3) with Dirichlet's integral (13) of Sec. 23 shows that (3) is much the easier to handle, since $\left(\dfrac{\sin nt}{\sin t}\right)^2$ is positive in (3) while in Dirichlet's integral the corresponding factor $\dfrac{\sin nt}{\sin t}$ oscillates over positive and negative values. Now

$$\int_0^{\pi/2} \left(\frac{\sin nt}{\sin t}\right)^2 dt = \frac{n\pi}{2}. \quad (4)$$

(Why?) From (4) and (3) we have

$$\sigma_{n-1} - s = \frac{2}{n\pi} \int_0^{\pi/2} \left[\frac{f(x_0 + 2t) + f(x_0 - 2t)}{2} - s\right]\left[\frac{\sin nt}{t}\right]^2 dt. \quad (5)$$

Hence, a necessary and sufficient condition that the Fourier series be summable $(C, 1)$ to the sum s is that the integral (5) should approach zero as $n \to +\infty$.

We show now that if $\varphi(t)$ is integrable in $(0, \pi/2)$ and if $\lim\limits_{t \to +0} \varphi(t) = 0$, then as $n \to +\infty$, $\dfrac{2}{n\pi} \displaystyle\int^{\pi/2} \varphi(t) \cdot \left(\dfrac{\sin nt}{\sin t}\right)^2 dt \to 0$.

Since $\varphi(t) \to 0$, for every $\epsilon > 0$ there exists a $\delta < \pi/2$, such that $|\varphi(t)| < \epsilon/2$ when $0 < t \leq \delta$. Hence

$$\left|\frac{2}{n\pi} \int_0^\delta \varphi(t) \cdot \left(\frac{\sin nt}{\sin t}\right)^2 dt\right| \leq \frac{\epsilon}{2} \cdot \frac{2}{n\pi} \int_0^\delta \left(\frac{\sin nt}{\sin t}\right)^2 dt < \frac{\epsilon}{2}. \quad (6)$$

Since $|\varphi(t)|$ is bounded for $0 < t < \pi/2$, there exists an $M > 0$ such that $|\varphi(t)| < M$. Then it is easy to show that

$$\left| \frac{2}{n\pi} \int_{\delta}^{\pi/2} \varphi(t) \cdot \left(\frac{\sin nt}{\sin t} \right)^2 dt \right| \leqq \frac{2M}{n\pi} \cdot \frac{\pi}{2} \cdot \frac{1}{\sin^2 \delta}, \tag{7}$$

when M and δ are fixed. Select an N sufficiently large so that the right member of (7) is less than $\epsilon/2$ for all $n > N$. Combining this with (6) and replacing $\varphi(t)$ by $\left[\dfrac{f(x_0 + 2t) + f(x_0 - 2t)}{2} - s \right]$, we have $|\sigma_{n-1} - s| < \epsilon$ for all $n > N$. Hence $\sigma_{n-1} \to S$. This proves Fejér's theorem.

An immediate corollary to this theorem is

THEOREM 27.2. *If $f(x)$ is continuous in $0 \leqq x \leqq 2\pi$, if $f(0) = f(2\pi)$, then for every x the Fourier series generated from $f(x)$ is summable $(C, 1)$ to $f(x)$.*

The truth of this theorem follows immediately from the observation that the hypotheses of Theorem 27.1 are met everywhere, that it is understood that $f(x) = f(x - 2k\pi)$, and that $f(x) = \frac{1}{2}[f(x + 0) + f(x - 0)]$ for all values of x.

An important consequence of Theorem 27.1 is

THEOREM 27.3. *Under the assumptions of Theorem 27.1, the Fourier series of $f(x)$ is uniformly summable $(C, 1)$ in any interval included in an interval where $f(x)$ is continuous.*

Proof. Since $f(x)$ is periodic and everywhere continuous, it is uniformly continuous for all x's (Theorem 8.7, Chap. IX), so that for any fixed $\epsilon > 0$ there exists a $\delta > 0$ such that for every x, $|f(x \pm 2t) - f(x)| < \epsilon/2$ when $|t| < \delta$. Hence

$$|\varphi(t)| \equiv |\varphi(t, x)| =$$

$$\frac{1}{2}|[f(x + 2t) - f(x)] + [f(x - 2t) - f(x)]| < \frac{\epsilon}{2} \tag{8}$$

for all values of x. Furthermore $f(x)$ is bounded since $f(x)$ is periodic and continuous everywhere, so that there exists a $K > 0$ such that $|f(x)| < K$ for all values of x.

Hence $|\varphi(t, x)| < 2K$ for all values of x and t. A repetition of the argument given in the proof of Theorem 27.1 shows that

$$\left| \frac{2}{n\pi} \int_{0}^{\pi/2} \varphi(t) \cdot \left(\frac{\sin nt}{\sin t} \right)^2 dt \right| < \frac{1}{n} \frac{2K}{\sin^2 \delta}. \tag{9}$$

We thus conclude that there exists a definite number N such that the right member of (9) is less than $\epsilon/2$ for every $n \geqq N$. Hence $|\sigma_{n-1} - s| < \epsilon$ for $n \geqq N$. Thus for every given ϵ there exists a definite number N independent of x such that for $n > N$, $|\sigma_{n-1}(x) - f(x)| < \epsilon$.

THEOREM 27.4 (*Weierstrass's Theorem for Polynomial Approximation*). *If $f(x)$ is continuous for $a \leqq x \leqq b$, and if ϵ is any positive number, it is possible to construct a polynomial $P_m(x)$ so that for all $a \leqq x \leqq b$, $|f(x) - P_m(x)| < \epsilon$.*

We shall merely outline the proof of this theorem. Transform the variable x so that (a, b) lies within $(0, 2\pi)$. By Theorem 27.3 we know that there exists a "trigonometric polynomial" $\sigma_n(x)$ such that $|f(x) - \sigma_n(x)| < \epsilon/2$ for all x's on the interval. Replace each $\sin kx$ and $\cos kx$ in $\sigma_n(x)$ by their corresponding power series. By using a sufficiently large number of terms in these power series we can obtain a polynomial $P_m(x)$ such that

$$|\sigma_n(x) - P_m(x)| < \epsilon/2$$

for every x on the interval. Theorem 27.4 then follows.

EXERCISES XXV

1. Show that $\frac{1}{2} + \cos x + \cos 2x + \cdots + \cos nx + \cdots$ is summable $(C, 1)$ to the "sum" 0, if $x \neq 2k\pi$.

2. Show that $\sin x + \sin 2x + \cdots$ is convergent to the "sum" 0, for $x = k\pi$; if $x \neq k\pi$, the series is divergent but summable $(C, 1)$ to the "sum" $\frac{1}{2} \operatorname{ctn} (x/2)$.

3. Show that $\cos x + \cos 3x + \cos 5x + \cdots$ is summable $(C, 1)$ to the "sum" 0, if $x \neq k\pi$.

4. Show that $\sin x + \sin 3x + \sin 5x + \cdots$ is summable $(C, 1)$ to the "sum" $\dfrac{1}{2 \sin x}$ if $x \neq k\pi$.

28. Fourier Integral Formula. A Fourier series of the form

$$f(x) = \frac{1}{2}a_0 + \sum_{n=1}^{\infty}\left(a_n \cos \frac{nx}{\lambda} + b_n \sin \frac{nx}{\lambda}\right) \qquad (1)$$

represents at points of convergence a function of period $2\pi\lambda$. Subject to the proper restrictions, the coefficients are obtainable from the relations

$$a_n = \frac{1}{\pi\lambda}\int_{-\pi\lambda}^{+\pi\lambda} f(t)\cos\left(\frac{nt}{\lambda}\right) dt,$$

$$b_n = \frac{1}{\pi\lambda}\int_{-\pi\lambda}^{+\pi\lambda} f(t)\sin\left(\frac{nt}{\lambda}\right) dt. \tag{2}$$

The entire theory of Fourier series may be applied to series of type (1).

Substituting (2) in (1), we have

$$f(x) = \frac{1}{2\pi\lambda}\int_{-\pi\lambda}^{+\pi\lambda} f(t)\,dt + \sum_{n=1}^{\infty}\frac{1}{\pi\lambda}\int_{-\pi\lambda}^{+\pi\lambda} f(t)\cos\frac{n(x-t)}{\lambda}\,dt. \tag{3}$$

Let

$$w_n = \frac{n}{\lambda}, \quad \text{and} \quad \varphi(w) = \frac{1}{\pi}\int_{-\pi\lambda}^{+\pi\lambda} f(t)\cos w(x-t)\,dt. \tag{4}$$

Then the right-hand member of (3) may (under suitable conditions) be approximated by means of $\sum_{n=1}^{\infty}(w_{n+1} - w_n)\varphi(w_n)$. Let $\lambda \to +\infty$. Thus (3) becomes

$$f(x) = \frac{1}{\pi}\int_0^{+\infty}\int_{-\infty}^{+\infty} f(t)\cos w(x-t)\,\partial t\,dw, \tag{5}$$

provided, of course, such a limit exists. This is known as *Fourier's integral formula*. The right member of (5) represents a function on $(-\infty, +\infty)$ in much the same manner that a Fourier series represents a function over a finite period.

In this development we have overlooked many difficulties. Thus, we have ignored the fact that $\varphi(w)$ is a function of λ and that the approximating series is infinite. A rigorous proof of (5) is quite difficult and will not be undertaken here. (See Bochner, "Fourier Series and Integrals.")

It can be shown that under suitable conditions

$$f(x) = \frac{1}{\pi}\int_{-\infty}^{+\infty}\int_{-\infty}^{+\infty} f(t)\cos w(x-t)\,\partial t\,dw$$

$$= \frac{1}{2}[f(x+0) + f(x-0)], \qquad -\infty < x < +\infty. \tag{6}$$

If $f(x)$ is an even function, (6) becomes the *Fourier Cosine Integral*:

$$f(x) = \frac{2}{\pi}\int_0^{+\infty}\int_0^{+\infty} f(t)\cos wt \cos wx \, \partial t \, dw$$

$$= \frac{1}{2}[f(x+0) + f(x-0)], \tag{7}$$

and if $f(x)$ is an odd function, (6) becomes the *Fourier sine integral*:

$$f(x) = \frac{2}{\pi}\int_0^{+\infty}\int_0^{+\infty} f(t)\sin wt \sin wx \, \partial t \, dw$$

$$= \frac{1}{2}[f(x+0) + f(x-0)], \tag{8}$$

provided, of course, that these limits exist.

EXERCISES XXVI

1. Let $f(t) = 1$ for $0 < t < 1$, $f(t) = 0$ for $t > 1$, $f(t) = f(-t)$. Show from (7) that

$$\frac{2}{\pi}\int_0^{+\infty} \frac{\sin w \cos wt}{w}\, dw = \begin{cases} 1 & \text{for} & 0 < t < 1, \\ \tfrac{1}{2} & \text{for} & t = 1, \\ 0 & \text{for} & t > 1. \end{cases}$$

2. Let $f(t) = e^{-\beta t}$ for $t > 0$, $f(t) = -f(-t)$. (a) from (7) show that $\int_0^{+\infty}\frac{w\sin wt}{w^2+\beta^2}\,dw = \frac{\pi}{2}e^{-\beta t}$; (b) from (8), show that $\int_0^{+\infty}\frac{\cos wt}{w^2+\beta^2}\,dw = \frac{\pi}{2\beta}e^{-\beta t}$.

29. Harmonic Analysis. Let the interval $0 \leqq x \leqq 2\pi$ be divided into n equal subintervals by the points $x_0 = 0$, x_1, $x_2, \cdots, x_{n-1}$, $x_n = 2\pi$. Let $f(x)$ be periodic of period 2π. We wish to construct a trigonometric polynomial

$$S_m(x) = \tfrac{1}{2}a_0 + \sum_{k=1}^m (a_k \cos kx + b_k \sin kx) \tag{1}$$

such that

$$S_m(x_i) = f(x_i). \qquad (i = 0, 1, 2, \cdots, n-1.) \tag{2}$$

Since S_m contains $(2m + 1)$ undetermined coefficients, and since we are imposing n conditions by (2), we shall require n to be odd and we shall determine m from the relation $2m + 1 = n$. By (2) for the case $i = 0$ $(x_0 = 0)$,

$$\tfrac{1}{2}a_0 + \sum_{k=1}^{m} a_k = f(0). \tag{3}$$

Likewise,

$$\tfrac{1}{2}a_0 + \sum_{k=1}^{m} (a_k \cos kx_1 + b_k \sin kx_1) = f(x_1), \tag{4}$$

. . . .

$$\tfrac{1}{2}a_0 + \sum_{k=1}^{m} (a_k \cos kx_{n-1} + b_k \sin kx_{n-1}) = f(x_{n-1}). \tag{5}$$

If we add Eqs. (3) to (5) and collect together terms having like values of k, we find that

$$a_0 = \frac{2}{n} \sum_{i=0}^{n-1} f(x_i) \tag{6}$$

since, for fixed $k > 0$, $\sum_{i=0}^{n-1} a_k \cos kx_i = \sum_{i=0}^{n-1} b_k \sin kx_i = 0$. In close analogy with the Euler formulas of Sec. 22, it is easily shown that

$$a_k = \frac{2}{n} \sum_{i=0}^{n-1} (\cos kx_i) f(x_i),$$

$$b_k = \frac{2}{n} \sum_{i=0}^{n-1} (\sin kx_i) f(x_i), \quad k = 1, 2, \cdots, \frac{n-1}{2}. \tag{7}$$

If the period l of $f(x)$ is not 2π, then it can be made equal to 2π by a suitable change of scale along the x-axis. Formulas (6) and (7) then hold in the new scale; if desired, we can return to the original scale by writing $x = (2\pi/l)x'$ in (6) and (7).

Another set of formulas, based on an even number n of intervals, is obtained by omitting the term $b_m \sin mk$ from S_m in (1), where now $2m = n$. It turns out that formulas (6) and (7) hold for $k = 0, 1, 2, \cdots, (n/2) - 1$, and in addition,

$$a_{n/2} = \frac{1}{n} \cdot \sum_{i=0}^{n-1} (-1)^i f(x_i).$$

For a description of other and more systematic methods of analysis, see Whittaker and Robinson, "Calculus of Observations."

EXERCISES XXVII

Represent the following functions over the interval $0 \leqq x \leqq 2\pi$ by trigonometric sums:

1. $f(x) = 3x$. Take $n = 5$.   2. $f(x) = x^2$. Take $n = 6$.

3. $f(x) = \begin{cases} -1 \text{ when } 0 \leqq x < \pi, \\ 2\pi - x \text{ when } \pi \leqq x \leqq 2\pi. \end{cases}$ Take $n = 7$.

30. Further Results. We shall not have space to pursue this subject further than to make a few general remarks. We do not know at the present time what are the necessary and sufficient conditions that a function be representable by its Fourier's series.

It is known that not all continuous functions are representable by their Fourier series. Continuous functions exist whose Fourier series are divergent. Furthermore, it is known that Fourier series may sometimes represent functions which are nowhere differentiable. The theory of summability has aided materially in studying the question as to whether a Fourier series of a function represents that function.

It can be shown that any Fourier series S, whether convergent or not, may be integrated term by term between any limits; *i.e.*, the sum of the integrals of the separate terms is the integral of the function $f(x)$ which generates the given Fourier series.

In 1898, J. W. Gibbs discovered a very curious phenomenon in connection with the series $\displaystyle\sum_{n=1}^{+\infty} \frac{\sin nx}{n}$. Gibbs noticed that in the neighborhood of the discontinuity at $x = 0$, the curves $y = s_n(x)$ "overshoot the mark." Let α_n be the abscissa of the greatest maximum of $s_n(x)$ on $0 < x < \pi$ and let β_n be the corresponding ordinate. As $\alpha_n \to 0$, β_n does not approach $\pi/2$, but instead approaches a value $h = (\pi/2)(1.089 \cdots)$. Thus the curves $y = s_n(x)$ approximate as a limit the configuration consisting of the graph of the function $f(x) = (\pi - x)/2$ in $0 < x < 2\pi$, and a strip of the y-axis from $y = -h$ to $y = +h$, where h exceeds the "jump" of the function by about 9 per cent.

This strange behavior is known as the *Gibbs phenomenon* and has been extensively studied in general Fourier series (see Fig. 147).

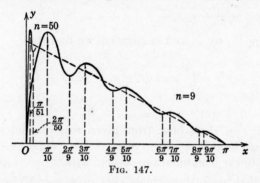

Fig. 147.

31. Systems of Orthogonal Functions. The *inner product* over $a \leqq x \leqq b$ of two real-valued functions $f(x)$ and $g(x)$ is defined to be

$$(f, g) \equiv \int_a^b f(x) \, g(x) \, dx. \tag{1}$$

If $(f, g) = 0$, the functions f and g are said to be *orthogonal*.* The *norm* of f is defined as

$$N(f) = (f, f) = \int_a^b f^2 \, dx. \tag{2}$$

If $N(f) = 1$, f is said to be *normalized*. If, for any function f, we let $\varphi = f/\sqrt{N(f)}$, then $N(\varphi) = (f/\sqrt{N(f)}, f/\sqrt{N(f)}) = 1$.

A system of normalized functions $\varphi_1(x)$, $\varphi_2(x)$, $\cdots$ for which

$$(\varphi_m, \varphi_n) = \begin{cases} 0 & \text{when} & m \neq n, \\ 1 & \text{when} & m = n, \end{cases} \tag{3}$$

are said to form a *normalized orthogonal*, or *orthonormal system*. For example, over $0 \leqq x \leqq 2\pi$,

$$\frac{1}{\sqrt{2\pi}}, \frac{\cos x}{\sqrt{\pi}}, \frac{\sin x}{\sqrt{\pi}}, \frac{\cos 2x}{\sqrt{\pi}}, \frac{\sin 2x}{\sqrt{\pi}}, \cdots \tag{4}$$

form a normalized orthogonal system.

The first n functions ($n = 2, 3, 4, \cdots$) of an orthogonal system $\varphi_1, \varphi_2, \cdots, \varphi_n, \cdots$, are always linearly independent.

---

* See Courant-Hilbert, "Mathematische Physik," I, pp. 40–47.

For suppose $\varphi_1, \cdots, \varphi_n$ were linearly dependent. Then there would exist constants $c_1, \cdots, c_n$ such that

$$c_1\varphi_1 + c_2\varphi_2 + \cdots + c_n\varphi_n = 0. \tag{5}$$

Multiplying (5) by φ_ν and integrating we find that

$$\sum_{k=1}^{n} c_k \int_a^b \varphi_k \varphi_\nu \, dx = c_\nu \int_a^b \varphi_\nu^2 \, dx = 0.$$

Hence $c_\nu = 0$, $\nu = 1, \cdots, n$.

We shall now show how, from given real continuous linearly independent functions $\alpha_1(x)$, $\alpha_2(x)$, $\cdots$, $\alpha_n(x)$, $\cdots$ we can construct linear combinations $\varphi_1(x)$, $\varphi_2(x)$, $\cdots$, $\varphi_n(x)$, $\cdots$ of them which are orthonormal. Let $\varphi_1 = \alpha_1/\sqrt{N(\alpha_1)}$, so that $N(\varphi_1) = (\varphi_1, \varphi_1) = 1$. Select c_{11} such that $\varphi_2' = \alpha_2 - c_{11}\varphi_1$ is orthogonal to φ_1; i.e., so that $(\varphi_1, \varphi_2') = (\varphi_1, \alpha_2) - c_{11}(\varphi_1, \varphi_1) = 0$. Then $c_{11} = (\varphi_1, \alpha_2)$. To normalize φ_2', let $\varphi_2 = \varphi_2'/\sqrt{N(\varphi_2')}$. It is evident that $(\varphi_1, \varphi_2) = 0$. Next let $\varphi_3' = \alpha_3 - c_{21}\varphi_1 - c_{22}\varphi_2$, where the c's are such that

$$(\varphi_1, \varphi_3') = (\varphi_1, \alpha_3) - c_{21} = 0, \qquad (\varphi_2, \varphi_3') = (\varphi_2, \alpha_3) - c_{22} = 0.$$

Thus $c_{21} = (\varphi_1, \alpha_3)$, $c_{22} = (\varphi_2, \alpha_3)$. Let $\varphi_3 = \varphi_3'/\sqrt{N(\varphi_3')}$. Then φ_3 is orthonormal to φ_1 and φ_2. In general, let

$$\varphi_{n+1} = \frac{\varphi_{n+1}'}{\sqrt{N(\varphi_{n+1}')}}, \qquad \varphi_{n+1}' = \alpha_{n+1} - \sum_{k=1}^{n} \varphi_k(\varphi_k, \alpha_{n+1}), \qquad \cdots\cdots$$

The set $\varphi_1, \varphi_2, \cdots$ so constructed forms an orthonormal system.

Let $\varphi_1, \varphi_2, \cdots$ be an orthonormal system, and let $f(x)$ be any real function of the real variable x on $a \leqq x \leqq b$. Let $c_k \equiv (f, \varphi_k)$. It can be shown from the fact that

$$\int_a^b \left(f - \sum_{k=1}^{n} c_k \varphi_k \right)^2 dx \geqq 0$$

that

$$\sum_{k=1}^{n} c_k^2 \leqq N(f), \tag{6}$$

provided $c_1, \cdots, c_n$ are independent. This inequality is called *Bessel's inequality.*

Let $f(x)$ be a given real function of the real variable x. What values must the coefficients γ_k have in order that f be approximated in the sense of "least squares" by means of the linear relation $\sum\limits_{k=1}^{n} \gamma_k \varphi_k$, where $\varphi_1, \cdots, \varphi_n$ form a normalized orthogonal system; i.e., in order that $M = \int_a^b \left(f - \sum\limits_{k=1}^{n} \gamma_k \varphi_k \right)^2 dx$ be a minimum? Now

$$M = \int_a^b f^2\, dx + \sum_{k=1}^{n} (\gamma_k - c_k)^2 - \sum_{k=1}^{n} c_k^2. \tag{7}$$

Hence in order that M be a minimum, $\gamma_k = c_k$ for all values of $k = 1, \cdots, n$.

If $M = 0$, then (7) with $c_k = (f, \varphi_k)$ gives

$$\sum_{k=1}^{\infty} c_k^2 = N(f). \tag{8}$$

An orthonormal system $\varphi_1, \varphi_2, \cdots$ is said to be *complete* if there exists no orthonormal system $\alpha_1, \alpha_2, \cdots$ of which $\varphi_1, \varphi_2, \cdots$ is a proper subset.

In order that $\varphi_1, \varphi_2, \cdots$ form a complete orthogonal system, it is sufficient that *completeness relation* (8) hold for all continuous functions f.

Suppose that throughout $a \leqq x \leqq b$, $f(x)$ can be represented by a convergent series of the form

$$f(x) = \sum_{k=1}^{\infty} c_k \varphi_k(x), \tag{9}$$

where $\varphi_1, \varphi_2, \cdots$ form a complete orthogonal system. If, furthermore, (9) is uniformly convergent, then the series obtained from (9) by multiplying by φ_n can be integrated term by term. Since the φ's are orthogonal, we have

$$\int_a^b f(x)\, \varphi_n(x)\, dx = c_n \int_a^b [\varphi_n(x)]^2\, dx, \tag{10}$$

from which we have

$$c_n = \frac{(f, \varphi_n)}{(\varphi_n, \varphi_n)}. \quad (n = 1, 2, \cdots) \quad (11)$$

If the φ's are normalized, then

$$c_n = (f, \varphi_n). \qquad (n = 1, 2, \cdots)$$

EXERCISES XXVIII

1. Show that (4) is an orthonormal system of functions over the interval $0 \leqq x \leqq 2\pi$.

2. Show that the system of Legendre polynomials form an orthogonal system. Find the normalizing factors for the Legendre polynomials.

3. Show that if the system $\varphi_1(x)$, $\varphi_2(x)$, $\cdots$ is orthogonal, then the system $\psi_1(x)$, $\psi_2(x)$, $\cdots$ with $\psi_k = \varphi_k(x)/\sqrt{(\varphi_k, \varphi_k)}$ is orthonormal.

4. Two complex functions f and g of a real variable x are said to be *orthogonal* if $(f, g^*) = (f^*, g) = 0$, where f^* is the conjugate of f, $\cdots$. If $N(f) = \int_a^b |f|^2 \, dx = 1$, then $f(x)$ is said to be *normalized*. Show that over $-\pi \leqq x \leqq +\pi$, $1/\sqrt{2\pi}$, $e^{ix}/\sqrt{2\pi}$, $e^{2ix}/\sqrt{2\pi}$, $\cdots$ is a normalized orthogonal system.

5. Show that (f, g) satisfies *Schwarz's inequality*

$$(f, g)^2 \leqq (f, f)(g, g). \tag{12}$$

Hint: $(f, g)^2 = (f, f)(g, g) - \frac{1}{2}\iint_K [f(x)g(\xi) - f(\xi)g(x)]^2 \, \partial x \, d\xi$.

6. Show that the equality in (12) holds if and only if f and g are proportional.

7. Construct from 1, x, x^2, $\cdots$, x^{n-1} a set of orthogonal functions for the interval $-1 \leqq x \leqq +1$. Do not normalize.

$$Ans. \quad 1, \ x, \ x^2 - \tfrac{1}{3}, \ x^3 - \tfrac{3}{5}x, \ \cdots.$$

8. Show that $f_0(x)$, $f_1(x)$, $\cdots$, $f_n(x)$, where

$$f_n(x) = \frac{d^n}{dx^n}[(x - a)^n(x - b)^n],$$

is a set of nonorthonormal orthogonal functions. Construct this set of functions from the set, 1, x, x^2, x^3, $\cdots$.

9. Prove Bessel's inequality (6).

10. Prove: If condition (8) is satisfied, any function orthogonal to every member of the system φ_1, φ_2, $\cdots$ vanishes identically.

11. Show that if any member of a complete system S be removed, the remaining system will not be a *complete* system.

12. Show that (f, g) has the following properties, where f and g are suitable complex functions of the real variable x and where a is a complex number:

$(f, ag) = a^*(f, g)$.

$(f, g_1 + g_2) = (f, g_1) + (f, g_2)$.

$N(af) = |a|N(f).$

$|(f, g)| \leqq N(f)N(g).$

$N(f_1 + f_2) \leqq Nf_1 + Nf_2.$

$[N(f + g)]^2 \leqq [N(f)]^2 + 2[N(f)][N(g)] + [N(g)]^2.$

$N(f - g) \geqq 0.$

$N(f - g) = 0$ if and only if $f = g.$

$N(f - h) \leqq N(f - g) + N(g - h).$

13. Prove:

If $\varphi_1, \varphi_2, \cdots, \varphi_n, \cdots$ is an orthonormal set of functions, then $\displaystyle\sum_{k=1}^{+\infty} a_k b_k{}^*$

is absolutely convergent for every f and g. Here $a_k = (f, \varphi_k)$, $b_k = (g, \varphi_k)$.

When $f = g$, $\displaystyle\sum_{k=1}^{+\infty} |a_k|^2 \leqq [N(f)]^2.$

14. Let $\varphi_1, \varphi_2, \cdots$ be a complete orthonormal set and suppose f and g are suitable functions. Show:

(a) If $(f, \varphi_n) = 0$ for every n, then $f = 0.$

(b) For every f and g, $(f, g) = \displaystyle\sum_{k=1}^{+\infty} a_k b_k{}^*, a_n = (f, \varphi_n), b_n = (g, \varphi_n).$ (*Parse-val's identity.*)

15. The functions $\varphi_1(x)$, $\varphi_2(x)$, $\cdots$ are said to be *orthogonal* (over the interval $a \leqq x \leqq b$) *relative to the weight function* $\rho(x)$ if

$$\int_a^b \rho(x)\varphi_m(x)\varphi_n(x)\,dx = 0 \qquad \text{when} \qquad m \neq n.$$

Verify that the following systems of functions are orthogonal with respect to the weight function indicated:

(a) The Legendre polynomials over the interval $-1 \leqq x \leqq 1$; $\rho(x) = 1.$

(b) The Hermite polynomials over the interval $-\infty < x < +\infty$; $\rho(x) = e^{-x^2}.$

(c) The Laguerre polynomials over the interval $0 \leqq x < \infty$; $\rho(x) = e^{-x}.$ (HINT: consider the differential equations satisfied by these functions.)   If

$$N(\varphi) = \int_a^b \rho(x)[\varphi(x)]^2\,dx,$$ show that $N(\varphi_n) = \dfrac{2}{2n+1}$ in (a); $N(\varphi_n) = 2^n n!$ in (b); and $N(\varphi_n) = (n!)^2$ in (c).

CHAPTER V

FUNCTIONS OF A COMPLEX VARIABLE

1. Introduction. In this chapter we shall study the elements of the theory of analytic functions of a complex variable. This theory has been found to be of the utmost importance and value, not only to mathematicians, but also to engineers and physicists. The theory of the two-dimensional flow of heat, electricity, and fluids is studied through the medium of analytic functions; the theory of maps is intimately related to the subject; the solution of many of the ordinary differential equations which arise in electric-circuit theory is greatly aided by the use of complex numbers; in the rapidly growing field of aerodynamics the methods of the theory have found wide application.

The early mathematical theory of analytic functions was largely developed under the influence of Cauchy (1789–1857), Riemann (1826–1866), Weierstrass (1815–1897), and their students.

PART A. COMPLEX NUMBERS

2. Complex Numbers. Let (x, y) be an ordered pair of real numbers. We shall represent the number pair (x, y) by the symbol* $x + yi$, and we shall speak of $x + yi$ as a *complex number*. In the notation $x + yi$, the symbols i, yi, and $+$ have (as yet) no meaning whatever, and $x + yi$ should be regarded as a single symbol. The number x is called the *real* part, and y the *imaginary* part, of the complex number $x + yi$; if $z = x + yi$, then the real and imaginary parts of z are sometimes denoted by $\Re(z)$ and $\Im(z)$, respectively. A complex number $0 + yi$ in which

---

* A number pair (x, y) may be represented in other ways, such as by a vector or a point. Because complex numbers and vectors are added in essentially the same way, complex numbers and vectors have many properties and applications in common. In fact, the only thing that distinguishes a complex number from a vector is the law defining multiplication, so that, as long as multiplication is not involved, complex numbers and vectors may be used indiscriminantly.

the real part is zero is called a *pure imaginary* number; the number $0 + 1i$ is called the *imaginary unit*. (It should be remembered that an imaginary number is in no way considered as an "imagined" number. We would prefer not to use the word imaginary, but its use is so universal that we retain the term here.)   We shall write $x + 0i$ merely as x, and $0 + yi$ as yi. Thus, $z = x + yi$ is representable by x alone if and only if $y = 0$; moreover, $z = x + yi$ is representable by 0 if and only if both $x = 0$ and $y = 0$.

If $z_1 = x_1 + y_1i$ and $z_2 = x_2 + y_2i$, where of course x_1, x_2, y_1, and y_2 are real numbers, then we define the *sum* of z_1 and z_2 to be the complex number

$$z_1 + z_2 = (x_1 + y_1i) + (x_2 + y_2i) = (x_1 + x_2) + (y_1 + y_2)i, \quad (1)$$

and the *product* of z_1 and z_2 to be the complex number

$$\begin{aligned} z_1z_2 &= (x_1 + y_1i)(x_2 + y_2i) \\ &= (x_1x_2 - y_1y_2) + (x_1y_2 + x_2y_1)i. \end{aligned} \quad (2)$$

It follows directly from (1) and (2) that

$$z_1 + z_2 = z_2 + z_1, \quad (3)$$
$$z_1 + (z_2 + z_3) = (z_1 + z_2) + z_3, \quad (4)$$
$$z_1z_2 = z_2z_1, \quad (5)$$
$$z_1(z_2z_3) = (z_1z_2)z_3, \quad (6)$$
$$z_1(z_2 + z_3) = z_1z_2 + z_1z_3, \quad (7)$$

these relations being known, respectively, as the commutative and associative laws for addition, and the commutative, associative, and distributive laws for multiplication.

If we set $y_1 = 0$ in (2), we see that

$$x_1z_2 = (x_1 + 0i)(x_2 + y_2i) = x_1x_2 + x_1y_2i. \quad (8)$$

In particular, if $x_1 = 1$, it follows by (8) that $1z_2 = z_2$. We shall denote the number $1i$ merely by i.

If we set $z_1 = y$ and $z_2 = i$ in (5), we see that $yi = iy$. Hence

$$x + yi = x + iy. \quad (9)$$

We define the symbol $x - yi$ to mean $x + (-y)i$. If $z = x + yi$, we define $-z$ to be $(-x) + (-y)i = -x - yi$. If we set $x_1 = -1$ in (8), it follows that $(-1)z_2 = -z_2$; in particular, $(-1)i = -i$.

We define the *difference* $z_1 - z_2$ to be $z_1 + (-z_2)$. By (1),

$$z_1 - z_2 = z_1 + (-z_2) = (x_1 + y_1i) + (-x_2 - y_2i)$$
$$= (x_1 - x_2) + (y_1 - y_2)i. \tag{10}$$

If $z_1 = z_2$, i.e., if $x_1 = x_2$ and $y_1 = y_2$, then by (10), $z_1 - z_2 = 0$. Conversely, if $z_1 - z_2 = 0$, then by (10),

$$(x_1 - x_2) + (y_1 - y_2)i = 0.$$

But, as remarked above, this situation occurs only when

$$x_1 - x_2 = 0 \quad \text{and} \quad y_1 - y_2 = 0,$$

i.e., when $x_1 = x_2$ and $y_1 = y_2$, so that $z_1 = z_2$. Thus, *two complex numbers are equal when and only when their difference is zero.*

If we set $x_1 = x_2 = 0$, $y_1 = y_2 = 1$ in (2), and if we denote ii by i^2, then*

$$i^2 = ii = (0 + 1i)(0 + 1i) = -1 + 0i = -1. \tag{11}$$

We define the *conjugate* z^* of $z = x + yi$ to be $z^* = x - yi$. Evidently,

$$zz^* = (x + yi)(x - yi) = x^2 + y^2 = z^*z. \tag{12}$$

Likewise

$$(z_1 + z_2)^* = z_1^* + z_2^*, \qquad (z_1z_2)^* = z_1^*z_2^*. \tag{13}$$

It is seen by (2) that *the product z_1z_2 of two complex numbers is zero if one (or both) of the factors z_1, z_2 are zero. Conversely, if the product $z_1z_2 = 0$, then either z_1 or z_2 (or both) must be zero.* The proof is quite simple: If $z_1z_2 = 0$, then

$$z_1^*(z_1z_2)z_2^* = 0.$$

But

$$z_1^*(z_1z_2)z_2^* = (z_1^*z_1)(z_2z_2^*) = (x_1^2 + y_1^2)(x_2^2 + y_2^2) = 0.$$

* Equation (11) must not be interpreted as showing that $i = \sqrt{-1}$. As indicated above, i denotes an ordered pair of real numbers, namely, the number pair $(0, 1)$, and Eq. (11) shows merely that the product of this number pair by itself is, according to (2), the number pair $(-1, 0)$. The operation of taking a square root of a complex number has not yet been defined, and it will be seen later that $\sqrt{-1}$ has meaning only when regarded as the result of an operation on the number pair $(-1, 0)$ leading to the number pair $(0, 1)$.

Hence either $x_1^2 + y_1^2 = 0$ or $x_2^2 + y_2^2 = 0$, or both. If $x_1^2 + y_1^2 = 0$, then $x_1 = y_1 = 0$, so that $z_1 = 0$. Likewise, if $x_2^2 + y_2^2 = 0$, then $z_2 = 0$.

If we set $x_1 = 1/u$, $u \neq 0$, in (8), it follows that

$$\frac{z_2}{u} = \frac{x_2}{u} + \frac{y_2}{u}i.$$

Thus we may divide a complex number by a real number (other than 0). If $z_1 = x_1 + y_1 i$ and $z_2 = x_2 + y_2 i$, and if there exists a complex number q such that

$$z_1 q = z_2, \tag{14}$$

then we say that z_2 and z_1 have the *quotient* $q = z_2/z_1$. To determine q we observe that, if (14) holds, then

$$z_1{}^* z_1 q = (x_1^2 + y_1^2)q = z_1{}^* z_2. \tag{15}$$

If $z_1 \neq 0$, so that $x_1^2 + y_1^2 \neq 0$, then by the latter part of (15),

$$q = \frac{z_1{}^* z_2}{x_1^2 + y_1^2} = \frac{(x_1 - y_1 i)(x_2 + y_2 i)}{x_1^2 + y_1^2}$$

$$= \frac{x_1 x_2 + y_1 y_2}{x_1^2 + y_1^2} + \frac{x_1 y_2 - x_2 y_1}{x_1^2 + y_1^2}i. \tag{16}$$

It is seen that this value of q satisfies (14), for

$$z_1 q = z_1 \frac{z_1{}^* z_2}{x_1^2 + y_1^2} = \frac{z_1 z_1{}^*}{x_1^2 + y_1^2} z_2 = z_2.$$

3. Geometric Representation of Complex Numbers.

Let a right-hand cartesian coordinate system be set up in a plane $\mathcal{P}$. Associate with each complex number $z = x + yi$ the corresponding point (x, y) in the plane $\mathcal{P}$. Then each complex number $z = x + yi$ is represented by exactly one point (x, y), and conversely, to each point (x, y) there corresponds exactly one

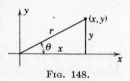

Fig. 148.

complex number $z = x + yi$. The x-axis is often called the *real axis* and the y-axis the *imaginary axis*. (Why?) The complex number $0 = 0 + 0i$ is represented by the origin of the coordinate system.

Let (r, θ) denote the polar coordinates of the point (x, y) constructed in the usual manner, with θ chosen so that r is positive. Then

$$r = \sqrt{x^2 + y^2} = \sqrt{zz^*}, \qquad \cos \theta = \frac{x}{r}, \qquad \sin \theta = \frac{y}{r}. \qquad (1)$$

The number r is called the *absolute value* (or *modulus, radius vector*) of the complex number $z = x + yi$. The symbol $|z|$ is also used to denote the absolute value of z, so that

$$|z| = r = \sqrt{zz^*}. \qquad (2)$$

The number θ is called the *amplitude* (or *arc, argument, angle*) of z. While for a given complex number $z \neq 0$, there is but one amplitude θ such that $0 \leq \theta < 2\pi$, there is also an amplitude between 2π and 4π, an amplitude between 4π and 6π, etc. The term amplitude may refer to the smallest positive number θ in (1), or it may refer to any number of the set $\theta + 2n\pi$, where n is any integer. The amplitude of z is sometimes denoted by amp z. It is readily shown (see Exs. I, 4, 5) that

$$|z_1| - |z_2| \leq |z_1 + z_2| \leq |z_1| + |z_2|, \qquad (3)$$

$$|z_1 z_2| = |z_1| \cdot |z_2|, \qquad \left|\frac{z_1}{z_2}\right| = \frac{|z_1|}{|z_2|} \text{ if } z_2 \neq 0, \qquad |z^*| = |z|. \qquad (4)$$

It follows from (1) that any complex number can be represented in the form

$$z = x + yi = r(\cos \theta + i \sin \theta). \qquad (5)$$

For example,

$$-5 = -5 + 0i = 5(\cos \pi + i \sin \pi),$$

$$5i = 0 + 5i = 5\left(\cos \frac{\pi}{2} + i \sin \frac{\pi}{2}\right).$$

However, θ in (5) may have infinitely many different values. Hence each complex number $z = x + yi$ may be represented in the form (5) in infinitely many ways. In fact, because $\cos(\theta + 2k\pi) = \cos \theta$ and $\sin(\theta + 2k\pi) = \sin \theta$ for any integer k, we may write

$$z = r(\cos \theta + i \sin \theta)$$
$$= r[\cos(\theta + 2k\pi) + i \sin(\theta + 2k\pi)]. \qquad (6)$$

Another method for representing geometrically a complex number $z_1 = x_1 + y_1 i$ is by means of vectors. By a vector we shall mean a directed line segment $\overrightarrow{OA}$. If O is the origin $(0, 0)$ and if A is the point (x_1, y_1), then the complex number

$$z_1 = x_1 + y_1 i$$

is represented by the vector $\overrightarrow{OA}$ (see Fig. 149). Thus, to each number z_1 there corresponds one vector $\overrightarrow{OA}$ from O, and conversely, to each vector $\overrightarrow{OA}$ from O there corresponds exactly one complex number z_1.

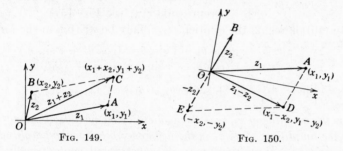

FIG. 149.   FIG. 150.

Using formula (1) of Sec. 2, we may give a geometric construction for the sum $z_1 + z_2$ of two complex numbers $z_1 = x_1 + y_1 i$ and $z_2 = x_2 + y_2 i$. Let z_1 and z_2 be represented by the vectors $\overrightarrow{OA}$ and $\overrightarrow{OB}$ as indicated in Fig. 149. If C is determined as the fourth vertex of the parallelogram $OACB$, then $\overrightarrow{OC}$ is the sum of $\overrightarrow{OA}$ and $\overrightarrow{OB}$, and $\overrightarrow{OC}$ represents $z_1 + z_2$. This construction is called the *parallelogram law of addition*.

In Fig. 150, $\overrightarrow{OE}$ represents $-z_2$. It is seen that $\overrightarrow{OD}$ is the sum of $\overrightarrow{OA}$ and $\overrightarrow{OE}$, and $\overrightarrow{OD}$ represents the difference $z_1 - z_2$.

To construct the vector representing the product $z_1 z_2$, let us write

$$z_1 z_2 = r_1(\cos \theta_1 + i \sin \theta_1) \cdot r_2(\cos \theta_2 + i \sin \theta_2) \qquad (7)$$
$$= r_1 r_2 [\cos (\theta_1 + \theta_2) + i \sin (\theta_1 + \theta_2)].$$

It is seen by (7) that *the modulus of $z_1 z_2$ is equal to the product of the moduli of z_1 and z_2*, and that *the amplitude of $z_1 z_2$ is the sum* *of the amplitudes of* z_1 *and* z_2. Let the vectors $\overrightarrow{OA}$ and $\overrightarrow{OB}$ represent z_1 and z_2, and let $\overrightarrow{OU}$ represent the number 1. On $\overrightarrow{OB}$ construct a triangle OBF similar to triangle OUA. Angle BOF equals angle UOA, and angle UOF is the sum of angles UOA and UOB. Moreover

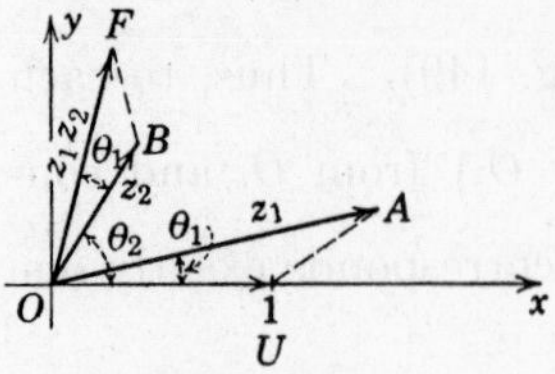

Fig. 151.

$$\frac{OF}{OB} = \frac{OA}{OU} = \frac{OA}{1},$$

so that $OF = OA \cdot OB$. Thus $\overrightarrow{OF}$ represents $z_1 z_2$ (see Fig. 151).

By (16) of Sec. 2, the quotient z_2/z_1 may be written in the form

$$q = \frac{z_2}{z_1} = \frac{z_1^* z_2}{z_1^* z_1} = \frac{r_1(\cos \theta_1 - i \sin \theta_1) r_2(\cos \theta_2 + i \sin \theta_2)}{r_1^2(\cos \theta_1 - i \sin \theta_1)(\cos \theta_1 + i \sin \theta_1)} \quad (8)$$

$$= \frac{r_2}{r_1} [\cos (\theta_2 - \theta_1) + i \sin (\theta_2 - \theta_1)].$$

Thus *the modulus of* z_2/z_1 *is the quotient of the moduli of* z_2 *and* z_1, *and the amplitude of* z_2/z_1 *is the difference between the amplitudes of* z_2 *and* z_1. A quotient may be constructed geometrically in much the same way as a product. Thus, in Fig. 151, $\overrightarrow{OA}$ represents the quotient of the complex number $\overrightarrow{OF}$ divided by the complex number $\overrightarrow{OB}$.

If in (8) we set $z_2 = 1$, $z_1 = z$, then (8) assumes the special form

$$\frac{1}{z} = \frac{1}{r}[\cos (0 - \theta) + i \sin (0 - \theta)]$$

$$= \frac{1}{r} (\cos \theta - i \sin \theta) = \frac{z^*}{r^2}. \quad (9)$$

Thus the modulus of $1/z$ is the reciprocal of the modulus of z, and the amplitude of $1/z$ is the negative of the amplitude of z.

If n is a positive integer and if $w = r(\cos \psi + i \sin \psi)$, then by (7) we have *De Moivre's theorem:*

$$w^n = [r(\cos \psi + i \sin \psi)]^n = r^n(\cos n\psi + i \sin n\psi). \quad (10)$$

We define an nth root of a number $z = R(\cos \theta + i \sin \theta)$ to be a number $w = r(\cos \psi + i \sin \psi)$ such that

$$w^n = z, \tag{11}$$

and we write $w = z^{1/n}$. By (6) we may write

$$z = R[\cos (\theta + 2k\pi) + i \sin (\theta + 2k\pi)], \tag{12}$$

where k is zero or any other integer, and where we may suppose θ to be the smallest nonnegative amplitude of z. By (10) and (11),

$$r^n(\cos n\psi + i \sin n\psi) = R[\cos (\theta + 2k\pi) + i \sin (\theta + 2k\pi)].$$

Hence

$$r = R^{1/n}, \qquad \psi = \frac{\theta + 2k\pi}{n}, \tag{13}$$

where $R^{1/n}$ denotes the positive real nth root of R. It follows that

$$w = z^{1/n} = \sqrt[n]{z} = R^{1/n}\left(\cos \frac{\theta + 2k\pi}{n} + i \sin \frac{\theta + 2k\pi}{n}\right). \tag{14}$$

By assigning to k the values $0, 1, 2, \cdots , n - 1$, we obtain n distinct complex numbers, each of which is an nth root of z.
If we assign to k any other positive or negative integral value, the resulting amplitude will differ by an integral multiple of 2π from an amplitude of one of the above roots, and we obtain merely another representation of this root. Thus there are exactly n distinct nth roots of any nonzero complex number. In fact, the points representing the nth roots of z all lie on a circle of radius $\sqrt{r}$ and form a regular polygon of n sides, one vertex having the amplitude θ/n. (See Fig. 152.)

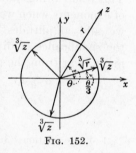

Fig. 152.

If p/q is any positive rational number, then by (10) and (14),

$$z^{p/q} = (z^{1/q})^p = r^{p/q}\left[\cos \frac{p}{q}(\theta + 2k\pi) + i \sin \frac{p}{q}(\theta + 2k\pi)\right].$$
$$(k = 0, 1, \cdots , q - 1) \tag{15}$$

This result also holds when p/q is a negative rational number, as may be seen by letting $p/q = -m$ and noting that

$$z^{-m} = \frac{1}{z^m} = \frac{1}{r^m[\cos m(\theta + 2k\pi) + i \sin m(\theta + 2k\pi)]}$$
$$= r^{-m}\{\cos [-m(\theta + 2k\pi)] + i \sin [-m(\theta + 2k\pi)]\}. \quad (16)$$

Example 1. Find the 5th roots of 32.

Since $32 = 32[\cos (0 + 2k\pi) + i \sin (0 + 2k\pi)]$, it follows that

$$32^{1/5} = \sqrt[5]{32}\left(\cos \frac{0 + 2k\pi}{5} + i \sin \frac{0 + 2k\pi}{5}\right).$$

By assigning k the values 0, 1, 2, 3, and 4 we find that the fifth roots of 32 are

$$2, \quad 2\left(\cos \frac{2\pi}{5} + i \sin \frac{2\pi}{5}\right), \quad 2\left(\cos \frac{4\pi}{5} + i \sin \frac{4\pi}{5}\right),$$

$$2\left(\cos \frac{6\pi}{5} + i \sin \frac{6\pi}{5}\right), \quad 2\left(\cos \frac{8\pi}{5} + i \sin \frac{8\pi}{5}\right).$$

In Sec. 8 we shall define the symbol $re^{i\theta}$ by the formula

$$z = re^{i\theta} = r(\cos \theta + i \sin \theta), \quad (17)$$

and we shall show that $re^{i\theta}$ is subject to the well-known laws of exponents. In particular,

$$(r_1 e^{i\theta_1})(r_2 e^{i\theta_2}) = r_1 r_2 e^{i(\theta_1 + \theta_2)}.$$

This result brings out the fact that we are merely restating a law of exponents when we say that "in multiplying complex numbers we add amplitudes" [cf. comment following (7)]. Likewise, the significance of division and the taking of powers or roots is made clear from the relations

$$\frac{r_1 e^{i\theta_1}}{r_2 e^{i\theta_2}} = \frac{r_1}{r_2}e^{i(\theta_1 - \theta_2)}, \quad (re^{i\theta})^n = r^n e^{in\theta}.$$

EXERCISES I

1. Prove relations (3) to (7) and (13) of Sec. 2. State these relations in words.

2. Show that $\Re(z) = (z + z^*)/2$ and that $\vartheta(z) = (z - z^*)/2i$.

3. Show that $|z_1 - z_2|$ is equal to the distance between the points representing z_1 and z_2.

4. Prove relations (4) of Sec. 3. [Hint: Use (2).] Show that

$$|z_1 z_2 \cdots z_n| = |z_1| \cdot |z_2| \cdots \cdots |z_n|$$

and that

$$|z^n| = |z|^n. \quad \quad (n \text{ a positive integer})$$

5. Prove relation (3) of Sec. 3.

6. Show that $\Re\left(\frac{z_1}{z_1 + z_2}\right) + \Re\left(\frac{z_2}{z_1 + z_2}\right) = 1.$

7. (a) If $z_1 = 2 + 3i$ and $z_2 = 5 - 7i$, find $z_1 + z_2$, $z_1 - z_2$, z_1z_2, and z_1/z_2. Verify your results by graphical constructions.

(b) Repeat part (a) with $z_1 = -1 + 2i$ and $z_2 = -2 - i$.

8. Find the modulus and amplitude of:

$1 + i\sqrt{3}$, -7, $-9i$, $24 - 23i$.   Represent these results graphically.

9. Find by numerical and graphical methods: $(3 - 4i)^2$, $(-1 + i\sqrt{2})^2$, $(1 - i)^3$, $(1 + i)^4$.

10. Find by numerical and graphical methods the n nth roots in each of the following cases: $\sqrt{1}$, $\sqrt[3]{1}$, $\sqrt[4]{1}$, $\sqrt[5]{-1}$, $\sqrt[7]{128}$, $\sqrt[3]{-8}$, $\sqrt[3]{2 + 3i}$, $\sqrt[5]{4 - 7i}$.

11. Plot the numbers $z_1 = 2e^{\pi i/4}$, $z_2 = 3e^{2\pi i/3}$, z_1z_2, z_1^2, z_1^3/z_2^2, $\sqrt{z_1}$, $z_1 + z_2$, $z_1 - z_2$.

12. If w_1, w_2, and 1 are the three cube roots of 1, show that $w_1 = w^2$, $w_1^2 = w_2$, $1 + w_1 + w_2 = 0$.

13. Let z be represented by the vector OP. Show that the operation of multiplying z by i may be interpreted as rotating $\overrightarrow{OP}$ counterclockwise through the angle $\pi/2$ without changing the length of $\overrightarrow{OP}$. Interpret the operation of multiplying z by: -1; a positive real number a; a negative real number a; $-i$; bi (b real, positive or negative); $2 + i$; $a + bi$; $re^{i\theta}$.

14. An airplane is flying in a horizontal plane and is headed due north. Its airspeed is 175 miles an hour and it is being carried to the east of north by a wind blowing in the direction of northeast at 50 miles an hour. Find an expression of the form $z = x + iy$ for the resultant velocity of the airplane. Express the resultant speed and direction in terms of z, and find these quantities numerically.

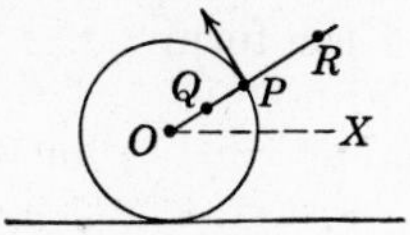

Fig. 153.

15. Let P denote a point on the circumference of a wheel 3 ft. in radius. The wheel rotates about its center at the rate of 120 r.p.m. Find an expression of the form $z = a + bi$ for the position of the point P at any time if at $t = 0$ seconds, P lies on the x-axis. Also, find a similar expression for the velocity of P at any time.

16. If in problem 15, Q and R are points on the line OP 30 and 40 in., respectively, from O, find expressions for the position and velocity of Q and R at any time.

17. Suppose that the wheel in problem 15 is a car wheel and that it rolls along a tangent straight track at a uniform rate of 75 m.p.h. Find expressions for the position and velocity of Q, P, and R.

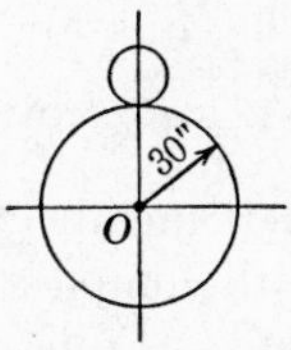

18. On the inner side of the wheel in Exs. 15 and 17 is mounted a circular gear with its center at the center of the wheel and an effective radius of 30 in. A smaller gear of effective radius 8 in. is mounted with center on a vertical line through O and is enmeshed with the larger gear. Find an expression for the position and velocity of a point S on the circumference of the smaller gear under the assumption of problem 15; also under the assumption of problem 17.

Fig. 154.

PART B.   FUNCTIONS OF A COMPLEX VARIABLE

4. Functions.   The definitions of a complex variable and of a function of a complex variable are quite similar to the definitions given in Chap. I, Sec. 2 for a real variable and for a function of a real variable.

A *complex variable* is a symbol having complex numbers for values.

If a complex variable w has one or more complex values for each value of the complex variable z in some subset D of the set of all complex numbers, then this variable w is called *a complex function of z defined over D*.   If to each value of z in D, there corresponds exactly one value of the variable w, then w is called *a single-valued complex function of z defined over D*.

A *polynomial (rational integral* function)* in the complex variable z is a function of z of the form

$$a_n z^n + a_{n-1} z^{n-1} + \cdots + a_0, \tag{1}$$

where $a_n, a_{n-1}, \cdots, a_0$ are complex constants and n is a positive integer or zero; if $a_n \neq 0$, the polynomial is said to be of degree n.

By a *rational (fractional) function of z* is meant the quotient of two polynomials in z having no common factor, i.e., a function w of the form

$$w = \frac{a_n z^n + a_{n-1} z^{n-1} + \cdots + a_0}{b_m z^m + b_{m-1} z^{m-1} + \cdots + b_0}, \tag{2}$$

where m and n may be any two nonnegative integers.

While a polynomial is defined for all values of z, the region of definition of the rational function (2) cannot include points where the denominator vanishes.

All algebraic complex functions which are not rational are called *irrational functions*.

Let $g_0(z), g_1(z), \cdots, g_n(z)$ be polynomials in z.   The equation

$$g_0(z)w^n + g_1(z)w^{n-1} + g_2(z)w^{n-2} + \cdots + g_n(z) = 0 \tag{3}$$

is said to be *reducible* if it is possible to express the left member of (3) as the product of two polynomials P and Q with complex coefficients, where neither P nor Q is merely a constant.   Equa-

---

* An integral function is sometimes called *entire*, since such a function is defined everywhere over the entire z-plane.

tion (3) is said to be *irreducible* if it is not reducible.   We say that w is a *complex algebraic function* of z when w and z are related by an irreducible equation of the form (3).

Evidently, all rational functions w are algebraic functions. All nonalgebraic functions are called *transcendental*.   For example, it is known that the logarithmic and trigonometric functions are transcendental.

If w is a complex function of $z = x + iy$, say $w = \phi(z)$, then w can be expressed in the form $w = u(x, y) + iv(x, y)$, where u and v are real functions of x and y.   That this is true is evident, for if $w = u + iv$, where w is a function of $z = x + iy$, then w, and hence u and v, must be determined for each pair of values of x and y in the domain of definition of w.   For example, if $w = 1/(z - 1)$ and $z = x + iy$, then

$$w = \frac{1}{(x + iy) - 1} = \frac{1}{(x - 1) + iy}$$
$$= \frac{(x - 1)}{(x - 1)^2 + y^2} + i\left[\frac{-y}{(x - 1)^2 + y^2}\right].$$

Conversely, every expression of the form $w = u(x, y) + iv(x, y)$ represents a function of $z = x + iy$, for the determination of z implies the determination of x and y, the determination of the functions u and v, and hence the determination of w.   Thus $(x^2 - y^2) + i(2xy) = (x + iy)^2$ and $x - iy$ are functions of $z = x + iy$.   (We shall show in a later section that $x - iy$ is not a rational function of $z = x + iy$.)

Suppose $w = f(z) = u + iv$, where $z = x + iy$.   If one attempts to graph w as a function of z, a figure in four dimensions is suggested by the presence of the four variables x, y, u, v. However, it is customary to represent the values of $z = x + iy$ by points in a z-plane with coordinates x and y, and to represent corresponding values of $w = f(z) = u + iv$ by points in a w-plane with coordinates u and v.   Thus, in Fig. 155, the point $(1, 2)$ in the z-plane and the point $(-3, 4)$ in the w-plane represent a pair of corresponding values of $z = x + iy$ and $w = z^2$.   Again, if z varies so as to trace out some path in the z-plane, then w varies in a corresponding manner to trace out a path in the w-plane.   Since $|z - z_0|$ represents the distance from z to z_0 (see Ex. I, 3), the condition $|z - z_0| < \delta$ implies that z lies in a circle with center z and radius δ; the condition $|w - w_0| < \epsilon$ admits of a similar interpretation in the w-plane.

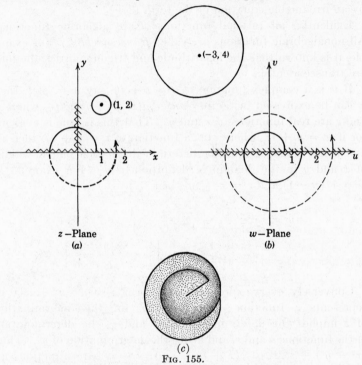

z –Plane
(a)

w –Plane
(b)

(c)
FIG. 155.

5. Limits and Continuity. The concepts of limit and continuity carry over directly from real variables to complex variables.

DEFINITION 5.1. *If $f(z)$ is a complex single-valued function of the complex variable z, if w_0 and z_0 are complex numbers, and if for each preassigned positive number ϵ there exists a positive number δ such that $|f(z) - w_0| < \epsilon$ for all values of z for which $0 < |z - z_0| < \delta$, then w_0 is denoted by* $\lim\limits_{z \to z_0} f(z)$, *and w_0 is referred to as the limit of $f(z)$ as $z \to z_0$.*

We leave it to the student in Ex. II, 2, to interpret this definition geometrically with the aid of Fig. 155. As in the case of real variables, this definition implies that $f(z)$ is defined over some circle about z_0 as center (except for z_0 itself). This definition may be extended in the manner indicated in Ex. IV, 27, of

Chap. I, and we shall make free use of this extension wherever occasion arises.

As an immediate consequence of Definition 5.1 we have

THEOREM 5.1.   *A necessary and sufficient condition that* $w = f(z) = u(x, y) + iv(x, y)$ *have the limit* $w_0 = u_0 + iv_0$ *as* $z = x + iy$ *approaches the limit* $z_0 = x_0 + iy_0$ *is that*

$$\lim_{x \to x_0, y \to y_0} u = u_0 \quad and \quad \lim_{x \to x_0, y \to y_0} v = v_0.$$

DEFINITION 5.2.   *If* $f(z)$ *is a complex single-valued function of* z, *and if* (1) $f(z_0)$ *exists,* (2) $\lim_{z \to z_0} f(z)$ *exists, and* (3) $\lim_{z \to z_0} f(z) = f(z_0)$, *then* f *is said to be continuous at* $z = z_0$.   *If* $f(z)$ *is continuous at each point* z *of some subset* D *of the set of all complex numbers, then* $f(z)$ *is said to be continuous over* D.   *If* $f(z)$ *is not continuous at* $z = z_0$, *then* $f(z)$ *is said to be discontinuous at* $z = z_0$, *and* z_0 *is called a point of discontinuity of* $f(z)$.

As an immediate consequence of this definition we have

THEOREM 5.2.   *A function* $f(z)$ *is continuous at* $z = z_0$ *when and only when* (1) $f(z_0)$ *exists, and* (2) *for each positive number* ϵ *there exists a positive number* δ *such that*

$$|f(z) - f(z_0)| < \epsilon \quad when \quad |z - z_0| < \delta.$$

This theorem is sometimes taken as the definition of continuity of $f(z)$ at $z = z_0$.

As an analogue of Theorem 5.1 we have

THEOREM 5.3.   *If* $z = x + iy$, *a necessary and sufficient condition that* $f(z) = u(x, y) + iv(x, y)$ *be continuous at* $z = z_0 = x_0 + iy_0$ *is that* $u(x, y)$ *and* $v(x, y)$ *be continuous at the point* (x_0, y_0).

A neighborhood of a point z_0 may be defined as in Sec. 15 of Chap. I.   We leave to the reader the proof of

THEOREM 5.4.   *If* $f(z)$ *is continuous at some point* z_0 *and if* $f(z_0) \neq 0$, *then there exists a neighborhood* N *of* z_0 *over which* $f(z) \neq 0$.

Suppose $f(z)$ is continuous at each point of some region D. Let z_0 be a point of D.   Then, ϵ being any arbitrarily selected positive number, there exists a positive number δ, depending in general upon ϵ and z_0, such that

$$|f(z) - f(z_0)| < \epsilon \quad when \quad |z - z_0| < \delta. \tag{1}$$

For a fixed ϵ, the value of δ may decrease if some other point z_1 of D is used instead of z_0, and δ may further decrease at another point z_2. In fact, it may be necessary to so restrict the value of δ that, as z_0 ranges over D, δ becomes arbitrarily small. However, if it is the case that, for any value of ϵ, there always exists a fixed δ independent of z_0 in D, and for which (1) holds, then we say that $f(z)$ is *uniformly continuous* over D.

Let R be a set of points in the z-plane. If there exists a positive number d such that $|z| < d$ for every point of R, then R is said to be *bounded*. A *simple closed curve* C in the z-plane is a continuous curve which divides the z-plane into exactly two parts, one of which is bounded; the bounded part, together with the bounding curve C, is called a *closed region*. (This concept may be described in many other ways, but we shall not go into the matter here.)

The following theorem is an extension of Theorem 8.7 of Chap. IX, and may be proved in the same manner as this latter theorem.

Theorem 5.5. *If a function $f(z)$ of a complex variable z is continuous over a bounded closed region D, then it is uniformly continuous over D.*

The following two theorems follow directly from Theorem 8.3 of Chap. IX.

Theorem 5.6. *If $f(z)$ is continuous throughout a bounded closed region D, then there exists a positive number M such that for all values of z in D, $|f(z)| < M$.*

Theorem 5.7. *If $f(z)$ is continuous throughout a bounded closed region D, then $|f(z)|$ has a finite least upper bound U in D, and $|f(z)|$ actually attains the value U at some point z_0 of D.*

EXERCISES II

1. Prove Theorems 5.1, 5.2, and 5.3.
2. Translate Definition 5.1 into geometric language.
3. Find the limit of $f(z) \equiv (x^3 - 3xy^2) + i(3x^2y - y^3)$ as z approaches $5 - 3i$.

4. Prove that $f(z) \equiv \log (x^2 + y^2) + i$ arc tan $\dfrac{2xy}{x^2 - y^2}$ is continuous for all finite values of $z = x + iy$ except $z = 0$.

5. Let $S_n \equiv \left(x - \dfrac{1}{n} \right)^2 + y^2 - \dfrac{1}{n^2} = 0$, $n = 1, 2, 3, \cdots$, be a sequence of circles. Prove $\lim\limits_{n \to +\infty} S_n$ exists and is the origin.

6. Prove that every polynomial in z is uniformly continuous in any given bounded region.

7. Let $f(z) = (z^2 + 1)/(z^2 - 1)$. Prove that in the region bounded by $x^2 + y^2 = \frac{1}{4}$, $|f(z)|$ has a finite least upper bound. Does $|f(z)|$ have a finite upper bound within the region bounded by $x^2 + y^2 = 1$? Discuss.

8. Give a geometric interpretation to the notion of uniform continuity.

6. Analytic Functions.   We shall define the derivative of a function $f(z)$ of a complex variable z in much the same manner as we did for a function of a real variable.

DEFINITION 6.1.   *Let $f(z)$ denote a complex, single-valued function of z.   The derivative of $f(z)$ with respect to z is defined to be that function $f'(z)$ of z such that*

$$f'(z_0) = \lim_{\Delta z \to 0} \frac{f(z_0 + \Delta z) - f(z_0)}{\Delta z} \tag{1}$$

at all points z_0 where the limit exists, and such that $f'(z)$ is defined for no other values of z.

The laws for differentiating functions of real variables can easily be extended without modification to functions of a complex variable.   That this may be expected follows from the fact that these laws depend, when the functions are suitably defined, upon the general theory of limits which, as we have seen above, hold equally well in the real and the complex number fields.   For example,

$$D_z(w_1 + w_2) = D_z w_1 + D_z w_2, \qquad D_z w^n = n w^{n-1} D_z w, \text{ etc.}$$

(See Sec. 5 of Chap. I, relations 1 to 22.)

The definition of the differentials $dz = dx + i\, dy$ and dw, where $w = f(z)$, are made in much the same manner as in the theory of real variables.   The higher derivatives and differentials follow as in the theory of real variables.

DEFINITION 6.2.   *A single-valued complex function $f(z)$ of the complex variable z is said to be analytic throughout a region D if $f(z)$ has a derivative at every point of D.*

Different writers have used, with various modifications, the terms *monogenic*, *holomorphic*, and *regular* in the sense that we have used the term *analytic*.

While there is a close analogy between the rules for differentiation in the real and complex fields, there is an important distinction between the two cases in respect to the type of limit involved.

Since $z = x + iy$, the increment Δz in z is $\Delta z = \Delta x + i\,\Delta y$. In order that $\Delta z \to 0$ both Δx and Δy must approach zero. We are thus faced with a double limit in the case of a complex variable. In order that the derivative of a function $f(z)$ exist at a point z_0, the difference quotient $[f(z_0 + \Delta z) - f(z_0)]/\Delta z$ must have the same limit no matter how Δx and Δy approach zero. There are many simple functions which do not have a derivative at any point. For instance, $f(z) \equiv x - iy$ is such a function, since the limit of the quotient

$$\frac{f(z + \Delta z) - f(z)}{\Delta z} = \frac{[(x + \Delta x) - i(y + \Delta y)] - [x - iy]}{\Delta x + i\,\Delta y}$$

$$= \frac{\Delta x - i\,\Delta y}{\Delta x + i\,\Delta y}$$

is dependent on the manner in which Δx and Δy approach zero. (For if we make $\Delta y \to 0$ and then $\Delta x \to 0$, then the limit of the difference quotient is $+1$, but if $\Delta x \to 0$ first and then $\Delta y \to 0$, the limit is -1.) We are thus led to the conclusion that the condition that a complex function $f(z)$ be analytic is far more restrictive than is apparent. However, it is due principally to this particular restriction that so many fruitful results appear. Analytic functions have many properties not possessed by complex functions in general. In the sections to follow many of these properties will be developed.

We shall now develop necessary conditions in order that $f(z) = u(x, y) + iv(x, y)$ be analytic, where $z = x + iy$. Suppose we first let $\Delta y = 0$ and then let $\Delta x \to 0$. We find that

$$\frac{df}{dz} = \lim_{\Delta z = \Delta x \to 0} \left(\frac{\Delta f}{\Delta z}\right)_y = \frac{\partial f}{\partial x} = \frac{\partial u}{\partial x} + i\,\frac{\partial v}{\partial x}. \tag{2}$$

Next, suppose we first let $\Delta x = 0$ and then $\Delta y \to 0$. We obtain

$$\frac{df}{dz} = \lim_{\Delta z = i\Delta y \to 0} \left(\frac{\Delta f}{\Delta z}\right)_x = \frac{1}{i}\frac{\partial f}{\partial y} = \frac{1}{i}\left[\frac{\partial u}{\partial y} + i\frac{\partial v}{\partial y}\right] = \frac{\partial v}{\partial y} - i\frac{\partial u}{\partial y}. \tag{3}$$

This leads us to the conclusion that if $f(z)$ is analytic, then

$$\frac{\partial f}{\partial x} = \frac{1}{i}\frac{\partial f}{\partial y}, \quad \text{or,} \quad \frac{\partial u}{\partial x} + i\frac{\partial v}{\partial x} = \frac{\partial v}{\partial y} - i\frac{\partial u}{\partial y} \tag{4}$$

From this, we have

$$\frac{\partial u}{\partial x} = \frac{\partial v}{\partial y}, \qquad \frac{\partial u}{\partial y} = -\frac{\partial v}{\partial x}. \tag{5}$$

This proves

THEOREM 6.1. *A necessary condition that $f(z) = u + iv$ be analytic at $z_0 = x_0 + iy_0$, is that Eqs. (5) be satisfied at z_0.*

Equations (5) are known as the *Cauchy-Riemann differential equations* or *conditions*.

We shall now inquire as to sufficient conditions that $f(z)$ be analytic. Since Eqs. (5) arose merely from the fact that the limit of $\Delta f/\Delta z$ is the same for two particular ways in which Δz was made to approach zero, it does not necessarily follow that Eqs. (5) give sufficient conditions that $f(z)$ be analytic. We now prove

THEOREM 6.2. *If the four first partial derivatives of u and v exist throughout a region D, and are continuous at all points of D, then the validity of the Cauchy-Riemann conditions is both a necessary and sufficient condition for $f(z) = u + iv$ to be analytic throughout D.*

From the assumptions on the existence of the first partial derivatives and their continuity, we find with the aid of the theorem of the mean,

$$\begin{aligned}
\Delta u &= u(x_0 + \Delta x, y_0 + \Delta y) - u(x_0, y_0) \\
&= u_x(x_0 + \theta_1 \cdot \Delta x, y_0 + \Delta y) \Delta x + u_y(x_0, y_0 + \theta_2 \cdot \Delta y) \Delta y, \\
&\qquad\qquad\qquad\qquad (0 < \theta_1 < 1, \, 0 < \theta_2 < 1) \\
&= [u_x(x_0, y_0) + \epsilon_1] \Delta x + [u_y(x_0, y_0) + \eta_1] \Delta y,
\end{aligned}$$

and

$$\Delta v = [v_x(x_0, y_0) + \epsilon_2] \Delta x + [v_y(x_0, y_0) + \eta_2] \Delta y.$$

Then making use of Eq. (5), we find

$$\Delta u + i \, \Delta v = (u_x + iv_x)(\Delta x + i \, \Delta y) + \rho,$$

where

$$\rho = [(\epsilon_1 + i\epsilon_2) \Delta x + (\eta_1 + i\eta_2) \Delta y].$$

Hence

$$\frac{f(z_0 + \Delta z) - f(z_0)}{\Delta z} = \frac{\Delta u + i \, \Delta v}{\Delta x + i \, \Delta y} = (u_x + iv_x) + \frac{\rho}{\Delta x + i \, \Delta y}.$$

Now $\left| \dfrac{\rho}{\Delta x + i\,\Delta y} \right| \leqq |\epsilon_1| + |\epsilon_2| + |\eta_1| + |\eta_2| \;\to\; 0 \;$ as $\; \Delta z \to 0.$
Hence $f(z)$ is analytic at z_0.

The necessity of the condition follows at once from the definition of analyticity.

Theorem 6.3. *If $f(z)$ is analytic throughout D, not only the first partial derivatives of u and v, but also those of higher orders all exist throughout D.*

We must postpone the proof of this theorem to Sec. 15.

Theorem 6.4. *A necessary condition that $u + iv$ be analytic in a region D is that in D, u and v satisfy Laplace's equation, i.e.,*

$$\frac{\partial^2 u}{\partial x^2} + \frac{\partial^2 u}{\partial y^2} = 0, \quad \text{and} \quad \frac{\partial^2 v}{\partial x^2} + \frac{\partial^2 v}{\partial y^2} = 0.$$

If $u + iv$ is analytic, $\partial u/\partial x = \partial v/\partial y$ and $\partial u/\partial y = -\partial v/\partial x$. By Theorem 6.3, we are assured of the existence of the higher partial derivatives of u and v. Differentiating, we see

$$\frac{\partial}{\partial x}\!\left(\frac{\partial u}{\partial x}\right) = \frac{\partial}{\partial x}\!\left(\frac{\partial v}{\partial y}\right), \qquad \frac{\partial}{\partial y}\!\left(\frac{\partial u}{\partial y}\right) = \frac{\partial}{\partial y}\!\left(-\frac{\partial v}{\partial x}\right),$$

so that

$$\frac{\partial^2 u}{\partial x^2} + \frac{\partial^2 u}{\partial y^2} = \frac{\partial^2 v}{\partial x\,\partial y} - \frac{\partial^2 v}{\partial y\,\partial x} = 0.$$

A similar proof holds with regard to v.

This theorem shows that, if we wish to construct an analytic function $u + iv$, we must select for u and v solutions of Laplace's equation.

If u is chosen so as to satisfy Laplace's equation, then we may obtain v so that $u + iv$ is analytic from the real line integral

$$v_1 = \int_{x_0,y_0}^{x,y}\!\left(-\frac{\partial u}{\partial y}\,dx + \frac{\partial u}{\partial x}\,dy\right)\!.$$

Since the value of this integral is independent of the path connecting (x_0, y_0) and (x, y), it follows from Theorem 18.13 of Chap. II that $\partial v_1/\partial x = -\partial u/\partial y$ and $\partial v_1/\partial y = \partial u/\partial x$. Thus $u + iv_1$ satisfies the conditions for analyticity and v_1 is a possible value for v. We shall leave it as an exercise to show that for a given u, if $u + iv$ is to be analytic, every possible v must have the form $v_1 + c$, where c is a constant.

If u is a solution of Laplace's equation, having second partial derivatives, then u is called a *harmonic function*, and v_1 is called its *harmonic conjugate*. This terminology appears in physical as well as mathematical literature. The Laplace differential equation is of great importance in theoretical physics and engineering.

EXERCISES III

1. Verify the rules for differentiation, given in Sec. 5 of Chap. I, directly from Definition 6.1.

2. Define the differential of w, where $w = f(z)$.

3. If $z = x + yi$, where $x = \phi(t)$, $y = \psi(t)$, and where t is a real variable, show that $dz = [\phi'(t) + i\psi'(t)] \, dt$.

4. Prove that $w = x^2 - y^2 + i(2xy)$ is analytic everywhere in any finite region of the z-plane; also for $w = z^3$; for

$$w = (x^4 - 6x^2y^2 + y^4) + i(4x^3y - 4xy^3).$$

5. Prove that if $f_1(z)$ and $f_2(z)$ are analytic in D, then so is $f_1(z) + f_2(z)$; $f_1(z) \cdot f_2(z); f_1(z)/f_2(z)$, except at those points for which $f_2(z) = 0$.

6. Prove that if $f(w)$ is analytic in some neighborhood N_1 of w_0, and if $w = \phi(z)$ is analytic in some neighborhood N_2 of z_0, then $f[\phi(z)]$ is an analytic function of z in some neighborhood of z_0.

7. Prove that any rational function of z is analytic except at those points where the denominator vanishes.

8. If $f(z) = \Re(z) = x$, show that f is not analytic.

9. If $f(z) = |z|^2 = x^2 + y^2$, show that the Cauchy-Riemann equations are satisfied only at $z = 0$. Is f analytic?

10. Is $3x - 3iy$ an analytic function of $z = x + iy$?

11. Given $u = x^2 - y^2$. Find a function v so that $u + iv$ is analytic.

$Ans.$ $v = \int_{x_0,y_0}^{x,y} -\frac{\partial u}{\partial y}\, dx + \frac{\partial u}{\partial x}\, dy = \int_{x_0,y_0}^{x,y} 2y\, dx + 2x\, dy = 2xy - 2x_0y_0.$

12. Find v so that $u + iv$ is analytic if:

(a) $u = \log_e \sqrt{x^2 + y^2}.$ $Ans.$ $v = \arctan y/x + c.$

(b) $u = x/(x^2 + y^2).$ $Ans.$ $w = 1/z.$

13. Find where the following functions of z are continuous:

(a) z^*,   (b) $\dfrac{z + z^*}{1 + |z|}$;   (c) $\dfrac{z^2 + z^{*2}}{|z|^2}.$

14. Examine each of the functions given in Ex. 13 for differentiability.

15. Given $f(z) = \sqrt{|xy|}$. Show that the Cauchy-Riemann equations are satisfied at $z = 0$, but that $f(z)$ has no derivative at $z = 0$.

16. Given $f(z) = \dfrac{2xy^2(x + iy)}{x^2 + y^4}$ when $z \neq 0$, $f(0) = 0$. Show that as

$z \to 0$ along any straight line, $\left[\dfrac{f(z) - f(0)}{z} \right] \to 0$; that as $z \to 0$ along

$x = y^2$, that $\left[\dfrac{f(z) - f(0)}{z} \right] \to 1$. Is $f(z)$ analytic at $z = 0$?

17. Given $f(z) = 3e^{-1/z^4}$ when $z \neq 0$, $f(0) = 0$. Show that f is analytic for all finite values of z except $z = 0$. [Hint: examine the behavior of $f(z)$ as $r \to +0$ with $z = re^{i\pi/4}$.]

18. Prove the assertion left as an exercise near the end of Sec. 6.

19. Show that the curves $u = $ const. and $v = $ const. are orthogonal when u and v are conjugate. Illustrate with the aid of Ex. 11.

20. Prove: (a) The transformation

$$w = \frac{\alpha z + \beta^*}{\beta z + \alpha^*},$$

where α and β are any two complex numbers satisfying the relation $\alpha\alpha^* - \beta\beta^* = 1$, transforms the circumference of the unit circle into itself and the interior of the circle into itself.

(b) If $\beta\beta^* - \alpha\alpha^* = 1$, the transformation maps the interior of the circle into the exterior.

21. Prove: The transformation $w = \dfrac{1}{2}\left(z + \dfrac{1}{z}\right)$ maps the circles with centers at the origin and the straight lines through the origin of the z-plane into confocal ellipses and hyperbolas, respectively, in the w-plane.

22. If z_1, z_2, z_3, z_4 be any four distinct points, then $\dfrac{z_1 - z_3}{z_2 - z_3} \div \dfrac{z_1 - z_4}{z_2 - z_4}$ is known as their *cross ratio*. Prove that the cross ratio is absolutely invariant (unaltered) by every transformation of the form

$$w = \frac{(\alpha z + \beta)}{(\gamma z + \delta)}, \qquad (\alpha\delta - \beta\gamma) \neq 0.$$

23. The general linear transformation is

$$w = \frac{az + b}{cz + d},$$

when a, b, c, d are constants and $ad - bc \neq 0$.

(a) Prove that all circles and straight lines in the z-plane are transformed by this relation into straight lines and circles in the w-plane.

(b) The points for which $z = w$ are called *fixed* or *invariant points*. Prove that there are two invariant points associated with the transformation given above. Are they always distinct?

(c) Prove that the family of circles through the two fixed points and the family of circles orthogonal to them transform into themselves.

24. Solve the equation

$$z^2 + 4z + 7 = 0.$$

25. The impedance Z of a certain electric-circuit element containing resistance R and reactance X is frequently expressed in the form

$$Z = R + Xi,$$

when the impressed e.m.f. is sinusoidal and of a definite frequency. R is always positive. If two such elements of impedance z_1 and z_2, respectively, are connected in series the impedance Z equivalent to the two impedances in series is $Z = z_1 + z_2$; but if the elements are connected in parallel, the impedance Z equivalent to the two impedances in parallel is given by the relation

$$\frac{1}{Z} = \frac{1}{z_1} + \frac{1}{z_2}.$$

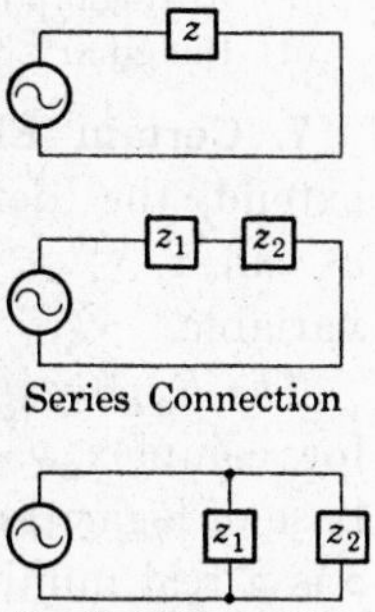

Let three circuit elements subject to a 60-cycle e.m.f. have impedances $z_1 = 11 + 820i$, $z_2 = 25 + 30i$, $z_3 = 7 - 3500i$, respectively:

Series Connection

(a) Find impedance equivalent to z_1 and z_2 in series.

(b) Find impedance equivalent to z_1 and z_2 in parallel.

(c) Find impedance equivalent to z_1, z_2, and z_3 in series.

Parallel Connection
Fig. 156.

(d) Find impedance equivalent to z_1, z_2, and z_3 in parallel.

(e) Find impedance equivalent to z_1 in series with z_2 and z_3 in parallel.

NOTE: In electrical engineering many writers use j in place of i, in order to reserve the use of i for current.

26. In the computation in connection with transmission line problems it is frequently necessary to find the values of $\sqrt{ZY}$ and $\sqrt{Z/Y}$, where Z is the series impedance of the line and Y the admittance of the line to ground. Suppose that for a 25 cycle line, $Z = 0.275 + 0.56i$ and

$$Y = (1.78)10^{-8} + (4.57)10^{-6}i.$$

Find $\sqrt{ZY}$ and $\sqrt{Z/Y}$.

27. In both electrical and mechanical work the complex number $Ae^{i(\omega t + \theta)}$ is of great utility.* If A, ω and θ are constants and t is time, this complex number is often called a *rotating vector*. Prove:

(a) That this vector is of constant length and rotates uniformly with frequency $f = \omega/2\pi$.

(b) The product of any two rotating vectors is a rotating vector with frequency equal to the sum of the frequencies of the two vectors.

(c) State and prove a theorem similar to (b) for the quotient of two rotating vectors.

(d) The sum or difference of two rotating vectors of the same frequency is a rotating vector of that frequency.

(e) Is (d) true with the word *same* removed?

28. (a) Find the frequency of each of the rotating vectors:

$$z_1 = 20e^{i(157t + 30°)}, \qquad z_2 = 15e^{i(157t - 45°)}, \qquad z_3 = 3e^{i(157t)}.$$

(b) Express each of the following in the form of a rotating vector: (1) $z_1 + z_2$, (2) $z_1 - z_2$, (3) $z_1 z_2$, (4) z_1/z_2, (5) $z_2 z_3$, (6) z_2/z_3.

* Some writers use $A\underline{/\omega t + \theta}$ in place of $Ae^{i(\omega t + \theta)}$.

29. Find the rotating vectors having the following properties:

(a) Real component is 5 cos $(377t - 30°)$.

(b) Imaginary component is 12 sin $(63t + 45°)$.

(c) Real component is 7 sin $(157t - 37°)$.

(d) Imaginary component is 3 cos $(157t + 21°)$.

7. Certain Elementary Functions.

In this section we shall extend the definitions of certain elementary real functions e^x, sin x, $\cdots$ to the field of analytic functions of a complex variable.

The Exponential Function e^z. In extending the definition of e^z for complex values of z, where $e = 2.718 \cdots$ is the natural base of logarithms, we wish: (i) e^z to be the real function e^x when z is a real number x; furthermore, we wish to preserve as far as possible the familiar properties enjoyed by e^x, namely, that (ii) for every $z = x + iy$, $e^z = u + iv$ be single-valued and analytic; (iii) that $de^z/dz = e^z$.

The last requirement implies by (2) of Sec. 6 that

$$\frac{\partial(u + iv)}{\partial x} = u + iv,$$

or

$$\frac{\partial u}{\partial x} = u, \qquad \frac{\partial v}{\partial x} = v.$$

A solution of the first of these differential equations is evidently of the form $u = e^x \varphi(y)$. By (ii), $\partial u/\partial y = -\partial v/\partial x$, and $\partial v/\partial x = v$, so that

$$v = -\frac{\partial u}{\partial y} = -e^x \frac{d\varphi(y)}{dy}.$$

Substituting these values of u and v in the equation

$$\frac{\partial u}{\partial x} = \frac{\partial v}{\partial y}$$

and dividing by e^x, we have

$$\frac{d^2\varphi(y)}{dy^2} + \varphi(y) = 0.$$

From the theory of differential equations we know that $\varphi(y)$ must be of the form

$$\varphi(y) = c_1 \cos y + c_2 \sin y,$$

so that

$$u = e^x \varphi(y) = e^x(c_1 \cos y + c_2 \sin y),$$
$$v = -e^x \frac{d\varphi(y)}{dy} = e^x(c_1 \sin y - c_2 \cos y).$$

By property (i), if $z = x$, $e^z = u + iv$ must be equal to e^x, so that when $y = 0$,

$$\Big]_{y=0} = c_1 e^x, \qquad v\Big]_{y=0} = -c_2 e^x,$$
$$u + iv\Big]_{y=0} = u + i(0)\Big]_{y=0} = e^x,$$

so that $c_1 = 1$ and $c_2 = 0$. We have now shown that

$$u = e^x \cos y, \qquad v = e^x \sin y,$$

and

$$e^z = e^{x+iy} = e^x[\cos y + i \sin y]. \tag{1}$$

We shall take formula (1) as the definition of e^z.

From (1), we see that $e^{z_1+z_2} = e^{z_1} \cdot e^{z_2}$, where $z_1 = x_1 + iy_1$ and $z_2 = x_2 + iy_2$, for

$$e^{z_1} \cdot e^{z_2} = [e^{x_1}(\cos y_1 + i \sin y_1)][e^{x_2}(\cos y_2 + i \sin y_2)]$$
$$= e^{x_1+x_2}[\cos (y_1 + y_2) + i \sin (y_1 + y_2)] = e^{z_1+z_2}.$$

By setting $x = 0$ in (1), we have

$$e^{iy} = \cos y + i \sin y. \tag{2}$$

It is easy to show that the function e^z is periodic, with period $2\pi i$; i.e., that $e^{z+2\pi i} = e^z$. In fact, e^z is also of the period $2n\pi i$ where n is any integer, but e^z has no other periods. To show this, suppose $p = p_1 + ip_2$ is a period of e^z. Then $e^{z+p} = e^z$. Dividing by e^z, we have $e^p = 1$. Hence

$$e^{p_1+p_2 i} = e^{p_1}(\cos p_2 + i \sin p_2) = 1,$$

so that $p_2 = 2n\pi$, $p_1 = 0$, and $p = p_1 + p_2 i = 2n\pi i$.

Replacing y by $(-y)$ in (2), we find

$$e^{-iy} = \cos y - i \sin y. \tag{3}$$

From (2) and (3), we see that

$$\cos y = \frac{e^{iy} + e^{-iy}}{2}, \qquad \sin y = \frac{e^{iy} - e^{-iy}}{2i}. \tag{4}$$

The Trigonometric Functions. We shall use formulas (4), which hold for y real, to define the trigonometric functions $\cos z$ and $\sin z$:

$$\cos z = \frac{e^{iz} + e^{-iz}}{2}, \qquad \sin z = \frac{e^{iz} - e^{-iz}}{2i}. \qquad (5)$$

It is easy to show that

$$\left. \begin{array}{l} \cos z = \cosh y \cos x - i \sinh y \sin x, \\ \sin z = \cosh y \sin x + i \sinh y \cos x. \end{array} \right\} \qquad (6)$$

Since e^z is single-valued and continuous for all z, it follows from Definition 5.2 and definitions (5) that $\cos z$ and $\sin z$ are single-valued and continuous everywhere.

Let $\cos z = u + iv$. From (6),

$$u = \cosh y \cos x, \qquad v = -\sinh y \sin x.$$

Evidently, u and v have continuous first partial derivatives which satisfy the Cauchy-Riemann equations

$$\frac{\partial u}{\partial y} = \sinh y \cos x = -\frac{\partial v}{\partial x}; \qquad \frac{\partial u}{\partial x} = -\cosh y \sin x = \frac{\partial v}{\partial y},$$

so we see that $\cos z$ is analytic everywhere.

From (5) a large number of trigonometric identities may be derived. For example,

$$\begin{array}{c} \cos^2 z + \sin^2 z = 1, \\ \sin (z_1 + z_2) = \sin z_1 \cos z_2 + \cos z_1 \sin z_2. \end{array} \qquad (7)$$

It is easy to show that $\cos z$ and $\sin z$ have the period $2n\pi$, where n is any integer, but have no other periods.

We define the other trigonometric functions of z as follows:

$$\tan z = \frac{\sin z}{\cos z}, \quad \operatorname{ctn} z = \frac{\cos z}{\sin z}, \quad \sec z = \frac{1}{\cos z}, \quad \csc z = \frac{1}{\sin z}. \qquad (8)$$

The Logarithmic Function. We define the logarithm of $z = x + iy$ to be that function $w = \log z$ which satisfies the exponential equation $e^w = z$. Let $w = u + iv$, and let $z = \rho e^{i\theta}$, where ρ and θ may be found from $z = x + iy$. Then

$$e^w = e^{u+iv} = e^u \cdot e^{iv} = z = \rho e^{i\theta}. \qquad (9)$$

Hence $e^u = \rho$ $(\rho > 0)$ and $v = \theta$. Thus

$$w = \log z = \log \rho + i\theta. \qquad (10)$$

Let θ_1, $0 \leqq \theta_1 < 2\pi$, be the *principal amplitude* of z. Then z has the amplitudes $\theta = \theta_1 + 2n\pi$, where n is any integer. Since $e^w = \rho e^{i[\theta_1 + 2n\pi]} = \rho e^{i\theta_1} = z$, we have

$$w = \log z = \log \rho + i(\theta_1 + 2n\pi). \tag{11}$$

Thus, the logarithmic function is infinitely many-valued and is defined for all values of z except $z = 0$. We call $\log \rho + i\theta_1$ the *principal value* of $\log z$.

If in (11) we restrict n to a particular value, w is then a particular *branch* of the logarithmic function which is single-valued and continuous in the interior of every region not containing $z = 0$ nor the positive x-axis (since θ_1 ranges from 0 to 2π). We shall now show that such a branch is analytic. Now

$$\frac{dz}{dw} = \frac{de^w}{dw} = e^w = z,$$

so that

$$\frac{dw}{dz} = \frac{1}{dz/dw} = \frac{1}{z}.$$

Thus, $w = \log z$ has a derivative at every point for which a branch of this function has been defined.

The logarithms of the positive real numbers are special cases of those of the complex numbers, namely, those cases in which the amplitude $\theta_1 = 0$. The logarithms of the negative real numbers may now be given an interpretation. If z is a negative real number $-R$, then the corresponding amplitude $\theta_1 = \pi$, so that

$$\log (-R) = \log \rho + in\pi.$$

Thus, $\log (-1) = \log 1 + in\pi = in\pi$; $\log (-4) = \log 4 + in\pi$; $\cdots$ which are all representable as definite sets of points in the complex plane.

The function $\log z$ obeys the usual laws for real variables:

$$\log (z_1 z_2) = \log z_1 + \log z_2, \tag{12}$$
$$\log z^a = a \log z, \tag{13}$$

where a is any complex number. The proof of (12) is quite short:

$$\begin{aligned}
\log z_1 + \log z_2 &= (\log \rho_1 + in_1\theta_1) + (\log \rho_2 + in_2\theta_2) \\
&= (\log \rho_1 + \log \rho_2) + i(n_1\theta_1 + n_2\theta_2) \\
&= \log \rho_1\rho_2 + i(n_1\theta_1 + n_2\theta_2) = \log (z_1 z_2),
\end{aligned}$$

since for each choice of n_1 and n_2 there is a value of $\log (z_1 z_2)$.

We shall define z^a, where a is any complex number, as

$$z^a = e^{a \log z}. \tag{14}$$

Since $\log z$ is infinitely many-valued, so is z^a, unless a is a rational real number.

We shall define a^z, where a and z are complex numbers, as

$$a^z = e^z \log a,$$

which in general is infinitely many-valued. We shall agree in any particular case as to the particular value we mean.

We define $w = \sin^{-1} z$ to be a solution of

$$z = \sin w = \frac{e^{iw} - e^{-iw}}{2i}. \tag{15}$$

Solving (15) for e^{iw}, we have

$$e^{iw} = iz \pm \sqrt{1 - z^2}. \tag{16}$$

From this we find, upon taking logarithms, that

$$w = -i \log (iz \pm \sqrt{1 - z^2}) = \sin^{-1} z, \tag{17}$$
$$w = i \log (-iz \pm \sqrt{1 - z^2}) = \sin^{-1} z.$$

Similar definitions may be given for $\cos^{-1} z$, $\tan^{-1} z$, etc.

EXERCISES IV

1. Prove that $e^{x+iy} = e^x \cdot e^{iy}$.
2. Prove that $e^{z+2\pi i} = e^z$, $e^{z+2n\pi i} = e^z$, where n is any integer.
3. Show from definitions (1) and (5) that
(a) $\cos z = \cosh y \cos x - i \sinh y \sin x$.
(b) $\sin z = \cosh y \sin x + i \sinh y \cos x$.
[Recall that $\cosh y \equiv (e^y + e^{-y})/2$, $\sinh y \equiv (e^y - e^{-y})/2$].
4. Prove that $\sin z$ is analytic everywhere.
5. Prove that the functions defined by (5) coincide with the real trigonometric functions $\cos x$ and $\sin x$, when $z = x$.
6. Prove relations (7).
7. Prove $\cos [z + (\pi/2)] = -\sin z$.
8. Prove $\cos (z + 2n\pi) = \cos z$; $\sin (z + 2n\pi) = \sin z$.
9. Prove that $\cos z$ and $\sin z$ have no other periods than $2\pi n$, where n is any integer.
10. From the definitions of the hyperbolic functions $\cosh z = (e^z + e^{-z})/2$, $\sinh z = (e^z - e^{-z})/2$, $\tanh z = (\sinh z)/(\cosh z)$, etc.,
Prove: $\cosh z = \cos iz$, $\sinh z = i \sin iz$,

$$\cosh^2 z - \sinh^2 z = 1, \quad \operatorname{sech}^2 z + \tanh^2 z = 1, \quad \operatorname{ctnh}^2 z - \operatorname{csch}^2 z = 1.$$

11. Prove that the hyperbolic functions $\cosh z$ and $\sinh z$ defined in Ex. (10) are analytic. Are $\tanh z$, $\operatorname{ctnh} z$, $\operatorname{csch} z$, $\operatorname{sech} z$ everywhere analytic?

12. The hyperbolic functions are periodic. Find all their periods.

13. Show that $\cosh (z_1 + z_2) = \cosh z_1 \cosh z_2 + \sinh z_1 \sinh z_2$.

14. Given $w = \log z = \log \rho + i\theta_1$, where $\rho = \sqrt{x^2 + y^2}$, and

$$\theta_1 = \tan^{-1} \frac{y}{x}$$

is a particular amplitude of z. Show that w is analytic almost everywhere.

15. Show that (13) is true provided that for each value of z^a, $\log z^a$ is suitably chosen.

16. Define $\cos^{-1} z$, $\tan^{-1} z$.

17. (a) Prove that $z = x + ib$ is the equation of a line parallel to the x-axis.

(b) What is the corresponding equation of a line parallel to the y-axis?

(c) Prove that $z = x + i(mx + b)$ is the equation of a line of slope m.

(d) Prove that $z - z_0 = ae^{i\theta}$ is the equation of a circle with center at z_0 and radius a.

(e) Of what locus is $z = x + iax^2$ the equation?

18. A point $z = re^{i\theta}$ moves in the z-plane with r and θ functions of the time t.

(a) Prove that the velocity of the point at any instant is given by

$$\dot{z} = \dot{r}e^{i\theta} + ire^{i\theta} \cdot \dot{\theta},$$

where $\dot{z}$ indicates the derivative of z with respect to time t.

(b) Prove that the acceleration is given by

$$\ddot{z} = \ddot{r}e^{i\theta} + 2i\dot{r}e^{i\theta} \cdot \dot{\theta} + ire^{i\theta} \cdot \ddot{\theta} - re^{i\theta}(\dot{\theta})^2.$$

(c) Find the x and y components of velocity.

(d) Find the direction of velocity.

(e) Find the x and y components of acceleration.

(f) Find the direction of acceleration.

(g) Find the radial component of velocity.

(h) Find the radial component of acceleration.

(i) Find the component of velocity orthogonal to the radius vector.

(j) Find the component of acceleration orthogonal to the radius vector.

19. The position of a particle in a plane is given by

$$z = 3t^2 e^{i \sin 3t}.$$

Find by the method of Ex. 18 the velocity and acceleration of the particle at time $t = \pi/3$ sec.

20. Prove that if $z = F(w)$ is analytic everywhere in a neighborhood of w_0, its derivative at that point is given by $\dfrac{dz}{dw} = \dfrac{1}{dw/dz}$.

21. Show that $w = z^2$ defines two families of curves $\varphi \equiv x^2 - y^2 = \varphi_1$, and $\psi \equiv 2xy = \psi_1$, which are orthogonal. (Here φ_1 and ψ_1 are constants.) Plot these curves.

22. Given $z = c \cos w = c \cos (\varphi + i\psi)$, where c is a constant. Show that the curves $\psi = $ constant and $\varphi = $ constant are orthogonal conics with common foci at $(\pm c, 0)$.

HINT: $\cos (\varphi + i\psi) = \cos \varphi \cosh \psi - i \sin \varphi \sinh \psi$.

The conics are

$$\frac{x^2}{c^2 \cosh^2 \psi} + \frac{y^2}{c^2 \sinh^2 \psi} = 1, \qquad \frac{x^2}{c^2 \cos^2 \varphi} - \frac{y^2}{c^2 \sin^2 \varphi} = 1.$$

23. Find at least one value of each of the following and express it in the form $x + iy$:

(a) 3^{5i}, (b) $3^{\sqrt{5}}$, (c) $(2 - 2i)^{\sqrt{3}}$, (d) $(\sqrt{3} + i)^{1+i}$, (e) i^i.

PART C.   COMPLEX INTEGRAL CALCULUS

8. Indefinite Integral. By an *integral* of a single-valued continuous function $f(z)$ of a complex variable, we shall mean a function $F(z)$ such that $D_z F(z) = f(z)$. We shall denote an arbitrary integral of $f(z)$ by $\int f(z)\, dz$, and we call $\int f(z)\, dz$ the *indefinite integral* of $f(z)$.

The various formulas for calculating the indefinite integral of a function of a real variable x given in Sec. 4, Chap. II can be shown to hold with x replaced by the complex variable z. Thus, $\int z^n\, dz = z^{n+1}/(n + 1) + C$, $n \neq -1$; etc.

The reader should note that the above definition is essentially that given for the indefinite integral of a real function of a real variable. However, while *every* real single-valued continuous function of a real variable has an indefinite integral, it is not true that every single-valued continuous function of a complex variable has an indefinite integral. In fact, the nonanalytic function $x - iy$ of the complex variable $z = x + iy$ is such a function; for while $x - iy$ is single-valued and continuous, there exists no (analytic) function $w = u + iv$ whose derivative is equal to $x - iy$. To show this, suppose $dw/dz = x - iy$. Then $dw/dz = \partial u/\partial x + i(\partial v/\partial x) = x - iy$ and

$$\frac{\partial u}{\partial x} = x, \qquad \frac{\partial v}{\partial x} = -y.$$

If w is analytic, then by the Cauchy-Riemann conditions, $\partial v/\partial x = -\partial u/\partial y$, so that $\partial u/\partial x = x$, and $\partial u/\partial y = y$. Forming the Laplacian, we have $\partial^2 u/\partial x^2 + \partial^2 u/\partial y^2 = 2$. Since u does not satisfy Laplace's equation, u cannot be the real part of an analytic function w, that is, a function having a derivative. We then conclude that there exists no function w having $x - iy$ for a derivative.

9. Definite Integral. Consider a continuous arc C connecting points A and B of a curve defined by the equations $x = \alpha(t), y = \beta(t)$, where on C, α and β are real differentiable functions of the real variable t.

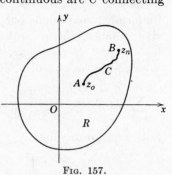

Suppose that as t varies from the value t_A to t_B, the point (x, y) moves along C "smoothly" from A to B.

Suppose $f(z) = u(x, y) + iv(x, y)$ is any complex function of z, continuous everywhere on C. Select

Fig. 157.

any n distinct consecutive points $z_0, z_1, \cdots, z_n$ on C, z_0 corresponding to A and z_n to B. Next, consider the sum

$$S_n \equiv \sum_{k=1}^{n} f(\zeta_k) \cdot (z_k - z_{k-1}), \tag{1}$$

where ζ_k is any point on C between z_{k-1} and z_k. We call $\lim_{\delta \to 0} \sum_{k=1}^{n} f(\zeta_k)(z_k - z_{k-1})$ the *complex line integral of $f(z)$* along the curve C (provided, of course, this limit exists), where δ is the largest of the numbers $|z_k - z_{k-1}|$ for any particular set of points $z_0, z_1, \cdots, z_n$, and we shall denote this limit by the symbol $S_C f(z) \, dz$.

To evaluate $S_C f(z) \, dz$, let us write

$$\zeta_k = \xi_k + i\eta_k, \qquad u_k = u(\xi_k, \eta_k), \qquad v_k = v(\xi_k, \eta_k),$$

$$S_n = \sum_{k=1}^{n} (u_k + iv_k)(x_k + iy_k - x_{k-1} - iy_{k-1}). \tag{2}$$

By the theorem of the mean,

$$x_k - x_{k-1} = \alpha(t_k) - \alpha(t_{k-1}) = \alpha'(\theta_k)(t_k - t_{k-1}),$$
$$y_k - y_{k-1} = \beta(t_k) - \beta(t_{k-1}) = \beta'(\psi_k)(t_k - t_{k-1}),$$

where $t_{k-1} \leqq \theta_k \leqq t_k$, $t_{k-1} \leqq \psi_k \leqq t_k$, so that (2) may be written

$$S_n = \sum_{k=1}^{n} (u_k + iv_k)[\alpha'(\theta_k) + i\beta'(\psi_k)](t_k - t_{k-1}). \tag{3}$$

Since α', β', u_k, v_k, are real and continuous on C, they are all uniformly* continuous on C. Hence, if ϵ be an arbitrary positive number, there exists a positive number δ, such that if $|t_k - t_{k-1}| < \delta$, then $|u_k\alpha'(\theta_k) - u(x_k, y_k)\alpha'(t_k)| < \epsilon$ for $k = 1$, $\cdots$, n. Consequently, as $\epsilon \to 0$ and $\delta \to 0$, we see that

$$\sum_{k=1}^{n} u_k\alpha'(\theta_k)(t_k - t_{k-1}) \quad \text{and} \quad \sum_{k=1}^{n} u(x_k, y_k)\alpha'(t_k)(t_k - t_{k-1})$$

both tend to the limit

$$\int_{t_A}^{t_B} u[\alpha(t), \beta(t)]\alpha'(t)\, dt.$$

By a repetition of this argument for the other products in (3), we find that S_n in (3) approaches the limit

$$\int_{t_A}^{t_B} (u + iv)[\alpha'(t) + i\beta'(t)]\, dt. \tag{4}$$

Since $\alpha'(t)\, dt = dx$, $\beta'(t)\, dt = dy$, we may write (4) in the form

$$\int_{t_A}^{t_B} f(z)\, dz = \int_{t_A}^{t_B} (u + iv)(dx + i\, dy)$$

$$= \int_{A}^{z_B} (u\, dx - v\, dy) + i\int_{z_A}^{z_B} (v\, dx + u\, dy), \tag{5}$$

where $dz = dx + i\, dy$, z_A = value of z at A, and z_B = value of z at B.

While $f(z)$ was not assumed to be analytic, it is evident that our argument and definition is valid for any function $f(z)$ analytic everywhere in any region R including the curve C.

Many of the formulas for real definite integrals hold for complex integrals. Thus, we may show that:

$$\int_C [f_1(z) + f_2(z)]\, dz = \int_C f_1(z)\, dz + \int_C f_2(z)\, dz,$$

$$\int_C kf(z)\, dz = k\int_C f(z)\, dz, \ k \text{ a constant,}$$

$$\int_{z_A}^{z_B} f(z)\, dz + \int_{z_B}^{z_E} f(z)\, dz = \int_{z_A}^{z_E} f(z)\, dz,$$

---

* See Chap. IX, Theorem 8.7.

where z_B lies on the path C connecting z_A and z_E,

$$\int_{z_1}^{z_1} f(z) \, dz = 0,$$

$$\int_C f(z) \, dz = -\int_{\overline{C}} f(z) \, dz,$$

where $\overline{C}$ denotes the arc C described in the opposite sense.

We shall now prove an important inequality. Consider the curve C defined by $x = \alpha(t)$, $y = \beta(t)$, where the derivatives $\alpha'(t)$ and $\beta'(t)$ are real continuous functions of the real variable t, for an appropriate domain of t. By Ex. X, 7, Chap. II, we know that the length L of the curve C connecting two points z_1 and z_2 is (if it exists)

$$L = \int_{t_1}^{t_2} \{[\alpha'(t)]^2 + [\beta'(t)]^2\}^{\frac{1}{2}} \, dt.$$

Theorem 9.1. *Let $f(z)$ be any complex function (not necessarily analytic) of the complex variable z, continuous along C. If along C, $|f(z)|$ is less than or equal to some positive constant M, and L is the length of the curve connecting z_1 and z_2, then*

$$\left| \int_{\substack{z_1 \\ C}}^{z_2} f(z) \, dz \right| \leqq ML.$$

Suppose $\lambda(t)$ is any continuous complex function of a real variable t. Since $\left| \sum_{k=1}^{n} \lambda(t_k)(t_k - t_{k-1}) \right| \leqq \sum_{k=1}^{n} |\lambda(t_k)|(t_k - t_{k-1})$, we find that

$$\left| \int_{t_1}^{t_2} \lambda(t) \, dt \right| \leqq \int_{t_1}^{t_2} |\lambda(t)| \, dt.$$

Consequently,

$$\left| \int_C f(z) \, dz \right| = \left| \int_{t_1}^{t_2} (u + iv)[\alpha'(t) + i\beta'(t)] \, dt \right|$$
$$\leqq \int_{t_1}^{t_2} M\{[\alpha'(t)]^2 + [\beta'(t)]^2\}^{\frac{1}{2}} \, dt = ML.$$

EXERCISES V

1. Show that $\int_C k \, dz = k(b - a)$, where C is any curve connecting $z = a$ and $z = b$. Do this by constructing the sum (3) and then letting $n \to +\infty$. Note that the result is independent of the path C.

2. Show that $\int_C z \, dz = \frac{1}{2}(b^2 - a^2)$ for all paths connecting $z = a$ and $z = b$.

3. Show that $\int_C (dz/z) = 2\pi i$, where C is a circle of radius ρ with center at the origin. (Hint: Let $x = \rho \cos \theta$, $y = \rho \sin \theta$, $z = x + iy$.)

4. Repeat Ex. 3 for $\int_C z^n\, dz$, when n is any integer.

5. Let C be a simple closed curve bounding a region D. If z is interior to D show that

$$\int_C \frac{dw}{(w-z)} = 2\pi i, \quad \text{and} \quad \int_C \frac{dw}{(w-z)^{m+1}} = 0, \quad m = \pm 1, \pm 2, \cdots.$$

$$\left(\text{Hint: Let } (w - z) = \rho e^{i\theta}. \text{ Then } \int_C \frac{dw}{w-z} = \int_C \frac{d\rho}{\rho} + i\int_C d\theta.\right)$$

What is the value of $\displaystyle\int_C \frac{dw}{(w-z)}$ when C encircles z k times?

Ans. $2k\pi i$.

10. Contours. Let $x = \alpha(t)$ and $y = \beta(t)$ define a *continuous arc of a curve* over some interval I of t, where $\alpha'(t)$ and $\beta'(t)$ are real continuous functions of the real variable t.

A continuous curve consisting of only a finite number of arcs of the type named will be called a *contour*. If the end point of the last arc is the same as the starting point of the first arc, then the contour will be said to be *closed*.

Suppose C is a closed contour. Furthermore, suppose: (1) There exists an interval $[a, b]$ such that, if $a < \bar{x} < b$, then the line $x = \bar{x}$ meets C in exactly two points, $y_1(\bar{x})$ and $y_2(\bar{x})$, with $y_1 < y_2$; if $\bar{x} < a$ or $\bar{x} > b$, the line $x = \bar{x}$ meets C nowhere, (2) There exists an interval $[c, d]$ such that if $c < \bar{y} < d$, then $y = \bar{y}$ meets C in exactly two points, $x_1(\bar{y})$ and $x_2(\bar{y})$, where $x_1 < x_2$; if $\bar{y} < c$ or $\bar{y} > d$, $y = \bar{y}$ meets C nowhere. (Such a curve bounds an axial region of the type described in Theorem 17.2 of Chap. II.) A point (x, y) such that $y_1(x) < x < y_2(x)$ and $x_1(y) < y < x_2(y)$ is said to be *interior* to C. A point not on C and not interior to C is said to be *outside* or *exterior* to C. A curve meeting all the conditions mentioned above is said to be a *simple closed contour* or a *simple closed curve.**

The student will no doubt feel that all of this phraseology is unnecessary. An accurate study of the matters at hand is really quite difficult and is beyond the scope of this book. However, while the correct statement of many theorems requires the

---

* For a rigorous definition and treatment, see R. L. Moore, "Foundations of Point Set Theory," Colloquium Lectures of the American Mathematical Society; also see A. Hurwitz and R. Courant, "Funktionentheorie."

greatest care at times, the reader will no doubt find his geometrical intuition an excellent guide and help.

Many of the theorems to follow and stated for simple closed
contours are readily extended to a more general class of curves.
We shall give several examples: (a) If C and C' are two simple
closed curves with one or more common arcs, but C and C'
lying outside each other, we can then form a new closed contour
C'' by deleting the common boundary K; (b) if all of C' is interior
to C, we can form a new closed curve C'' the interior of which

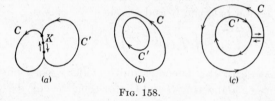

Fig. 158.

consists of points outside C' but interior to C; (c) the region
indicated in Fig. 158 (c).

11. Cauchy's Integral Theorem.   A theorem upon which the
entire theory of analytic functions can be built is the following
one, due to Cauchy.

THEOREM 11.1 (*Cauchy's Theorem*).   *If $f(z)$ is single-valued and
analytic within and on a simple closed curve C, then $\int_C f(z)\,dz = 0$.*

Consider the integral in (5) of Sec. 9 over the simple closed
curve C:

$$\int_C f(z)\,dz = \int_C (u\,dx - v\,dy) + i\int_C (v\,dx + u\,dy). \quad (1)$$

Since $f(z)$ is analytic, $\partial u/\partial y = -\partial v/\partial x$ and $\partial v/\partial y = \partial u/\partial x$.
It follows directly from Theorem 18.1 of Chap. II that the two
integrals in the right member of (1) are each zero, so that

$$\int_C f(z)\,dz = 0.$$

12. Certain Extensions of Cauchy's Theorem.   It is quite
evident that we can extend Cauchy's theorem to any closed
contour of the types mentioned in Sec. 10.

There are many different forms in which this theorem may be
stated.   Suppose that z_0 and z_1 are two points connected by two
different curves C and C', such that C and C' reversed together
make up a simple closed curve or a closed contour of one of the

types defined in Sec. 10.   Suppose $f(z)$ is a function analytic in the entire region enclosed by C and C', including the curves themselves.   Then Cauchy's theorem states that

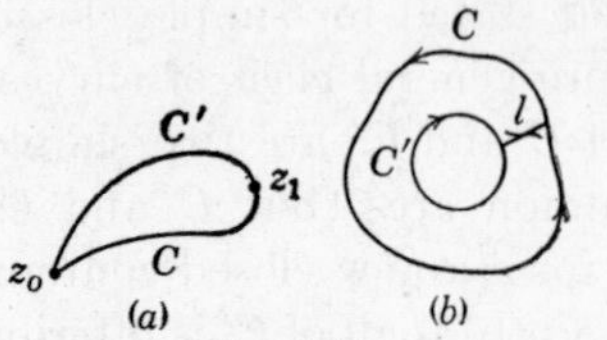

$$\int_C f(z)\,dz = \int_{C'} f(z)\,dz. \qquad (1)$$

(a)   (b)
Fig. 159.

Suppose C and C' are simple closed curves, the latter of which lies entirely inside C.   If $f(z)$ is analytic and single-valued everywhere in the enclosed region between C and C', then

$$\int_C f(z)\,dz = \int_{C'} f(z)\,dz. \qquad (2)$$

The reason for this becomes quite evident when one draws a simple curve l connecting C and C'; for then the curve C described counterclockwise, the curve C' clockwise, and the curve l, described in both directions, as indicated in the figure, form a closed curve Γ; and

$$\int_\Gamma f(z)\,dz = \int_C f(z)\,dz - \int_{C'} f(z)\,dz$$
$$+ \int_l f(z)\,dz - \int_l f(z)\,dz. \qquad (3)$$

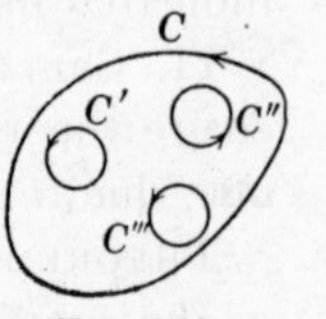

Fig. 160.

Since the left hand integral of (3) around Γ is zero, (2) results.   Similar results may be obtained for the case where there are a finite number of contours: C', C'', $\cdots$, inside C, and if $f(z)$ is analytic in the region within, then

$$\int_C f(z)\,dz = \int_{C'} f(z)\,dz + \int_{C''} f(z)\,dz + \cdots. \qquad (4)$$

It could be shown that certain of the assumptions stated in Cauchy's theorem are not necessary.   For example: $f(z)$ need not be analytic on C, it being only necessary that f be analytic inside C and continuous up to and on C.   Without going into the detail of the rigorous proof of this fact, we remark that, if $f(z)$ is continuous,

$$\int_C f(z)\,dz = \lim_{C' \to C} \int_{C'} f(z)\,dz, \qquad (5)$$

where C' is a simple closed curve lying inside C, and tending to C.

The right-hand side of (5) is zero for all of the curves C' inside C, so that the left-hand side of (5) is zero.

13. Relation between Definite and Indefinite Integrals.   The following theorem due to Goursat is an immediate consequence of Cauchy's theorem.

THEOREM 13.1.   *If $f(z)$ is analytic throughout a region D bounded by a simple closed curve, then $\int_{z_1}^{z_2} f(z)\, dz$ is independent of the path connecting z_1 and z_2, where the path of integration must lie entirely inside of D.*

THEOREM 13.2.   *If $f(z)$ is analytic in a region D bounded by a simple closed curve, then $\int_{z_0}^{z} f(w)\, dw = F(z)$ is also analytic in D (if the path joining z_0 to z lies entirely in D), and the derivative of F with respect to z is $f(z)$.*

Consider

$$F(z + \Delta z) - F(z) = \int_{z}^{z+\Delta z} f(w)\, dw,$$

where the integral is taken along the straight line connecting z and $z + \Delta z$.   Then

$$\frac{F(z + \Delta z) - F(z)}{\Delta z} - f(z) = \frac{1}{\Delta z}\int_{z}^{z+\Delta z} [f(w) - f(z)]\, dw.$$

Let $\epsilon > 0$.   Since $f(z)$ is continuous in D, there exists a $\delta > 0$ such that for every $|w - z| < \delta$, $|f(w) - f(z)| < \epsilon$.   Hence if $|\Delta z| < \delta$,

$$\left| \frac{F(z + \Delta z) - F(z)}{\Delta z} - f(z) \right| < \epsilon,$$

so that $F(z)$ is analytic and $dF/dz = f(z)$.   It is proved in the following theorem that the function $F(z) + C$ represents the indefinite integral of $f(z)$.

THEOREM 13.3.   *Let $F(z)$ and $G(z)$ be analytic functions such that throughout a region D, $F'(z) \equiv f(z)$ and $G'(z) \equiv f(z)$.   Then $F - G$ is a constant, and $\int_{a}^{b} f(z)\, dz = F(b) - F(a) = G(b) - G(a)$.*

Since $F'(z) \equiv G'(z)$, $(d/dz)\,[F(z) - G(z)] \equiv 0$.   Write

$$F(z) - G(z) = u + iv.$$

Then $\partial u/\partial x = \partial u/\partial y = \partial v/\partial x = \partial v/\partial y = 0$.   (Why?)   Hence u and v are both constants, so that $F(z) - G(z)$ is a constant.   Therefore, in D,

$$\int_{a}^{b} f(z)\, dz = F(b) - F(a) = G(b) - G(a).$$

SERIES WHOSE TERMS ARE COMPLEX NUMBERS

14. Complex Numbers and Sequences. A large part of the definitions and theorems referring to sequences and series of real numbers given in Chap. IV hold when the arbitrary real numbers are replaced by complex numbers. In fact, subject to a few minor alterations, this situation extends equally well to the proofs. Throughout Chap. IV we have prefixed the symbol c to the theorems and definitions which remain valid word for word when arbitrary real numbers are replaced by complex numbers and the numerical values of real numbers are replaced by the absolute values of the corresponding complex numbers. Theorems and definitions referring to real numbers in which the symbols $<$ and $>$ play an essential part either do not hold for complex numbers, or require considerable modification.

For a résumé of the definitions and theorems valid for complex numbers the reader is advised to reread the preceding sections of Chap. IV in which the prefix c appears, with the terms "arbitrary real numbers" replaced by "arbitrary complex numbers."

One of the most important theorems which is easily extended to complex numbers is the Cauchy-Toeplitz theorem.

The problem of reducing the convergence or divergence of complex sequences to the corresponding problem in real sequences is easily solved by splitting up the terms into real and imaginary parts. The following theorems are all easily proved:

THEOREM 14.1. *A necessary and sufficient condition that the sequence $\{z_n\} = \{x_n + iy_n\}$ converge to $X + iY$ is that the real parts x_n converge to X and the imaginary parts y_n converge to Y.*

An immediate and important consequence of Theorem 14.1 is

THEOREM 14.2. *A necessary and sufficient condition for the convergence of a complex sequence $\{z_n\}$ is that for every arbitrary positive number ϵ, there exists a positive number n_0 such that for every $n > n_0$ and every $n_1 > n_0$, $|z_{n_1} - z_n| < \epsilon$.*

The theorem regarding series of complex terms corresponding to Theorem 14.1 is

THEOREM 14.3. *A necessary and sufficient condition that the series Σz_n of complex terms converge is that the series $\Sigma \Re(z_n)$ of the real parts of Σz_n, and the series $\Sigma \Im(z_n)$ of the imaginary parts of Σz_n each converge. If these two series have the sums S_R and S_I, respectively, then the sum S of Σz_n is $S = S_R + iS_I$.*

The distinction between *absolute* and *nonabsolute convergence* of series of real terms remains the same for series of complex terms. Since for every complex number $z = x + iy$,

$$|x| \leqq |z| \leqq |x| + |y| \quad \text{and} \quad |y| \leqq |z| \leqq |x| + |y|,$$

we have

Theorem 14.4. *A necessary and sufficient condition that the complex series Σz_n be absolutely convergent is that the series $\Sigma \Re(z_n)$ and $\Sigma \Im(z_n)$ both be absolutely convergent.*

In general, all results proved for absolutely convergent series of real terms may be used in the theory of absolutely convergent series of complex numbers.

The theory of real power series developed in Part C of Chap. IV remains valid without essential change for complex power series—series of the form $\Sigma a_n(z - z_0)^n$, when the quantities a_n, z, and z_0 are complex. However, the geometrical interpretation is somewhat different: The power series $\Sigma a_n(z - z_0)^n$ converges—and absolutely—for every z interior to the circle C of radius r about z_0, and diverges for all points outside C. This circle is known as *the circle of convergence* of the power series.

The results obtained in Part D of Chap. IV in regard to series $\Sigma f_n(x)$ of real variable terms remain essentially the same for series of complex terms, but in place of the common *interval* of definition we now assume a common *region* of definition.

Theorem 14.5. *A power series represents an analytic function inside its circle of convergence.*

Suppose $f(z) = \sum_{n=0}^{\infty} a_n z^n$ is convergent for $|z| < R$. If $\rho < R$, then $|a_n \rho^n| \leqq K$, where K is some fixed positive number, for $a_n \rho^n$ is bounded. Let $g(z) = \sum_{n=1}^{\infty} n a_n z^{n-1}$. Then

$$\frac{f(z + \Delta z) - f(z)}{\Delta z} - g(z) = \sum_{n=0}^{\infty} a_n \left\{ \frac{(z + \Delta z)^n - z^n}{\Delta z} - n z^{n-1} \right\}$$

when $|z| + |\Delta z| < \rho$. Since

$$\left| \frac{(z + \Delta z)^n - z^n}{\Delta z} - n z^{n-1} \right| = \left| \frac{n(n-1)}{1 \cdot 2} z^{n-2} \Delta z + \cdots + \Delta z^{n-1} \right|$$

$$\leqq \frac{(|z| + |\Delta z|)^n - |z|^n}{|\Delta z|} - n|z|^{n-1},$$

we conclude that

$$\left| \frac{f(z + \Delta z) - f(z)}{\Delta z} - g(z) \right| \leqq K \sum_{n=1}^{\infty} \frac{1}{\rho^n} \left[\frac{(|z| + |\Delta z|)^n - |z|^n}{|\Delta z|} - n|z|^{n-1} \right]$$

$$= K \left[\frac{1}{|\Delta z|} \left(\frac{\rho}{\rho - |z| - |\Delta z|} - \frac{\rho}{\rho - |z|} \right) - \frac{\rho}{(\rho - |z|)^2} \right]$$

$$= \frac{K\rho|\Delta z|}{(\rho - |z| - |\Delta z|)(\rho - |z|)^2}.$$

This expression $\to 0$ as $\Delta z \to 0$. Hence $f'(z) = g(z)$.

A uniformly convergent series of analytic functions of a complex variable may be integrated term by term along any path lying in the region of uniform convergence.

A series of analytic functions may be differentiated term by term at any point within a region where the derived series is uniformly convergent.

EXERCISES VI

1. Show that Σz^n converges with the sum $1/(1 - z)$ in the interior of the unit circle, and diverges everywhere else.

2. Show that $\Sigma(z^n/n^2)$ converges within and on the boundary of the unit circle.

3. Show that $\Sigma(z^n/n)$ is convergent within the unit circle C; conditionally convergent on the boundary, except where $z = 1$; divergent at $z = 1$; and divergent exterior to C.

4. Where is $\Sigma(z^{4n}/4n)$ convergent? $\Sigma(z^n/n!)$?

15. Cauchy's Integral Formula and Its Extensions. The following theorem is known as *Cauchy's integral formula*. It expresses the value of $f(z)$ at any point z interior to C in terms of the values of $f(z)$ on C, that is, in terms of its boundary values. Thus, if $f(z)$ represents a physical quantity whose value has been measured only along C, Cauchy's formula enables one to compute $f(z)$ within C from these values.

THEOREM 15.1. *If $f(z)$ is analytic inside and on a simple closed curve C and z is any point interior to C, then*

$$f(z) = \frac{1}{2\pi i} \int_C \frac{f(w)}{w - z} \, dw. \tag{1}$$

The function $\dfrac{f(w)}{w - z}$ is analytic everywhere within C except at $w = z$. Hence, if Γ is any circle with center at z inside C, then

$$\int_C \frac{f(w)}{w - z}\, dw = \int_\Gamma \frac{f(w)}{w - z}\, dw.$$

Let ρ be the radius of the circle Γ. Since $f(w)$ is continuous, we can select ρ small enough that with w on Γ, $|f(w) - f(z)| < \epsilon$. Now

$$\int_\Gamma \frac{f(w)}{w - z}\, dz = f(z) \int_\Gamma \frac{dw}{w - z} + \int_\Gamma \frac{f(w) - f(z)}{w - z}\, dw.$$

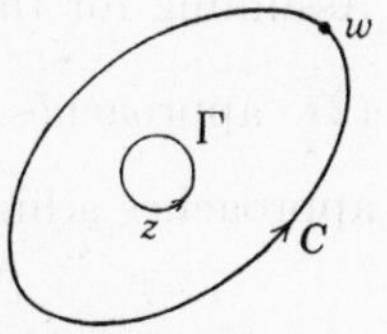

Fig. 161.

By Ex. V, 5, the first term on the right is equal to $2\pi i\, f(z)$; by Theorem 9.1 the absolute value of the second term cannot exceed $(\epsilon/\rho)2\pi\rho = 2\pi\epsilon$. Hence

$$\left| \int_C \frac{f(w)}{w - z}\, dw - 2\pi i\, f(z) \right| < 2\pi\epsilon.$$

The left-hand member vanishes since it is independent of ϵ. Hence

$$f(z) = \frac{1}{2\pi i} \int_C \frac{f(w)}{w - z}\, dw.$$

An important extension of Theorem 15.1 is given by

THEOREM 15.2. *If $f(z)$ is analytic throughout an open region* D bounded by a simple closed curve C, then its derivatives of all orders exist at each point of D and each derivative is analytic throughout D. In fact,*

$$f'(z) = \frac{1}{2\pi i} \int_C \frac{f(w)}{(w - z)^2}\, dw, \cdots,$$

$$f^{(n)}(z) = \frac{n!}{2\pi i} \int_C \frac{f(w)}{(w - z)^{n+1}}\, dw.$$

Let z and $z + h$ be two neighboring points inside D. By Theorem 15.1,

$$f(z + h) = \frac{1}{2\pi i} \int_C \frac{f(w)}{w - z - h}\, dw,$$

$$f(z) = \frac{1}{2\pi i} \int_C \frac{f(w)}{w - z}\, dw, \tag{1'}$$

---

* An *open region* is a set S of points such that any point of S can be made the center of a circle which contains in its interior only points of S.

so that

$$\frac{f(z + h) - f(z)}{h} = \frac{1}{2\pi i}\int_C \frac{f(w)}{(w - z)(w - z - h)}\,dw. \qquad (2)$$

Assuming for the moment that as $h \to 0$, the right-hand side of (2) approaches $\dfrac{1}{2\pi i}\displaystyle\int_C \dfrac{f(w)}{(w - z)^2}\,dw$, the left-hand side also approaches a limit, and

$$f'(z) = \frac{1}{2\pi i}\int_C \frac{f(w)}{(w - z)^2}\,dw. \qquad (3)$$

By a repetition of this argument we obtain

$$f''(z) = \frac{2}{2\pi i}\int_C \frac{f(w)}{(w - z)^3}\,dw, \qquad \cdots,$$

$$f^{(n)}(z) = \frac{n!}{2\pi i}\int_C \frac{f(w)}{(w - z)^{n+1}}\,dw, \qquad \cdots. \qquad (4)$$

We shall now verify the assumption made immediately prior to equation (3). Consider the difference

$$\int_C \frac{f(w)}{(w - z)(w - z - h)}\,dw - \int_C \frac{f(w)}{(w - z)^2}\,dw$$

$$= h\int_C \frac{f(w)}{(w - z)^2(w - z - h)}\,dw. \qquad (5)$$

Let the minimum value of $|w - z|$ as w describes C be δ and furthermore suppose $|f(w)| \leqq M$ on C. Then if L be the length of C, and if $|h| < \delta$,

$$\left|\int_C \frac{f(w)}{(w - z)^2(w - z - h)}\,dw\right| \leqq \frac{ML}{\delta^2(\delta - |h|)}. \qquad (6)$$

The right member of (6) is bounded as $|h| \to 0$, so that (5) approaches zero as $|h| \to 0$.

Theorem 15.3 (*Morera's Theorem*). *If $f(z)$ is single-valued and continuous throughout a region D bounded by a simple closed curve C, and the integral $\int_{C_2} f(w)\,dw$ vanishes when computed over any closed curve C_2 in D, then $f(z)$ is analytic in D.*

The value of

$$F(z) = \int_{z_0}^{z} f(w)\,dw$$

is independent of the path C_2 of integration. Since $f(w)$ is continuous, the difference

$$\frac{F(z+h) - F(z)}{h} - f(z) = \frac{1}{h} \int_z^{z+h} [f(w) - f(z)] \, dw$$

tends to zero as $h \to 0$ when the path of integration is a straight line. Hence $dF(z)/dz = f(z)$ and $F(z)$ is analytic. Our theorem is now immediate, since the derivative of an analytic function is analytic (Theorem 15.2).

Morera's theorem is in a sense the converse of Cauchy's theorem.

As another extension of Cauchy's integral formula, we have

THEOREM 15.4 (*Taylor's Theorem*). *Let $f(z)$ be single-valued and analytic throughout the interior of a region D, where D is bounded by the simple closed curve C. Suppose z and a are both interior to D. Then*

$$f(z) = f(a) + f'(a)(z - a) + \frac{f''(a)}{2!}(z - a)^2$$

$$+ \cdots + \frac{f^{(n-1)}(a)}{(n-1)!}(z - a)^{n-1} + R_n, \quad (7)$$

where

$$R_n = (z - a)^n P_n(z), \quad (8)$$

where

$$P_n(z) = \frac{1}{2\pi i} \int_C \frac{f(w)}{(w - a)^n (w - z)} \, dw \quad (9)$$

is analytic throughout the interior of D.

From Cauchy's integral formula,

$$f(z) = \frac{1}{2\pi i} \int_C \frac{f(w)}{w - z} \, dw$$

$$= \frac{1}{2\pi i} \int_C \frac{f(w)}{w - a} \left[\frac{1}{1 - [(z - a)/(w - a)]} \right] dw. \quad (10)$$

Since

$$\frac{1}{1 - u} = 1 + u + u^2 + \cdots u^{n-1} + \frac{u^n}{1 - u},$$

$$\frac{1}{1 - \dfrac{z - a}{w - a}} = 1 + \frac{z - a}{w - a} + \left(\frac{z - a}{w - a} \right)^2 + \cdots$$

$$+ \left(\frac{z - a}{w - a} \right)^{n-1} + \frac{(z - a)^n}{(w - a)^{n-1}(w - z)}. \quad (11)$$

Substituting (11) in (10), we find that

$$f(z) = \frac{1}{2\pi i}\int_C \frac{f(w)}{w-a}\,dw + \frac{(z-a)}{2\pi i}\int_C \frac{f(w)}{(w-a)^2}\,dw$$

$$+\;\cdots\;+ \frac{(z-a)^{n-1}}{2\pi i}\int_C \frac{f(w)}{(w-a)^n}\,dw$$

$$+ \frac{(z-a)^n}{2\pi i}\int_C \frac{f(w)}{(w-a)^n(w-z)}\,dw. \quad (12)$$

From Theorems 15.1 and 15.2, we can write (12) in the form (7).

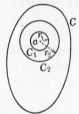

An Inequality for $P_n(z)$. Let C_1 and C_2 be two circles of radii r_1 and r_2, respectively, $r_2 > r_1$, with centers at a, such that the region within and on C_2 lies interior to the region D in Theorem 15.4. By (2) of Sec. 12, if z is within C_2, the integral (3) is unchanged when C is replaced by C_2. If, furthermore, z is interior to C_1, then for all

Fig. 162.   values of w on C_2,

$$|w-a| = r_2, \qquad |w-z| > r_2 - r_1, \qquad |f(w)| \leq M,$$

where M is the maximum value of $|f(w)|$ on C_2. By Theorem 9.1,

$$\left|\int_C f(z)\,dz\right| \leq ML,$$

$$|P_n(z)| \leq \frac{1}{2\pi}\frac{M}{r_2^n(r_2-r_1)}2\pi r_2 = \frac{M}{r_2^{n-1}(r_2-r_1)},$$

where z is within C_1, $|z-a| < r_1$. Hence

$$|R_n| = |z-a|^n|P_n(z)| < \frac{Mr_1^n}{r_2^{n-1}(r_2-r_1)} = M\frac{r_1}{(r_2-r_1)}\left(\frac{r_1}{r_2}\right)^{n-1}.$$

Since $r_2 > r_1$, it follows that for every z within C_1, $R_n \to 0$ as $n \to +\infty$.

Theorem 15.5 (*Cauchy's Inequality*). *If* $f(z) = \displaystyle\sum_{n=0}^{\infty} a_n(z-z_0)^n$ *converges for* $|z-z_0| < r$, *if* $0 < \rho < r$, *and if* M *is a number which* $|f(z)|$ *never exceeds along the circumference* $|z-z_0| = \rho$, *then* $|a_n| \leq (M/\rho^n)$, $(n = 0, 1, 2, \cdots)$.

By Taylor's theorem, $a_n = \dfrac{1}{2\pi i}\displaystyle\int_C \frac{f(z)}{(z-z_0)^{n+1}}\,dz$, and by Theorem 9.1, $|a_n| \leq M/\rho^n$.

As a corollary to this theorem we have

Theorem 15.6.   *If $f(z)$ is analytic within the circle $|z - z_0| < r$, then $|f(z)|$ at an interior point of this circle never exceeds the maximum M of $|f(z)|$ on the boundary of this circle.   In other words, $|f(z)|$ cannot have a maximum at an interior point z.*

16. Taylor's Series.   In the preceding section we discussed Taylor's theorem:

$$f(z) = f(a) + f'(a)(z - a) + \frac{f''(a)}{2!}(z - a)^2$$
$$+ \cdots + \frac{f^{(n-1)}(a)}{(n-1)!}(z - a)^{n-1} + R_n,$$

and it is seen that, if C be a circle about a such that C and the region interior to it are within a region T throughout which $f(z)$ is analytic, and if z is interior to C, then $R_n \to 0$ as $n \to +\infty$.   We then write

$$f(z) = f(a) + f'(a)(z - a) + \frac{f''(a)}{2!}(z - a)^2$$
$$+ \cdots + \frac{f^{(n)}(a)}{n!}(z - a)^n + \cdots. \quad (1)$$

The infinite series in (1) is called *Taylor's series*.   This series converges and is equal to $f(z)$ at every point z within C', where C' is any circle throughout the interior of which $f(z)$ is analytic. If $a = 0$, the series is known as *Maclaurin's series*.

It is frequently difficult to establish the validity of a Taylor's series for a real function of a real variable x.   The method of this section often is helpful in such cases: Let $S(x)$ be a real Taylor's series about $x = a$ generated from the real function $f(x)$. In the series $S(x)$, replace x by z.   The resulting series $S(z)$ will converge everywhere within C, where C is the largest circle about the real point a within which $f(z)$ is analytic. C cuts out on the x-axis the interval of convergence I of the original series $S(x)$; and within I the value of $f(x)$ must be equal to the value of its Taylor's series $S(x)$.   Thus, in this manner we could conclude that the binomial series

$$1 + mz + \frac{m(m - 1)}{2}z^2$$
$$+ \cdots + \frac{m(m - 1) \cdots (m - n + 1)}{n!}z^n + \cdots$$

for $(1 + z)^m$ converges to the value of $(1 + x)^m$ at every point of the interval $-1 < x < +1$, since $(1 + z)^m$ is analytic within a unit circle with center at $z = 0$. Again the method shows us immediately that a Maclaurin's series for e^{-1/x^2} does not converge to the value of e^{-1/x^2} since e^{-1/z^2} is not analytic at $z = 0$.

Theorem 16.1. *Let $f(x)$ be a real function of the real variable x representable by a real Taylor's series $S(x)$ within the interval of convergence $(a - R) < x < (a + R)$. Then the power series $S(z)$, found from $S(x)$ by replacing x by z is a power series in $(z - a)$, convergent throughout a circle C of radius R about a, and represents a function $f(z)$ analytic within C and is equal to $f(x)$ when $z = x$. This function $f(z)$ of z is the only function analytic throughout C and which coincides with $f(x)$ on an interval about a of the x-axis.*

Suppose there were two such functions $f_1(z)$ and $f_2(z)$, each representable by Taylor's series and whose values coincide along $(a - R) < x < (a + R)$. By an argument similar to that given in Theorem 13.2, Chap. IV, their coefficients would coincide, and $f_1(z) \equiv f_2(z)$.

A theorem analogous to the one proved in an earlier section— that an analytic function is completely determined within a closed curve by its values on the curve—is

Theorem 16.2. *Let $f(z)$ be single-valued and analytic throughout T. Then $f(z)$ is completely determined at every point of T when we know either (1) the value of f and all its derivatives at an interior point of T, or (2) its values at the points of an infinite set having a limiting point within T.*

A combination of Taylor's series and Theorem 14.5 leads to

Theorem 16.3. *A necessary and sufficient condition that a function should be expressible in a power series is that it should be analytic in a region.*

17. Liouville's Theorem. If $f(z)$ is analytic for all finite values of z, then the Taylor's series $f(z) = \sum_{n=0}^{\infty} a_n z^n$ converges for all values of z. If $f(z)$ is bounded, that is, if $|f(z)| \leq M$, then by Theorem 15.5, $|a_n| \leq M/r^n$ for all values of r and n. If $n > 0$, $Mr^{-n} \to 0$ as $r \to +\infty$. Hence $a_n = 0$ for $n > 0$ and $f(z) = a_0$, a constant. Hence we have

Theorem 17.1 *(Liouville's Theorem). There exists no bounded function other than a constant which is everywhere analytic and finite.*

More generally, it is possible to prove

Theorem 17.2. *If $f(z)$ is analytic for all finite values of z, and as $|z| \to +\infty, |f(z)| = O(|z|^k)$, then $f(z)$ is a polynomial of degree not greater than k.*

Theorem 17.3 (*Fundamental Theorem of Algebra*). *If $f(z)$ is a polynomial of degree greater than zero with complex coefficients, then $f(z) = 0$ has at least one root.*

Suppose that $f(z) \neq 0$ for all complex numbers z. Then $\varphi(z) = 1/f(z)$ is everywhere analytic and finite, for $f(z)$ is a polynomial, $f(z) \neq 0$, $\lim\limits_{z \to \infty} \varphi(z) = 0$. Hence, there exists a circle C of radius r with center at the origin and a positive number M such that for every circle of radius $R > r$, $|\varphi(z)| < M$ for all values of z outside C. Also, on and within C, $\varphi(z)$ is continuous so that $|\varphi(z)|$ has a maximum value M for all values of z within or on C. By Liouville's theorem we conclude that $\varphi(z) = 1/f(z)$ is a constant. But this cannot be true since $f(z)$ is of degree > 0. Hence $f(z)$ must vanish for at least one value of z.

18. Zeros of Analytic Functions. A value a of z such that $f(a) = 0$ is called a *zero* of $f(z)$. An analytic function $f(z)$ is said to have *a zero of order m* at $z = a$ if

$$f(a) = f'(a) = \cdots = f^{(m-1)}(a) = 0, \qquad f^{(m)}(a) \neq 0.$$

Theorem 18.1. *Let $p_1, p_2, \cdots, p_n, \cdots$ be a set S of points with limit point p inside the region D. If $f(z)$ is analytic in D, and if $f(z) = 0$ at each point of S, then $f(z) = 0$ everywhere in D.*

For convenience we may suppose that p is the point $z = 0$.

Then $f(z) = \sum\limits_{n=0}^{\infty} a_n z^n$ is analytic in some region, $|z| < R$, enclosing $z = 0$. Suppose that one or more of the coefficients $a_0, a_1, \cdots$ in the series is not zero. Let $a_k \neq 0$ be the first such nonzero coefficient. Then $f(z) = z^k(a_k + a_{k+1}z + \cdots)$, $|z| < R$. The series is convergent for $z = \rho$, $0 < \rho < R$. Hence $|a_n|\rho^n \leq K$, for $a_n\rho^n$ is bounded. Then

$$|f(z)| \geq |z|^k \left(|a_k| - \frac{K|z|}{\rho^{k+1}} - \frac{K|z|^2}{\rho^{k+2}} - \cdots \right)$$

$$= |z|^k \left[|a_k| - \frac{K|z|}{\rho^k(\rho - |z|)} \right].$$

Except at the point $z = 0$, the right-hand side here is positive for $|z|$ sufficiently small. But by hypothesis $f(z)$ has zeros arbitrarily close to, but not coincident with, $z = 0$. We have reached a contradiction, and we conclude that all the coefficients $a_0, a_1, \cdots$ must vanish. Hence $f(z) = 0$ everywhere inside the circle of convergence of the series.

THEOREM 18.2. *If $f(z)$ is analytic in a region D including $z = a$, and if $f(z)$ does not vanish identically, there exists a circle $|z - a| = r$ $(r > 0)$ inside which $f(z)$ vanishes nowhere except possibly at $z = a$, i.e., the zeros of $f(z)$ are isolated points.*

Theorem 18.2 follows directly from Theorem 18.1.

EXERCISES VII

1. Show that $\sin z$ has zeros of order one at $z = 0$, $\pm\pi$, $\pm 2\pi$, $\cdots$, and no others.

2. Find all the zeros of $\cos z$.

3. Prove: If $f(z)$ is analytic in D and vanishes at all points along any arc of a continuous curve in D, then it must vanish identically.

4. Prove: If $f_1(z)$ and $f_2(z)$ are analytic in D, and have the same values at an infinite set S of points having a limit point p, then $f_1(z) \equiv f_2(z)$ throughout D.

5. In Ex. 4 suppose $f_1(z) \cdot f_2(z) \equiv 0$ throughout D. Prove that either $f_1(z)$ or $f_2(z)$ vanishes throughout D.

6. Show that if $f(z) = \sum_{n=0}^{\infty} a_n(z - a)^n$ has a zero of order m at $z = a$, then $a_0 = a_1 = \cdots = a_{m-1} = 0$, $a_m \neq 0$.

19. Laurent's Series. An important generalization of Taylor's series is one which gives us a method for representing a function analytic everywhere outside a circle C by means of a series of positive or negative powers of $(z - a)$ convergent everywhere outside C.

We shall have need of some terminology relating to the behavior of a function $f(z)$ as z becomes infinite.

DEFINITION 19.1. *A function $f(z)$ is said to be analytic at the ideal point $z = \infty$, ("at infinity") if $f(z)$ is carried by the transformation $w = 1/(z - a)$ into a function $\varphi(w)$ analytic at $w = 0$.*

Suppose $f(z)$ is analytic everywhere exterior to a circle C of center a including the point $z = \infty$. Let $\varphi(w)$ denote the value of $f(z)$ when $w = 1/(z - a)$. Then $\varphi(w)$ is analytic in w everywhere interior to some circle C_1 about $w = 0$. By Sec. 16, φ may be expanded into a Taylor's series valid throughout the interior of C_1,

$$\varphi(w) = a_0 + a_1 w + a_2 w^2 + \cdots . \tag{1}$$

Since $f(z) = \varphi(w)$, we can express $f(z)$ by the series

$$f(z) = a_0 + \frac{a_1}{z - a} + \frac{a_2}{(z - a)^2} + \cdots \tag{2}$$

which converges everywhere outside C including $z = \infty$. The expansion (2) is known as a *development* of $f(z)$ about $z = \infty$.

Example 1. The function

$$\log (1 + z) = z - \frac{z^2}{2} + \cdots + \frac{(-1)^{n-1} z^n}{n} + \cdots$$

converges everywhere within a circle C of radius $r = 1$ whose center is at $z = 0$. Let $z = 1/w$. Then

$$\log \left(1 + \frac{1}{w}\right) = \frac{1}{w} - \frac{1}{2w^2} + \cdots + \frac{(-1)^{n-1}}{n w^n} + \cdots$$

converges everywhere exterior to the circle C.

We shall now prove

THEOREM 19.1 (*Laurent's Theorem*). *Let T be the region bounded by the concentric circles C_1 and C_2 with center at a. Let $f(z)$ be analytic and single-valued within and on the boundaries of T. Then $f(z)$ can be represented in the form*

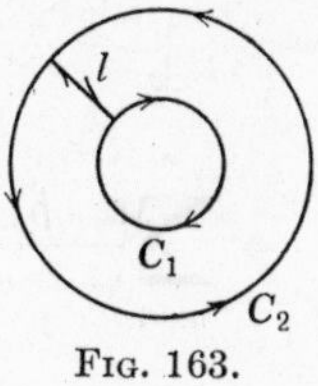

$$f(z) = \sum_{n = -\infty}^{n = +\infty} a_n (z - a)^n, \tag{3}$$

FIG. 163.

where

$$a_n = \frac{1}{2\pi i} \int \frac{f(w)\, dw}{(w - a)^{n+1}} \tag{4}$$

for all values of n, the integral being taken around any simple closed contour which passes around the ring.

Consider the integral $\dfrac{1}{2\pi i} \displaystyle\int_C \dfrac{f(w)}{w - z}\, dw$, where z is a point of T, taken around the boundary C and cut l as indicated in Fig. 163. By Cauchy's integral theorem,

$$f(z) = \frac{1}{2\pi i}\int_{C_2} \frac{f(w)}{w - z}\, dw + \frac{1}{2\pi i}\int_{C_1} \frac{f(w)}{w - z}\, dw, \qquad (5)$$

since the two integrals taken along l in opposite directions have the sum zero, $f(z)$ being single-valued. As in the proof of Taylor's theorem,

$$\frac{1}{2\pi i}\int_{C_2} \frac{f(w)}{w - z}\, dw = \sum_{n=0}^{\infty} a_n(z - a)^n,$$

where

$$a_n = \frac{1}{2\pi i}\int_{C_2} \frac{f(w)}{(w - a)^{n+1}}\, dw. \qquad (6)$$

Since

$$\frac{1}{z - w} = \frac{1}{z - a} + \frac{w - a}{(z - a)^2} + \cdots + \frac{(w - a)^{n-1}}{(z - a)^n} + \cdots, \qquad (7)$$

a series uniformly convergent on C_1, the second integral in (5) is equal to

$$\frac{1}{2\pi i}\int_{C_1} \frac{f(w)}{w - z}\, dw = \frac{1}{z - a}\frac{1}{2\pi i}\int_{C_1} f(w)\, dw$$

$$+ \cdots + \frac{1}{(z - a)^n}\frac{1}{2\pi i}\int_{C_1} (w - a)^{n-1}f(w)\, dw + \cdots \qquad (8)$$

$$= \sum_{n=1}^{\infty} \frac{b_n}{(z - a)^n}, \qquad \text{where} \qquad b_n = \frac{1}{2\pi i}\int_{C_1} (w - a)^{n-1}f(w)\, dw.$$

Combining the series in (6) and (8), we obtain (3).

If $f(z)$ is analytic inside C_1, each b_n in (8) is 0 (by Cauchy's theorem), and (3) is simply Taylor's series. It should be noticed that the series in (6) converges, not only in T, but everywhere in C_2. The series (8) converges everywhere outside C_1.

EXERCISES VIII

1. Expand $1/(z^2 - 3z + 2)$ by Laurent's series valid for a region outside the unit circle C_1 with center at $z = 0$ and inside the circle C_2 of radius 2 with center at $z = 0$.

Ans. $\cdots - (1/z^3) - (1/z^2) - (1/z) - \frac{1}{2} - (z/4) - (z^2/8) - \cdots$.

Find an expansion valid inside C_1; outside C_2.

2. Expand $\dfrac{(z-1)(z-2)}{(z-3)(z-4)}$ in the neighborhood of $z = \infty$.

3. Show that $e^{\frac{1}{2}\omega\left(z-\frac{1}{z}\right)} = \sum\limits_{n=-\infty}^{n=+\infty} a_n z^n$ where

$$a_n = \frac{1}{2\pi}\int_0^{2\pi} \cos\,(n\theta - \omega\sin\,\theta)\;d\theta.$$

PART D. SINGULARITIES OF SINGLE-VALUED ANALYTIC FUNCTIONS

20. Singularities.   A point z_0 is said to be a *singular point* of a single-valued function $f(z)$ if $f(z)$ does not have a derivative at z_0, or if every neighborhood of z_0 contains points other than z_0 at which $f(z)$ has no derivative.

If z_0 is such a point that there exists a neighborhood of z_0 throughout which $f(z)$ is analytic, except at z_0, then z_0 is said to be an *isolated singular point* of the function $f(z)$.

If $f(z)$ is single-valued and analytic, we may expand $f(z)$ in a Laurent series of powers of $(z - a)$, and we may take the inner circle C_1 (see Sec. 19) arbitrarily small.   Thus

$$f(z) = \sum_{n=0}^{\infty} a_n(z-a)^n + \sum_{n=1}^{\infty} b_n(z-a)^{-n}. \quad (0 < |z - a| < R). \quad (1)$$

We shall consider three cases: (1) the case when all the b_n are zero; (2) the case when the series of negative powers of $(z - a)$ contains only a finite number of terms; (3) the case where the series of negative terms does not terminate.

If all the b_n are zero, the first series in (1) is analytic and represents $f(z)$ for $|z - a| < R$, except possibly at $z = a$.   The function $f(z) = 3$, $z \neq a$, with $f(a) = 0$ is an example of such a function.   This case is of no particular interest.

In case (2), $f(z)$ is said to have a *pole* at the point $z = a$.   If b_m is the last nonzero coefficient in (1), then

$$f(z) = \sum_{n=0}^{\infty} a_n(z-a)^n + \sum_{n=1}^{m} b_n(z-a)^{-n}, \quad (2)$$

and the pole at $z = a$ is said to be of *order m*; if $m = 1$, the order is *simple*; if $m = 2$, the order is *double*; $\cdots$.

If $f(z)$ has a pole of order m at $z = a$, then $(z - a)^m f(z)$ is analytic and does not vanish at $z = a$.   Hence

$$\varphi(z) = \frac{1}{(z - a)^m f(z)} \qquad (3)$$

is analytic and does not vanish at $z = a$, so that the function

$$\frac{1}{f(z)} = (z - a)^m \varphi(z) \qquad (4)$$

has a zero of order m.

If $f(z)$ has a zero of order m, then $1/f(z)$ has a pole of order m. The finite series

$$\sum_{n=1}^{m} b_n (z - a)^{-n} \qquad (5)$$

is called *the principal part of* $f(z)$ *at* $z = a$.

THEOREM 20.1.   *If* $f(z)$ *has a pole at* $z = a$, *then* $|f(z)| \to +\infty$ *as* $z \to a$.

Evidently,

$$\left| \sum_{n=1}^{m} b_n (z - a)^{-n} \right| = |z - a|^{-m} \cdot \left| \sum_{n=1}^{m} b_n (z - a)^{m-n} \right|$$

$$\geqq |z - a|^{-m} \left\{ |b_m| - \sum_{n=1}^{m-1} |b_n| \cdot |z - a|^{m-n} \right\}.$$

Since the terms enclosed in the braces approaches $|b_m|$ as $z \to a$, the entire expression on the right $\to +\infty$ as $z \to a$.

THEOREM 20.2.   *Let* A *be a nonzero constant.   If*

$$\frac{f(z)}{|z - a|^{-k}} \to A$$

as $|z - a| \to 0$, $z = a$ *is a singular point for* $f(z)$ *of at most a pole of order* k; *if* $f(z)$ *is bounded,* $f(z)$ *has no singular point except possibly that of the trivial type mentioned in case* (1).

In case (3), where the expansion of $f(z)$ in powers of $(z - a)$ leads to a nonterminating series of negative powers, the point $z = a$ is called an *essential singularity* of $f(z)$.   Then

$$f(z) = \sum_{n=1}^{+\infty} a_n (z - a)^n + \sum_{n=1}^{+\infty} \frac{b_n}{(z - a)^n}, \qquad (6)$$

where the second series in (6) does not terminate, but is convergent for all values of z except $z = a$.

THEOREM 20.3 (*Weierstrass Theorem*). *If $f(z)$ has an essential singularity at $z = a$, and if C is any complex number, then for every positive number ρ and ϵ, there exists a point z in the circle $|z - a| < \rho$ at which $|f(z) - C| < \epsilon$ [i.e., $f(z)$ tends to any given limit as $z \to a$ through a suitable sequence of values].*

Suppose that ρ and M are any two positive numbers. If, for every point z such that $|z - a| < \rho$, $|f(z)| \leq M$, then by Theorem 9.1

$$|b_n| = \left| \frac{1}{2\pi i} \int_{C_1} (w - a)^{n-1} f(w) \, dw \right| \leq M R_1^n,$$

where R_1 is the radius of C_1. Since this is true for all positive numbers M and R_1, it follows, upon letting $R_1 \to 0$, that $b_n = 0$ for $n \geq 1$. But this indicates that $f(z)$ has no essential singularity, contrary to hypothesis. Thus, there exist values of z in the circle $|z - a| < \rho$ for which $|f(z)| > M$. Let C be any finite complex number. We consider two cases:

(I) $f(z) - C$ has no zeros inside every circle $|z - a| = \rho$.

(II) $f(z) - C$ has such zeros.

Case (I). Select a ρ sufficiently small that, for $|z - a| < \rho$, $f(z) - C$ has no zero. Then $g(z) \equiv \dfrac{1}{f(z) - C}$ is analytic for $0 < |z - a| < \rho$. $g(z)$ has an essential singularity at $z = a$; for $f(z) = \dfrac{1}{g(x)} + c$ would be analytic if $g(z)$ had a pole, while $f(z)$ would be analytic or else have a pole if $g(z)$ were analytic. From our earlier discussion we know that there exists a point z in $|z - a| < \rho$ such that $|g(z)| > 1/\epsilon$, so that $|f(z) - C| < \epsilon$.

Case (II). If $f(z) - C$ has zeros within every circle $|z - a| = \rho$ the theorem follows immediately.

Singularities at Infinity. We shall define the properties of $f(z)$ in the neighborhood of $z = \infty$ as those of $\varphi(w) = f(1/w)$ in a neighborhood of $w = 0$. We say that $f(z)$ has a *simple pole* at infinity if $\varphi(w)$ has the same property at $w = 0$; etc. For example, $f(z) \equiv z^3$ has a triple pole at $z = \infty$ since $f(1/w) = 1/w^3$ has a triple pole at $w = 0$. Similar definitions may be given for other types of singularities at $z = \infty$.

THEOREM 20.4. *A function which is analytic everywhere, including infinity, is a constant.*

By Laurent's theorem, since $f(z)$ is analytic for all finite values

of z, $f(z) = \displaystyle\sum_{n=0}^{\infty} a_n z^n$, $f\left(\dfrac{1}{w}\right) = \displaystyle\sum_{n=0}^{\infty} \dfrac{a_n}{w^n}$. Hence $f(z) = a_0$ since

$f(1/w)$ is analytic at $w = 0$ and $a_n = 0$ for all $n > 0$.

THEOREM 20.5. *A function $f(z)$ which has no singularities other than poles is a rational function.*

Suppose that the number of poles of $f(z)$ were infinite. Then the set of poles would have a limit point (finite or infinite), and at such a point $f(z)$ would have an essential singularity, contrary to hypothesis. Hence the number of poles is finite.

Suppose the poles of $f(z)$ are of multiplicities α, β, $\cdots$, κ at the finite points a, b, $\cdots$, k, respectively. Then the function $g(z) \equiv f(z)(z - a)^\alpha \cdots (z - k)^\kappa$ is analytic except at infinity, where it may have at most a pole. Then

$$g(z) = \sum_{n=0}^{\infty} a_n z^n, \qquad g\left(\frac{1}{w}\right) = \sum_{n=0}^{\infty} \frac{a_n}{w^n}.$$

This latter series must terminate, since the singularity (if there is one) of $g(1/w)$ at the origin is a pole. This means that $g(z)$ is a polynomial, so that $f(z)$ is the quotient of two polynomials.

We leave the proof of the following theorem to the reader.

THEOREM 20.6. *A rational function has no singularities other than poles.*

EXERCISES IX

1. Show that ctn z and csc z have simple poles at $z = 0$, $\pm\pi$, $\pm 2\pi$, $\cdots$.
2. Show that tan z and sec z have simple poles at $z = \pm \pi/2, \pm \frac{3}{2}\pi$, $\cdots$.
3. Show that csc (z^2) has one double pole and an infinity of simple poles.
4. Locate the poles of each of the following functions:

$$\frac{1}{\cos z + \cos a}, \frac{1}{\sin z - \sin a}, \frac{1}{1 + z^2}, \frac{1}{1 + z^4}, \frac{1}{1 + 2z^2 + z^4}.$$

5. Discuss the type of singularity present in: sin $(1/z)$, $1/z$, $(1/z)\sin (1/z)$, $e^{1/z}$, cos $(1/z)$.
6. Prove Theorem 20.2.
7. Prove Theorem 20.6.
8. Show that each of the following functions have isolated essential singularities at $z = 0$: sin $(1/z)$, $e^{1/z}$, cos $(1/z)$.

9. Show that $e^{1/z}$ actually takes every value except 0 an infinite number of times in a neighborhood of $z = 0$. Show that $e^{1/z} \to 0$ as $z \to 0$ along the negative real axis.

10. Show that csc $(1/z)$ has a nonisolated essential singularity at $z = 0$. Show that this singular point is the limit point of the poles $z = 1/n\pi$.

21. Analytic Functions Defined by Integrals. We shall now indicate how we may extend the discussion of Sec. 33 in Chap. II to complex integrals.

THEOREM 21.1.   *Let $f(z, w)$ be an analytic function of z in a region D for each value of w on the boundary C of D. Suppose $f(z, w)$ is a continuous function of the complex variables z and w when z ranges over D and w lies on C. Then in D*

$$F(z) \equiv \int_C f(z, w)\, dw$$

is an analytic function of z in D, and

$$\frac{dF(z)}{dz} \equiv \int_C \frac{\partial f}{\partial z}\, dw.$$

THEOREM 21.2   *Suppose C in Theorem 21.1 goes to infinity, such that on any bounded part of C, $f(z, w)$ is analytic in z, and continuous in z and w. Further suppose that on any bounded part of C, subject to the restrictions of Theorem 21.1, $\int_C f(z, w)\, dw$ is uniformly convergent. Then the conclusions of Theorem 21.1 remain valid.*

EXERCISES X

1. Show that $F(z) = \int_0^\infty e^{-w} w^{z-1}\, dw$ is analytic for the region $\Re(z) > 0$.

2. In what region does the integral $\int_0^\infty e^{-2w^2}\, dw$ represent an analytic function?

22. Residues. In the neighborhood of an isolated singularity at $z = a$, a one-valued analytic function $f(z)$ may be expanded in the form

$$f(z) = \sum_{n=0}^{+\infty} a_n(z - a)^n + \sum_{n=1}^{+\infty} b_n(z - a)^{-n}. \tag{1}$$

The coefficient b_1 in this expansion is called the *residue* of $f(z)$ at $z = a$. By Laurent's expansion

$$b_1 = \frac{1}{2\pi i} \int_C f(z)\, dz, \tag{2}$$

where C is any circle with center at $z = a$ containing no other singularity of $f(z)$.

If $z = a$ is a simple pole of $f(z)$,

$$b_1 = \lim_{z \to a} (z - a) f(z). \tag{3}$$

Theorem 22.1. *Let $f(z)$ be single-valued and analytic everywhere within and on a simple closed curve C, except perhaps at a finite number of singularities z_1, z_2, $\cdots$, z_n, in the interior of C. Let R_1, R_2, $\cdots$, R_n denote the residues of $f(z)$ at z_1, $\cdots$, z_n, respectively. Then*

$$\int_C f(z)\, dz = 2\pi i (R_1 + R_2 + \cdots + R_n).$$

Let C_1, C_2, $\cdots$, C_n be circles with centers at z_1, $\cdots$, z_n, having radii so small that C_1, $\cdots$, C_n are all inside C and do not overlap. Then $f(z)$ is analytic in the region between C and these circles, so by Cauchy's theorem

$$\int_C f(z)\, dz = \int_{C_1} f(z)\, dz + \cdots + \int_{C_n} f(z)\, dz.$$

Since $\int_{C_i} f(z)\, dz = 2\pi i R_i$, the result follows.

EXERCISES XI

1. Expand $1/z$ inside a circle with center at i.
2. Expand $1/z^2$ inside a circle with center at (-1).
3. Expand $1/z^2$ in powers of $(z + i)$.
4. Expand $1/(z - 1)$ about $z = 0$ for a region inside a unit circle with center at $z = 0$. Expand $1/(z - 1)$ about $z = \infty$. In the latter case what is the region of convergence? Repeat for $\dfrac{z + 1}{(z + 3)(z + 2)}$.

5. Expand $\dfrac{1}{z^2(z + 1)^3}$ about $z = 0$; about $z = -1$.

6. Find the residue of $f(z) = \dfrac{1}{(z - a)(x - z)}$ at $z = a$. *Ans.* $\dfrac{1}{x - a}$.

7. Find the residue of $f(z) = \dfrac{1}{(z - a)^M (x - z)}$ at $z = a$.

$$Ans. \quad \frac{1}{(x - a)^M}.$$

8. Show that the zeros and poles of analytic functions are necessarily isolated.

9. Show that the reciprocal of a function analytic at a cannot have an essential singularity at a.

10. Let C be a circle of radius R and center ζ.   Show that

$$f(\zeta) = \frac{1}{2\pi r} \int_C f(z) \, ds$$

is the arithmetic mean of the values of $f(z)$ on C.

11. If the function $u(x, y)$ is harmonic; i.e., satisfies

$$\frac{\partial^2 u}{\partial x^2} + \frac{\partial^2 u}{\partial y^2} = 0,$$

there exists an analytic function whose real part equals $u(x, y)$.

23. Contour Integration.   The theory of residues is quite useful in evaluating a large number of real definite integrals.   In this method we usually take as a part of the contour the real axis, the remaining portion of the contour usually being made to tend to ∞.   We shall resort to examples to explain the method.

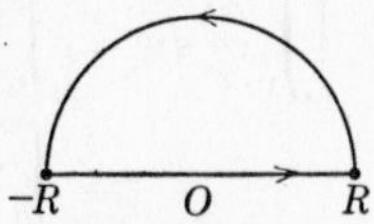

Fig. 164.

Example 1.   Show that the real integral $\int_0^{+\infty} dx/(1 + x^2) = \pi/2$.
Consider the integral

$$\int_C \frac{dz}{1 + z^2} \tag{1}$$

taken around the contour C consisting of the real axis from $-R$ to $+R$, and a semicircle on this line segment as diameter above it.   Evidently

$$\frac{1}{1 + z^2} = \frac{1}{2i}\left(\frac{1}{z - i} - \frac{1}{z + i} \right),$$

This integral has poles at $z = i$ and $z = -i$.   If we select $R > 1$, then the integrand has a pole at $z = i$ inside C, and by (3) of Sec. 22, this residue is $1/2i$.   By Theorem 22.1, the integral (1) is equal to π.   On the semicircle, $|1 + z^2| \geqq R^2 - 1$, so that the absolute value of the integral around the semicircle does not exceed $\pi R/(R^2 - 1)$.   Hence, as $R \to \infty$, the integral around the semicircle tends to 0, and

$$\int_C \frac{dz}{1 + z^2} = \lim_{R \to \infty} \int_{-R}^{+R} \frac{dx}{1 + x^2} = \pi.$$

Since $1/(1 + x^2)$ is an even function, the given integral has the value $\pi/2$.

Example 2.   Consider the integral

$$\int_C \frac{e^{iz}}{z} \, dz$$

over the contour C indicated in Fig. 165, where $0 < \rho < R$, ρ small and R large. Since e^{iz}/z is analytic and has no singularity inside C, its integral is zero, i.e.,

$$\int_\rho^R \frac{e^{ix}}{x} dx + \int_\Gamma \frac{e^{iz}}{z} dz + \int_{-R}^{-\rho} \frac{e^{ix}}{x} dx + \int_\gamma \frac{e^{iz}}{z} dz = 0. \tag{2}$$

The sum of the first and third integrals is equal to

$$\int_\rho^R \frac{e^{ix} - e^{-ix}}{x} dx = 2i \int_\rho^R \frac{\sin x}{x} dx.$$

Now

$$\left| \int_\Gamma \frac{e^{iz}}{z} dz \right| = \left| \int_0^\pi e^{iRe^{i\theta}} i \, d\theta \right| \leq \int_0^\pi e^{-R \sin \theta} \, d\theta$$

$$\leq \int_0^\delta d\theta + \int_\delta^{\pi-\delta} e^{-R \sin \delta} \, d\theta + \int_{\pi-\delta}^\pi d\theta < 2\delta + \pi e^{-R \sin \delta}.$$

By selecting δ arbitrarily small but fixed, then by choosing R sufficiently large, the middle integral here can be made as small as we please. Hence the integral along Γ tends to zero as $R \to \infty$.

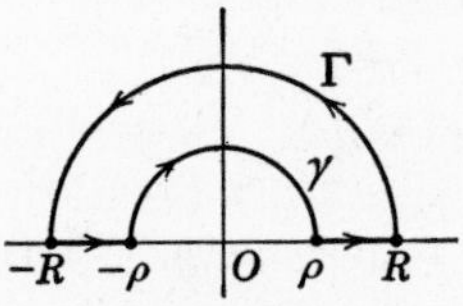

FIG. 165.

Now

$$\int_\gamma \frac{e^{iz}}{z} dz = \int_\gamma \frac{dz}{z} + \int_\gamma \frac{e^{iz} - 1}{z} dz. \tag{3}$$

By Theorem 15.4,

$$\frac{e^{iz} - 1}{z} = \frac{1 + z + \dfrac{z^2}{2!} + \cdots - 1}{z} = 1 + \frac{z}{2!} + \cdots.$$

Thus $\left| \dfrac{e^{iz} - 1}{z} \right|$ is bounded for all z with $|z| < \rho_0$, where ρ_0 is sufficiently small. The last integral in (3) approaches 0 as $\rho \to 0$. (Why?) Since

$$\int_\gamma \frac{dz}{z} = \int_\pi^0 i \, d\theta = -i\pi,$$

we obtain from (2) by letting $\rho \to 0$ and $R \to \infty$,

$$2i \int_0^\infty \frac{\sin x}{x} dx - i\pi = 0.$$

Hence

$$\int_0^\infty \frac{\sin x}{x} dx = \frac{\pi}{2}.$$

EXERCISES XII

1. Show $\displaystyle\int_{-\infty}^{+\infty} \frac{\sin kx}{1 + x^2}\, dx = 0$, and $\displaystyle\int_{0}^{+\infty} \frac{\cos kx}{1 + x^2}\, dx = \frac{\pi}{2} e^{-k}.$

HINT: Consider $\displaystyle\int_{C} \frac{e^{ikz}\, dz}{1 + z^2}$, $k > 0$, around the semicircle of Example 1. Sec. 23.

2. Show $\displaystyle\int_{0}^{+\infty} \frac{x^{a-1}}{1 + x}\, dx = \frac{\pi}{\sin a\pi}.$

HINT: Consider $\displaystyle\int_{C} \frac{z^{a-1}}{1 + z}\, dz$, $0 < a < 1$, along the contour C given above.

3. Evaluate by contour integration:

(a) $\displaystyle\int_{0}^{+\infty} \frac{dx}{1 + x^4}.$

(b) $\displaystyle\int_{0}^{+\infty} \frac{x^2\, dx}{1 + x^4}.$

(c) $\displaystyle\int_{0}^{+\infty} \frac{\cos x}{9 + x^2}\, dx.$

(d) $\displaystyle\int_{0}^{+\infty} \frac{\sin^2 x}{x^2}\, dx.$

(e) $\displaystyle\int_{0}^{+\infty} \cos x^2\, dx = \int_{0}^{+\infty} \sin x^2\, dx.$

24. Analytic Continuation.

Let $f_1(z)$ and $f_2(z)$ be analytic functions defined over the regions D_1 and D_2, respectively. Suppose D_1 and D_2 have a common part D, and suppose $f_1(z) \equiv f_2(z)$ over D. If we let $f(z)$ be such that $f(z) \equiv f_1(z)$ over D_1 and $f(z) \equiv f_2(z)$ over D_2, then $f(z)$ is analytic over the combined region $D_1 + D_2$ and $f(z)$ is called an *analytic continuation* of either $f_1(z)$ or $f_2(z)$.

Suppose $f(z)$ is represented by the series $\displaystyle\sum_{n=0}^{\infty} a_n(z - z_0)^n$ convergent in the region $|z - z_0| < R$, and suppose z_1 is a point in this region other than z_0. By Theorem 13.3 of Chap. IV we may represent $f(z)$ by the series $\displaystyle\sum_{n=0}^{\infty} b_n(z - z_1)^n$. If this series converges anywhere outside the region $|z - z_0| < R$, then this series determines an analytic continuation of the function represented by $\displaystyle\sum_{n=0}^{\infty} a_n(z - z_0)^n$. It may be shown that all possible continuations of $f(z)$ may be obtained by repeated applications of this method.

While the above determination of $f(z)$ can be shown to be unique for the region $D_1 + D_2$, yet, in general, if the domain of definition of $f_1(z)$ is extended to an arbitrary point z_0 not in D_1 by different successions of regions $D_2, D_3, \cdots$ and $D_2', D_3', \cdots$, different values may be obtained for the extended function f_1 at z_0.

EXERCISE XIII

1. Show that the function $f(z) = z - \tfrac{1}{2}z^2 + \tfrac{1}{3}z^3 - \cdots$ can be continued analytically by the representation

$$f(z) = \log 2 - \frac{1 - z}{2} - \frac{(1 - z)^2}{2 \cdot 2^2} - \frac{(1 - z)^3}{3 \cdot 2^3} - \cdots.$$

PART E.   CONFORMAL MAPPING.   APPLICATIONS

25. Conformal Mapping. As we have previously remarked, equations of the type $w = f(z)$ may be regarded as transformations which define a correspondence between points of the w and z-planes. As a point z moves along any curve C in the z-plane, the corresponding point (or points) w will trace a curve (or curves) Γ in the w-plane. We then say that the curve C in the z-plane is *mapped* upon Γ in the w-plane. Likewise, if z ranges over a region S in the z-plane, then w ranges over a region (or regions) Σ in the w-plane and we say that S is *mapped* upon Σ.

We say that the mapping $w = f(z)$ is *biunique* if the function $w = f(z)$ gives but one value of w in Σ for each value of z in S, and if there exists an *inverse* function $z = F(w)$ defined throughout Σ such that $z = F(w)$ gives but one value of z in S for each w in Σ. What are the necessary properties of $f(z)$ to be fulfilled in order that the mapping $w = f(z)$ be biunique?

Let (x, y) be a point P in S, and let (u, v) be the corresponding point Q in Σ. Suppose $w = f(z)$ is analytic and single-valued in S, where $z = x + iy$ and $w = u + iv$,

$$u = u(x, y), \qquad v = v(x, y). \tag{1}$$

From Theorem 20.2 of Chap. I, we know that if $J(u, v/x, y) \neq 0$ over S, then equations (1) can be solved for x and y as functions of u and v,

$$x = x(u, v), \qquad y = y(u, v), \tag{2}$$

the solution (2) is unique, and equations (2) define the *inverse* function $z = F(w) = x(u, v) + iy(u, v)$. But $f(z)$ being analytic, $\partial u/\partial x = \partial v/\partial y$ and $\partial u/\partial y = -\partial v/\partial x$, so that

$$J\!\left(\frac{u,\,v}{x,\,y}\right) = \begin{vmatrix} \dfrac{\partial u}{\partial x} & \dfrac{\partial u}{\partial y} \\[2mm] \dfrac{\partial v}{\partial x} & \dfrac{\partial v}{\partial y} \end{vmatrix} = \left(\frac{\partial u}{\partial x}\right)^2 + \left(\frac{\partial v}{\partial x}\right)^2 = \left|\frac{\partial u}{\partial x} + i\frac{\partial v}{\partial x}\right|^2 = |f'(z)|^2.$$

Hence *a sufficient condition that* $w = f(z)$ *define a biunique correspondence between the points of* S *and* Σ *is that* $f'(z) \neq 0$ *over* S.

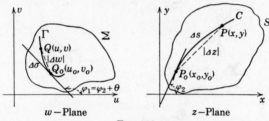

w — Plane   z — Plane

Fig. 166.

Let P_0 be the point in S corresponding to the complex number z_0, and let Q_0 be the point of Σ corresponding to the complex number $w_0 = f(z_0)$. Through P_0 draw some curve C in S. Let Γ be the curve through Q_0 in Σ corresponding to C. Select some point P on C distinct from P_0 and call Q the corresponding point on Γ. Let Δs be the length of the arc $\overparen{P_0P}$ of C and let $\Delta\sigma$ be the length of the arc $\overparen{Q_0Q}$ of Γ. Since $f(z)$ is continuous over S [for $f(z)$ is analytic over S], $\Delta\sigma \to 0$ as $\Delta s \to 0$. Assume $f(z)$ to be such that the *scale* is constant at Q_0, i.e., $\lim\limits_{\Delta s \to 0} (\Delta\sigma/\Delta s)$ exists and is the same for *all* curves (having arc lengths) in S with initial point P_0. The length of the chord $\overline{P_0P}$ in S is $|z - z_0| = |\Delta z|$, and the length of the chord $\overline{Q_0Q}$ in Σ is $|w - w_0| = |\Delta w|$. Assume $f(z)$ to be such that

$$\lim_{\Delta s \to 0}\frac{\Delta\sigma}{\Delta s} = \lim_{\Delta s \to 0}\left|\frac{\Delta w}{\Delta z}\right|.$$

If $w = f(z)$ is analytic in S, we know that $\lim\limits_{\Delta s \to 0} (\Delta w/\Delta s) = f'(z_0)$, no matter how $\Delta z \to 0$ and $\Delta s \to 0$. Thus the *scale function* for f at z_0 is $|f'(z_0)|$.

Let C_1 and C_2 be two curves in S through z_0, intersecting at an angle α. Suppose C_1 and C_2 are then mapped by the transformation $w = f(z)$ into the curves Γ_1 and Γ_2 on the w-plane. If the angle between Γ_1 and Γ_2 is equal to α, the mapping is said to be *isogonal*. If the sense of rotation of a tangent is preserved, an isogonal transformation is called *conformal*. We shall now show that *the transformation $w = f(z)$ is conformal when $f(z)$ is analytic with $f'(z) \neq 0$ over S*. Suppose $f'(z_0) \neq 0$. Write $f'(z_0)$, Δw, and Δz in the polar forms $f'(z_0) = \rho e^{i\theta}$, $\Delta w = \rho_1 e^{i\theta_1}$, $\Delta z = \rho_2 e^{i\theta_2}$,

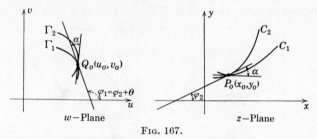

w-Plane z-Plane

Fig. 167.

$(\rho, \rho_1, \rho_2 > 0)$, where θ_1 and θ_2 are taken as the principal amplitudes of Δw and Δz, respectively. Then

$$f'(z_0) = \lim_{\Delta z \to 0} \frac{\Delta w}{\Delta z} = \lim_{\Delta z \to 0} \frac{\rho_1 e^{i\theta_1}}{\rho_2 e^{i\theta_2}} = \rho e^{i\theta},$$

and

$$\rho = \lim_{\Delta z \to 0} \frac{\rho_1}{\rho_2}, \qquad \theta = \lim_{\Delta z \to 0} (\theta_1 - \theta_2).$$

Let φ_2 be the angle which the tangent to C at P_0 makes with the x-axis and φ_1 the angle which the tangent to Γ at Q_0 makes with the u-axis. Then as $\Delta z \to 0$, $\theta_2 \to \varphi_2$ and $\theta_1 \to \varphi_1$. Hence $\theta = \varphi_1 - \varphi_2$. Here θ is the angle through which the curve C is turned during the mapping process. Since $f'(z_0)$ is a non-vanishing constant, θ is a constant for all curves through z_0. Thus, every curve through z_0 is turned through the same angle θ. In particular C_1 and C_2 make the same angle as Γ_1 and Γ_2. Thus the mapping is not only isogonal, but it is conformal.

The scale function $|f'(z_0)| = |\rho e^{i\theta}| = \rho = \lim_{\Delta z \to 0} (\rho_1/\rho_2)$ is known as the *ratio of magnification*.

If the curves C_1 and C_2 are mapped onto the w-plane by the conjugate $w^* = u - iv$ of w, the resulting configuration is symmetric (with respect to the u-axis) to the configuration resulting from $w = f(z)$, for the direction from Γ_1 to Γ_2 is merely reversed in the mapping w^*.   Mapping with w^* is thus *isogonal with reversal of angle.*

Example 1.   Discuss the transformation $w = z^2$ and its inverse.

Since $w = u + iv = z^2 = (x + iy)^2 = x^2 - y^2 + 2xyi$, then
$$u = x^2 - y^2, \qquad v = 2xy.$$

The ratio of magnification at (x_0, y_0) is $|f'(z_0)| = |2z_0| = 2\sqrt{x_0^2 + y_0^2}$. Evidently, the greater the distance from (x_0, y_0) to $(0, 0)$, the greater is the magnification.   The representation will be conformal everywhere except when $f'(z_0) = 2z_0 = 0$.

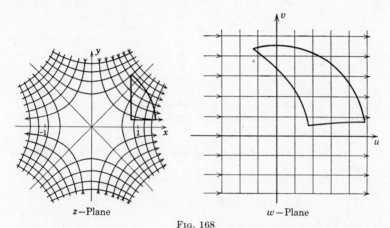

z—Plane   w—Plane

Fig. 168

If we let $z = \rho e^{i\theta}$, then $w = z^2 = \rho^2 e^{i(2\theta)} \equiv \lambda e^{i\psi}$.   Since $\psi = 2\theta$, we see that if z describes an arc subtending an angle θ at $(0, 0)$, then w describes an arc in the w-plane which subtends an angle 2θ at its origin.   In fact, half the z-plane maps into the whole of the w-plane.   Evidently, the positive x-axis maps into the positive u-axis, the positive y-axis corresponds to the negative u-axis, and the first quadrant of the z-plane is mapped on the upper half of the w-plane (see Fig. 155(a) and (b)).

The straight lines $x = c_1$ in the z-plane map into the family of parabolas

$$\begin{aligned} u &= c_1^2 - y^2, \\ v &= 2c_1 y, \end{aligned} \qquad \text{or} \qquad v^2 = 4c_1^2(c_1^2 - u), \qquad (\mathcal{P}_1)$$

on the w-plane, and the family of lines $y = c_2$ maps into the family of parabolas

$$\begin{aligned} u &= x^2 - c_2^2, \\ v &= 2c_2 x, \end{aligned} \qquad \text{or} \qquad v^2 = 4c_2^2(u + c_2^2). \qquad (\mathcal{P}_2)$$

The families $(\mathcal{P}_1)$ and $(\mathcal{P}_2)$ are orthogonal.

The straight lines $u = k_1$, $v = k_2$, on the w-plane map into the orthogonal families of hyperbolas

$$x^2 - y^2 = k_1, \qquad 2xy = k_2$$

As a further illustration, the region indicated in Fig. 168 of the z-plane maps into the indicated region in the w-plane.

EXERCISES XIV

Discuss each of the following transformations and their inverses. Illustrate with sketches. State where the conformal property fails (if anywhere). Give the magnification.

1. $w = z^3$.
2. $w = z^n$.
3. $w = z^{-1}$.
4. $w = z^{-n}$.
5. $w = e^z$.
6. $w = \sin z$.
7. $w = \cosh z$.
8. $w = \log z$.

9. $w = (1-z)/(1+z)$.
10. $w = \log \dfrac{z-1}{z+1}$.

11. $w = z + (1/z)$.
12. $w = 2z + (3/z)$.
13. $w = \sqrt{z}$.
14. $w = \tan z$.
15. $w = z + e^z$.

16. Reconsider Exs. III, 20 to 23, from the point of view of conformal mapping.

17. Let A, B, C be three complex constants. (a) Then

$$(A + A^*)zz^* + Bz + B^*z^* + C + C^* = 0 \qquad \text{(i)}$$

is a real circle or a straight line if

$$BB^* > (A + A^*)(C + C^*). \qquad \text{(ii)}$$

(b) Prove conversely that every real circle and every real straight line can be represented by such an equation with the restriction given in (a).

18. Consider the transformations

$$w = z + \lambda, \qquad \text{(iii)}$$
$$w = \mu z, \qquad \text{(iv)}$$
$$w = \frac{1}{z}. \qquad \text{(v)}$$

(a) Show that (v) transforms those circles and lines of (i) for which $C + C^* = 0$ into straight lines which pass through $z = 0$. (For this reason, straight lines which pass through $z = \infty$ are called circles.)

(b) Prove that the result of applying successively any finite number of transformations of the form

$$w = \frac{\alpha z + \beta}{\gamma z + \delta}, \qquad \text{(vi)}$$

when α, β, γ, δ are constants and

$$\alpha\delta - \beta\gamma \neq 0, \tag{vii}$$

is a transformation of form (vi).

(c) Show that any (bilinear) transformation (vi) can be obtained by means of transformations (iii), (iv), (v), and hence (vi) transforms circles into circles.

(d) Show that the inverse transformation of (vi) is

$$z = \frac{-\delta w + \beta}{\gamma w - \alpha}, \qquad (\alpha\delta - \beta\gamma) \neq 0. \tag{viii}$$

(e) Show that the result of first performing the transformation (vi) and then the transformation

$$\bar{w} = \frac{\alpha_1 w + \beta_1}{\gamma_1 w + \delta_1}, \qquad (\alpha_1\delta_1 - \beta_1\gamma_1) \neq 0 \tag{ix}$$

results in a third transformation of the same type,

$$\bar{w} = \frac{Az + B}{\Gamma z + \Delta},$$

with

$$A\Delta - B\Gamma = (\alpha\delta - \beta\gamma)(\alpha_1\delta_1 - \beta_1\gamma_1) \neq 0.$$

This shows that the set of all bilinear transformations forms a *group*.

(f) If the point $z = \infty$ be added to the z-plane show that every bilinear transformation forms a one-to-one transformation of the closed z-plane into itself.

(g) Show that if $\gamma \neq 0$, $w = \alpha/\gamma$ in (vii) corresponds to $z = \infty$, and $w = \infty$ in (vi) to $z = -\delta/\gamma$. If $\gamma = 0$, then $z = \infty$ corresponds to $w = \infty$.

(h) By computing dw/dz, show that the transformation is conformal except at $z = \infty$ and $z = -\delta/\gamma$.

A function $w = f(z)$ is said to transform the neighborhood of z_0 conformally into a neighborhood of $w = \infty$ if $\eta = 1/f(z)$ transforms the neighborhood of z_0 conformally into a neighborhood of $\eta = 0$. $w = f(z)$ is said to transform the neighborhood of $z = \infty$ conformally into a neighborhood of w_0 if $w = \phi(\xi) = f(1/\xi)$ transforms the neighborhood of $\xi = 0$ conformally into a neighborhood of w_0. (Here w_0 may be ∞.)

(i) Prove: Every bilinear transformation gives a one-to-one conformal representation of the entire closed z-plane on the entire closed w-plane.

The theory of the bilinear transformation has found wide application in certain branches of engineering, for example as in the theory of "circle diagrams" as used by some electrical engineers.

19. Let us consider a fluid flowing over the z-plane. Let the components of velocity at $z = x + iy$ be $u(x, y)$ and $v(x, y)$. Recall that the *velocity potential* $\varphi(x, y)$ is defined by the relation

$$\varphi(x_0, y_0) = \int_{a,b}^{x_0,y_0} u\,dx + v\,dy,$$

where $d\varphi = u\,dx + v\,dy$ is exact. Likewise the *stream function* $\psi(x, y)$ is given by

$$\psi(x_0, y_0) = \int_{a,b}^{x_0,y_0} -v\,dx + u\,dy,$$

where again $d\psi = -v\,dx + u\,dy$ is exact. The function

$$w = f(z) = \varphi + i\psi$$

is an analytic function of z. (Why?) We shall call w the *general potential function*. The *streamlines* lie along $\psi = $ const.

Example 1. Suppose $w = z^2 = (x + iy)^2 = (x^2 - y^2) + (2xy)i$. Since $w = \varphi + i\psi$, we see that $\varphi = x^2 - y^2$, $\psi = 2xy$, and $u = \partial\varphi/\partial x = 2x$, $v = \partial\varphi/\partial y = -2y$. We can also find u and v from the fact that

$$\frac{dw}{dz} = u - iv = 2z = 2x + 2yi.$$

Example 2. Given $\varphi = x^2 - y^2$. Find ψ.

Solution. $\psi = \displaystyle\int_{0,0}^{x,y} -v\,dx + u\,dy = \int_{0,0}^{x,y} -\frac{\partial\varphi}{\partial y}\,dx + \frac{\partial\varphi}{\partial x}\,dy$

$$= \int_{0,0}^{x,y} 2y\,dx + 2x\,dy = 2xy.$$

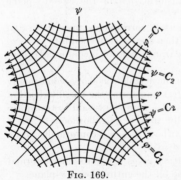

Fig. 169.

(a) Give a physical interpretation to ψ.

(b) Prove that the curves $\varphi = $ const. and $\psi = $ const. are orthogonal.

(c) Show that $dw/dz = u - iv$.

(d) Show that $u = \partial\varphi/\partial x = \partial\psi/\partial y$, $v = \partial\varphi/\partial y = -\partial\psi/\partial x$.

(e) Show that in polar coordinates

$$d\varphi = n\,dr + cr\,d\theta,$$
$$d\psi = nr\,d\theta - c\,dr,$$

where n is the component of the velocity in the direction of the radius vector, and c is the component normal to the radius vector at the point (r, θ).

(f) Given $\psi = 2xy$, find φ. (Fig. 169.)

(g) If $w = (a + ib)z$, find $\varphi, \psi, u, v, dw/dz$.

(h) If $w = \log z = \log r + i\theta$, find $\varphi, \psi, u, v, dw/dz$.

Ans. $\varphi = \log r$, $\psi = \theta$, $c = 0$, $u = (\cos\theta)/r$, $v = (\sin\theta)/r$, $dw/dz = 1/z$.

(i) Prove the velocity at any point is inversely proportional to the lengths of the intercepts on successive lines φ = const. cut off between adjacent lines ψ = const.

(j) Fluid flows with constant velocity U parallel to the x-axis. Show that $\varphi = Ux$, $\psi = Uy$, and that $w = \varphi + i\psi = Uz$.

(k) Show that, if fluid flows with constant velocity V parallel to the y-axis, then $w = -iVz$.

(l) If the fluid flows with constant velocity at an angle of 30° with the x-axis, find w. Find w when the components U and V are constant. [*Ans.* $w = (U - iV)z$.] Find the streamlines in this case, and plot.

(m) Show that the velocity along a streamline at any point is directly proportional to the space rate of change of velocity potential at this point in the direction of the streamline, and hence is inversely proportional to the spacing of the curves φ = const. along the streamline.

(n) Show that, for the flow $w = \varphi + i\psi$, the divergence of the velocity of the fluid equals

$$(\partial U/\partial x) + (\partial V/\partial y) = 0.$$

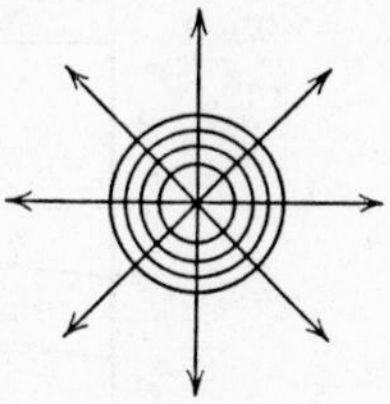

20. Suppose a fluid flows over a plane surface. A point P from which the fluid flows out (in) in all directions in a uniform manner is called a *source* (*sink*). The

Fig. 170.

total flow per unit of time across a small closed curve about P is called the *strength* of the source. The strength is taken to be positive for a source, negative for a sink. Suppose n denotes the radial velocity of the fluid from source O at a distance r from O. Then the strength m of the source is $m = 2\pi r n$. If O is the origin, then the x and y components of the radial velocity are

$$u = \frac{m \cos \theta}{2\pi r} = \frac{m}{2\pi} \frac{x}{x^2 + y^2}, \qquad v = \frac{m \sin \theta}{2\pi} \frac{1}{r} = \frac{m}{2\pi} \frac{y}{x^2 + y^2}.$$

Since $d\varphi = u\, dx + v\, dy$, we see $\varphi = (m/2\pi) \log r = (m/4\pi) \log (x^2 + y^2)$. The stream function is $\psi = (m/2\pi) \operatorname{Tan}^{-1} (y/x) = (m/2\pi)\theta$, so that $w = \varphi + i\psi = (m/2\pi) \log z = (m/2\pi) \log (x + iy)$. Show that this motion is irrotational. (HINT: Show circulation is zero.) (Fig. 170.)

Prove that if the source is at (a, b),

$$\varphi = \frac{m}{4\pi} \log [(x - a)^2 + (y - b)^2], \qquad \psi = \frac{m}{2\pi} \operatorname{Tan}^{-1} \frac{(y - b)}{(x - a)},$$

and

$$w = \frac{m}{2\pi} \log [z - (a + ib)].$$

21. Prove that, if two rectilinear-plane flow fields of potentials w_1 and w_2 be superimposed, the resulting flow field is represented by $w = w_1 + w_2$.

22. Show that, if a source be assumed at the origin and a rectilinear flow along the x-axis be superimposed, the potential of the resulting flow is $w = -Uz + (m/2\pi) \log z$. Plot a few streamlines. (Fig. 171.)

23. Repeat Ex. 22 with a sink instead of a source.

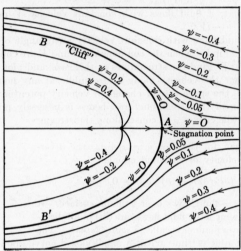

FIG. 171.

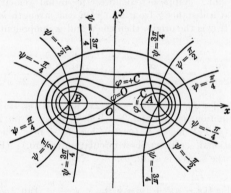

FIG. 172.

24. Repeat Ex. 22 for two sources of equal strength located at $(a, 0)$ and $(-a, 0)$. (HINT: Add w_1 and w_2.) (Fig. 172.)

Ans. $\varphi = (m/2\pi) \log r_1 r_2$, $w = (m/2\pi) \log (z + a)(z - a)$.

Find u and v. Write equation of streamlines and plot. (NOTE: All streamlines pass through one source or the other.)

Find a *point of stagnation*, that is, a point where the velocity is zero. Show that the y-axis passing through the stagnation point separates the two parts of the joint field. This means that this streamline can be replaced by a rigid smooth barrier without in the least interfering with the flow from either source.   We may then suppress the flow from either source without in any way disturbing that from the other.   We thus arrive at the field on one side of the y-axis as representing the flow for a source placed near an indefinite straight barrier.

25. Repeat Ex. 22 for two sinks of equal strength.

26. Repeat Ex. 22 for two sources of unequal strength.

$$Ans. \quad w = (m_1/2\pi) \log (z + a) + (m_2/2\pi) \log (z - a).$$

Find u, v, and the point of stagnation.   Find the streamline passing through the stagnation point.

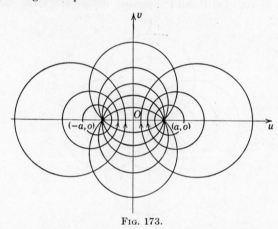

Fig. 173.

27. Repeat Ex. 22 for a source and sink of equal strength.

$$Ans. \quad w = \frac{m}{2\pi} \log \frac{z - a}{z + a}.$$

Plot streamlines.   Show that there is no point of stagnation (Fig. 173).

28. Repeat Ex. 22 for source and sink of unequal strength.

$$Ans. \quad w = (m_1/2\pi) \log (z + a) - (m_2/2\pi) \log (z - a).$$

Show that the streamlines are partly open and partly closed.   Find the point of stagnation.

29. Repeat Ex. 22 for rectilinear flow with source and sink of equal strength. $\qquad Ans. \quad w = -Uz + \dfrac{m}{2\pi} \log \dfrac{z - a}{z + a}.$

Plot streamlines.   Find the point of stagnation.

30. In a field known as *vortex* flow in a plane outside a circular barrier of radius r,

$$n = \text{velocity along radius} = 0,$$

$$c = \text{velocity perpendicular to radius} = \frac{\Gamma}{2\pi r},$$

where Γ is the *strength* of the *vortex core*.   Then

$$d\varphi = cr \, d\theta + n \, dr, \qquad \text{so that} \qquad \varphi = \frac{\Gamma}{2\pi}\theta,$$

and

$$d\psi = nr\, d\theta - c\, dr, \qquad \psi = -\frac{\Gamma}{2\pi} \log \frac{r}{a}.$$

For the ideal vortex sheet, a may be taken very small. Then

$$w = \frac{\Gamma}{2\pi}\theta - i\frac{\Gamma}{2\pi} \log \frac{r}{a} = -\frac{i\Gamma}{2\pi} \log z.$$

Compare w for a vortex with w for a simple source.

31. Let P at $(a, 0)$ be a source of strength m and P' at $(-a, 0)$ be a sink of strength $(-m)$. Let P and P' approach the origin O along the real axis

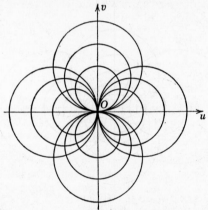

FIG. 174.

in such a way that $2ma = k$ is a constant. Find the velocity potential. What is the stream function? What are the lines of flow? Lines of equal velocity potential? Plot. (Fig. 174.) This case is known as the *plane doublet* of strength k.   *Ans.* $w = -M/z$, where $M = am/\pi$.

32. Find the general potential function for the following types of flow:

(a) A superposition of a rectilinear flow with a doublet.

(b) A superposition of a rectilinear flow, a doublet flow, and a vortex flow, the vortex center being at the doublet.

$$Ans. \quad w = -Uz - (M/z) - iK \log z.$$

Plot streamlines and find points of stagnation.

33. Suppose sources of strengths $k_1, k_2, \cdots, k_n$ occur at the points $\alpha_1, \alpha_2, \cdots, \alpha_n$, respectively, and sinks $s_1, s_2, \cdots, s_m$ occur at the points $\beta_1, \beta_2, \cdots, \beta_m$, respectively. Show that

$$w = \log \frac{(z - \alpha_1)^{k_1}(z - \alpha_2)^{k_2} \cdots (z - \alpha_n)^{k_n}}{(z - \beta_1)^{s_1}(z - \beta_2)^{s_2} \cdots (z - \beta_m)^{s_m}}, \qquad \text{where} \qquad w = \varphi + i\psi.$$

34. Determine the value of n so that $w = z^n$ will determine an irrotational flow of a fluid between two walls making an angle $60°$ with each other. Find velocity potential and direction of flow at the point $z_0 = 3$; at $z_1 = 3(e^{50°i})$.

35. In a certain electrostatic field the lines of equipotential are given by $\psi = c_1$ and the lines of force are given by $\varphi = c_2$, where c_1 and c_2 are arbitrary constants. Make a map to show these lines for the case when $w = \varphi + i\psi$:

(a) $w = z$;
(b) $w = z^2$;
(c) $w = 1/z$;
(d) $w = z^3$;
(e) $w = z^{\frac{1}{2}}$;
(f) $w = z^{\frac{2}{3}}$;
(g) $w = z^{\frac{3}{2}}$.
(h) $w = z^n$;
(i) $z = w + e^w$.

36. Wires pierce the complex plane at $P(1, 0)$ and $P'(-1, 0)$. The wire through P carries a current of two units and the wire through P' a current one unit. The function $w = \varphi + i\psi$ determines the equipotential lines and the lines of force in the magnetic field about the two conductors. Show that $w = \log \dfrac{(z-1)^2}{(z+1)}$. Find points of equilibrium. Map.

37. (a) We defined $w = \varphi + i\psi$ with the assumption of irrotational flow. Under this assumption, show that

$$\frac{\partial^2 \varphi}{\partial x^2} + \frac{\partial^2 \varphi}{\partial y^2} = 0, \qquad \frac{\partial^2 \psi}{\partial x^2} + \frac{\partial^2 \psi}{\partial y^2} = 0.$$

(b) Suppose $\psi = x^2 + y^2$ for a certain flow. Find u and v. Show that a general potential function does not exist. (Why?)

(c) Plot the streamlines in (b).

(d) Calculate the circulation around a circle of radius a with center at the origin. (*Ans.* $-4\pi a^2$.) Note that $(\partial^2 \psi/\partial x^2) + (\partial^2 \psi/\partial y^2) = -4$. $2w = -4$ is called the *vorticity* and w is the angular velocity of the vortex.

38. Consider the mapping function $w = 1/z$, with $w \equiv \varphi + i\psi$.

(a) Express φ and ψ as functions of x and y.

(b) Make two diagrams showing how the z-plane is mapped into the w-plane. Into what curves do $\varphi = $ const. map in the z-plane? The curves $\psi = $ const.?

(c) Find all invariant points which are unchanged by the transformation.

Ans. $z = 1, -1$.

(d) Find the singular points (i.e., points where $dw/dz = 0$).

(e) The unit circle $z = e^{i\theta}$ is transformed into what curve in the w-plane?

(f) Quadrant I of the z-plane outside the unit circle is transformed into what region in the w-plane?

(g) Quadrant I of the z-plane inside the unit circle is transformed into what region of the w-plane?

39. Consider the mapping function $w = \dfrac{1}{2}\left(z + \dfrac{1}{z}\right)$.

(a) Find φ and ψ, when $w \equiv \varphi + i\psi$ is a general potential function.

(b) Into what curves in the z-plane do the curves $\varphi = $ const. map? $\psi = $ const.?

(c) Find the invariant points of the transformation.

Ans. $z = 0, 1, -1$.

(d) Find the singular points.

Ans. $z = 1, -1$.

(e) Show that the unit circle in the z-plane is transformed into the portion of the φ-axis between $(1, 0)$ and $(-1, 0)$.

(f) Show that the positive half of the real axis in the z-plane is transformed into the real axis of φ between 1 and $+\infty$.

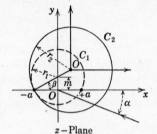

z – Plane

(g) Into what does the negative half of the real axis map?

(h) Let $z = re^{i\theta}$. Show that the lines $\theta = $ const. go into hyperbolas with foci $(\pm 1, 0)$, $(\varphi^2/\cos^2 \theta) - (\psi^2/\sin^2 \theta) = 1$.

(i) Show that the circles $r = $ const. go into ellipses:

$$\frac{4\varphi^2}{(r + r^{-1})^2} + \frac{4\psi^2}{(r - r^{-1})^2} = 1.$$

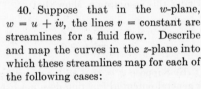
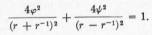

w – Plane
Fig. 175.

40. Suppose that in the w-plane, $w = u + iv$, the lines $v = $ constant are streamlines for a fluid flow. Describe and map the curves in the z-plane into which these streamlines map for each of the following cases:

(a) $w = 3z$.   (b) $w = z^2$.
(c) $w = z^3$.   (d) $w = z^4$.
(e) $w = z^{2/3}$.   (f) $(w = z^n$.

41. Describe how each of the following curves in the z-plane is mapped into the w-plane by means of the transformation $w = z + (2/z)$. Make a map in each case. Plot $\psi = 0.5$, 1, 2, 3, in each case.

(a) The circle $z = \sqrt{2}e^{i\theta}$.

(b) A circle of radius 1.2 with center at $(0.1, 0)$.

(c) A circle of radius 1.2 with center at $(0, 0.1)$.

(d) A circle of radius 1.2 with center at $(0.1, 0.1)$.

(e) The circle of radius 2.0 and center at $(0.5, 1.0)$, and the circle of radius 1.3 and center at $(0, 0.7)$.

For the transformation used above, find the singular points; the stagnation points; and map the stream lines $\psi = $ const.

The methods of complex variables have been found quite useful in aerodynamics. The preceding problem is taken from the *Joukowsky-aerofoil theory*, where transformations of the form $w = z + (a^2/z)$ are used. A typical figure is shown in Fig. 175. By varying the center and radius of the circle, various figures may be obtained resembling aerofoil shapes.

PART F.   ELLIPTIC INTEGRALS

26. Introduction. We have seen in Chap. II that every integral of the type

$$\int R(x, \sqrt[n]{ax + b}) \, dx \qquad \text{or} \qquad \int R(x, \sqrt{ax^2 + bx + c}) \, dx,$$

where R is a rational function of the arguments indicated, can be evaluated in terms of elementary functions. (See Chap. II, Secs. 7, 8.)

We here wish to study certain integrals having algebraic integrands which cannot be evaluated in terms of only "elementary functions." In particular, an important class of integrals which require new functions for their evaluation are integrals of the type

$$\int R(x, \sqrt{a_0 x^3 + a_1 x^2 + a_2 x + a_3}) \, dx, \qquad (1)$$

and

$$\int R(x, \sqrt{a_0 x^4 + a_1 x^3 + a_2 x^2 + a_3 x + a_4}) \, dx. \qquad (2)$$

It can be shown that the functions introduced to evaluate (2) can be used to evaluate (1). The evaluation of (2) can be reduced to the evaluation of the following types of integrals, known as Legendre's normal forms:

$$u \equiv \int_0^x \frac{dt}{\sqrt{(1 - t^2)(1 - k^2 t^2)}}, \qquad (3)$$

$$\int_0^x \sqrt{\frac{1 - k^2 t^2}{1 - t^2}} \, dt, \qquad (4)$$

$$\int_0^x \frac{dt}{(t^2 - a)\sqrt{(1 - t^2)(1 - k^2 t^2)}}. \qquad (5)$$

These integrals are called *incomplete elliptic integrals* of the *first*, *second*, and *third kind*, respectively. It is customary to take $0 < k^2 < 1$ in these integrals. More generally, any integral of the type (2), in which

$$a_0 x^4 + a_1 x^3 + a_2 x^2 + a_3 x + a_4 = 0$$

has no multiple roots, is called an *elliptic integral*. The variables x and t may be either complex or real.

Upon substituting $t = \sin \psi$ in the integrals (3), (4), and (5), we obtain, respectively,

$$\int_{\psi=0}^{\psi=\varphi} \frac{d\psi}{\sqrt{1 - k^2 \sin^2 \psi}} \equiv F(k, \varphi), \qquad (6)$$

$$\int_{\psi=0}^{\psi=\varphi} \sqrt{1 - k^2 \sin^2 \psi}\, d\psi \equiv E(k,\,\varphi), \tag{7}$$

$$\int_{\psi=0}^{\psi=\varphi} \frac{d\psi}{(\sin^2 \psi - a)\sqrt{1 - k^2 \sin^2 \psi}}. \tag{8}$$

The integral

$$\int_{\psi=0}^{\psi=\pi/2} \frac{d\psi}{\sqrt{1 - k^2 \sin^2 \psi}} = \int_0^1 \frac{dt}{\sqrt{(1 - t^2)(1 - k^2 t^2)}}$$

$$= F\!\left(k,\,\frac{\pi}{2}\right) \equiv K(k), \qquad (0 < k^2 < 1) \tag{9}$$

is called *the complete elliptic integral of the first kind.* The integral

$$\int_{\psi=0}^{\psi=\pi/2} \frac{d\psi}{\sqrt{1 - k'^2 \sin^2 \psi}}$$

$$= \int_0^1 \frac{dt}{\sqrt{(1 - t^2)(1 - k'^2 t^2)}} \equiv K'(k') \tag{10}$$

is called the *associated elliptic integral of the first kind,* and $k' = \sqrt{1 - k^2}$ is *the modulus complementary to the modulus k.*

27. The Elliptic Functions sn u, cn u, dn u. Let the elliptic integral in (6) in Sec. 26 be denoted by z. Then the relation

$$z = F(k,\,\varphi) \tag{1}$$

defines z as a function of k and φ. The number φ is known as the *amplitude* of the integral z, and k the *modulus* of z. Suppose that k is fixed. Then (1) defines φ as a function of z which we denote by

$$\varphi = \text{am } z. \tag{2}$$

Since $x = \sin \varphi$ and z is equal to the integral u given in (3) in Sec. 26,

$$x = \sin (\text{am } u), \tag{3}$$

or more briefly,

$$x = \text{sn } u. \tag{4}$$

The expressions $\sqrt{1 - x^2}$ and $\sqrt{1 - k^2 x^2}$ appearing in (3) in Sec. 26 define the functions cn u and dn u,

$$\pm\sqrt{1 - \text{sn}^2 u} = \pm\sqrt{1 - x^2} = \cos (\text{am } u) \equiv \text{cn } u, \tag{5}$$

$$\pm\sqrt{1 - k^2 \text{sn}^2 u} = \pm\sqrt{1 - k^2 x^2} = \Delta \cos (\text{am } u) \equiv \text{dn } u. \tag{6}$$

[The sign to be used may be determined from (5) or (6) in Sec. 3.]
To complete the definitions of these functions we require

$$\text{sn } 0 = 0, \quad \text{cn } 0 = 1, \quad \text{dn } 0 = 1. \tag{7}$$

The functions sn, cn, and dn are called the *Jacobi elliptic functions*.

28. Derivatives of Elliptic Functions. Upon differentiating the integral u in equation (3) of Sec. 26, we find that

$$\frac{du}{dx} = \frac{1}{\sqrt{(1 - x^2)(1 - k^2 x^2)}}. \tag{1}$$

Since $\dfrac{dx}{du} = \dfrac{1}{du/dx}$ and $x = \text{sn } u$, we have

$$\frac{d \text{ sn } u}{du} = \sqrt{(1 - x^2)(1 - k^2 x^2)} = \sqrt{1 - \text{sn}^2 u} \cdot \sqrt{1 - k^2 \text{ sn}^2 u}$$

$$= \text{cn } u \text{ dn } u. \tag{2}$$

From (5) and (6) of Sec. 27, we find that

$$\frac{d \text{ cn } u}{du} = \frac{-\text{sn } u \dfrac{d \text{ sn } u}{du}}{\sqrt{1 - \text{sn}^2 u}} = -\text{sn } u \text{ dn } u, \tag{3}$$

and

$$\frac{d \text{ dn } u}{du} = -k^2 \text{ sn } u \text{ cn } u. \tag{4}$$

By means of Maclaurin's series we find that

$$\text{sn } u = u - (1 + k^2)\frac{u^3}{3!} + (1 + 14k^2 + k^4)\frac{u^5}{5!} + \cdots, \tag{5}$$

$$\text{cn } u = 1 - \frac{u^2}{2!} + (1 + 4k^2)\frac{u^4}{4!}$$
$$- (1 + 44k^2 + 16k^4)\frac{u^6}{6!} + \cdots, \tag{6}$$

$$\text{dn } u = 1 - k^2\frac{u^2}{2!} + k^2(4 + k^2)\frac{u^4}{4!}$$
$$- k^2(16 + 44k^2 + k^4)\frac{u^6}{6!} + \cdots. \tag{7}$$

These series may be shown to converge.

From (5), (6), and (7) it is easy to see that sn is odd and that cn and dn are even functions, i.e.,

$$\text{sn } (-u) = -\text{sn } (u), \text{ cn } (-u) = \text{cn } (u), \text{ dn } (-u) = \text{dn } (u). \tag{8}$$

29. Addition Formulas. We shall indicate how it may be shown that

$$\text{sn }(u + v) = \frac{\text{sn }u \cdot \text{cn }v \cdot \text{dn }v + \text{sn }v \cdot \text{cn }u \cdot \text{dn }u}{1 - k^2 \text{ sn}^2 u \cdot \text{sn}^2 v}, \tag{1}$$

$$\text{cn }(u + v) = \frac{\text{cn }u \cdot \text{cn }v - \text{sn }u \cdot \text{sn }v \cdot \text{dn }u \cdot \text{dn }v}{1 - k^2 \text{ sn}^2 u \cdot \text{sn}^2 v}, \tag{2}$$

$$\text{dn }(u + v) = \frac{\text{dn }u \cdot \text{dn }v - k^2 \text{ sn }u \cdot \text{sn }v \cdot \text{cn }u \cdot \text{cn }v}{1 - k^2 \text{ sn}^2 u \cdot \text{sn}^2 v} \tag{3}$$

We shall suppose $s_1 = \text{sn }u$ and $s_2 = \text{sn }v$, where u and v vary so that

$$u + v = b, \tag{4}$$

where b is a constant. Differentiating with respect to u, it can be shown that

$$du + dv = 0, \tag{5}$$

$$\frac{\ddot{s}_1 s_2 - \ddot{s}_2 s_1}{\dot{s}_1 s_2 - \dot{s}_2 s_1} = -\frac{2k^2 s_1 s_2 (\dot{s}_1 s_2 + \dot{s}_2 s_1)}{1 - k^2 s_1^2 s_2^2}, \tag{6}$$

where dots indicate differentiation with respect to u. Integrating (6), we obtain the solution

$$\frac{\dot{s}_1 s_2 - \dot{s}_2 s_1}{1 - k^2 s_1^2 s_2^2} = C, \tag{7}$$

or

$$\frac{\text{cn }u \cdot \text{dn }u \cdot \text{sn }v + \text{cn }v \cdot \text{dn }v \cdot \text{sn }u}{1 - k^2 \cdot \text{sn}^2 u \cdot \text{sn}^2 v} = C. \tag{8}$$

Let G denote the left-hand member of (8). We note that both (8) and (4) are solutions of (5). From the theory of differential equations, it can then be concluded that C is a function of $b = u + v$, so that

$$G \equiv C(u + v). \tag{9}$$

Setting $v = 0$ in (9), we see that $\text{sn }u = c(u)$. Hence the addition relation (1) follows. Relations (2) and (3) follow from (1). Similar relations can be shown to hold for sn $(u - v)$, etc., using relations (8) of Sec. 28.

30. The Periods of the Elliptic Functions. We consider K as defined by Eq. (9) in Sec. 26. Then sn $K = 1$, cn $K = 0$, dn $K = k' = \sqrt{1 - k^2}$, the real positive root being used if $k < 1$. Substituting $v = K$ in formulas (1) to (3) of Sec. 29, we have

$$\operatorname{sn}(u + K) = \frac{\operatorname{cn} u}{\operatorname{dn} u}, \tag{1}$$

$$\operatorname{cn}(u + K) = -k'\frac{\operatorname{sn} u}{\operatorname{dn} u}, \tag{2}$$

$$\operatorname{dn}(u + K) = \frac{k'}{\operatorname{dn} u}. \tag{3}$$

In (1) to (3) of Sec. 29, replace v by $u + K$; we find that

$$\operatorname{sn}(u + 2K) = -\operatorname{sn} u, \tag{4}$$
$$\operatorname{cn}(u + 2K) = -\operatorname{cn} u, \tag{5}$$
$$\operatorname{dn}(u + 2K) = \operatorname{dn} u. \tag{6}$$

Replacing u by $(u + 2K)$ in (4) to (6), we have

$$\operatorname{sn}(u + 4K) = \operatorname{sn} u, \tag{7}$$
$$\operatorname{cn}(u + 4K) = \operatorname{cn} u, \tag{8}$$
$$\operatorname{dn}(u + 4K) = \operatorname{dn} u. \tag{9}$$

Consider the sum

$$\begin{aligned}
K + iK' &= \int_{\psi=0}^{\psi=\pi/2} \frac{d\psi}{\sqrt{1 - k^2 \sin^2 \psi}} \\
&+ i \int_{\psi=0}^{\psi=\pi/2} \frac{d\psi}{\sqrt{1 - k'^2 \sin^2 \psi}} \cdot (k' = \sqrt{1 - k^2})
\end{aligned} \tag{10}$$

Let $\csc \beta = \sqrt{1 - k'^2 \sin^2 \psi}$. Then we find from (9) and (10) of Sec. 26,

$$\begin{aligned}
K' &= \frac{1}{i} \int_{\beta=\pi/2}^{\sin \beta = 1/k} \frac{d\beta}{\sqrt{1 - k^2 \sin^2 \beta}} \\
&= \frac{1}{i} \int_1^{1/k} \frac{dx}{\sqrt{(1 - x^2)(1 - k^2 x^2)}}.
\end{aligned} \tag{11}$$

Hence

$$\begin{aligned}
K + iK' &= \int_{\psi=0}^{\psi=\pi/2} \frac{d\psi}{\sqrt{1 - k^2 \sin^2 \psi}} + \int_{\beta=\pi/2}^{\sin \beta = 1/k} \frac{d\beta}{\sqrt{1 - k^2 \sin^2 \beta}} \\
&= \int_{\psi=0}^{\sin \psi = 1/k} \frac{d\psi}{\sqrt{1 - k^2 \sin^2 \psi}}.
\end{aligned} \tag{12}$$

From (5) and (6) of Sec. 27 and (12), we see that

$$\text{sn } (K + iK') = \frac{1}{k}, \tag{13}$$

$$\text{cn } (K + iK') = -\frac{ik'}{k}, \tag{14}$$

$$\text{dn } (K + iK') = 0. \tag{15}$$

Substituting (13) to (15) in (1) to (3) of Sec. 29 in succession, we obtain

$$\text{sn } (u + K + iK') = \frac{\text{dn } u}{k \text{ cn } u}, \tag{16}$$

$$\text{cn } (u + K + iK') = -\frac{ik'}{k \text{ cn } u}, \tag{17}$$

$$\text{dn } (u + K + iK') = \frac{ik' \text{ sn } u}{\text{cn } u}, \tag{18}$$

and

$$\text{sn } (u + 2K + 2iK') = -\text{ sn } u, \tag{19}$$
$$\text{cn } (u + 2K + 2iK') = \text{cn } u, \tag{20}$$
$$\text{dn } (u + 2K + 2iK') = -\text{dn } u. \tag{21}$$

By a similar method, we could prove

$$\text{sn } (u + iK') = \frac{1}{k \text{ sn } u}, \tag{22}$$

$$\text{cn } (u + iK') = -\frac{i \text{ dn } u}{k \text{ sn } u}, \tag{23}$$

$$\text{dn } (u + iK') = -\frac{i \text{ cn } u}{\text{sn } u}, \tag{24}$$

$$\text{sn } (u + 2iK') = \text{sn } u, \tag{25}$$
$$\text{cn } (u + 2iK') = -\text{ cn } u, \tag{26}$$
$$\text{dn } (u + 2iK') = -\text{ dn } u, \tag{27}$$
$$\text{sn } (u + 4iK') = \text{sn } u, \tag{28}$$
$$\text{cn } (u + 4iK') = \text{cn } u, \tag{29}$$
$$\text{dn } (u + 4iK') = \text{dn } u. \tag{30}$$

Hence

  THEOREM 30.1. *The functions* sn *u,* cn *u,* dn *u are doubly periodic;* sn *u having the periods* 4K *and* 2iK, cn *u having the periods* 4K *and* 2K + 2iK', *and* dn *u having the periods* 2K *and* 4iK'.

31. The Cases k = 0; k = 1. If $k = 0$, the integral (3) of Sec. 26 becomes

$$u = \int_0^x \frac{dt}{\sqrt{1 - t^2}} = \sin^{-1} x. \tag{1}$$

This shows that $x = \operatorname{sn} u = \sin u$, $\operatorname{cn} u = \cos u$, $\operatorname{dn} u = 1$ if $k = 0$. Also, $K = \pi/2$, and the period $4K = 2\pi$. K' has no significance here. (Why?)

If $k = 1$, (3) of Sec. 26 becomes

$$u = \int_0^x \frac{dt}{1 - t^2} = \tanh^{-1} x. \tag{2}$$

Thus,

$$x = \operatorname{sn} u = \tanh u,$$

so that $\operatorname{cn} u = \operatorname{sech} u$, and $\operatorname{dn} u = \operatorname{sech} u$. If $k = 1$, $K' = \pi/2$ so that the period $4iK' = 2\pi i$. K is of no significance.

32. Complex Elliptic Integrals. Complex line integrals may be used to obtain many important results. We shall illustrate the use of complex line integrals by giving a second proof of Theorem 30.1. We shall now consider the complex elliptic integral

$$w = \int_0^z f(z)\, dz, \qquad f(z) \equiv \frac{1}{\sqrt{(1 - z^2)(1 - k^2 z^2)}} \tag{1}$$

over various paths in the complex plane, where $w = u + iv$ and where $z = x + iy$. The integrand $f(z)$ has poles at $z = \pm 1$, $\pm(1/k)$, while at all other points $f(z)$ is analytic. Let w_0 be the value of w when (1) is evaluated along any arbitrarily given path Γ_1 in the z-plane joining the point $z = 0$ to the point $z_0 = x_0 + iy_0$ (see Fig. 176); thus

$$w_0 = {}_{\Gamma_1}\!\!\int_0^{z_0} f(z)\, dz. \tag{2}$$

The path Γ_1 may be deformed in any manner whatsoever and not change the value of w_0, provided that in the deformation no point is encountered at which $f(z)$ ceases to be analytic. Let Γ_2 be a path which, together with Γ_1, incloses the singular points $z = -1$ and $z = +1$. The value of the integral w taken around Γ_2 from 0 to z_0, will not be changed if Γ_2 be deformed into the curve Γ_3, where Γ_3 consists of a piece of the real axis from $z = 0$

to $z = 1 - r$, a circle C_1 of radius r with center at $z = 1$, the piece of the real axis from $z = 1 - r$ to $z = -1 + r$, a circle C_2 with radius r and center at $z = -1$, and a portion of the real axis from $z = -1 + r$ to $z = 0$, and the curve Γ_1 from 0 to z_0. Γ_3

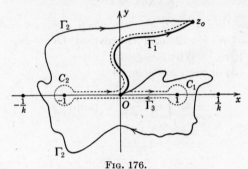

FIG. 176.

is indicated by the dotted curve in the figure. The value of w along Γ_3 is then equal to the sum

$$\int_0^{1-r} f(x)\, dx + \int_{C_1} f(z)\, dz + \int_{1-r}^0 - f(x)\, dx + \int_0^{-1+r} - f(x)\, dx$$
$$+ \int_{C_2} - f(z)\, dz + \int_{-1+r}^0 f(x)\, dx + _{(\Gamma_1)}\int_0^{z_0} f(z)\, dz, \quad (3)$$

where the changes in sign of the radical in $f(z)$ are due to passage around a singular point.

The value of the integral around the circle C_1 can be found as follows: Let $(1 - z) = re^{-i\phi}$, then $dz = ire^{-i\phi}\, d\phi$. The integral reduces to

$$\int_{C_1} f(z)\, dz = r^{1/2} \int_0^{2\pi} G(\phi)\, d\phi, \quad (4)$$

where $G(\phi)$ is bounded and is independent of r. A similar expression may be obtained for $\int_{C_2} f(z)\, dz$.

The sum of the remaining integrals in (3) is equal to

$$4 \int_0^{1-r} f(x)\, dx + w_0. \quad (5)$$

We have now seen that the value of (4) does not depend on r. Let $r \to 0$. We find

$$_{(\Gamma_2)}\int_0^{z_0} f(z)\, dz = \lim_{r \to 0} \left[4 \int_0^{1-r} f(x)\, dx + w_0 \right] = 4K + w_0. \quad (6)$$

But the value z_0 of z in (1) and (2) is the same, hence

$$\text{sn } (4K + w_0) = \text{sn } w_0. \tag{7}$$

Let Γ_4 be a path which, together with Γ_1, inclose the singular points $z = 1$ and $z = 1/k$. Deform Γ_4 into the path Γ_5 indicated in Fig. 177. It can be shown by a method similar to that given above, that

$$_{(\Gamma_4)}\!\int_0^{z_0} f(z)\,dz = 2iK' + w_0,$$

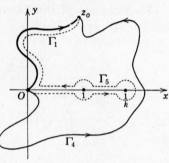

so that

$$\text{sn } (2iK' + w_0) = \text{sn } w_0. \quad (8)$$

All of the various relations found in Sec. 30 can be obtained by similar methods applied to various other paths.

We now consider the integral $\int_0^z f(z)\,dz$ around a path Γ_6 con-

FIG. 177.

sisting of the circle $z = Re^{i\theta}$ and the portion of the imaginary axis between $z = -iR$ and $z = +iR$, where $R > 1/k$. Deform the path Γ_6 into the path Γ_7 indicated in Fig. 178, where Γ_7 consists of that portion of the real axis between $z = 1$ and $z = 1/k$. The integral along Γ_7 is $\int_{\Gamma_7} f(x)\,dx = 2iK'$, by equa-

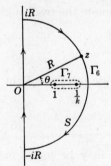

tion (11) of Sec. 30. The integral $\int_S f(z)\,dz$ around the semicircle S is of the form $(1/R)\int_{-\pi/2}^{+\pi/2} F(\theta)\,d\theta$, where $F(\theta)$ remains finite as $R \to +\infty$. Hence by letting $R \to +\infty$, we have

$$2\int_0^\infty f(z\ dz = 2iK',$$

or

$$\int_0^\infty \frac{dz}{\sqrt{(1 - z^2)(1 - k^2 z^2)}} = iK'. \tag{9}$$

FIG. 178.

THEOREM 32.1. *The elliptic functions* sn u, cn u, *and* dn u *have simple poles at* $w = iK'$, *with residues* $1/k$, $-i/k$, *and* $-i$, *respectively.*

By (22) of Sec. 30, (5) of Sec. 28 and an inversion of the series for sn w,

$$\text{sn } (w + iK') = \frac{1}{k\ \text{sn } w} = \frac{1}{kw} + \frac{1 + k^2}{6k}w + \cdots .$$

Upon substituting $w + iK'$ for w, we have

$$\text{sn } w = \frac{1}{k(w - iK')} + \frac{1 + k^2}{6k}(w - iK') + \cdots .$$

This shows that sn u has a simple pole with residue $1/k$ at $w = iK'$. A similar proof holds for cn u and dn u.

33. Integrals of the Second and Third Type. Consider the elliptic integral (7) of Sec. 26. When $\varphi = \pi/2$, this integral is denoted by

$$E \equiv E\left(k, \frac{\pi}{2}\right) \tag{1}$$

From (7) of Sec. 26,

$$E(k, \varphi + \pi) = \int_0^\pi \sqrt{1 - k^2 \sin \varphi}\, d\varphi$$
$$+ \int_\pi^{\varphi + \pi} \sqrt{1 - k^2 \sin \varphi}\, d\varphi. \tag{2}$$

In the second integral of (2) let $\varphi = \psi + \pi$; we find that this integral reduces to

$$\int_0^\varphi \sqrt{1 - k^2 \sin^2 \psi}\, d\psi = E(k, \varphi).$$

By (1) we see that

$$E(k, \varphi + \pi) = 2E + E(k, \varphi). \tag{3}$$

In (7) of Sec. 26, set $x = \text{sn } u$ and let $E(u)$ denote the resulting integral. We find

$$E(u) = \int_0^u \text{dn}^2 u\, du = u - k^2 \int_0^u \text{sn}^2 u\, du. \tag{4}$$

By setting $t = \text{sn } \beta$ and $a = \text{sn}^2 \alpha$, the elliptic integral (5) of Sec. 26 can be written

$$\int_{\beta=0}^{\beta=u} \frac{d\beta}{\text{sn}^2 \beta - \text{sn}^2 \alpha}. \tag{5}$$

The various values of $E(k, \varphi)$, E, K, $\cdots$ may be found in tables or may be computed by expansions into power series.

34. The Weierstrass Elliptic Function p(u). The elliptic integral

$$u = \int_x^{+\infty} \frac{dt}{\sqrt{4t^3 - g_2 t - g_3}}$$
$$= \int_x^\infty \frac{dt}{\sqrt{4(t - e_1)(t - e_2)(t - e_3)}}, \tag{1}$$

defines x as a function of u,

$$x = p(u), \tag{2}$$

known as the *Weierstrass elliptic function.* Evidently

$$p'(u) = \sqrt{4p^3(u) - g_2 p(u) - g_3},$$

and $p(u)$ is a solution of the equation

$$\left(\frac{d\phi}{dx}\right)^2 = 4\phi^3 - g_2\phi - g_3. \tag{3}$$

The integral (1) can be reduced to one of the first kind. This may be done by setting $t = e_3 + (g^2/\tau^2)$ in the second form of (1), taking $g^2 = e_1 - e_3$ and $k^2 = (e_2 - e_3)/(e_1 - e_3)$. There results

$$u = \frac{1}{g}\int_0^t \frac{d\tau}{\sqrt{(1 - \tau^2)(1 - k^2\tau^2)}}, \tag{4}$$

from which we have

$$t = \text{sn } (gu). \tag{5}$$

It can be shown that

$$p(u) = e_3 + \frac{g^2}{\text{sn}^2 (gu)}. \tag{6}$$

From (6) and Sec. 30 it can be shown that

$$\begin{aligned} p(u + 2w) &= p(u), \\ p(u + 2iw') &= p(u), \end{aligned} \tag{7}$$

where $w = K/g$, $w' = K'/g$.

THEOREM 34.1. *The function $p(u)$ is doubly periodic with periods $2w$ and $2iw'$.*

From (6) and (1) it can be shown that

$$p(w) = e_1 = e_3 + q^2, \; p(w + w') = e_2 = e_3 + k^2 g^2, \; p(w') = e_3, \tag{8}$$

$$w = \int_{e_1}^\infty h(x)\, dx, \qquad w' = \int_{e_3}^\infty h(x)\, dx,$$

$$w + w' = \int_{e_2}^\infty h(x)\, dx, \qquad w = \int_2^{e_3} h(x)\, dx, \tag{9}$$

where $h(x) = (4x^3 - g_2 x - g_3)^{-\frac{1}{2}}$.

35. Certain Applications. We shall give two examples illustrating the applications of elliptic integrals.

Example 1. Let a pendulum of length l and mass m be supported at O. Since $s = l\theta$, $d^2s/dt^2 = l\,d^2\theta/dt^2$. By Newton's laws of motion (see Fig. 179)

$$m\frac{d^2s}{dt^2} = -mg\sin\theta.$$

Hence

$$\frac{d^2\theta}{dt^2} = -\frac{g}{l}\sin\theta.$$

Multiply both sides by $2\dfrac{d\theta}{dt}$ and integrate. Then

$$\left(\frac{d\theta}{dt}\right)^2 = \frac{2g}{l}(\cos\theta + c).$$

If α is the maximum value of θ, then $\theta = \alpha$ when $d\theta/dt = 0$ and $c = -\cos\alpha$. If we take the square root and reciprocal of both sides and integrate again, we find that

$$t = \sqrt{\frac{l}{g}}\int_0^{\theta_0}\frac{d\theta}{\sqrt{2(\cos\theta - \cos\alpha)}}, \tag{1}$$

where $t = 0$ when $\theta = 0$. To reduce this integral to standard form, write

$$(\cos\theta - \cos\alpha) = (1 - \cos\alpha) - (1 - \cos\theta) = 2\left(\sin^2\frac{\alpha}{2} - \sin^2\frac{\theta}{2}\right)$$

$$= 2\left(1 - \frac{\sin^2\dfrac{\theta}{2}}{\sin^2\dfrac{\alpha}{2}}\right)\sin^2\frac{\alpha}{2} = 2k^2\cos^2\phi,$$

where $k = \sin\dfrac{\alpha}{2}$, $\sin\phi = \dfrac{1}{k}\sin\dfrac{\theta}{2}$. Hence (1) becomes

$$t = \sqrt{\frac{l}{g}}\int_0^{\phi_0}\frac{d\phi}{\sqrt{1 - k^2\sin^2\phi}}. \tag{2}$$

Since we wish to regard t, and not ϕ, as the independent variable in connection with the motion of the pendulum, we write

$$\phi = \text{amp}\left(\sqrt{\frac{g}{l}}\,t\right).$$

To obtain a geometric representation of ϕ, we observe that

$$\sin \phi = \frac{\sin(\theta/2)}{\sin(\alpha/2)} = \sqrt{\frac{1-\cos\theta}{1-\cos\alpha}} = \sqrt{\frac{l-l\cos\theta}{l-l\cos\alpha}} = \sqrt{\frac{SP'}{SE'}}.$$

(See Fig. 180.)   We may remove the radical by constructing the right triangle $E'MS$:

$$\sqrt{\frac{SP'}{SE'}} = \sqrt{\frac{SP'}{SE'} \cdot \frac{P'E'}{P'E'}} = \frac{P'M}{E'M}.$$

Hence $\phi = \angle SE'M$. Since $\angle E'MS$ is a right angle, it follows that, E being fixed, M moves about a circle with center at the mid-point of $E'S$.

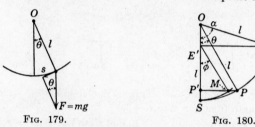

FIG. 179.   FIG. 180.

Example 2. Find the length of an arc of the ellipse $x = a \sin \psi$ $y = b \cos \psi$.

By Ex. X, 7, of Chap. II, the arc length of the ellipse from $(0, b)$ to the point (x, y) is

$$s = \int_0^\phi \sqrt{a^2 \cos^2 \psi + b^2 \sin^2 \psi}\, d\psi. \tag{3}$$

Since $b^2 = a^2(1 - e^2)$, (3) may be written

$$s = \int_0^\phi \sqrt{1 - e^2 \sin^2 \psi}\, d\psi = aE(e, \phi). \tag{4}$$

When $\phi = \pi/2$, $s = aE$ is the quarter arc of the ellipse.

EXERCISES XV

1. Evaluate each of the integrals in equations (3), (4), (5), (6), (7), (8) of Sec. 26 for the case where $k = 0$; the case where $k = 1$.
2. Tabulate the values of sn u, cn u, dn u at $u = 0$, K, iK', $K + iK'$.
3. Find expressions for sn $(u - v)$, cn $(u - v)$, dn $(u - v)$.
4. Prove: sn $(u + v)$ sn $(u - v) = (\text{sn}^2 u - \text{sn}^2 v)/(1 - k^2 \text{sn}^2 u \text{sn}^2 v)$.
5. Prove: $\text{sn}^2 u = (1 - \text{cn } 2u)/(1 + \text{cn } 2u)$.
6. Evaluate: sn $(2K - u)$, cn $(2K - u)$, dn $(2K - u)$.
7. Prove: $p(-u) = p(u)$.
8. Verify (6) and obtain (8) of Sec. 29.
9. Show that the length of the circumference of the hyperbola $(x^2/a^2) - (y^2/b^2) = 1$ of eccentricity e is equal to

$$(b^2/ae)\, F(\phi, k) + ae \tan \phi \sqrt{1 - k^2 \sin^2 \phi} - aeE(\phi, k),$$

where $\tan \phi = aey/b^2$, $k = 1/e$.

10. Find the arc of the hyperbola cut off by the latus rectum if $e = 1.3$, $e = 2$.

11. Evaluate $\int d\theta / \sqrt{a - \cos \theta}$, $a > 1$ in terms of elliptic functions.

12. From (9) of Sec. 32 show $\operatorname{sn}(ik') = \infty$, $\operatorname{cn}(ik') = \infty$, $\operatorname{dn}(ik') = \infty$.

13. Complete the proof of Theorem 32.1.

14. Express (4) of Sec. 33 as a power series. Use (5) of Sec. 28.

15. Verify (4), (6), (7), and (8) of Sec. 34.

16. (a) Express $\operatorname{sn} 2u$, $\operatorname{cn} 2u$, $\operatorname{dn} 2u$ in terms of functions of u.

(b) Express $\operatorname{sn} \frac{1}{2}u$, $\operatorname{cn} \frac{1}{2}u$, $\operatorname{dn} \frac{1}{2}u$ as functions of u.

(c) Show that

$$\operatorname{sn} \frac{K}{2} = (1 + k')^{-\frac{1}{2}}, \qquad \operatorname{cn} \frac{K}{2} = \sqrt{k'}(1 + k')^{-\frac{1}{2}}, \qquad \operatorname{dn} \frac{K}{2} = \sqrt{k'}.$$

17. Show that $\displaystyle\int_0^\phi \frac{d\phi}{\sqrt{1 - \mu^2 \sin^2 \phi}} = \frac{1}{\mu}\int_0^\psi \frac{d\psi}{\sqrt{1 - \mu^{-2} \sin^2 \psi}}$, $\mu > 1$,

$\sin^2 \psi = \mu^2 \sin^2 \phi$.

18. Using Ex. 17, find the arc length of the lemniscate $r^2 = 2a^2 \cos 2\phi$. Also, the arc length from $\phi = 0$ to $\phi = 30°$.

19. Compute: $\int_0^\phi d\theta / \sqrt{1 - 0.1 \sin^2 \theta}$ to find K; $\operatorname{sn}(2K/3)$; $F(\pi/8, 1/\sqrt{10})$. Check against a table of elliptic integrals.

20. Evaluate:

(a) $\displaystyle\int_1^5 \frac{dx}{\sqrt{(x^2 - 1)(1 - 0.1x^2)}}.$ (b) $\displaystyle\int_0^1 \frac{dx}{\sqrt{(25 - x^2)(1 + 4x^2)}}.$

(c) $\displaystyle\int_0^{10} \frac{dx}{\sqrt{(1 + x^2)(4 + 9x^2)}}.$

21. In connection with Example 1 above: (a) Find geometric representations for $\operatorname{sn} \sqrt{g/l}\, t$, $\operatorname{cn}\sqrt{g/l}\, t$, $\operatorname{dn} \sqrt{g/l}\, t$; (b) show that if $4T$ is the period of oscillation of the pendulum then $T = \sqrt{l/g}K$; (c) show that

$$\operatorname{sn} \sqrt{\frac{g}{l}}(t + 2T) = -\operatorname{sn} \sqrt{\frac{g}{l}}t,$$

$$\operatorname{cn} \sqrt{\frac{g}{l}}(t + 2T) = -\operatorname{cn} \sqrt{\frac{g}{l}}t,$$

$$\operatorname{dn} \sqrt{\frac{g}{l}}(t + 2T) = \operatorname{dn} \sqrt{\frac{g}{l}}t.$$

22. Repeat Example 1 for the case when the bob goes completely around the circle and the velocity at the bottom is v_0; also when the bob just reaches the top of the swing.

23. Find the period of a pendulum oscillating through the following angles: $10°$, $90°$, $180°$, $330°$. In each case find the instant at which the pendulum makes an angle of $5°$ with the vertical.

24. Examine $\displaystyle\int_0^{z_0} \frac{dz}{\sqrt{(1-z^2)(1-k^2z^2)}}$ for the difference in its values corresponding to two paths Γ_1 and Γ_2 connecting $z = 0$ and $z = z_0$, where Γ_1 and Γ_2 taken together enclose $z = 1$; same for $z = 1/k$.

25. Repeat Ex. 24 for $\displaystyle\int_{z_0}^{\infty} \frac{dz}{2\sqrt{(z-e_1)(z-e_2)(z-e_3)}}$ corresponding to two paths Γ_1 and Γ_2 which taken together enclose two of the distinct points e_1, e_2, e_3.

26. Repeat Ex. 25 for the case when Γ_1 and Γ_2 together enclose one of the distinct points e_1, e_2, e_3.

CHAPTER VI

ALGEBRA AND VECTOR ANALYSIS

PART A. ALGEBRA

1. Determinants. Consider the system of m linear homogeneous equations in the n variables x_1, x_2, $\cdots$, x_n:

$$\begin{cases} a_{11}x_1 + a_{12}x_2 + \cdots + a_{1n}x_n = 0, \\ a_{21}x_1 + a_{22}x_2 + \cdots + a_{2n}x_n = 0, \\ \cdots \cdots \cdots \cdots \cdots \cdots \cdots \cdots \cdots \cdots \\ a_{m1}x_1 + a_{m2}x_2 + \cdots + a_{mn}x_n = 0, \end{cases}$$

where the coefficients a_{ij} ($i = 1, 2, \cdots, m; j = 1, 2, \cdots, n$) are any real or complex numbers.* The properties of this system of equations, such as consistence, redundancy, solutions other than $x_1 = x_2 = \cdots = x_n = 0$, etc., are completely determined by the values and positions of the numbers a_{ij}. This suggests that a study of the properties of arrays of numbers may be useful.

Special importance attaches to the case where $m = n$, that is, the case where the array **A**

$$\begin{bmatrix} a_{11} & a_{12} & \cdots & a_{1n} \\ a_{21} & a_{22} & \cdots & a_{2n} \\ \cdot & \cdot & & \cdot \\ \cdot & \cdot & & \cdot \\ \cdot & \cdot & & \cdot \\ a_{n1} & a_{n2} & \cdots & a_{nn} \end{bmatrix} \tag{1}$$

is square. Such an array **A** will be referred to as an $n \times n$ array, or a square array of order n. Associated with such an array,

---

* We shall assume, unless otherwise specified, that the arrays and matrices with which we are working have elements which are complex numbers. Most of the results stated in the present treatment of the theory of determinants and matrices are valid under more general hypotheses on the algebraic system in which the elements of the arrays and matrices lie. Such generality is not necessary for our present purposes. For a more thorough treatment the reader is referred to the comprehensive works of MacDuffee and Wedderburn mentioned in the bibliography.

644

there is a number $d(\mathbf{A})$, called the *determinant* of $\mathbf{A}$, defined by

$$d(\mathbf{A}) = \Sigma(-1)^h a_{1i_1} a_{2i_2} \cdots a_{ni_n}, \tag{2}$$

where the summation is taken over all permutations $i_1, i_2, \cdots,$ i_n of the integers $1, 2, \cdots, n$, and where h is the number of successive interchanges of two i's which would be necessary to permute the order $i_1, i_2, \cdots, i_n$ into the order $1, 2, \cdots, n$. It is obvious that the order $i_1, i_2, \cdots, i_n$ might be brought into the order $1, 2, \cdots, n$ by a variety of sequences of interchanges. However, it can be shown that for a given order, the number of such interchanges is either always even or always odd, regardless of the chain of interchanges employed. Thus, while h is not uniquely determined for any given term in (2), $(-1)^h$ is unique.

A symbolism frequently used in place of $d(\mathbf{A})$ is

$$\begin{vmatrix} a_{11} & a_{12} & \cdots & a_{1n} \\ a_{21} & a_{22} & \cdots & a_{2n} \\ \cdot & \cdot & & \cdot \\ \cdot & \cdot & & \cdot \\ \cdot & \cdot & & \cdot \\ a_{n1} & a_{n2} & \cdots & a_{nn} \end{vmatrix}$$

We note that the determinant is defined for a square array only; hence there will be no ambiguity if we omit the word square in speaking of the determinant of an array.

Example 1. Let $\mathbf{A}$ be the third order array

$$\begin{bmatrix} a_{11} & a_{12} & a_{13} \\ a_{21} & a_{22} & a_{23} \\ a_{31} & a_{32} & a_{33} \end{bmatrix}.$$

The possible permutations (i_1, i_2, i_3) are $(1, 2, 3)$, $(1, 3, 2)$, $(2, 1, 3)$, $(2, 3, 1)$, $(3, 1, 2)$ and $(3, 2, 1)$, and

$$d(\mathbf{A}) = \Sigma(-1)^h a_{1i_1} a_{2i_2} a_{3i_3} = a_{11}a_{22}a_{33} - a_{11}a_{23}a_{32} - a_{12}a_{21}a_{33}$$
$$+ a_{12}a_{23}a_{31} + a_{13}a_{21}a_{32} - a_{13}a_{22}a_{31}.$$

It is possible to eliminate the variables $x_2, \cdots, x_n$ from a system of equations whose array of coefficients is (1) in such a way that the coefficient of x_1 in the resulting equation is exactly $d(\mathbf{A})$. Without going into greater detail on this point, we remark that this suggests at least one important reason for studying this number associated with a square array.

The calculation of the determinant of an array by (2) becomes a laborious process where $n > 3$, and consequently it is advisable to investigate some properties of determinants which will enable us to shorten the computation.

THEOREM 1.1. *If* **B** *is the array obtained from* **A** *by interchanging rows and columns, then* $d(\mathbf{B}) = d(\mathbf{A})$.

If in (2) we rearrange the factors a_{rs} in each term so that the column indices are in the order $1, 2, \cdots, n$, we have

$$d(\mathbf{A}) = \Sigma(-1)^h a_{1i_1} a_{2i_2} \cdots a_{ni_n} = \Sigma(-1)^h a_{j_1 1} a_{j_2 2} \cdots a_{j_n n}$$
$$= \Sigma(-1)^h b_{1j_1} b_{2j_2} \cdots b_{nj_n}, \quad (3)$$

where the b_{rs} are the elements of **B**. The sequence of interchanges necessary to bring $j_1, j_2, \cdots, j_n$ into the order $1, 2, \cdots, n$ can be taken as the reverse of the sequence of interchanges by which we brought $i_1, i_2, \cdots, i_n$ into the order $1, 2, \cdots, n$. Hence $(-1)^h$ determines the sign on each term in the last member of (3) so that we can write

$$d(\mathbf{B}) = \Sigma(-1)^h b_{1j_1} b_{2j_2} \cdots b_{nj_n} = d(\mathbf{A}).$$

Example 2. $\begin{vmatrix} 3 & 1 \\ 2 & 5 \end{vmatrix} = \begin{vmatrix} 3 & 2 \\ 1 & 5 \end{vmatrix} = 13.$

Theorem 1.1 is important for the reason that any theorem on determinants resulting from a property of the rows of the array will automatically furnish a theorem on determinants which results from the same property of the columns.

THEOREM 1.2. *If all the elements of a row (column) of an array* **A** *are zero, then* $d(\mathbf{A}) = 0$.

The proof follows directly from (2) and Theorem 1.1.

THEOREM 1.3. *If the array* **B** *results from the array* **A** *by the interchange of two rows (columns) of* **A**, *then* $d(\mathbf{B}) = -d(\mathbf{A})$.

Suppose that rows j and k of **A**, $j < k$, are interchanged to form **B**. Then

$$d(\mathbf{B}) = \Sigma(-1)^h a_{1i_1} a_{2i_2} \cdots a_{ji_k} \cdots a_{ki_j} \cdots a_{ni_n}$$
$$= \Sigma(-1)^{h+1} a_{1i_1} a_{2i_2} \cdots a_{ji_j} \cdots a_{ki_k} \cdots a_{ni_n}$$
$$= (-1)\Sigma(-1)^h a_{1i_1} a_{2i_2} \cdots a_{ji_j} \cdots a_{ki_k} \cdots a_{ni_n}$$
$$= -d(\mathbf{A}).$$

Theorem 1.4.   *If two rows (columns) of an array **A** are identical, then $d(\mathbf{A}) = 0$.*

From Theorem 1.3 the interchange of the two identical rows (columns) yields $d(\mathbf{A}) = -d(\mathbf{A})$, whence $d(\mathbf{A}) = 0$.

Theorem 1.5.   *Let $\mathbf{A}_1$, $\mathbf{A}_2$, $\cdots$, $\mathbf{A}_k$ be $n \times n$ arrays which have all their rows (columns), with the exception of the jth, in common.   Then*

$$d(\mathbf{A}_1) + d(\mathbf{A}_2) + \cdots + d(\mathbf{A}_k) = d(\mathbf{B}),$$

*where **B** is an array which has those same rows (columns) in common with $\mathbf{A}_1$, $\cdots$, $\mathbf{A}_k$, and whose element in the jth row (column) and sth column (row), $s = 1, 2, \cdots, n$, is equal to the sum of the elements in the jth row (column) and sth column (row) of each of the arrays $\mathbf{A}_1$, $\mathbf{A}_2$, $\cdots$, $\mathbf{A}_k$.*

Let the elements of the jth row of $\mathbf{A}_m$ be denoted by $a_{j1}^{(m)}$, $\cdots$, $a_{jn}^{(m)}$.   Then

$$d(\mathbf{A}_1) + d(\mathbf{A}_2) + \cdots + d(\mathbf{A}_k) = \Sigma(-1)^h a_{1i_1} \cdots a_{ji_j}^{(1)} \cdots a_{ni_n}$$
$$+ \Sigma(-1)^h a_{1i_1} \cdots a_{ji_j}^{(2)} \cdots a_{ni_n}$$
$$+ \cdots + \Sigma(-1)^h a_{1i_1} \cdots a_{ji_j}^{(\kappa)} \cdots a_{ni_n}$$
$$= \Sigma(-1)^h a_{1i_1} \cdots (a_{ji_j}^{(1)} + a_{ji_j}^{(2)} + \cdots + a_{ji_j}^{(k)}) \cdots a_{ni_n} = d(\mathbf{B}).$$

Example 3. $\begin{vmatrix} a & b & c \\ d & e & f \\ g_1 & h_1 & k_1 \end{vmatrix} + \begin{vmatrix} a & b & c \\ d & e & f \\ g_2 & h_2 & k_2 \end{vmatrix} = \begin{vmatrix} a & b & c \\ d & e & f \\ g_1 + g_2 & h_1 + h_2 & k_1 + k_2 \end{vmatrix}.$

Theorem 1.6.   *If the array **B** is formed from an array **A** by multiplying each of the elements of some row (column) by a number k, then $d(\mathbf{B}) = kd(\mathbf{A})$.*

The proof is left to the reader.

Definition 1.1.   *By the linear combination*

$$k_1(a_{11}, a_{12}, \cdots, a_{1n}) + k_2(a_{21}, a_{22}, \cdots, a_{2n})$$
$$+ \cdots + k_n(a_{n1}, a_{n2}, \cdots, a_{nn})$$

*of the rows of an array **A**, we shall mean the row of elements obtained by forming the same combination of elements in like positions in those rows; that is, the row*

$$(k_1 a_{11} + k_2 a_{21} + \cdots + k_n a_{n1}, \; k_1 a_{12} + k_2 a_{22} + \cdots + k_n a_{n2},$$
$$\cdots, \; k_1 a_{1n} + k_2 a_{2n} + \cdots + k_n a_{nn}).$$

We do not exclude the possibility of any or all of the k_i being zero. A similar definition will be understood for a linear combination of the columns of an array.

Theorem 1.7. *If* **B** *is an array arising from an array* **A** *by adding to a fixed row (column) of* **A** *a linear combination of the remaining rows (columns) of* **A**, *then* $d(\mathbf{B}) = d(\mathbf{A})$.

Theorem 1.7 is a consequence of Theorems 1.4, 1.5, and 1.6.

Example 4. Consider the array

$$\mathbf{B} = \begin{bmatrix} a & b + k_1a + k_2c & c \\ d & e + k_1d + k_2f & f \\ g & h + k_1g + k_2l & l \end{bmatrix} \text{ arising from the array } \mathbf{A} = \begin{bmatrix} a & b & c \\ d & e & f \\ g & h & l \end{bmatrix}$$

by the linear combination of the columns indicated. The determinant of **B** is equal to the determinant of **A**, for

$$\begin{vmatrix} a & b + k_1a + k_2c & c \\ d & e + k_1d + k_2f & f \\ g & h + k_1g + k_2l & l \end{vmatrix} = \begin{vmatrix} a & b & c \\ d & e & f \\ g & h & l \end{vmatrix} + \begin{vmatrix} a & k_1a & c \\ d & k_1d & f \\ g & k_1g & l \end{vmatrix} + \begin{vmatrix} a & k_2c & c \\ d & k_2f & f \\ g & k_2l & l \end{vmatrix} = \begin{vmatrix} a & b & c \\ d & e & f \\ g & h & l \end{vmatrix}.$$

Definition 1.2. *By the symbol* $\mathbf{A}\begin{smallmatrix} r_1 & \cdots & r_k \\ s_1 & \cdots & s_k \end{smallmatrix}$ *we shall understand the square minor array formed from the array* **A** *by selecting from* **A** *the elements in rows* $r_1 \cdots r_k$ *and columns* $s_1 \cdots s_k$, *in those orders. If the same columns as rows are selected, the minor array is called a principal minor array.*

Theorem 1.8 (*Laplace's Expansion by Minors*). *From the array* **A**, *let any distinct rows* $r_1, r_2, \cdots r_k$ *be selected. Then*

$$d(A) = \Sigma(-1)^h d\left(\mathbf{A}\begin{smallmatrix} r_1 & \cdots & r_k \\ i_1 & \cdots & i_k \end{smallmatrix}\right) \cdot d\left(\mathbf{A}\begin{smallmatrix} r_{k+1} & \cdots & r_n \\ i_{k+1} & \cdots & i_n \end{smallmatrix}\right),$$

where h is equal to the number of any set of interchanges which would be necessary to bring the order $i_1, i_2, \cdots, i_n$ *into the order* $r_1, r_2, \cdots, r_n$, *and where the summation is to be taken over the* $\binom{n}{k}^*$ *ways of choosing the combinations* $i_1, i_2, \cdots, i_k$ *from the integers* $1, 2, \cdots, n$.

The proof of this theorem is a little lengthy and will not be included here.

$$^*\binom{n}{k} = \frac{n!}{k!(n-k)!}.$$

Example 5.

$$\begin{vmatrix} a_{11} & a_{12} & a_{13} & a_{14} \\ a_{21} & a_{22} & a_{23} & a_{24} \\ a_{31} & a_{32} & a_{33} & a_{34} \\ a_{41} & a_{42} & a_{43} & a_{44} \end{vmatrix}$$

$$= (-1)^1 \, d(\mathbf{A}_{12}^{13}) \, d(\mathbf{A}_{34}^{24}) + (-1)^0 \, d(\mathbf{A}_{13}^{13}) \, d(\mathbf{A}_{24}^{24}) + (-1)^1 \, d(\mathbf{A}_{14}^{13}) \, d(\mathbf{A}_{23}^{24})$$
$$+ (-1)^1 \, d(\mathbf{A}_{23}^{13}) \, d(\mathbf{A}_{14}^{24}) + (-1)^2 \, d(\mathbf{A}_{24}^{13}) \, d(\mathbf{A}_{13}^{24}) + (-1)^3 \, d(\mathbf{A}_{34}^{13}) \, d(\mathbf{A}_{12}^{24})$$

$$= - \begin{vmatrix} a_{11} & a_{12} \\ a_{31} & a_{32} \end{vmatrix} \cdot \begin{vmatrix} a_{23} & a_{24} \\ a_{43} & a_{44} \end{vmatrix} + \begin{vmatrix} a_{11} & a_{13} \\ a_{31} & a_{33} \end{vmatrix} \cdot \begin{vmatrix} a_{22} & a_{24} \\ a_{42} & a_{44} \end{vmatrix}$$

$$- \begin{vmatrix} a_{11} & a_{14} \\ a_{31} & a_{34} \end{vmatrix} \cdot \begin{vmatrix} a_{22} & a_{23} \\ a_{42} & a_{43} \end{vmatrix} - \begin{vmatrix} a_{12} & a_{13} \\ a_{32} & a_{33} \end{vmatrix} \cdot \begin{vmatrix} a_{21} & a_{24} \\ a_{41} & a_{44} \end{vmatrix}$$

$$+ \begin{vmatrix} a_{12} & a_{14} \\ a_{32} & a_{34} \end{vmatrix} \cdot \begin{vmatrix} a_{21} & a_{23} \\ a_{41} & a_{43} \end{vmatrix} - \begin{vmatrix} a_{13} & a_{14} \\ a_{33} & a_{34} \end{vmatrix} \cdot \begin{vmatrix} a_{21} & a_{22} \\ a_{41} & a_{42} \end{vmatrix}.$$

Of particular importance is the case of Theorem 1.8 where $k = 1$. Let $(-1)^{r+s} \cdot d\left(\mathbf{A}_{1, \, 2, \, \cdots, \, s-1, \, s+1, \, \cdots, \, n}^{1, \, 2, \, \cdots, \, r-1, \, r+1, \, \cdots, \, n}\right)$ be denoted by A_{rs}. A_{rs} is called the *cofactor* of a_{rs}. From Theorem 1.8 we can obtain

THEOREM 1.9. $d(\mathbf{A}) = \displaystyle\sum_{i=1}^{n} a_{ri} A_{ri}; \qquad d(\mathbf{A}) = \displaystyle\sum_{i=1}^{n} a_{is} A_{is}.$ The proof is left to the reader.

Example 6.

$$\begin{vmatrix} a_{11} & a_{12} & a_{13} \\ a_{21} & a_{22} & a_{23} \\ a_{31} & a_{32} & a_{33} \end{vmatrix} = - a_{21} \begin{vmatrix} a_{12} & a_{13} \\ a_{32} & a_{33} \end{vmatrix} + a_{22} \begin{vmatrix} a_{11} & a_{13} \\ a_{31} & a_{33} \end{vmatrix} - a_{23} \begin{vmatrix} a_{11} & a_{12} \\ a_{31} & a_{32} \end{vmatrix}.$$

THEOREM 1.10. $\displaystyle\sum_{i=1}^{n} a_{ri} A_{pi} = 0 \; if \; r \neq p; \; \sum_{i=1}^{n} a_{is} A_{ip} = 0 \; if \; s \neq p.$

By Theorem 1.9, $\displaystyle\sum_{i=1}^{n} a_{ri} A_{pi}$ is the determinant of an array $\mathbf{B}$, the rth and pth rows of which are identical, both being the rth row of $\mathbf{A}$. By Theorem 1.4, $d(\mathbf{B}) = \displaystyle\sum_{i=1}^{n} a_{ri} A_{pi} = 0$. The proof of the second half of the theorem is similar to that of the first half.

We conclude with an example of the use of some of the preceding results in the evaluation of a determinant.

Example 7. Evaluate the determinant

$$\Delta = \begin{vmatrix} 2 & 6 & 1 & 8 \\ 3 & -4 & -5 & 2 \\ -1 & -1 & 4 & 3 \\ -8 & -10 & 11 & 6 \end{vmatrix}.$$

Subtracting 2 times column 3 from column 1, 6 times column 3 from column 2, and 8 times column 3 from column 4, there results by Theorem 1.7

$$\Delta = \begin{vmatrix} 0 & 0 & 1 & 0 \\ 13 & 26 & -5 & 42 \\ -9 & -25 & 4 & -29 \\ -30 & -76 & 11 & -82 \end{vmatrix}.$$

By a Laplace expansion according to the elements of the first row, we find that

$$\Delta = \begin{vmatrix} 13 & 26 & 42 \\ -9 & -25 & -29 \\ -30 & -76 & -82 \end{vmatrix}.$$

The expansion of this determinant would involve considerable arithmetic. Hence we continue to manipulate the array as before. Subtracting twice the first column from the second and 3 times the first column from the third column, we have

$$\Delta = \begin{vmatrix} 13 & 0 & 3 \\ -9 & -7 & -2 \\ -30 & -16 & 8 \end{vmatrix} = 2\begin{vmatrix} 13 & 0 & 3 \\ -9 & -7 & -2 \\ -15 & -8 & 4 \end{vmatrix}.$$

Subtracting 4 times the third column from the first, we have

$$\Delta = 2\begin{vmatrix} 1 & 0 & 3 \\ -1 & -7 & -2 \\ -31 & -8 & 4 \end{vmatrix}.$$

Further,

$$\Delta = 2\begin{vmatrix} 1 & 0 & 0 \\ -1 & -7 & 1 \\ -31 & -8 & 97 \end{vmatrix},$$

whence by a Laplace expansion according to elements of the first row,

$$\Delta = 2\begin{vmatrix} -7 & 1 \\ -8 & 97 \end{vmatrix} \quad \text{and from (2) we find } \Delta = 2(-679 + 8) = -1342.$$

EXERCISES I

1. By eliminating x_2 and x_1 in turn from the set of equations

$$\begin{cases} a_{11}x_1 + a_{12}x_2 = b_1, \\ a_{21}x_1 + a_{22}x_2 = b_2, \end{cases}$$

show that if $d(\mathbf{A}) \neq 0$, where $\mathbf{A} = \begin{bmatrix} a_{11} & a_{12} \\ a_{21} & a_{22} \end{bmatrix}$, the solution of this system is $x_1 = d(\mathbf{B}_1)/d(\mathbf{A})$, $x_2 = d(\mathbf{B}_2)/d(\mathbf{A})$, where $\mathbf{B}_1$ ($\mathbf{B}_2$) is the array obtained from $\mathbf{A}$ by replacing column one (two) by the column $\begin{Bmatrix} b_1 \\ b_2 \end{Bmatrix}$.

2. Show that the system of equations in Ex. 1 has no solution if $d(\mathbf{A}) = 0$ and either $d(\mathbf{B}_1)$ or $d(\mathbf{B}_2)$ is not zero.

3. Evaluate: (a) $\begin{vmatrix} 2 & 4 & 7 \\ -3 & 1 & 0 \\ 2 & 0 & 2 \end{vmatrix}$; (b) $\begin{vmatrix} 3 & 1 & 2 & 6 \\ 4 & -2 & 1 & 3 \\ -2 & 0 & 3 & 1 \\ 2 & 4 & 2 & -5 \end{vmatrix}$,

(1) by using the definition of a determinant; (2) by using the theorems on determinants to simplify the computation.

4. Verify Theorems 1.1, 1.3, 1.6, 1.9 and 1.10 for the array

$$\begin{bmatrix} 2 & -1 & 4 \\ 3 & 2 & 11 \\ -8 & 6 & 4 \end{bmatrix}.$$

5. By using Theorems 1.3, 1.5 and 1.6, express

$$\begin{vmatrix} 1 & 2 & 3 \\ 4 & 5 & 7 \\ -2 & 4 & 4 \end{vmatrix} - 2\begin{vmatrix} 4 & 5 & 7 \\ 3 & 4 & -2 \\ 3 & 6 & 9 \end{vmatrix}$$

as the determinant of a single array.

6. Show, without expanding, that

$$\begin{vmatrix} 2 & 3 & 1 & 4 \\ 5 & -1 & -2 & 0 \\ 17 & 10 & -6 & 5 \\ 8 & 5 & -6 & -3 \end{vmatrix} = 0.$$

7. Expand the determinant in Ex. 6 by a Laplace expansion according to columns 1 and 4.

8. Prove Theorem 1.4 by using Theorem 1.8.

9. The function of n variables

$$F(x_1, x_2, \cdots, x_n) = (x_1 - x_2)(x_1 - x_3) \cdots (x_1 - x_n)(x_2 - x_3) \cdots$$
$$(x_2 - x_n) \cdots (x_{n-1} - x_n)$$

is called the *alternating function* of order n. Show that, if two variables x_i and x_j, $i \neq j$ are interchanged, the alternating function changes sign. (HINT: First prove the result for interchange of two successive variables and on that basis prove the general case.)

10. Prove, by use of the alternating function, that the number of interchanges necessary to bring the order $i_1, i_2, \cdots, i_n$ (or the order $x_{i_1}, x_{i_2}, \cdots, x_{i_n}$) into the order $1, 2, \cdots, n$ (or the order $x_1, x_2, \cdots, x_n$) is either always even or always odd.

2. Matrices and Their Elementary Properties. We say that two $m \times n$ arrays are *equal* if and only if the elements in like positions in the two arrays are equal. Let $A = [a_{rs}]$ and $B = [b_{rs}]$ be two square arrays. We define the sum $A + B$ of the arrays to be the array $[a_{rs} + b_{rs}]$, and the product AB of the arrays to be the array $\left[\sum_{i=1}^{n} a_{ri}b_{is} \right]$. The product of a number k and a square array A is defined to be the array each element of which is k times the corresponding element of A.

Example 1. If

$$A = \begin{bmatrix} 3 & 2 & -3 \\ 1 & 0 & 2 \\ 2 & -1 & -1 \end{bmatrix} \quad \text{and} \quad B = \begin{bmatrix} 1 & 2 & 1 \\ -1 & 4 & 5 \\ 0 & -4 & 2 \end{bmatrix}$$

then

$$A + B = \begin{bmatrix} 3+1 & 2+2 & -3+1 \\ 1-1 & 0+4 & 2+5 \\ 2+0 & -1-4 & -1+2 \end{bmatrix} = \begin{bmatrix} 4 & 4 & -2 \\ 0 & 4 & 7 \\ 2 & -5 & 1 \end{bmatrix},$$

and

$$AB = \begin{bmatrix} (3)(1) + (2)(-1) + (-3)(0) & (3)(2) + (2)(4) + (-3)(-4) \\ (1)(1) + (0)(-1) + (2)(0) & (1)(2) + (0)(4) + (2)(-4) \\ (2)(1) + (-1)(-1) + (-1)(0) & (2)(2) + (-1)(4) + (-1)(-4) \end{bmatrix}$$

$$\begin{matrix} (3)(1) + (2)(5) + (-3)(2) \\ (1)(1) + (0)(5) + (2)(2) \\ (2)(1) + (-1)(5) + (-1)(2) \end{matrix} \Bigg] = \begin{bmatrix} 1 & 26 & 7 \\ 1 & -6 & 5 \\ 3 & 4 & -5 \end{bmatrix}.$$

A member of a set of arrays of order n, for which equality, addition, and multiplication are defined as above, is called a *matrix of order n* (plural matrices). That is to say, matrices are arrays for which the above addition and multiplication processes and definition of equality are assumed. An array is not a matrix until such concepts are defined. On the other hand, a matrix is always an array, and hence all the results of the preceding section can be rephrased in terms of the determinant of a matrix. A matrix will frequently be denoted by placing double bars about the array. The notation ( ) is also used. Where the order is known, $\|a_{rs}\|$, where r is the row index and s is the column index, is unambiguous and will be used.

The determinant of the array of coefficients of a system of n linear homogeneous equations in n variables characterizes that system only partially.   On the other hand, the properties of the matrix of coefficients will give a complete characterization. Moreover, we shall find other valuable applications of the notion and properties of a matrix.   We proceed to investigate these properties.

THEOREM 2.1.   *Addition of matrices is associative and commutative; that is* $A + B = B + A$ *and* $A + (B + C) = (A + B) + C$. The proof is elementary and is left to the reader.

THEOREM 2.2.   *Multiplication of matrices is associative, but not, in general, commutative.*

Let $A = \|a_{rs}\|$, $B = \|b_{rs}\|$, $C = \|c_{rs}\|$ be matrices of order n.

$$(AB)C = \left\|\sum_{i=1}^{n} a_{ri}b_{is}\right\| \cdot \|c_{rs}\| = \left\|\sum_{i,j=1}^{n} a_{ri}b_{ij}c_{js}\right\|$$

$$= \left\|\sum_{i=1}^{n} a_{ri}\left(\sum_{j=1}^{n} b_{ij}c_{js}\right)\right\| = A(BC).$$

The matrices of Example 1 are not commutative, as the reader may easily verify.

THEOREM 2.3 (*Distributive Laws*).   *If* A, B, *and* C *are matrices of order* n, *then* $A(B + C) = AB + AC$; $(B + C)A = BA + CA$. The proof is left to the reader.

DEFINITION 2.1.   *The symbol* δ_{ij}(*Kronecker's delta*) *is defined to be unity if* $i = j$ *and* 0 *if* $i \neq j$.   (*Thus* $\delta_{34} = 0$, $\delta_{33} = 1$.)

DEFINITION 2.2.   *The main diagonal of a matrix is the set of positions along which the row and column indices are equal.*

For instance, the elements of the main diagonal of

$$\begin{Vmatrix} a_{11} & a_{12} & a_{13} \\ a_{21} & a_{22} & a_{23} \\ a_{31} & a_{32} & a_{33} \end{Vmatrix}$$

are a_{11}, a_{22}, and a_{33}.

DEFINITION 2.3.   *A diagonal matrix is a matrix all of whose elements off the main diagonal are zero.*

DEFINITION 2.4.   *A scalar matrix is a diagonal matrix whose main diagonal elements are all equal.*

By Definition 2.1, a scalar matrix can be written as $\|k\delta_{rs}\|$. The reader will easily verify that a scalar matrix of order n is commutative with every matrix of order n.   The converse also holds, viz.,

THEOREM 2.4. *If* **A** *is a matrix of order* n *and if* **AX** = **XA** *for every matrix* **X** *of order* n, *then* **A** *is a scalar matrix.*

Since **AX** = **XA**,

$$\sum_{i=1}^{n} a_{ri}x_{is} = \sum_{i=1}^{n} x_{ri}a_{is} \qquad (r, s = 1, 2, \cdots, n) \qquad (1)$$

for all matrices **X**, that is, for all values of x_{is} and x_{ri}. Take $x_{rs} = \delta_{rp}\delta_{sq}$. Then (1) must hold for this choice of x_{rs}, for every p and q.

Substituting in (1), we have

$$\sum_{i=1}^{n} a_{ri}\delta_{ip}\delta_{sq} = \sum_{i=1}^{n} \delta_{rp}\delta_{iq}a_{is}$$

If $q = s$ and $r \neq p$ this gives $a_{rp} = 0$ for every r and every $p \neq r$, while for $q = s$ and $r = p$, it gives $a_{rr} = a_{ss}$ for every r and s. Hence **A** is scalar.

By analogy with the ordinary number system (real or complex), the zero matrix **O** should be such a matrix that **A** + **O** = **A** for every matrix **A**. By definition of addition of matrices it is evident that **O** is a matrix each of whose elements is zero. Again by analogy the identity (or unit) matrix **I** should be a matrix such that **IA** = **AI** = **A** for every **A**. From Theorem 2.4, **I** must be scalar, and it is then further seen that each element of the main diagonal must be 1. Hence **I** = (δ_{rs}). These matrices **O** and **I** play much the same roles in matric algebra that 0 and 1 do in ordinary algebra.

A matrix **A** when multiplied on either side by a scalar matrix $\|k\delta_{rs}\|$, yields a matrix each element of which is k times the corresponding element of **A**. The product $\|k\delta_{rs}\|$**A** is what we defined earlier as k**A**. $\|k\delta_{rs}\|$ itself can be written as k**I**. By virtue of this definition, the meaning of the difference of two matrices is determined. For

$$\textbf{A} - \textbf{B} = \textbf{A} + (-1)\textbf{B} = \textbf{A} + (-\textbf{I}) \cdot \textbf{B};$$

and $(-\textbf{I} \cdot \textbf{B})$ is a matrix each element of which is the negative of the corresponding element of **B**.

THEOREM 2.5. *If* **A** *and* **B** *are matrices of order* n,

$$d(\textbf{AB}) = d(\textbf{A}) \cdot d(\textbf{B}).$$

Let **A** = $\|a_{rs}\|$ and **B** = $\|b_{rs}\|$. Consider the square array of order $2n$:

$$
\mathbf{M} = \begin{bmatrix}
a_{11} & a_{12} & \cdots & a_{1n} & 0 & 0 & \cdots & 0 \\
a_{21} & a_{22} & \cdots & a_{2n} & 0 & 0 & \cdots & 0 \\
\cdot & \cdot & & \cdot & \cdot & \cdot & & \cdot \\
\cdot & \cdot & & \cdot & \cdot & \cdot & & \cdot \\
a_{n1} & a_{n2} & \cdots & a_{nn} & 0 & 0 & \cdots & 0 \\
-1 & 0 & \cdots & 0 & b_{11} & b_{12} & \cdots & b_{1n} \\
0 & -1 & \cdots & 0 & b_{21} & b_{22} & \cdots & b_{2n} \\
\cdot & \cdot & & \cdot & \cdot & \cdot & & \cdot \\
\cdot & \cdot & & \cdot & \cdot & \cdot & & \cdot \\
0 & 0 & \cdots & -1 & b_{n1} & b_{n2} & \cdots & b_{nn}
\end{bmatrix}
$$

By a Laplace expansion according to rows $1, 2, \cdots, n$ it is clear that $d(\mathbf{M}) = d(\mathbf{A}) \cdot d(\mathbf{B})$. By Theorem 1.7,

$$
d(\mathbf{M}) = \begin{vmatrix}
a_{11} & a_{12} & \cdots & a_{1n} & \sum_{i=1}^{n} a_{1i}b_{i1} & \cdots & \sum_{i=1}^{n} a_{1i}b_{in} \\
a_{21} & a_{22} & \cdots & a_{2n} & \sum_{i=1}^{n} a_{2i}b_{i1} & \cdots & \sum_{i=1}^{n} a_{2i}b_{in} \\
\cdot & \cdot & & \cdot & \cdot & & \cdot \\
\cdot & \cdot & & \cdot & \cdot & & \cdot \\
\cdot & \cdot & & \cdot & \cdot & & \cdot \\
a_{n1} & a_{n2} & \cdots & a_{nn} & \sum_{i=1}^{n} a_{ni}b_{i1} & \cdots & \sum_{i=1}^{n} a_{ni}b_{in} \\
-1 & 0 & \cdots & 0 & 0 & \cdots & 0 \\
0 & -1 & \cdots & 0 & 0 & \cdots & 0 \\
\cdot & \cdot & & \cdot & \cdot & & \cdot \\
\cdot & \cdot & & \cdot & \cdot & & \cdot \\
0 & 0 & \cdots & -1 & 0 & \cdots & 0
\end{vmatrix}
$$

By a Laplace expansion according to rows $n + 1, n + 2, \cdots, 2n$,

$$
d(\mathbf{M}) = \begin{vmatrix}
\sum_{i=1}^{n} a_{1i}b_{i1} & \cdots & \sum_{i=1}^{n} a_{1i}b_{in} \\
\cdot & & \cdot \\
\cdot & & \cdot \\
\cdot & & \cdot \\
\sum_{i=1}^{n} a_{ni}b_{i1} & \cdots & \sum_{i=1}^{n} a_{ni}b_{in}
\end{vmatrix} = d(\mathbf{AB}).
$$

Definition 2.5. *Let* **A** *be any array. The order ρ of a minor square array of* **A** *of maximum order whose determinant is not zero is called the rank of* **A**.

Example 2. The matrix $\begin{Vmatrix} 3 & 2 & -1 \\ 6 & 4 & -2 \\ 6 & 4 & -2 \end{Vmatrix}$ is of rank 1, since the determinant of **A** is zero and the determinant of every minor square array of order 2 is zero, and since there are minor arrays of order one whose determinants are not zero—that is, there are nonzero elements.

If the determinant of a matrix is not zero, then the rank of the matrix is equal to its order. A matrix whose order exceeds its rank is called *singular*.

Theorem 2.6. *Associated with every nonsingular matrix* **A** *there is a unique matrix,* **B**, *such that* **AB** = **BA** = **I**.

Let **B** denote the matrix $\left\Vert \dfrac{A_{sr}}{d(\mathbf{A})} \right\Vert$ where A_{sr} is the cofactor of a_{sr}.

Then $\mathbf{AB} = \left\Vert \dfrac{1}{d(\mathbf{A})} \cdot \sum_{i=1}^{n} a_{ri} A_{si} \right\Vert$. By Theorems 1.9 and 1.10,

$\sum_{i=1}^{n} a_{ri} A_{si} = \delta_{rs} d(\mathbf{A})$ and hence $\mathbf{AB} = (\delta_{rs}) = \mathbf{I}$. A similar argument will show that **BA** = **I**. It remains to show that **B** is unique. Let **C** be any matrix for which **AC** = **I**. Then

$$\mathbf{B} = \mathbf{B(AC)} = \mathbf{(BA)C} = \mathbf{I} \cdot \mathbf{C} = \mathbf{C}.$$

Definition 2.6. *The matrix* **B** *of Theorem 2.6 is called the inverse of* **A**, *and is written* $\mathbf{A}^{-1}$.

Corollary 2.6. *If* **A** *is nonsingular,* $d(\mathbf{A}^{-1}) = 1/d(\mathbf{A})$.
For $d(\mathbf{A}) \cdot d(\mathbf{A}^{-1}) = d(\mathbf{AA}^{-1}) = d(\mathbf{I}) = 1$.

Example 3. Let $\mathbf{A} = \begin{Vmatrix} 2 & 2 \\ -3 & 1 \end{Vmatrix}$. Then $A_{11} = 1$, $A_{12} = 3$, $A_{21} = -2$, $A_{22} = 2$, and $d(\mathbf{A}) = 8$. Hence $\mathbf{A}^{-1} = \begin{Vmatrix} \frac{1}{8} & -\frac{1}{4} \\ \frac{3}{8} & \frac{1}{4} \end{Vmatrix}$.

Theorem 2.7. *Let* **A** *be a nonsingular matrix of order n and let* **B** *be an arbitrary matrix of order n. The rank of* **B** *is equal to the rank of* **AB**.

Let ρ be the rank of **B**. If $\rho = n$, then by Theorem 2.5, $d(\mathbf{AB}) = d(\mathbf{A}) \cdot d(\mathbf{B}) \neq 0$ and hence the rank of **AB** is n and is equal to the rank of **B**. Let us assume, then, that $\rho < n$. The reader can verify that the determinant of every square minor array of order $\rho + 1$ of the product matrix **AB** can be represented as a linear combination, with coefficients which are polynomials in the elements of **A**, of $n^{\rho+1}$ determinants of minor arrays of order $\rho + 1$ of **B**. But since the determinant of every square minor array of order $\rho + 1$ of **B** is zero, the rank ρ' of **AB** is not greater than ρ.

Now let **AB** = **C**. Since **A** is nonsingular it has an inverse and **B** = **A**⁻¹**C**. Now as before it can be shown that the rank ρ of **A**⁻¹**C** is not greater than the rank ρ' of **C**. Hence $\rho = \rho'$, or the rank of **AB** is equal to the rank of **B**.

EXERCISES II

1. (a) If $A = \begin{Vmatrix} 2 & 0 & 2 \\ -3 & 1 & 1 \\ 4 & -1 & 6 \end{Vmatrix}$ and $B = \begin{Vmatrix} 3 & 4 & 6 \\ -2 & 1 & 1 \\ 7 & 3 & 5 \end{Vmatrix}$,

find **A** + **B**, **A** − **B**, **B** − **A**, **AB**, and **BA**.

(b) Verify Theorem 2.5.

2. Prove Theorem 2.1.

3. Prove Theorem 2.3.

4. If **O** is the zero matrix of order n, and **A** is any nth order matrix, what matrix is **OA**? **AO**?

5. What are the ranks of the arrays

$$\begin{bmatrix} 2 & 1 & -3 \\ -4 & -2 & 6 \end{bmatrix}; \quad \begin{bmatrix} 2 & 1 & 3 & 5 \\ -2 & 3 & 1 & 15 \end{bmatrix}; \quad \begin{bmatrix} 2 & 1 & 0 \\ 3 & 5 & -3 \\ 9 & 8 & -3 \end{bmatrix}.$$

6. If $A = \begin{Vmatrix} 1 & 2 & -1 \\ 2 & 6 & -2 \\ 1 & 4 & 0 \end{Vmatrix}$, find **A**⁻¹, if it exists.

7. The *adjoint* matrix of **C** = $\|c_{rs}\|$, is the matrix $\|C_{sr}\|$, where C_{sr} is the cofactor of c_{sr}. It is denoted by **C**ᴬ. If **C** is nonsingular of order n, prove that

(a) $C^{-1} = \dfrac{1}{d(C)} C^A$; (b) $d(C^A) = [d(C)]^{n-1}$.

8. Show that if **A** is singular, there exists no matrix **B** such that **AB** = **I**.

9. By the method used in the proof of Theorem 2.5 show that if **C** is singular there is a matrix **B**, different from the zero matrix **O**, such that **CB** = **BC** = **O**. What is the matrix **B** derived in this way? Show that **B**, for which **CB** = **BC** = **O**, is not unique.

10. Prove that if **C** is singular, so is **C**ᴬ.

11. If **A** = $\|a_{rs}\|$ and **B** = $\|b_{rs}\|$ are third-order matrices, show that the determinant of every two rowed minor array of **AB** can be written as a linear combination of determinants of two rowed minor arrays of **AB**, with coefficients which are polynomials in the elements of **A**.

3. Elementary Matrices and Equivalence. An *elementary operation* or *transformation upon the rows of a matrix* **A** is a transformation upon the rows of **A** of one or more of the following types:

(I) *The interchange of two rows.*

(II) *The addition to the elements of a row of k times the corresponding elements of another row.*

(III) *The multiplication of the elements of a row by a number h.*

Each of these elementary operations can be effected by multiplying on the left by a certain elementary matrix, an elementary matrix being the matrix obtained by performing the elementary operation under consideration upon the identity matrix **I**.

Elementary operations upon the columns of a matrix **A** are defined in a similar manner.

If $I_{(ij)}$ denotes the elementary matrix obtained from the identity matrix by interchanging the ith and jth rows without disturbing the remaining $(n-2)$ rows, then the effect of multiplying **A** on the left by $I_{(ij)}$, giving $I_{(ij)}A$, is to interchange row i and row j of **A**. $I_{(ij)}$ is said to be an *elementary matrix of type* I.

The effect of multiplying **A** on the right by $I_{(ij)}$, giving $AI_{(ij)}$, is to interchange column i and column j.

Let $H_{(ij)} = I + (h)_{(ij)}$ $(i \neq j)$ denote the matrix obtained from the identity matrix **I** by inserting an element h in the ith row, jth column. The effect of multiplying **A** on the left by $H_{(ij)}$, giving $H_{(ij)}A$, is to add to the elements of the ith row of **A**, h times the elements of the jth row of **A**. $H_{(ij)}$ is said to be an *elementary matrix of type* II. The operation $AH_{(ij)}$ adds to the elements of the jth column of **A**, h times the elements of the ith column of **A**.

The operation $H_{(ji)}AH_{(ij)}$ upon **A** adds to the jth row h times the ith row, and adds to the jth column h times the ith column.

Let $J_{(ii)} = I + (k)_{(ii)}$, denote the matrix obtained from the identity matrix **I** by replacing the element in row i column i by k. The effect of multiplying **A** on the left by $J_{(ii)}$, giving $J_{(ii)}A$, is to multiply each element in the ith row of **A** by k. The operation $AJ_{(ii)}$ multiplies each element in the ith column of **A** by k. $J_{(ii)}$ is called an *elementary matrix of type* III.

It is easy to see that the inverse of an elementary matrix is an elementary matrix of the same type.

Evidently, if **B** is derived from **A** by a finite number of successive elementary transformations $P_1, P_2, \cdots, P_m$ upon the rows of **A**, $P_1A, \cdots$, then $B = P_m P_{m-1} P_{m-2} \cdots P_1 A$.

If **C** is derived from **A** by a finite number of successive elementary transformations $T_1, \cdots, T_n$ upon the columns of **A**, $AT_1, \cdots$, then $C = AT_1 T_2 \cdots T_n$.

In general, if **D** is obtained from **A** by a finite number of elementary transformations upon the rows and columns of **A**, then **D** is equivalent to **A**, that is, $D = RAS$, where **R** and **S** are the products of elementary matrices.

DEFINITION 3.1.   *The matrix* **B** *is said to be equivalent to the matrix* **A** *if there exist nonsingular matrices* **P** *and* **Q** *such that* $A = PBQ$.

We note that the ranks of equivalent matrices are equal.

We shall now prove

THEOREM 3.1.   *Every matrix* **A** *of rank* ρ *is equivalent to a diagonal matrix* $\|h_1, h_2, \cdots, h_\rho, 0, \cdots, 0\|$.

Suppose the rank of **A** is ρ. Then, if necessary, a shifting of rows and columns can be performed by means of elementary transformations so that the minor determinant of order ρ in the upper left-hand corner is not zero. By adding, if necessary, some other row to the first row, we can make the element in the (1, 1) position $\neq 0$. Next, by elementary transformations make the elements of the first column below the diagonal equal to zero. By elementary transformations every element in the first row save a_{11} can be made zero without disturbing the first column of zeros. Denote the resulting matrix by $\bar{B}$.

Next, repeat this general process by working with the last $(n-1)$ rows and columns of $\bar{B}$; then with the last $(n-2)$ rows and columns; etc. In this way **A** can be reduced to an equivalent matrix

$$
B = \left\|
\begin{matrix}
h_1 & 0 & \cdot & \cdot & 0 & 0 & \cdot & \cdot & \cdot & 0 \\
0 & h_2 & \cdot & \cdot & 0 & & & \cdot & & \cdot \\
& & \cdot & \cdot & & & & & & \\
& & \cdot & \cdot & \cdot & & & & & \\
0 & 0 & \cdot & \cdot & h_\rho & 0 & \cdot & \cdot & \cdot & 0 \\
0 & \cdot & \cdot & \cdot & 0 & & & & & \\
\cdot & & & \cdot & & & & & & \\
\cdot & & & \cdot & & & & M & & \\
\cdot & & & \cdot & & & & & & \\
0 & \cdot & \cdot & \cdot & 0 & & & & &
\end{matrix}
\right\|.
$$

Evidently $\mathbf{M} = 0$, for if but one element of $\mathbf{M}$ were not zero, $\mathbf{B}$, and hence $\mathbf{A}$, would be of rank $(\rho + 1)$, whereas $\mathbf{A}$ is of rank ρ.

EXERCISES III

1. (a) Show that the determinant of an elementary matrix of types I or II is unity.

(b) Show that if $\mathbf{A}$ is derived from $\mathbf{B}$ by elementary transformations on the rows and columns of $\mathbf{B}$ of types I and II, then $d(\mathbf{A}) = d(\mathbf{B})$.

2. (a) By elementary transformations, reduce the matrix

$$\mathbf{A} = \begin{Vmatrix} 4 & 2 & 5 \\ 3 & -1 & 0 \\ 7 & 4 & 4 \end{Vmatrix}$$

to a diagonal matrix $\mathbf{D}$.

(b) What are the matrices $\mathbf{P}$ and $\mathbf{Q}$ of (a) such that

$$\mathbf{D} = \mathbf{PAQ}?$$

(c) Verify the result of (a) by showing by direct matric multiplication that $\mathbf{PAQ} = \mathbf{D}$.

4. Linear Forms, Linear Transformations. Suppose we have a product of two matrices $\mathbf{AB}$ where the columns of $\mathbf{B}$, with one exception, consist entirely of zeros. Then the same columns of the product matrix $\mathbf{AB}$ consist entirely of zeros, i.e.,

$$\begin{Vmatrix} a_{11} & a_{12} & \cdots & a_{1n} \\ a_{21} & a_{22} & \cdots & a_{2n} \\ \vdots & \vdots & & \vdots \\ a_{n1} & a_{n2} & \cdots & a_{nn} \end{Vmatrix} \begin{Vmatrix} 0 & 0 & \cdots & b_1 & \cdots & 0 \\ 0 & 0 & \cdots & b_2 & \cdots & 0 \\ \vdots & \vdots & & \vdots & & \vdots \\ 0 & 0 & \cdots & b_n & \cdots & 0 \end{Vmatrix}$$

$$= \begin{Vmatrix} 0 & 0 & \cdots & \sum_{i=1}^{n} a_{1i}b_i & \cdots & 0 \\ 0 & 0 & \cdots & \sum_{i=1}^{n} a_{2i}b_i & \cdots & 0 \\ \vdots & \vdots & & \vdots & & \vdots \\ 0 & 0 & \cdots & \sum_{i=1}^{n} a_{ni}b_i & \cdots & 0 \end{Vmatrix}$$

We shall make frequent use of the following abbreviated notation for such a relation, whenever no confusion is likely to arise:

$$
\begin{Vmatrix}
a_{11} & a_{12} & \cdots & a_{1n} \\
a_{21} & a_{22} & \cdots & a_{2n} \\
\cdot & \cdot & & \cdot \\
\cdot & \cdot & & \cdot \\
a_{n1} & a_{n2} & \cdots & a_{nn}
\end{Vmatrix}
\begin{Bmatrix}
b_1 \\
b_2 \\
\cdot \\
\cdot \\
b_n
\end{Bmatrix}
=
\begin{Bmatrix}
\sum_{i=1}^{n} a_{1i}b_i \\
\sum_{i=1}^{n} a_{2i}b_i \\
\cdot \\
\cdot \\
\sum_{i=1}^{n} a_{ni}b_i
\end{Bmatrix},
$$

or more briefly,

$$
\mathbf{A}\{\mathbf{b}\} = \left\{ \sum_{i=1}^{n} a_{ri}b_i \right\},
$$

where $\{\ \}$ signifies a column of elements and $\{\mathbf{b}\} \equiv \{b_r\}$. We can think of this abridged notation as defining the product of a matrix and a column array, in that order. Similarly we may define the symbolic abbreviation

$$
(\mathbf{c})\mathbf{A} = \left(\sum_{i=1}^{n} c_i a_{is} \right)
$$

where $(\ \ )$ denotes a row array, or more properly, a matrix all of whose rows, with one exception, consist entirely of zeros.

Further, if $\mathbf{A}$ has only one nonzero row $a_1, a_2, \cdots, a_n$ and $\mathbf{B}$ one nonzero column, $b_1, b_2, \cdots, b_n$ then the product matrix $\mathbf{E}$ will have (at most) only one non-zero element and we may introduce for the identity $\mathbf{AB} = \mathbf{E}$, the abridgment

$$
(\mathbf{a})\{\mathbf{b}\} = \sum_{i=1}^{n} a_i b_i,
$$

wherever no confusion is likely to arise.

A set of linear equations (or transformations)

$$
\left.
\begin{aligned}
a_{11}x_1 + a_{12}x_2 + \cdots + a_{1n}x_n &= y_1, \\
a_{21}x_1 + a_{22}x_2 + \cdots + a_{2n}x_n &= y_2, \\
\cdots\cdots\cdots\cdots\cdots\cdots\cdots\cdots\cdots \\
a_{n1}x_1 + a_{n2}x_2 + \cdots + a_{nn}x_n &= y_n,
\end{aligned}
\right\}
\tag{1}
$$

can now be written by use of the abridged notation as the single matric equation

$$A\{x\} = \{y\},$$

where $A = \|a_{rs}\|$.

If $d(A) \neq 0$, the inverse A^{-1} of A exists. Multiplying on the left of each side of equation (1) by A^{-1}, we have

$$A^{-1}\{y\} = A^{-1}A\{x\} = I\{x\} = \{x\}.$$

In other words, if the matrix A of the system (1) is nonsingular,

$$\{x\} = A^{-1}\{y\} \tag{2}$$

is the (unique) solution of (1). Equation (2) is known as *Cramer's rule*.

If $d(A) = 0$, the system (1) is said to be *singular*.

Various interpretations may be placed upon eqs. (1) and its solution (2). Equations (1) may be looked upon as an operation which transforms an array $\{x\}$ into a new array $\{y\}$.

If $x_1, x_2, \cdots , x_n$ be thought of as the coordinates of a point P in n-space, then the point P' of coordinates $y_1, y_2, \cdots , y_n$ is said to be derived from P by the linear homogeneous transformation (1).

Any homogeneous linear function is called a *linear form*. Hence eqs. (1) may be said to consist of n linear forms $y_1, \cdots , y_n$.

Suppose the x's in (1) are subjected to the linear transformation B with coefficients b_{rs},

$$\{x\} = B\{z\}. \tag{3}$$

By (1),

$$y_i = \sum_{p=1}^{n} a_{ip}x_p = \sum_{p=1}^{n} a_{ip}\sum_{j=1}^{n} b_{pj}z_j = \sum_{j=1}^{n} d_{ij}z_j, \tag{4}$$

where

$$d_{ij} = \sum_{p=1}^{n} a_{ip}b_{pj}. \tag{5}$$

From the definition of the product AB of two matrices A and B, it is clear that

$$D = (d_{ij}) = AB.$$

In other words, under transformation (3), (1) becomes

$$\{y\} = A\{x\} = D\{z\}, \qquad \text{where} \qquad D = AB. \tag{6}$$

$AB = D$ is called the *product* of the linear transformations A and B.

Theorem 4.1. *A linear transformation with matrix B replaces a system of linear forms with matrix A, by a system of linear forms with matrix AB.*

It is important to notice the one-to-one correspondence (isomorphism) between the linear transformations and their matrices which is preserved under multiplication. This shows why the definition of multiplication of matrices is made as it is.

We shall leave to the reader the proof of the following theorems:

Theorem 4.2. *If A, B, C be the matrices of three linear transformations, then $A(BC) = (AB)C$, that is, the product of linear transformations is associative.*

Theorem 4.3. *The sum of the two arrays $A\{y\}$ and $B\{y\}$ of the same number of rows is the row array $C\{y\}$ where $C = A + B$.*

We noted that if $d(A) \neq 0$ in (1), (2) gives the unique solution of (1). If $d(A) = 0$, the above method can not be employed. However, a parametric solution can be obtained by the use of the diagonal form $D = PAQ$.   (See Sec. 3.)

We shall consider the equations (1) with coefficients in a field F,* and with $d(A) = 0$.† Let the matrix A be reduced by means of nonsingular elementary transformations of matrices P and Q to an equivalent diagonal form $D = PAQ$, where D has r nonzero consecutive diagonal elements $\alpha_1, \alpha_2, \cdots, \alpha_r$, all rational in the coefficients a_{ij}. Let n new variables ξ_i be introduced by means of the linear relations

---

* A *field* of numbers is a set S of numbers such that the sum, difference, product, and quotient (provided the divisor is not zero) of any two numbers of S are again in S. Thus the set of all rational numbers, the set of all real numbers, and the set of all complex numbers each constitutes a field. The set of all positive rational numbers is, however, not a field. (Why?) Neither is the set of all integers. (Why?)

Although the results we shall obtain in this and later sections, as well as the results of preceding sections, are valid for a more general domain than a field of numbers, where no particular field is specified, the student may think of some familiar field such as the complex field or the real field, when studying the work in this chapter.

† The student is advised to work carefully Exs. 5 to 13 at the end of this section before attempting to read the remainder of this section.

$$\{\xi\} = \left\{\begin{matrix} \xi_1 \\ \cdot \\ \cdot \\ \cdot \\ \xi_n \end{matrix}\right\} = Q^{-1}\left\{\begin{matrix} x_1 \\ \cdot \\ \cdot \\ \cdot \\ x_n \end{matrix}\right\}. \tag{7}$$

Then from (7) and (1) we have

$$D\{\xi\} = PAQ\{\xi\} = PAQQ^{-1}\{x\} = PA\{x\} = P\{y\}. \tag{8}$$

In (8),

$$D\{\xi\} = \left\{\begin{matrix} \alpha_1\xi_1 \\ \cdot \\ \cdot \\ \cdot \\ \alpha_r\xi_r \\ 0 \\ \cdot \\ \cdot \\ \cdot \\ 0 \end{matrix}\right\} \tag{9}$$

consists of a column of r nonzero elements followed by $(n - r)$ zeros. The right-hand member $P\{y\}$ of (8) is a column array consisting of n homogeneous linear functions of the y_i whose coefficients are the elements of the respective rows of P,

$$P\{y\} = \left\|\begin{matrix} p_{11} & \cdots & p_{1n} \\ \cdot & & \cdot \\ \cdot & & \cdot \\ p_{n1} & \cdots & p_{nn} \end{matrix}\right\| \left\{\begin{matrix} y_1 \\ \cdot \\ \cdot \\ \cdot \\ y_n \end{matrix}\right\} = \left\{\begin{matrix} \eta_1 \\ \cdot \\ \eta_r \\ \cdot \\ \eta_n \end{matrix}\right\} = \{n\}. \tag{10}$$

Evidently, the equation (8), $D\{\xi\} = P\{y\} = \{n\}$ can be solved for the ξ_i if the last $(n - r)$ elements of the column $\{n\}$ are zero. In case this is so, we have $\alpha_1\xi_1 = \eta_1$, $\alpha_2\xi_2 = \eta_2$, $\cdots$, $\alpha_r\xi_r = \eta_r$ from which we find

$$\xi_1 = \frac{\eta_1}{\alpha_1}, \qquad \xi_2 = \frac{\eta_2}{\alpha_2}, \qquad \cdots, \qquad \xi_r = \frac{\eta_r}{\alpha_r}.$$

The remaining $(n - r)$ of the ξ_i are arbitrary, for they do not affect the value of $\mathbf{D}\{\boldsymbol{\xi}\}$. From (7), $\{\mathbf{x}\} = \mathbf{Q}\{\boldsymbol{\xi}\}$, so that each x_i is a linear function of all the ξ_i with coefficients in F.

Thus, if the last $(n - r)$ elements of $\{\mathbf{n}\}$ are zero, the general solution for x_i involves exactly $(n - r)$ parameters $\xi_{r+1}, \cdots, \xi_n$; for throughout the entire argument, the expressions used have been obtained by rational operations involving only the elements a_{ij} of $\mathbf{A}$ and the n variables $y_1, \cdots, y_n$. Since $\mathbf{P}$ and $\mathbf{Q}$ are nonsingular the argument given above may be reversed.

If any one of the last $(n - r)$ elements η_{r+i} do not vanish, no solution to (1) exists in case $d(\mathbf{A}) = 0$. In this case the equations (1) are *inconsistent* (or *incompatible*). In order to state the conditions for consistency in a more general form we shall consider the following $n \times (n + 1)$ array $\mathbf{B}$ formed by augmenting the matrix $\mathbf{A}$ by the column $\{\mathbf{y}\}$,

$$\mathbf{B} \equiv \begin{Vmatrix} a_{11} & \cdots & a_{1n} & y_1 \\ \cdot & & \cdot & \cdot \\ \cdot & & \cdot & \cdot \\ a_{n1} & \cdots & a_{nn} & y_n \end{Vmatrix}, \tag{11}$$

and shall show that the n non-homogeneous equations

$$\mathbf{A}\{\mathbf{x}\} = \{\mathbf{y}\}$$

are consistent and solvable for r of the variables $\{\mathbf{x}\}$ in terms of $(n - r)$ arbitrary parameters, if and only if the rank of $\mathbf{B}$ is equal to the rank r of $\mathbf{A}$.

We shall consider the identity

$$\begin{Vmatrix} p_{11} & \cdots & p_{1n} & 0 \\ \cdot & & \cdot & \cdot \\ \cdot & & \cdot & \cdot \\ p_{n1} & \cdots & p_{nn} & 0 \\ 0 & \cdots & 0 & 1 \end{Vmatrix} \begin{Vmatrix} a_{11} & \cdots & a_{1n} & y_1 \\ \cdot & & \cdot & \cdot \\ \cdot & & \cdot & \cdot \\ a_{n1} & \cdots & a_{nn} & y_n \\ 0 & \cdots & 0 & 0 \end{Vmatrix} \begin{Vmatrix} q_{11} & \cdots & q_{1n} & 0 \\ \cdot & & \cdot & \cdot \\ \cdot & & \cdot & \cdot \\ q_{n1} & \cdots & q_{nn} & 0 \\ 0 & \cdots & 0 & 1 \end{Vmatrix}$$

$$= \begin{Vmatrix} \alpha_1 & 0 & \cdots & 0 & 0 & \cdots & 0 & \eta_1 \\ 0 & \alpha_2 & \cdots & & & & & \\ & & \cdot & & & & \cdot & \\ 0 & \cdots & \alpha_r & 0 & \cdots & 0 & \eta_r \\ 0 & \cdots & 0 & 0 & \cdots & \cdot & \cdot \\ & & & \cdot & & & & \\ 0 & \cdots & 0 & 0 & \cdots & 0 & \eta_n \\ 0 & \cdots & 0 & 0 & \cdots & 0 & 0 \end{Vmatrix} \equiv \tilde{\mathbf{D}}, \tag{12}$$

or more briefly

$$\tilde{P}B\tilde{Q} = \tilde{D}. \tag{13}$$

If r is the rank of A, then the rank of $\tilde{D}$ must be r at least, for one of its r-rowed minors (in D) is the nonzero product $\alpha_1 \cdots \alpha_r$. Furthermore, the rank of $\tilde{D}$ can exceed r if and only if at least one element η_{r+i} $(i > 0)$ in the last $(n - r)$ rows and the final column of $\tilde{D}$ is not zero. Since P and Q are nonsingular, $\tilde{P}$ and $\tilde{Q}$ are also, hence, by Theorem 2.7 the rank of B is equal to the rank of $\tilde{D}$. Thus, the last $(n - r)$ elements of $P\{y\} = \{n\}$ are zero and the equations (1) are consistent and parametrically solvable, if and only if the matrices A and B have the same rank r.

The results given above are readily generalized to cover the cases where the number of equations in (1) is $m \neq n$.

Theorem 4.4. *Given the linear equations with coefficients in a field F*

$$y_r = \sum_{s=1}^{n} a_{rs}x_s \qquad (r = 1, \cdots, m) \tag{14}$$

of array $A \equiv [a_{rs}]$. Let r be the rank of A and ρ be the rank of B, the augmented array derived from A by annexing the column $\{y\}$. If $\rho > r$, equations (14) are inconsistent. If $\rho = r$, certain r of the equations determine uniquely r of the unknowns as linear functions of the remaining $(n - r)$ unknowns; for all values of the latter the expressions for these r unknowns satisfy also the remaining $(m - r)$ equations.

A set of elements $z_1, z_2, \cdots, z_n$ (row arrays, matrices, polynomials, numbers, etc.) are said to be *linearly independent* with respect to a field of numbers F (real, rational, or complex) in which we are working, if no linear combination of them,

$$a_1z_1 + a_2z_2 + \cdots + a_nz_n,$$

with coefficients a_i in the field F, is zero unless

$$a_1 = a_2 = \cdots = a_n = 0.$$

If numbers a_i not all zero do exist such that the above combination is zero, then the $z_1, z_2, \cdots, z_n$ are said to be *linearly dependent* relative to F. It is necessary to specify the field F. For example, consider the numbers $1, \sqrt{3}$; they are linearly independent relative to the rational field but are linearly dependent relative to the real field. Similarly, 1 and i are linearly independent relative to the rational field or the real field but are linearly dependent relative to the complex field.

A particularly important case of Theorem 4.4 occurs when (1) consists of m homogeneous linear equations with

$$y_1 = \cdots = y_m = 0,$$

that is,

$$\sum_{s=1}^{n} a_{rs} x_s = 0. \qquad (r = 1, \cdots, m) \quad (15)$$

Theorem 4.5. *Given the homogeneous equations* (15) *with coefficients in a field F. Let r be the rank of* $\mathbf{A} \equiv [a_{rs}]$. *Then* (15) *has* $(n - r)$ *linearly independent solutions in F, while every other solution is linearly dependent on them* [*i.e., r equations may be selected from* (15), *whose matrix has a non-vanishing r-rowed determinant and these r equations determine uniquely r of the unknowns as homogeneous linear functions, with coefficients in F, of the remaining* $(n - r)$ *unknowns: for all values of the latter, the expressions for the r unknowns satisfy* (15)].

An immediate consequence of this theorem is

Corollary 4.5. *Equations* (15) *have solutions not all zero if and only if* $r < n$. *In particular, n homogeneous linear equations in n unknowns have solutions not all zero if and only if the determinant of the coefficients of the unknowns is zero.*

If the m homogeneous eqs. (15) have the two solutions $\{\mathbf{u}\} \equiv (u_1, \cdots, u_n)$ and $\{\mathbf{v}\} \equiv (v_1, \cdots, v_n)$, then (15) have the solution $(\alpha u_1 + \beta v_1, \cdots, \alpha u_n + \beta v_n)$ where α and β are any two unknowns in F. The solutions $\{\mathbf{u}\}$ and $\{\mathbf{v}\}$ are linearly dependent if there exists in F constants α and β, not both zero, such that $\alpha\{\mathbf{u}\} + \beta\{\mathbf{v}\} = \{\mathbf{O}\}$; but linearly independent if no such constants α and β exist in F. This notion can readily be extended to any number of solutions. Thus, in Theorem 4.5 any system (15) of rank $r < n$ has $(n - r)$ linearly independent solutions while every solution is linearly dependent upon them.

We are now in a position to state an important theorem on linear dependence.

Theorem 4.6. *Let* $\mathbf{S}$ *be a set of n row arrays (column arrays) of m elements each, and let the elements of these arrays lie in a field*

F. The arrays of S *are linearly independent relative to F, if and only if the rectangular array composed of these rows (columns) is of rank r = n. If r < n, there are exactly n − r linearly independent linear relations among the rows (columns) of* S.

The proof follows immediately from Theorem 4.5 and Corollary 4.5 when we ask for the solutions of the system of equations

$$x_1 \left\{ \begin{array}{c} a_{11} \\ a_{21} \\ \cdot \\ \cdot \\ \cdot \\ a_{m1} \end{array} \right\} + x_2 \left\{ \begin{array}{c} a_{12} \\ a_{22} \\ \cdot \\ \cdot \\ \cdot \\ a_{m2} \end{array} \right\} + \cdots + x_n \left\{ \begin{array}{c} a_{1n} \\ a_{2n} \\ \cdot \\ \cdot \\ \cdot \\ a_{mn} \end{array} \right\} = 0.$$

Note that if $m < n$, Theorem 4.6 states that the arrays of S are always linearly dependent.

Theorem 4.6 may be applied to any entities capable of representation as row or column arrays. As particularly important instances of such, we mention vectors of order m, linear forms in m variables, and polynomials of degree m in one variable.

Example 1. The polynomials $x^3 - 2x^2 + 1$, $x^3 - 3x^2 - x + 3$, and $2x^3 - 3x^2 + x$ are linearly dependent. For if these polynomials are represented respectively by the row arrays $(1, -2, 0, 1)$, $(1, -3, -1, 3)$ and $(2, -3, 1, 0)$ the array

$$\begin{bmatrix} 1 & -2 & 0 & 1 \\ 1 & -3 & -1 & 3 \\ 2 & -3 & 1 & 0 \end{bmatrix}$$

is easily seen to be of rank 2. The third row is linearly dependent on rows one and two. Theorem 4.6 also tells us that there is just one independent linear relation among these polynomials.

We leave the proof of the following theorem to the reader:

THEOREM 4.7. *If* $\{\mathbf{x}^{(1)}\}, \cdots, \{\mathbf{x}^{(q)}\}$ *are q solutions of* (15),

$$A\{\mathbf{x}\} = \{\mathbf{O}\}, then \left\{ \sum_{j=1}^{q} \alpha_j \, x^{(j)} \right\} is \ a \ solution \ of \ (15), \ the \ \alpha_j \ being \ in$$

the field F.

EXERCISES IV

1. (a) Let the variables x_1, x_2 be subjected to the transformation

$$\begin{array}{r} x_1 = x_1' \cos \theta - x_2' \sin \theta, \\ x_2 = x_1' \sin \theta + x_2' \cos \theta. \end{array} \right\} \tag{1}$$

What is the geometric interpretation of this transformation? What is the matrix of the transformation? Is the transformation nonsingular?

(b) Find, by matric methods, the inverse transformation.

(c) If the variables x_1' and x_2' are subjected to the transformation

$$\left.\begin{array}{l} x_1' = x_1'' \cos \alpha - x_2'' \sin \alpha, \\ x_2' = x_1'' \sin \alpha + x_2'' \cos \alpha, \end{array}\right\} \tag{2}$$

verify by direct substitution, that the matrix of the transformation carrying x_1, x_2 into x_1'', x_2'' is the product of the matrices of transformations (1) and (2).

(d) Verify that the matrices of transformations (1) and (2) are commutative. Is there any reason for this?

2. Prove that if **A** is equivalent to **B**, then **B** is equivalent to **A**.

3. Prove that if **A** is equivalent to **B** and **B** is equivalent to **C**, then **A** is equivalent to **C**. What are the transforming matrices under which **A** is equivalent to **C**?

4. Is a matrix equivalent to itself?

Solve the systems of equations in Exs. 5 to 13 by following the procedure outlined below:

(a) Find the rank r of the array of coefficients.

(b) Find the rank of the array of coefficients augmented by the column of constant terms, thus determining whether or not the system is consistent. (See Theorem 4.4.)

(c) In case the system is consistent, choose a subset of r of the equations whose array of coefficients is of rank r, and solve by Cramer's rule for the r unknowns corresponding to the minor of rank r in terms of the $n - r$ remaining unknowns.

(d) Verify by direct substitution that these solutions satisfy each equation of the system.

5. $\begin{cases} 2x - 3y = 5, \\ x + y = 0. \end{cases}$

6. $\begin{cases} 2x + 3y = 4, \\ 6x + 9y = 12. \end{cases}$

7. $\begin{cases} 5x - 7y = 8, \\ 10x - 14y = 7. \end{cases}$

8. $\begin{cases} 2x + y - 6z = -4, \\ 5x - 3y + 14z = -12, \\ -3x + 2y - 10z = 7. \end{cases}$

9. $\begin{cases} 3x - 4y + 20z = -8, \\ -x + y - 6z = 2, \\ 3x - 5y + 22z = -10. \end{cases}$

10. $\begin{cases} x + 6y - 32z = 0, \\ x - 2y + 5z = 3, \\ 4x - 2z = -9. \end{cases}$

11. $\begin{cases} 2x + 3y + 5z = 0, \\ 3x + 4y + 6z = 0, \\ x + 3y + 7z = 0. \end{cases}$

12. $\begin{cases} x - 2y + z = 0, \\ 3x + 5y + 2z = 0, \\ 4x + 3y + 3z = 0. \end{cases}$

13. $\begin{cases} 3x - y - 2z = 4, \\ -2x + 3y + 4z = -1, \\ x + 9y + 10z = 8, \\ 13x - 2y - 6z = 19. \end{cases}$

14. Show that the linear forms $3x - 2y + z$, $x + y - 6z$, and $2x + 2y$ are linearly independent relative to the complex field.

15. Show that the polynomials $x^2 - 3x + 2$, $5x^2 - 2x + 7$, $3x^2 + 2$, and $2x^2 - x + 2$ are linearly dependent relative to the complex field, and find a particular linear combination of them, with coefficients not all zero, which is identically equal to zero.

16. Consider the pair of straight lines

$$\begin{cases} a_1x + b_1y + c_1 = 0 \\ a_2x + b_2y + c_2 = 0. \end{cases}$$

If $A \equiv \begin{Vmatrix} a_1 & b_1 \\ a_2 & b_2 \end{Vmatrix}$ and $B \equiv \begin{bmatrix} a_1 & b_1 & c_1 \\ a_2 & b_2 & c_2 \end{bmatrix}$, discuss the points of intersection of the lines in the following cases: (a) $d(A) \neq 0$; (b) the rank of A is 1 and the rank of B is 2; (c) the rank of A is 1 and the rank of B is 1.

17. Make a discussion similar to that of Ex. 16 for the case of three straight lines in the plane.

5. Bilinear Forms and Equivalent Matrices. The second-degree polynomial

$$G \equiv \sum_{i,j=1}^{n} a_{ij}x_iy_j$$

in the $2n$ variables $x_1, x_2, \cdots, x_n, y_1, y_2, \cdots, y_n$ is called a *bilinear form.* In the abridged notation we may write

$$G = (x)A\{y\},$$

where $(x) \equiv (x_1, x_2, \cdots, x_n)$, $\{y\}$ is a similar column array, and $A \equiv \|a_{rs}\|$. A is called the matrix of the form G.

DEFINITION 5.1. *The transpose of a matrix A, denoted by A^T, is the matrix resulting from A by interchanging the rows and columns of A. Thus if $A \equiv \|a_{rs}\|$, $A^T = \|a_{sr}\|$.*

Example 1. $\begin{Vmatrix} 2 & 3 \\ -1 & 4 \end{Vmatrix}^T = \begin{Vmatrix} 2 & -1 \\ 3 & 4 \end{Vmatrix}.$

It is easy to prove
THEOREM 5.1.

$$(A + B)^T = A^T + B^T;$$
$$(A + B + \cdots + K)^T = A^T + B^T + \cdots + K^T.$$

THEOREM 5.2.

$$(AB)^T = B^TA^T; \quad (AB \cdots K)^T = K^T \cdots B^TA^T.$$

THEOREM 5.3. $(A^T)^{-1} = (A^{-1})^T.$

If the variables of G are subjected to the nonsingular linear transformations

$$\{\mathbf{x}\} = \mathbf{P}\{\bar{\mathbf{x}}\}, \qquad \{\mathbf{y}\} = \mathbf{Q}\{\bar{\mathbf{y}}\}$$

where $\mathbf{P} \equiv \|p_{rs}\|$ and $\mathbf{Q} \equiv \|q_{rs}\|$, then writing $\{\mathbf{x}\}^T = (\mathbf{x}) = (\bar{\mathbf{x}})\mathbf{P}^T$, G becomes

$$\mathbf{G} = (\bar{\mathbf{x}})\mathbf{P}^T \cdot \mathbf{A} \cdot \mathbf{Q}\{\bar{\mathbf{y}}\} = (\bar{\mathbf{x}}) \cdot \mathbf{P}^T\mathbf{A}\mathbf{Q} \cdot \{\bar{\mathbf{y}}\},$$

Thus, under nonsingular transformations of the variables, the matrix of the bilinear form in the new variables $\bar{x}_i$, $\bar{y}_i$ is equivalent to the matrix of the form involving the old variables x_i, y_i.

This is an instance of the use of the idea of equivalence of matrices. As in the case of equivalence we see that the rank of the matrix of G (called the rank of the bilinear form) is an invariant under nonsingular linear transformations of the variables.

EXERCISES V

1. Prove that $(\mathbf{A}^T)^T = \mathbf{A}$.
2. Prove Theorem 5.1.
3. Prove Theorem 5.2.
4. Prove Theorem 5.3.
5. Make a briefer statement of Theorem 1.1.

6. Congruence of Matrices. As a particular kind of equivalence of matrices, we take up the study of the congruence of matrices. *Congruence* is the case of equivalence wherein $\mathbf{P} = \mathbf{Q}^T$. (See Sec. 3.)

DEFINITION 6.1. *A matrix* $\mathbf{A}$ *is called symmetric, if* $\mathbf{A}^T = \mathbf{A}$.

DEFINITION 6.2. *If two matrices* $\mathbf{A}$ *and* $\mathbf{B}$ *are so related that there exists a nonsingular matrix* $\mathbf{P}$ *such that* $\mathbf{P}^T\mathbf{A}\mathbf{P} = \mathbf{B}$, *then* $\mathbf{B}$ *is said to be congruent to* $\mathbf{A}$.

If $\mathbf{A}$ is symmetric and $\mathbf{B}$ is congruent to $\mathbf{A}$, then $\mathbf{B}$ is also symmetric. For if $\mathbf{B} = \mathbf{P}^T\mathbf{A}\mathbf{P}$, then by Theorem 5.2

$$\mathbf{B}^T = \mathbf{P}^T\mathbf{A}^T\mathbf{P} = \mathbf{P}^T\mathbf{A}\mathbf{P} = \mathbf{B}.$$

A *quadratic form* in n variables x_1, x_2, $\cdots$, x_n is a homogeneous polynomial of the second degree in x_1, x_2, $\cdots$, x_n. A quadratic form is a particular type of bilinear form. A quadratic form Q may be written in the symmetric form

$$Q = \sum_{i,j=1}^{n} a_{ij}x_ix_j,$$

where $a_{ij} = a_{ji}$. The matrix $\mathbf{A} = \|a_{rs}\|$ is called the matrix of the quadratic form. By virtue of the symmetric way in which Q is written it is clear that $\mathbf{A}$ is symmetric. In the abridged notation of Sec. 4, Q may be written

$$Q = (\mathbf{x})\mathbf{A}\{\mathbf{x}\}$$

where $(\mathbf{x})$ is the row array $(x_1, \cdots, x_n)$ and $\{\mathbf{x}\}$ is the similar column array.

If the variables $x_1, x_2, \cdots, x_n$ are subjected to the nonsingular linear transformation

$$\{\mathbf{x}\} = \mathbf{C}\{\mathbf{y}\}, \qquad \mathbf{C} = \|C_{rs}\|$$

then, since $(\mathbf{x}) = \{\mathbf{x}\}^T = (\mathbf{y})\mathbf{C}^T$

$$Q = (\mathbf{y})\mathbf{C}^T \cdot \mathbf{A} \cdot \mathbf{C}\{\mathbf{y}\} = (\mathbf{y}) \cdot \mathbf{C}^T\mathbf{A}\mathbf{C} \cdot \{\mathbf{y}\}.$$

Thus the matrix $\mathbf{A}$ of Q is transformed into a congruent symmetric matrix under the linear transformation of the variables.

Theorem 6.1. *Every symmetric matrix* $\mathbf{A}$ *of rank* ρ *with elements in a field* F *is congruent in* F *to a diagonal matrix*

$$[d_1, d_2, \cdots, d_\rho, 0, \cdots, 0], \qquad d_i \neq 0.$$

We consider the matrix

$$\mathbf{A} = \begin{Vmatrix} a_{11} & \cdots & a_{1n} \\ \cdot & & \cdot \\ \cdot & & \cdot \\ a_{n1} & \cdots & a_{nn} \end{Vmatrix}$$

of rank ρ.

If the principal minor of order ρ in the upper left corner of $\mathbf{A}$ is singular, then an elementary transformation matrix $\mathbf{P}_1$ can be found such that $\mathbf{B} = \mathbf{P}_1^T\mathbf{A}\mathbf{P}_1$ where the principal minor of order ρ in the upper left corner of $\mathbf{B}$ is nonsingular. If $b_{11} = 0$, some $b_{1k} \neq 0$. (Why?) In this case select a matrix $\mathbf{P}_2$ which adds row k to row 1 and column k to column 1, giving $\mathbf{C} = \mathbf{P}_2^T\mathbf{B}\mathbf{P}_2$ in which $c_{11} = 2b_{1k} \neq 0$. Now select a $\mathbf{P}_3$ which adds $-c_{1k}/c_{11}$ times the first row to the kth row and $-c_{1k}/c_{11}$ times the first column to the kth column, $(k = 2, 3, \cdots, n)$, giving $\mathbf{E} = \mathbf{P}_3^T\mathbf{C}\mathbf{P}_3$, in which all the elements of the first row and first column are zero except e_{11}. Now proceed similarly with the lower right minor of order $(n - 1)$, and so on, until the diagonal matrix

$$\mathbf{D} \equiv \|d_1, d_2, \cdots, d_\rho, 0, \cdots, 0\|$$

is reached.   Since

$$\mathbf{P}_s^T \cdots \mathbf{P}_3^T\mathbf{P}_2^T\mathbf{P}_1^T\mathbf{A}\mathbf{P}_1\mathbf{P}_2\mathbf{P}_3 \cdots \mathbf{P}_s = \mathbf{P}^T\mathbf{A}\mathbf{P} = \mathbf{D}$$

with $\mathbf{P} = \mathbf{P}_1\mathbf{P}_2\mathbf{P}_3 \cdots \mathbf{P}_s$ we see that $\mathbf{A}$ is congruent to $\mathbf{D}$. Since $\mathbf{P}$ is nonsingular and $\mathbf{A}$ is of rank ρ, so is $\mathbf{D}$ of rank ρ (Theorem 2.7).

An immediate consequence of the proof of Theorem 6.1 is

THEOREM 6.2.   *Let* $\mathbf{A}_i$ *be the principal minor of order* i *in the upper left hand corner of the symmetric matrix* $\mathbf{A}$. *If* $d(\mathbf{A}_i) \neq 0$, *then* d_i *in Theorem* 6.1 *can be determined as a rational function of the elements of* $\mathbf{A}_i$ *alone.*

The truth of this theorem becomes obvious, since in the beginning of the proof of Theorem 6.1, if $d(\mathbf{A}_i) \neq 0$, none of the first i rows and columns need be interchanged with any of the last $(n - i)$ rows and columns.

We shall now prove Sylvester's famous theorem known as the "law of inertia" (1852).

THEOREM 6.3.   *Let the field of numbers be the real or rational field. If* $\mathbf{D} = \|d_1, d_2, \cdots, d_\rho, 0, \cdots, 0\|$ *is congruent with* $\mathbf{H} = \|h_1, h_2, \cdots, h_r, 0, \cdots, 0\|$, *then the number of positive d's is exactly equal to the number of positive h's.*

Proof.   By Theorem 2.7, $r = \rho$. Suppose $\mathbf{A}$ and $\mathbf{B}$ are any two congruent matrices

$$\mathbf{A} = \mathbf{P}^T\mathbf{B}\mathbf{P}.$$

Let $x_1, \cdots, x_n$ be indeterminants which are denoted by (x) when written as a row array and by $\{\mathbf{x}\}$ when written as a column array.   Construct the quadratic form

$$(\mathbf{x})\mathbf{A}\{\mathbf{x}\} = (\mathbf{x})\mathbf{P}^T\mathbf{B}\mathbf{P}\{\mathbf{x}\}.$$

Let $\{\mathbf{y}\} = \mathbf{P}\{\mathbf{x}\}$.   Then

$$(\mathbf{x})\mathbf{A}\{\mathbf{x}\} = (\mathbf{y})\mathbf{B}\{\mathbf{y}\}.$$

If $\mathbf{A} = \mathbf{H}$ and $\mathbf{B} = \mathbf{D},$ then

$$\sum_{r=1}^{n} h_r x_r^2 = \sum_{i=1}^{n} d_i y_i^2.$$

Suppose the h's and d's are so numbered that

$$h_1 > 0, \quad \cdots, \quad h_\lambda > 0, \quad h_{\lambda+1} < 0, \quad \cdots, \quad h_\rho < 0,$$
$$d_1 > 0, \quad \cdots, \quad d_\mu > 0, \quad d_{\mu+1} < 0, \quad \cdots, \quad d_\rho < 0,$$

and suppose that $\mu < \lambda$.　Then

$$h_1 x_1^2 + \cdots + h_\lambda x_\lambda^2 - d_{\mu+1} y_{\mu+1}^2 - \cdots - d_\rho y_\rho^2$$
$$= d_1 y_1^2 + \cdots + d_\mu y_\mu^2 - h_{\lambda+1} x_{\lambda+1}^2 - \cdots - h_\rho x_\rho^2.$$

Select $x_{\lambda+1} = \cdots = x_n = 0$ and $x_1, \cdots, x_\lambda$ not all zero so that the μ ($\mu < \lambda$) linear forms $y_1, \cdots, y_\mu$ are all zero.　This last can be done according to Corollary 4.5.　But this implies $h_1 x_1^2 + \cdots + h_\lambda x_\lambda^2 = 0$ for the x's not all zero; this is a contradiction of our hypothesis, hence $\mu \geqq \lambda$.　But the relation between $\mathbf{H}$ and $\mathbf{D}$ is mutual, so that a similar argument would lead to the result $\mu \leqq \lambda$.　Hence $\lambda = \mu$.

The number $2\lambda - \rho = \sigma$ is called the *signature* of $\mathbf{D}$ and is the number of positive terms diminished by the number of negative terms in the canonical form $\mathbf{D}$.　The two integer invariants ρ and σ determine the number of positive and the number of negative terms in $\mathbf{D}$, the canonical form of $\mathbf{A}$.

In Theorem 6.1, if F is the real field, every positive d_i can be reduced to 1, and every negative d_i to -1, by an elementary transformation of type III in the real field.　Thus,

THEOREM 6.4.　*Two real symmetric matrices are congruent in the real field if and only if they have the same rank ρ, and the same signature σ.*

EXERCISES VI

1. Is a matrix congruent to itself?
2. Prove that if $\mathbf{A}$ is congruent to $\mathbf{B}$, then $\mathbf{B}$ is congruent to $\mathbf{A}$.
3. Prove that if $\mathbf{A}$ is congruent to $\mathbf{B}$ and $\mathbf{B}$ is congruent to $\mathbf{C}$, then $\mathbf{A}$ is congruent to $\mathbf{C}$.
4. If $\mathbf{A} = \mathbf{P}^T \mathbf{B} \mathbf{P}$, what is $d(\mathbf{A})$?
5. (a) Write the quadratic form

$$Q = 2x_1^2 + 3x_2^2 - 2x_3^2 + x_1 x_2 - 3x_1 x_3 + 4x_2 x_3$$

in symmetric form.　What is the matrix of this form?

(b) Write Q in the abridged matric notation.

6. Verify, by direct substitution, the law of transformation of the matrix of a quadratic form in the case of the form

$$x_1^2 + 4x_1 x_2 + x_2^2$$

and the transformation

$$\begin{cases} x_1 = 2x_1' - 3x_2', \\ x_2 = x_1' + x_2'. \end{cases}$$

7. Reduce each of the quadratic forms of Ex. 5 and 6 to a form which contains only the squares of the variables, by reducing its matrix to a diagonal form by transformations involving rational coefficients. What is the single transformation on the variables, in each case, which will accomplish this reduction?

8. Using results of Ex. 7, reduce each form further to a form in which the coefficient of each square term is $+1$ or -1, by using real transformations. What is the signature of each form?

9. Using results of Ex. 8 reduce each form further to a sum of squares with coefficients $+1$, by using complex transformations.

7. Transformation of Reference Frame. In Sec. 4 we remarked that a row array (or a column array) could be considered as the coordinates of a point in n-space. If we think of this point as the end point of a vector directed from the origin of coordinates, then such a row or column array defines the vector completely. The elements of the array can be thought of as the components of the vector in the n independent principal directions of the axes of the reference frames.

Suppose that two vectors $\{x\}$ and $\{y\}$ referred respectively to two reference frames X and Y are related by

$$\{x\} = A\{y\}, \qquad A \equiv \|a_{rs}\|.$$

Let us change from the frame X to a new frame $\bar{X}$ by the nonsingular transformation

$$\{x\} = P\{\bar{x}\}, \qquad P \equiv \|p_{rs}\|,$$

and let us likewise change from frame Y to a new frame $\bar{Y}$ by the nonsingular transformation

$$\{y\} = Q\{\bar{y}\}, \qquad Q \equiv \|q_{rs}\|.$$

Then the relation between the vectors $\{\bar{x}\}$ and $\{\bar{y}\}$, which are the transforms of $\{x\}$ and $\{y\}$, respectively, is

$$P\{\bar{x}\} = AQ\{\bar{y}\}$$

or

$$\{\bar{x}\} = P^{-1}AQ\{\bar{y}\};$$

in particular, if the same transformation is made for both frames, then

$$\{\bar{x}\} = P^{-1}AP\{\bar{y}\}.$$

DEFINITION 7.1. *If two matrices* A *and* B *are so related that* $A = P^{-1}BP$, *where* P *is a nonsingular matrix, then* A *is said to be similar to* **B**. *It is clear that similarity is another instance of equivalence.*

Let **A** be a matrix of order n and let λ be an indeterminate. The determinant $d(\mathbf{A} - \lambda\mathbf{I})$ is a polynomial of degree n in λ. This polynomial is called the *characteristic function* of **A**, and the equation $\varphi(\lambda) = d(\mathbf{A} - \lambda\mathbf{I}) = 0$ is called the *characteristic equation* of **A**.

A curious theorem, whose proof will be omitted here, is the famous

THEOREM 7.1 (*Hamilton-Cayley Theorem*). *Every matrix satisfies its characteristic equation, when the constant term c of the equation is replaced by c*I.

That is, if in the function $\varphi(\lambda)$, λ is replaced by **A** and the constant term c by $c\mathbf{I}$ then the resulting matrix is the zero matrix.

Example 1. Let $\mathbf{A} = \left\|\begin{matrix} 3 & 1 \\ -2 & 2 \end{matrix}\right\|$. Then $\mathbf{A} - \lambda\mathbf{I} = \left\|\begin{matrix} 3 - \lambda, & 1 \\ -2, & 2 - \lambda \end{matrix}\right\|$, and $\varphi(\lambda) = d(\mathbf{A} - \lambda\mathbf{I}) = \lambda^2 - 5\lambda + 8$. Replacing λ in $\varphi(\lambda)$ by **A**, we find

$$\left\|\begin{matrix} 7 & 5 \\ -10 & 2 \end{matrix}\right\| - 5\left\|\begin{matrix} 3 & 1 \\ -2 & 2 \end{matrix}\right\| + 8\left\|\begin{matrix} 1 & 0 \\ 0 & 1 \end{matrix}\right\| = \left\|\begin{matrix} 0 & 0 \\ 0 & 0 \end{matrix}\right\|.$$

EXERCISES VII

1–4. Solve Exs. 1, 2, 3, 4 of Ex. VI for the case of similar matrices.

5. Find the characteristic equation of the matrix

$$\mathbf{A} = \left\|\begin{matrix} 2 & 2 & -1 \\ 3 & 0 & 2 \\ -5 & 6 & 2 \end{matrix}\right\|$$

and verify the Hamilton-Cayley theorem for **A**.

6. Show, without direct verification and without computing $\mathbf{A}^{-1}$, that the matrix $\mathbf{A} = \left\|\begin{matrix} 2 & 3 \\ -1 & -2 \end{matrix}\right\|$ is its own inverse.

7. Show that any matrix similar to **A** of Ex. 6 is its own inverse.

8. *The Method of Symmetric Components.* Let E_1, E_2, E_3, and I_1, I_2, I_3 be the vector representations in frame $\mathcal{F}_1$ of the voltages and currents in phases 1, 2, and 3, respectively, of a three-phase electrical system $\mathcal{S}$. The Kirchhoff equations for $\mathcal{S}$ are

$$\left\|\begin{matrix} z_{11} & z_{12} & z_{13} \\ z_{21} & z_{22} & z_{23} \\ z_{31} & z_{32} & z_{33} \end{matrix}\right\| \left\{\begin{matrix} I_1 \\ I_2 \\ I_3 \end{matrix}\right\} = \left\{\begin{matrix} E_1 \\ E_2 \\ E_3 \end{matrix}\right\}, \quad \text{or} \quad \mathbf{z}\{\mathbf{I}\} = \{\mathbf{E}\}, \quad (1)$$

where the elements z_{ii} are lumped impedances in phase i ($i = 1, 2, 3$), and z_{ij} are the lumped impedances common to phases i and j. Suppose the voltages and currents are referred to a new reference frame $\mathfrak{F}_2$ by means of the equations

$$
\left\{\begin{array}{c} E_1 \\ E_2 \\ E_3 \end{array}\right\} = \left\|\begin{array}{ccc} 1 & 1 & 1 \\ 1 & a^{-1} & a^{-2} \\ 1 & a^{-2} & a^{-4} \end{array}\right\| \left\{\begin{array}{c} E_1^{(0)} \\ E_1^{(1)} \\ E_1^{(2)} \end{array}\right\}, \quad \left\{\begin{array}{c} I_1 \\ I_2 \\ I_3 \end{array}\right\} = \left\|\begin{array}{ccc} 1 & 1 & 1 \\ 1 & a^{-1} & a^{-2} \\ 1 & a^{-2} & a^{-4} \end{array}\right\| \left\{\begin{array}{c} I_1^{(0)} \\ I_1^{(1)} \\ I_1^{(2)} \end{array}\right\}, \quad (2)
$$

or

$$
\{E\} = S\{\overline{E}\}, \qquad \{I\} = S\{\overline{I}\},
$$

where a is the primitive cube root of unity; i.e., $a = -\frac{1}{2} + j(\sqrt{3}/2)$, with $j^2 = -1$. Then under (2), (1) gives

$$
\overline{z}\{\overline{I}\} = \{\overline{E}\}, \qquad \text{where} \qquad \overline{z} = S^{-1}zS. \tag{3}
$$

The term $E_1^{(k)}$ in $\{\overline{E}\}$ is called the kth sequence component of the voltage in phase 1, $k = 1, 2, 3$; and the element $I_1^{(k)}$ in $\{\overline{I}\}$, the kth sequence component of the current in phase 1. The sequence components for phase r are defined by means of

$$
\left\{\begin{array}{c} E_r^{(0)} \\ E_r^{(1)} \\ E_r^{(2)} \end{array}\right\} = \left\|\begin{array}{ccc} b_{11} & b_{12} & b_{13} \\ b_{21} & b_{22} & b_{23} \\ b_{31} & b_{32} & b_{33} \end{array}\right\| \left\{\begin{array}{c} E_1^{(0)} \\ E_1^{(1)} \\ E_1^{(2)} \end{array}\right\}, \tag{4}
$$

where $b_{ij} = \delta_{ij}a^{(1-i)(r-1)}$, $\delta_{ij} = 0$ if $i \neq j$, $\delta_{ij} = 1$ if $i = j$.

(a) Express $\overline{z}$ in terms of z_{ij}.

(b) Show that $\overline{z}$ reduces to a diagonal matrix when $\mathscr{J}$ is electrically symmetrical, that is, when $z_{11} = z_{22} = z_{33}$, $z_{12} = z_{23} = z_{13} = z_{21} = z_{32} = z_{31}$.

(c) Solve (2) for $\{\overline{E}\}$ in terms of $\{E\}$.

(d) Suppose

$$
E_1 = (100) + j(0), \quad E_2 = -(2.7) - j(32.3), \quad \text{and} \quad E_3 = -(37.3) + j(2.3).
$$

Find the sequence components for phase 1; phase 2; phase 3. Graph your results on the complex plane. Illustrate each step in the theory graphically.

(e) Generalize this method for the case of an n-phase electrical system.*

PART B.   VECTOR ANALYSIS

8. Introduction. In formulating the properties of vectors, there are several points of view which may be adopted. For example, we may use the Gibbs notation **V** for a vector, and develop the subject of vector analysis along geometrical lines, or along the line of a generalized or abstract algebra. On the other hand, we may build up the vector concept from the point of view of invariants of transformations. We shall adopt this latter viewpoint because it leads directly to the extension of vector analysis called tensor analysis (see Part D of this chapter).

* Burington, *Matrices in Circuit Theory, J. Math. Physics*, December, 1935.

9. Concept of a Vector. In this work we shall use as a reference framework a system of three mutually perpendicular axes meeting in a point O, as shown in Fig. 181. We shall agree that these axes are so lettered as to form a *right-handed* system. (In such a system rotation of a right-handed screw, with axis along OZ, from the positive x-axis through $90°$ to the positive y-axis

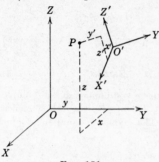

Fig. 181.

causes the screw to advance along the positive z-axis.) A point P is then specified by its Cartesian coordinates (x, y, z) relative to the frame $OXYZ$.

If another reference frame $O'X'Y'Z'$ be used, its position may be specified with reference to the frame $OXYZ$ by the coordinates (x_0, y_0, z_0) of the new origin O' and by the direction cosines of the angles which $O'X'$, $O'Y'$, $O'Z'$ make with OX, OY, OZ. As indicated in the array listed below, we shall let $a_{11}, a_{12}, a_{13}, a_{21}, \cdots$ denote the direction cosines of $O'X'$ with OX, $O'X'$ with OY, $O'X'$ with OZ, $O'Y'$ with OX, $\cdots$, respectively,

$$\begin{array}{c}\begin{array}{ccc}OX & OY & OZ\end{array}\\ \begin{array}{c}O'X'\\O'Y'\\O'Z'\end{array}\begin{bmatrix}a_{11} & a_{12} & a_{13}\\a_{21} & a_{22} & a_{23}\\a_{31} & a_{32} & a_{33}\end{bmatrix}.\end{array} \tag{1}$$

By virtue of the well-known formula

$$\cos\theta = \cos\alpha_1\cos\alpha_2 + \cos\beta_1\cos\beta_2 + \cos\gamma_1\cos\gamma_2, \tag{2}$$

we have the following relations among the above direction cosines:

$$\begin{aligned}a_{11}^2 + a_{12}^2 + a_{13}^2 = 1, && a_{21}a_{31} + a_{22}a_{32} + a_{23}a_{33} = 0, &\cdots\,;\\a_{11}^2 + a_{21}^2 + a_{31}^2 = 1, && a_{12}a_{13} + a_{22}a_{23} + a_{32}a_{33} = 0, &\cdots,\end{aligned} \tag{3}$$

the last relation, for example, expressing the fact that $\theta = YOZ$ is a right angle.

Let (x, y, z) and (x', y', z') be the coordinates of the same point P relative to the two frames $OXYZ$ and $O'X'Y'Z'$, respectively. Let α, β, γ, α' be the direction angles of $O'P$ with OX, OY, OZ, $O'X'$. Then by (1) and (2),

$$x' = O'P \cos \alpha' = O'P[a_{11} \cos \alpha + a_{12} \cos \beta + a_{13} \cos \gamma]$$
$$= a_{11}(x - x_0) + a_{12}(y - y_0) + a_{13}(z - z_0).$$

Similarly, we find

$$\begin{aligned} y' &= a_{21}(x - x_0) + a_{22}(y - y_0) + a_{23}(z - z_0), \\ z' &= a_{31}(x - x_0) + a_{32}(y - y_0) + a_{33}(z - z_0). \end{aligned} \tag{4}$$

By Sec. 4, these equations may be combined into the single matric equation

$$\left\{ \begin{array}{c} x' \\ y' \\ z' \end{array} \right\} = \left\| \begin{array}{ccc} a_{11} & a_{12} & a_{13} \\ a_{21} & a_{22} & a_{23} \\ a_{31} & a_{32} & a_{33} \end{array} \right\| \left\{ \begin{array}{c} x - x_0 \\ y - y_0 \\ z - z_0 \end{array} \right\}. \tag{5}$$

By the method used to derive (4), we have

$$\left\{ \begin{array}{l} x - x_0 = a_{11}x' + a_{21}y' + a_{31}z', \\ y - y_0 = a_{12}x' + a_{22}y' + a_{32}z', \\ z - z_0 = a_{13}x' + a_{23}y' + a_{33}z'. \end{array} \right. \tag{6}$$

It is easy to see that (6) is the inverse of (4).

Consider two points P_1 and P_2 and an operation that carries P_1 into P_2. This operation involves the concept of *magnitude* (the distance between the two points), and the concept of *direction*. These two characteristics are possessed by many physical quantities and are frequently represented by the geometric operation mentioned above. Such physical quantities are known as *vector quantities*. A *vector quantity* is said to be described when its magnitude and direction are specified. If one end point, say P_1, of the segment representing a vector quantity be chosen at random, then the other end point is definitely determined by the magnitude and direction of the segment representing the vector quantity. A vector quantity may be represented by any one of a system of equal, parallel, and similarly directed vector segments. The term *vector* is commonly used to denote either a physical vector quantity or its geometric representation.

The magnitude and direction of the translation of P_1 to P_2 are commonly specified or *represented* by the projections of the directed segment $\overrightarrow{P_1P_2}$ on the coordinate axes. These projections of the same segment $\overrightarrow{P_1P_2}$ are of course different in different reference frames. For example, if (x_1, y_1, z_1) and (x_2, y_2, z_2) are the coordinates of P_1 and P_2, respectively, in the reference frame $\mathfrak{F}$ the representation of the segment $\overrightarrow{P_1P_2}$ in this frame is $(x_2 - x_1, y_2 - y_1, z_2 - z_1)$. If (x_1', y_1', z_1') and (x_2', y_2', z_2') are the coordinates of P_1 and P_2, respectively, in the frame $\mathfrak{F}'$, then the representation of $\overrightarrow{P_1P_2}$ in frame $\mathfrak{F}'$ is $(x_2' - x_1', y_2' - y_1', z_2' - z_1')$. As in (4) and (6), the two representations are related by

$$\left.\begin{aligned}
x_2' - x_1' &= a_{11}(x_2 - x_1) + a_{12}(y_2 - y_1) + a_{13}(z_2 - z_1), \\
y_2' - y_1' &= a_{21}(x_2 - x_1) + a_{22}(y_2 - y_1) + a_{23}(z_2 - z_1), \\
z_2' - z_1' &= a_{31}(x_2 - x_1) + a_{32}(y_2 - y_1) + a_{33}(z_2 - z_1),
\end{aligned}\right\} \quad (7)$$

and the inverse is

$$\left.\begin{aligned}
x_2 - x_1 &= a_{11}(x_2' - x_1') + a_{21}(y_2' - y_1') + a_{31}(z_2' - z_1'), \\
y_2 - y_1 &= a_{12}(x_2' - x_1') + a_{22}(y_2' - y_1') + a_{32}(z_2' - z_1'), \\
z_2 - z_1 &= a_{13}(x_2' - x_1') + a_{23}(y_2' - y_1') + a_{33}(z_2' - z_1').
\end{aligned}\right\} \quad (8)$$

Suppose the measurement of a certain (physical, geometrical, or other) entity involves the determination of three numbers relative to a reference frame. Are these three numbers for a certain frame $\mathfrak{F}$ the representation in frame $\mathfrak{F}$ of a definite vector? In other words, is the quantity measured a vector quantity?

Example 1. Let $\rho(x, y, z)$ be the density of the gas at any point in a jet and let P be a point in the jet. For each frame $\mathfrak{F}$ we can determine three numbers, $\dfrac{\partial\rho}{\partial x}\Big]_P$, $\dfrac{\partial\rho}{\partial y}\Big]_P$, $\dfrac{\partial\rho}{\partial z}\Big]_P$. Are these three numbers the components of a vector?

Example 2. Let us determine three numbers for each reference frame in the following way: Let Φ be a surface containing the point P. For each frame $\mathfrak{F}$ pass three planes through P parallel to the coordinate planes of $\mathfrak{F}$ and cutting Φ in three plane sections C_1, C_2, C_3 with curvatures K_1, K_2, K_3 at P. Are the numbers K_1, K_2, K_3, determined in this way for each frame $\mathfrak{F}$, the components of a vector?

Example 3. Suppose rays of light (of a certain wave length) are radiating from a point P in a heterogeneous medium such that the velocities of the rays are different in different directions. For each frame $\mathfrak{F}$ we can determine three numbers V_1, V_2, V_3, namely, the actual velocities of the rays in the directions of the three axes. Are these three numbers the components of a vector?

Example 4. Let A_t, B_t, C_t denote the market values of the common stock of General Motors, Pennsylvania Railroad, and United States Steel at a fixed time t. Are these three numbers the components of a vector?

It is evident that, if (A_x, A_y, A_z) are three numbers determined for a quantity Q relative to frame $\mathfrak{F}$, it is *always* possible to construct a directed line segment $\overrightarrow{P_1P_2}$ such that the measures of its projections on OX, OY, OZ are (A_x, A_y, A_z). But for Q to be called a vector quantity, it is necessary that the numbers (A'_x, A'_y, A'_z), determined for Q relative to any other frame $\mathfrak{F}'$, be the measures of the projections of the *same* segment $\overrightarrow{P_1P_2}$ on $O'X'$, $O'Y'$, $O'Z'$.

It is seen that $\partial\rho/\partial x$, $\partial\rho/\partial y$, $\partial\rho/\partial z$ in Example 1 represent the vector quantity called the normal derivative of ρ in Sec. 22 of Chap. I. On the other hand, the velocities V_1, V_2, V_3 of the rays in Example 3 may be quite unrelated* in different frames, so that V_1, V_2, V_3 do not represent a vector. In Example 4, A_t, B_t, C_t do not represent a vector since they are not measured relative to any three-dimensional frame $\mathfrak{F}$. We leave it to the student to answer the question in Example 2.

We shall now put the preceding criterion in analytic form. Suppose a quantity is represented by a line segment $\overrightarrow{P_1P_2}$ with projections on the axes of $\mathfrak{F}$ of measures (A_x, A_y, A_z). Then

$$A_x = x_2 - x_1, \qquad A_y = y_2 - y_1, \qquad A_z = z_2 - z_1;$$

if the quantity represented by $\overrightarrow{P_1P_2}$ is a vector quantity, then A'_x, A'_y, A'_z must be the measures of the projections of $\overrightarrow{P_1P_2}$ on the axes of $\mathfrak{F}'$, that is, if the quantity is a vector quantity, then it must be the case that

$$A'_x = x'_2 - x'_1, \qquad A'_y = y'_2 - y'_1, \qquad A'_z = z'_2 - z'_1,$$

where by (7) and (8),

$$\left.\begin{array}{l} A'_x = a_{11}A_x + a_{12}A_y + a_{13}A_z, \\ A'_y = a_{21}A_x + a_{22}A_y + a_{23}A_z, \\ A'_z = a_{31}A_x + a_{32}A_y + a_{33}A_z, \end{array}\right\} \tag{9}$$

* Consider the case where P is on the bounding surface between a crystal of iceland spar and a solution of sugar in water in a magnetic field.

and

$$A_x = a_{11}A'_x + a_{21}A'_y + a_{31}A'_z,$$
$$A_y = a_{12}A'_x + a_{22}A'_y + a_{32}A'_z, \Bigg\} \qquad (10)$$
$$A_z = a_{13}A'_x + a_{23}A'_y + a_{33}A'_z.$$

These relations enable us to lay down

DEFINITION 9.1. *If, in any manner whatever, a set of three numbers* (A_x, A_y, A_z) *is determined for each frame* $\mathfrak{F}$, *then these numbers are said to represent a vector* **A,** *provided that,* (A'_x, A'_y, A'_z) *being the set of numbers determined for any other frame* $\mathfrak{F}'$, *the two sets* (A_x, A_y, A_z) *and* (A'_x, A'_y, A'_z) *are related by* (9) *and* (10), *where the numbers* a_{ij} *are the coefficients in the transformation* (4) *connecting* $\mathfrak{F}$ *and* $\mathfrak{F}'$.

Here **A** denotes the vector itself, and not any particular representation of it. Another interpretation of this symbol **A** is that **A** represents all possible representations of the vector, any two of the representations in Cartesian frames being connected with each other by Eqs. (9) and (10). We shall call A_x, A_y, A_z the components of the vector **A** in frame $\mathfrak{F}$.

A convenient notation for the relation (9) is (see Sec. 4)

$$\begin{Bmatrix} A'_x \\ A'_y \\ A'_z \end{Bmatrix} = \begin{Vmatrix} a_{11} & a_{12} & a_{13} \\ a_{21} & a_{22} & a_{23} \\ a_{31} & a_{32} & a_{33} \end{Vmatrix} \begin{Bmatrix} A_x \\ A_y \\ A_z \end{Bmatrix}, \quad \text{or} \quad \{\mathbf{A}'\} = \mathfrak{a}\{\mathbf{A}\}. \quad (11)$$

It is essential to realize that those properties of vectors that are of importance are principally those which are essentially independent of the particular representation used. Thus, the common length of the representative segments $\overrightarrow{P_1P_2}$ of a vector **A** is quite independent of the particular reference frame used. This length A has the value

$$A = +\sqrt{A_x^2 + A_y^2 + A_z^2} \qquad (12)$$

in the frame $\mathfrak{F}$, and the value $A' = +\sqrt{A_x'^2 + A_y'^2 + A_z'^2}$ in the frame $\mathfrak{F}'$. That $A = A'$, or

$$A_x^2 + A_y^2 + A_z^2 = A_x'^2 + A_y'^2 + A_z'^2 \qquad (13)$$

is easily shown from Eqs. (3) and (9).

We shall call the *length* A of the vector **A** the *magnitude* of **A.** A quantity, such as A, which is independent of the reference frame used, is known as an *invariant* or *scalar quantity*.

Let **A** and **B** be two vector quantities. These vectors **A** and **B,** while they perhaps arise from different physical or mathematical situations and consequently are not necessarily the *same* vectors, are said to be *equal* when they have the same representative segments, or when any representative segment of the first is equal, parallel, and similarly directed to any representative segment of the second. Thus, we say that **A** is equal to **B** if, in frame $\mathfrak{F}$, $A_x = B_x$, $A_y = B_y$, and $A_z = B_z$. Equations (9) then show that, in frame $\mathfrak{F}'$, $A'_x = B'_x$, $A'_y = B'_y$, and $A'_z = B'_z$, i.e., *if two vectors have identical representations in any frame $\mathfrak{F}$, they have identical representations in any other frame $\mathfrak{F}'$, and the two vectors are said to be equal.* Thus, the equality of two vectors as defined above is another example of a relationship between two vectors which is independent of the frame used.

10. Vector Algebra. We shall now develop the laws of vectors.

Product of a Vector by a Scalar. Let **A** be an arbitrary vector whose components with reference to frame $\mathfrak{F}$ are (A_x, A_y, A_z) and whose components with reference to frame $\mathfrak{F}'$ are (A'_x, A'_y, A'_z). Let m be a real number, i.e., the measure of any scalar quantity. Multiply each equation in (9) by m. It is now evident that the set of numbers (mA_x, mA_y, mA_z) transforms by (9) of Sec. 9 into the set (mA'_x, mA'_y, mA'_z). Hence these two sets of numbers are the representations (in frames $\mathfrak{F}$ and $\mathfrak{F}'$) of a vector. We shall denote this vector by m**A** or **A**m and we shall call m**A** the *product* of the vector **A** by the scalar m. The magnitude of m**A** is equal to $|m|$ times the magnitude of **A,** where $|m|$ is the numerical value of m. If $m \neq 0$, any representative segment of the vector m**A** is parallel to any representative segment of **A,** the two segments being similarly directed in case $m > 0$, and oppositely directed if $m < 0$. If $m = 0$, m**A** has components $(0, 0, 0)$ in every frame, and is independent of **A.** Since the magnitude of (0)**A** is zero, (0)**A** does not possess direction. We call this vector, whose components with reference to any frame are $(0, 0, 0)$, the *zero vector*, and we shall denote it by **O.**

It is easy to show that if m and n are any two scalar quantities, and if **A** is any arbitrary vector,

$$m\mathbf{A} + n\mathbf{A} = (m + n)\mathbf{A}. \tag{1}$$

Sum and Difference of two Vectors. Consider two vectors **A** and **B,** with components (A_x, A_y, A_z) and (B_x, B_y, B_z) with reference to a frame $\mathfrak{F}$, and components (A_x', A_y', A_z') and (B_x', B_y', B_z') in frame $\mathfrak{F}'$. Construct the algebraic sums $(A_x + B_x, A_y + B_y, A_z + B_z)$ and $(A_x' + B_x', A_y' + B_y', A_z' + B_z')$. Since these two sets of numbers satisfy (9) of Sec. 9, these sets are the representations of a vector which we shall denote by $\mathbf{A} + \mathbf{B}$.

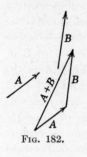

One method for finding a representative segment of $\mathbf{A} + \mathbf{B}$ is to choose the initial point of a representative segment of $\mathbf{B}$ as the end point of a representative segment of $\mathbf{A}$, so that the segment from the initial point of the segment representing $\mathbf{A}$ to the end point of the segment representing $\mathbf{B}$ is the representative segment of $\mathbf{A} + \mathbf{B}$ (see Fig. 182).

Fig. 182.

Since

$$A_x + B_x = B_x + A_x,\; A_y + B_y = B_y + A_y,\; A_z + B_z = B_z + A_z,$$

it follows that addition of vectors is *commutative*, i.e.,

$$\mathbf{A} + \mathbf{B} = \mathbf{B} + \mathbf{A}. \tag{2}$$

We define $-\mathbf{B}$ to be $(-1)\mathbf{B}$, and we define the *difference* $\mathbf{A} - \mathbf{B}$ by the relation

$$\mathbf{A} - \mathbf{B} = \mathbf{A} + (-\mathbf{B}).$$

Thus, to construct a representative segment of $\mathbf{A} - \mathbf{B}$, construct a representative segment of $-\mathbf{B}$ by reversing the direction of the representative segment of $\mathbf{B}$ and then add according to the method given above.

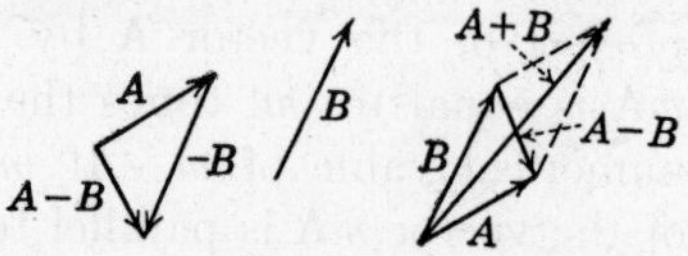

Evidently, if two adjacent sides of a parallelogram represent vectors $\mathbf{A}$ and $\mathbf{B}$, one diagonal represents the sum, and the other, the difference of $\mathbf{A}$ and $\mathbf{B}$.

Fig. 183.

Care must be taken in applying the above theory of vectors to physical problems, for even though a physical quantity may have magnitude and direction it may not be a vector, and it does not follow that the laws of composition of vectors are isomorphic with the laws of the physical quantities at hand. Moreover, even though the laws for compounding the physical quantities are consistent with those for compounding vectors, it does not necessarily follow that the physical quantity is fully described by a magnitude and direction. Examples illustrating these possibilities abound in the literature, notable cases appearing in the study of the rotation of rigid bodies.

Unit Vectors. A *unit vector* is a vector whose magnitude is unity. Associated with any cartesian frame $\mathfrak{F}$ there is a particular set of unit vectors of great utility. These *fundamental unit vectors* have their representative segments along the three coordinate axes; in frame $\mathfrak{F}$ they have representations $(1, 0, 0)$, $(0, 1, 0)$, $(0, 0, 1)$, and are commonly denoted by **i, j, k,** respectively.

If **A** is an arbitrary vector whose representation in frame $\mathfrak{F}$ is (A_x, A_y, A_z), then

$$(A_x, A_y, A_z) = A_x(1, 0, 0)$$
$$+ A_y(0, 1, 0) + A_z(0, 0, 1) \quad (3)$$

where $A_x(1, 0, 0) \equiv (A_x, 0, 0), \cdots$. Hence we may write

$$\mathbf{A} = A_x\mathbf{i} + A_y\mathbf{j} + A_z\mathbf{k}. \quad (4)$$

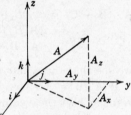

Fig. 184.

Scalar Product of Two Vectors. Let **A** and **B** be two arbitrary vectors. With reference to frame $\mathfrak{F}$, the direction cosines of any representative segments of the two vectors **A** and **B** with respect to the x, y, and z-axes are $(A_x/A, A_y/A, A_z/A)$ and $(B_x/B, B_y/B, B_z/B)$, respectively. If θ is the angle between any pair of representative segments of **A** and **B,** then by (2) of Sec. 9,

$$\cos\theta = \frac{A_xB_x + A_yB_y + A_zB_z}{AB},$$

so that

$$AB\cos\theta = A_xB_x + A_yB_y + A_zB_z. \quad (5)$$

From equations (9) and (3) of Sec. 9, we can prove that

$$A'_xB'_x + A'_yB'_y + A'_zB'_z = A_xB_x + A_yB_y + A_zB_z. \quad (6)$$

Hence the value of the expression (5) is *invariant*, that is, is independent of the reference frame $\mathfrak{F}$ used. This number, $AB\cos\theta$, is called the *scalar* (or *dot*) *product* of the vectors **A** and **B,** and is commonly denoted by **A** · **B,** so that

$$\mathbf{A}\cdot\mathbf{B} = AB\cos\theta = A_xB_x + A_yB_y + A_zB_z \quad (7)$$

$$= (A_x, A_y, A_z)\begin{Bmatrix} B_x \\ B_y \\ B_z \end{Bmatrix}.$$

It is an immediate consequence of (7) that the scalar product of two vectors obeys the *commutative law:*

$$\mathbf{A} \cdot \mathbf{B} = \mathbf{B} \cdot \mathbf{A}. \qquad (8)$$

From (7) it follows that

$$\mathbf{A} \cdot \mathbf{A} = \mathbf{A}^2 = A^2 \cos 0 = A^2. \qquad (9)$$

In other words, the scalar product of **A** by itself is equal to the square of its magnitude.

Since, for any reference frame $\mathfrak{F}$,

$$
\begin{aligned}
\mathbf{A} \cdot (\mathbf{B} + \mathbf{C}) &= A_x(B_x + C_x) + A_y(B_y + C_y) + A_z(B_z + C_z) \\
&= (A_x B_x + A_y B_y + A_z B_z) + (A_x C_x + A_y C_y + A_z C_z) \\
&= (\mathbf{A} \cdot \mathbf{B}) + (\mathbf{A} \cdot \mathbf{C}), \qquad (10)
\end{aligned}
$$

we see that the scalar product also obeys the distributive law.

If $\mathbf{A} \cdot \mathbf{B} = AB \cos \theta = 0$, then at least one of the vectors is zero, or else the vectors have perpendicular representative segments. In this latter case we shall say that the vectors are perpendicular. Hence *a necessary and sufficient condition that two nonzero vectors be perpendicular is that their scalar product be zero.* It is evident that

$$\mathbf{i} \cdot \mathbf{j} = \mathbf{j} \cdot \mathbf{i} = 0, \qquad \mathbf{j} \cdot \mathbf{k} = \mathbf{k} \cdot \mathbf{j} = 0, \qquad \mathbf{i} \cdot \mathbf{k} = \mathbf{k} \cdot \mathbf{i} = 0, \qquad (11)$$

since, for example, $\mathbf{i} \cdot \mathbf{j} = (1)(0) + (0)(1) + (0)(0) = 0$ by (7). We shall now prove

Theorem 10.1. *If a set of three numbers (A_x, A_y, A_z) is determined for each reference frame $\mathfrak{F}$, if **B** is an arbitrary vector with representation (B_x, B_y, B_z) in $\mathfrak{F}$, and if $A_x B_x + A_y B_y + A_z B_z$ has the same value for every frame $\mathfrak{F}$, then (A_x, A_y, A_z) is the representation in $\mathfrak{F}$ of a vector **A**.*

To prove the theorem we must show that (9) of Sec. 9 holds for any two frames $\mathfrak{F}$ and $\mathfrak{F}'$. Let $\mathbf{B}^{(1)}$ be the vector whose representation in $\mathfrak{F}'$ is $(1, 0, 0)$. By (10) of Sec. 9 the representation in $\mathfrak{F}$ of $\mathbf{B}^{(1)}$ is (a_{11}, a_{12}, a_{13}), and by hypothesis,

$$A_x' \equiv (1)A_x' + (0)A_y' + (0)A_z' = a_{11}A_x + a_{12}A_y + a_{13}A_z.$$

Similarly, with the aid of the vectors $\mathbf{B}^{(2)}$ and $\mathbf{B}^{(3)}$ whose representations in $\mathfrak{F}'$ are $(0, 1, 0)$ and $(0, 0, 1)$, we find that

$$
\begin{aligned}
A_y' &= a_{21}A_x + a_{22}A_y + a_{23}A_z, \\
A_z' &= a_{31}A_x + a_{32}A_y + a_{33}A_z.
\end{aligned}
$$

Hence (A_x, A_y, A_z) and (A'_x, A'_y, A'_z) are related by (9), and (A_x, A_y, A_z) is the representation in $\mathfrak{F}$ of a vector **A**.

Vector Product of Two Vectors. Let **A** and **B** be two arbitrary vectors which have neither the same nor opposite directions, i.e., such that $A_x:A_y:A_z \neq B_x:B_y:B_z$ in every frame $\mathfrak{F}$. At any point P construct the representation segments for **A** and **B**. These segments determine a plane M. If **C** is any vector perpendicular to the plane of **A** and **B**, then the scalar product of **C** with **A**, and with **B**, must be zero, i.e.,

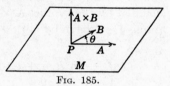

Fig. 185.

$$C \cdot A = C_xA_x + C_yA_y + C_zA_z = 0,$$
$$C \cdot B = C_xB_x + C_yB_y + C_zB_z = 0,$$

where (A_x, A_y, A_z), (B_x, B_y, B_z), (C_x, C_y, C_z) are the representations of **A**, **B**, **C** in any frame $\mathfrak{F}$. Solving for C_x, C_y, C_z, we find that

$$C_x = k(A_yB_z - A_zB_y),$$
$$C_y = k(A_zB_x - A_xB_z), \qquad (12)$$
$$C_z = k(A_xB_y - A_yB_x),$$

where k is a constant of proportionality. By hypothesis, the coefficients of k are not all zero. By (12) of Sec. 9,

$$C^2 = C_x^2 + C_y^2 + C_z^2 = k^2[(A_x^2 + A_y^2 + A_z^2)(B_x^2 + B_y^2 + B_z^2) - (A_xB_x + A_yB_y + A_zB_z)^2]$$

$$= k^2[A^2B^2 - (AB \cos \theta)^2] = k^2A^2B^2(\sin^2 \theta),$$

where we take θ as the smaller angle from **A** to **B**. Hence

$$C = \pm kAB \sin \theta. \qquad (13)$$

Since the magnitudes of **A**, **B**, **C**, and the angle θ between **A** and **B**, are independent of the reference frame $\mathfrak{F}$, it follows that k is independent of $\mathfrak{F}$. Let us determine **C** by taking $k = +1$ in (12). Hence the representation of **C** in $\mathfrak{F}$ is

$$C_x = A_yB_z - A_zB_y,$$
$$C_y = A_zB_x - A_xB_z, \qquad (14)$$
$$C_z = A_xB_y - A_yB_x.$$

In the particular frame $\mathfrak{F}'$ such that the representation of **A** is $(A, 0, 0)$ and of B is $(B \cos \theta, B \sin \theta, 0)$ with $0 < \theta < 180°$, it follows from (14) that $C_x = C_y = 0$, $C_z = AB \sin \theta > 0$.

Hence **A**, **B**, **C**, form a right-hand system when **A** is rotated through the smaller angle θ to **B**. Since C_z in $\mathcal{F}'$ is the magnitude C, (13) reduces to

$$C = AB \sin \theta. \tag{15}$$

The vector **C** is called the *vector product* of **A** and **B** and is denoted by the symbol **A** $\times$ **B**. Using the unit vectors **i**, **j**, **k** in frame $\mathcal{F}$, we have by (14)

$$
\begin{aligned}
\mathbf{C} &= \mathbf{A} \times \mathbf{B} \\
&= (A_y B_z - A_z B_y)\mathbf{i} + (A_z B_x - A_x B_z)\mathbf{j} + (A_x B_y - A_y B_x)\mathbf{k} \\
&= \begin{vmatrix} \mathbf{i} & \mathbf{j} & \mathbf{k} \\ A_x & A_y & A_z \\ B_x & B_y & B_z \end{vmatrix}.
\end{aligned} \tag{16}
$$

In case the angle θ between the segments representing vectors **A** and **B** is $0°$ or $180°$, we define the vector product of **A** and **B** to be the zero vector. As particular instances of (16), we have

$$\mathbf{i} \times \mathbf{j} = \begin{vmatrix} \mathbf{i} & \mathbf{j} & \mathbf{k} \\ 1 & 0 & 0 \\ 0 & 1 & 0 \end{vmatrix} = \mathbf{k}, \quad \mathbf{j} \times \mathbf{k} = \mathbf{i}, \quad \mathbf{k} \times \mathbf{i} = \mathbf{j}. \tag{17}$$

Fig. 186.

It follows from (16) that

$$\mathbf{A} \times \mathbf{B} = -\mathbf{B} \times \mathbf{A}, \tag{18}$$

which shows that the vector product is not commutative. Moreover, it follows from (16) that the distributive law holds, i.e.,

$$\mathbf{A} \times (\mathbf{B} + \mathbf{C}) = \mathbf{A} \times \mathbf{B} + \mathbf{A} \times \mathbf{C}, \tag{19}$$

and

$$
\begin{aligned}
(\mathbf{A} + \mathbf{B}) \times (\mathbf{C} + \mathbf{D}) \\
= \mathbf{A} \times \mathbf{C} + \mathbf{A} \times \mathbf{D} + \mathbf{B} \times \mathbf{C} + \mathbf{B} \times \mathbf{D}. \tag{20}
\end{aligned}
$$

From (14) we find that the magnitude C of the vector product $\mathbf{C} = \mathbf{A} \times \mathbf{B}$ is equal to

$$
\begin{aligned}
C = AB \sin \theta = [(A_y B_z - A_z B_y)^2 + (A_z B_x - A_x B_z)^2 \\
+ (A_x B_y - A_y B_x)^2]^{1/2}. \tag{21}
\end{aligned}
$$

This magnitude C may be interpreted as the area of a parallelogram whose coterminal edges are representative segments of **A** and **B**.

If $\mathbf{i}$, $\mathbf{j}$, $\mathbf{k}$ be in frame $\mathfrak{F}$, then the representations of $\mathbf{i}$, $\mathbf{j}$, $\mathbf{k}$ in frame $\mathfrak{F}'$ are, by (9) of Sec. 9,

$$(a_{11}, a_{21}, a_{31}), \qquad (a_{12}, a_{22}, a_{32}), \qquad (a_{13}, a_{23}, a_{33}).$$

Let $\mathbf{i}'$, $\mathbf{j}'$, $\mathbf{k}'$ be the fundamental unit vectors for frame $\mathfrak{F}'$. Then the representation of the vector product $\mathbf{j} \times \mathbf{k} = \mathbf{i}$ in frame $\mathfrak{F}'$ yields

$$\mathbf{i} = \mathbf{j} \times \mathbf{k} = \begin{vmatrix} \mathbf{i}' & \mathbf{j}' & \mathbf{k}' \\ a_{12} & a_{22} & a_{32} \\ a_{13} & a_{23} & a_{33} \end{vmatrix}$$

$$= \begin{vmatrix} a_{22} & a_{32} \\ a_{23} & a_{33} \end{vmatrix} \mathbf{i}' - \begin{vmatrix} a_{12} & a_{32} \\ a_{13} & a_{33} \end{vmatrix} \mathbf{j}' + \begin{vmatrix} a_{12} & a_{22} \\ a_{13} & a_{23} \end{vmatrix} \mathbf{k}'. \qquad (22)$$

But the representation of $\mathbf{i}$ in $\mathfrak{F}'$ is (a_{11}, a_{21}, a_{31}), so that

$$a_{11} = \begin{vmatrix} a_{22} & a_{32} \\ a_{23} & a_{33} \end{vmatrix}, \; a_{21} = - \begin{vmatrix} a_{12} & a_{32} \\ a_{13} & a_{33} \end{vmatrix}, \; a_{31} = \begin{vmatrix} a_{12} & a_{22} \\ a_{13} & a_{23} \end{vmatrix}. \qquad (23)$$

These fundamental relationships among the direction cosines supplement those given in (3) of Sec. 9. Similar equations may be found for (a_{12}, a_{22}, a_{32}) and (a_{13}, a_{23}, a_{33}).

If we interchange the frames $\mathfrak{F}$ and $\mathfrak{F}'$, we find that

$$a_{11} = \begin{vmatrix} a_{22} & a_{23} \\ a_{32} & a_{33} \end{vmatrix}, \; a_{12} = - \begin{vmatrix} a_{21} & a_{23} \\ a_{31} & a_{33} \end{vmatrix}, \; a_{13} = \begin{vmatrix} a_{21} & a_{22} \\ a_{31} & a_{32} \end{vmatrix}. \qquad (24)$$

Similar equations may be found for (a_{21}, a_{22}, a_{23}) and (a_{31}, a_{32}, a_{33}).

By (23) together with the other six similar relationships among the nine direction cosines, we may verify that the set of three numbers $(A_y B_z - A_z B_y, \; A_z B_x - A_x B_z, \; A_x B_y - A_y B_x)$ is the representation in frame $\mathfrak{F}$ of a vector. For, from (9) of Sec. 9 and the corresponding equations in B_x, B_y, B_z,

$$\begin{aligned} A_y' B_z' - A_z' B_y' = &(a_{22} a_{33} - a_{32} a_{23})(A_y B_z - A_z B_y) \\ &+ (a_{23} a_{31} - a_{33} a_{23})(A_z B_x - A_x B_z) \\ &+ (a_{21} a_{32} - a_{31} a_{22})(A_x B_y - A_y B_x). \end{aligned}$$

By (23) and other similar relations, we have

$$\begin{aligned} A_y' B_z' - A_z' B_y' = a_{11}(A_y B_z - A_z B_y) + a_{12}(A_z B_x - A_x B_z) \\ + a_{13}(A_x B_y - A_y B_x). \end{aligned}$$

Similar expressions can be found for

$$A_z' B_x' - A_x' B_z' \qquad \text{and} \qquad A_x' B_y' - A_y' B_x',$$

from which we see that the three numbers under consideration actually satisfy the requirements of (9) of Sec. 9, that they be a representation of a vector in frame $\mathfrak{F}$.

The Scalar Triple Product.   Let **A**, **B**, and **C** be three vectors. The scalar quantity

$$\mathbf{A} \cdot (\mathbf{B} \times \mathbf{C}) = (A_x\mathbf{i} + A_y\mathbf{j} + A_z\mathbf{k}) \cdot \begin{vmatrix} \mathbf{i} & \mathbf{j} & \mathbf{k} \\ B_x & B_y & B_z \\ C_x & C_y & C_z \end{vmatrix}$$

$$= \begin{vmatrix} A_x & A_y & A_z \\ B_x & B_y & B_z \\ C_x & C_y & C_z \end{vmatrix} = \begin{vmatrix} A_x & B_x & C_x \\ A_y & B_y & C_y \\ A_z & B_z & C_z \end{vmatrix} \quad (25)$$

is called the *scalar triple product* of **A**, **B**, and **C**.

It is seen that $\mathbf{A} \cdot (\mathbf{B} \times \mathbf{C})$ is independent of the reference frame, i.e.,

$$\begin{vmatrix} A'_x & B'_x & C'_x \\ A'_y & B'_y & C'_y \\ A'_z & B'_z & C'_z \end{vmatrix} = \begin{vmatrix} A_x & B_x & C_x \\ A_y & B_y & C_y \\ A_z & B_z & C_z \end{vmatrix}. \quad (26)$$

A particularly short proof is as follows: From the equations (9) of Sec. 9 for **A**, **B**, and **C**, construct the product matrix

$$\begin{Vmatrix} A'_x & B'_x & C'_x \\ A'_y & B'_y & C'_y \\ A'_z & B'_z & C'_z \end{Vmatrix} = \begin{Vmatrix} a_{11} & a_{12} & a_{13} \\ a_{21} & a_{22} & a_{23} \\ a_{31} & a_{32} & a_{33} \end{Vmatrix} \begin{Vmatrix} A_x & B_x & C_x \\ A_y & B_y & C_y \\ A_z & B_z & C_z \end{Vmatrix}. \quad (27)$$

Since the determinant of the left-hand side of (27) is equal to the product of the determinants of the right-hand side, and the determinant of $\mathbf{a}$ is 1, we have (26).

It is readily shown from (25) that

$$\mathbf{A} \cdot (\mathbf{B} \times \mathbf{C}) = \mathbf{B} \cdot (\mathbf{C} \times \mathbf{A}) = \mathbf{C} \cdot (\mathbf{A} \times \mathbf{B}) = (\mathbf{A} \times \mathbf{B}) \cdot \mathbf{C}$$
$$= (\mathbf{B} \times \mathbf{C}) \cdot \mathbf{A} = (\mathbf{C} \times \mathbf{A}) \cdot \mathbf{B}, \quad (28)$$
$$\mathbf{A} \cdot (\mathbf{B} \times \mathbf{C}) = -\mathbf{A} \cdot (\mathbf{C} \times \mathbf{B}), \cdots,$$

and

$$\mathbf{A} \cdot (\mathbf{B} \times \mathbf{C}) = \mathbf{A} \cdot [\mathbf{B} \times (\mathbf{C} + m\mathbf{A} + n\mathbf{B})].$$

By (28), the positions of the dot, cross, and letters is immaterial so long as the cyclic order of the letters is preserved.   Hence we shall denote each member of (28) by

$$[\mathbf{A}, \mathbf{B}, \mathbf{C}] = [\mathbf{B}, \mathbf{C}, \mathbf{A}] = [\mathbf{C}, \mathbf{A}, \mathbf{B}].$$

The triple product $\mathbf{A} \cdot (\mathbf{B} \times \mathbf{C})$ may be interpreted as the volume of a parallelopiped whose coterminal edges are representative segments of $\mathbf{A}$, $\mathbf{B}$, and $\mathbf{C}$, respectively. The truth of this is immediately evident when one writes

$$\mathbf{A} \cdot (\mathbf{B} \times \mathbf{C}) = A(BC \sin \theta) \cos \varphi$$

by (15) and (8), noting that $BC \sin \theta$ is the area of the base and $A \cos \varphi$ is the altitude.

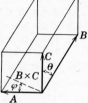

Fig. 187.

The Vector Triple Product. The vector product $\mathbf{A} \times (\mathbf{B} \times \mathbf{C})$ is called the *vector triple product.* The following relationships may be proved readily:

$$\mathbf{A} \times (\mathbf{B} \times \mathbf{C}) = (\mathbf{A} \cdot \mathbf{C})\mathbf{B} - (\mathbf{A} \cdot \mathbf{B})\mathbf{C}. \qquad (29)$$
$$\mathbf{A} \times (\mathbf{B} \times \mathbf{C}) + \mathbf{B} \times (\mathbf{C} \times \mathbf{A}) + \mathbf{C} \times (\mathbf{A} \times \mathbf{B}) = 0. \quad (30)$$
$$\mathbf{A} \times (\mathbf{B} \times \mathbf{C}) = (\mathbf{C} \times \mathbf{B}) \times \mathbf{A}. \qquad (31)$$

EXERCISES VIII

1. Show that Eqs. (3) of Sec. 9 may be concisely written by means of the equations $\mathfrak{a}\mathfrak{a}^T = \mathbf{I}$ and $\mathfrak{a}^T\mathfrak{a} = \mathbf{I}$. For example,

$$\mathfrak{a}^T\mathfrak{a} \equiv \begin{Vmatrix} a_{11} & a_{21} & a_{31} \\ a_{12} & a_{22} & a_{32} \\ a_{13} & a_{23} & a_{33} \end{Vmatrix} \begin{Vmatrix} a_{11} & a_{12} & a_{13} \\ a_{21} & a_{22} & a_{23} \\ a_{31} & a_{32} & a_{33} \end{Vmatrix} = \begin{Vmatrix} 1 & 0 & 0 \\ 0 & 1 & 0 \\ 0 & 0 & 1 \end{Vmatrix}.$$

Also, prove that the determinant of $\mathfrak{a}$ is 1.

2. If $\mathbf{A}$ is a unit vector, give a geometric interpretation to $\mathbf{A} \cdot \mathbf{B}$.

3. Prove (17), (18), (19), (20) of Sec. 10.

4. Derive the twelve other relations analogous to (23) and (24) of Sec. 10.

5. Find the x-, y-, and z-components of the representation of the vector $\mathbf{A} \times (\mathbf{B} \times \mathbf{C})$ in frame $\mathfrak{F}$.

6. Prove relations (29), (30), (31), using unit vectors $\mathbf{i}$, $\mathbf{j}$, $\mathbf{k}$.

7. Prove: $\mathbf{A} \times (\mathbf{B} \times \mathbf{C})$ is a vector in the plane of $\mathbf{B}$ and $\mathbf{C}$. Hence it is a linear combination of $\mathbf{B}$ and $\mathbf{C}$.

8. Given: $\mathbf{A} = 3\mathbf{i} + 20\mathbf{j} - 15\mathbf{k}$, $\mathbf{C} = 7\mathbf{i} + 11\mathbf{j} - 2\mathbf{k}$,
$\mathbf{B} = 2\mathbf{i} + 5\mathbf{k}$, $\mathbf{D} = \mathbf{i} - 4\mathbf{j} - 7\mathbf{k}$.

Compute:

(a) $\mathbf{A} + \mathbf{B}$.

(b) $\mathbf{A} + \mathbf{C} - \mathbf{D}$.

(c) $\mathbf{A} \cdot \mathbf{B}$, $\mathbf{A} \cdot \mathbf{A} = A^2$.

(d) $\mathbf{A} \times \mathbf{B}$.

(e) $\mathbf{A} \cdot \mathbf{C} - \mathbf{B} \cdot \mathbf{C}$.

(f) $\mathbf{A} \times \mathbf{B} + \mathbf{B} \times \mathbf{A}$.

(g) $\mathbf{A} \times \mathbf{C} - \mathbf{C} \times \mathbf{B}$.

(h) $\mathbf{A} \times (\mathbf{B} + \mathbf{C})$.

(i) $\mathbf{A} \times (\mathbf{B} \times (\mathbf{C} \times \mathbf{D}))$.

(j) $\mathbf{A} \cdot (\mathbf{B} \times \mathbf{C})$.

(k) $\dfrac{\mathbf{A} \cdot \mathbf{C}}{\mathbf{A} \cdot \mathbf{A}}\mathbf{A}$.

(l) $\dfrac{\mathbf{A} \times \mathbf{C}}{\mathbf{A} \cdot \mathbf{A}} \times \mathbf{A}$.

(m) Find the cosine of the angle between $\mathbf{A}$ and $\mathbf{B}$; $\mathbf{A}$ and $\mathbf{C}$.

9. Given $\mathbf{r} = \mathbf{A}e^t + \mathbf{B}e^{-t}$ where $\mathbf{A}$ and $\mathbf{B}$ are fixed vectors and t is a variable parameter. (a) Find $d\mathbf{r}/dt$. (b) Prove that $d^2\mathbf{r}/dt^2 = \mathbf{r}$.

10. If $\mathbf{A}$, $\mathbf{B}$, $\mathbf{C}$ are the position vectors of the vertices of a triangle, show that the position vector of the point of intersection of the medians is $\frac{1}{3}(\mathbf{A} + \mathbf{B} + \mathbf{C})$.

11. Let $\mathbf{A}$, $\mathbf{B}$, $\mathbf{C}$ be the vector sides of a triangle so directed that $\mathbf{C} = \mathbf{A} - \mathbf{B}$. Deduce the law of cosines from the identity $\mathbf{C} \cdot \mathbf{C} = (\mathbf{A} - \mathbf{B}) \cdot (\mathbf{A} - \mathbf{B})$.

12. Show that a necessary and sufficient condition that the vectors $\mathbf{A}$, $\mathbf{B}$, $\mathbf{C}$ be coplanar is that $\mathbf{A} \cdot (\mathbf{B} \times \mathbf{C}) = 0$.

13. Show that the volume of the tetrahedron with vertices at $(0, 0, 0)$, (x_1, y_1, z_1), (x_2, y_2, z_2), (x_3, y_3, z_3) is

$$V = \tfrac{1}{6}\begin{vmatrix} x_1 & y_1 & z_1 \\ x_2 & y_2 & z_2 \\ x_3 & y_3 & z_3 \end{vmatrix}.$$

14. Let $\mathbf{A}$ and $\mathbf{B}$ be adjacent vector sides of a parallelogram. Show that the sum of the squares of the diagonals is equal to the sum of the squares of the sides.

15. Why is it that division of two vectors is not defined?

16. Prove that if m and n are scalar quantities

$$\mathbf{A} \times (\mathbf{B} + m\mathbf{A}) = \mathbf{A} \times \mathbf{B} = (\mathbf{A} + n\mathbf{B}) \times \mathbf{B}.$$

17. Three vectors $\mathbf{A}$, $\mathbf{B}$, $\mathbf{C}$ are called *linearly dependent* if there exist three numbers x, y, z, not all zero, such that

$$x\mathbf{A} + y\mathbf{B} + z\mathbf{C} = 0.$$

(a) Show that a necessary and sufficient condition that three vectors be linearly dependent is that they be coplanar.

(b) Show that the vectors $\mathbf{i} - \mathbf{j}$, $\mathbf{j} - \mathbf{k}$, $\mathbf{k} - \mathbf{i}$ are coplanar.

18. Let O be a fixed point of a rigid body, and let a force $\mathbf{F}$ be applied to the body at the point P whose position vector $\overrightarrow{OP} = \mathbf{r}$. Show that the torque $\mathbf{T}$ resulting from $\mathbf{F}$ is given by the relation $\mathbf{T} = \mathbf{r} \times \mathbf{F}$.

19. (a) Show that the vector equation of the straight line through the point with position vector $\mathbf{a}$ and parallel to the vector $\mathbf{b}$ is $\mathbf{r} = \mathbf{a} + u\mathbf{b}$, where u is a real parameter.

(b) Show that the vector equation of the straight line through the points with position vectors $\mathbf{a}$ and $\mathbf{b}$ is $\mathbf{r} = \mathbf{a} + u(\mathbf{b} - \mathbf{a}) = \mathbf{b} + v(\mathbf{a} - \mathbf{b})$, where u and v are real parameters.

(c) Show the points with position vectors $\mathbf{a}$, $\mathbf{b}$, $\mathbf{c}$ are collinear if and only if $\mathbf{a}$, $\mathbf{b}$, $\mathbf{c}$ are linearly dependent (see Ex. 17.)

20. Show that the vector equation of the plane determined by the given conditions is as indicated:

(a) Through the point with position vector $\mathbf{a}$, and parallel to $\mathbf{b}$ and $\mathbf{c}$: $\mathbf{r} = \mathbf{a} + u\mathbf{b} + v\mathbf{c}$.

(b) Through the points with position vectors $\mathbf{a}$, $\mathbf{b}$, $\mathbf{c}$:

$$\mathbf{r} = \mathbf{a} + u(\mathbf{b} - \mathbf{a}) + v(\mathbf{c} - \mathbf{a}).$$

Express this relation in other forms.

(c) Through the point with position vector **a** and perpendicular to **a**: $(\mathbf{r} - \mathbf{a}) \cdot \mathbf{a} = 0$.

(d) Show that the points with position vectors **a, b, c, d** are coplanar if and only if **a, b, c, d** are linearly dependent.

11. Vector Fields. If with each point of a region of space there is associated a definite vector **A,** we have what is known as a *vector field.* Examples in physics of vector fields are abundant. Thus, at each point in the atmosphere of the earth we can associate a vector representing the velocity of wind; at each point of an electrostatic field we can associate a vector representing the force acting on a unit charge at the point; etc.

In a vector field, the components (A_x, A_y, A_z) (relative to any frame $\mathfrak{F}$) of the vector **A** associated with a point P in that field are functions of the coordinates (x, y, z) of the point P. A vector field is said to be *continuous* when (A_x, A_y, A_z) are continuous functions of (x, y, z) at every point of the field. The vector field is said to be *differentiable* if each of the derivatives in the array

$$\begin{bmatrix} \dfrac{\partial A_x}{\partial x} & \dfrac{\partial A_x}{\partial y} & \dfrac{\partial A_x}{\partial z} \\[2mm] \dfrac{\partial A_y}{\partial x} & \dfrac{\partial A_y}{\partial y} & \dfrac{\partial A_y}{\partial z} \\[2mm] \dfrac{\partial A_z}{\partial x} & \dfrac{\partial A_z}{\partial y} & \dfrac{\partial A_z}{\partial z} \end{bmatrix} \tag{1}$$

exists at all points of the field. In general, we shall confine ourselves to vector fields which are continuous and differentiable (to any order), unless we specifically state otherwise.

If $\mathcal{C}$ is a curve in a vector field such that, at each point P on the curve, the associated vector **A** at P has the direction of the tangent to the curve, then $\mathcal{C}$ is called a *vector line* of the field. The vector lines of a field may be obtained by integrating the equations (see Sec. 22 of Chap. III)

$$\frac{dx}{A_x} = \frac{dy}{A_y} = \frac{dz}{A_z}. \tag{2}$$

Recall from Sec. 23 of Chap. I that a scalar point function $\Phi(P)$ is a function whose value at any point P is independent of the particular frame of reference used. Let (x, y, z) and (x', y', z')

denote the coordinates of P in frames $\mathfrak{F}$ and $\mathfrak{F}'$, respectively.
If $\varphi(x, y, z)$ represents this function in $\mathfrak{F}$ and if $\varphi'(x', y', z')$
represents this function in $\mathfrak{F}'$, then the functions $\varphi(x, y, z)$ and
$\varphi'(x', y', z')$ are such that

$$\varphi'(x', y', z') \equiv \varphi(x, y, z). \tag{3}$$

Differentiating (3), we find that

$$\frac{\partial \varphi'}{\partial x'} = \frac{\partial \varphi}{\partial x}\bigg)_{y,z}\frac{\partial x}{\partial x'} + \frac{\partial \varphi}{\partial y}\bigg)_{x,z}\frac{\partial y}{\partial x'} + \frac{\partial \varphi}{\partial z}\bigg)_{x,y}\frac{\partial z}{\partial x'}, \tag{4}$$

where by (6) of Sec. 9, $\partial x/\partial x' = a_{11}$, $\partial y/\partial x' = a_{12}$, $\partial z/\partial x' = a_{13}$.
Similar relations can be found for $\partial \varphi'/\partial y'$, $\partial \varphi'/\partial z'$.   We then have

$$\left\{\begin{array}{c} \dfrac{\partial \varphi'}{\partial x'} \\[2mm] \dfrac{\partial \varphi'}{\partial y'} \\[2mm] \dfrac{\partial \varphi'}{\partial z'} \end{array}\right\} = \left\|\begin{array}{ccc} a_{11} & a_{12} & a_{13} \\ a_{21} & a_{22} & a_{23} \\ a_{31} & a_{32} & a_{33} \end{array}\right\| \left\{\begin{array}{c} \dfrac{\partial \varphi}{\partial x} \\[2mm] \dfrac{\partial \varphi}{\partial y} \\[2mm] \dfrac{\partial \varphi}{\partial z} \end{array}\right\}. \tag{4'}$$

Comparing this equation with (9) of Sec. 9, we see that
$(\partial \varphi/\partial x, \partial \varphi/\partial y, \partial \varphi/\partial z)$ is the representation in $\mathfrak{F}$ of a vector.
This vector is known as the *gradient* of the scalar point function
Φ, and is commonly written **grad** Φ.   (See Sec. 22, Chap. 1.)
The square of the magnitude of **grad** Φ is a scalar denoted by
$\Delta_1\Phi$, and with reference to frame $\mathfrak{F}$ is given by

$$\Delta_1\varphi = \left(\frac{\partial \varphi}{\partial x}\right)^2 + \left(\frac{\partial \varphi}{\partial y}\right)^2 + \left(\frac{\partial \varphi}{\partial z}\right)^2. \tag{5}$$

By (14) of Sec. 9 and by Ex. XIX, 36 of Chap. I, we see that $\Delta_1\Phi$
is an *invariant*, i.e.,

$$\Delta_1\varphi' = \left(\frac{\partial \varphi'}{\partial x'}\right)^2 + \left(\frac{\partial \varphi'}{\partial y'}\right)^2 + \left(\frac{\partial \varphi'}{\partial z'}\right)^2$$

$$= \left(\frac{\partial \varphi}{\partial x}\right)^2 + \left(\frac{\partial \varphi}{\partial y}\right)^2 + \left(\frac{\partial \varphi}{\partial z}\right)^2 = \Delta_1\varphi. \tag{6}$$

The operator denoted by Δ_1, and whose representation in
frame $\mathfrak{F}$ is

$$\Delta_1 \equiv \left(\frac{\partial}{\partial x}\right)^2 + \left(\frac{\partial}{\partial y}\right)^2 + \left(\frac{\partial}{\partial z}\right)^2,$$

where $(\partial/\partial x)^2$ operating on φ means $(\partial\varphi/\partial x)^2$, is called the *first
differential operator*.

.It follows directly from (9) of Sec. 9 that the set of differentials (dx, dy, dz) is the representation in $\mathfrak{F}$ of a vector. Likewise, if a curve C is given in the parametric form $x = x(s)$, $y = y(s)$, $z = z(s)$, when s is arc length along C, then $(dx/ds, dy/ds, dz/ds)$ is the representation in $\mathfrak{F}$ of a *unit* vector **t** in the direction of C at the point (x, y, z) on C.

Consider the family of surfaces $\phi(x, y, z) = k$. Then

$$d\phi = 0 = (\partial\phi/\partial x)\, dx + (\partial\phi/\partial y)\, dy + (\partial\phi/\partial z)\, dz.$$

Let (x, y, z) be the coordinates of a point P on one of the surfaces S of the family. Then (dx, dy, dz) is the representation of an arbitrary vector in the tangent plane to S at P. Evidently $d\phi$ is the scalar product of the vectors

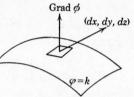

$$(\partial\phi/\partial x,\ \partial\phi/\partial y,\ \partial\phi/\partial z) = \mathbf{grad}\ \phi$$

and (dx, dy, dz). Since this product is zero, it follows that **grad** ϕ at any point

Fig. 188.

P is normal to that surface of the family $\phi(x, y, z) = k$ which passes through P, and **grad** ϕ is directed toward the side of the surface on which ϕ is increasing.

The directional derivative of ϕ in an arbitrary direction **t** is

$$\frac{d\phi}{ds} = \frac{\partial\phi}{\partial x}\frac{dx}{ds} + \frac{\partial\phi}{\partial y}\frac{dy}{ds} + \frac{\partial\phi}{\partial z}\frac{dz}{ds}$$

$$= \frac{\partial\phi}{\partial x}l + \frac{\partial\phi}{\partial y}m + \frac{\partial\phi}{\partial z}n = (\mathbf{grad}\ \phi)\cdot\mathbf{t}, \tag{7}$$

where l, m, n are the direction cosines of the unit tangent vector **t** at (x, y, z). Thus $d\phi/ds$ is the component of **grad** ϕ in the direction **t**. The maximum value of the directional derivative of ϕ at any point is known as the *normal derivative* of ϕ at the point; by (7), this maximum value is attained when **t** is taken in the direction of **grad** ϕ, and this maximum value is

$$\frac{d\phi}{dn} = \text{magnitude of } \mathbf{grad}\ \phi = +\sqrt{\Delta_1\phi}. \tag{8}$$

Thus, the directional derivative at (x, y, z) has a maximum value when s is measured normal to the surface of the family

$$\phi(x, y, z) = k$$

at (x, y, z). The normal is directed in the sense in which ϕ increases. If θ is the angle between this normal and the direction s, then by (7),

$$\frac{d\phi}{ds} = \frac{d\phi}{dn}\cos\theta. \tag{9}$$

Divergence of a Vector. Associated with any vector field **A** is a scalar point function whose representation in $\mathfrak{F}$ is

$$\frac{\partial A_x}{\partial x} + \frac{\partial A_y}{\partial y} + \frac{\partial A_z}{\partial z},$$

known as the *divergence* of **A,** and denoted by div **A** (see Sec. 20, Chap. II):

$$\text{div } \mathbf{A} = \frac{\partial A_x}{\partial x} + \frac{\partial A_y}{\partial y} + \frac{\partial A_z}{\partial z}. \tag{10}$$

We shall show the invariant character of div **A** by showing that for any two frames $\mathfrak{F}$ and $\mathfrak{F}'$,

$$\frac{\partial A_x'}{\partial x'} + \frac{\partial A_y'}{\partial y'} + \frac{\partial A_z'}{\partial z'} = \frac{\partial A_x}{\partial x} + \frac{\partial A_y}{\partial y} + \frac{\partial A_z}{\partial z}. \tag{11}$$

Now from (9) of Sec. 9 and (4),

$$\frac{\partial A_x'}{\partial x'} = \frac{\partial}{\partial x'}(a_{11}A_x + a_{12}A_y + a_{13}A_z)$$

$$= \left(\frac{\partial x}{\partial x'}\frac{\partial}{\partial x} + \frac{\partial y}{\partial x'}\frac{\partial}{\partial y} + \frac{\partial z}{\partial x'}\frac{\partial}{\partial z}\right)(a_{11}A_x + a_{12}A_y + a_{13}A_z)$$

$$= \left(a_{11}\frac{\partial}{\partial x} + a_{12}\frac{\partial}{\partial y} + a_{13}\frac{\partial}{\partial z}\right)(a_{11}A_x + a_{12}A_y + a_{13}A_z)$$

$$= a_{11}^2\frac{\partial A_x}{\partial x} + a_{12}^2\frac{\partial A_y}{\partial y} + a_{13}^2\frac{\partial A_z}{\partial z} + a_{11}a_{12}\left(\frac{\partial A_y}{\partial x} + \frac{\partial A_x}{\partial y}\right) \tag{12}$$

$$+ a_{11}a_{13}\left(\frac{\partial A_z}{\partial x} + \frac{\partial A_x}{\partial z}\right) + a_{12}a_{13}\left(\frac{\partial A_z}{\partial y} + \frac{\partial A_y}{\partial z}\right).$$

(In the second step the usual order of the factors has been inverted.) Similar expressions can also be found for $\partial A_y'/\partial y'$ and $\partial A_z'/\partial z'$. Upon adding these results and simplifying by (3) of Sec. 9, we obtain (11).

We shall denote by $\boldsymbol{\nabla}$ the vector operator whose representation in frame $\mathfrak{F}$ is $(\partial/\partial x,\ \partial/\partial y,\ \partial/\partial z)$. For example, in frame $\mathfrak{F}$,

$$\text{grad } \varphi \equiv \boldsymbol{\nabla}\varphi = \left(\mathbf{i}\frac{\partial}{\partial x} + \mathbf{j}\frac{\partial}{\partial y} + \mathbf{k}\frac{\partial}{\partial z}\right)\varphi = \mathbf{i}\frac{\partial\varphi}{\partial x} + \mathbf{j}\frac{\partial\varphi}{\partial y} + \mathbf{k}\frac{\partial\varphi}{\partial z}, \tag{13}$$

$$\boldsymbol{\nabla}\cdot\boldsymbol{\nabla}\varphi = \boldsymbol{\nabla}^2\varphi = \left(\mathbf{i}\frac{\partial}{\partial x} + \mathbf{j}\frac{\partial}{\partial y} + \mathbf{k}\frac{\partial}{\partial z}\right)\cdot\left(\mathbf{i}\frac{\partial\varphi}{\partial x} + \mathbf{j}\frac{\partial\varphi}{\partial y} + \mathbf{k}\frac{\partial\varphi}{\partial z}\right) \tag{14}$$

$$= \frac{\partial^2\varphi}{\partial x^2} + \frac{\partial^2\varphi}{\partial y^2} + \frac{\partial^2\varphi}{\partial z^2}.$$

In matrix notation, **grad** φ has the representation in $\mathfrak{F}$

$$\left(\frac{\partial}{\partial x}, \frac{\partial}{\partial y}, \frac{\partial}{\partial z}\right)\varphi = \left(\frac{\partial \varphi}{\partial x}, \frac{\partial \varphi}{\partial y}, \frac{\partial \varphi}{\partial z}\right),$$

and $\nabla \cdot$ **grad** φ has the representation in $\mathfrak{F}$

$$\left(\frac{\partial}{\partial x}, \frac{\partial}{\partial y}, \frac{\partial}{\partial z}\right)\left\{\begin{matrix}\dfrac{\partial \varphi}{\partial x} \\[4pt] \dfrac{\partial \varphi}{\partial y} \\[4pt] \dfrac{\partial \varphi}{\partial z}\end{matrix}\right\} = \frac{\partial^2 \varphi}{\partial x^2} + \frac{\partial^2 \varphi}{\partial y^2} + \frac{\partial^2 \varphi}{\partial z^2}.$$

If $\mathbf{A} = \mathbf{grad}\ \phi$, where ϕ is a scalar point function, then

$$\operatorname{div} \mathbf{A} = \operatorname{div} \mathbf{grad}\ \phi = \nabla \cdot \mathbf{grad}\ \phi = \nabla^2 \phi = \frac{\partial^2 \phi}{\partial x^2} + \frac{\partial^2 \phi}{\partial y^2} + \frac{\partial^2 \phi}{\partial z^2}. \quad (15)$$

The representation of the vector $\mathbf{A}$ in $\mathfrak{F}$ is $(\partial\phi/\partial x, \partial\phi/\partial y, \partial\phi/\partial z)$. By (11), $\partial A_x/\partial x + \partial A_y/\partial y + \partial A_z/\partial z$ is a scalar point function. Since $A_x = \partial\phi/\partial x, \cdots, A_x' = \partial\phi'/\partial x', \cdots,$ we have from (11)

$$\frac{\partial^2 \phi'}{\partial x'^2} + \frac{\partial^2 \phi'}{\partial y'^2} + \frac{\partial^2 \phi'}{\partial z'^2} = \frac{\partial^2 \phi}{\partial x^2} + \frac{\partial^2 \phi}{\partial y^2} + \frac{\partial^2 \phi}{\partial z^2}. \quad (16)$$

This scalar point function $\nabla^2\phi$ is known as the *Laplacian* (or *second differential parameter*) of ϕ and in $\mathfrak{F}$ is denoted by $\Delta_2\phi = \partial^2\phi/\partial x^2 + \partial^2\phi/\partial y^2 + \partial^2\phi/\partial z^2$. The operator $\Delta_2 \equiv \operatorname{div} \mathbf{grad}$ is called the *Laplacian operator*. If ψ is any scalar point function, then

$$\operatorname{div}(\psi\,\mathbf{A}) = \nabla \cdot \psi\mathbf{A} = \psi \operatorname{div} \mathbf{A} + \mathbf{A} \cdot \mathbf{grad}\ \psi. \quad (17)$$

Let (A_x, A_y, A_z) be the components of a vector $\mathbf{A}$ in frame $\mathfrak{F}$. We shall show that $(\Delta_2 A_x, \Delta_2 A_y, \Delta_2 A_z)$ are the components in $\mathfrak{F}$ of a vector which we shall denote by $\Delta_2\mathbf{A}$. Suppose (A_x', A_y', A_z') is the representation of $\mathbf{A}$ in any other frame $\mathfrak{F}'$. Then by (9) of Sec. 9,

$$A_x' = a_{11}A_x + a_{12}A_y + a_{13}A_z, \cdots.$$

Let $\Delta_2' \equiv \dfrac{\partial^2}{\partial x'^2} + \dfrac{\partial^2}{\partial y'^2} + \dfrac{\partial^2}{\partial z'^2}.$ From the invariant character of Δ_2 as shown in (16), $\Delta_2' A_x' = \Delta_2 A_x'.$ (See Ex. IX, 9.) Hence

$$\Delta_2' A_x' = \Delta_2 A_x' = \Delta_2(a_{11}A_x + a_{12}A_y + a_{13}A_z)$$
$$= a_{11}\Delta_2 A_x + a_{12}\Delta_2 A_y + a_{13}\Delta_2 A_z, \cdots.$$

In other words,

$$\begin{Bmatrix} \Delta_2' A_x' \\ \Delta_2' A_y' \\ \Delta_2' A_z' \end{Bmatrix} = \begin{Vmatrix} a_{11} & a_{12} & a_{13} \\ a_{21} & a_{22} & a_{23} \\ a_{31} & a_{32} & a_{33} \end{Vmatrix} \begin{Bmatrix} \Delta_2 A_x \\ \Delta_2 A_y \\ \Delta_2 A_z \end{Bmatrix}. \tag{18}$$

This shows that $\Delta_2 \mathbf{A}$ is a vector.

Curl of a Vector.   We define the *curl* of a vector field $\mathbf{A}$ to be

$$\operatorname{curl} \mathbf{A} \equiv \nabla \times \mathbf{A}. \tag{19}$$

It can be shown that **curl A** is a vector.   In frame $\mathfrak{F}$, the components of **curl A** are (see Sec. 21 of Chap. II),

$$\left(\frac{\partial A_z}{\partial y} - \frac{\partial A_y}{\partial z},\ \frac{\partial A_x}{\partial z} - \frac{\partial A_z}{\partial x},\ \frac{\partial A_y}{\partial x} - \frac{\partial A_x}{\partial y} \right).$$

The representation of **curl A** in $\mathfrak{F}$ is frequently written in the form

$$\begin{vmatrix} \mathbf{i} & \mathbf{j} & \mathbf{k} \\ \dfrac{\partial}{\partial x} & \dfrac{\partial}{\partial y} & \dfrac{\partial}{\partial z} \\ A_x & A_y & A_z \end{vmatrix}. \tag{19'}$$

For some purposes it is convenient to denote the x, y, and z components of **curl A** by $\operatorname{curl}_x \mathbf{A}$, $\operatorname{curl}_y \mathbf{A}$, and $\operatorname{curl}_z \mathbf{A}$.   (Many writers use the notation **rot A** for **curl A**.)

We define $\mathbf{\Theta}$, $\mathbf{\Psi}$, $\mathbf{\Phi}$ to be matrix operators whose representations in frame $\mathfrak{F}$ are given by

$$\mathbf{\Theta} \equiv \begin{Vmatrix} 0 & -\dfrac{\partial}{\partial z} & \dfrac{\partial}{\partial y} \\ \dfrac{\partial}{\partial z} & 0 & -\dfrac{\partial}{\partial x} \\ -\dfrac{\partial}{\partial y} & \dfrac{\partial}{\partial x} & 0 \end{Vmatrix}, \qquad \mathbf{\Psi} \equiv \begin{Vmatrix} \nabla^2 & 0 & 0 \\ 0 & \nabla^2 & 0 \\ 0 & 0 & \nabla^2 \end{Vmatrix},$$

$$\mathbf{\Phi} \equiv \begin{Vmatrix} \dfrac{\partial^2}{\partial x^2} & \dfrac{\partial^2}{\partial x\, \partial y} & \dfrac{\partial^2}{\partial x\, \partial z} \\ \dfrac{\partial^2}{\partial y\, \partial x} & \dfrac{\partial^2}{\partial y^2} & \dfrac{\partial^2}{\partial y\, \partial z} \\ \dfrac{\partial^2}{\partial z\, \partial x} & \dfrac{\partial^2}{\partial z\, \partial y} & \dfrac{\partial^2}{\partial z^2} \end{Vmatrix}. \tag{20}$$

Writing **A** in frame $\mathfrak{F}$ as a column array $\{\mathbf{A}\}$ and using the "row-by-column" rule for the product, it is easy to see that **curl A** may be written in the form

$$\mathbf{curl\ A} = \Theta\{\mathbf{A}\}, \tag{21}$$

that is,

$$\mathbf{curl\ A} = \left\{\begin{array}{c} \operatorname{curl}_x \mathbf{A} \\ \operatorname{curl}_y \mathbf{A} \\ \operatorname{curl}_z \mathbf{A} \end{array}\right\} = \left\|\begin{array}{ccc} 0 & -\dfrac{\partial}{\partial z} & \dfrac{\partial}{\partial y} \\[2mm] \dfrac{\partial}{\partial z} & 0 & -\dfrac{\partial}{\partial x} \\[2mm] -\dfrac{\partial}{\partial y} & \dfrac{\partial}{\partial x} & 0 \end{array}\right\| \left\{\begin{array}{c} A_x \\ A_y \\ A_z \end{array}\right\}. \tag{21'}$$

Also, it is clear from (18), that $\Delta_2\mathbf{A}$ may be written in the form

$$\Delta_2\mathbf{A} = \Psi\{\mathbf{A}\}, \tag{22}$$

that is, in the form

$$\Delta_2\mathbf{A} = \left\{\begin{array}{c} \Delta_2 A_x \\ \Delta_2 A_y \\ \Delta_2 A_z \end{array}\right\} = \left\|\begin{array}{ccc} \nabla^2 & 0 & 0 \\ 0 & \nabla^2 & 0 \\ 0 & 0 & \nabla^2 \end{array}\right\| \left\{\begin{array}{c} A_x \\ A_y \\ A_z \end{array}\right\}. \tag{22'}$$

It is an immediate consequence of these definitions that

$$\mathbf{curl\ grad}\ \phi = 0, \qquad \operatorname{div} \mathbf{curl\ A} = 0. \tag{23}$$

For example, by (21'), we have

$$\mathbf{curl\ grad}\ \phi = \left\|\begin{array}{ccc} 0 & -\dfrac{\partial}{\partial z} & \dfrac{\partial}{\partial y} \\[2mm] \dfrac{\partial}{\partial z} & 0 & -\dfrac{\partial}{\partial x} \\[2mm] -\dfrac{\partial}{\partial y} & \dfrac{\partial}{\partial x} & 0 \end{array}\right\| \left\{\begin{array}{c} \dfrac{\partial\phi}{\partial x} \\[2mm] \dfrac{\partial\phi}{\partial y} \\[2mm] \dfrac{\partial\phi}{\partial z} \end{array}\right\}$$

$$= \left\{\begin{array}{c} 0 - \dfrac{\partial}{\partial z}\left(\dfrac{\partial\phi}{\partial y}\right) + \dfrac{\partial}{\partial y}\left(\dfrac{\partial\phi}{\partial z}\right) \\[2mm] \dfrac{\partial}{\partial z}\left(\dfrac{\partial\phi}{\partial x}\right) + 0 - \dfrac{\partial}{\partial x}\left(\dfrac{\partial\phi}{\partial z}\right) \\[2mm] -\dfrac{\partial}{\partial y}\left(\dfrac{\partial\phi}{\partial x}\right) + \dfrac{\partial}{\partial x}\left(\dfrac{\partial\phi}{\partial y}\right) + 0 \end{array}\right\} = \left\{\begin{array}{c} 0 \\ 0 \\ 0 \end{array}\right\}. \tag{24}$$

We shall leave it to the student to prove div **curl A** = 0.

The gradient of the divergence of a vector field **A** may be computed from the definitions given. The result may readily be seen to be written in the form, for frame $\mathfrak{F}$,

$$\textbf{grad} \text{ div } \mathbf{A} = \Phi\{A\}, \tag{25}$$

that is, as

$$\textbf{grad} \text{ div } \mathbf{A} = \begin{Vmatrix} \dfrac{\partial^2}{\partial x^2} & \dfrac{\partial^2}{\partial x\,\partial y} & \dfrac{\partial^2}{\partial x\,\partial z} \\[2mm] \dfrac{\partial^2}{\partial y\,\partial x} & \dfrac{\partial^2}{\partial y^2} & \dfrac{\partial^2}{\partial y\,\partial z} \\[2mm] \dfrac{\partial^2}{\partial z\,\partial x} & \dfrac{\partial^2}{\partial z\,\partial y} & \dfrac{\partial^2}{\partial z^2} \end{Vmatrix} \begin{Bmatrix} A_x \\ A_y \\ A_z \end{Bmatrix}$$

$$= \begin{Bmatrix} \dfrac{\partial^2 A_x}{\partial x^2} + \dfrac{\partial^2 A_y}{\partial x\,\partial y} + \dfrac{\partial^2 A_z}{\partial x\,\partial z} \\[2mm] \dfrac{\partial^2 A_x}{\partial y\,\partial x} + \dfrac{\partial^2 A_y}{\partial y^2} + \dfrac{\partial^2 A_z}{\partial y\,\partial z} \\[2mm] \dfrac{\partial^2 A_x}{\partial z\,\partial x} + \dfrac{\partial^2 A_y}{\partial z\,\partial y} + \dfrac{\partial^2 A_z}{\partial z^2} \end{Bmatrix}. \tag{26}$$

From (20), we find upon multiplying the matrix operators that $\theta\theta = \theta^2 = \Phi - \Psi$, for

$$\theta^2 = \begin{Vmatrix} 0 & -\dfrac{\partial}{\partial z} & \dfrac{\partial}{\partial y} \\[2mm] \dfrac{\partial}{\partial z} & 0 & -\dfrac{\partial}{\partial x} \\[2mm] -\dfrac{\partial}{\partial y} & \dfrac{\partial}{\partial x} & 0 \end{Vmatrix} \cdot \begin{Vmatrix} 0 & -\dfrac{\partial}{\partial z} & \dfrac{\partial}{\partial y} \\[2mm] \dfrac{\partial}{\partial z} & 0 & -\dfrac{\partial}{\partial x} \\[2mm] -\dfrac{\partial}{\partial y} & \dfrac{\partial}{\partial x} & 0 \end{Vmatrix}$$

$$= \begin{Vmatrix} -\dfrac{\partial^2}{\partial z^2} - \dfrac{\partial^2}{\partial y^2} & \dfrac{\partial^2}{\partial y\,\partial x} & \dfrac{\partial^2}{\partial z\,\partial x} \\[2mm] \dfrac{\partial^2}{\partial x\,\partial y} & -\dfrac{\partial^2}{\partial z^2} - \dfrac{\partial^2}{\partial x^2} & \dfrac{\partial^2}{\partial z\,\partial y} \\[2mm] \dfrac{\partial^2}{\partial x\,\partial z} & \dfrac{\partial^2}{\partial y\,\partial z} & -\dfrac{\partial^2}{\partial y^2} - \dfrac{\partial^2}{\partial x^2} \end{Vmatrix} \tag{27}$$

$$= \begin{Vmatrix} \dfrac{\partial^2}{\partial x^2} & \dfrac{\partial^2}{\partial x\,\partial y} & \dfrac{\partial^2}{\partial x\,\partial z} \\[2mm] \dfrac{\partial^2}{\partial y\,\partial x} & \dfrac{\partial^2}{\partial y^2} & \dfrac{\partial^2}{\partial y\,\partial z} \\[2mm] \dfrac{\partial^2}{\partial z\,\partial x} & \dfrac{\partial^2}{\partial z\,\partial y} & \dfrac{\partial^2}{\partial z^2} \end{Vmatrix} - \begin{Vmatrix} \nabla^2 & 0 & 0 \\ 0 & \nabla^2 & 0 \\ 0 & 0 & \nabla^2 \end{Vmatrix} = \Phi - \Psi.$$

The curl of the curl of a vector field may be found quite simply, using the relations developed above:

curl curl A $= \theta\theta\{A\} = \theta^2\{A\} = (\Phi - \Psi)\{A\} = \Phi\{A\} - \Psi\{A\}$
$= $ **grad** div **A** $- \nabla^2$**A**.

From (21′) if ϕ be any scalar point function, we find

$$\text{curl } \phi\mathbf{A} = \theta\{\phi\mathbf{A}\} = \begin{Vmatrix} 0 & -\dfrac{\partial}{\partial z} & \dfrac{\partial}{\partial y} \\ \dfrac{\partial}{\partial z} & 0 & -\dfrac{\partial}{\partial x} \\ -\dfrac{\partial}{\partial y} & \dfrac{\partial}{\partial x} & 0 \end{Vmatrix} \begin{Bmatrix} \phi A_x \\ \phi A_y \\ \phi A_z \end{Bmatrix}$$

$$= \phi \begin{Vmatrix} 0 & -\dfrac{\partial}{\partial z} & \dfrac{\partial}{\partial y} \\ \dfrac{\partial}{\partial z} & 0 & -\dfrac{\partial}{\partial x} \\ -\dfrac{\partial}{\partial y} & \dfrac{\partial}{\partial x} & 0 \end{Vmatrix} \begin{Bmatrix} A_x \\ A_y \\ A_z \end{Bmatrix} + \begin{Bmatrix} -A_y\dfrac{\partial \phi}{\partial z} + A_z\dfrac{\partial \phi}{\partial y} \\ +A_x\dfrac{\partial \phi}{\partial z} - A_z\dfrac{\partial \phi}{\partial x} \\ -A_x\dfrac{\partial \phi}{\partial y} + A_y\dfrac{\partial \phi}{\partial x} \end{Bmatrix}$$

$$= \phi \text{ curl } \mathbf{A} + \text{grad } \phi \times \mathbf{A}.$$

EXERCISES IX

1. Given the scalar point function $\varphi = (x^2 + y^2 + z^2)^{-\frac{1}{2}}$.
(a) Find the directional derivative of φ in the direction of the vector $x\mathbf{i} + y\mathbf{j} + z\mathbf{k}$ at the point (x_0, y_0, z_0). (b) Find **grad** φ at (x_0, y_0, z_0). (c) Find div **grad** φ. (d) If $\mathbf{A} = 3\mathbf{i} + 20\mathbf{j} - 15\mathbf{k}$, find $\nabla \cdot (\varphi\mathbf{A})$. (e) If

$$\mathbf{B} = 3x\mathbf{i} + 20y\mathbf{j} - 15z\mathbf{k},$$

find $\nabla \cdot (\varphi\mathbf{B})$.
2. Repeat Ex. 1 when (a) $\varphi = xyz$. (b) $\varphi = x^2 + y^2 + z^2$. (c) $\varphi = \log (x^2 + y^2 + z^2)$.
3. Given $\mathbf{A} = 3xy\,\mathbf{i} + 20yz^2\,\mathbf{j} - 15xz\,\mathbf{k}$, $\mathbf{B} = x^2\,\mathbf{i} - \sin y\,\mathbf{j} + e^z\mathbf{k}$, and a point function $\varphi = y^2 - xz$. Find

(a) **curl A**.   (b) div **A**.   (c) $\nabla \cdot \mathbf{B} - $ div **A**.
(d) $\nabla \cdot \nabla\mathbf{A} = \Delta_2\mathbf{A}$.   (e) $\nabla \cdot (\nabla \times \mathbf{A})$.   (f) $\nabla \times (\nabla \times \mathbf{A})$.
(g) $\nabla \times (\mathbf{A} \times \mathbf{B})$.   (h) $\nabla(\mathbf{A} \cdot \mathbf{B})$.   (i) $\Delta_1\varphi$.
(j) $\nabla \times \nabla\varphi$.   (k) $\nabla \cdot (\varphi\mathbf{A})$.

4. Find the divergence and curl of

(a) $\mathbf{r} = x\mathbf{i} + y\mathbf{j} + z\mathbf{k}$. (b) $\mathbf{r} = \dfrac{x}{r}\mathbf{i} + \dfrac{y}{r}\mathbf{j} + \dfrac{z}{r}\mathbf{k}$, where $r = \sqrt{x^2 + y^2 + z^2}$.

5. Let **A** and **B** be vectors whose components are functions of x, y, and z. φ is a point function and α is a scalar. Prove:

(a) div **curl A** = 0.   (b) **curl grad** φ = 0.

(c) div **A** $\times$ **B** = $-$**A** $\cdot$ **curl B** $+$ **B** $\cdot$ **curl A**.

(d) (**B** $\cdot$ **grad**)**A** = (**B** $\cdot$ **grad** A_x)**i** $+$ (**B** $\cdot$ **grad** A_y)**j** $+$ (**B** $\cdot$ **grad** A_z)**k**.

(e) **curl A** $\times$ **B** = **A** div **B** $-$ **B** div **A** $+$ (**B** $\cdot$ **grad**)**A** $-$ (**A** $\cdot$ **grad**)**B**.

(f) div α**A** = α div **A** $+$ **A** $\cdot$ $\boldsymbol{\nabla}\alpha$.

(g) **curl** φ**A** = φ **curl A** $+$ ($\boldsymbol{\nabla}\varphi$) $\times$ **A**.

(h) **grad** (**A**^{2}/2) = (**A** $\cdot$ **grad**)**A** $+$ **A** $\times$ **curl A**.

6. Show that if $\Phi(x, y, z)$ be a point function, and if spherical coordinates r, θ, ϕ are used,

$$\mathbf{grad}\ \Phi = \mathbf{r}_1\frac{\partial\Phi}{\partial r} + \frac{\boldsymbol{\theta}_1}{r}\frac{\partial\Phi}{\partial\theta} + \frac{\boldsymbol{\phi}_1}{r\sin\theta}\frac{\partial\Phi}{\partial\phi},$$

where $\mathbf{r}_1$, $\boldsymbol{\theta}_1$, and $\boldsymbol{\phi}_1$ are unit vectors in the direction of increasing r, θ, and ϕ, respectively.

7. Prove that $\boldsymbol{\nabla}\Phi$ is perpendicular to the surface $\Phi(x, y, z)$ = constant.

8. Show that $\boldsymbol{\nabla} \cdot \boldsymbol{\nabla}(1/r) = 0$.

9. Let **A** be a vector with representation (A_x, A_y, A_z) in frame $\mathfrak{F}$. Show by direct differentiation that $\Delta_2' A_x' = \Delta_2 A_x'$.

12. Derivative of a Vector. Let C be a curve each point of which is associated with a vector of a vector field **A**. Let the parametric equation of the curve in frame $\mathfrak{F}$ be

$$x = x(\lambda), \qquad y = y(\lambda), \qquad z = z(\lambda),$$

where λ is an independent real parameter, independent of the frame $\mathfrak{F}$. The components (A_x, A_y, A_z) of **A** in frame $\mathfrak{F}$ are functions of (x, y, z), and hence of the independent variable λ. Since λ is independent of the frame used, we may differentiate (9) of Sec. 9 with respect to λ. Since the direction cosines a_{11}, a_{12}, a_{13}, $\cdot\ \cdot\ \cdot$ are constants, we find

$$\frac{dA_x'}{d\lambda} = a_{11}\frac{dA_x}{d\lambda} + a_{12}\frac{dA_y}{d\lambda} + a_{13}\frac{dA_z}{d\lambda}, \text{ etc.,} \tag{1}$$

or

$$\left\{\begin{matrix}\dfrac{dA_x'}{d\lambda}\\[2mm]\dfrac{dA_y'}{d\lambda}\\[2mm]\dfrac{dA_z'}{d\lambda}\end{matrix}\right\} = \left\|\begin{matrix}a_{11} & a_{12} & a_{13}\\ a_{21} & a_{22} & a_{23}\\ a_{31} & a_{32} & a_{33}\end{matrix}\right\|\left\{\begin{matrix}\dfrac{dA_x}{d\lambda}\\[2mm]\dfrac{dA_y}{d\lambda}\\[2mm]\dfrac{dA_z}{d\lambda}\end{matrix}\right\}. \tag{1'}$$

This shows that $dA_x/d\lambda$, $dA_y/d\lambda$, $dA_z/d\lambda$ are the components in $\mathfrak{F}$ of a vector which we will denote by $d\mathbf{A}/d\lambda$. This vector is known as the *derivative of the vector* $\mathbf{A}$ *with respect to* λ. The proof that $d\mathbf{A}/d\lambda$ is a vector depends essentially on the fact that the direction cosines a_{11}, a_{12}, $\cdots$ which fix the relative orientation of the two frames, are independent of the parameter λ.

From the vector $d\mathbf{A}/d\lambda$, the vector $d^2\mathbf{A}/d\lambda^2$, known as the second derivative of the vector $\mathbf{A}$, whose components in $\mathfrak{F}$ are $d^2A_x/d\lambda^2$, $d^2A_y/d\lambda^2$, $d^2A_z/d\lambda^2$ may be found.

From the definition of the derivative of a vector $\mathbf{A}$, we can readily prove the following relationships: Let m be a scalar, and let $\mathbf{A}$ and $\mathbf{B}$ be arbitrary vector fields. Then

$$\frac{d(m\mathbf{A})}{d\lambda} = m\frac{d\mathbf{A}}{d\lambda} + \frac{dm}{d\lambda}\mathbf{A}, \tag{2}$$

$$\frac{d(\mathbf{A}\cdot\mathbf{B})}{d\lambda} = \mathbf{A}\cdot\frac{d\mathbf{B}}{d\lambda} + \frac{d\mathbf{A}}{d\lambda}\cdot\mathbf{B}, \qquad \frac{d(\mathbf{A}\cdot\mathbf{A})}{d\lambda} = 2\mathbf{A}\cdot\frac{d\mathbf{A}}{d\lambda}, \tag{3}$$

$$\frac{d(\mathbf{A}\times\mathbf{B})}{d\lambda} = \mathbf{A}\times\frac{d\mathbf{B}}{d\lambda} + \frac{d\mathbf{A}}{d\lambda}\times\mathbf{B}. \tag{4}$$

If $\mathbf{A}$ is a vector of fixed magnitude, then $\mathbf{A}\cdot\mathbf{A} = A^2$ is a constant, $\dfrac{d(\mathbf{A}\cdot\mathbf{A})}{d\lambda} = \dfrac{dA^2}{d\lambda} = 0$, so that $\mathbf{A}\cdot\dfrac{d\mathbf{A}}{d\lambda} = 0$. The last equation shows that $d\mathbf{A}/d\lambda$ is perpendicular to $\mathbf{A}$ when $\mathbf{A}$ is of constant magnitude.

From (4), we find that

$$\frac{d}{d\lambda}\left(\mathbf{A}\times\frac{d\mathbf{A}}{d\lambda}\right) = \mathbf{A}\times\frac{d^2\mathbf{A}}{d\lambda^2} + \frac{d\mathbf{A}}{d\lambda}\times\frac{d\mathbf{A}}{d\lambda}.$$

But the vector product of equal vectors is equal to zero. Hence

$$\frac{d}{d\lambda}\left(\mathbf{A}\times\frac{d\mathbf{A}}{d\lambda}\right) = \mathbf{A}\times\frac{d^2\mathbf{A}}{d\lambda^2}. \tag{5}$$

Line and Surface Integrals. The various line and surface integral definitions and theorems which we studied in Chap. II may all be written in the notation of vector analysis. This fact has already been pointed out in Chap. II. For example, the definite integral $\mathsf{S}_a^b\,\mathbf{f}(\lambda)\,d\lambda$ is defined by the formula

$$\mathsf{S}_a^b\mathbf{f}(\lambda)\,d\lambda = \lim_{\Delta\lambda\to 0}\sum_{i=1}^{n}\mathbf{f}(\lambda_i)\,\Delta_i\lambda,$$

where λ is a real parameter, and $f(\lambda)$ is a vector function of λ.
As a further example, *Gauss's law* may be written in the form

$$S_K \, E \cdot dA = S_R \nabla \cdot E \, dV = 4\pi S_R \, \rho \, dV,$$

where E is the electric intensity, and ρ is the charge density.

EXERCISES X

1. Let r be the position vector of a point on a plane curve represented
in polar coordinates (r, θ). Then r is the magnitude of r, and $r = r r_1$,
where r_1 is a unit vector in the direction of r. Show that the velocity is

$$\frac{dr}{dt} = V = \frac{dr}{dt} r_1 + r \frac{d\theta}{dt} n,$$

where n is a unit vector perpendicular to r.

2. If r is the position vector of a particle of mass m, and if F is the force
acting on this particle, then $F = m \, dv/dt$, where $v = dr/dt$. Prove:

(a) The x, y, z components of F are $m \, d^2x/dt^2$, $m \, d^2y/dt^2$, $m \, d^2z/dt^2$.

(b) If the path of the particle is in the (r, θ)-plane, then (see Ex. 1)

$$F = m\left[\frac{d^2r}{dt^2} - r\left(\frac{d\theta}{dt}\right)^2\right]r_1 + m\left[2\frac{dr}{dt}\frac{d\theta}{dt} + r\frac{d^2\theta}{dt^2}\right]n.$$

3. A particle P moves in a plane with constant angular velocity ω about
a fixed point O. Show that, if the time rate of increase of its acceleration
is parallel to PO, then $\dddot{r} = \frac{1}{3}r\omega^2$.

4. Find the time rate of change of momentum M when the mass is a
function of the time. Show that dM/dt has the direction of $\ddot{r}$ if the mass
is constant.

5. (a) The "areal velocity" A of a moving point P about a fixed point
O is the rate of sweeping out of vector area by the line OP. Show that A
is the magnitude of the vector $\frac{1}{2}r \times V$. If we write $A = \frac{1}{2}H$, show that
$H = r^2\omega = pv$, where p is the length of the perpendicular from O to the
tangent at P, and v is the speed of P.

(b) If the point P moves under the action of a central force $F = \mu r$,
then $m \, d^2r/dt^2 = \mu r$. Hence $r \times (d^2r/dt^2) = 0$. Show as a result that

$$\frac{d}{dt}\left(r \times \frac{dr}{dt}\right) = 0,$$ and hence by part (a) that A is a constant.

6. Find the path of a particle P with position vector r relative to O
when P is acted on by a central force directed toward O and varying inversely
with r^2. [HINTS: (1) $m\ddot{r} = -\dfrac{\mu m}{r^2}\dfrac{r}{r}$. (2) $r \times V = Hk = r^2\omega k$, where k

is a unit vector perpendicular to the plane of the orbit, and ω is the angular
velocity of r. (3) The orbit is given by $H^2/\mu r = 1 + e \cos \theta$.]

7. A rigid body rotates about an axis OA with uniform angular velocity
ω. Let ω be a vector of magnitude ω in the direction OA, and such that a

right-hand screw would advance in the direction ω when turning with the body. Let $\mathbf{r} = \overrightarrow{OP}$ be the position vector of any point P in the body, and let $\mathbf{V}$ be the velocity of P.

(a) Show that $\mathbf{V} = \omega \times \mathbf{r}$.

(b) Show that curl $\mathbf{V} = 2\omega$.

(c) Find the acceleration vector $\mathbf{A} = d\mathbf{V}/dt$.

(d) Give the physical interpretation of the results in (a), (b), and (c).

8. (a) Let $\mathbf{r}$ be the position vector of a moving particle relative to a fixed point P. If we regard the momentum as localized along a straight line through the particle, the *moment of the momentum* $\mathbf{M} = m\dot{\mathbf{r}}$ of the particle about P is called the *angular momentum* $\mathbf{H}$ of the particle about P. Show that $\mathbf{H} = \mathbf{r} \times (m\dot{\mathbf{r}})$. Show that the rate of increase of angular momentum is $d\mathbf{H}/dt = \mathbf{r} \times \mathbf{F}$, where $\mathbf{F} = m\ddot{\mathbf{r}}$ is the resultant force acting on the particle. This relation $d\mathbf{H}/dt = \mathbf{r} \times \mathbf{F}$ is called the *principle of angular momentum*.

(b) Show that the kinetic energy of the particle P in part (a) is $\frac{1}{2}\mathbf{A} \cdot \mathbf{H}$, where $\mathbf{A}$ is the areal velocity in Ex. 5.

9. Let $\mathfrak{F}_1$ and $\mathfrak{F}_2$ be two frames of reference having a common origin O, and let ω be the angular velocity at any instant of $\mathfrak{F}_2$ relative to $\mathfrak{F}_1$. Let $\mathbf{r}$ be a vector function of the time t. If $(d\mathbf{r}/dt)_1$ is the vector in frame $\mathfrak{F}_1$ representing the time rate of change of $\mathbf{r}$ with reference to frame $\mathfrak{F}_1$, and if $(d\mathbf{r}/dt)_2$ has a similar interpretation with respect to frame $\mathfrak{F}_2$, then by Ex. 7,

$$\left(\frac{d\mathbf{r}}{dt}\right)_1 = \left(\frac{d\mathbf{r}}{dt}\right)_2 + \omega \times \mathbf{r}, \tag{1}$$

or

$$\mathbf{V}_1 = \mathbf{V}_2 + \omega \times \mathbf{r}, \tag{2}$$

where $\omega \times \mathbf{r}$ is the velocity relative to $\mathfrak{F}_1$ of that point P_2 fixed in frame $\mathfrak{F}_2$ whose position vector at the instant in question is $\mathbf{r}$. By regarding $\mathbf{V}_1$ as the position vector of a moving point, we see that

$$\mathbf{A}_1 \equiv \left(\frac{d\mathbf{V}_1}{dt}\right)_1 = \left(\frac{d\mathbf{V}_1}{dt}\right)_2 + \omega \times \mathbf{V}_1. \tag{3}$$

Likewise,

$$\left(\frac{d\omega}{dt}\right)_1 = \left(\frac{d\omega}{dt}\right)_2 + \omega \times \omega = \left(\frac{d\omega}{dt}\right)_2, \tag{4}$$

If we substitute (2) in (3), then by (4) we have *Coriolis' theorem:*

$$\mathbf{A}_1 = \mathbf{A}_2 + 2\omega \times \mathbf{V}_2 + \frac{d\omega}{dt} \times \mathbf{r} + \omega \times (\omega \times \mathbf{r}), \tag{5}$$

where $\mathbf{A}_2 = (d\mathbf{V}_2/dt)_2$. If we multiply both sides of (5) by the mass m of a moving particle with position vector $\mathbf{r}$, we have, upon transposing terms and writing $\omega \times (\omega \times \mathbf{r}) = (\mathbf{r} \cdot \omega)\omega - \omega^2 \mathbf{r}$,

$$m\mathbf{A}_2 = \mathbf{F} + m\omega^2\mathbf{r} - m(\mathbf{r} \cdot \omega)\omega - 2m(\omega \times \mathbf{V}_2) - m \quad \times \mathbf{r}, \qquad (6$$

where $\mathbf{F} = m\mathbf{A}_1$. Give the physical interpretation of each term of this result. The term $2m(\omega \times \mathbf{V}_2)$ is called the *Coriolis force*. The term $-m\omega \times (\omega \times \mathbf{r}) = m\omega^2\mathbf{r} - m(\mathbf{r} \cdot \omega)\omega$ is called the *centrifugal force*. Show that the term $-m\ddot{\varrho}$ is to be added to the right member of (6) when the origin of frame $\mathfrak{F}_2$ moves relative to the frame $\mathfrak{F}_1$ with position vector ϱ.

10. Let $\mathbf{r} \equiv \mathbf{r}(\lambda) = x(\lambda)\mathbf{i} + y(\lambda)\mathbf{j} + z(\lambda)\mathbf{k}$ be the position vector of a point on a curve C, where λ is a real independent parameter. The *differential* $d\mathbf{r}$ of $\mathbf{r}$ is defined to be $d\mathbf{r} = dx\,\mathbf{i} + dy\,\mathbf{j} + dz\,\mathbf{k}$. Let $f(x, y, z)$ be a scalar point function. Show that the differential df in the direction $d\mathbf{r}$ is $\nabla f \cdot d\mathbf{r}$.

11. (a) If a vector $\mathbf{A}$ is of constant magnitude, show that $d\mathbf{A}$ is perpendicular to $\mathbf{A}$.

(b) If the magnitude of $\mathbf{A}$ is identically 1, show that the magnitude of $d\mathbf{A}$ is equal to the angle $d\theta$ between $\mathbf{A}$ and $\mathbf{A} + d\mathbf{A}$.

12. Show that the area of the triangle with sides $\mathbf{r}$, $d\mathbf{r}$, and $\mathbf{r} + d\mathbf{r}$ is the magnitude of the vector $\frac{1}{2}(\mathbf{r} \times d\mathbf{r})$.

13. Prove the following formulas:

$$\int \left(\mathbf{F} \cdot \frac{d\mathbf{G}}{dt} + \frac{d\mathbf{F}}{dt} \cdot \mathbf{G} \right) dt = \mathbf{F} \cdot \mathbf{G} + C.$$

$$\int \left(\mathbf{F} \cdot \frac{d\mathbf{F}}{dt} \right) dt = \frac{1}{2}(\mathbf{F} \cdot \mathbf{F}) + C.$$

$$\int \frac{d\mathbf{F}}{dt} \cdot \frac{d^2\mathbf{F}}{dt^2}\, dt = \frac{1}{2} \frac{d\mathbf{F}}{dt} \cdot \frac{d\mathbf{F}}{dt} + C.$$

$$\int \mathbf{F} \times \frac{d^2\mathbf{F}}{dt^2}\, dt = \mathbf{F} \times \frac{d\mathbf{F}}{dt} + \mathbf{C}.$$

14. Show that the center of gravity of a body is the point whose position vector $\bar{\mathbf{r}}$ is given by

$$\bar{\mathbf{r}} = \frac{1}{M} \mathbf{S}_{\mathbf{R}}\, \mu\mathbf{r}\, dV,$$

where M is the mass of the body and μ is the density at any point whose position vector is $\mathbf{r}$.

15. Interpret $\mathbf{S}_C\, \mathbf{F} \cdot d\mathbf{r}$ when (a) $\mathbf{F}$ is the force acting on a particle at any point, (b) $\mathbf{F}$ is the velocity of a fluid at any point.

16. Interpret $\mathbf{S}_S\, \mathbf{F} \cdot d\mathbf{A}$ when (a) $\mathbf{F}$ is the electric or magnetic flux of a field at any point, (b) $\mathbf{F}$ is the velocity of a fluid at any point.

17. (a) Show that $\mathbf{r} = (\cos nt)\mathbf{a} + (\sin nt)\mathbf{b}$ is a solution of the differential equation $\frac{d^2\mathbf{r}}{dt^2} + n^2\mathbf{r} = 0$, and also of the equation $\mathbf{r} \times \frac{d\mathbf{r}}{dt} = n\mathbf{a} \times \mathbf{b}$.

(b) Show that **r** in part (a) traces out an ellipse with center at the origin, and that the motion is that due to a central force proportional to **r**.

18. Consider a perfect nonviscous fluid in which the density ρ and pressure p are functions of the time t. Let **v** denote the velocity of the fluid at the point P and at time t. Show that the acceleration of the fluid at P is $\dfrac{d\mathbf{v}}{dt} = \dfrac{\partial \mathbf{v}}{\partial t} + \mathbf{v} \cdot \nabla\mathbf{v}$. Show that the angular velocity ω about P is given by $\omega = \frac{1}{2}\nabla \times \mathbf{v}$, where **v** refers to the velocity at P. If ω is everywhere zero, **v** is called *irrotational*.

19. Show that any irrotational vector is the gradient of a scalar point function. If the motion of the fluid is irrotational, we shall write $\mathbf{v} = -\nabla\Phi$, where Φ is called the *velocity potential*. A surface $\Phi = $ constant is known as an *equipotential surface*. Those curves in a fluid having everywhere the direction of **v** are called *streamlines*. The equations of these lines are $dx/v_x = dy/v_y = dz/v_z$.

20. Show that $\nabla\Phi$ is normal to $\Phi = $ constant. This shows that the stream lines are normal to the equipotential surfaces.

21. Show from the equation of continuity [Chap. II, Sec. 20, eq. (18)] that $\partial\rho/\partial t = -\nabla \cdot (\rho\mathbf{v})$. From this, show that $d\rho/dt + \rho\nabla \cdot \mathbf{v} = 0$. What does this equation become when the fluid is incompressible; incompressible and irrotational?   *Ans.* $\nabla \cdot \nabla\Phi = 0$.

22. In exactly the same way that the space rate of change of velocity determines the rate of expansion of a fluid at a point (see Sec. 20, Chap. II), just so the space rate of change of unit pressure p at P within a fluid determines the force acting per unit of volume at P due to the surrounding fluid. Show in detail that this force is $-\nabla p$. Then show that the equation of motion is $\rho\, d\mathbf{v}/dt = \rho\mathbf{F} - \nabla p$, where **F** is the external force per unit mass of the fluid. If **F** is derivable from a potential, we shall write $\mathbf{F} = -\nabla\Omega$.

23. Show that the condition for irrotational motion of a fluid is that the circulation be zero around every closed curve.

Remark. It can be shown that, if $\mathbf{F} = -\nabla\Omega$, then the circulation around every closed curve is constant with respect to time.

The converse of this result may also be proved.

24. Give the physical interpretation of the relation

$$\iiint_R (X^2 + Y^2 + Z^2)\partial z\, \partial y\, dx = \iint_S \varphi\frac{\partial\varphi}{\partial n}\, dS$$

when φ is the velocity potential of a fluid (see Ex. XII, 4, Chap. II), and X, Y, Z are the components of velocity. Show that the kinetic energy of the fluid is $E = \dfrac{1}{2}\iint_S \rho\varphi\dfrac{\partial\varphi}{\partial n}\, dS$.

25. It has been shown in Ex. 18 that a fluid of velocity $\mathbf{V}(x, y, z)$ at $P(x, y, z)$ has an instantaneous rotation about an axis parallel to $\nabla \times \mathbf{V}$. A *vortex line* is a curve which at each of its points is tangent to the instantaneous axis of rotation. A *vortex tube* is the surface generated by the set of vortex lines drawn through each point of a closed curve. A *vortex* is the fluid

contained in such a tube.   On the surface of a vortex tube the vector $\nabla \times V$ is everywhere perpendicular to the normal to the tube.

The *circulation* around a closed path C is defined to be $\int_C V \cdot dR$.

(a) Show that the circulation is the product of the length of the path and the average velocity along the path.

(b) Let c_1 and c_2 be two closed curves on the surface of a vortex tube both drawn once around the tube in the same direction.   Denote the portion of the surface of the tube between c_1 and c_2 by D.   Show by means of Stokes's theorem that the circulation around a path containing c_1 and c_2 is zero, and thus prove that the circulation is independent of the position of the path on the surface of a vortex tube.   The strength of the enclosed vortex is taken to be the circulation $\int_{c_1} V \cdot dR$.

(c) Show that $\int_D n \cdot \nabla \times dA$ is also a measure of the strength of a vortex.

(d) If the velocity V of a fluid is perpendicular to a surface D at all points P of D, show that the vortex lines through points of D all lie on D.

(e) Find the value of $\int_A V \cdot n \, dA$ over the surface of a cube whose faces lie on $x = 0$, $y = 0$, $z = 0$, $x = 2$, $y = 2$, $z = 2$, when

$$V = (x^2 + y^2)i + (2xy)j + (x^2 - y^2)k.$$

26. Suppose the field of a vector F is *conservative*, that is, suppose $\int_C F \cdot dR = 0$ around every closed curve C.

If P_0 is a fixed point and $P(x, y, z)$ is a variable point, the quantity $-\int_{P_0}^{P} F \cdot dR$ is called the *potential* at P.

(a) Find the potential at P if a particle is attracted toward the origin with a force inversely proportional to the square of the distance from the origin.

(b) Find the potential at P if a particle is attracted toward the origin with a force inversely proportional to the distance from the origin.

(c) Find a potential for the centrifugal force of a particle of mass M which rotates with constant angular velocity about the z-axis.

27. Find the value of $\int_A F \cdot n \, dA$ over a sphere of radius r when

$$F = axi + byj + czk,$$

a, b, and c being constants.   Show that the above integral over any simple closed surface S is three times the volume enclosed by S.

28. Show that $\int_R \nabla \times F \, dV = 0$, where F is a vector normal to the boundary S of R at each point of S.

29. Let R be the position vector from the origin to the point $P(x, y, z)$. Show that the unit vectors tangent to the coordinate curves are:

(a) $i_1 = \partial R/\partial r$, $i_2 = (1/r)(\partial R/\partial \theta)$, $i_3 = k$ when the cylindrical coordinates r, θ, and z are used;

(b) Find an expression for the acceleration $d^2R/dt^2 = a_1 i_1 + a_2 i_2 + a_3 i_3$ for the case (a).   (Hint: Show that $\partial i_1/\partial \theta = i_2$, $\partial i_2/\partial \theta = -i_1$, $\partial i_3/\partial \theta = 0$.)

(c) $i_1 = \partial R/\partial r$, $i_2 = (1/r)(\partial R/\partial \theta)$, $i_3 = (1/r \sin \theta)(\partial R/\partial \phi)$, when spherical coordinates r, θ, and ϕ are used.

(d) Repeat (b) for the case of spherical coordinates as given in (c).   Hint: $\partial i_1/\partial \phi = i_3 \sin \theta$, $\partial i_2/\partial \phi = i_3 \cos \theta$, $\partial i_3/\partial \phi = -i_1 \sin \theta - i_2 \cos \theta$; $\partial i_1/\partial \theta = i_2$, $\partial i_2/\partial \theta = -i_1$, $\partial i_3/\partial \theta = 0$.

(e) Calculate ∇r, $\nabla \theta$, $\nabla \theta$ for Case (c).

PART C.   SOME DIFFERENTIAL GEOMETRY

13. Space Curves.   Let the point P trace out a space curve C along which the parameter is λ.   Let $\mathbf{r}$ be the position vector of the point P whose coordinates with reference to frame $\mathfrak{F}$ are (x, y, z), i.e., $\mathbf{r} = x\mathbf{i} + y\mathbf{j} + z\mathbf{k}$. From the definition of the derivative of $\mathbf{r}$ at P, the vector $d\mathbf{r}/d\lambda$ has the direction of the tangent at P to the curve C, the tangent being drawn in the direction of increasing λ.   We shall let s denote the arc length along the curve, measured from some fixed point in the direction in which λ increases.   Then $d\mathbf{r}/ds$ *is a unit vector in the direction of the tangent,* for

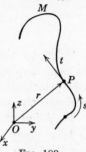

FIG. 189.

$$\left(\frac{d\mathbf{r}}{ds}\right)^2 = \left(\frac{dx}{ds}\mathbf{i} + \frac{dy}{ds}\mathbf{j} + \frac{dz}{ds}\mathbf{k}\right)^2 = \cos^2 \alpha + \cos^2 \beta + \cos^2 \gamma = 1.$$

Let $\mathbf{t} = d\mathbf{r}/ds$, where $\mathbf{t}$ is a unit vector.   Then if

$$v = \frac{ds}{d\lambda} = \sqrt{\left(\frac{dx}{d\lambda}\right)^2 + \left(\frac{dy}{d\lambda}\right)^2 + \left(\frac{dz}{d\lambda}\right)^2}, \tag{1}$$

we have

$$\frac{d\mathbf{r}}{d\lambda} = v\mathbf{t}. \tag{2}$$

By (2) of Sec. 12, we see that

$$\frac{d^2\mathbf{r}}{d\lambda^2} = v\frac{d\mathbf{t}}{d\lambda} + \frac{dv}{d\lambda}\mathbf{t}. \tag{3}$$

Since $\mathbf{t}$ is a vector of constant unit length, $d\mathbf{t}/d\lambda$ is a vector perpendicular to $\mathbf{t}$.   We define the direction of the *principal normal* to C to be the direction of $d\mathbf{t}/d\lambda$ at P.   Let $\mathbf{n}$ denote the unit vector along this principal normal.   Then, using a prime to denote differentiation with respect to s, we see that

$$\mathbf{t}' \equiv \frac{d\mathbf{t}}{ds} = \frac{\mathbf{n}}{\rho} = \kappa\mathbf{n},$$

so that

$$\mathbf{n} = \rho\mathbf{t}' = \rho\mathbf{r}'' \tag{4}$$

defines the positive number ρ which is known as the *radius of curvature* of the curve C at the point P; κ is called the *curvature* of the curve C at P.

Since $\dfrac{dt}{d\lambda} = \dfrac{dt}{ds}\dfrac{ds}{d\lambda}$, $\dfrac{dt}{d\lambda} = v\dfrac{\mathbf{n}}{\rho}$. Substituting this relation in (3), we find that

$$\frac{d^2\mathbf{r}}{d\lambda^2} = v^2\frac{\mathbf{n}}{\rho} + \frac{dv}{d\lambda}\mathbf{t}. \tag{5}$$

If λ denotes time, then $ds/d\lambda$ represents the speed v of P along its path, $dv/d\lambda$ is the rate of change of speed, and (5) shows that the (principal) normal component of the vector acceleration is v^2/ρ, and the tangential component is dv/dt.

We define the *osculating plane* to the curve C at the point P to be a plane passing through P and parallel to the vectors $\mathbf{n}$ and $\mathbf{t}$. From (5) we see that the vector $d^2\mathbf{r}/d\lambda^2$ lies in the osculating plane. If C is a plane curve, C lies entirely in the osculating plane and the principal normal is then the ordinary normal directed toward the center of curvature.

The equation of the osculating plane is

$$(\mathbf{R} - \mathbf{r}) \cdot (\mathbf{t} \times \mathbf{n}) = \begin{vmatrix} X - x & Y - y & Z - z \\ t_1 & t_2 & t_3 \\ n_1 & n_2 & n_3 \end{vmatrix} = 0, \tag{6}$$

where $\mathbf{R}$ is the current point on the plane. This may also be written

$$(\mathbf{R} - \mathbf{r}) \cdot \left(\frac{d\mathbf{r}}{d\lambda} \times \frac{d^2\mathbf{r}}{d\lambda^2}\right) = 0. \tag{7}$$

The equation of the principal normal at P is

$$\mathbf{R} = \mathbf{r} + u\mathbf{n}, \tag{8}$$

where u is a parameter.

EXERCISES XI

1. Given $x = \lambda$, $y = \lambda^2$, $z = \lambda^3$. Find the equation of the tangent line to C at $\lambda = \lambda_0$. Find the equation of the osculating plane to C at the point $\lambda = \lambda_0$. Find the equation of the principal normal to C at $\lambda = \lambda_0$. Find the curvature of C at $\lambda = \lambda_0$. What special form do these results assume when $\lambda = s$?

2. From the definition of the osculating plane derive its equation (6). Derive the equation of the osculating plane in the form (7). Write (7) in determinant form.

3. Show that the plane containing "two consecutive tangents at P" to C is the osculating plane at P. In other words, if P and $\bar{P}$ be two neighboring points on C, show that the osculating plane is the limiting position attained by a plane passing through the tangents to C at P and $\bar{P}$ as $\bar{P}$ approaches P as a limit.

4. By squaring (4) show that

$$\frac{1}{\rho^2} = \left(\frac{d^2\mathbf{r}}{ds^2}\right)^2 = \left(\frac{d^2x}{ds^2}\right)^2 + \left(\frac{d^2y}{ds^2}\right)^2 + \left(\frac{d^2z}{ds^2}\right)^2.$$

5. Show that the direction cosines of $\mathbf{n}$ are

$$\rho x'', \; \rho y'', \; \rho z'', \qquad \text{where} \qquad x'' = \frac{d^2x}{ds^2}, \; \cdots .$$

14. Binormal. Torsion. The normal to the osculating plane at P is called the *binormal*. Let $\mathbf{b}$ be a unit vector parallel to this binormal and so directed that $\mathbf{t}$, $\mathbf{n}$, $\mathbf{b}$ form a right-handed system of mutually perpendicular unit vectors. Then

$$\mathbf{t} \cdot \mathbf{n} = \mathbf{n} \cdot \mathbf{b} = \mathbf{b} \cdot \mathbf{t} = 0,$$
$$\mathbf{t} \times \mathbf{n} = \mathbf{b}, \quad \mathbf{n} \times \mathbf{b} = \mathbf{t}, \quad \mathbf{b} \times \mathbf{t} = \mathbf{n}. \tag{1}$$

We take the positive direction along the binormal as that of $\mathbf{b}$. Then the equation of the binormal at P is

$$\mathbf{R} = \mathbf{r} + u\mathbf{b}. \tag{2}$$

The vector $d\mathbf{b}/ds = \mathbf{b}'$ is perpendicular to $\mathbf{b}$, for $\mathbf{b}$ is of constant length. Since $\mathbf{t} \cdot \mathbf{b} = 0$ it follows that $\mathbf{t} \cdot \mathbf{b}' + \mathbf{t}' \cdot \mathbf{b} = 0$. From (4) of Sec. 13, $\mathbf{t}' = (1/\rho)\mathbf{n}$, so that $\mathbf{t} \cdot \mathbf{b}' + (1/\rho)\mathbf{n} \cdot \mathbf{b} = 0$. Since $\mathbf{n}$ is perpendicular to $\mathbf{b}$, $\mathbf{n} \cdot \mathbf{b} = 0$, so that $\mathbf{t} \cdot \mathbf{b}' = 0$. Hence we find that $\mathbf{t}$, as well as $\mathbf{b}$, is perpendicular to $\mathbf{b}'$. Thus $\mathbf{b}' \equiv d\mathbf{b}/ds = -\tau\mathbf{n}$, where the con-stant τ is called the *torsion* of the curve at the point P.

Fig. 190.

It represents the rate of rotation of the osculating plane. Torsion is agreed to be positive when the rotation (with s increasing) of the binormal increases in the same sense as that of a right-handed screw traveling in the direction of $\mathbf{t}$.

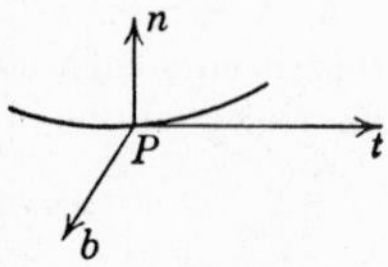

Since $\mathbf{n} = \mathbf{b} \times \mathbf{t}$, it follows that

$$\frac{d\mathbf{n}}{ds} = \tau\mathbf{b} - \kappa\mathbf{t}, \tag{3}$$

where $\kappa = 1/\rho$. Formula (4) of Sec. 13, and (2) and (3), are called the *Serret-Frenet formulas:*

$$\mathbf{t}' = \kappa\mathbf{n}, \qquad \mathbf{n}' = \tau\mathbf{b} - \kappa\mathbf{t}, \qquad \mathbf{b}' = -\tau\mathbf{n}. \qquad (4)$$

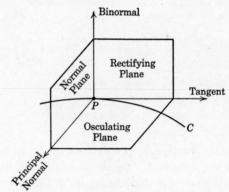

Fig. 191.

EXERCISES XII

1. Show that (2) may be written $\mathbf{R} = \mathbf{r} + v\mathbf{r}' \times \mathbf{r}''$, where v is a parameter. (HINT: $\mathbf{b} = \mathbf{t} \times \mathbf{n}$.)

2. Show that the direction cosines of the binormal are

$$\rho(y'z'' - z'y''), \; \rho(z'x'' - x'z''), \; \rho(x'y'' - y'x'').$$

3. In Ex. XI, 1, find the equation of the binormal at $\lambda = \lambda_0$, and find a formula for the torsion τ. Find the Serret-Frenet formulas for this curve.

4. Show that $\tau = \dfrac{1}{\kappa^2}[\mathbf{r}', \, \mathbf{r}'', \, \mathbf{r}'''] = [\mathbf{t}, \, \mathbf{n}, \, \mathbf{n}']$.

5. A *circular helix* is a curve drawn on a circular cylinder of radius a so that it cuts each element of the cylinder at a constant angle β. Its parametric equations in rectangular coordinates are

$$x = a \cos \theta, \qquad y = a \sin \theta, \qquad z = a\theta \cot \beta. \qquad (5)$$

Hence the position vector $\mathbf{r}$ of a point P on (5) is

$$\mathbf{r} = (a \cos \theta)\mathbf{i} + (a \sin \theta)\mathbf{j} + (a\theta \cot \beta)\mathbf{k},$$

where $\mathbf{i}, \mathbf{j}, \mathbf{k}$ are unit vectors along the x-, y-, and z-axes. Find $\mathbf{t} = \mathbf{r}'$. Using the fact that $\mathbf{r}'$ is a unit vector, show that $a^2\theta'^2 = \sin^2 \beta$. Find $\mathbf{r}'' = \kappa\mathbf{n}$. From the relation $\kappa^2 = \mathbf{r}'' \cdot \mathbf{r}''$ ($\mathbf{n}$ being a unit vector), show that $\kappa = a\theta'^2$. Find $\mathbf{n}$. Find $\tau = (1/a) \sin \beta \; \cos \beta$ from Ex. 4.

6. Show that $\kappa = \tau = \dfrac{1}{3a(1 + u^2)^2}$ for the curve

$$\mathbf{r} = a(3u - u^3)\mathbf{i} + 3au^2\mathbf{j} + a(3u + u^3)\mathbf{k}.$$

7. Find κ and τ for the curve

$$x = a(u - \sin u), \qquad y = a(1 - \cos u), \qquad z = bu.$$

8. Show that a curve is uniquely determined, except for its position in space, when κ and τ are given in the *intrinsic equations*

$$\kappa = f(s), \qquad \tau = g(s). \tag{6}$$

[Hint: Let C and C_1 be two curves such that κ and τ are given for each by (6).] Let $\mathbf{t}$, $\mathbf{n}$, $\mathbf{b}$ refer to C and let $\mathbf{t}_1$, $\mathbf{n}_1$, $\mathbf{b}_1$ refer to C_1. Show that

$$\frac{d}{ds}(\mathbf{t} \cdot \mathbf{t}_1 + \mathbf{n} \cdot \mathbf{n}_1 + \mathbf{b} \cdot \mathbf{b}_1) = 0,$$

and hence that

$$\mathbf{t} \cdot \mathbf{t}_1 + \mathbf{n} \cdot \mathbf{n}_1 + \mathbf{b} \cdot \mathbf{b}_1 = \text{const.} \tag{7}$$

Place C and C_1 so that $\mathbf{t} = \mathbf{t}_1$, $\mathbf{n} = \mathbf{n}_1$, $\mathbf{b} = \mathbf{b}_1$ at some point P_0. Then the constant in (7) is 3. Using the fact that the maximum value of each of the quantities $\mathbf{t} \cdot \mathbf{t}_1$, $\mathbf{n} \cdot \mathbf{n}_1$, and $\mathbf{b} \cdot \mathbf{b}_1$ is 1, show that $\mathbf{t} = \mathbf{t}_1$, $\mathbf{n} = \mathbf{n}_1$, $\mathbf{b} = \mathbf{b}_1$ all along C and C_1. Since $\mathbf{t} - \mathbf{t}_1 \equiv 0$, show that $\mathbf{r} - \mathbf{r}_1$ is a constant and deduce the theorem.

15. Surfaces. The parametric equations

$$x = \xi(u, v), \qquad y = \eta(u, v), \qquad z = \zeta(u, v) \tag{1}$$

represent a surface S in rectangular coordinates. We write (1) in the abbreviated form

$$\begin{aligned}\mathbf{r} = \mathbf{r}(u, v) &= x\mathbf{i} + y\mathbf{j} + z\mathbf{k} \tag{2}\\ &= \xi(u, v)\mathbf{i} + \eta(u, v)\mathbf{j} + \zeta(u, v)\mathbf{k},\end{aligned}$$

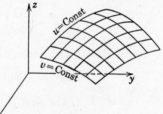

Fig. 192.

where $\mathbf{i}$, $\mathbf{j}$, $\mathbf{k}$ are unit vectors along the x, y, z-axes. We call $\mathbf{r}$ the position vector of a point (x, y, z) on S. If in (2) we set $u = u_0$, then (2) represents a curve C on the surface S along which v alone varies. Likewise, if we set $v = v_0$ we obtain another curve C' on S. All curves C and C' obtained from the relation $u = u_0$ or from the relation $v = v_0$ are called *parametric curves* on S. Again, the pair of numbers (u, v) are called the *parametric* or *curvilinear coordinates* of the point (x, y, z) on S. It is seen that the curves $u = u_0$ and $v = v_0$ are analogous to the lines $x = x_0$ and $y = y_0$ in the xy-plane.

We introduce the notation

$$\mathbf{r}_1 = \frac{\partial \mathbf{r}}{\partial u} = \frac{\partial \xi(u, v)}{\partial u}\mathbf{i} + \frac{\partial \eta(u, v)}{\partial u}\mathbf{j} + \frac{\partial \zeta(u, v)}{\partial u}\mathbf{k}; \ \mathbf{r}_2 = \frac{\partial \mathbf{r}}{\partial v};$$

$$\mathbf{r}_{11} = \frac{\partial^2 \mathbf{r}}{\partial u^2}; \qquad \mathbf{r}_{12} = \frac{\partial^2 \mathbf{r}}{\partial u \, \partial v}; \qquad \mathbf{r}_{22} = \frac{\partial^2 \mathbf{r}}{\partial v^2}.$$

By Sec. 13, the vector $\mathbf{r}_1$ is tangent to the parametric curve $v = \text{const.}$ at the point $\mathbf{r}$, and $\mathbf{r}_2$ is tangent to $u = \text{const.}$ at the point $\mathbf{r}$.

The equations $u = \phi(s)$, $v = \psi(s)$ represent a curve C on the surface S in (1), s being the arc length of C. The unit tangent to C is given by

$$\mathbf{t} = \frac{d\mathbf{r}}{ds} = \mathbf{r}_1\frac{du}{ds} + \mathbf{r}_2\frac{dv}{ds}.$$

Since $\mathbf{t} \cdot \mathbf{t} = 1$, we have

$$1 = \mathbf{r}_1^2\left(\frac{du}{ds}\right)^2 + 2\mathbf{r}_1 \cdot \mathbf{r}_2\frac{du}{ds}\frac{dv}{ds} + \mathbf{r}_2^2\left(\frac{dv}{ds}\right)^2. \tag{3}$$

We define

$$E = \mathbf{r}_1^2 = \left(\frac{\partial x}{\partial u}\right)^2 + \left(\frac{\partial y}{\partial u}\right)^2 + \left(\frac{\partial z}{\partial u}\right)^2,$$

$$F = \mathbf{r}_1 \cdot \mathbf{r}_2 = \frac{\partial x}{\partial u}\frac{\partial x}{\partial v} + \frac{\partial y}{\partial u}\frac{\partial y}{\partial v} + \frac{\partial z}{\partial u}\frac{\partial z}{\partial v}, \tag{4}$$

$$G = \mathbf{r}_2^2 = \left(\frac{\partial x}{\partial v}\right)^2 + \left(\frac{\partial y}{\partial v}\right)^2 + \left(\frac{\partial z}{\partial v}\right)^2.$$

Using this notation and writing (3) in differential form, we have

$$ds^2 = E \, du^2 + 2F \, du \, dv + G \, dv^2. \tag{5}$$

We call E, F, G the *first fundamental magnitudes* for the surface (1), and we call (5) the *quadratic differential form* for arc length.

Let C and C' be two curves on S intersecting at P, and let s and σ be the arc lengths of C and C'. Then

$$\frac{d\mathbf{r}}{ds} = \mathbf{r}_1\frac{du}{ds} + \mathbf{r}_2\frac{dv}{ds}, \qquad \frac{d\mathbf{r}}{d\sigma} = \mathbf{r}_1\frac{du}{d\sigma} + \mathbf{r}_2\frac{dv}{d\sigma},$$

and if ψ is the angle between C and C',

$$\cos \psi = \frac{d\mathbf{r}}{ds} \cdot \frac{d\mathbf{r}}{d\sigma} = E\frac{du}{ds}\frac{du}{d\sigma} + F\left(\frac{du}{ds}\frac{dv}{d\sigma} + \frac{du}{d\sigma}\frac{dv}{ds}\right) + G\frac{dv}{ds}\frac{dv}{d\sigma}. \tag{6}$$

It follows that C and C' are orthogonal at P if $(d\mathbf{r}/ds) \cdot (d\mathbf{r}/d\sigma) = 0$, i.e., if

$$E\frac{du}{ds}\frac{du}{d\sigma} + F\left(\frac{du}{ds}\frac{dv}{d\sigma} + \frac{du}{d\sigma}\frac{dv}{ds}\right) + G\frac{dv}{ds}\frac{dv}{d\sigma} = 0. \qquad (7)$$

To eliminate s and σ from (7), let us write $\dfrac{du}{ds} = \left(\dfrac{du}{dv}\right)_c\dfrac{dv}{ds}$, $\dfrac{du}{d\sigma} = \left(\dfrac{du}{dv}\right)_{c'}\dfrac{dv}{d\sigma}$, where, for example, $\left(\dfrac{du}{dv}\right)_c$ indicates that $\dfrac{du}{dv}$ is to be computed along C. If we substitute these relations in (7) and then divide by $\dfrac{dv}{ds}\dfrac{dv}{d\sigma}$, we find that C and C' are orthogonal when

$$E\left(\frac{du}{dv}\right)_c\left(\frac{du}{dv}\right)_{c'} + F\left[\left(\frac{du}{dv}\right)_c + \left(\frac{du}{dv}\right)_{c'}\right] + G = 0. \qquad (8)$$

We *define* the area A of a region K on the surface S by the formula

$$A = \iint_K \sqrt{EG - F^2}\, \partial v\, du. \qquad (9)$$

We shall show that (9) is an invariant for all coordinate systems Let

$$\mathbf{r}_1 = x_u\mathbf{i} + y_u\mathbf{j} + z_u\mathbf{k}, \qquad \mathbf{r}_2 = x_v\mathbf{i} + y_v\mathbf{j} + z_v\mathbf{k}.$$

By (4) and Ex. XXI, 7 of Chap. I,

$$\begin{aligned}
\sqrt{EG - F^2} &= \sqrt{(x_u^2 + y_u^2 + z_u^2)(x_v^2 + y_v^2 + z_v^2)} \\
&\qquad\qquad - (x_u x_v + y_u y_v + z_u z_v) \\
&= J\left(\frac{x, y}{u, v}\right)\sqrt{1 + \left[\frac{J(x, z/u, v)}{J(x, y/u, v)}\right]^2 + \left[\frac{J(y, z/u, v)}{J(x, y/u, v)}\right]^2} \\
&= J\left(\frac{x, y}{u, v}\right)\sqrt{1 + z_x^2 + z_y^2}.
\end{aligned}$$

Hence (9) assumes the form

$$A = \iint_K \sqrt{1 + z_x^2 + z_y^2}\, J\left(\frac{x, y}{u, v}\right) \partial v\, du. \qquad (10)$$

By Sec. 19 of Chap. II, (10) reduces to

$$A = \iint_K \sqrt{1 + z_x^2 + z_y^2}\, \partial y\, dx. \qquad (11)$$

This result agrees with (20) of Sec. 17, Chap. II. Hence the area A is independent of the uv-coordinate system (2).

As a special application of (9), consider the surface of revolution

$$x = u \cos \phi, \qquad y = u \sin \phi, \qquad z = f(u).$$

By (9) and Ex. XIII, 3,

$$A = \int_a^b \int_0^{2\pi} \sqrt{(1 + z'^2)u^2}\, \partial\phi\, du = \int_a^b 2\pi u \sqrt{1 + z'^2}\, du$$
$$= \int_0^{s_1} 2\pi u\, ds.$$

A normal to a surface S at a point $\mathbf{r}$ is perpendicular to $\mathbf{r}_1$ and $\mathbf{r}_2$, and hence is parallel to $\mathbf{r}_1 \times \mathbf{r}_2$. We define the *unit normal* $\mathbf{n}$ to S at $\mathbf{r}$ by the relation

$$\mathbf{n} = \frac{\mathbf{r}_1 \times \mathbf{r}_2}{|\mathbf{r}_1 \times \mathbf{r}_2|} = \frac{\mathbf{r}_1 \times \mathbf{r}_2}{H}, \tag{12}$$

where $H = |\mathbf{r}_1 \times \mathbf{r}_2|$.

We define the *second fundamental magnitudes* L, M, N by the formulas

$$L = \mathbf{n} \cdot \mathbf{r}_{11}, \qquad M = \mathbf{n} \cdot \mathbf{r}_{12}, \qquad N = \mathbf{n} \cdot \mathbf{r}_{22}. \tag{13}$$

We shall show the geometric significance of these quantities in Exs. XIII, 7 to 13.

EXERCISES XIII

1. Let (u_0, v_0) and $(u_0 + du, v_0 + dv)$ be two points on the surface (2). Show that $r_1\, du$ is approximately the arc length along the parametric curve

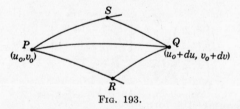

Fig. 193.

$v = v_0$ from (u_0, v_0) to $(u_0 + du, v_0)$, and hence that $E\, du^2$ is approximately the square of this length. Interpret $F\, du\, dv$ and $G\, dv^2$ similarly. Hence deduce that (5) is a form of the law of cosines as applied to the triangle PQR in Fig. 193.

2. Show that the parametric curves are orthogonal if and only if $F = 0$.

3. Show that the equations

$$x = u \cos \phi, \qquad y = u \sin \phi, \qquad z = f(u)$$

represent a surface of revolution with axis along the z-axis. Describe the parametric curves $u = u_0$ and $\phi = \phi_0$. Write

$$r = (u \cos \phi)\mathbf{i} + (u \sin \phi)\mathbf{j} + f(u)\mathbf{k},$$

and show that

$$E = 1 + f'^2, \qquad F = 0, \qquad G = u^2.$$

Compute ds^2 and interpret the formula geometrically.

4. Compute ds^2 for the surface

$$x = u \cos \phi, \qquad y = u \sin \phi, \qquad z = c\phi.$$

Describe the parametric curves on this surface.

5. Show that $H^2 = EG - F^2$. (HINT: If ω is the angle between the parametric curves at $\mathbf{r}$, then $\cos \omega = F/\sqrt{EG}$. Compute $\sin \omega$ in two ways.)

6. Show that

$$\mathbf{n} \cdot \mathbf{r}_1 \times \mathbf{r}_2 = H, \qquad \mathbf{r}_1 \times \mathbf{n} = \frac{1}{H}(F\mathbf{r}_1 - E\mathbf{r}_2), \qquad \mathbf{r}_2 \times \mathbf{n} = \frac{1}{H}(G\mathbf{r}_1 - F\mathbf{r}_2).$$

7. Show that

$$HL = \mathbf{r}_1 \times \mathbf{r}_2 \cdot \mathbf{r}_{11}, \qquad HM = \mathbf{r}_1 \times \mathbf{r}_2 \cdot \mathbf{r}_{12}, \qquad HN = \mathbf{r}_1 \times \mathbf{r}_2 \cdot \mathbf{r}_{22}.$$

8. Compute L, M, N and $\mathbf{n}$ for the surfaces of Exs. 3 and 4.

9. If $\mathbf{r} + d\mathbf{r}$ is the position vector of the point $(u + du, v + dv)$, then by Taylor's series,

$$(\mathbf{r} + d\mathbf{r}) = \mathbf{r} + (\mathbf{r}_1\, du + \mathbf{r}_2\, dv) + \tfrac{1}{2}(\mathbf{r}_{11}\, du^2 + 2\mathbf{r}_{12}\, du\, dv + \mathbf{r}_2\, dv^2) + \cdots.$$

The distance D from the point $\mathbf{r} + d\mathbf{r}$ to the tangent plane at $\mathbf{r}$ is $\mathbf{n} \cdot d\mathbf{r}$. Show that D is approximately $\tfrac{1}{2}(L\, du^2 + 2M\, du\, dv + N\, dv^2)$. What is the geometric interpretation of L, M, and N?

10. Show that

$$L = -\mathbf{n}_1 \cdot \mathbf{r}_1, \qquad M = -\mathbf{n}_1 \cdot \mathbf{r}_2 = -\mathbf{n}_2 \cdot \mathbf{r}_1, \qquad N = -\mathbf{n}_2 \cdot \mathbf{r}_2.$$

HINT: Differentiate relations of the type $\mathbf{n} \cdot \mathbf{r}_1 = 0$ with respect to u or v.

11. Show that

$$H^2\mathbf{n}_1 = (FM - GL)\mathbf{r}_1 + (FL - EM)\mathbf{r}_2,$$
$$H^2\mathbf{n}_2 = (FN - GM)\mathbf{r}_1 + (FM - EN)\mathbf{r}_2.$$

HINT: Since $\mathbf{n}_1$ is perpendicular to $\mathbf{n}$, we can write $\mathbf{n}_1 = a\mathbf{r}_1 + b\mathbf{r}_2$. Determine a and b by forming the products $\mathbf{n}_1 \cdot \mathbf{r}_1$ and $\mathbf{n}_1 \cdot \mathbf{r}_2$.

12. Show that

$$H\mathbf{n}_1 \times \mathbf{n}_2 = T^2\mathbf{n}, \qquad \mathbf{n} \cdot \mathbf{n}_1 \times \mathbf{n}_2 = \frac{T^2}{H},$$

where $T^2 = LN - M^2$.

13. Show that

$$H\mathbf{n} \cdot \mathbf{n}_1 \times \mathbf{r}_1 = EM - FL, \qquad H\mathbf{n} \cdot \mathbf{n}_1 \times \mathbf{r}_2 = FM - GL,$$
$$H\mathbf{n} \cdot \mathbf{n}_2 \times \mathbf{r}_1 = EN - FM, \qquad H\mathbf{n} \cdot \mathbf{n}_2 \times \mathbf{r}_2 = FN - GM.$$

14. Find the equation of the tangent plane to the surface of Ex. 3 at (u_0, ϕ_0). Repeat for Ex. 4.

16. Certain Curves on a Surface. We say that a *normal section* of a surface S at a point P is a section cut by a plane containing the normal $\mathbf{n}$ at P. For convenience, we take the principal normal of the section in the direction of $\mathbf{n}$, so that κ for the section is positive when the section is concave on the side on which $\mathbf{n}$ lies. If $\mathbf{r}$ moves along a normal section, we have

$$\kappa_n = \mathbf{n} \cdot \mathbf{r}'' = \mathbf{n} \cdot (\mathbf{r}_1 u'' + \mathbf{r}_2 v'' + \mathbf{r}_{11} u'^2 + 2\mathbf{r}_{12} u'v' + \mathbf{r}_{22} v'^2)$$
$$= Lu'^2 + 2Mu'v' + Nv'^2 \tag{1}$$

$$= \frac{L\left(\dfrac{du}{dv}\right)^2 + 2M\dfrac{du}{dv} + N}{E\left(\dfrac{du}{dv}\right)^2 + 2F\dfrac{du}{dv} + G}, \tag{2}$$

where the last formula is obtained with the aid of (5) in Sec. 15. We call κ_n the *normal curvature* of S at P in the direction du/dv.

Now suppose $\mathbf{r}$ traces out an arbitrary curve C on the surface S. Let θ be the angle between the surface normal $\mathbf{n}$ and the principal normal $\mathbf{r}''/\kappa$ of C at a point P. Then

$$\cos \theta = \frac{\mathbf{n} \cdot \mathbf{r}''}{\kappa} = \frac{1}{\kappa}(Lu'^2 + 2Mu'v' + Nv'^2). \tag{3}$$

If C_n is the normal section of S at P tangent to C, then by (1),

$$\kappa_n = (Lu'^2 + 2Mu'v' + Nv'^2). \tag{4}$$

Since C and C_n are tangent, $Lu'^2 + 2Mu'v' + Nv'^2$ is the same for the two curves at P by (2) since du/dv is the same for C and C_n at P. By (3) and (4), we have *Meusnier's theorem:*

$$\kappa_n = \kappa \cos \theta. \tag{5}$$

This formula shows that, of all curves on S through P with a given direction, the normal section in this direction has the least curvature.

If C is a curve on a surface S such that, at a point P,

$$[\mathbf{t}, \mathbf{n}, \mathbf{n}'] = 0, \tag{6}$$

where $\mathbf{n}$ is the unit surface normal, the direction of C at P is called a *principal direction* of S at P. By Ex. VIII, 12, (6) implies that $\mathbf{n}'$ is parallel to $\mathbf{t}$. Write (6) in the form $\mathbf{n} \cdot \mathbf{n}' \times \mathbf{r}' = 0$, i.e.,

$$\mathbf{n} \cdot \left(\mathbf{n}_1\frac{du}{ds} + \mathbf{n}_2\frac{dv}{ds}\right) \times \left(\mathbf{r}_1\frac{du}{ds} + \mathbf{r}_2\frac{dv}{ds}\right) = 0.$$

Then

$$\mathbf{n} \cdot \mathbf{n}_1 \times \mathbf{r}_1\left(\frac{du}{ds}\right)^2 + \{\mathbf{n} \cdot \mathbf{n}_2 \times \mathbf{r}_1 + \mathbf{n} \cdot \mathbf{n}_1 \times \mathbf{r}_2\}\frac{du}{ds}\frac{dv}{ds}$$
$$+ \mathbf{n} \cdot \mathbf{n}_2 \times \mathbf{r}_2\left(\frac{dv}{ds}\right)^2 = 0.$$

By Ex. XIII, 13, this may be written as

$$(EM - FL)\left(\frac{du}{dv}\right)^2 + (EN - GL)\frac{du}{dv} + (FN - GM) = 0. \quad (7)$$

This equation determines two values for du/dv which we may write as $(du/dv)_1$ and $(du/dv)_2$. By (8) of Sec. 15, the directions determined by $(du/dv)_1$ and $(du/dv)_2$ are orthogonal. We have thus shown that, if $EM - FL$ and $FN - GM$ are not both zero, i.e., if $E:F:G \neq L:M:N$, then at any point P on a surface S there are two principal directions, and these two directions are orthogonal. A curve C on S along which (7) is satisfied identically is called a *line of curvature*. It follows that there are two families of lines of curvature on a surface S, one curve of each family going through any given point P.

Let us now determine du/dv in (2) so that κ_n is a maximum or minimum. Write (2) in the form

$$\kappa_n = \frac{L\lambda^2 + 2M\lambda + N}{E\lambda^2 + 2F\lambda + G}, \quad (8)$$

where $\lambda = du/dv$. If we differentiate (8) with respect to λ and set the result equal to zero, we obtain the equation

$$(E\lambda^2 + 2F\lambda + G)(L\lambda + M)$$
$$(L\lambda^2 + 2M\lambda + N)(E\lambda + F) = 0. \quad (9)$$

This equation evidently reduces to (7). It may be shown (in general) that, of the two values of κ_n in (8) resulting from the two values of λ determined in (9), one is a maximum and the other is a minimum. Hence the principal directions at P are the directions of maximum and minimum normal curvature.

If we write (9) in the form

$$\frac{L\lambda + M}{E\lambda + F} = \frac{L\lambda^2 + 2M\lambda + N}{E\lambda^2 + 2F\lambda + G},$$

we see by (8) that

$$(E\kappa_n - L)\lambda + (F\kappa_n - M) = 0. \tag{10}$$

Write (8) in the form

$$(E\kappa_n - L)\lambda^2 + 2(F\kappa_n - M)\lambda + (G\kappa_n - N) = 0. \tag{11}$$

Multiply (10) by λ and subtract from (11). We obtain

$$(F\kappa_n - M)\lambda + (G\kappa_n - N) = 0. \tag{12}$$

Elimination of λ from (10) and (12) leads to the equation

$$H^2\kappa_n^2 - (EN - 2FM + GL)\kappa_n + T^2 = 0, \tag{13}$$

which determines the maximum value κ_1 and the minimum value κ_2 of κ_n at a point P on S.

It follows by (4) of Sec. 15 and Ex. XIII, 10, that (10) and (12) may be written as

$$\mathbf{r}_1 \cdot [(\kappa\mathbf{r}_1 + \mathbf{n}_1)\lambda + (\kappa\mathbf{r}_2 + \mathbf{n}_2)] = 0,$$
$$\mathbf{r}_2 \cdot [(\kappa\mathbf{r}_1 + \mathbf{n}_1)\lambda + (\kappa\mathbf{r}_2 + \mathbf{n}_2)] = 0,$$

where κ denotes either κ_1 or κ_2. Since $\lambda = du/dv$ these relations in turn may be written (by the usual manipulations with differentials) in the form

$$\mathbf{r}_1 \cdot \left[\kappa\frac{d\mathbf{r}}{ds} + \frac{d\mathbf{n}}{ds}\right] = 0, \qquad \mathbf{r}_2 \cdot \left[\kappa\frac{d\mathbf{r}}{ds} + \frac{d\mathbf{n}}{ds}\right] = 0.$$

But $d\mathbf{r}/ds$ and $d\mathbf{n}/ds$ both lie in the tangent plane to S at P. Thus $[\kappa(d\mathbf{r}/ds) + (d\mathbf{n}/ds)]$ lies in the tangent plane and is perpendicular to both $\mathbf{r}_1$ and $\mathbf{r}_2$. Hence

$$\kappa\frac{d\mathbf{r}}{ds} + \frac{d\mathbf{n}}{ds} = 0, \tag{14}$$

where $\mathbf{r}$ and $\mathbf{n}$ range along a line of curvature, and where (14) is called *Rodrigues's formula*.

We define $J = \kappa_1 + \kappa_2$ to be the *first (mean) curvature* of S at a point P, and we define $K = \kappa_1\kappa_2$ to be the *second (specific, total, Gauss) curvature* of S at P. It follows by (13) that

$$J = \frac{1}{H^2}(EN - 2FM + GL), \qquad K = \frac{T^2}{H^2}.$$

A *geodesic* is a curve on a surface S whose principal normal at each point coincides with the surface normal **n**. By Meusnier's theorem, the geodesic curvature is the normal curvature in the direction of the geodesic. It can be shown that (with certain restrictions) the geodesic joining two points A and B is the shortest of all curves on S joining A and B. (A taut thread stretched on S from A to B assumes the position of shortest length, this being also the position such that at each point the tension in the thread tends to produce no lateral motion, i.e., **t**$'$ is along **n**. (See Ex. I, 11, of Chap. VIII.) By the defining property of a geodesic,

$$\mathbf{r}'' \equiv \mathbf{r}_1 u'' + \mathbf{r}_2 v'' + \mathbf{r}_{11} u'^2 + 2\mathbf{r}_{12} u'v' + \mathbf{r}_{22} v'^2 = \kappa \mathbf{n}, \quad (15)$$

where **n** is the surface normal. If we form the scalar product of each side of (15) with $\mathbf{r}_1$ and $\mathbf{r}_2$, we obtain the differential equations of the geodesics on S:

$$\begin{aligned} Eu'' + Fv'' + \tfrac{1}{2}E_1 u'^2 + E_2 u'v' + (F_2 - \tfrac{1}{2}G_1)v'^2 &= 0, \\ Fu'' + Gv'' + (F_1 - \tfrac{1}{2}E_2)u'^2 + G_1 u'v' + \tfrac{1}{2}G_2 v'^2 &= 0, \end{aligned} \quad (16)$$

where $E_1 = \partial E/\partial u$, etc.

Since the principal normal of a geodesic is the surface normal at any point, it follows by Ex. XII, 4, that

$$\tau = [\mathbf{t}, \mathbf{n}, \mathbf{n}'],$$

where **n** is now the surface normal. Since $[\mathbf{t}, \mathbf{n}, \mathbf{n}'] = 0$ in the direction of a line of curvature, it follows that the torsion of a geodesic is 0 in the direction of a line of curvature. Moreover, $[\mathbf{t}, \bar{\mathbf{n}}, \bar{\mathbf{n}}']$ being identically zero only along a plane curve ($\bar{\mathbf{n}}$ being the principal normal), it follows that if a geodesic is either a plane curve or a line of curvature, it has both of these properties.

It turns out that geodesics play much the same role on a surface that straight lines do in a plane. For example, one may set up "polar" coordinates on a surface using geodesic distance, and one may measure the curvature of a curve relative to the tangent geodesic. But many of those properties are better dealt with by tensor analysis, and we pass over them here. See, for example, Weatherburn, "Differential Geometry"; Eisenhart, "Differential Geometry;" Levi-Civita, "Absolute Differential Calculus."

EXERCISES XIV

1. Find J and K for the surfaces of Exs. XIII, 3 and 4; also find the differential equations for the lines of curvature.

2. The differential equations representing the lines of curvature being $du/dv = 0$ and $dv/du = 0$, show by (7) and Ex. XIII, 2, that the parametric curves are the lines of curvature when and only when $F = M = 0$.

3. Show that $\kappa_1 = L/E$, $\kappa_2 = N/G$ when the parametric curves are the lines of curvature. Let κ_n be the normal curvature in a direction making an angle ψ with the direction in which κ_1 is taken. Use the preceding result to prove *Euler's formula:*

$$\kappa_n = \kappa_1 \cos^2 \psi + \kappa_2 \sin^2 \psi.$$

4. Show that (16) may be written in the following alternative forms:

$$\left.\begin{aligned}
\frac{d}{ds}(Eu' + Fv') &= \frac{1}{2}(E_1 u'^2 + 2F_1 u'v' + G_1 v'^2), \\
\frac{d}{ds}(Fu' + Gv') &= \frac{1}{2}(E_2 u'^2 + 2F_2 u'v' + G_2 v'^2),
\end{aligned}\right\} \tag{17}$$

$$\left.\begin{aligned}
u'' + lu'^2 + 2mu'v' + nv'^2 &= 0, \\
v'' + \lambda u'^2 + 2\mu u'v' + \nu v'^2 &= 0,
\end{aligned}\right\} \tag{18}$$

where $l, m, n, \lambda, \mu, \nu$ are certain expressions in E, F, G and their derivatives; also

$$\frac{d^2 v}{du^2} = n\left(\frac{dv}{du}\right)^3 + (2m - \nu)\left(\frac{dv}{du}\right)^2 + (l - 2\mu)\frac{dv}{du} - \lambda. \tag{19}$$

Since (19) is a second order equation, there exists (in general) exactly one geodesic on a surface S through a given point in a given direction.

5. Show that the geodesics in a plane are straight lines.

6. Show that the geodesics on a sphere are arcs of great circles.

7. Show that the geodesics on a circular cylinder are helices.

8. Find the geodesics on a right circular cone.

17. Maps. Let S and S' be two surfaces. If, by any means there is made to correspond to each point of S exactly one point of S', then we say that S is *transformed into,* or *mapped upon,* S'. If, moreover, exactly one point of S has any given point of S' for its image, then the mapping is said to be *biunique.* For example, a geographic map is a mapping of (part or all of) the earth's surface upon either a sheet of paper or a sphere. Again, the usual operation of projection maps one plane or surface upon another. More generally, if F is a family of curves in space such that through each point there is one and only one curve, and if S and S' both cut all curves of the family F, then this family maps S on S'.

A simple way to establish a mapping of two surfaces S and S' is to represent each surface by equations of the form (1) or (2) of

Sec. 15 using the same parameters u and v. Then the pair of numbers (u, v) determines exactly one point on each surface (assuming the ranges of u and v to be the same) and a mapping M of S upon S' is established by associating these pairs of points. Arc lengths on S and S' are then given by

$$\left. \begin{array}{l} ds^2 = E\, du^2 + 2F\, du\, dv + G\, dv^2, \\ d\sigma^2 = \overline{E}\, du^2 + 2\overline{F}\, du\, dv + \overline{G}\, dv^2. \end{array} \right\} \tag{1}$$

At any particular point P the ratio $ds/d\sigma$ is constant for all directions du/dv if and only if

$$\frac{\overline{E}}{E} = \frac{\overline{F}}{F} = \frac{\overline{G}}{G} = \rho^2, \tag{2}$$

where, however, ρ may be a function of u and v. We say that the mapping M is *conformal* if (2) holds, and as $\rho = d\sigma/ds$, we

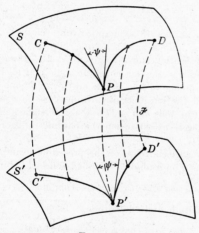

FIG. 194.

call ρ the *magnification*. A relation $f(u, v) = 0$ determines a curve C on S and a curve C' on S'; the relation $g(u, v) = 0$ determines curves D and D' on S and S'. If C and D intersect at P, C' and D' intersect at P', and if ψ is the angle between C and D, with ψ' the angle between C' and D', then it is seen by (6) of Sec. 15 and (2) that $\cos \psi = \cos \psi'$. By proper choice of signs, we have $\psi = \psi'$. Thus angles are preserved at every point by conformal mapping. It follows that infinitesimal figures in the neighborhood of P and P' are similar in shape, though the ratio of their linear dimensions is ρ.

Example 1. We shall construct a conformal mapping of the surface S of revolution

$$x = w \cos \phi, \qquad y = w \sin \phi, \qquad z = f(w) \tag{3}$$

on a plane. We first observe from Ex. XIII, 3, that

$$ds^2 = (1 + f'^2) \, dw^2 + w^2 \, d\phi^2. \tag{4}$$

Let us change the parameter w to a new parameter u by the relation

$$du = \frac{\sqrt{1 + f'^2(w)}}{w} \, dw. \tag{5}$$

(This is merely a change of scale along the curves $v = $ const.) Then (4) becomes

$$ds^2 = w^2(du^2 + d\phi^2). \tag{6}$$

If we use ku and kv as rectangular coordinates in a plane M, then

$$d\sigma^2 = k^2(du^2 + d\phi^2). \tag{7}$$

By (6) and (7), the surface (3) is mapped conformally on M, where corresponding points on S and M have the same coordinates (u, ϕ) and where at any point the magnification is k/w as given by (2). Because a straight line l in M cuts all lines $u = u_0$ at a constant angle and all lines $\phi = \phi_0$ at a constant angle, the image of l on S cuts all the meridians $\phi = \phi_0$ at a constant angle and all the parallels of latitude $u = u_0$ at a constant angle. If the equation of l in M is $aku + bk\phi + c = 0$, the equation of the image of l on S is $au + b\phi + c = 0$ (when the parametric coordinates on S are taken as u and ϕ).

Example 2. As a special case of the preceding example, we shall map a sphere S of radius a on a plane. We may represent S in the form

$$x = a \cos \varphi \cos \theta, \qquad y = a \cos \varphi \sin \theta, \qquad z = a \sin \varphi,$$

where φ denotes latitude and θ longitude. Then

$$ds^2 = a^2 \cos^2 \varphi \, (\sec^2 \varphi \, d\varphi^2 + d\theta^2).$$

If we introduce the variable α by the relation

$$d\alpha = \sec \varphi \, d\varphi,$$

so that $\alpha = \log \tan \left(\dfrac{\varphi}{2} + \dfrac{\pi}{4} \right)$, then

$$ds^2 = a^2 \cos^2 \varphi (d\alpha^2 + d\theta^2). \tag{8}$$

Let $x = k\theta$ and $y = k\alpha$. Then $d\sigma^2 = k^2(d\alpha^2 + d\theta^2)$. Since condition (2) is met, the sphere is mapped conformally on the plane. Moreover, any straight line on the plane represents the image of a curve on the sphere cutting all meridians at a constant angle. The magnification is $k/(a \cos \varphi)$.

Because this magnification is large for values of φ near $\pi/2$, this mapping, called *Mercator's projection*, causes areas near the poles to appear unduly large. This mapping may be obtained geometrically as follows: Let L be the axis of the sphere through the poles, and let C be a cylinder with L for axis and tangent to the sphere along the equator. The mapping is effected by projecting each point P of the sphere onto C by a line through P perpendicular to L. C may now be rolled out into a plane.

If instead of $x = k\theta$ and $y = k\alpha$, we take $x = ke^{-\alpha} \cos \theta$, $y = ke^{-\alpha} \sin \theta$, then

$$d\sigma^2 = dx^2 + dy^2 = k^2 e^{-2\alpha}(d\alpha^2 + d\theta^2),$$

and we have another type of conformal mapping of a sphere on a plane called *stereographic projection*. This mapping may be obtained geometrically by taking the xy-plane tangent to the sphere at the south pole; if P is a point on the sphere, the image P' of P in the plane is found by projecting P onto the plane from the north pole. It is seen that meridians project into straight lines through the origin, and parallels of latitude project into circles with center at the origin.

EXERCISES XV

1. Show that the surfaces $x = u \cos \phi$, $y = u \sin \phi$, $z = c\phi$, and $x = u \cos \phi$, $y = u \sin \phi$, $z = c \cosh^{-1} u/c$ can be mapped conformally on to each other with linear magnification identically one.

2. Determine $f(v)$ so that the surface $x = u \cos v$, $y = u \sin v$, $z = f(v)$ can be mapped conformally on a surface of revolution with linear magnification identically one.

PART D.   TENSOR ANALYSIS

18. Definition of a Tensor. In Sec. 9 we said that if three functions $A_x(x, y, z)$, $A_y(x, y, z)$, $A_z(x, y, z)$ transform according to the law (9) when the coordinates (x, y, z) are transformed by (8), then A_x, A_y, A_z are the components of a vector. We shall now generalize this concept.   Let

$$x'^\alpha = \chi^\alpha(x^1, x^2, \cdots, x^n) \qquad (\alpha = 1, 2, \cdots, n) \qquad (1)$$

represent a transformation of coordinates in n-dimensional space, where we use superscripts, instead of subscripts, to distinguish the variables.   Suppose that the Jacobian

$$J\left(\frac{\chi^1, \cdots, \chi^n}{x^1, \cdots, x^n}\right)$$

of (1) exists and is $\neq 0$, so that (1) has an inverse:

$$x^i = \psi^i(x'^1, x'^2, \cdots, x'^n). \qquad (i = 1, 2, \cdots, n.) \qquad (2)$$

DEFINITION 18.1.   *If, in any manner whatever, a set of n functions $F^1(x^1, \cdots, x^n), \cdots, F^n(x^1, \cdots, x^n)$ is determined for each coordinate system* (1) *and* (2), *and if these functions transform according to the law**

$$F'^\alpha(x'^1, \cdots, x'^n) = \sum_i F^i(x^1, \cdots, x^n) \frac{\partial x'^\alpha}{\partial x^i},$$

$$(\alpha = 1, 2, \cdots, n). \quad (3)$$

then we say that the functions $F^1, \cdots, F^n$ are the components in the coordinate system $(x^1, \cdots, x^n)$ of a contravariant tensor of order one, and $F'^1, \cdots, F'^n$ are the components of this tensor in the coordinate system $(x'^1, \cdots, x'^n)$.

Since (9) of Sec. 9 is a special case of (3), a contravariant tensor of order one is sometimes called a *contravariant vector*.

If $F^1(x^1, \cdots, x^n), \cdots, F^n(x^1, \cdots, x^n)$ are any given functions in the coordinate system $(x^1, \cdots, x^n)$, a tensor may always be constructed by *defining* the functions

$$F'^1(x'^1, \cdots, x'^n), \cdots, F'^n(x'^1, \cdots, x'^n)$$

for every other coordinate system $(x'^1, \cdots, x'^n)$ by means of (3). (See Ex. XVI, 3.)

Example 1. Let a unit of *distance* be selected in Euclidean 3-space. If a fluid is moving with velocity **V** at any point, and if (x^1, x^2, x^3) are the rectangular coordinates in frame $\mathfrak{F}$ of a certain particle P, with x^1, x^2, x^3 representing distance along the axes, then $dx^1/dt, dx^2/dt, dx^3/dt$ are the components of velocity of P parallel to the axes. Under the transformation (1) we have

$$\frac{dx'^\alpha}{dt} = \sum_i \frac{\partial x'^\alpha}{\partial x^i} \frac{dx^i}{dt}. \quad (\alpha = 1, 2, 3.) \quad (4)$$

At any instant the derivatives dx^i/dt are functions of the position of P, i.e., of (x^1, x^2, x^3). Since (4) is of the form (3), dx^i/dt and dx'^α/dt are components of a contravariant tensor of order one.

Example 2. Let us regard the differentials dx^i in the coordinate system $(x^1, \cdots, x^n)$ as defined at each point $(x^1, \cdots, x^n)$, i.e., dx^i are given functions of $(x^1, \cdots, x^n)$. Then in another system $(x'^1, \cdots, x'^n)$ the differentials dx'^α are given by

* Since the range of all indices in this discussion is from 1 to n unless otherwise indicated, we shall write $\sum\limits_i$ instead of $\sum\limits_{i=1}^{n}$.

$$dx'^{\alpha} = \sum_i \frac{\partial x'^{\alpha}}{\partial x^i} dx^i. \qquad (\alpha = 1, \cdots, n.) \tag{5}$$

Since the differentials dx^i and dx'^{α} are functions of the coordinates alone, and since (5) is of the form (3), it follows that dx^i and dx'^{α} are components of a contravariant tensor of order one.

Example 3. Let $\mathfrak{F}$ and $\mathfrak{F}'$ be any two reference frames of axes with common origin O, where the axes may be orthogonal or oblique, and where the scales along the axes in each frame may be arbitrary and distinct (i.e., not based on the unit of distance), but such that the coordinates in $\mathfrak{F}$ and $\mathfrak{F}'$ are related by the transformation

$$x'^{\alpha} = \sum_i a_i^{\alpha} x^i, \tag{6}$$

where a_i^{α} are constants. Since $\partial x'^{\alpha}/\partial x^i = a_i^{\alpha}$, we see from (6) that

$$x'^{\alpha} = \sum_i \frac{\partial x'^{\alpha}}{\partial x^i} x^i.$$

Hence by (3), x^i and x'^{α} are components of a contravariant tensor of order one with respect to transformations (6). Since the coordinates x^i of a point Q transform as a contravariant tensor, it follows that we may represent the components in frame $\mathfrak{F}$ of an arbitrary contravariant tensor of order one as the coordinates in $\mathfrak{F}$ of a point Q when we consider only frames $\mathfrak{F}$ related by (6). It is common to regard the segment $\overrightarrow{OQ}$ as "representing" the tensor itself. Thus, in Example 1 consider the motion of the particle P at a certain instant. For convenience choose a frame $\mathfrak{F}$ having its origin at P at this instant. Then we may represent dx^1/dt, dx^2/dt, dx^3/dt as the coordinates in $\mathfrak{F}$ of a point Q. By the preceding remark, the coordinates of Q in any other frame $\mathfrak{F}'$ represent the transforms of dx^i/dt in $\mathfrak{F}'$, and $\overrightarrow{PQ}$ represents the tensor with components dx^i/dt. However, in curvilinear coordinate systems this representation is not always possible. Moreover, it must be remembered that dx'^{α}/dt represent the actual components of the velocity $\mathbf{V}$ in frame $\mathfrak{F}'$ only when x'^{α} represent distance. For example, if x^i is based on the unit of distance, and if $x'^i = 5x^i$, then dx'^i/dt is 5 times the component of velocity along OX^i. The question of scales and velocity components will be taken up in the next section.

DEFINITION 18.2. *If, in any manner whatever, a set of n functions $F_1(x^1, \cdots x^n), \cdots, F_n(x^1, \cdots, x^n)$ is determined for each coordinate system (1) and (2), and if these functions transform according to the law*

$$F'_\alpha = \sum_i F_i \frac{\partial x^i}{\partial x'^\alpha}, \qquad (\alpha = 1, \cdots, n.) \qquad (7)$$

then we say that the functions $F_1, \cdots, F_n$ are the components in the coordinate system $(x^1, \cdots, x^n)$ of a covariant tensor of order one, and $F'_1, \cdots, F'_n$ are the components of this tensor in the coordinate system $(x'^1, \cdots, x'^n)$.

Example 4. Let φ be a point function. If φ_i denotes $\dfrac{\partial \varphi(x^1, x^2, x^3)}{\partial x^i}$ and

if φ'_α denotes $\dfrac{\partial \varphi'(x'^1, x'^2, x'^3)}{\partial x'^\alpha}$, where $\varphi(x^1, x^2, x^3)$ and $\varphi'(x'^1, x'^2, x'^3)$ are the

representations of the point function φ in the respective coordinate systems (see Sec. 23 of Chap. I), then

$$\varphi'_\alpha = \sum_i \varphi_i \frac{\partial x^i}{\partial x'^\alpha}. \qquad (\alpha = 1, 2, 3.) \quad (8)$$

Since (8) is of the form (7), φ_i are the components of a covariant tensor of order one. We denote the tensor having these components by **grad** φ and we refer to this tensor as the *gradient* of φ.

It should be noticed that we use a superscript, as in F^i, to indicate the components of a contravariant tensor, and a subscript, as in F_i, to indicate the components of a covariant tensor.

If φ is a point function with representations $\varphi(x^1, \cdots, x^n)$ and $\varphi'(x'^1, \cdots, x'^n)$ in the respective coordinate systems indicated, then

$$\varphi'(x'^1, \cdots, x'^n) = \varphi(x^1, \cdots, x^n). \qquad (9)$$

Because of this relation between the representations of φ, we speak of φ as a *tensor of order zero*, or as a *scalar* or *invariant*.

To prove certain properties of tensors, we shall need a generalization of the result in Ex. XX, 21, of Chap. I. According to the usual rules of differentiation, we have by (2) and (1),

$$\frac{\partial x^i}{\partial x^j} = \sum_\alpha \frac{\partial x^i}{\partial x'^\alpha} \frac{\partial x'^\alpha}{\partial x^j}.$$

Let the Kronecker delta δ^i_j denote 1 when $i = j$ and 0 when $i \neq j$. Since $\partial x^i/\partial x^j = \delta^i_j$, we have

$$\sum_\alpha \frac{\partial x^i}{\partial x'^\alpha} \frac{\partial x'^\alpha}{\partial x^j} = \delta^i_j. \qquad (10)$$

It is evident, for example, that $\sum_j F^j \delta^i_j = F^i$ and that

$$\sum_i F_i \delta^i_j = F_j.$$

Example 5. If F^i and G_i are the components of any contravariant and covariant vectors respectively, then $\sum_i F^i G_i$ is a scalar point function.

To show this, we have by (3), (7), and (10),

$$F'^\alpha G'_\alpha = \left(\sum_i F^i \frac{\partial x'^\alpha}{\partial x^i} \right) \left(\sum_j G_j \frac{\partial x^j}{\partial x'^\alpha} \right) = \sum_{i,j} F^i G_j \frac{\partial x'^\alpha}{\partial x^i} \frac{\partial x^j}{\partial x'^\alpha}.$$

Hence

$$\sum_\alpha F'^\alpha G'_\alpha = \sum_{i,j} \left(\sum_\alpha F^i G_j \frac{\partial x'^\alpha}{\partial x^i} \frac{\partial x^j}{\partial x'^\alpha} \right) = \sum_{i,j} F^i G_j \delta^j_i = \sum_i F^i G_i,$$

the change of order of summation being merely a rearrangement of terms, and the last term being obtained by summing first with respect to j while treating i as fixed. Since the relation $\sum_\alpha F'^\alpha G'_\alpha = \sum_i F^i G_i$ is of the form (9), $\sum_i F^i G_i$ is a scalar point function.

THEOREM 18.1. *Let n functions G_i be determined for each coordinate system. If $\sum_i F^i G_i$ is a scalar for every contravariant vector*[*] F^i, then G_i is a covariant vector.*

By hypothesis, $\sum_\alpha F'^\alpha G'_\alpha = \sum_i F^i G_i$, that is,

$$\sum_\alpha F'^\alpha G'_\alpha - \sum_i F^i G_i = 0.$$

Since F^i is a vector, it follows by (3) that

$$\sum_\alpha \left(\sum_i F^i \frac{\partial x'^\alpha}{\partial x^i} G'_\alpha \right) - \sum_i F^i G_i$$

$$= \sum_i \left(\sum_\alpha G'_\alpha \frac{\partial x'^\alpha}{\partial x^i} F^i \right) - \sum_i F^i G_i = 0.$$

* For convenience we shall often speak of "a tensor F^i" instead of "a tensor having components F^i in the coordinate system $(x^1, \cdots , x^n)$."

Hence

$$\sum_i \left(\sum_\alpha G_\alpha' \frac{\partial x'^\alpha}{\partial x^i} - G_i \right) F^i = 0.$$

Since this relation holds for every vector F^i, the coefficients of F^i in this relation must each be zero. Hence G_i is a covariant vector. (To see this, interchange the primed and unprimed letters in (7).)

Example 6. Considering only reference frames $\mathfrak{F}$ related by (6), so that x^i is a contravariant vector, it follows by Theorem 18.1 that if the relation

$$\sum_i u_i x^i = 1 \tag{11}$$

is to hold for all frames $\mathfrak{F}$, then u_i must be a covariant tensor. (It is manifest that 1 is a scalar point function.) Now (11) is the equation of a plane not through the origin. If we define the *coordinates of a plane* to be the reciprocals of its intercepts on the coordinate axes, then u_i are the coordinates of the plane (11). Thus the coordinates of a fixed plane transform like the components of a covariant tensor. This leads us to the counterpart of the result obtained in Example 3: We may represent the components in frame $\mathfrak{F}$ of an arbitrary covariant tensor F_i of order one as the reciprocals of the intercepts in $\mathfrak{F}$ of a plane M when we consider only frames $\mathfrak{F}$ related as in (6). It is common to regard the plane M as "representing" the tensor itself.

EXERCISES XVI

1. Show by (3) that

$$F^i = \sum_\alpha F'^\alpha \frac{\partial x^i}{\partial x'^\alpha}. \tag{12}$$

Hint: Multiply each equation (3) by $\partial x^j/\partial x'^\alpha$, respectively, add the results, interchange the order of summation in the right member, and use (10). Deduce the analogous form of (7). This shows that the law of transformation of tensors has an inverse.

2. Show that if $F''^\lambda = \sum_\alpha F'^\alpha (\partial x''^\lambda / \partial x'^\alpha)$, then it follows from (3) that

$F''^\lambda = \sum_i F^i (\partial x''^\lambda / \partial x^i)$. Deduce the analogous relation for F_i. (This shows that the law of transformation of tensors is transitive.)

It follows from Exs. 1 and 2 that the components of a tensor are uniquely defined for each coordinate system, and that it is immaterial what series of transformations is followed to get from one coordinate system to another.

3. A tensor has components 1, x, $x^2 - yz$ in the (x, y, z) rectangular coordinate system. Find the components of this tensor in cylindrical, polar, and parabolic coordinates if this tensor is (a) contravariant, (b) covariant. Parabolic coordinates are given by the relations

$$x = \xi\eta \cos \varphi, \qquad y = \xi\eta \sin \varphi, \qquad z = \tfrac{1}{2}(\xi^2 - \eta^2).$$

4. Write (3) and (7) in matric form, using upper indices for row numbers and lower indices for column numbers. Note that a contravariant vector is represented by a one-column matrix and a covariant vector by a one-row matrix.

5. According to (11), $\displaystyle\sum_{\alpha} u_\alpha x'^\alpha = \sum_i u_i x^i$. Use this relation and (6) to show that $u'_\alpha = \displaystyle\sum_i A^i_\alpha u_i$, where A^i_α is $1/a$ times the cofactor of a^α_i in the determinant $a = |a^\beta_j|$. (The matrix $\|A^i_\alpha\|$ is the inverse of the matrix $\|a^\beta_j\|$.)

6. Show that if the components of a vector (either contravariant or covariant) are all zero at a point P in one coordinate system, then they are all zero at P in every coordinate system.

19. Tensors of Higher Order.   The concept of a tensor may be extended as indicated in

DEFINITION 19.1.   *If, in any manner whatever, a set of n^2 functions $F^{ij}(x^1, \cdots, x^n)$ (where $i, j = 1, \cdots, n$) is determined for each coordinate system, and if these functions transform according to the law*

$$F'^{\alpha\beta} = \sum_{i,j} F^{ij}\frac{\partial x'^\alpha}{\partial x^i}\,\frac{\partial x'^\beta}{\partial x^j}, \tag{1}$$

then we say that the functions F^{ij} are the components of a contravariant tensor of order two.   If a set of n^2 functions transforms according to the law

$$F'_{\alpha\beta} = \sum_{i,j} F_{ij}\frac{\partial x^i}{\partial x'^\alpha}\,\frac{\partial x^j}{\partial x'^\beta}, \quad \text{or} \quad F'^\alpha_\beta = \sum_{i,j} F^i_j\frac{\partial x'^\alpha}{\partial x^i}\,\frac{\partial x^j}{\partial x'^\beta}, \tag{2}$$

then F_{ij} are the components of a covariant tensor of order two, and F^i_j are the components of a mixed tensor of order two.

Tensors with components F^{ijk}, F^{ij}_{klm}, $\cdots$ are similarly defined.   The tensor F^{ij}_{klm} is of order 5; also, we say that F^{ij}_{klm} is contravariant of order 2, and covariant of order 3.

Example 1. Let F^i and G^j be contravariant vectors. If $\varphi^{ij} = F^iG^j$ and $\varphi'^{\alpha\beta} = F'^{\alpha}G'^{\beta}$, then

$$\varphi'^{\alpha\beta} = \left(\sum_i F^i \frac{\partial x'^{\alpha}}{\partial x^i}\right)\left(\sum_j F^j \frac{\partial x''^{\beta}}{\partial x^j}\right) = \sum_{i,j} \varphi^{ij} \frac{\partial x'^{\alpha}}{\partial x^i}\frac{\partial x''^{\beta}}{\partial x^j}. \tag{3}$$

Hence φ^{ij} are the components of a contravariant tensor of order two. (φ^{ij} is called the *outer product* of F^i and G^j.) However, not every tensor ψ^{ij} can be represented as a product in this way.

Example 2. The Kronecker delta δ^i_j are the components in *every* coordinate system of a mixed tensor of order two, for if δ^i_j are taken as the components of a tensor in the coordinate system $(x^1, \cdots, x^n)$, then these components transform into

$$\eta'^{\alpha}_{\beta} = \sum_{i,j} \delta^i_j \frac{\partial x'^{\alpha}}{\partial x^i}\frac{\partial x^i}{\partial x'^{\beta}} = \sum_i \frac{\partial x'^{\alpha}}{\partial x^i}\frac{\partial x^i}{\partial x'^{\beta}} = \delta^{\alpha}_{\beta}, \tag{4}$$

where in $\displaystyle\sum_{i,j}$ we sum first over j treating i as fixed. Hence δ^{α}_{β} are the components of this tensor in the system $(x'^1, \cdots, x'^n)$.

It is readily seen that *the sum or difference of two tensors of the same order and type is a tensor of this order and type.* For example, if $\varphi^{ij} = F^{ij} + G^{ij}$, then φ^{ij} is a tensor by virtue of (1).

The product of any two tensors (regardless of order or type) *is a tensor.* This is illustrated by Example 1. Again, if

$$\varphi^{ijk}_{lm} = F^{ij}G^k_{lm},$$

where F^{ij} and G^k_{lm} are tensors, then it is readily proved as in Example 1 that φ^{ijk}_{lm} is a tensor contravariant of order 3 and covariant of order 2.

If F^{ij}_{klm} are the components of a mixed tensor, then $\varphi^i_{kl} = \displaystyle\sum_j F^{ij}_{klj}$ is a set of n^3 functions, each of which is the sum of n of the functions F^{ij}_{klm}. Since

$$\varphi'^{\alpha}_{\beta\gamma} = \sum_{\delta} F'^{\alpha\delta}_{\beta\gamma\delta} = \sum_{\delta}\left(\sum_{i,j,k,l,m} F^{ij}_{klm} \frac{\partial x'^{\alpha}}{\partial x^i}\frac{\partial x'^{\delta}}{\partial x^j}\frac{\partial x^k}{\partial x'^{\beta}}\frac{\partial x^l}{\partial x'^{\gamma}}\frac{\partial x^m}{\partial x'^{\delta}}\right)$$

$$= \sum_{i,j,k,l,m} F^{ij}_{klm}\delta^m_j \frac{\partial x'^{\alpha}}{\partial x^i}\frac{\partial x^k}{\partial x'^{\beta}}\frac{\partial x^l}{\partial x'^{\gamma}} = \sum_{i,k,l}\left(\sum_j F^{ij}_{klj}\right)\frac{\partial x'^{\alpha}}{\partial x^i}\frac{\partial x^k}{\partial x'^{\beta}}\frac{\partial x^l}{\partial x'^{\gamma}},$$

where $\displaystyle\sum_j F^{ij}_{klj} = \varphi^i_{kl}$, it follows that φ^i_{kl} are the components of a tensor. The process of summing the components of a tensor of order r over any contravariant and covariant index is called *contraction*, and the resulting functions are the components of a tensor of order $r - 2$. A contracted tensor may evidently be contracted again; for example, $\psi_l = \sum_i \varphi_{il}^i$ are the components of a covariant vector. If we contract the tensor δ_j^i we obtain the scalar $\sum_i \delta_i^i = n$.

Since tensors may be multiplied and contracted to give tensors, we may combine the two operations to obtain new tensors. For example,

$$\varphi_{kl}^i = \sum_j F^{ij}G_{jkl}, \qquad \psi^{ijl} = \sum_k F_k G^{ijkl}, \qquad \theta_{il} = \sum_{j,k} F^{jk}G_{ijkl}$$

are components of tensors. The combined process of multiplication and contraction is called *inner multiplication*.

If F_{klm}^{ij} is a tensor, and if, for example, $F_{klm}^{ij} = F_{mlk}^{ij}$ for every set of values of the indices, then F_{klm}^{ij} is said to be *symmetric* in the indices k and m. If a tensor is symmetric in every pair of contravariant indices and in every pair of covariant indices, then the tensor is said to be *symmetric*. If interchange of any pair of indices of the same type causes merely a change of sign of the component in question, then the tensor is called *skew symmetric*.

Example 3. If g_{ij} is a covariant tensor, then because dx^i is a contravariant tensor (see Example 2 of Sec. 18), $\sum_{i,j} g_{ij}\, dx^i dx^j$ is an invariant (scalar point function), i.e.,

$$\sum_{\alpha,\beta} g'_{\alpha\beta}\, dx'^\alpha\, dx'^\beta = \sum_{i,j} g_{ij}\, dx^i\, dx^j. \tag{5}$$

If $(x^1, \cdots, x^n)$ are rectangular coordinates with each coordinate representing distance along the respective axis, then the element of arc-length is

$$ds^2 = (dx^1)^2 + (dx^2)^2 + \cdots + (dx^n)^2.$$

If we define g_{ij} in this coordinate system by the relations

$$g_{ij} = \begin{cases} 1 & \text{when} \quad i = j, \\ 0 & \text{when} \quad i \neq j, \end{cases} \tag{6}$$

then

$$ds^2 = \sum_{i,j} g_{ij}\, dx^i\, dx^j. \tag{7}$$

If we now use (6) to define g_{ij} as a covariant tensor for all other coordinate systems by the first part of (2), then, because of (5), (7) holds in *every* coordinate system (see Ex. XVII, 7). The tensor g_{ij} in (7) is called the *fundamental metric tensor* for n-dimensional Euclidean space, and ds is the *magnitude* of the tensor with components dx^i.

Example 4. In rectangular coordinates (based on the unit of distance) the *magnitude* F of the vector with components F^i is given by

$$F^2 = \sum_{i,j} g_{ij} F^i F^j, \tag{8}$$

where g_{ij} is given by (6). Since $\sum_{i,j} g_{ij} F^i F^j$ is an invariant, F is a scalar point function and (8) gives the magnitude F of the tensor F^i in every coordinate system. We say that F^i is a *unit tensor* if $F = 1$. In the same manner, the scalar product $\sum_{i,j} g_{ij} F^i G^j$ of the tensors F^i and G^j is an invariant for every coordinate system. Since in rectangular coordinates we have

$$FG \cos \theta = \sum_{i,j} g_{ij} F^i G^j, \tag{9}$$

where θ is the angle between the vectors F^i and G^j, it follows that $FG \cos \theta$, and hence $\cos \theta$, is an invariant for all coordinate systems; however, θ has as yet no interpretation in curvilinear coordinates since we have as yet no geometric representation for a tensor F^i in curvilinear coordinates. We now give this representation in

Theorem 19.1. *Let F^i be the components of a tensor in an arbitrary coordinate system $(x^1, \cdots, x^n)$. Let each component F^i be represented at any point P by a line segment $\overrightarrow{PP^i}$ along the tangent at P to the parametric curve of parameter x^i (i.e., the curve with equations $x^j = $ constant for all $j \neq i$, x^i alone being variable), the length of $\overrightarrow{PP^i}$ being the magnitude of the component F^i. Then the vector sum $\overrightarrow{PQ}$ of all the line segments $\overrightarrow{PP^i}$ represents the given tensor in every coordinate system.*

The magnitude of the component F^i is computed as the magnitude of the tensor with components

$$0, 0, \cdots, 0, F^i, 0, \cdots, 0. \tag{10}$$

By (8),

$$|F^i|^2 = (\text{magnitude of } F^i)^2 = g_{ii} F^i F^i, \tag{11}$$

since all the F's in (8) are 0 except F^i. By (9), we have for two different tensors of the type indicated in (10),

$$|F^i| \cdot |F^j|(\cos \theta)_{ij} = g_{ij}F^iF^j, \tag{12}$$

where θ is as yet undefined.   By (11) and (12),

$$F^2 = \sum_{i,j} g_{ij}F^iF^j = \sum_i |F^i|^2 + \sum_{i \neq j} |F^i| \cdot |F^j|(\cos \theta)_{ij}, \tag{13}$$

where in $\displaystyle\sum_{i,j}$ we sum first for equal i, j and then for distinct i, j.

But if we regard $\overrightarrow{PP^i}$ and $\overrightarrow{PQ}$ as vectors (in the elementary sense),

$$\overrightarrow{PQ}^2 = \left(\sum_i \overrightarrow{PP^i}\right) \cdot \left(\sum_i \overrightarrow{PP^i}\right)$$

$$= \sum_i (\overrightarrow{PP^i})^2 + \sum_{i \neq j} (\overrightarrow{PP^i})(\overrightarrow{PP^j}) \cos (\theta_{ij}), \tag{14}$$

where $\cdot$ indicates the elementary scalar product and θ_{ij} is the angle between $\overrightarrow{PP^i}$ and $\overrightarrow{PP^j}$.   Since (13) and (14) hold for every tensor F^i, $(\cos \theta)_{ij} = \cos (\theta_{ij})$ and the theorem follows at once.

In applying Theorem 19.1 care must be taken to distinguish between the *magnitude* of a component F^i [which by (8) is invariant for all scales in all coordinate systems] and the *numerical value* of F^i (which depends, for example, upon the scales of the variables x^i).

If the tensor F^i has components of unit magnitude, then by (11), $F^i = 1/\sqrt{g_{ii}}$ since $|F^i| = 1$, and by (12),

$$\cos \theta_{ij} = \frac{g_{ij}}{\sqrt{g_{ii}g_{jj}}}. \tag{15}$$

Let g_{ij} be any symmetric covariant tensor.   We write

$$g = \begin{vmatrix} g_{11} & \cdots & g_{1n} \\ \cdot & & \cdot \\ \cdot & & \cdot \\ \cdot & & \cdot \\ g_{n1} & \cdots & g_{nn} \end{vmatrix}, \qquad g^{ij} = \frac{1}{g} \text{ (cofactor of } g_{ij} \text{ in } g). \tag{16}$$

It is readily proved that g^{ij} is symmetric (see Ex. XVII, 9). Moreover, $\displaystyle\sum_k g_{jk}g^{ik}$ is $1/g$ times the expansion of the determinant obtained by replacing the ith row in g by the jth row.   By Theorem 1.10,

$$\sum_k g_{jk}g^{ik} = \delta_j^i. \tag{17}$$

If F^i is an arbitrary vector, then $G_j = \sum_k g_{jk}F^k$ is an arbitrary vector. Since g_{ij} and g^{ij} are symmetric, we have by (17),

$$\sum_j g^{ij}G_j = \sum_{j,k} g^{ij}(g_{jk}F^k) = \sum_k \delta_k^i F^k = F^i. \tag{18}$$

Since F^i is a vector, it follows by Ex. XVII, 10 that g^{ij} is a tensor.

If F^i is a given contravariant tensor, then $F_j \equiv \sum_i g_{ij}F^i$ is a covariant tensor. Since g_{ij} is symmetric, $F_j = \sum_i g_{ji}F^i$. We call F_j the *tensor associated with* F^i, and we speak of the components F_j as the *covariant components* of the tensor with contravariant components F^i. Let A^i be the tensor associated with F_j by the law $A^i = \sum_j g^{ij}F_j$. If $F_j = \sum_k g_{jk}F^k$, then by (17),

$$A^i = \sum_j g^{ij}F_j = \sum_{j,k} g^{ij}g_{jk}F^k = \sum_k \delta_k^i F^k = F^i.$$

Hence contracting with respect to g_{ij} and g^{ij} are inverse operations, and the roles of F^i and F_j are interchangeable. In rectangular coordinates where g_{ij} is given by (6) and g^{ij} is numerically equal to g_{ij}, F^i and F_j are numerically equal. This accounts for the fact that no distinction was made between contravariant and covariant vectors in Part B of this chapter.

The idea of associated tensors may be generalized; for example, if

$$F^i{}_j = \sum_k F^{ik}g_{jk}, \qquad \text{or} \qquad G_i{}^j{}_k = \sum_l G_{ilk}g^{jl},$$

then $F^i{}_j$ and F^{ik} are associated, and $G_i{}^j{}_k$ and G_{ilk} are associated. Note that the indices should be spaced to show which index is raised or lowered, for, in general, tensors like $F^i{}_j = \sum_k F^{ik}g_{jk}$ and $\varphi_j{}^i = \sum_k F^{ki}g_{kj}$ are not the same.

Example 5. In rectangular coordinates, where g_{ij} are given by (6), we have

$$g^{ij} = \begin{cases} 1 & \text{when} & i = j, \\ 0 & \text{when} & i \neq j. \end{cases}$$

If F_i are the components in a rectangular coordinate system of a covariant tensor, if p is the distance from the origin to the plane M representing F_i (see Example 6 of Sec. 18), and if we define the magnitude F of the tensor with components F_i to be $1/p$, then in rectangular coordinates we have

$$F^2 = \sum_{i,j} g^{ij} F_i F_j, \tag{19}$$

as may be seen by writing the equation of the plane M in normal form. Since $\sum_{i,j} g^{ij} F_i F_j$ is an invariant, (19) gives the magnitude F in *every* coordinate system. If F^i is the associate vector of F_i, and if in (8) and (19) the summation is carried out over j, then both of these equations may be written as

$$F^2 = \sum_i F^i F_i, \tag{20}$$

showing that the magnitude of a vector and its associate is the same. In rectangular coordinates, the components F_i are direction numbers of a normal N upon the plane M representing the tensor F_i; moreover, in rectangular coordinates, the associate vectors F_i and F^i are numerically the same. Hence the line segment representing F^i is parallel to N. It follows that the angle θ between the planes representing F_i and G_i is equal to the angle θ between the line segments representing F^i and G^i. Thus, by (9),

$$\sum_{i,j} g^{ij} F_i G_j = \sum_j F^i G_j = \sum_j F_j G^j = \sum_{i,j} g_{ij} F^i G^i = FG \cos \theta, \tag{21}$$

this relation holding in *every* coordinate system.

If a set of functions transforms, for example, by the law

$$F'^{\alpha} = J^p \sum_i F^i \frac{\partial x'^{\alpha}}{\partial x^i}, \quad \text{or} \quad F_{\gamma}'^{\alpha\beta} = J^p \sum_{i,j,k} F_k^{ij} \frac{\partial x'^{\alpha}}{\partial x^i} \frac{\partial x'^{\beta}}{\partial x^j} \frac{\partial x^k}{\partial x'^{\gamma}},$$

where J is the Jacobian $\dfrac{\partial(x^1, \cdots, x^n)}{\partial(x'^1, \cdots, x'^n)}$ of the coordinate transformation, then these functions are called the *components of a relative tensor of weight p.* It is evident that the sum of two relative tensors of the same type and weight p is again a relative tensor of this same type and weight p. The product of any two relative tensors of weights p and q, respectively, is a relative tensor of weight $p + q$. Contraction of a relative tensor does not alter its weight.

Example 6. Let

$$e^{ijk} = e_{ijk} = \begin{cases} 1 \text{ when } ijk \text{ is an even permutation of } 123, \\ -1 \text{ when } ijk \text{ is an odd permutation of } 123, \\ 0 \text{ when two or more of the indices } ijk \text{ are equal.} \end{cases}$$

It follows from Sec. 1, (2), that

$$e^{\alpha\beta\gamma} \begin{vmatrix} a_1^1 & a_2^1 & a_3^1 \\ a_1^2 & a_2^2 & a_3^2 \\ a_1^3 & a_2^3 & a_3^3 \end{vmatrix} = \sum_{i,j,k} e^{ijk} a_i^\alpha a_j^\beta a_k^\gamma, \tag{22}$$

$$e_{\alpha\beta\gamma} \begin{vmatrix} a_1^1 & a_2^1 & a_3^1 \\ a_1^2 & a_2^2 & a_3^2 \\ a_1^3 & a_2^3 & a_3^3 \end{vmatrix} = \sum_{i,j,k} e_{ijk} a_\alpha^i a_\beta^j a_\gamma^k, \tag{23}$$

where all indices range over 1, 2, 3. The symbols $e^{ii\cdots n} = e_{ij\ldots n}$ with n indices may be defined in a similar manner and may be used to represent the expansion of determinants of order n. If we divide both sides of (23) by the coefficient of $e_{\alpha\beta\gamma}$ and replace a_α^i by $\partial x^i / \partial x'^\alpha$, we have

$$J^{-1} \sum_{i,j,k} e_{ijk} \frac{\partial x^i}{\partial x'^\alpha} \frac{\partial x^i}{\partial x'^\beta} \frac{\partial x^k}{\partial x'^\gamma} = e_{\alpha\beta\gamma}, \tag{24}$$

where $J = \dfrac{\partial(x^1, x^2, x^3)}{\partial(x'^1, x'^2, x'^3)}$. Hence in three-dimensional space e_{ijk} are the components in every coordinate system of a third order covariant relative tensor of weight -1. By Ex. XXI, 14, of Chap. I, $\dfrac{\partial(x'^1, x'^2, x'^3)}{\partial(x^1, x^2, x^3)} = J^{-1}$. Hence it may be shown [as in (24)] that in three-dimensional space e^{ijk} is a relative tensor of weight $+1$. In n-dimensional space, $e_{ij\ldots n}$ and $e^{ii\cdots n}$ (with n indices) are the components in every coordinate system of relative tensors of weights -1 and $+1$.

Example 7. If g_{ij} is a covariant tensor in three-dimensional space, and if

$$g = \begin{vmatrix} g_{11} & g_{12} & g_{13} \\ g_{21} & g_{22} & g_{23} \\ g_{31} & g_{32} & g_{33} \end{vmatrix},$$

then g is a scalar of weight $+2$, for by Example 6,

$$g' = \sum_{\alpha,\beta,\gamma} e^{\alpha\beta\gamma} g'_{1\alpha} g'_{2\beta} g'_{3\gamma}$$

$$= J \sum_{\substack{\alpha,\beta,\gamma \\ i,j,k \\ l,m,n,p,q,r}} e^{ijk} g_{lm} g_{np} g_{qr} \frac{\partial x'^{\alpha}}{\partial x^i} \frac{\partial x'^{\beta}}{\partial x^j} \frac{\partial x'^{\gamma}}{\partial x^k} \frac{\partial x^l}{\partial x'^1} \frac{\partial x^m}{\partial x'^{\alpha}} \frac{\partial x^n}{\partial x'^2} \frac{\partial x^p}{\partial x'^{\beta}} \frac{\partial x^q}{\partial x'^3} \frac{\partial x^r}{\partial x'^{\gamma}}$$

$$= J \sum_{\substack{i,j,k \\ l,m,n,p,q,r}} e^{ijk} g_{lm} g_{np} g_{qr} \delta_i^m \delta_j^p \delta_k^r \frac{\partial x^l}{\partial x'^1} \frac{\partial x^n}{\partial x'^2} \frac{\partial x^q}{\partial x'^3}$$

$$= J \sum_{l,m,n,p,q,r} e^{mpr} g_{lm} g_{np} g_{qr} \frac{\partial x^l}{\partial x'^1} \frac{\partial x^n}{\partial x'^2} \frac{\partial x^q}{\partial x'^3} = J \sum_{l,n,q} g e_{lnq} \frac{\partial x^l}{\partial x'^1} \frac{\partial x^n}{\partial x'^2} \frac{\partial x^q}{\partial x'^3}$$

$$= JgJ = J^2 g.$$

It follows at once that $\sqrt{g}$ is a scalar of weight $+1$. Hence in three-dimensional space $\sqrt{g} e_{ijk}$ is a tensor of weight 0, i.e., an ordinary or *absolute* tensor. It may be shown in a similar manner that, if g_{ij} is a tensor in n-dimensional space, then $\sqrt{g} e_{ij\ldots n}$ (n indices) is an absolute tensor in n-dimensional space. Since $1/g' = J^{-2}(1/g)$, $1/\sqrt{g}$ is of weight -1 and $(1/\sqrt{g})e^{ij\ldots n}$ is an absolute tensor in n-dimensional space. For brevity, we shall write

$$\epsilon_{ij\ldots n} = \sqrt{g} e_{ij\ldots n}, \qquad \epsilon^{ij\ldots n} = \frac{1}{\sqrt{g}} e^{ij\ldots n}, \tag{25}$$

where $g = 1$ in rectangular coordinates.

Example 8. In rectangular coordinates in three-dimensional space,

$$\varphi^i = \sum_{j,k} \epsilon^{ijk} F_j G_k = FG \sin\theta \, v^i \tag{26}$$

is the *vector product* of the vectors F_j and G_k, where v^i is a unit vector orthogonal to F_i and G_i. Because (26) is in tensor form, it defines φ^i in every coordinate system.

EXERCISES XVII

1. State the law of transformation for the tensor F^i_{jkl}.

2. (a) Prove the statements made in the two paragraphs following Example 2.

(b) Prove the properties stated of relative tensors.

3. (a) Show that if the components of a tensor are symmetric (skew symmetric) in one coordinate system, then they are symmetric (skew symmetric) in every coordinate system.

(b) Show that if a_{ij} is any tensor, then $a_{ij} + a_{ji}$ is a symmetric tensor and $a_{ij} - a_{ji}$ is a skew-symmetric tensor. Represent a_{ij} as the sum of a symmetric and a skew-symmetric tensor.

4. Prove relation (5) directly from the tensor laws of transformation.

5. Show that if F^{ijklm}_{npq} is a tensor, then $\sum_l F^{ijklm}_{npl}$ and $\sum_{i,l} F^{ijklm}_{nil}$ are tensors.

6. Show that φ^i_{kl}, ψ^{ijl}, and θ_{il} (preceding Example 3) are tensors if F^{ij}, G_{jkl}, $\cdots$, are tensors.

7. (a) If (r, θ) are polar coordinates (r based on the unit of distance, θ in radians), find g_{ij} and ds^2. If s_r and s_θ represent arc length along the parametric curves, find ds_r and ds_θ as the magnitudes of dr and $d\theta$. Represent your results geometrically, and illustrate the significance of Theorem 19.1.

(b) Prove the following formulas:

$$ds^2 = dr^2 + r^2\, d\theta^2 + r^2 \sin^2\theta\, d\phi^2 \text{ in spherical polar coordinates.}$$
$$ds^2 = dr^2 + r^2\, d\theta^2 + dz^2 \text{ in cylindrical coordinates.}$$
$$ds^2 = (\xi^2 + \eta^2)(d\xi^2 + d\eta^2) + \xi^2\eta^2\, d\varphi^2 \text{ in parabolic coordinates.}$$

In each case find the differential of arc length along the parametric curves, represent your results geometrically, and illustrate the significance of Theorem 19.1.

8. A coordinate system is called *orthogonal* if $g_{ij} = 0$ for $i \neq j$ in this system. Find ds^2 and θ_{ij} in such a system. Show that $g^{ii} = 1/g_{ii}$, $g^{ij} = 0$ for $i \neq j$.

9. If g_{ij} is symmetric, show that g^{ij} is symmetric.

10. Show that if the set of functions F^{ij} is such that $\sum_j F^{ij}G_j$ is a vector for every vector G_j, then F^{ij} is a tensor. Generalize this result.

11. If g^{ij} is any (absolute) contravariant tensor, show that the determinant $|g^{ij}|$ is an invariant of weight -2.

12. (a) If $F^i_{(\lambda)}$, are vectors in three-dimensional space, where (λ) serves merely to distinguish the various vectors, $\lambda = 1, 2, 3$, show that the determinant $|F^i_{(\lambda)}|$ is an invariant of weight -1.

(b) Give the analogue of part (a) for covariant vectors.

13. If F^i_j is a mixed tensor, show that the cofactors of the determinant $|\mathrm{F}^i_j|$ are the components of a tensor.

14. Show that if $a_{ij}F^iF^j$ is an invariant for every vector F^i, then the quantities $a_{ij} + a_{ji}$ are the components of a tensor.

15. Show that in oblique Cartesian coordinates $g_{ij} = \cos\theta_{ij}$, where θ_{ij} is the angle between OX^i and OX^j, and where $\theta_{ii} = 0$ for all i.

16. If λ^i and μ^i are unit vectors, and if θ is the angle between them, show that

$$\sin^2\theta = \sum_{i,j,m,n} (g_{ij}g_{mn} - g_{im}g_{jn})\lambda^i\lambda^j\mu^m\mu^n.$$

17. Show that $\epsilon_{ij\cdots n}$ and $\epsilon^{ij\cdots n}$ are associated tensors. (Hint: In three dimensions, $ge_{\alpha\beta\gamma} = \sum_{i,j,k} e^{ijk}g_{\alpha i}g_{\beta j}g_{\gamma k}$.)

18. Show that g_{ij}, g^{ij}, and δ^i_j are associate tensors.

19. In three-dimensional space if F^i is the associate of F_i, and G^i that of G_i, and if $\varphi^{ii} = F^iG^j - F^jG^i$, show that φ^{ii} is skew symmetric and that $\sum_{j,k} \frac{1}{2}\epsilon_{ijk}\varphi^{ik}$ are the covariant components of the vector product of F_i and G_i.

20. (a) In three-dimensional space, if F^{ii} is a skew-symmetric contravariant tensor, show that $\sqrt{g}F^{23}$, $\sqrt{g}F^{31}$, $\sqrt{g}F^{12}$ are the components of the covariant vector $\sum_{j,k} \frac{1}{2}\epsilon_{ijk}F^{ik}$.

(b) If G_{ij} is a skew-symmetric covariant tensor, show that $(1/\sqrt{g})G_{23}$, $(1/\sqrt{g})G_{31}$, $(1/\sqrt{g})G_{12}$ are the components of a contravariant vector.

(c) If G_{ij} is skew-symmetric, and if $\varphi^i = \sum_{j,k} \epsilon^{iik}G_{ij}$, show that

$$G_{ij} = \frac{1}{2}\sum_k \epsilon_{ijk}\varphi^k.$$

21. If λ^i is a unit vector, show that the cosines of the angles it makes with the parametric lines are $(1/\sqrt{g_{ii}})\lambda_i$.

22. In three dimensional space, show that the element of volume in any coordinate system is given by

$$dV = \sqrt{g}\, dx^1\, dx^2\, dx^3,$$

where g is given by (16) with g_{ij} the fundamental metric tensor.

20. The Covariant Derivative.

It was shown in Example 4 of Sec. 18 that $F_i \equiv \partial F/\partial x^i$ are the components of a covariant tensor when F is a point function. However, if F_i is an arbitrary covariant tensor of order one, it is not the case that the n^2 functions $\partial F_i/\partial x^j$ are the components of a tensor, for

$$\frac{\partial F'_\alpha}{\partial x'^\beta} = \frac{\partial}{\partial x'^\beta}\sum_k F_k \frac{\partial x^k}{\partial x'^\alpha} = \sum_k\left[\left(\sum_j \frac{\partial F_k}{\partial x^j}\frac{\partial x^j}{\partial x'^\beta}\right)\frac{\partial x^k}{\partial x'^\alpha} + F_k \frac{\partial^2 x^k}{\partial x'^\alpha\, \partial x'^\beta}\right].$$

$$(1)$$

The presence of the last term shows that $\partial F_k/\partial x^j$ does not transform as a covariant tensor. We shall now define a quantity $F_{i,j}$ (in terms of $\partial F_i/\partial x^j$) which transforms according to the tensor law. Let g_{ij}, g, and g^{ij} be the tensors in (16) of Sec. 19. The quantities

$$[ij,\, k] = \frac{1}{2}\left(\frac{\partial g_{ik}}{\partial x^j} + \frac{\partial g_{jk}}{\partial x^i} - \frac{\partial g_{ij}}{\partial x^k}\right), \qquad \left\{\begin{matrix} k \\ ij \end{matrix}\right\} = \sum_l g^{kl}\, [ij,\, l] \quad (2)$$

are called the *Christoffel symbols of the first and second kinds*. These quantities are evidently symmetric in i and j (since g_{ij} is symmetric). From the relation

$$g'_{\alpha\beta} = \sum_{i,j} g_{ij} \frac{\partial x^i}{\partial x'^{\alpha}} \frac{\partial x^j}{\partial x'^{\beta}},$$

with similar formulas for $g'_{\alpha\delta}$ and $g'_{\beta\delta}$, we have

$$\frac{\partial g'_{\alpha\beta}}{\partial x'^{\delta}} = \sum_{i,j,l} \frac{\partial g_{ij}}{\partial x^l} \frac{\partial x^l}{\partial x'^{\delta}} \frac{\partial x^i}{\partial x'^{\alpha}} \frac{\partial x^j}{\partial x'^{\beta}}$$
$$+ \sum_{i,j} g_{ij}\left[\frac{\partial^2 x^i}{\partial x'^{\delta} \partial x'^{\alpha}} \frac{\partial x^j}{\partial x'^{\beta}} + \frac{\partial x^i}{\partial x'^{\alpha}} \frac{\partial^2 x^j}{\partial x'^{\delta} \partial x'^{\beta}} \right],$$

$$\frac{\partial g'_{\alpha\delta}}{\partial x'^{\beta}} = \sum_{i,j,l} \frac{\partial g_{il}}{\partial x^j} \frac{\partial x^j}{\partial x'^{\beta}} \frac{\partial x^i}{\partial x'^{\alpha}} \frac{\partial x^l}{\partial x'^{\delta}}$$
$$+ \sum_{i,l} g_{il}\left[\frac{\partial^2 x^i}{\partial x'^{\beta} \partial x'^{\alpha}} \frac{\partial x^l}{\partial x'^{\delta}} + \frac{\partial x^i}{\partial x'^{\alpha}} \frac{\partial^2 x^l}{\partial x'^{\beta} \partial x'^{\delta}} \right],$$

$$\frac{\partial g'_{\beta\delta}}{\partial x'^{\alpha}} = \sum_{i,j,l} \frac{\partial g_{jl}}{\partial x^i} \frac{\partial x^i}{\partial x'^{\alpha}} \frac{\partial x^j}{\partial x'^{\beta}} \frac{\partial x^l}{\partial x'^{\delta}}$$
$$+ \sum_{j,l} g_{jl}\left[\frac{\partial^2 x^i}{\partial x'^{\alpha} \partial x'^{\beta}} \frac{\partial x^l}{\partial x'^{\delta}} + \frac{\partial x^j}{\partial x'^{\beta}} \frac{\partial^2 x^l}{\partial x'^{\alpha} \partial x'^{\delta}} \right].$$

Since the second sum in each of these equations may be written with summation indices i and j, we may combine these equations to show that

$$[\alpha\beta, \delta]' = \sum_{i,j,l} [ij, l] \frac{\partial x^i}{\partial x'^{\alpha}} \frac{\partial x^j}{\partial x'^{\beta}} \frac{\partial x^l}{\partial x'^{\delta}} + \sum_{i,j} g_{ij} \frac{\partial^2 x^i}{\partial x'^{\alpha} \partial x'^{\beta}} \frac{\partial x^j}{\partial x'^{\delta}}. \quad (3)$$

If we multiply both sides of (3) by $g'^{\gamma\delta} \, \partial x^k / \partial x'^{\gamma}$ and sum over γ and δ, we find that

$$\sum_{\gamma} \left\{ \begin{matrix} \gamma \\ \alpha\beta \end{matrix} \right\}' \frac{\partial x^k}{\partial x'^{\gamma}} = \sum_{i,j} \left\{ \begin{matrix} k \\ ij \end{matrix} \right\} \frac{\partial x^i}{\partial x'^{\alpha}} \frac{\partial x^j}{\partial x'^{\beta}} + \frac{\partial^2 x^k}{\partial x'^{\alpha} \partial x'^{\beta}}, \quad (4)$$

since $\displaystyle\sum_{\gamma,\delta} g'^{\gamma\delta} \frac{\partial x^k}{\partial x'^{\gamma}} \frac{\partial x^l}{\partial x'^{\delta}} = g^{kl}$, and $\displaystyle\sum_{j} g_{ij} g^{kj} = \delta_i^k$. If we solve (4) for $\partial^2 x^k/\partial x'^{\alpha}\,\partial x'^{\beta}$ and substitute the result in (1), we have

$$\frac{\partial F'_{\alpha}}{\partial x'^{\beta}} = \sum_{k,j}\frac{\partial F_k}{\partial x^j}\frac{\partial x^k}{\partial x'^{\alpha}}\frac{\partial x^j}{\partial x'^{\beta}}$$

$$+ \sum_{\gamma}\left(\sum_k F_k\frac{\partial x^k}{\partial x'^{\gamma}}\right)\left\{\begin{matrix}\gamma\\ \alpha\beta\end{matrix}\right\}' - \sum_{i,j}\sum_k F_k\left\{\begin{matrix}k\\ ij\end{matrix}\right\}\frac{\partial x^i}{\partial x'^{\alpha}}\frac{\partial x^j}{\partial x'^{\beta}}.$$

In the first term we may change the summation index k to i. If we collect the first and last terms, and transpose the middle term, we have

$$\frac{\partial F'_{\alpha}}{\partial x'^{\beta}} - \sum_{\gamma}F'_{\gamma}\left\{\begin{matrix}\gamma\\ \alpha\beta\end{matrix}\right\}' = \sum_{i,j}\left(\frac{\partial F_i}{\partial x^j} - \sum_k F_k\left\{\begin{matrix}k\\ ij\end{matrix}\right\}\right)\frac{\partial x^i}{\partial x'^{\alpha}}\frac{\partial x^j}{\partial x'^{\beta}}. \quad (5)$$

Thus the quantity

$$F_{i,j} \equiv \frac{\partial F_i}{\partial x^j} - \sum_k F_k\left\{\begin{matrix}k\\ ij\end{matrix}\right\} \quad (6)$$

transforms as a second order covariant tensor. We call the tensor $F_{i,j}$ the *covariant derivative of the tensor F_i with respect to the tensor g_{ij}*. It may be shown in a similar manner that

$$F^i_{,j} \equiv \frac{\partial F^i}{\partial x^j} + \sum_k F^k\left\{\begin{matrix}i\\ jk\end{matrix}\right\} \quad (7)$$

is a mixed tensor. We call $F^i_{,j}$ the *covariant derivative of F^i with respect to g_{ij}*. Since

$$\left\{\begin{matrix}k\\ ij\end{matrix}\right\} = \left\{\begin{matrix}k\\ ji\end{matrix}\right\}, \quad (8)$$

$F_{i,j}$ is symmetric if and only if $\partial F_i/\partial x^j = \partial F_j/\partial x^i$, i.e., when F_i is the gradient of a scalar point function F. By (8),

$$F_{i,j} - F_{j,i} = \frac{\partial F_i}{\partial x^j} - \frac{\partial F_j}{\partial x^i}. \quad (9)$$

We call this quantity the *curl* of the vector F_i. Since the difference between two tensors is a tensor, the quantity (9) is a tensor. In three-dimensional space the quantity

$$\varphi^k = \sum_{i,j}\epsilon^{kji}F_{i,j} \quad (10)$$

is a contravariant vector.   In rectangular coordinates the components of φ^i reduce to the quantities given in (21) of Sec. 11 since $\sqrt{g} = 1$.   (In Part B of this chapter we omitted the proof of the fact that φ^k were the components of a vector.   We have now supplied this proof by tensor methods.)   In general orthogonal coordinates (u, v, w), g_{ij} have the values

$$g_{11} = e_1^2, \qquad g_{22} = e_2^2, \qquad g_{33} = e_3^2, \qquad g_{ij} = 0 \text{ when } i \neq j;$$
$$ds^2 = e_1^2 \, du^2 + e_2^2 \, dv^2 + e_3^2 \, dw^2, \tag{11}$$

where e_1, e_2, e_3 are functions of (u, v, w).   By (10) the components of φ^i are

$$\varphi^1 = \frac{1}{\sqrt{g}}\left(\frac{\partial F_3}{\partial v} - \frac{\partial F_2}{\partial w}\right), \qquad \varphi^2 = \frac{1}{\sqrt{g}}\left(\frac{\partial F_1}{\partial w} - \frac{\partial F_3}{\partial u}\right),$$
$$\varphi^3 = \frac{1}{\sqrt{g}}\left(\frac{\partial F_2}{\partial u} - \frac{\partial F_1}{\partial v}\right). \tag{12}$$

(This relation holds for arbitrary coordinates.)   Let $\mathfrak{F}_i$ denote the magnitude of the component F_i, so that $\mathfrak{F}_i = \sqrt{g^{ii}}F_i$.   By Ex. XVII, 8, $F_i = e_i\mathfrak{F}_i$.   If we denote the vector with components φ^i by curl F (not to be confused with the general concept of curl given above), and if we denote the magnitude of φ^i by $(\text{curl } F)^i$, so that $(\text{curl } F)^i = e_i\varphi^i$, we have

$$(\text{curl } F)^1 = \frac{1}{e_2 e_3}\left\{\frac{\partial (e_3\mathfrak{F}_3)}{\partial v} - \frac{\partial (e_2\mathfrak{F}_2)}{\partial w}\right\},$$
$$(\text{curl } F)^2 = \frac{1}{e_3 e_1}\left\{\frac{\partial (e_1\mathfrak{F}_1)}{\partial w} - \frac{\partial (e_3\mathfrak{F}_3)}{\partial u}\right\}, \tag{13}$$
$$(\text{curl } F)^3 = \frac{1}{e_1 e_2}\left\{\frac{\partial (e_2\mathfrak{F}_2)}{\partial u} - \frac{\partial (e_1\mathfrak{F}_1)}{\partial v}\right\}.$$

The *divergence* of the vector F^i is taken to be $\sum_i F^i{}_{,i}$.   By (6),

$$\sum_i F^i{}_{,i} = \sum_i \left(\frac{\partial F^i}{\partial x^i} + \sum_j F^j \left\{\begin{matrix} i \\ ij \end{matrix}\right\}\right)$$
$$= \sum_i \frac{\partial F^i}{\partial x^i} + \sum_j \left(\sum_{i,l} F^j \frac{1}{2} g^{il}\left(\frac{\partial g_{il}}{\partial x^j} + \frac{\partial g_{jl}}{\partial x^i} - \frac{\partial g_{ij}}{\partial x^l}\right)\right). \tag{14}$$

Since $g_{mn} = g_{nm}$, $\quad \sum_i \sum_l g^{il}(\partial g_{il}/\partial x^i) = \sum_l \sum_i g^{il}(\partial g_{ij}/\partial x^l)$, and the last two terms of the last sum cancel out (after summation). Moreover,

$$\sum_{i,l} \frac{1}{2} g^{il} \frac{\partial g_{il}}{\partial x^i} = \frac{1}{2g} \frac{\partial}{\partial x^i} g = \frac{1}{\sqrt{g}} \frac{\partial}{\partial x^j} \sqrt{g}.$$

Hence (14) reduces to

$$\sum_i \frac{\partial F^i}{\partial x^i} + \sum_j F^j \frac{1}{\sqrt{g}} \frac{\partial}{\partial x^j} \sqrt{g}. \tag{15}$$

Thus the divergence of the vector F^i is given by

$$\sum_i F^i_{,i} = \frac{1}{\sqrt{g}} \sum_i \frac{\partial}{\partial x^i} (F^i \sqrt{g}). \tag{16}$$

In any coordinate system for which g is constant, this expression reduces to the form given in (10) of Sec. 11. If $\mathfrak{F}^i$ denotes the magnitude of the component F^i, so that by (11), $\mathfrak{F}^i = \frac{1}{e_i} F^i$, (16) reduces for orthogonal coordinates in three-dimensional space to the form

$$\text{div } F = \frac{1}{e_1 e_2 e_3}\left[\frac{\partial}{\partial u}(e_2 e_3 \mathfrak{F}_1) + \frac{\partial}{\partial v}(e_3 e_1 \mathfrak{F}_2) + \frac{\partial}{\partial w}(e_1 e_2 \mathfrak{F}_3) \right]. \tag{17}$$

Since the magnitude of the ith component of grad U is $\frac{1}{e_i}\frac{\partial U}{\partial x^i}$, we have

$$\text{div grad } U = \frac{1}{e_1 e_2 e_3}\left[\frac{\partial}{\partial u}\left(\frac{e_2 e_3}{e_1} \frac{\partial U}{\partial u}\right) + \frac{\partial}{\partial v}\left(\frac{e_3 e_1}{e_2} \frac{\partial U}{\partial v}\right) \right. $$
$$\left. + \frac{\partial}{\partial w}\left(\frac{e_1 e_2}{e_3} \frac{\partial U}{\partial w}\right) \right]. \tag{18}$$

This reduces to the Laplacian when the e's are constants.

EXERCISES XVIII

1. Show that in any orthogonal coordinate system,

$$[ij, k] = 0, \qquad [ij, i] = -[ii, j] = e_i \frac{\partial e_i}{\partial x^j}, \qquad [ii, i] = e_i \frac{\partial e_i}{\partial x^i};$$

$$\begin{Bmatrix} k \\ ij \end{Bmatrix} = 0, \qquad \begin{Bmatrix} j \\ ii \end{Bmatrix} = \frac{e_i}{e_j^2} \frac{\partial e_i}{\partial x^j}, \qquad \begin{Bmatrix} i \\ ij \end{Bmatrix} = \frac{\partial \log e_i}{\partial x^j}, \qquad \begin{Bmatrix} i \\ ii \end{Bmatrix} = \frac{\partial \log e_i}{\partial x^i},$$

where $e_i^2 = g_{ii}$, and i, j, k are distinct.

2. Compute the divergence, Laplacian, and curl in polar, cylindrical, and parabolic coordinates.

3. Show that if F^i is a contravariant vector, then $F^i{}_{,j}$ is a mixed tensor of order two.

4. Show that $F_{ij,k} \equiv \dfrac{\partial F_{ij}}{\partial x^k} - \sum_h F_{ih} \left\{ \begin{matrix} h \\ jk \end{matrix} \right\} - \sum_h F_{hj} \left\{ \begin{matrix} h \\ ik \end{matrix} \right\},$

$$F^{ij}{}_{,k} \equiv \dfrac{\partial F^{ij}}{\partial x^k} + \sum_h F^{ih} \left\{ \begin{matrix} j \\ hk \end{matrix} \right\} + \sum_h F^{hj} \left\{ \begin{matrix} i \\ hk \end{matrix} \right\},$$

$$F^i_{j,k} \equiv \dfrac{\partial F^i_j}{\partial x^k} + \sum_h F^h_j \left\{ \begin{matrix} i \\ hk \end{matrix} \right\} - \sum_h F^i_h \left\{ \begin{matrix} h \\ jk \end{matrix} \right\},$$

are tensors. These quantities are called the *covariant derivatives* of F_{ij}, F^{ij}, F^i_j respectively.

5. Write the formulas for the covariant derivatives of several higher order tensors.

6. Show that $g_{ij,k} = g^{ij}{}_{,k} = \delta^i_{j,k} = 0$, i.e., that the tensors g_{ij}, g^{ij}, and δ^i_j behave like constants under covariant differentiation.

7. Show that the rules for covariant differentiation of the sum, difference, outer and inner product of two tensors are the same as for ordinary differentiation of scalars.

8. Show that $F_{,ij} - F_{,ji} = 0$. Find formulas for $F_{i,jk}$ and $F_{i,jk} - F_{i,kj}$.

9. Show that if $\varphi_{ij} = F_{i,j} - F_{j,i}$, then

$$\varphi_{ij,k} + \varphi_{jk,i} + \varphi_{ki,j} = \frac{\partial \varphi_{ij}}{\partial x^k} + \frac{\partial \varphi_{jk}}{\partial x^i} + \frac{\partial \varphi_{ki}}{\partial x^j} = 0.$$

What theorem of ordinary vector analysis is a special case of this result?

10. Show that $[ij, k] = \displaystyle\sum_l g_{lk} \left\{ \begin{matrix} l \\ ij \end{matrix} \right\}.$

11. Show that the Laplacian of U in general coordinates is given by

$$\nabla^2 \varphi = \frac{1}{\sqrt{g}} \sum_{i,j} \frac{\partial}{\partial x^i} \left(\sqrt{g}\, g^{ij} \frac{\partial \varphi}{\partial x^i} \right).$$

12. Show that the *divergence* of the tensor a^{ij} is

$$\sum_j a^{ij}{}_{,j} = \frac{1}{\sqrt{g}} \sum_j \frac{\partial}{\partial x^i} (a^{ij} \sqrt{g}) + \sum_{j,k} a^{jk} \left\{ \begin{matrix} i \\ jk \end{matrix} \right\}.$$

To what form does this reduce when the g's are constants?

CHAPTER VII

PARTIAL DIFFERENTIAL EQUATIONS

1. Introduction. A partial differential equation is an equation involving partial derivatives. Explicit solutions of such equations can be written down in only a relatively few cases. The theoretical questions involved in the study of such equations are so great that we shall not undertake to do more than note certain equations of importance in applied mathematics and to indicate certain methods for their solution. We shall not consider the problems relating to the existence of solutions, or to the validity of the operations upon the series involved.

The solution of a partial differential equation usually involves arbitrary functions, in much the same way that the solutions of ordinary differential equations involve arbitrary constants. In the applications of the theory to physical problems, the problem usually involves the determination of a particular function which satisfies the differential equation and which, at the same time, meets other conditions—frequently called *boundary conditions*—of the physical problem.

2. A Simple Form of Partial Differential Equation. Euler's Equation. We shall first consider the equation

$$\frac{\partial^2 z}{\partial x \, \partial y} = 0. \tag{1}$$

Integrating with respect to y, we have

$$\frac{\partial z}{\partial x} = \varphi_1(x),$$

where φ_1 is an arbitrary function of x. Integrating with respect to x, we find

$$z = \varphi(x) + \psi(y),$$

where φ and ψ are arbitrary functions of x and y, respectively.

We shall now consider the *general Euler equation*,

$$a\frac{\partial^2 z}{\partial x^2} + 2b\frac{\partial^2 z}{\partial x \, \partial y} + c\frac{\partial^2 z}{\partial y^2} = 0, \tag{2}$$

where a, b, c are constants.

We shall change the independent variables by means of the linear transformations

$$\xi = \alpha x + \beta y, \tag{3}$$
$$\eta = \gamma x + \delta y.$$

Evidently,

$$\frac{\partial z}{\partial x} = \frac{\partial z}{\partial \xi}\frac{\partial \xi}{\partial x} + \frac{\partial z}{\partial \eta}\frac{\partial \eta}{\partial x} = \alpha\frac{\partial z}{\partial \xi} + \gamma\frac{\partial z}{\partial \eta}, \cdots, \tag{4}$$

$$\frac{\partial^2 z}{\partial x^2} = \left(\alpha\frac{\partial}{\partial \xi} + \gamma\frac{\partial}{\partial \eta}\right)^2 z, \cdots.$$

Substituting these relations in Eq. (2), we have

$$(a\alpha^2 + 2b\alpha\beta + c\beta^2)\frac{\partial^2 z}{\partial \xi^2} + (a\gamma^2 + 2b\gamma\delta + c\delta^2)\frac{\partial^2 z}{\partial \eta^2}$$
$$+ 2[a\alpha\gamma + b(\alpha\delta + \beta\gamma) + c\beta\delta]\frac{\partial^2 z}{\partial \xi\,\partial \eta} = 0. \tag{5}$$

If we select $\alpha = \gamma = 1$, $\beta = \lambda_1$, $\delta = \lambda_2$, where λ_1 and λ_2 are the roots of the quadratic

$$a + 2b\lambda + c\lambda^2 = 0, \tag{6}$$

Eq. (5) reduces to

$$[a + b(\lambda_1 + \lambda_2) + c\lambda_1\lambda_2]\frac{\partial^2 z}{\partial \xi\,\partial \eta} = 0,$$

or

$$\frac{2}{c}(ac - b^2)\frac{\partial^2 z}{\partial \xi\,\partial \eta} = 0. \tag{7}$$

If $b^2 - ac > 0$, Eq. (2) is said to be *hyperbolic*, if $b^2 - ac = 0$, Eq. (2) is said to be *parabolic*, and if $b^2 - ac < 0$, Eq. (2) is said to be *elliptic*. If $ac \neq b^2$, then (7) reduces to

$$\frac{\partial^2 z}{\partial \xi\,\partial \eta} = 0,$$

which has the solution

$$z = \varphi(\xi) + \psi(\eta) = \varphi(x + \lambda_1 y) + \psi(x + \lambda_2 y). \tag{8}$$

If $ac = b^2$, then $\lambda_1 = \lambda_2$, and $\xi = \eta$. In Eq. (5), set $\alpha = 1$, $\beta = \lambda$, γ and δ arbitrary, we find

$$\frac{\partial^2 z}{\partial \eta^2} = 0, \tag{9}$$

which has the solution

$$z = \varphi(\xi) + \eta\psi(\xi) = \varphi(x + \lambda y) + (\gamma x + \delta y)\cdot\psi(x + \lambda y). \quad (10)$$

The method given above applies to the equation of a stretched string,

$$\frac{\partial^2 u}{\partial t^2} = a^2\frac{\partial^2 u}{\partial x^2}, \qquad a^2 = \frac{\tau}{\rho}. \quad (11)$$

Set $\xi = x + \lambda_1 t$, $\eta = x + \lambda_2 t$, with $\lambda^2 - a^2 = 0$, $\lambda_1 = a$, $\lambda_2 = -a$. We then find

$$u = \varphi(x + at) + \psi(x - at). \quad (12)$$

EXERCISES I*

1. Show that

$$z = Y_0 + Y_1 x + Y_2 x^2 + \cdots + Y_{m-1}x^{m-1} + X_0 + X_1 y + X_2 y^2$$
$$+ \cdots + X_{n-1}y^{n-1},$$

where the Y's are arbitrary functions of y and the X's are arbitrary functions of x, is a solution of $\partial^{m+n}z/\partial x^m\,\partial y^n = 0$.

2. Show that $z = c_1 \sin wx + c_2 \cos wx$, where c_1 and c_2 are arbitrary functions of y, is a solution of $\partial^2 z/\partial x^2 = -a^2 z$.

3. Show that $z = \varphi_1(x + ay) + \varphi_2(x - ay)$, where φ_1 and φ_2 are arbitrary functions, is a solution of the equation $(\partial^2 z/\partial y^2) - a^2(\partial^2 z/\partial x^2) = 0$.

4. Find a partial differential equation having the primitive

$$(x - a)^2 + (y - b)^2 + z^2 = 1,$$

and show that $z^2 - 1 = 0$ is a singular solution.

5. Find the partial differential equation representing each of the following families:

(a) $z = (x + a)(y + b)$.   (b) $\dfrac{x^2}{a^2} + \dfrac{y^2}{b^2} - \dfrac{z^2}{c^2} = 0$.

(c) $z = ax^2 + 2bxy + cy^2 + dx + ey$.

(d) A family of conical surfaces with vertex at (α, β, γ).

$$Ans. \quad (x - \alpha)\frac{\partial z}{\partial x} + (y - \beta)\frac{\partial z}{\partial y} = z - \gamma.$$

(e) A family of cylinders where generators are parallel to the line $x = \alpha z$, $y = \beta z$.

(f) A family of surfaces of revolution with OZ as axis.

$$Ans. \quad xq - yp = 0.$$

(g) A family of surfaces generated by lines parallel to a fixed plane and intersecting a fixed normal to that plane.   *Ans.* $xp + yq = 0$.

* We shall frequently use the notation $p = \partial z/\partial x$, $q = \partial z/\partial y$, $r = \partial^2 z/\partial x^2$, $s = \partial^2 z/\partial x\,\partial y$, $t = \partial^2 z/\partial y^2$.

6. Find partial differential equations for each of the following by eliminating the arbitrary functions:

(a) $x + y + z = \varphi(x^2 + y^2 + z^2)$.   (b) $\varphi(x^2 + y^2, z - xy) = 0$.

(c) $\varphi(x/y, y/z, z/x) = 0$.

7. Let $u(x, y, z)$ and $v(x, y, z)$ be any two differentiable functions of x, y, and z. Show that if $\Phi(v)$ be any arbitrary function of v, then this function may always be eliminated from $u = \Phi(v)$.

3. Linear Partial Differential Equations of the First Order.
We shall consider equations of the form

$$P\frac{\partial z}{\partial x} + Q\frac{\partial z}{\partial y} = R, \tag{1}$$

where P, Q, and R are any three continuous differentiable functions of (x, y, z) in a region D of space, and such that P and Q do not both vanish simultaneously. It can be shown that under quite general conditions (1) has a solution. We shall obtain a solution to (1) by constructing a family of solutions to the total differential equation (3) given below.

Suppose

$$z = g(x, y) \tag{2}$$

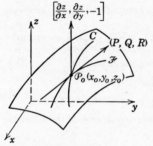

FIG. 195.

is a solution of (1). To each point in D there corresponds a definite direction whose direction numbers are P, Q, and R. The normal to the surface (2) at a point $\mathcal{P}$ has direction components $[\partial z/\partial x, \partial z/\partial y, -1]$. Equation (1) indicates that the direction P, Q, R is orthogonal to the direction $[\partial z/\partial x, \partial z/\partial y, -1]$. This means that at any point on the surface (2), $[P, Q, R]$ determine a vector **V** in the tangent plane to (2). We seek a family $\mathcal{F}$ of curves such that at each point $\mathcal{P}$ of (2) each curve of $\mathcal{F}$ through $\mathcal{P}$ is tangent to the vector **V** at $\mathcal{P}$. This family $\mathcal{F}$ is defined by the system of ordinary differential equations

$$\frac{dy}{dx} = \frac{Q}{P}, \qquad \frac{dz}{dx} = \frac{R}{P},$$

or

$$\frac{dx}{P} = \frac{dy}{Q} = \frac{dz}{R}. \tag{3}$$

Through each point $\mathcal{P}$ of (2) there passes a curve of $\mathfrak{F}$. Let $\mathfrak{F}$, the solution of (3), be given parametrically by

$$x = f_1(t, x_0, y_0, z_0), \; y = f_2(t, x_0, y_0, z_0), \; z = f_3(t, x_0, y_0, z_0), \quad (4)$$

or by

$$u(x, y, z) = c_1 = u(x_0, y_0, z_0), \; v(x, y, z) = c_2 = v(x_0, y_0, z_0). \quad (4')$$

Suppose C is any curve in D which does not coincide along any arc with any of the curves of $\mathfrak{F}$. A curve of $\mathfrak{F}$ passes through each point (x_0, y_0, z_0) of C. We shall show that the one-parameter family $\mathcal{G}$ of curves taken from $\mathfrak{F}$ in this manner forms a surface

$$z = \phi(x, y). \quad (5)$$

Suppose the solution (4) is written in nonparametric form

$$y = g(x, x_0, y_0, z_0), \qquad z = h(x, x_0, y_0, z_0). \quad (6)$$

Now suppose in (4) x_0 is fixed, and has the value $x_0 = 0$. Then rewrite (6) as

$$y = \beta(x, y_0, z_0), \qquad z = \gamma(x, y_0, z_0). \quad (7)$$

Since $y_0 = \beta(0, y_0, z_0), \, z_0 = \gamma(0, y_0, z_0)$,

$$\frac{\partial y}{\partial y_0} = 1, \qquad \frac{\partial y}{\partial z_0} = 0, \qquad \frac{\partial z}{\partial y_0} = 0, \qquad \frac{\partial z}{\partial z_0} = 1. \quad (8)$$

Let the equation of the curve C be

$$z_0 = \delta(y_0), \qquad x = x_0 = 0, \quad (9)$$

where δ has a continuous first derivative. Substitute (9) in (7). Since $\partial y / \partial y_0 \neq 0$, the resulting expression may be solved for y_0, giving, say

$$y_0 = \omega(x, y), \quad (10)$$

where ω has a continuous first derivative. By means of (9) and (10) y_0 and z_0 may be eliminated from the second equation of (7), leading to an expression of the form given in (5).

In equations (4), we may always regard (in the neighborhood of (x_0, y_0, z_0)) the parameter t as x when $P \neq 0$, and as y when $Q \neq 0$ at that point (x_0, y_0, z_0). This shows that our proof is general if $P \neq 0$ at (x_0, y_0, z_0), for otherwise, it is only necessary to interchange the role of x and y.

The curves $\mathfrak{F}$ whose equations are (4) are called the *characteristics* of the differential equation (1).

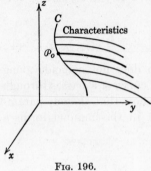

FIG. 196.

The normal at any point $\mathcal{P}$ of the surface (5) is perpendicular to the particular curve γ_P of (4) through $\mathcal{P}$. The direction numbers of γ_P are P, Q, R and those of the normal to γ_P at $\mathcal{P}$ are ϕ_x, ϕ_y, -1. Hence *the surface* (5) *is an integral surface of* (1), since (1) is satisfied.

If the curve C is given by the equations

$$x = \xi(\lambda), \qquad y = \eta(\lambda), \qquad z = \zeta(\lambda), \tag{11}$$

where λ is a parameter, the equation for the surface (5) may be written [by substituting (11) in (4)] in the form

$$x = f_1[t, \xi(\lambda), \eta(\lambda), \zeta(\lambda)], \qquad y = f_2[t, \xi(\lambda), \eta(\lambda), \zeta(\lambda)],$$
$$z = f_3[t, \xi(\lambda), \eta(\lambda), \zeta(\lambda)]. \tag{12}$$

Any solution of (1) yields a surface $z = \psi(x, y)$ which is generated by a one-parameter family of curves (4). This fact follows immediately from the observation that through each of the points of the surface passes a curve (4), and each curve of this sort lies entirely in the surface.

It can be shown that $\Phi(u, v) = 0$ *is the general solution of equation* (1), *where* Φ *is an arbitrary function and where*

$$u(x, y, z) = c_1, \qquad v(x, y, z) = c_2$$

is the general solution of equations (3).

Example 1. Find a solution of $x\dfrac{\partial z}{\partial x} + (y + 3x^2 y^2 e^{x^3})\dfrac{\partial z}{\partial y} = 0$. Here $P = x$, $Q = y + 3x^2 y^2 e^{x^3}$, $R = 0$. We suppose $z = g(x, y)$ is a solution of the given equation. The family $\mathfrak{F}$ of characteristics of the given equation is defined by

$$\frac{dx}{x} = \frac{dy}{y + 3x^2 y^2 e^{x^3}} = \frac{dz}{0}. \tag{3'}$$

A solution of this equation is

$$u \equiv \frac{x}{y} + e^{x^3} = c_1, \qquad v \equiv z = c_2. \qquad (4')$$

Hence the surface $z = (x/y) + e^{x^3}$ is a particular solution of the given equation.

The general solution of the given equation is

$$\Phi(u, v) \equiv \Phi\left(\frac{x}{y} + e^{x^3}, z\right) = 0.$$

Example 2. Solve $p + q = 1$.

Here $P = Q = R = 1$, and $dx/1 = dy/1 = dz/1$ have the (characteristic) solution $x - y = c_1$, $x - z = c_2$. The characteristic through (x_0, y_0, z_0) is $x - y = x_0 - y_0$, $x - z = x_0 - z_0$. We select $x = 0$, $z = e^{-y}$ in the yz-plane for the curve C. Pick a point, say $(0, y_0, e^{-y_0})$, on C. The characteristic through this point is $x - y = -y_0$, $x - z = -e^{-y_0}$. These are the equations of a surface $\mathcal{S}$ generated by the characteristics when y_0 is a parameter. The equation of the integral surface $\mathcal{S}$ is found, upon eliminating the parameter y_0, to be $z - x = e^{x-y}$. The general solution of the given equation is $\Phi(x - y, x - z) = 0$.

Example 3. Solve $(x^2 - y^2 - z^2)p + (2xy)q = 2xz$. Here

$$P = x^2 - y^2 - z^2, \qquad Q = 2xy, \qquad R = 2xz.$$

The solutions of $\dfrac{dx}{x^2 - y^2 - z^2} = \dfrac{dy}{2xy} = \dfrac{dz}{2xz}$ are the characteristics

$$\frac{y}{z} = c_1, \qquad \frac{x^2 + y^2 + z^2}{z} = c_2.$$

Consider the curve C with equations $x = 0$, $z = y^3$ in the yz-plane. We select the characteristic through $x_0 = 0$, $z_0 = y_0^3$, namely,

$$\frac{y}{z} = \frac{1}{y_0^2}, \qquad \frac{x^2 + y^2 + z^2}{z} = \frac{y_0^2 + y_0^6}{y_0^3}.$$

These are the parametric equations of a surface generated by the characteristics through curve C with y_0 as the parameter. Upon eliminating y_0, we have

$$y^3(x^2 + y^2 + z^2)^2 - z(y^2 + z^2)^2 = 0,$$

which is a solution of the given equation. The general solution is

$$\Phi\left(\frac{y}{z}, \frac{x^2 + y^2 + z^2}{z}\right) = 0.$$

EXERCISES II

1. (a) Show that the equation of the tangent plane to the surface

$$z = f(x, y) \text{ at } (x_0, y_0) \text{ is } \quad \frac{\partial z}{\partial x}\Big]_0 (x - x_0) + \frac{\partial z}{\partial y}\Big]_0 (y - y_0) - (z - z_0) = 0.$$

(b) Show that the equation of the normal to the tangent plane at the

point (x_0, y_0, z_0) is
$$\frac{x - x_0}{\dfrac{\partial z}{\partial x}\Big]_0} = \frac{y - y_0}{\dfrac{\partial z}{\partial y}\Big]_0} = \frac{z - z_0}{-1}.$$

2. Find the equations of the tangent plane and the normal to each of the following surfaces at the points indicated:

  (a) $x^2 + y^2 + z^2 = 14$ at $(1, 3, -2)$.

  (b) $z = \log xy$ at $(1, e, 1)$.

  (c) $z = \mathrm{Tan}^{-1}(y/x)$ at $(2, -2, -\pi/4)$.

  3. Solve: $dx/x = dy/y = dz/z$.   *Ans.* $x = c_1 y$, $x = c_2 z$.

  4. Find a solution of $\dfrac{dx}{y^2 z(z+1)} = \dfrac{dy}{x^2 z(z+1)} = \dfrac{dz}{xy^2(1+z)}$ which

passes through the point $(1, 0, -2)$.   *Ans.* $x^3 - y^3 = 1$, $x^2 - z^2 = -3$.

  5. Solve: $dx/s = dy/t = dz/2st = dt/0 = ds/0$.

                Ans. $s = c_1$, $t = c_2$, $tx - sy = c_3$, $2tx - z = c_4$.

  6. Solve: $yz\,dx + xz\,dy + dz = 0$.   (HINT: set $z =$ constant.)

                                Ans. $xy + \log c_1 z = 0$.

  7. Find a solution for $(x + z)\,dx + y\,dy - z\,dz = 0$ on the surface $3z = x^2 + y^2$.

  8. (a) Find integral curves of $2y\,dx + x\,dy - dz = 0$ on the surface $x + y - z = 0$.

  (b) Also, on $y^2 = x$.

  9. Solve: $yz^2 + (xyz + 1)(\partial z/\partial x) = 0$ by assuming $y = y_0$ is a constant.   *Ans.* $ze^{xyz} = \varphi(y)$, where φ is an arbitrary function of y.

  10. Solve: $(x \operatorname{ctn} xz - y)(\partial z/\partial y) = z$.   *Ans.* $\log \sin xz = yz + \varphi(x)$.

  11. Find a particular integral of each of the following equations, using the method of Sec. 3:

  (a) $(\cos x + \sin x)\dfrac{\partial z}{\partial x} + (\sin x - \cos x)\dfrac{\partial z}{\partial y} = 0.$

                       Ans. $z = y + \log(\cos x + \sin x)$.

  (b) $x\dfrac{\partial z}{\partial x} + y(1 - x)\dfrac{\partial z}{\partial y} = 0.$ *Ans.* $z = \log \dfrac{x}{y} - x.$

  (c) $x \log x\dfrac{\partial z}{\partial x} + (\log x - y)\dfrac{\partial z}{\partial y} = 0.$ *Ans.* $z = \tfrac{1}{2}(\log x)^2 - y \log x.$

  12. (a) Prove that if $z = g(x, y)$ is a solution of (1) in Sec. 3, then $z = \Phi(g)$ is also a solution of (1), where Φ is an arbitrary function of g.

$$\left\{ \text{Hint: } P\frac{\partial z}{\partial x} + Q\frac{\partial z}{\partial y} = P\left[\Phi'(g)\frac{\partial g}{\partial x}\right] + Q\left[\Phi'(g)\frac{\partial g}{\partial y}\right] = \Phi'(g)\left[P\frac{\partial g}{\partial x} + Q\frac{\partial g}{\partial y}\right].\right\}$$

It can be shown that (1) has no other solutions not contained in $z = \Phi(g)$.

(b) Use (a) to find general solutions to the equations given in Ex. 11 above. Thus the answer to part (b) is $z = \Phi[\log (x/y) - x]$.

13. Find a solution to Example 2 above when the curve C is taken to be $y = x^2$, $z = x^3$, and when the point P is taken to be (x_0, x_0^2, x_0^3).

Ans. $(x - y)^3 = (y - z)(x - 2y + z)$.

Also find the general solution.

14. Solve $xp + yq - z = 0$, using $y^2 = 4x$, $z = 1$, for the curve C, and (x_1, y_1, z_1) for the point P. Find the general solution.

15. Prove the statement made at the end of Sec. 3 that a general solution of (1) is $\Phi(u, v) = 0$.

16. (a) Prove: *If $f(x, y, z) = 0$ is a solution of $Pp + Qq = R$, then*
$$g = f(x, y, z)$$
is a solution of $P(x, y, z)(\partial g/\partial x) + Q(x, y, z)(\partial g/\partial y) + R(x, y, z)(\partial g/\partial z) = 0$, when x, y, z are independent variables. Show that the converse is also true.

(b) Solve $(xyz - x)(\partial g/\partial x) + (y - xyz)(\partial g/\partial y) + (xz - yz)(\partial g/\partial z) = 0$.

Ans. $g = \Phi(x + y + \log z, \log xy + z)$.

17. Find an integral surface for $p - q = 0$ through the curve $x = s$, $y = s^2$, $z = s^3$, where s is a parameter.

18. Given $xp + yq = z$. (a) Show that the parametric equations of the characteristics are $\log x = t + c_1$, $\log y = t + c_2$, $\log z = t + c_3$, where t is a parameter. (b) Find the characteristic at the point where $t = 0$ through the curve $x = s^2$, $y = 2s$, $z = 1$, where s is a parameter. (c) By eliminating s and t from the result found in (b), show that $y^2 = 4xz$ is an integral surface of the given equation.

19. Solve each of the following equations. Interpret your solutions geometrically.

(a) $3p + 5q = 0$.

(b) $py = qx$.

(c) $p(x - 3) + q(x - 5) = z - 7$.

(d) $p + qz = 0$.

(e) $py - qx = 1$.

(f) $3(p + q) = z$.

(g) $px + qz + y = 0$.

(h) $\dfrac{p}{x} + \dfrac{q}{y} = \dfrac{1}{z}$.

(i) $xp + yq = nz$.

(j) $x^2p + y^2q = z^2$.

(k) $(x + y)p + (y - x)q = 0$.

20. Find integrals for each of the equations in Ex. 19 which pass through the curves:

(a) $x^2 + y^2 - 1 = 0$, $z = 0$.

(b) $y = 3x$, $z = 1$.

(c) $x = y$, $z = 0$.

(d) $x = y = z$.

21. Show that $z = \alpha x + \beta y + c$, with α and β subject to the relation $G(\alpha, \beta) = 0$, is a solution of the differential equation $G(p, q) = 0$.

22. Find integrals for:

(a) $pq - 1 = 0$.

(b) $p^2 + 1 - q = 0$.

23. Solve:

(a) $p - q + (x - y)s = 0.$ (b) $x(r - t) + 2p = 0.$
(c) $r^2 + 2p + z = 0.$ (d) $r^2 = y + z.$
(e) $r^2 - 5p + 6z = 0.$

4. General First-order Partial Differential Equations. We now consider the partial differential equation

$$G(x, y, z, p, q) = 0, \qquad \left(p = \frac{\partial z}{\partial x}, \; q = \frac{\partial z}{\partial y}\right) \qquad (1)$$

where the function G is assumed to have continuous first partial derivatives throughout a region D. We shall suppose that G_p and G_q do not both vanish at any point (x, y, z) in D. We

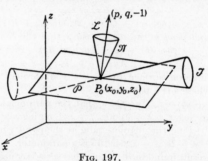

FIG. 197.

shall furthermore suppose that p and q can assume any values whatever within D.

Select a fixed point (x_0, y_0, z_0) in D, and consider the lines $\mathcal{L}$ passing through this point with direction numbers $[p, q, -1]$, and which satisfy (1), so that $G(x_0, y_0, z_0, p, q) = 0$. [This relation shows that at (x_0, y_0, z_0) only certain directions are possible.] These lines $\mathcal{L}$ generate a cone $\mathfrak{N}$, and their normal planes through (x_0, y_0, z_0), represented by

$$z - z_0 = p(x - x_0) + q(y - y_0), \qquad (2)$$

envelope a cone $\mathfrak{I}$. The rulings of $\mathfrak{I}$ are determined by (2) and by

$$0 = (y - y_0) + \frac{\partial p}{\partial q}(x - x_0), \qquad (3)$$

or by

$$\frac{x - x_0}{G_p} = \frac{y - y_0}{G_q}, \qquad (4)$$

where

$$\frac{\partial G(x_0, y_0, z_0, p, q)}{\partial p} = G_p, \qquad \frac{\partial G(x_0, y_0, z_0, p, q)}{\partial q} = G_q.$$

Let a solution of (1) be the surface S with equation

$$z = \psi(x, y). \tag{5}$$

At (x_0, y_0, z_0), the tangent plane $\mathcal{P}$ to S is given by (2). The ruling of cone $\mathcal{J}$ which lies in $\mathcal{P}$ also lies in the plane (4). This shows that at every point of S a direction is determined.

We shall show that the surface S may be generated by a one-parameter family of curves $\mathcal{C}$, each curve of $\mathcal{C}$ being tangent at every one of its points to the direction associated with that point. The differential equation

$$\frac{dx}{G_p} = \frac{dy}{G_q} \tag{6}$$

with z given by (5) has for a solution in the neighborhood of (x_0, y_0) a one-parameter family of curves $\mathcal{C}_2$ which sweep out this neighborhood exactly once. The cylinders on $\mathcal{C}_2$ as directrices, with elements parallel to the z-axis, cut from S the curves $\mathcal{C}$, and these curves $\mathcal{C}$ sweep out that portion of S in the neighborhood of (x_0, y_0, z_0) exactly once.

We shall introduce in (6) a parameter t:

$$\frac{dx}{G_p} = \frac{dy}{G_q} = dt. \tag{7}$$

Along the curves $\mathcal{C}$, $dz = p\, dx + q\, dy = (pG_p + qG_q)\, dt$. Hence (6) becomes

$$\frac{dx}{G_p} = \frac{dy}{G_q} = \frac{dt}{pG_p + qG_q} = dt. \tag{8}$$

Along $\mathcal{C}$,

$$dp = r\, dx + s\, dy, \qquad dq = s\, dx + t\, dy, \tag{9}$$

where

$$r = \frac{\partial^2 z}{\partial x^2} = \frac{\partial p}{\partial x}, \qquad s = \frac{\partial^2 z}{\partial x\, \partial y} = \frac{\partial p}{\partial y} = \frac{\partial q}{\partial x}, \qquad t = \frac{\partial^2 z}{\partial y^2} = \frac{\partial q}{\partial y}. \tag{10}$$

Hence

$$dp = (rG_p + sG_q)\, dt, \qquad dq = (sG_p + tG_q)\, dt. \tag{11}$$

The function (5) satisfies Eq. (1) identically. By (1),

$$G_x + pG_z + rG_p + sG_q = 0, \; G_y + qG_z + sG_p + tG_q = 0, \quad (12)$$

where $G_x = \partial G/\partial x$, $G_y = \partial G/\partial y$, $G_z = \partial G/\partial z$. By (11) and (12),

$$G_x + pG_z + \frac{dp}{dt} = 0, \qquad G_y + qG_z + \frac{dq}{dt} = 0. \qquad (13)$$

Equations (8) and (13) give

$$\frac{dx}{G_p} = \frac{dy}{G_q} = \frac{dz}{pG_p + qG_q} = \frac{-dp}{G_x + pG_z} = \frac{-dq}{G_y + qG_z} = dt. \quad (14)$$

This system (14) involving five dependent variables x, y, z, p, q, and the independent variable t define a family of curves:

$$\left. \begin{array}{l} x = f_1(t; x_0, y_0, z_0, p_0, q_0), \\ y = f_2(t; x_0, y_0, z_0, p_0, q_0), \\ z = f_3(t; x_0, y_0, z_0, p_0, q_0), \\ p = f_4(t; x_0, y_0, z_0, p_0, q_0), \\ q = f_5(t; x_0, y_0, z_0, p_0, q_0). \end{array} \right\} \qquad (15)$$

We shall assume that at $t = 0$, $x = x_0$, $y = y_0$, $\cdots$, $q = q_0$.

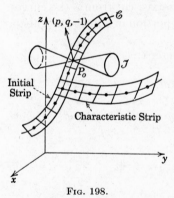

Fig. 198.

These equations (15) define the family known as the *characteristics* of the given differential equation. The first three equations in (15) determine a curve $\mathcal{C}$ through (x_0, y_0, z_0), and the last two determine for each point of $\mathcal{C}$ a definite normal having direction numbers $[p, q, -1]$, and a tangent plane perpendicular to this normal. We can think of $\mathcal{C}$ as being imbedded in a narrow strip of surface $\mathcal{S}$ such that at each point of $\mathcal{C}$, the tangent plane to the surface has the position belonging to that point. Such a strip is known as a *characteristic strip* lying in the surface $\mathcal{S}$. $\mathcal{S}$ can be thought of as being made up of a one parameter family of such characteristic strips.

Example 1. Given $G \equiv xp^2 + yq - xz = 0$.
The normal planes (2) at (x_0, y_0, z_0) are given by

$$z - z_0 = p(x - x_0) + q(y - y_0). \qquad (2')$$

The rulings of cone $\mathfrak{Z}$ are determined by (2') and (4).

Since $P = G_p = 2px_0$, and $Q = G_q = y_0$, Eq. (4) is

$$\frac{x - x_0}{2px_0} = \frac{y - y_0}{y_0}. \tag{4'}$$

The planes (2') through (x_0, y_0, z_0) envelope the cone $\mathfrak{Z}$ whose rulings are given by (2') and (4'). Eliminating p and q from (4'), (2') and

$$G(x_0, y_0, z_0, p, q) \equiv x_0 p^2 + y_0 q - x_0 z_0 = 0, \tag{1'}$$

we may obtain the equation of the cone $\mathfrak{Z}$.

Example 2. Given $G(x, y, z, p, q) \equiv pq + z(p + q) = 0$. Find the equation of the cone $\mathfrak{Z}$ through (x_0, y_0, z_0).

The normal planes (2) at (x_0, y_0, z_0) are given by

$$z - z_0 = p(x - x_0) + q(y - y_0), \tag{2''}$$

and the rulings of $\mathfrak{Z}$ are given by (2'') and

$$\frac{x - x_0}{q + z_0} = \frac{y - y_0}{p + z_0}, \tag{4''}$$

where

$$G(x_0, y_0, z_0, p, q) \equiv pq + z_0(p + q) = 0. \tag{1''}$$

Eliminating p and q from (2'') and (4''), and substituting in (1''), we have the equation of the cone $\mathfrak{Z}$, the envelope of the family of planes (2'') subject to the restriction (1'').

The rulings of the cone $\mathfrak{Z}$ are found from (2''), (4''), i.e.,

$$p(x - x_0) + q(y - y_0) - (z - z_0) = 0, \tag{2'''}$$

and

$$(p + z_0)(x - x_0) - (q + z_0)(y - y_0) = 0, \tag{4'''}$$

to be

$$\frac{x - x_0}{q + z_0} = \frac{y - y_0}{p + z_0} = \frac{z - z_0}{2pq + z_0(p + q)}.$$

By (1''), $q = -z_0 p/(p + z_0)$, so that the equations for the rulings on the cone may be written

$$\frac{x - x_0}{z_0^2} = \frac{y - y_0}{(p + z_0)^2} = \frac{z - z_0}{-z_0 p^2}.$$

Example 3. Find the characteristic strips for $G \equiv pq - z = 0$.

Equations (14) are

$$\frac{dx}{q} = \frac{dy}{p} = \frac{dz}{2pq} = \frac{dp}{p} = \frac{dq}{q} = \frac{dt}{q}, \tag{14'}$$

where the parameter t has been introduced. The characteristics of the given equation through (x_0, y_0, z_0) are the solutions to (14'), namely, [recalling that at $t = 0$, $(x, y, z) = (x_0, y_0, z_0)$],

$$\begin{cases} \dfrac{p}{q} = c_1 = \dfrac{p_0}{q_0}, \qquad p_0 q_0 = z_0, \\[2mm] z - pq = c_2 = z_0 - p_0 q_0, \\[2mm] y - p = c_3 = y_0 - p_0, \\[2mm] x - \dfrac{y}{c_1} = c_4 = x_0 - \dfrac{y_0 q_0}{p_0}, \\[2mm] x - t = c_5 = x_0. \end{cases}$$

EXERCISES III

1. Show that the family of planes $z - z_0 = a(x - x_0) + b(y - y_0)$ envelope a cone with vertex (x_0, y_0, z_0), where a and b are dependent parameters subject to the relation $G(a, b) = 0$, and where G is a suitable arbitrary function. Show that the rulings of the cone are determined by the given family of planes and $\dfrac{x - x_0}{\partial G / \partial a} = \dfrac{y - y_0}{\partial G / \partial b}$.

2. Find the envelope of the family of ellipses $(x^2/a^2) + (y^2/b^2) = 1$ of constant area $\pi ab = k$. *Ans.* $xy = \pm k/2\pi$.

3. Find the envelope of the family of circles having their centers on the line $y = 3x$ and tangent to the y-axis.

4. (a) Find the envelope of $\alpha x + \beta y + \alpha\beta z = 1$.
(b) Find the envelope in case (a) if $\alpha = -\beta$.

5. (a) Find the characteristic strips for $xp + p^2 - q = 0$.
Ans. $q = c_1$, $y = -t + c_2$, $\log p = -t + c_3$, $xp + p^2 = c_4$,

$$z = (c_1 - c_4) \log p - \frac{p^2}{2} + c_5,$$

(b) Using $x_0 p_0 + p_0^2 - q_0 = 0$, eliminate x_0 from the equations of the characteristic strips in (a), thus leaving four initial constants, y_0, z_0, p_0, q_0.

6. Find characteristic strips for $pq = 1$.

7. Show that in case $G(x, y, z, p, q) = 0$ is linear, the cone $\mathfrak{I}$ degenerates to a line.

8. From equations (2) and (4) of Sec. 4 show that the solutions of

$$\frac{dx}{G_p} = \frac{dy}{G_q} = \frac{dz}{pG_p + qG_q}$$

are curves $\mathfrak{C}$ in space having the direction of some ruling on the cone $\mathfrak{I}$.

9. Show that if we demand that the curves $\mathfrak{C}$ in Ex. 8 lie on the surface $z = \psi(x, y)$, then $\partial p/\partial y = \partial q/\partial x$. If we further require that the curves $\mathfrak{C}$ also satisfy $G(x, y, z, p, q) = 0$, show that $\mathfrak{C}$ satisfy Eq. (14).

5. The Method of Characteristics.
Throughout Sec. 4 we have assumed a definite solution (5) of (1). In this section we

shall discuss methods of constructing general solutions of type (5), Sec. 4, by means of characteristic strips.

We shall suppose that $G(x, y, z, p, q)$ is continuous and has continuous first and second order derivatives throughout a neighborhood $\mathcal{G}$ of the point (a, b, c, α, β) in the space R of the variables (x, y, z, p, q), where (x, y, z) is a point interior to the region D of Sec. 4. We shall furthermore suppose that

$$G(a, b, c, \alpha, \beta) = 0,$$

and that in $\mathcal{G}$, G_p and G_q are not both simultaneously zero. Let $(x_0, y_0, z_0, p_0, q_0)$ be an arbitrary point of $\mathcal{G}$. The system (14) of Sec. 4 defines a four-parameter family of curves (15) which sweep out $\mathcal{G}$ exactly once.

The first three equations of (14) define a family of curves $\mathcal{C}$. Let C_1 be the curve of $\mathcal{C}$ passing through (a, b, c, α, β). Any solution of

$$G(x, y, z, p, q) = 0, \tag{1}$$

say

$$z = \Phi(x, y), \tag{2}$$

with $c = \Phi(a, b)$, $\alpha = \Phi_x(a, b)$, and $\beta = \Phi_y(a, b)$, where Φ is continuous and has continuous first-order partial derivatives throughout a neighborhood of (a, b), must contain the curve C_1 and the corresponding characteristic strip. This result follows from the fact that C_1 and its characteristic strip are uniquely determined by the initial values corresponding to (a, b, c, α, β).

The curve C_1 is tangent at (a, b, c) to a plane T_1 through (a, b, c, α, β) whose normal has direction numbers $[\alpha, \beta, -1]$.

Let Γ be any curve not tangent to C_1 but tangent to T_1 at (a, b, c). Suppose the equations of Γ are

$$x = \omega_1(u), \qquad y = \omega_2(u), \qquad z = \omega_3(u), \tag{3}$$

where $\omega_i(u)$ and its first derivative are both continuous, $i = 1, 2, 3$. We suppose that at (a, b, c), $u = 0$; and that $\omega_1'(0)$, $\omega_2'(0)$, $\omega_3'(0)$ do not all vanish together. From the third equation of (3), we find upon differentiating that

$$\omega_3'(0) = \alpha\omega_1'(0) + \beta\omega_2'(0). \tag{4}$$

[Evidently $\omega_1'(0)$ and $\omega_2'(0)$ are not both zero, for if they were, we see from (4) that $\omega_3'(0)$ would also vanish, contrary to hypothesis.]

We shall indicate the proof of

Theorem 5.1. *The equation $G(x, y, z, p, q) = 0$ has exactly one solution satisfying the conditions placed upon Φ in (2), and this solution is such that the curve Γ lies on the surface $z = \Phi(x, y)$.*

We shall select from (15) of Sec. 4 by means of Γ a one-parameter family of characteristic strips which sweep out the solution of (1). We require a solution such that the values of p and q on Γ, say p_0, q_0, satisfy the restrictions

$$G[\omega_1(u), \ \omega_2(u), \ \omega_3(u), \ p_0, \ q_0] = 0, \tag{5}$$

$$\omega_1'(u)p_0 + \omega_2'(u)q_0 = \omega_3'(u). \tag{6}$$

The latter condition follows from the fact that (2) must be satisfied identically along Γ, and that at any point on Γ,

$$\Phi_x[\omega_1(u), \ \omega_2(u)] = p_0, \qquad \Phi_y[\omega_1(u), \ \omega_2(u)] = q_0.$$

It can be shown (see Ex. IV, 4), that Eqs. (5) and (6) can be solved for p_0, q_0. Suppose these solutions are

$$p_0 = \omega_4(u), \qquad q_0 = \omega_5(u). \tag{7}$$

Then $\omega_1(u), \omega_2(u), \cdots, \omega_5(u)$ are the values which $x_0, y_0, \cdots, q_0$ have in (15) of Sec. 4. The functions $\omega_1, \omega_2, \omega_3$ depend on the selection of Γ, while ω_4, ω_5 depend directly on $\omega_1, \omega_2, \omega_3$. In other words, the first three equations of (15) in Sec. 4 determine a surface which represents an integral solution (2) of (1).

We shall restate Theorem 5.1 in a form independent of the curve Γ. Let

$$\begin{aligned} x_0 &= \omega_1(u), & y_0 &= \omega_2(u), & z_0 &= \omega_3(u), \\ p_0 &= \omega_4(u), & q_0 &= \omega_5(u) \end{aligned} \tag{8}$$

be each continuous with continuous first derivatives in the neighborhood of $u = 0$, and suppose that

$$a = \omega_1(0), \ b = \omega_2(0), \ c = \omega_3(0), \ \alpha = \omega_4(0), \ \beta = \omega_5(0). \tag{9}$$

Furthermore, suppose that

$$G(x_0, y_0, z_0, p_0, q_0) = 0, \qquad \text{at} \qquad u = 0, \tag{10}$$

$$\frac{\partial z}{\partial u} = p\frac{\partial x}{\partial u} + q\frac{\partial y}{\partial u}, \qquad \text{at} \qquad t = 0, \qquad u = 0, \tag{11}$$

$$\begin{vmatrix} G_p & G_q \\ \dfrac{\partial x}{\partial u} & \dfrac{\partial y}{\partial u} \end{vmatrix} \neq 0, \qquad \text{at} \qquad t = 0, \qquad u = 0. \tag{12}$$

Then x, y, $\cdot \cdot \cdot$, q are given by (15) in Sec. 4, the functions $\omega_1(u)$, $\cdot \cdot \cdot$, $\omega_5(u)$ replacing the functions x_0, y_0, $\cdot \cdot \cdot$, q_0 in $f_1, f_2, \cdot \cdot \cdot , f_5$.

THEOREM 5.2. *If conditions* (8), (9), (10), (11), *and* (12) *hold, the first three equations of* (15) *in Sec. 4 define a surface* $z = \Phi(x, y)$ *which is a solution of* (1).

Proof. By Eqs. (14) of Sec. 4 and (8), we find

$$\frac{\partial x}{\partial t} = G_p, \qquad \frac{\partial y}{\partial t} = G_q, \qquad \frac{\partial z}{\partial t} = pG_p + qG_q,$$

$$\frac{\partial p}{\partial t} = -(G_x + pG_z), \qquad \frac{\partial q}{\partial t} = -(G_y + qG_z), \qquad (13)$$

$$\frac{\partial x}{\partial u}\bigg]_{t=0} = \omega_1'(u), \cdot \cdot \cdot , \frac{\partial q}{\partial u}\bigg]_{t=0} = \omega_5'(u). \qquad (14)$$

By (13), (12) gives

$$\begin{vmatrix} G_p & G_q \\ \dfrac{\partial x}{\partial u} & \dfrac{\partial y}{\partial u} \end{vmatrix} = \begin{vmatrix} \dfrac{\partial x}{\partial t} & \dfrac{\partial y}{\partial t} \\ \dfrac{\partial x}{\partial u} & \dfrac{\partial y}{\partial u} \end{vmatrix} \neq 0, \qquad \text{at} \qquad t = 0, \qquad u = 0. \quad (15)$$

By Sec. 20, Chap. I, the first two equations of (15), Sec. 4 can be solved for t and u in terms of x and y, so that the first three equations of (15), Sec. 4 are the equations of a surface S,

$$z = \Phi(x, y), \qquad (16)$$

where Φ is continuous with continuous first partial derivatives. This surface S contains both the curves C_1 and Γ. By Lemma 5.2 below $\Phi(x, y)$ satisfies the given differential equation (1).

For a more thorough treatment the reader is referred to Horn, "Partiale Differentialgleichungen"; Bieberbach, "Differentialgleichungen"; or the works of Goursat, "Cours d'analyse," Tome II, and "Dérivées partielles du premier ordre."

Lemma 5.1. In the preceding notation,

$$\frac{\partial z}{\partial t} = p\frac{\partial x}{\partial t} + q\frac{\partial y}{\partial t}, \qquad (17)$$

$$\frac{\partial z}{\partial u} = p\frac{\partial x}{\partial u} + q\frac{\partial y}{\partial u}. \qquad (18)$$

Equation (17) is an immediate consequence of equation (15) of Sec. 4.

Consider the function

$$W(t, u) = \frac{\partial z}{\partial u} - p\frac{\partial x}{\partial u} - q\frac{\partial y}{\partial u}. \tag{19}$$

By (11), $W = 0$ when $t = u = 0$. Now from (19) and (17), we find

$$\frac{\partial W}{\partial t} = \frac{\partial^2 z}{\partial t\,\partial u} - p\frac{\partial^2 x}{\partial t\,\partial u} - q\frac{\partial^2 y}{\partial t\,\partial u} - \frac{\partial p}{\partial t}\frac{\partial x}{\partial u} - \frac{\partial q}{\partial t}\frac{\partial y}{\partial u}, \tag{20}$$

$$0 = \frac{\partial^2 z}{\partial u\,\partial t} - p\frac{\partial^2 x}{\partial u\,\partial t} - q\frac{\partial^2 y}{\partial u\,\partial t} - \frac{\partial p}{\partial u}\frac{\partial x}{\partial t} - \frac{\partial q}{\partial u}\frac{\partial y}{\partial t}. \tag{21}$$

Subtracting (21) from (20) and using (13), we obtain

$$\frac{\partial W}{\partial t} = (G_x + pG_z)\frac{\partial x}{\partial u} + (G_y + qG_z)\frac{\partial y}{\partial u} + G_p\frac{\partial p}{\partial u} + G_q\frac{\partial q}{\partial u}. \tag{22}$$

Differentiating (1) with respect to u, we have

$$0 = \frac{\partial G}{\partial u} = G_x\frac{\partial x}{\partial u} + G_y\frac{\partial y}{\partial u} + G_z\frac{\partial z}{\partial u} + G_p\frac{\partial p}{\partial u} + G_q\frac{\partial q}{\partial u}. \tag{23}$$

Subtracting (23) from (22), we find

$$\frac{\partial W}{\partial t} = pG_z\frac{\partial x}{\partial u} + qG_z\frac{\partial y}{\partial u} - G_z\frac{\partial z}{\partial u} = -G_z W. \tag{24}$$

Let u be fixed, though arbitrary. Then integrating with respect to t, we have

$$W = W_0 e^{-\int_0^t G_z\,dt}. \tag{25}$$

Since $W_0 = W(0, u) = 0$, we see that $W \equiv 0$. Equation (18) now follows from (19).

Lemma 5.2.   The function $z = \Phi(x, y)$, where Φ and its first partial derivatives are continuous, satisfies the equation

$$G(x, y, z, p, q) = 0.$$

By Sec. 20 of Chap. I,

$$\Phi_x(x, y) = \frac{\dfrac{\partial(z, y)}{\partial(t, u)}}{\dfrac{\partial(x, y)}{\partial(t, u)}}, \qquad \Phi_y(x, y) = \frac{\dfrac{\partial(x, z)}{\partial(t, u)}}{\dfrac{\partial(x, y)}{\partial(t, u)}}. \tag{26}$$

Substituting (17) and (18) in (26) expanded, we find that

$$\Phi_x = p, \qquad \Phi_y = q. \tag{27}$$

This shows that Φ satisfies the differential equation (1).

Example 1.   Given $xp + p^2 - q = 0$.   (a) Using for the initial curve Γ, $x_0 = 0$, $y_0 = u$, $z_0 = u$, compute p and q for the initial strip. Here $G \equiv xp + p^2 - q$, $\omega_1(u) = 0$, $\omega_2(u) = u$, $\omega_3(u) = u$.   (b) Find an integral surface for the given equation.

Solution.   In Ex. III, 5, we found the strip through $(x_0, y_0, z_0, p_0, q_0)$ to be

$$x = \frac{q_0}{p_0}e^t - p_0 e^{-t}, \qquad y = y_0 - t, \qquad z = z_0 + \frac{p_0^2}{2}(1 - e^{-2t}),$$

$$p = p_0 e^{-t}, \qquad q = q_0.$$

From (5), we find

$$0 \cdot p_0 + p_0^2 - q_0 = 0, \qquad 0 \cdot p_0 + 1 \cdot q_0 = 1,$$

so that p and q for the initial strip are $p_0 = 1$, $q_0 = 1$.   Hence, the initial characteristic strip is

$$x_0 = 0, \qquad y_0 = u, \qquad z_0 = u, \qquad p_0 = 1, \qquad q_0 = 1.$$

The first three equations of (15) in Sec. 4 give the parametric equations of a surface which is an integral solution of the given equation, namely,

$$x = e^t - e^{-t}, \qquad y = u - t, \qquad z = u + \tfrac{1}{2}(1 - e^{-2t}).$$

Eliminating u and t, we have the integral surface $z = \Phi(x, y)$, i.e.,

$$z = y + \log \frac{x + \sqrt{x^2 + x}}{2} + \frac{x}{x + \sqrt{x^2 + 4}}.$$

Evidently the curve Γ lies on this surface.

EXERCISES IV

1. Solve Example 1 above if Γ is the curve $x_0 = u$, $y_0 = 0$, $z_0 = u^2$.

$$Ans. \; z = \frac{x^2 e^y}{3e^{-y} - 2e^y}.$$

2. Find integral surfaces for each of the following equations, using the indicated initial curve Γ:

(a) $pq - 1 = 0$, $\Gamma: x_0 = 0$, $y_0 = e^u$, $z_0 = u$.

(b) $2p^2 y = q$, $\Gamma: x_0 = u$, $y_0 = 0$, $z_0 = u^3$.

(c) $pq = z$, $\Gamma: x_0 = u$, $y_0 = 1 - u$, $z_0 = 1$.   *Ans.* $4z = (1 + x + y)^2$.

3. Find integral surfaces, selecting your own curve Γ, for:

(a) $zp(x + y) + p(q - p) - z^2 = 0$.   (b) $pq - px = qy$.

4. Show that Eq. (5) in Sec. 5 can be solved for p_0 and q_0.

HINT: (a) when $u = 0$, and $p_0 = \alpha$, $q_0 = \beta$, Eqs. (5) hold by hypothesis. (b) The Jacobian J of G and $L \equiv \omega_3' - p_0\omega_1' - q_0\omega_2'$ with respect to p_0 and q_0 does not vanish, for if $J = 0$, then the projections of C_1 and Γ on the xy-plane would be tangent at (a, b).   Recall Eq. (4).

5. Prove Eqs. (27).

6. The Principal Equations of Mathematical Physics. The chief partial differential equations of classical mathematical physics are, with a few exceptions, included in the general second order partial differential equation

$$\sum_{r=1}^{n}\sum_{s=1}^{n} a_{rs}\frac{\partial^2\varphi}{\partial x_r\,\partial x_s} + \sum_{r=1}^{n} b_r\frac{\partial\varphi}{\partial x_r} + c\varphi = F, \tag{1}$$

where all the a's, b's, c, and F are functions of n independent variables $x_1,\ x_2,\ x_3,\ \cdots,\ x_n$.

Included in this class of differential equations are the following important types:

$$\nabla^2\varphi \equiv \frac{\partial^2\varphi}{\partial x^2} + \frac{\partial^2\varphi}{\partial y^2} + \frac{\partial^2\varphi}{\partial z^2} = 0, \text{ (Laplace's equation)} \tag{2}$$

$$\nabla^2\varphi = -e, \qquad\qquad\qquad \text{(Poisson's equation)} \tag{3}$$

$$\frac{\partial\varphi}{\partial t} - a^2\,\nabla^2\varphi = 0, \tag{4}$$

$$\frac{\partial\varphi}{\partial t} - a^2\,\nabla^2\varphi = a^2 e, \tag{5}$$

$$\frac{\partial^2\varphi}{\partial t^2} - a^2\,\nabla^2\varphi = 0, \tag{6}$$

$$\frac{\partial^2\varphi}{\partial t^2} - a^2\,\nabla^2\varphi = a^2 e, \tag{7}$$

$$\frac{\partial^2\varphi}{\partial t^2} + a^2\,\nabla^2\varphi = 0, \tag{8}$$

$$\frac{\partial^2\varphi}{\partial t^2} + a^2\,\nabla^2\varphi = a^2 e. \tag{9}$$

In all of these equations, e, a, t, and φ denote the measures of certain physical quantities.

Equations (2), (3), $\cdots$, (7) are all examples of

$$a\frac{\partial^2\varphi}{\partial t^2} + b\frac{\partial\varphi}{\partial t} + c\nabla^2\varphi = -ce. \quad \text{(Telegraph equation)} \tag{10}$$

7. Laplace's Equation in Two Variables. The general solution of the Laplace equation

$$\frac{\partial^2\varphi}{\partial x^2} + \frac{\partial^2\varphi}{\partial y^2} = 0 \tag{1}$$

is of the form

$$\varphi = f_1(x + iy) + f_2(x - iy), \qquad i^2 = -1, \tag{2}$$

where f_1 and f_2 are arbitrary functions.   In practice this solution has been found to be too general, because of the difficulty of determining the functions so as to satisfy given boundary conditions.

A number of methods have been found useful for solving (1), but in many of them a general solution is not found, but rather a particular solution which may satisfy the given conditions.

A method which has been found quite useful depends upon assuming the solution to be a product of functions each of which contains only one of the variables.   Such a solution is only a particular solution, but the combination of a number of such particular solutions often results in a sufficiently general solution.

For instance, suppose we assume

$$\varphi = X(x) \cdot Y(y), \tag{3}$$

where X is a function of x only and Y is a function of y only. We wish to determine X and Y in such a manner that φ will satisfy equation (1).

Substituting (3) in (1), we find

$$\frac{X''}{X} + \frac{Y''}{Y} = 0. \tag{4}$$

Now this equality cannot hold unless each fraction in (4) is equal to a constant, for X''/X is a function of x only and Y''/Y is a function of y only, and such a function of x cannot equal such a function of y unless the functions are both constant and of the same value.   Thus

$$\frac{1}{X}\frac{d^2X}{dx^2} = -w^2, \qquad \frac{1}{Y}\frac{d^2Y}{dy^2} = w^2. \tag{5}$$

These equations are ordinary differential equations.   Their solutions are

$$X = c_1 \cos wx + c_2 \sin wx, \qquad Y = c_3 e^{wy} + c_4 e^{-wy}. \tag{6}$$

We thus conclude that

$$\varphi = (c_1 \cos wx + c_2 \sin wx)(c_3 e^{wy} + c_4 e^{-wy}) \tag{7}$$
$$= e^{wy}(A \cos wx + B \sin wx) + e^{-wy}(C \cos wx + D \sin wx),$$

where c_1, c_2, c_3, c_4, A, B, C, and D are arbitrary constants, is a solution of (1).

Since w may be assigned any value, it follows that there are infinitely many solutions of the type (7). In particular, the solutions for $w = 0, 1, 2, \cdots, n$ are, respectively,

$$\varphi_0 = A_0 + C_0,$$
$$\varphi_1 = e^y(A_1 \cos x + B_1 \sin x) + e^{-y}(C_1 \cos x + D_1 \sin x), \quad \cdots, \quad (8)$$
$$\varphi_n = e^{ny}(A_n \cos nx + B_n \sin nx) + e^{-ny}(C_n \cos nx + D_n \sin nx).$$

It is evident from the linearity of (1) that the sum of any finite number of solutions of (1) is a solution of (1). Thus,

$$\varphi = \varphi_0 + \varphi_1 + \cdots + \varphi_n \tag{9}$$

is a solution of (1). We shall assume this to be true when we let $n \rightarrow +\infty$. (This of course needs proof, and by no means necessarily follows from the assumptions made.) We thus assume

$$\varphi = \sum_{w=0}^{\infty} [e^{wy}(A_w \cos wx + B_w \sin wx)$$
$$+ e^{-wy}(C_w \cos wx + D_w \sin wx)] \tag{10}$$

as a solution of (1).

We must now determine the constants in (10) so that (10) will satisfy the given (boundary) conditions of the particular problem at hand. To illustrate the application of such boundary conditions we shall consider the following example:

The fundamental equation for the conduction of heat through a substance in which the quantity of heat created (or destroyed) per second per unit of volume is A has been shown to be (see Sec. 20, equation (20), Chap. II)

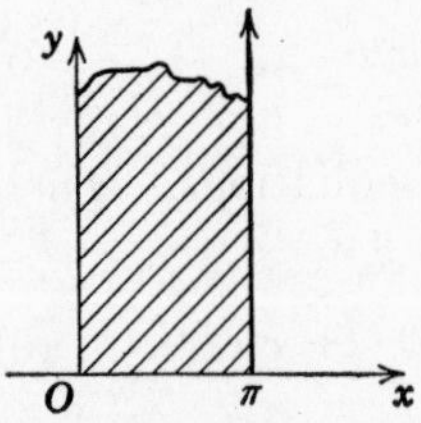

$$\frac{\partial^2 \varphi}{\partial x^2} + \frac{\partial^2 \varphi}{\partial y^2} + \frac{\partial^2 \varphi}{\partial z^2} = h^2 \frac{\partial \varphi}{\partial t} + \mu A, \tag{11}$$

where h and μ are constants.*

If the flow is steady, that is, independent of time, then $\partial \varphi/\partial t = 0$. If we further suppose that $A = 0$ and the flow of heat is in planes parallel to the xy-plane, φ is independent of z, so that $\partial^2 \varphi/\partial z^2 = 0$. Equation (11) then reduces to Eq. (1).

Fig. 199.

---

* $h^2 = c\rho/K$, where ρ is the density of the body, c its specific heat and $\mu = 1/K$, where K is conductivity of the substance.

We now seek a solution of (1) for the case when the heat flows in a rectangular plate of breadth π and of infinite length, the end being maintained at unit temperature, and the long edges at zero temperature. We consider the case when no heat is allowed to escape from either surface of the plate.

For convenience, we locate the end of the plate on the x-axis, and one of the long edges on the y-axis. The problem now consists of solving Eq. (1) subject to the boundary conditions

$$\varphi = 0 \qquad \text{where} \qquad x = 0, \tag{12}$$
$$\varphi = 0 \qquad \text{where} \qquad x = \pi, \tag{13}$$
$$\varphi = 1 \qquad \text{where} \qquad y = 0 \qquad \text{for} \qquad 0 < x < \pi, \tag{14}$$
$$\varphi = 0 \qquad \text{where} \qquad y = +\infty, \tag{15}$$

where the last condition arises from the nature of the physical problem.

We shall attempt to make (10) a solution of our problem. The boundary condition (15) shows that (10) must not contain terms in e^{wy}, so that $A_w = 0$, $B_w = 0$ for $w = 1, 2, \cdots$. From (12), we see

$$0 = \sum_{w=0}^{\infty} C_w e^{-wy} \tag{16}$$

for all values of y. Hence for all values of w, $C_w = 0$. Solution (10) is now reduced to the form

$$\varphi = \sum_{w=0}^{\infty} D_w e^{-wy} \sin wx, \tag{17}$$

which satisfies conditions (12), (13) and (15). In order that condition (14) be satisfied, we must determine (if possible) the D_w's so that

$$1 = \sum_{w=0}^{\infty} D_w \sin wx, \qquad \text{for} \qquad 0 < x < \pi. \tag{18}$$

This is a Fourier series for the expansion of 1. From Chap. IV, Sec. 26, Example 1, we have

$$1 = \frac{4}{\pi} \left(\sin x + \frac{1}{3} \sin 3x + \frac{1}{5} \sin 5x + \cdots \right), \qquad 0 < x < \pi. \tag{19}$$

By comparison of (18) and (19), we see that

$$D_w = \frac{4}{w\pi} \text{ for } w \text{ odd}, \qquad D_w = 0 \text{ for } w \text{ even}.$$

We have now shown (subject to questions of convergence, etc.) that

$$\varphi = \frac{4}{\pi}\left(e^{-y} \sin x + \frac{1}{3}e^{-3y} \sin 3x + \frac{1}{5}e^{-5y} \sin 5x + \cdots \right) \quad (20)$$

is a solution of (1) which satisfies boundary conditions (12), $\cdots$, (15). (This does not, however, show that the solution is unique.)

8. Laplace's Equation in Three Variables. We consider the equation

$$\frac{\partial^2 \varphi}{\partial x^2} + \frac{\partial^2 \varphi}{\partial y^2} + \frac{\partial^2 \varphi}{\partial z^2} = 0. \quad (1)$$

This equation becomes, when (x, y, z) are replaced by cylindrical coordinates, $x = r \cos \theta$, $y = r \sin \theta$,

$$\frac{\partial^2 \varphi}{\partial r^2} + \frac{1}{r}\frac{\partial \varphi}{\partial r} + \frac{1}{r^2}\frac{\partial^2 \varphi}{\partial \theta^2} + \frac{\partial^2 \varphi}{\partial z^2} = 0. \quad (2)$$

We shall attempt to find a particular solution of (2) by assuming

$$\varphi = R\Theta Z, \quad (3)$$

where R is a function of r only, Θ is a function of θ only, and Z is a function of z only. Substituting (3) in (2), we find

$$\frac{1}{Z}\frac{d^2Z}{dz^2} = -\frac{1}{R}\frac{d^2R}{dr^2} - \frac{1}{rR}\frac{dR}{dr} - \frac{1}{r^2\Theta}\frac{d^2\Theta}{d\theta^2}. \quad (4)$$

Since the right-hand term in equation (4) does not change when z varies, it follows that $(1/Z)(d^2Z/dz^2)$ does not change with z. Hence

$$\frac{1}{Z}\frac{d^2Z}{dz^2} = w^2, \quad (5)$$

where w is a constant. A solution of (5) is

$$Z = c_1 e^{wx} + c_2 e^{-wx}. \quad (6)$$

From (4) and (5) we find

$$\frac{r^2}{R}\frac{d^2R}{dr^2} + \frac{r}{R}\frac{dR}{dr} + w^2 r^2 = -\frac{1}{\Theta}\frac{d^2\Theta}{d\theta^2} \quad (7)$$

from which we conclude that both the right and left-hand members of (7) are constant. Let this constant be k^2. Then

$$\frac{d^2\Theta}{d\theta^2} = -k^2\Theta, \tag{8}$$

so that

$$\Theta = C_3 \cos k\theta + C_4 \sin k\theta. \tag{9}$$

From (7) and (8), we conclude that

$$r^2\frac{d^2R}{dr^2} + r\frac{dR}{dr} + (w^2r^2 - k^2)R = 0. \tag{10}$$

Substituting $wr = x$ in (10), we find (10) reduces to a Bessel equation

$$x^2\frac{d^2R}{dx^2} + x\frac{dR}{dx} + (x^2 - k^2)R = 0. \tag{11}$$

If k is fractional, a solution of (11) is

$$R = C_5J_k(x) + C_6J_{-k}(x) = C_5J_k(wr) + C_6J_{-k}(wr); \tag{12}$$

if k is an integer,

$$R = C_5J_k(wr) + C_6K_k(wr). \tag{13}$$

The various values of R, Θ, and Z found above when substituted in (3) give a solution φ of (2). The sum of any finite number of such solutions is also a solution of (2). A particular solution of importance occurs when w is a fixed constant and k assumes positive integral values. In this case, the sum of a finite number of terms of

$$\varphi = \sum_{k=0}^{+\infty} [e^{wz}(A_k \cos k\theta + B_k \sin k\theta)$$
$$+ e^{-wz}(C_k \cos k\theta + D_k \sin k\theta)]J_k(wz) \tag{14}$$

is a solution of (2). We shall assume that the limit of this sum as $n \to +\infty$ is also a solution of (2).

If Eq. (1) be written in spherical coordinates $x = r \cos \theta \sin \phi$, $y = r \sin \theta \sin \phi$, $z = r \cos \phi$, (1) becomes

$$r^2\frac{\partial^2\varphi}{\partial r^2} + 2r\frac{\partial\varphi}{\partial r} + \frac{\partial^2\varphi}{\partial\phi^2} + \operatorname{ctn} \phi\frac{\partial\varphi}{\partial\phi} + \csc^2 \phi \frac{\partial^2\varphi}{\partial\theta^2} = 0. \tag{15}$$

We shall consider the special case when φ is independent of θ, and hence $\partial\varphi/\partial\theta = 0$. Equation (15) may then be reduced to

$$r^2\frac{\partial^2\varphi}{\partial r^2} + 2r\frac{\partial\varphi}{\partial r} + \frac{\partial^2\varphi}{\partial\phi^2} + \text{ctn } \phi\frac{\partial\varphi}{\partial\phi} = 0. \tag{16}$$

We seek a particular solution of (16) by setting

$$\varphi = R\Phi, \tag{17}$$

where R is a function of r only and Φ is a function of ϕ only. Following the procedure used above, we find

$$r^2\frac{d^2R}{dr^2} + 2r\frac{dR}{dr} - w^2R = 0, \tag{18}$$

$$\frac{d^2\Phi}{d\phi^2} + \text{ctn } \phi\frac{d\Phi}{d\phi} + w^2\Phi = 0, \tag{19}$$

where w is any constant.

Solving (18) by the method of Sec. 19, Chap. III, we find

$$R = c_1 r^k + \frac{c_2}{r^{k+1}}, \tag{20}$$

where

$$k = -\tfrac{1}{2} + \sqrt{w^2 + \tfrac{1}{4}}.$$

Equation (19) can be written in the form

$$\frac{d^2\Phi}{d\phi^2} + \text{ctn } \phi\frac{d\Phi}{d\phi} + k(k+1)\Phi = 0. \tag{21}$$

If in (21), we set $u = \cos\phi$, we obtain a Legendre equation

$$(1 - u^2)\frac{d^2\Phi}{du^2} - 2u\frac{d\Phi}{du} + k(k+1)\Phi = 0. \tag{22}$$

A particular solution of importance occurs when k is taken as a positive integer, in which case a solution of (22) is the Legendre polynomial

$$\Phi = P_k(u) = P_k(\cos\phi). \tag{23}$$

Combining the various solutions obtained, we find

$$\varphi = \sum_{k=0}^{+\infty}\left(A_k r^k + \frac{B_k}{r^{k+1}}\right)P_k(\cos\phi) \tag{24}$$

for a solution of (16), provided of course that the series converges.

EXERCISES V

1. Solve the problem given in Sec. 7 for the case where condition (14) is replaced by the condition $\varphi = \sin x$ when $y = 0$, $0 < x < \pi$.

2. (a) Show that Laplace's equation (1) becomes

$$\frac{\partial^2 \varphi}{\partial r^2} + \frac{1}{r^2} \frac{\partial^2 \varphi}{\partial \theta^2} + \frac{1}{r} \frac{\partial \varphi}{\partial r} = 0, \tag{21}$$

when x and y are replaced by polar coordinates (r, θ).

(b) By means of the method given above and placing $\varphi = R\Theta$, where R is a function of r only and Θ is a function of θ only, show that equation (21) leads to

$$r^2 \frac{d^2 R}{dr^2} + r \frac{dR}{dr} - w^2 R = 0, \qquad \frac{d^2 \Theta}{d\theta^2} = - w^2 \Theta. \tag{22}$$

(c) From (22) show that

$$R = C_1 r^w + c_2 r^{-w},$$
$$\Theta = C_3 \cos w\theta + C_4 \sin w\theta.$$

(d) Show that

$$\varphi = \sum_{w=0}^{+\infty} [r^w (A_w \cos w\theta + B_w \sin w\theta) + r^{-w}(C_w \cos w\theta + D_w \sin w\theta)]$$

is a solution of (21).

3. Give examples from the theory of heat, sound, light, electricity, $\cdots$, to illustrate the importance of the equations (1) to (10) given in Sec. 6.

4. Show that $V = \dfrac{1}{r} g\left(t - \dfrac{r}{c}, \dfrac{z - r}{x - iy} \right)$ satisfies $\nabla^2 V = \dfrac{1}{c^2} \dfrac{\partial^2 v}{\partial t^2}$ an equation fundamental in light and sound. Here $r^2 = x^2 + y^2 + z^2$, $i^2 = -1$, and g is arbitrary.

5. Write the equation of continuity for the conduction of heat, Sec. 7, Eq. (11), in cylindrical coordinates, in spherical coordinates.

6. Solve the equation of continuity (11) in Sec. 7, assuming that the flow of heat is steady and takes place radially outward from the axis of a cylinder. Assume that φ_1 and φ_2 are the temperatures of the cylindrical isothermals of radius a and b, respectively. Find the quantity of heat crossing an isothermal per unit of length per unit of time.

$$Ans. \quad \varphi = \frac{(\varphi_1 - \varphi_2) \log r - (\varphi_2 \log a - \varphi_1 \log b)}{\log a - \log b}.$$

7. (a) Solve Eq. (11), Sec. 7 in the case of steady flow of heat in the direction of the x-axis, with the temperature being given as $\varphi = \varphi_0$ at $x = 0$,

$\varphi = \varphi_1$ at $x = d$. $\qquad\qquad Ans. \quad \varphi = \dfrac{(\varphi_1 - \varphi_0)}{d} x + \varphi_0.$

(b) Find the quantity of heat that flows across an area S of any isothermal in time t. $\quad\quad Ans. \quad Q = -\int\int_S K\frac{\partial\varphi}{\partial x}t\,dS = \frac{K(\varphi_0 - \varphi_1)St}{d}.$

(c) Find the quantity of heat contained in the slab bounded by the planes $x = 0$ and $x = d$. $\quad\quad$ *Ans.* $\int_0^d c\rho Sv\,dx = \frac{1}{2}c\rho Sd(\varphi_0 + \varphi_1).$

8. (a) Solve Eq. (11), Sec. 7 in the case of steady flow of heat flowing out from a point, assuming the temperature $\varphi = \varphi_a$ for $r = a$, and $\varphi = \varphi_b$ for $r = b$, for all time. $(b > a)$.

$$Ans. \quad \varphi = (\varphi_a - \varphi_b)\frac{ab}{(b-a)}\frac{1}{r} + \frac{\varphi_b b - \varphi_a a}{(b-a)}.$$

(b) Find the quantity of heat that flows across any isothermal in time t.

$$Ans. \quad 4\pi kt(\varphi_a - \varphi_b)\frac{ab}{(b-a)}.$$

(c) Find the quantity of heat contained between the isothermals $r = a$ and $r = b$.

$$Ans. \quad 4\pi\rho c\left\{(\varphi_a - \varphi_b)\frac{ab(a+b)}{2} + (b\varphi_b - a\varphi_a)\left(\frac{a^2 + ab + b^2}{3}\right)\right\}.$$

9. Consider a thin plate bounded by the lines

$$x = 0, \quad x = l, \quad y = 0, \quad y = +\infty.$$

Suppose that the temperature on the edge $y = 0$ is given by $f(x)$, where f is independent of the time; and suppose that on the other edges of the plate, it is always 0. Suppose that the heat cannot escape from either surface of the plate, and that the effect of initial conditions has vanished, so that the temperature everywhere is independent of the time. Find an expression for the temperature at any point (x, y) of the plate. [Hint: Try

$$\varphi = \sum b_n \sinh\frac{n\pi y}{l}\sin\frac{n\pi x}{l}.\ ]$$

10. Consider a rectangular plate bounded by

$$x = 0, \quad x = l, \quad y = 0, \quad y = h$$

under steady-state conditions and suppose that the boundary conditions are as indicated below:

$$\varphi = 0 \quad \text{for} \quad x = 0, \quad \varphi = 0 \quad \text{for} \quad x = l,$$
$$\varphi = 0 \quad \text{for} \quad y = 0, \quad \varphi = f(x) \quad \text{for} \quad y = h.$$

Find the temperature at any point (x, y) in the plate.

11. Consider the rectangular plate in Ex. 10, but subject to the boundary conditions:

$$\varphi = 0 \quad \text{for} \quad x = 0, \quad \varphi = 0 \quad \text{for} \quad x = l,$$
$$\varphi = \psi(x) \quad \text{for} \quad y = 0, \quad \varphi = f(x) \quad \text{for} \quad y = h.$$

Find the steady-state solution for the temperature at any point in this plate.

12. Given a thin bar of length l, of uniform cross section whose surface is impervious to heat and from which no radiation occurs. Let one end of the bar be taken as the origin and let distances along the bar be denoted by x. Suppose that the temperature φ satisfies the following conditions: (a) $\varphi = 0$ for $x = 0$ and $x = l$ for all values of time t; (b) $\varphi = f(x)$ for $t = 0$,

$$\varphi \neq \infty \text{ at } t = \infty. \quad \left(\text{Hint: } \varphi = \sum b_n e^{-(1/h^2)(n\pi/l)^2 t} \sin \frac{n\pi x}{l}. \right)$$

13. Solve Ex. 12 when the initial temperature is given by $\varphi = \dfrac{cx(l - x)}{l^2}$.

14. Solve Ex. 12 if the ends of the bar are impervious to heat. The boundary conditions are: (a) $\partial\varphi/\partial x = 0$ for $x = 0$ and $x = l$ for all values of t; (b) $\varphi = f(x)$ for $t = 0$, $\varphi \neq \infty$ for $t = \infty$. (Hint:

$$\varphi = a_0 + \sum a_n e^{-(1/h^2)(n\pi/l)^2 t} \cos \frac{n\pi x}{l}. \Big)$$

15. Solve Ex. 12 for the case when the ends are maintained at different temperatures. Suppose: (a) For all values of t, $\varphi = \varphi_1$ for $x = 0$ and $\varphi = \varphi_2$ for $x = l$; (b) $\varphi = f(x)$ for $t = 0$, $\varphi \neq \infty$ at $t = \infty$.

$$\textit{Ans.} \quad \varphi = \frac{(\varphi_2 - \varphi_1)}{l} x + \varphi_1 + \sum b_n e^{-(1/h^2)(n\pi/l)^2 t} \sin \frac{n\pi x}{l},$$

where

$$b_n = \frac{2}{l} \int_0^l \left[f(x) - \frac{(\varphi_2 - \varphi_1)}{l} x - \varphi_1 \right] \sin \frac{n\pi x}{l} \, dx.$$

16. A rod of length l radiates heat according to the law

$$\frac{\partial\varphi}{\partial t} = K \frac{\partial^2\varphi}{\partial x^2} - h\varphi.$$

Both ends of the rod are maintained at temperature zero, and the initial temperature distribution is given. Find φ. Here (a) $\varphi = 0$ when $x = 0$ and $x = l$; (b) $\varphi = f(x)$ at $t = 0$, $\varphi \neq \infty$ at $t = \infty$. (Hint: Let $\varphi = e^{-ht}u$.)

$$\textit{Ans.} \quad \varphi = \sum b_n e^{-h + k(n\pi/l)^2 t} \sin \frac{n\pi x}{l}.$$

17. Find an expression for the steady-state temperature over a semicircular plate of radius a if the circumference of the plate is maintained at 50°C. and the boundary diameter is kept at 0°C. (Hint: Use Laplace's equation in polar coordinates.)

18. By means of the transformation

$$\partial y/\partial x = p, \ \partial y/\partial t = q, \qquad u = px + qt - y,$$

show that the equation of propagation of plane waves of sound,

$$\left(\frac{\partial y}{\partial x}\right)^{n+1}\frac{\partial^2 y}{\partial t^2} = a^2 \frac{\partial^2 y}{\partial x^2}$$

can be written $p^{n+1}\,\partial^2 u/\partial p^2 = a^2\,\partial^2 u/\partial q^2$.

19. Show that $F[x - a \log g,\ y - b \log g] = 0$ is a solution of

$$a\left(p\frac{\partial g}{\partial z} + \frac{\partial g}{\partial x}\right) + b\left(q\frac{\partial g}{\partial z} + \frac{\partial g}{\partial y}\right) = g,$$

where a and b are constants, and where F and g are arbitrary functions of x, y, and z. Is $g(x, y, z) = 0$ a solution?

20. Show that $y = f_1(x - ct) + f_2(x + ct)$ is a solution of the wave equation $\partial^2 y/\partial t^2 = c^2\,\partial^2 y/\partial x^2$. Show that when plotted, $f_1(x)$ and $f_1(x - ct)$ are exactly the same shape, but taken as a whole $f_1(x - ct)$ is displaced by a distance ct to the right of $f_1(x)$. This shows that $f_1(x - ct)$ is an irregular wave traveling to the right with uniform velocity c. State a similar result with regard to $f_2(x + ct)$, a wave which travels to the left.

21. (a) Show that $y = \cos \dfrac{2\pi}{\tau}\left(t - \dfrac{x}{c}\right)$ is a solution of $\dfrac{\partial^2 y}{\partial t^2} = c^2 \dfrac{\partial^2 y}{\partial x^2}$.

(b) By plotting this solution for successive values of the time t show that y represents an infinite train of progressive harmonic waves. The *wave length* is given by $\lambda = c\tau$, where τ is the *period* (the time taken for a complete wave to pass a fixed point) and where c is the velocity of the wave.

22. A string of length l and density ρ is under tension T. Its initial velocity and position are given. Find its position at any time. (See Chap. VIII, Sec. 7, Example 3.) In other words, solve $\partial^2 y/\partial t^2 = c^2\,\partial^2 y/\partial x^2$, $c^2 = T/\rho$, with $y = 0$ at $x = 0$ and at $x = l$; $y = f(x)$, $\partial y/\partial t = \phi(x)$ at $t = 0$.

$$Ans. \quad y = \sum_{n=1}^{\infty} b_n \sin \frac{n\pi x}{l} \cos \frac{n\pi ct}{l} + \sum_{n=1}^{\infty} b'_n \sin \frac{n\pi x}{l} \sin \frac{n\pi ct}{l},$$

where

$$b_n = \frac{2}{l}\int_0^l f(x) \sin \frac{n\pi x}{l}\,dx \quad \text{and} \quad b'_n = \frac{2}{n\pi c}\int_0^l \phi(x) \sin \frac{n\pi x}{l}\,dx.$$

23. Solve Ex. 22 for the case when damping is taken into account and $\partial^2 y/\partial t^2 = c^2\,\partial^2 y/\partial x^2 - 2k\,\partial y/\partial t$.

$$Ans. \quad y = \sum b_n e^{-kt} \sin \frac{n\pi x}{l} \cos \mu t + \sum \left(b'_n + \frac{b_n k}{\mu}\right) e^{-kt} \sin \frac{n\pi x}{l} \sin \mu t,$$

where

$$\mu = \sqrt{\frac{n^2\pi^2 c^2}{l^2} - k^2},\ b_n = \frac{2}{l}\int_0^l f(x) \sin \frac{n\pi x}{l}\,dx,\ \text{and}$$

$$b'_n = \frac{2}{l\mu}\int_0^l \phi(x) \sin \frac{n\pi x}{l}\,dx.$$

24. (a) Solve Ex. 22 for the case when $\partial y/\partial t = 0$. Find an expression for the kinetic energy. (HINT: K.E. $= \frac{1}{2}\int_0^l \rho\dot{y}^2\, dx$.)

$$Ans. \quad K.E. = \frac{\rho l}{4}\sum b_n^2\left(\frac{n\pi c}{l}\right)^2 \sin^2\frac{n\pi ct}{l}.$$

(b) Show that the potential energy of the string is given by

$$\frac{\rho c^2}{2}\int_0^l \left(\frac{\partial y}{\partial x}\right)^2 dx = \frac{\rho l}{4}\sum b_n^2\left(\frac{n\pi c}{l}\right)^2 \cos^2\frac{n\pi ct}{l}.$$

25. Show that for a string of unlimited length with

$$y = \varphi(x) \text{ and } \dot{y} = \psi(x) \text{ at } t = 0,$$

$$y = \frac{1}{2}[\varphi(x - ct) + \varphi(x + ct)] + \frac{1}{2c}\int_{x-ct}^{x+ct} \psi(\xi)\, d\xi.$$

26. Solve Ex. 25 when $\varphi(x) = 0$ and $\psi(x) = 5x$.

27. Show that for a semiinfinite string, stretching from $(0, 0)$ to $(+\infty, 0)$, with $y = 0$ at $x = 0$ for all values of t, $y = f(ct - x) - f(ct + x)$.

28. (a) Solve $\partial^2 y/\partial t^2 = c^2\, \partial^2 y/\partial x^2$, by assuming a solution of the form $y = J(t) \cdot X(x)$ as in Secs. 7 and 8.

(b) Express your solution in the form

$$y = \sum_{n=1}^{\infty}\left(C_n \cos\frac{n\pi ct}{l} + D_n \sin\frac{n\pi ct}{l}\right)\sin\frac{n\pi x}{l}.$$

(c) Show that if the string starts from rest, all the D_n vanish.

(d) Show that if the string starts from the equilibrium position with given velocities, every C_n vanishes.

(e) Show that the sum of the potential and kinetic energies is

$$\left(\frac{n^2\pi^2}{4l}\right)P\sum_{n=1}^{\infty}(C_n^2 + D_n^2),$$

where $P = \rho c^2$ is the tension.

(f) Show that the fundamental pitch has frequency $c/2l = (1/2l)\sqrt{P/\rho}$.

(g) From (f), deduce methods for varying the fundamental pitch of a string.

29. *Harp String.* A harp string is set into motion by plucking. Suppose its initial position is given by

$$y = (b/a)x \text{ for } 0 \leq x \leq a; \qquad y = \frac{b(l - x)}{(l - a)}, \text{ for } a \leq x \leq l.$$

(a) Assuming the string is at rest at this initial position, find the position of the string at any later instant. Use Ex. 28 (b).

Ans. $y = \dfrac{2bl^2}{\pi^2 a(l-a)} \displaystyle\sum_{n=1}^{\infty} \dfrac{1}{n^2} \sin \dfrac{n\pi a}{l} \sin \dfrac{n\pi x}{l} \cos \dfrac{n\pi ct}{l}$, where $0 \leqq x \leqq l, 0 \leqq t$.

(b) Show that the harmonic of order n is absent when the string is plucked at one of its nodes (if $\sin n\pi a/l = 0$).

(c) Prove that all even harmonics disappear when the string is plucked at its mid-point.

(d) Show that the motion of the string is the resultant of two equal waves, moving with velocity c in opposite directions. [Hint: In the answer to (a) set $2 \sin \dfrac{n\pi x}{l} \cos \dfrac{n\pi ct}{l} = \sin \dfrac{n\pi}{l}(x-ct) + \sin \dfrac{n\pi}{l}(x+ct)$.]

30. Show that $w = \displaystyle\sum_{m,n=1}^{\infty} A_{mn} \sin\left(\dfrac{m\pi x}{a}\right) \sin\left(\dfrac{n\pi y}{b}\right) \cos (pct + a)$ is a

solution of $\dfrac{\partial^2 w}{\partial t^2} = c^2\left(\dfrac{\partial^2 w}{\partial x^2} + \dfrac{\partial^2 w}{\partial y^2}\right)$. Show that $w = 0$ when $x = 0$, $y = 0$, $x = a$, and $y = b$, where m and n are positive integers satisfying

$$\left(\dfrac{p}{\pi}\right)^2 = \left(\dfrac{m}{a}\right)^2 + \left(\dfrac{n}{b}\right)^2.$$

Here w is one solution of the equation for a vibrating membrane of fixed rectangular boundary.

31. The equation for a vibrating membrane with a fixed boundary is
$\dfrac{\partial^2 w}{\partial t^2} = c^2\left(\dfrac{\partial^2 w}{\partial r^2} + \dfrac{1}{r}\dfrac{\partial w}{\partial r}\right).$

(a) Show that $w = A J_0(nr) \cos (nct + a)$ is a solution of this equation.

(b) Solve the equation for a vibrating membrane, assuming a solution of the form $w = T(t) \cdot R(r)$.

(c) Show that $w = \displaystyle\sum_{k=0}^{\infty} (a_k \cos \lambda_k at + b_k \sin \lambda_k at) J_0(\lambda_k r)$ is also a solution, where $\lambda_0, \lambda_1, \cdots$ are the positive roots of $J_0(x)$.

32. In Ex. 30, suppose the vibrating membrane is started with the shape $z = f(x, y)$. Show that

$$A_{m,n} = \dfrac{4}{ab} \int_0^a \int_0^b f(x, y) \sin \dfrac{m\pi x}{a} \sin \dfrac{n\pi y}{b} \partial y \, dx.$$

33. Show that $\Sigma(a_n \cos n\phi + b_n \sin n\phi) J_n(r)$ is a solution of

$$\dfrac{\partial^2 V}{\partial r^2} + \dfrac{1}{r}\dfrac{\partial V}{\partial r} + \dfrac{1}{r^2}\dfrac{\partial^2 V}{\partial \phi^2} + V = 0.$$

34. Show that $r^{-\frac{1}{2}}J_{m+\frac{1}{2}}(r)P_n^m(\cos\theta)[a_{n,m}\cos m\phi + b_{n,m}\sin m\phi]$ satisfies $(\partial^2 V/\partial x^2) + (\partial^2 V/\partial y^2) + (\partial^2 V/\partial z^2) + V = 0$, where P_n^m is given in Chap. III, Sec. 32, Eq. (23).

35. Show that Laplace's equation in polar coordinates has a solution of the form

$$V = \sum_{n=0}^{\infty}\sum_{m=0}^{\infty}(A_n r^n + B_n r^{-(n+1)})(a_m \cos m\theta + b_m \sin m\theta)P_n^m(\cos\phi).$$

36. A thin bar of uniform section is bent into a circular ring of radius a One normal section N of the ring is maintained at constant temperature Heat radiates from the ring.   Show that the temperature is given by

$$\varphi = \frac{\varphi_0 \cosh\lambda(x - \pi a)}{\cosh\lambda\pi a}, \qquad \lambda = \sqrt{\frac{ep}{k\sigma}},$$

where σ is the cross-sectional area, k is the conductivity, e is its emissivity, p the perimeter, x represents arc length from the section N, and φ_0 is the temperature at N.   (HINT: $\partial^2\varphi/\partial x^2 = \lambda^2\varphi$; $\varphi = \varphi_0$ for $x = 0$, $\partial\varphi/\partial x = 0$ for $x = \pm\pi a$.)

37. A steam pipe 20 cm. in diameter is insulated by a layer of asbestos of conductivity 0.0008 and 3 cm. thick.   If the outer surface is at 20°C. and the inner surface is at 250°C., find the heat loss in calories per day for 1 m. of pipe.

9. Harmonic Functions.

Let $\Phi(x, y)$ be a function which over a region $\mathfrak{R}$ is continuous and has continuous derivatives of the first and second orders, except perhaps at certain definite points called *singular points*.   If

$$\frac{\partial^2\Phi}{\partial x^2} + \frac{\partial^2\Phi}{\partial y^2} = 0, \tag{1}$$

then Φ is called a *plane harmonic function*.   A function $V(x, y, z)$, which over a region $\mathfrak{D}$ of space is continuous and has continuous derivatives of the first and second orders (except at perhaps certain definite points, called singular points), and which satisfies

$$\frac{\partial^2 V}{\partial x^2} + \frac{\partial^2 V}{\partial y^2} + \frac{\partial^2 V}{\partial z^2} = 0, \tag{2}$$

is called a *space harmonic function*.

Harmonic functions have been studied in various places in this book.   We shall now state a few of the theorems concerning such functions.

THEOREM 9.1. *Let* $\Re$ *(or* $\mathfrak{D}$ *) be a region bounded by a simple closed curve* C *(or surface* S *).* (I) *If upon and within* $\Re$ *(or* $\mathfrak{D}$ *) the harmonic function* $V(x, y)$ *, [or* $V(x, y, z)$ *], has no singularities, the line integral of the normal derivative* of* V *along* C *(or over* S *) vanishes.* (II) *If* $V(x, y)$ *, [or* $V(x, y, z)$ *], has continuous first and second partial derivatives, and if the line (or surface) integral along every closed curve (surface) in a region* $\Re$ *(or* $\mathfrak{D}$ *) vanishes, then* V *is harmonic.*

In the case of $V(x, y)$, by Green's theorem, (Chap. II, Sec. 18)

$$\int_C \frac{dV}{dn}\, ds = \int_C \frac{\partial V}{\partial x}\, dy - \frac{\partial V}{\partial y}\, dx = \int\int_{\Re} \nabla^2 V\, \partial x\, dy. \qquad (3)$$

If V is harmonic, $\nabla^2 V = 0$ and part I of Theorem 9.1 follows. If the left member of (3) vanishes for all closed curves, the right member must vanish for every region, and consequently $\nabla^2 V \equiv 0$, or that V is harmonic. We leave the space case to Ex. 1 below.

THEOREM 9.2. *The average value of a harmonic function* V *over a circle (or sphere) in which* V *has no singularities is equal to the value of* V *at the center of the circle.*

Proof. Translate the coordinate axes so that the center of the circle is at the origin O. Assume the radius of the circle to be a. Then

$$\frac{dV(r, \theta)}{dn} = \frac{\partial V(r, \theta)}{\partial r}, \qquad ds = a\, d\theta,$$

and by (3) we may write

$$\int_0^{2\pi} \frac{\partial V}{\partial r}\, d\theta = 0.$$

Hence (Theorem 17.2 in Chap. II)

$$\int_0^a \int_0^{2\pi} \frac{\partial V}{\partial r} \partial\theta\, dr = \int_0^{2\pi} \int_0^a \frac{\partial V}{\partial r} \partial r\, d\theta$$

$$= \int_0^{2\pi} [V(a, \theta) - V(0, \theta)]\, d\theta = 0,$$

where $V(0, \theta) = V(0, 0) \equiv V_0$.

It follows that

$$V_0 = \frac{1}{2\pi} \int_0^{2\pi} V(a, \theta)\, d\theta. \qquad (4)$$

---

* By normal derivative we here mean the directional derivative in the direction normal to C at any point on C.

COROLLARY 9.21.   *A harmonic function having no singularities within a region cannot have a maximum or minimum at any point within the region.*

We shall prove this for the case of $V(x, y)$.   Suppose the function had a maximum (or minimum) at a point P in the region. Then this point may be inclosed in a circle with center P and radius sufficiently small that on the boundary the value of the function is always less (greater) than its value at P.   This contradicts the assertion of the preceding theorem.

COROLLARY 9.22.   *A harmonic function having no singularities within a region* $\mathcal{R}$, *and having a constant value on the boundary of the region* $\mathcal{R}$, *is constant throughout* $\mathcal{R}$.

The maximum and minimum values of the function must occur on the boundary of the region.   If the function is constant, these maximum and minimum values are equal, and the function is a constant throughout the region.

COROLLARY 9.23.   *Two harmonic functions having identical values upon a closed contour* C *and having no singularities within* C *are identical throughout the region bounded by* C.

The difference between the two functions is harmonic with the constant value zero on the boundary.   By the preceding corollary, the difference has the value zero within the entire region bounded by C.

The theorems given above remain true when the region is allowed to become infinite, provided proper account of the behavior of the function at infinity is taken into consideration.

THEOREM 9.3.   *If the normal derivative of a real harmonic function* V *(having no singularities on or within a given contour* C) *vanishes identically along* C, *then* V *is a constant.*

By Green's theorem (see Ex. XIV, 10, of Chap. II)

$$\int_C V \frac{dV}{dn} \, ds = \int\int_R \left[\left(\frac{\partial V}{\partial x} \right)^2 + \left(\frac{\partial V}{\partial y} \right)^2 \right] \partial x \, dy.$$

If along C, $dV/dn = 0$, then $\partial V/\partial x = 0$, $\partial V/\partial y = 0$, so that V is a constant.

COROLLARY 9.31.   *Two harmonic functions* V_1 *and* V_2 *having identically equal normal derivatives along a closed contour (within which they have no singularities) differ at most by an additive constant.*

This is proved in much the same manner as Corollary 9.23.

The above theorems are of great importance in mathematical physics. Thus, the problem of finding the potential distribution in a body in which a steady flow of electricity exists is the problem of solving Laplace's equation; the problem of finding the distribution of temperature in a body supporting a steady flow of heat involves the solving of Laplace's equation. Many other examples of this type have been mentioned throughout the text. A particularly notable case occurs in the study of irrotational motion of incompressible fluids.

As examples of the physical interpretation of the theorems given above, Corollary 9.23 applied to the steady flow of heat states that the temperature within a closed region is fully determined by the temperatures on the boundary; Corollary 9.31 states that except for an additive constant the temperature distribution inside a region is determined by the rate of flow of heat across the boundary.

Potential Integrals. Let $\rho(x, y, z)$ be a function defined over a region $\mathfrak{D}$ of space. By the *potential* of ρ at (ξ, η, ζ) is meant the integral

$$\Phi(\xi, \eta, \zeta) = \iiint_{\mathfrak{D}} \frac{\rho(x, y, z)\ \partial x\ \partial y\ dz}{\sqrt{(x - \xi)^2 + (y - \eta)^2 + (z - \zeta)^2}}$$
$$= \int_{\mathfrak{D}} \frac{\rho\ dV}{r}.$$

It is possible to prove

THEOREM 9.4. *The potential integral Φ satisfies Laplace's or Poisson's equation,*

$$\frac{\partial^2 \Phi}{\partial \xi^2} + \frac{\partial^2 \Phi}{\partial \eta^2} + \frac{\partial^2 \Phi}{\partial \zeta^2} = 0 \qquad or \qquad \frac{\partial^2 \Phi}{\partial \xi^2} + \frac{\partial^2 \Phi}{\partial \eta^2} + \frac{\partial^2 \Phi}{\partial \zeta^2} = -4\pi\rho,$$

according as the point (ξ, η, ζ) lies outside or inside the body of density $\rho(x, y, z)$.

An extended treatment of the potential integral and its application to electricity, magnetism, and other fields of physics will not be undertaken here. (See O. D. Kellogg, "Foundations of Potential Theory.")

EXERCISES VI

1. Complete the proof of Theorem 9.1.
2. Complete the proof of Theorem 9.2.

3. Complete the proof of Corollary 9.21.

4. Prove Corollary 9.22 for the space case.

5. Under what conditions are each of the following functions harmonic:

(a) $ax + by + cz + d$.

(b) $ax^2 + 2bxy + cy^2$.

(c) The sum (or difference) of two harmonic functions.

(d) The product of two harmonic functions.

(e) $\sin x \cosh y$.

(f) $f(ax + by + cz)$.   *Ans.* If $a^2 + b^2 + c^2 = 0$.

(g) $(z + ix \cos a + iy \sin a)^n$.

6. A space harmonic function V_n which is homogeneous of degree n is called a *solid spherical harmonic of degree n.* Show that the following are harmonics of degrees -1, 0, 1, 2, n, respectively; r^{-1}, 1, $ax + by + cz$, $x^2 - y^2 + yz$, $(z + ix)^n$.

7. A function U_n related to V_n in Ex. 6 by $U_n = V_n r^{-n}$ is called *a surface spherical harmonic of degree n.*

Show that a necessary and sufficient condition that a function $U_n(\theta, \phi)$, in polar coordinates, should be a surface spherical harmonic of degree n is that U_n satisfy $n(n + 1)U_n + \dfrac{1}{\sin \theta} \dfrac{\partial}{\partial \theta}\left(\sin \theta \cdot \dfrac{\partial U_n}{\partial \theta}\right) + \dfrac{1}{\sin^2 \theta} \dfrac{\partial^2 U_n}{\partial \phi^2} = 0.$

8. Show that if V_n is a solid spherical harmonic of degree n, then $r^{-2n-1}V_n$ is a solid spherical harmonic of degree $(-n - 1)$.

9. Show that $r^m V_n$ is a solid spherical harmonic if $m = 0$, or if $m = -2n - 1$.

10. Prove that the Legendre coefficient $P_n(\cos \theta)$ is a surface spherical harmonic of degree n.

11. Show that $[\cos \theta + i \sin \theta \cos (\phi - a)]^n$ is a surface harmonic of degree n.

12. Show that $U = f(\chi + i\phi) + F(\chi - i\phi)$ is a surface spherical harmonic of degree zero, where f and F are arbitrary functions and $\chi = \log \tan \frac{1}{2}\theta$.

13. Prove Theorem 9.4.   (See Kellogg, "Potential Theory.")

CHAPTER VIII

CALCULUS OF VARIATIONS. DYNAMICS

PART A. CALCULUS OF VARIATIONS

1. Introduction. It is well known that many physical phenomena are governed by laws which state, in effect, that the phenomena occur in such a manner that some physical or geometrical quantity has a maximum or minimum value. For example:

(a) When a ray of light travels through a substance, the velocity of the ray at any point P depends on the index of refraction of the substance at P. If the index of refraction varies from point to point in the substance, but is the same in all directions at any one point, then the ray follows that particular path from point A to point B for which the time required to go from A to B is a minimum:

Fig. 200.

(b) If a soap-bubble film is stretched over a twisted loop of wire, the film assumes such a shape that it forms a surface of minimum area.

(c) The distribution of electron charges within an atom in its lowest "state" of excitation is such that the internal energy of the atom is a minimum.

(d) If a metallic object A and a needle B are charged electrically until a spark jumps between them, the path of the spark is such that the "resistance" along it is a minimum. This path may not be along the line of shortest distance from B to A, for the conductivity of air is greater in the neighborhood of sharp points or corners on A.

Again, many physical problems arise in which we must design something so as to make some physical quantity a minimum. Thus:

(e) The longitudinal section of a dirigible or bullet must be determined so that the air resistance to it in flight is a minimum.

Certain purely geometric problems are of interest; in particular,

784

(f) Determine the shortest curve lying on a given warped surface S and passing through two given points A and B on S.

In all the above examples the quantity to be minimized may be represented by a line or surface integral, and the minimization is to be effected by proper choice of the curve or surface along which the integral is evaluated.   Thus, in (a) the time t required by the ray to go along the path C from A to B is $t = \int_A^B \dfrac{ds}{v(x,\, y,\, z)}$, where v is the velocity of the ray at $(x,\, y,\, z)$ (as determined by the index of refraction) and where s denotes arc length along C; the actual path followed by the ray is the one along which this integral takes on its minimum value.   Again, in (b) the surface area is $\iint_K \sqrt{1 + (z_x)^2 + (z_y)^2}\, \partial x\, dy$, and this integral is to be minimized by proper choice of the surface $z = f(x,\, y)$, z of course being subject to the condition that it represent a surface bounded by the given twisted loop.   These, and many other physical and geometrical questions lead us to the following *fundamental problem of the calculus of variations:*

Given a line or surface integral J.   To determine the curve C or surface S (subject to given initial or boundary conditions) along which J must be taken so that the value of J is a maximum or minimum.

2. Euler's Equation.   We shall first consider the problem of determining y as such a function $f(x)$ that

$$y = y_0 \quad \text{at} \quad x = a, \qquad y = y_1 \quad \text{at} \quad x = b, \qquad (1)$$

and such that, of all* functions y meeting (1),

$$J = \int_a^b F(x,\, y,\, p)\, dx \qquad (2)$$

is minimized by $y = f(x)$, where $p = y' = dy/dx$.   [We need consider only the case of a minimum, for (2) is maximized by minimizing $\int_a^b -F(x,\, y,\, p)\, dx$.]   In geometric language, we are to determine the curve $y = f(x)$ joining the given points $(a,\, y_0)$ and $(b,\, y_1)$ along which the line integral (2) is a minimum.

---

* For simplicity, we shall not itemize obvious technical conditions, such as that y must be differentiable and that y must be such that the point $(x,\, y,\, z)$ remains in the domain of definition of F; nor shall we try to list the less obvious conditions, for the analysis of these conditions is a long and highly technical problem.

It must be carefully observed in (2) that y is not a parameter in the way that α is a parameter in the integral $I = \int_a^b F(x, \alpha)\, \partial x$ (see Part E of Chap. II). Since I has a definite value for each value of α, it may be possible to compute $dI/d\alpha$, and to minimize I by setting $dI/d\alpha = 0$. On the other hand, if we write $y = f(x)$ in J, we see that the value of J depends upon the form of the

function $y = f(x)$ as a whole. Since the form of y may vary in an arbitrary manner, and since the value of J may vary much or little, depending on the exact way the form of y changes, J may not have a derivative with respect to y, in which case we cannot minimize J by setting $dJ/dy = 0$.

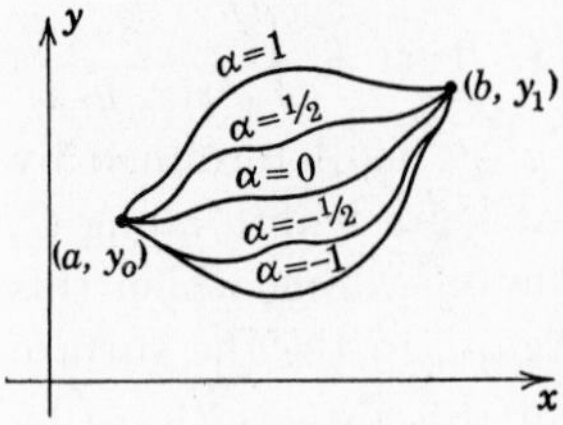

Fig. 201.

We shall avoid this difficulty by representing y in a specific way as a variable function of x, so that we may minimize J by the method indicated above for I. To construct this representation of y, let us suppose that the integral (2) is minimized by the particular function

$$y = f(x), \tag{3}$$

where $y_0 = f(a)$, $y_1 = f(b)$, and where we consider the value of J only for functions y which meet condition (1). Moreover, let $\eta(x)$ be an arbitrary function such that

$$\eta(a) = \eta(b) = 0, \tag{4}$$

and let α be a real parameter. Then

$$y = f(x) + \alpha \cdot \eta(x) \tag{5}$$

represents a variable function of x such that, for each value of α, the graph of (5) goes through the point (a, y_0) and (b, y_1) (see Fig. 201). We speak of the function (5) as a *variation* of the function (3). If we substitute (5) in (2), the value of the resulting integral is a function of α, i.e.

$$J(\alpha) = \int_a^b F[x, f(x) + \alpha \cdot \eta(x), f'(x) + \alpha \cdot \eta'(x)]\, dx. \tag{6}$$

By the definition of $f(x)$ in (3), $J(\alpha)$ has a minimum at $\alpha = 0$. Hence

$$\left. \frac{dJ(\alpha)}{d\alpha} \right]_{\alpha=0} = 0, \qquad \left. \frac{d^2 J(\alpha)}{d\alpha^2} \right]_{\alpha=0} \geqq 0. \tag{7}$$

By Leibnitz's rule (see Sec. 33, Chap. II),

$$\frac{dJ(\alpha)}{d\alpha} = \int_a^b \frac{\partial F}{\partial \alpha}\, dx$$

$$= \int_a^b \{\eta F_y[x, f(x) + \alpha \cdot \eta(x), f'(x) + \alpha \cdot \eta'(x)]$$

$$+ \eta' F_p[(x, f(x) + \alpha \cdot \eta(x), f'(x) + \alpha \cdot \eta'(x)]\}\, dx, \quad (8)$$

where $F_y = \dfrac{\partial F}{\partial y}\Big]_{x,p}$ and $F_p = \dfrac{\partial F}{\partial p}\Big]_{x,y}$. By (7) and (8),

$$\frac{dJ(\alpha)}{d\alpha}\Big]_{\alpha=0} = \int_a^b [\eta F_y(x, y, p) + \eta' F_p(x, y, p)]\, dx = 0, \quad (9)$$

where $y = f(x)$ of (3). Integrating the last term of (9) by parts, we have:

$$\int_a^b \eta' F_p(x, y, p)\, dx = [\eta(x) F_p(x, y, p)]_a^b - \int_a^b \left[\eta \frac{dF_p(x, y, p)}{dx} \right] dx.$$

$$(10)$$

By (4), the first term of the right member of (10) is zero, so that (9) becomes

$$\int_a^b \eta(x) \left[F_y - \frac{dF_p}{dx} \right] dx = 0. \quad (11)$$

Since $\eta(x)$ is arbitrary in (11) (except for condition (4)), it follows that

$$F_y(x, y, p) - \frac{dF_p(x, y, p)}{dx} = 0, \quad (12)$$

where y is the function $f(x)$ in (3). To show this, suppose there were a point $x = c$ in the interval $a \leq x \leq b$ at which

$$F_y - (dF_p/dx) > 0.$$

In view of the continuity of F_y and (dF_p/dx), $F_y - (dF_p/dx) > 0$ over some interval δ about $x = c$; $\eta(x)$ being arbitrary, we may take $\eta(x)$ as a function which is positive in δ and zero elsewhere. It is apparent that

$$\int_a^b \eta(x) \left[F_y - \frac{dF_p}{dx} \right] dx > 0,$$

in contradiction with (11). Hence the point $x = c$ does not exist. It may be shown in the same way that $F_y - (dF_p/dx)$ is never negative.

Equation (12) is known as *Euler's equation*, and a solution of (12) is called an *extremal* of (2). Equation (12) may be expanded into the form

$$F_{pp}\frac{d^2y}{dx^2} + F_{vp}\frac{dy}{dx} + F_{xp} - F_y = 0. \tag{13}$$

Since (13) is of the second order, its solution involves two arbitrary constants. These constants are just sufficient to determine a particular solution satisfying (1); in other words, *there is (in general) exactly one solution of Euler's equation meeting condition* (1), *and it is this solution which gives us* $f(x)$ *in* (3).

So far all we have proved is this: If there exists a function $y = f(x)$ which minimizes (2), then this function is the solution of (13) meeting condition (1). We have reached no conclusion in regard to the case where the integral (2) is such that there exists no function (3) which minimizes it. Since we do not yet know how to tell whether or not a given integral (2) has a minimizing function (3), we do not yet know if the solution of (13) meeting (1) actually minimizes (2). Now to show that this solution does minimize (2) it might be thought sufficient to show

that $\dfrac{d^2J(\alpha)}{dx^2}\bigg]_{\alpha=0} > 0$ for every function $\eta(x)$ in (6). Unfortu-

nately, this is not the case, for proving that $\dfrac{d^2J}{d\alpha^2}\bigg]_{\alpha=0} > 0$ for every

function η in (6) would show at best merely that $f(x)$ minimizes (2) with respect to variations of the particular type (5); since it is possible to construct variations of (3) in infinitely many other ways, we would not know that $f(x)$ minimizes (2) with respect to every possible kind of variation. To obtain a condition which insures that $f(x)$ minimizes (2) is a long and difficult problem.* In what follows we must rely on geometric or physical evidence to decide whether or not $f(x)$ minimizes (2).

It often happens in the applications of this subject that we desire, not a function which minimizes (2), but merely a function

which makes $\dfrac{dJ(\alpha)}{d\alpha}\bigg]_{\alpha=0} = 0$. Such a function is said to make

* Bolza, "Calculus of Variations."

the integral (2) *stationary* and is readily obtained as the proper solution of (13).

In many books on mathematics and physics a notation is used somewhat different from the one which we have introduced. The function $\alpha \cdot \eta(x)$ in (5) is denoted by δy and $\alpha \cdot \eta'(x)$ by $\delta y'$. Consequently,

$$\alpha \cdot \eta(x) \equiv \delta y, \qquad \alpha \cdot \eta'(x) \equiv \delta y',$$

$$\delta\!\left(\frac{dy}{dx}\right) = \frac{d}{dx}(\delta y), \qquad \delta(dy) = d(\delta y),$$

$$\frac{dJ}{d\alpha}\delta\alpha \equiv \delta J = \int_a^b \delta F \, dx = \int_a^b (F_y \delta y + F_{y'} \delta y') \, dx.$$

The use of this notation is dropping out since the representation of variations by differentials is unsuited to the more exacting methods of modern analysis.

EXERCISES I

1. Show that the Euler equations for $J = \int_a^b F(x, y, z, y', z') \, dx$ are

$$F_y - \frac{d}{dx}F_{y'} = 0, \qquad F_z - \frac{d}{dx}F_{z'} = 0. \tag{14}$$

[HINT: Vary $y = f(x)$ by the function $\alpha \cdot \eta(x)$ and vary $z = g(x)$ by the function $\alpha \cdot \xi(x)$.]   Generalize this result.

2. Show that the Euler equation for $J = \int_a^b F(x, y, y', y'') \, dx$ is

$$F_y - \frac{d}{dx}F_{y'} + \frac{d^2}{dx^2}F_{y''} = 0. \tag{15}$$

[HINT: In addition to (4) require that $\eta'(a) = \eta'(b) = 0$.]   Generalize this result.   (See Bolza, "Calculus of Variations.")

3. If the integrand F in (2) does not contain x explicitly, show that a first integral of Euler's equation (12) is

$$F - y'F_p = C. \tag{16}$$

[HINT: If F does not contain x explicitly, then

$$\frac{d}{dx}(F - y'F_p) \equiv y'\left(F_y - \frac{d}{dx}F_p\right).\bigg]$$

4. Show that the Euler equation for $J = \iint_K F(x, y, u, p, q) \, \partial x \, dy$ is

$$F_u - \frac{\partial F_p}{\partial x}\bigg)_y - \frac{\partial F_q}{\partial y}\bigg)_x = 0, \tag{17}$$

where $p = \partial u/\partial x, \; q = \partial u/\partial y$.

Hint: Vary $u(x, y)$ by the function $\alpha \cdot \eta(x, y)$ under the condition that $\eta(x, y) = 0$ along the boundary of K. Since

$$\frac{\partial}{\partial x}(\eta F_p) = \eta_x F_p + \eta \frac{\partial F_p}{\partial x},$$

it follows by Green's theorem that

$$\int\int_K \eta_x F_p \, \partial x \, dy = \int_C \eta F_p \, dy - \int\int_K \eta \frac{\partial F_p}{\partial x} \, \partial x \, dy,$$

where the line integral is zero by the definition of $\eta(x, y)$.

5. Generalize the result of Ex. 4 to
   (a) The integral $J = \int\int\int_R F(x, y, z, u, u_x, u_y, u_z) \, dV$.
   (b) The integral $J = \int\int_K F(x, y, u, v, u_x, u_y, v_x, v_y) \, dA$.
   (c) The integral $J = \int\int_K F(x, y, u, u_x, u_y, u_{xx}, u_{xy}, u_{yy}) \, dA$.

6. Show that Euler's equation for the integral

$$t = \int_{s_0}^{s_1} \frac{ds}{v(x, y)} = \int_a^b \frac{\sqrt{1 + y'^2}}{v(x, y)} \, dx$$

is

$$\frac{vy''}{1 + y'^2} - v_x y' + v_y = 0,$$

and integrate it when $v(x, y) = kx$ (see Sec. 1).

7. Show that Euler's equation for the integral

$$S = 2\pi \int_a^b y\sqrt{1 + y'^2} \, dx$$

is

$$\sqrt{1 + p^2} - \frac{d}{dx} \frac{yp}{\sqrt{1 + p^2}} = 0,$$

where S represents the area of a surface of revolution, and integrate this equation. [Hint: Write $d/dx = p(d/dy)$.]

8. If P is a particle falling along a curved path in a vertical plane, then the speed of P is $v = \sqrt{2gy}$, where y is the vertical distance fallen from rest. Hence the total time t of travel along the path is

$$t = \int_0^{s_1} \frac{ds}{v} = \frac{1}{\sqrt{2g}} \int_0^a \sqrt{\frac{1 + y'^2}{y}} \, dx.$$

Find the Euler equation for this integral, and solve it, showing that the solution represents a cycloid. (Note hint in Ex. 7.)

This is called the problem of the *brachystochrone*, i.e., the problem of finding the path of quickest descent from a point A to a point B below A, but not on the vertical line through A. Compare this problem with Ex. 6 as to physical significance.

9. Show that the Euler equation for the integral

$$\int\int_K \left[\left(\frac{\partial u}{\partial x} \right)^2 + \left(\frac{\partial u}{\partial y} \right)^2 \right] \partial x \, dy$$

is

$$\frac{\partial^2 u}{\partial x^2} + \frac{\partial^2 u}{\partial y^2} = 0,$$

and for the integral

$$\int\int\int_V \left[\left(\frac{\partial u}{\partial x} \right)^2 + \left(\frac{\partial u}{\partial y} \right)^2 + \left(\frac{\partial u}{\partial z} \right)^2 \right] dV$$

is

$$\frac{\partial^2 u}{\partial x^2} + \frac{\partial^2 u}{\partial y^2} + \frac{\partial^2 u}{\partial z^2} = 0.$$

10. Show that the Euler equation for the integral

$$S = \int\int_K \sqrt{1 + z_x^2 + z_y^2} \, \partial x \, dy$$

is

$$(1 + z_y^2)z_{xx} - 2z_x z_y z_{xy} + (1 + z_x^2)z_{yy} = 0.$$

11. Find the Euler equation for the integral

$$s = \int_a^b \sqrt{E + F\frac{dv}{du} + G\left(\frac{dv}{du}\right)^2} \, du$$

for arc length on a surface. Using this result, find the shortest curve between two given points on:

(a) A sphere.   (b) A cylinder of revolution.

(c) A cone of revolution.   (d) Any surface of revolution.

(e) The helicoid $x = r \cos \theta$, $y = r \sin \theta$, $z = k\theta$.

12. Show that the solution of the Euler equation for the integral

$$J = \int_A^B y'^2(y' + 1)^2 \, dx, \tag{18}$$

which passes through the points A and B is the straight line

$$y = mx + n \tag{19}$$

joining A and B.

Suppose that A and B are such that $-1 < m < 0$, so that $J > 0$ along (19). Then A and B may be joined by a broken line segment C such that each part of C has slope $m = 0$ or -1; moreover, C may be constructed

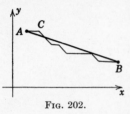

so that the maximum distance from C to the line (19) is arbitrarily small. It is seen that the value of J along C is 0. Hence the line (19) does *not* minimize J.

FIG. 202.

The broken line C is called a *discontinuous* solution for J since y' along C is discontinuous. A *continuous* solution is one along which y' is continuous at every point. Show that, by properly rounding the corners of C, a path $\overline{C}$ may be obtained along which y' is continuous and such that J has a value as close to zero as we please. Show that there exists no continuous solution which gives J its minimum value 0. Define the specific class of paths from A to B with respect to which J is minimized by the line (19).

3. Conditions of Constraint. It sometimes happens that an integral $J = \int_a^b F(x, y, p)\, dx$ has no minimum when $y = f(x)$ is restricted merely by the condition that $y = y_0$ when $x = a$ and $y = y_1$ when $x = b$. For example, $\int_a^b y\, dx$ has no minimum, and the Euler equation for this integral has no solution. In such a case, we are at liberty to impose an extra condition, or *constraint*, on $y = f(x)$. This condition may assume many forms, but we shall consider only the one in which $y = f(x)$ is required to make a second integral

$$K = \int_a^b G(x, y, p)\, dx \qquad (1)$$

have a specified constant value K_0.

To obtain the Euler equation for J under the condition that $K = K_0$, suppose

$$y = f(x) \qquad (2)$$

minimizes J, where $y_0 = f(a)$, $y_1 = f(b)$, and $K = K_0$ for this function. Let $\eta(x)$ and $\xi(x)$ be arbitrary functions such that

$$\eta(a) = \eta(b) = \xi(a) = \xi(b) = 0, \qquad (3)$$

and let α and β be real parameters. Construct the variation

$$y = f(x) + \alpha \cdot \eta(x) + \beta \cdot \xi(x). \qquad (4)$$

By the condition $K \equiv K_0$, we must have

$$\phi(\alpha, \beta) \equiv \int_a^b G(x, f + \alpha\eta + \beta\xi, f' + \alpha\eta' + \beta\xi')\, dx - K_0 \equiv 0. \qquad (5)$$

By Sec. 20 of Chap. I, (5) determines β as a single-valued function of α in the neighborhood of $\alpha = 0$, $\beta = 0$ if [cf. (11) of Sec. 2]

$$\phi_\beta(0, 0) \equiv \int_a^b [\xi G_y(x, f, f') + \xi' G_p(x, f, f')] \, dx$$

$$\equiv \int_a^b \xi\left(G_y - \frac{dG_p}{dx}\right) dx \neq 0. \tag{6}$$

Unless $G_y - (dG_p/dx) \equiv 0$, ξ may be determined so that (6) is met. Assuming (6) to hold, we have

$$\frac{dJ(\alpha)}{d\alpha}\bigg]_{\alpha=0} = \int_a^b [(\eta + \beta'\xi)F_y + (\eta' + \beta'\xi')F_p] \, dx \tag{7}$$

$$= \int_a^b (\eta F_y + \eta' F_p) \, dx + \beta' \int_a^b (\xi F_y + \xi' F_p) \, dx = 0,$$

where

$$\beta' = \frac{d\beta}{d\alpha}\bigg]_{\alpha=0} = -\frac{\phi_\alpha(0, 0)}{\phi_\beta(0, 0)} = -\frac{\int_a^b (\eta G_y + \eta' G_p) \, dx}{\int_a^b (\xi G_y + \xi' G_p) \, dx}.$$

Hence (7) may be written in the form

$$\int_a^b (\eta F_y + \eta' F_p) \, dx + \rho \int_a^b (\eta G_y + \eta' G_p) \, dx = 0, \tag{8}$$

where

$$\rho = -\frac{\int_a^b (\xi F_y + \xi' F_p) \, dx}{\int_a^b (\xi G_y + \xi' G_p) \, dx}.$$

Since ρ is a constant, we may write (8) in the form

$$\int_a^b [\eta(F_y + \rho G_y) + \eta'(F_p + \rho G_p)] \, dx = 0,$$

from which we obtain the Euler equation

$$(F_y + \rho G_y) - \frac{d}{dx}(F_p + \rho G_p) = 0, \tag{9}$$

where ρ may be regarded as a parameter, since its value depends upon the choice of ξ.

EXERCISES II

1. Show that $\int_a^b y \, dx$ is maximized by a circle when the total arc length of the curve $y = f(x)$ from $x = a$ to $x = b$ is to have a given value

$$l = \int_a^b \sqrt{1 + y'^2} \, dx.$$

2. Generalize Ex. I, 4, in the manner suggested by the discussion in Sec. 3 showing that the Euler equation is

$$(F_u + \rho G_u) - \frac{\partial}{\partial x}(F_p + \rho G_p) - \frac{\partial}{\partial y}(F_q + \rho G_q) = 0.$$

3. Let A and B be two given points (x_0, y_0) and (x_1, y_1), with $y_0 > 0$, $y_1 > 0$. Find the curve C of length l joining A and B such that

(a) C generates a surface of revolution of minimum area through A and B when revolved about the x-axis.

(b) C bounds with the lines $y = 0$, $x = x_0$, $x = x_1$, a region of maximum area.

4. Variable End Points. Let us now minimize

$$J = \int_a^{x_1} F(x, y, p)\, dx, \tag{1}$$

where $y = f(x)$ is subject to the condition

$$y = y_0 \quad \text{at} \quad x = a, \quad y = y_1 \quad \text{at} \quad x = x_1, \tag{2}$$

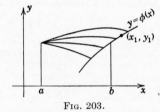

and where the point (x_1, y_1) is free to move along the curve

$$y = \phi(x). \tag{3}$$

Suppose (1) is minimized by $y = f(x)$, and that this curve meets the curve (3) at $x = b$. It is evident that $y = f(x)$ must satisfy Euler's equation

Fig. 203.

(12) of Sec. 2, for if $y = f(x)$ minimizes (1) under the conditions (2), then *a fortiori*, $y = f(x)$ minimizes (1) when the curve (3) is replaced by the fixed point $(b, \phi(b))$. To determine further the nature of $y = f(x)$, let us construct the variation

$$y = f(x) + \alpha \cdot \eta(x), \tag{4}$$

where

$$\eta(a) = 0, \quad \eta(b) \neq 0. \tag{5}$$

Then

$$J(\alpha) = \int_a^{x_1} F(x, f(x) + \alpha \cdot \eta(x), f'(x) + \alpha \cdot \eta'(x))\, dx, \tag{6}$$

where the upper limit x_1 is a function of α, so that $dJ(\alpha)/d\alpha$ involves the factor $dx_1/d\alpha$. To avoid this factor, let us change the independent parameter in (6) from α to h as follows: Let $x_1 = b + h$. Then by (2), (3), (4),

$$f(b + h) + \alpha \cdot \eta(b + h) = \phi(b + h). \tag{7}$$

Since $\eta(b) \neq 0$, $\eta(b + h) \neq 0$ for sufficiently small h. By (7), α is determined as a function of h:

$$\alpha = \alpha(h) = \frac{\phi(b + h) - f(b + h)}{\eta(b + h)}. \tag{8}$$

Since $x_1 = b$ when $\alpha = 0$, $h = 0$ when $\alpha = 0$, i.e., $\alpha(0) = 0$, and by (8)

$$\phi(b) - f(b) = 0. \tag{9}$$

Hence

$$\alpha'(0) = \lim_{h \to 0} \frac{\phi(b + h) - f(b + h) - [\phi(b) - f(b)]}{\eta(b + h) \cdot h}$$
$$= \frac{\phi'(b) - f'(b)}{\eta(b)}. \tag{10}$$

It follows by (6) and Sec. 33 of Chap. II that

$$\frac{dJ(h)}{dh}\Bigg]_{h=0} = \int_a^b [\alpha'(0)\eta F_y + \alpha'(0)\eta' F_p] \, dx + F[b, f(b), f'(b)],$$
$$= \alpha'(0)\eta F_p \Bigg]_a^b + \alpha'(0)\int_a^b \eta \left[F_y - \frac{dF_p}{dx} \right] dx$$
$$+ F[b, f(b), f'(b)] = 0. \tag{11}$$

Since $y = f(x)$ satisfies Euler's equation, the last integral vanishes. By (10), (11) reduces to

$$[\phi'(b) - f'(b)] F_p[b, f(b), f'(b)] + F[b, f(b), f'(b)] = 0. \tag{12}$$

Equation (12) is referred to as a *transversality* condition. It serves to determine a particular solution of Euler's equation in the following way: One of the two constants of integration in the general solution of Euler's equation is determined by the condition that $f(a) = y_0$; the other constant is determined by the condition that the equations

$$\phi(x) - f(x) = 0, \qquad (\phi' - f')F_p + F = 0$$

have a common solution $x = b$, so that (9) and (12) hold.

It is evident that a condition similar to (12) may be obtained for the case where the left end point is variable, and that both of these conditions hold when both end points are variable.

A physical interpretation of this discussion is given by (d) in Sec. 1.

EXERCISES III

1. Show that if the right end point of Ex. I, 7 is free to move along (3) of Sec. 4, then the minimizing solution of Ex. I, 7, is normal to (3).

2. Extend the discussion of Sec. 3 to the case of a variable end point, showing that the transversality condition is obtained from (12) by replacing F by $(F + \rho G)$ in (12).

3. Let C_1 and C_2 be two nonintersecting curves in the xy-plane or in space. Show that the curve C of shortest length from C_1 to C_2 is a straight line normal to C_1 and C_2.

PART B. ANALYTICAL DYNAMICS*

5. Laws of Classical Mechanics.

We shall consider a system S of n point particles of masses $m_1, m_2, \cdots, m_n$ with position

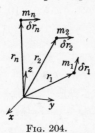

FIG. 204.

vectors $r_1, r_2, \cdots, r_n$, respectively. Suppose that the particles of this system are acted on by impressed forces $F_1^i, F_2^i, \cdots, F_n^i$, respectively (the superscript i denotes "impressed"), and suppose that the particles are given arbitrary (*virtual*) displacements $\delta r_1, \delta r_2, \cdots, \delta r_n$, respectively, subject of course to consistency with the constraints of the system.

The *principle of virtual displacements* or *virtual work* (first given by John Bernoulli in 1717) states that the condition for equilibrium of the system under the action of the forces is

$$F_1^i \cdot \delta r_1 + F_2^i \cdot \delta r_2 + \cdots + F_n^i \cdot \delta r_n = 0. \qquad (1)$$

D'Alembert's Principle. This principle was first given by D'Alembert in his "Traité de dynamique," published in 1743. It is "a general principle for finding the motions of several bodies which react on each other in any fashion." We shall give Mach's statement of the principle. (See Mach, "Mechanics.")

Let S be the system of n particles given above. If the particles were perfectly free to move, the forces $F_1^i, F_2^i, \cdots, F_n^i$, would give them accelerations $a_1 = F_1^i/m_1, \cdots, a_n = F_n^i/m_n$. How-

* See WEBSTER, "Dynamics of Particles"; WHITTAKER, "Analytical Dynamics"; LINDSEY and MORGENAU, "Foundations of Physics."

ever, owing to the constraints of the system, the actual accelerations are such as would be produced in free particles by the (*effective*) forces $\mathbf{F}_1^e, \mathbf{F}_2^e, \cdots, \mathbf{F}_n^e$. The vector differences

$$\mathbf{F}_1^i - \mathbf{F}_1^e = \mathbf{V}_1, \cdots, \mathbf{F}_n^i - \mathbf{F}_n^e = \mathbf{V}_n, \tag{2}$$

are thought of as the portions of the impressed forces which are "not effective." *This system of forces* $\mathbf{V}_1, \cdots, \mathbf{V}_n$ *must be such that the system* $\mathcal{S}$ *of particles must remain in equilibrium.* (The $\mathbf{V}$'s are sometimes called "lost forces.") In other words, the principle states that $\sum\limits_{j=1}^{n} \mathbf{V}_j \cdot \delta\mathbf{r}_j = 0$ where the $\delta\mathbf{r}_j$ are subject to the constraints on the system $\mathcal{S}$. The effective forces $\mathbf{F}_1^e$, $\mathbf{F}_2^e, \cdots, \mathbf{F}_n^e$ are considered to be $m_1\ddot{\mathbf{r}}_1, m_2\ddot{\mathbf{r}}_2, \cdots, m_n\ddot{\mathbf{r}}_n$, respectively. ($\dot{\mathbf{r}}_j = d\mathbf{r}_j/dt, \ddot{\mathbf{r}}_j = d^2\mathbf{r}_j/dt^2, \cdots$.)

D'Alembert's principle provides a single fundamental formula from which all other laws of classical mechanics may be derived. Lagrange in his "Mécanique analytique" (1788) used this principle as the starting point for the developments of his very general and powerful methods.

6. Hamilton's Principle. We consider the system $\mathcal{S}$ of Sec. 5 acted upon by a system of impressed forces $\mathbf{F}_1, \cdots, \mathbf{F}_n$. We shall assume that the classical laws of mechanics are valid. By D'Alembert's principle and the principle of virtual displacements (see Sec. 5), the motion of the system $\mathcal{S}$ is given by

$$\sum_{j=1}^{n} (m_j\ddot{\mathbf{r}}_j - \mathbf{F}_j) \cdot \delta\mathbf{r}_j = 0, \tag{1}$$

where $\delta\mathbf{r}_j$ is the "virtual displacement" of the jth particle. Since

$$\frac{d}{dt}(\dot{\mathbf{r}}_j \cdot \delta\mathbf{r}_j) = \ddot{\mathbf{r}}_j \cdot \delta\mathbf{r}_j + \frac{1}{2}\delta(v_j^2), \qquad \text{where} \qquad \dot{\mathbf{r}}_j \cdot \dot{\mathbf{r}}_j = v_j^2, \tag{2}$$

$$\sum_{j=1}^{n} m_j\frac{d}{dt}(\dot{\mathbf{r}}_j \cdot \delta\mathbf{r}_j) = \sum_{j=1}^{n} m_j\ddot{\mathbf{r}}_j \cdot \delta\mathbf{r}_j + \sum_{j=1}^{n} \frac{m_j}{2}\delta(v_j^2). \tag{3}$$

Integrating (3) with respect to time from $t = t_0$ to $t = t_1$, we have

$$\int_{t_0}^{t_1} \sum_{j=1}^{n} m_j\frac{d}{dt}(\dot{\mathbf{r}}_j \cdot \delta\mathbf{r}_j) = \int_{t_0}^{t_1} \sum_{j=1}^{n} m_j\ddot{\mathbf{r}}_j \cdot \delta\mathbf{r}_j + \int_{t_0}^{t_1} \sum_{j=1}^{n} \frac{m_j}{2}\delta(v_j^2), \tag{4}$$

and

$$\sum_{j=1}^{n} m_j \dot{\mathbf{r}}_j \cdot \delta \mathbf{r}_j \Bigg]_{t_0}^{t_1} = \int_{t_0}^{t_1} \sum_{j=1}^{n} m_j \ddot{\mathbf{r}}_j \cdot \delta \mathbf{r}_j + \int_{t_0}^{t_1} \sum_{j=1}^{n} \frac{m_j}{2} \delta(v_j^2). \tag{5}$$

We shall now consider the class of all motions of the system S in which the path of m_j begins at a given fixed point P_j and ends at a given point Q_i, $(j = 1, \cdots, n)$ in other words, the class of motions for which the $\delta \mathbf{r}_j$ are all zero at times t_0 and t_1. Then (5) shows that

$$\int_{t_0}^{t_1} \left(\delta T + \sum_{j=1}^{n} m_j \ddot{\mathbf{r}}_j \cdot \delta \mathbf{r}_j \right) dt = 0, \tag{6}$$

where $T \equiv \sum_{j=1}^{n} \frac{1}{2} m_j v_j^2$ is known as the *kinetic energy* of the system. From (1)

$$\sum_{j=1}^{n} \mathbf{F}_j \cdot \delta \mathbf{r}_j = \sum_{j=1}^{n} m_j \ddot{\mathbf{r}}_j \cdot \delta \mathbf{r}_j. \tag{7}$$

If there exists a function $V(\mathbf{r}_1, \mathbf{r}_2, \cdots, \mathbf{r}_n)$ of the position vectors of the n particles of S which has the property that

$$-\delta V = \sum_{j=1}^{n} \mathbf{F}_j \cdot \delta \mathbf{r}_j, \tag{8}$$

then the system S is said to be *conservative*. In this case (6) may be written

$$\delta \int_{0}^{t_1} (T - V)\, dt = 0 \tag{9}$$

If no such function V exists, the system S is said to be *non-conservative*. We have shown

Hamilton's Principle. *If we compare a dynamical* path with varied paths which have the same termini and which are described in the same time, then the time integral (6), [or (9)], has a stationary value for the dynamical path.*

* A *dynamical path* may be thought of as a path actually followed by the moving system S.

This principle may be taken as a fundamental postulate from which all the forms of classical dynamics may be deduced.

7. Lagrange's Equations. We return to the consideration of the system S, constrained or not. Suppose that the coordinates x_j, y_j, z_j of the jth particle are functions of m independent real parameters q_1, q_2, $\cdots$, q_m,

$$x_j = x_j(q_1, q_2, \cdots, q_m), \qquad y_j = y_j(q_1, q_2, \cdots, q_m), \quad (1)$$
$$z_j = z_j(q_1, q_2, \cdots, q_m),$$

or in the vector notation, $\mathbf{r}_j = \mathbf{r}_j(q_1, q_2, \cdots, q_m)$.

By Sec. 6, the kinetic energy of the system is

$$T = \tfrac{1}{2}\sum_{j=1}^{n} m_j(\dot{x}_j^2 + \dot{y}_j^2 + \dot{z}_j^2) = \tfrac{1}{2}\sum_{r=1}^{m}\sum_{s=1}^{m}\tau_{rs}\dot{q}_r\dot{q}_s, \quad (2)$$

where

$$\tau_{rs} = \sum_{p=1}^{n} m_p\frac{\partial x_p}{\partial q_r}\frac{\partial x_p}{\partial q_s}, \quad (3)$$

since

$$\dot{x}_j = \sum_{k=1}^{m}\frac{\partial x_j}{\partial q_k}\dot{q}_k, \qquad \dot{y}_j = \sum_{k=1}^{m}\frac{\partial y_j}{\partial q_k}\dot{q}_k, \qquad \dot{z}_j = \sum_{k=1}^{m}\frac{\partial z_j}{\partial q_k}\dot{q}_k. \quad (4)$$

The q_k used here are known as *generalized coordinates* and the $\dot{q}_k$ are called *generalized velocities*. We have shown that *the kinetic energy of* S *is a homogeneous quadratic form in the generalized velocities* $\dot{q}_k$, the coefficients τ_{rs} being functions of only the generalized coordinates q_k.   The τ_{rs} are such that for all assignable values of q_k and $\dot{q}_k$, T *shall be positive.*

We define δW, the *element of work*, to be $\delta W = \sum\limits_{j=1}^{n}\mathbf{F}_j \cdot \delta\mathbf{r}_j$. By means of (1) and (4), we find

$$\delta W = \sum_{j=1}^{n}\mathbf{F}_j \cdot \delta\mathbf{r}_j = \sum_{j=1}^{m}Q_j\delta q_j, \qquad \text{where} \qquad Q_j = \sum_{k=1}^{n}\mathbf{F}_k \cdot \frac{\partial\mathbf{r}_k}{\partial q_j}. \quad (5)$$

The term Q_j is called the *generalized force* for the jth particle due to the fact that $\sum\limits_{j=1}^{m}Q_j\delta q_j$ represents the total work done on S by the actual external forces $\mathbf{F}_1, \cdots, \mathbf{F}_n$ incident to the displacements $\delta \mathbf{r}_1, \cdots, \delta \mathbf{r}_n$.

We shall now apply Hamilton's principle to this system S in order to deduce the equations of motion in terms of the generalized coordinates q_k.

From (6) of Sec. 6,

$$\int_{t_0}^{t_1} (\delta T + \delta W) \, dt = \int_{t_0}^{t_1} \left(\delta T + \sum_{j=1}^{m} Q_j \delta q_j \right) dt = 0. \tag{6}$$

Now

$$\delta T = \sum_{k=1}^{m} \left(\frac{\partial T}{\partial q_k} \delta q_k + \frac{\partial T}{\partial \dot{q}_k} \delta \dot{q}_k \right), \quad \text{and} \quad \delta \dot{q}_k = \frac{d}{dt} \delta q_k. \tag{7}$$

Substitute (7) in (6) and integrate by parts the second terms in each set of δT. Since each $\delta q_s = 0$, $s = 1, \cdots, m$ at $t = t_0$ and at $t = t_1$, the integrated part vanishes, and we have

$$\int_{t_0}^{t_1} \left[\sum_{k=1}^{m} \left\{ \frac{\partial T}{\partial q_k} - \frac{d}{dt} \left(\frac{\partial T}{\partial \dot{q}_k} \right) + Q_k \right\} \delta q_k \right] dt = 0. \tag{8}$$

Now if each δq_k is arbitrary, $k = 1, \cdots, m$, the integral (8) vanishes only if the coefficient of every δq_k is equal to zero, so that

$$\frac{d}{dt} \left(\frac{\partial T}{\partial \dot{q}_k} \right) - \frac{\partial T}{\partial q_k} = Q_k. \quad (k = 1, \cdots, m) \tag{9}$$

If the system S is conservative, there exists a function $V(q_1, \cdots, q_m)$, known as the *potential energy*, such that

$$dV = -dW, \quad \text{and} \quad Q_k = -\frac{\partial V}{\partial q_k}. \quad (k = 1, \cdots, m) \tag{10}$$

In this case, the equations (9) of motions for S may be written

$$\frac{d}{dt} \left(\frac{\partial T}{\partial \dot{q}_k} \right) - \frac{\partial T}{\partial q_k} = -\frac{\partial V}{\partial q_k}. \quad (k = 1, \cdots, m) \tag{11}$$

Equation (11) is sometimes written

$$\frac{d}{dt} \left(\frac{\partial L}{\partial \dot{q}_k} \right) - \frac{\partial L}{\partial q_k} = 0, \, (k = 1, \cdots, m) \tag{12}$$

where $L \equiv T - V$ is known as the *kinetic potential* or *Lagrangian function*.

Equations (9) are known as *Lagrange's equations of motion* for the system S. Equations (9) are of the second order and hence their solution involves $2m$ arbitrary constants. The solution of (9) will express each q_k as a function of the time and the $2m$ constants which must be fixed by the initial conditions of the particles in system S.

If N of the coordinates $q_1, \cdots, q_m$ are essential to fix the configuration of a system at a given instant, the system S is said to have N *degrees of freedom.*

If we multiply each of the equations (9) by the corresponding velocity $\dot{q}_k$, and then add the results for $s = 1, \cdots, m$, we obtain

$$\sum_{k=1}^{m} \left[\frac{d}{dt}\left(\frac{\partial T}{\partial \dot{q}_k} \right) - \frac{\partial T}{\partial q_k} \right] \dot{q}_k = \sum_{k=1}^{m} Q_k \dot{q}_k, \qquad (13)$$

The right member of (13) is the time rate at which the applied forces do work on the system. Equation (13) is called the *equation of activity* in generalized coordinates.

We shall illustrate the use of Lagrange's equations.

Example 1. A particle of mass m moves freely in a plane. Show from Lagrange's equations that the equations of motion of the particle are

$$m\left[\frac{d^2 r}{dt^2} - r\left(\frac{d\phi}{dt} \right)^2 \right] = R, \qquad \frac{m}{r} \frac{d}{dt}\left(r^2 \frac{d\phi}{dt} \right) = \Phi, \qquad (9')$$

where R is the component of the force $\mathbf{F}$ impressed on the particle along the radius vector, Φ is the component of $\mathbf{F}$ normal to the radius vector, and where $x = r \cos \phi$, $y = r \sin \phi$.

Solution. The square of the speed of the particle is

$$v^2 = \dot{x}^2 + \dot{y}^2 = \dot{r}^2 + r^2 \dot{\phi}^2.$$

Hence the kinetic energy is

$$T = \frac{m}{2}(\dot{r}^2 + r^2 \dot{\phi}^2).$$

By (9) of Sec. 7, we obtain (9').

Example 2. Suppose a particle P of mass m is moving about a fixed point O in such a manner that the potential energy V of P is a function of r alone. It follows that P is acted on by a force which is always directed toward O, and such a force is called a *central force.* We shall find the equations of motion of P.

The Lagrangian function for P is

$$L = T - V$$
$$= \tfrac{1}{2}m(\dot{x}^2 + \dot{y}^2 + \dot{z}^2) - V(r) = \tfrac{1}{2}m[\dot{r}^2 + r^2\dot{\theta}^2 + r^2(\sin^2\theta)\dot{\phi}^2] - V(r).$$

Let $q_1 = r$, $q_2 = \theta$, $q_3 = \phi$. Then the Lagrangian equations (12) of Sec. 7 are

$$\frac{d}{dt}(m\dot{r}) - mr[\dot{\theta}^2 + (\sin^2\theta)\dot{\phi}^2] + \frac{dv}{dr} = 0, \tag{14}$$

$$\frac{d}{dt}(mr^2\,\dot{\theta}) - mr^2(\sin\theta\cos\theta)\dot{\phi}^2 = 0, \tag{15}$$

$$\frac{d}{dt}[mr^2(\sin^2\theta)\dot{\phi}] = 0. \tag{16}$$

By (16), we have

$$\dot{\phi} = \frac{C}{mr^2\sin^2\theta}, \tag{17}$$

where C is a constant. Substitution of (17) in (14) and (15) leads to two equations which do not involve ϕ in any way. Hence the motion is in a plane. Let us choose the coordinate axes so that this plane is the plane $\phi = 0$. Then $C = 0$ and (14), (15) reduce to

$$\frac{d}{dt}(m\dot{r}) - mr\dot{\theta}^2 + \frac{dv}{dr} = 0, \qquad \frac{d}{dt}(mr^2\dot{\theta}) = 0. \tag{18}$$

Integration of this latter equation leads to *Kepler's law of motion:*

$$mr^2\dot{\theta} = \text{const.},$$

i.e., *radial area is swept out at a constant rate.*

Example 3. Find the differential equation for a vibrating string with fixed ends l units apart.

Solution. We assume that the string vibrates in a fixed plane, that the displacement from its position of equilibrium is always small, that the direction of the tangent at any point P varies by only a small amount. Moreover, we neglect the component of motion parallel to the x-axis. The kinetic energy is then given by

$$T = \int_0^l \frac{1}{2}\rho\left(\frac{\partial y}{\partial t}\right)^2 dx,$$

where ρ is the mass per unit length of the string. We assume ρ constant. If the stretching is uniform and if the potential energy is proportional to the square of the amount of stretching, and if $\sigma = l' - l$, where l' is the length of the string at any instant, then

$$\sigma = \int_0^l \sqrt{1 + \left(\frac{\partial y}{\partial x}\right)^2}\, dx - l.$$

By hypothesis, $\partial y/\partial x$ is small, and $\sqrt{1 + (\partial y/\partial x)^2}$ is approximately $1 + \frac{1}{2}(\partial y/\partial x)^2$. Hence the potential energy V is approximately

$$V = \int_0^l \frac{p}{2}\left(\frac{\partial y}{\partial x}\right)^2 dx,$$

where p is a constant of proportionality. Thus Hamilton's integral takes the form

$$\int_{t_0}^{t_1} (T - V)\, dt = \int_{t_0}^{t_1} \int_0^l \left[\frac{\rho}{2}\left(\frac{\partial y}{\partial t}\right)^2 - \frac{p}{2}\left(\frac{\partial y}{\partial x}\right)^2\right] \partial x\, dt.$$

By Ex. I, 4, in which $x = x$, $y = t$, and $u = y$, the Euler equation is

$$\frac{p}{2}\frac{\partial^2 y}{\partial x^2} - \frac{\rho}{2}\frac{\partial^2 y}{\partial t^2} = 0,$$

or if we write $c^2 = p/\rho$,

$$\frac{\partial^2 y}{\partial t^2} = c^2 \frac{\partial^2 y}{\partial x^2}.$$

EXERCISES IV

1. By Hamilton's principle find the equations of motion of a projectile whose trajectory lies in a vertical plane.
   Ans. $d^2x/dt^2 = 0,\ (d^2y/dt^2) - g = 0.$

2. By Hamilton's principle find the equations of motion of a particle acted on by a force with components X, Y, Z parallel respectively to the x-, y-, z-axes.

3. (a) By Hamilton's principle find the equations of motion for a simple pendulum.   *Ans.* $(d^2\theta/dt^2) + (g/a) \sin\ \theta = 0.$

   (b) Find the tension in the pendulum string.
   Ans. $R = m[g \cos\ \theta + a(d\theta/dt)^2].$

4. Suppose a particle of mass m is constrained to move on a rough horizontal circle of radius a by a force R directed toward the center of the path. Let the initial velocity be v_0 and let the particle be resisted by the air with a force proportional to the square of its velocity. Suppose the resisting force due to the roughness of the path is $R\mu$, where μ is the coefficient of friction. Find the equations of motion.

   [Hint: $\delta W = R\delta r - k(r^2\dot\theta^2)r\delta\theta - \mu R r \delta\theta.$]

$$Ans. \quad \theta = \frac{1}{(ka/m) + \mu} \log\left[1 + \left(\frac{ka}{m} + \mu\right)\frac{v_0 t}{a}\right].$$

5. (a) A particle of mass m moves freely in space. Show that the equations of motion are

$$m\left[\frac{d^2r}{dt^2} - r\left(\frac{d\phi}{dt}\right)^2\right] = R, \qquad \frac{m}{r}\frac{d}{dt}\left(r^2\frac{d\phi}{dt}\right) = \Phi, \qquad m\frac{d^2z}{dt^2} = Z,$$

in cylindrical coordinates, where R is the component of the force $\mathbf{F}$ impressed on the particle along the radius vector, Φ is the component of $\mathbf{F}$ normal to the radius vector and to the z-axis, and Z is the component of $\mathbf{F}$ parallel to the z-axis.

(b) Show that in spherical coordinates these equations become

$$m\left\{\frac{d^2r}{dt^2} - r\left[\left(\frac{d\theta}{dt}\right)^2 + (\sin^2\theta)\left(\frac{d\phi}{dt}\right)^2\right]\right\} = R,$$

$$\frac{m}{r}\left[\frac{d}{dt}\left(r^2\frac{d\theta}{dt}\right) - r^2\sin\theta\cos\theta\left(\frac{d\phi}{dt}\right)^2\right] = \Theta,$$

$$\frac{m}{r\sin\theta}\frac{d}{dt}\left(r^2\sin^2\theta\frac{d\phi}{dt}\right) = \Phi,$$

where Θ is the component of $\mathbf{F}$ normal to the radius vector and in the plane of this vector and the z-axis, and Φ is the component normal to R and Θ.

6. A mass of four units is supported by a string passing over a weightless smooth pulley with rigid axis. The other end of the string is attached to the axis of a smooth pulley of mass one unit. Over this pulley there passes a string at whose ends are masses of one and two units. Find the equations of motion of each of the moving parts if the system starts from rest.

Ans. $\ddot{x} = g/23$ for mass 4.

7. Find the equations of motion of a string vibrating in three dimensions.

Ans. $\partial^2 y/\partial t^2 = c^2(\partial^2 y/\partial x^2)$, $\partial^2 z/\partial t^2 = c^2(\partial^2 z/\partial x^2)$.

8. A string vibrates longitudinally (i.e., along its own line). If $u(x)$ is the displacement of the particle originally at x, show that

$$\frac{\partial^2 u}{\partial t^2} = b^2\frac{\partial^2 u}{\partial x^2}.$$

9. Find the equation of motion of a vibrating drum head. (Hint: The potential energy is approximately $(p/2)\iint[(\partial z/\partial x)^2 + (\partial z/\partial y)^2]\,dS$.)

$$Ans.\ \frac{\partial^2 z}{\partial t^2} = c^2\left(\frac{\partial^2 z}{\partial x^2} + \frac{\partial^2 z}{\partial y^2}\right).$$

10. Find the equation of motion of a uniform straight rod which vibrates in a plane. Assume that the potential energy of the rod is proportional to the integral of the square of the curvature $\partial^2 u/\partial x^2$ (approximately).

Ans. $(\partial^2 u/\partial t^2) + c^2(\partial^4 u/\partial x^4) = 0.$

11. Find the equations of motion for the propagation of sound waves.

Hint: Let φ be the velocity potential. The potential energy of the medium under disturbance is approximately proportional to

$$\iiint_V \left(\frac{\partial\varphi}{\partial t}\right)^2 dV.$$

The kinetic energy is the volume integral of $\text{grad}^2\,\varphi$.

Ans. $\partial^2 u/\partial t^2 = c^2\,\nabla^2\varphi.$

12. A uniform flexible cord of fixed length is supported from two fixed points. Find the shape assumed by the cord when its center of gravity is as low as possible.

13. The ends of a uniform flexible cord of fixed length slide freely on fixed wires in a vertical plane. Show that the cord meets the wires at right angles when the cord is in equilibrium.

8. Hamilton's Canonical Equations.   Consider the dynamical system S of n degrees of freedom whose configuration is described by the generalized coordinates $q_1, \cdots, q_n$. By the *generalized momentum* p_k associated with the coordinate q_k we shall mean the quantity $p_k = \partial L / \partial \dot{q}_k$, where L is the Lagrangian function. (Thus for a single particle, if $q = x$, and $L = \frac{1}{2} m \dot{x}^2$, then $p = \partial L / \partial \dot{x} = m \dot{x}$.) For certain purposes it is often useful to express the dynamical equations in terms of the q's and the p's rather than the q's and the $\dot{q}$'s. By the *Hamiltonian function H* we shall mean the function

$$H = \sum_{k=1}^{n} p_k \dot{q}_k - L. \tag{1}$$

The total differential of H is

$$dH = \sum_{k=1}^{n} p_k \, d\dot{q}_k + \sum_{k=1}^{n} \dot{q}_k \, dp_k - \sum_{k=1}^{n} \frac{\partial L}{\partial \dot{q}_k} \, d\dot{q}_k - \sum_{k=1}^{n} \frac{\partial L}{\partial q_k} \, dq_k. \tag{2}$$

Since $p_k = \partial L / \partial \dot{q}_k$, we have

$$dH = \sum_{k=1}^{n} \dot{q}_k \, dp_k - \sum_{k=1}^{n} \frac{\partial L}{\partial q_k} \, dq_k. \tag{3}$$

Since dH depends only upon the differentials dq_k and dp_k, but not $d\dot{q}_k$, $H \equiv H(p, q)$ is a function of the q's and p's alone. Hence we may write

$$dH = \sum_{k=1}^{n} \frac{\partial H}{\partial q_k} \, dq_k + \sum_{k=1}^{n} \frac{\partial H}{\partial p_k} \, dp_k. \tag{4}$$

Comparing (3) and (4), we find

$$\frac{\partial H}{\partial q_k} = -\frac{\partial L}{\partial q_k} = -\dot{p}_k, \qquad \frac{\partial H}{\partial p_k} = \dot{q}_k. \ (k = 1, \cdots, n). \tag{5}$$

That $\partial L/\partial q_k = \dot{p}_k$ follows directly from Eqs. (12) of Sec. 7 and $p_k = \partial L/\partial \dot{q}_k$. The $2n$ partial differential equations (5) are known as the *Hamilton canonical equations of motion.*

From (4), we find

$$\dot{H} = \sum_{k=1}^{n} \frac{\partial H}{\partial q_k} \dot{q}_k + \sum_{k=1}^{n} \frac{\partial H}{\partial p_k} \dot{p}_k. \tag{6}$$

Substituting (5) in (6), we see that

$$\dot{H} = 0 \qquad \text{or} \qquad H = \text{const.} \tag{7}$$

If we assume that the potential energy is not an explicit function of $\dot{q}_k$, then $p_k = \dfrac{\partial L}{\partial \dot{q}_k} = \dfrac{\partial(T - V)}{\partial \dot{q}_k} = \dfrac{\partial T}{\partial \dot{q}_k}$, from which (1) gives

$$H = \sum_{k=1}^{n} \frac{\partial T}{\partial \dot{q}_k} \dot{q}_k - L. \tag{8}$$

Since T is a homogeneous quadratic form in the $\dot{q}$'s, we know by Euler's formula (Chap. I, Ex. XIX, 38) that

$$2T = \sum_{k=1}^{n} \frac{\partial T}{\partial \dot{q}_k} \dot{q}_k, \tag{9}$$

From (8) and (9), we find

$$H = 2T - L = T + V. \tag{10}$$

This shows that *the Hamiltonian function is the total energy of the system S.*

If L, and hence H, are explicit functions of the time it can be shown that Hamilton's equations (5) still hold. However, $\dot{H} = \dot{L}$ rather than $\dot{H} = 0$.

Example 1. For a free particle of mass m, $L = \frac{1}{2}m(\dot{x})^2$, $p = m\dot{x}$, $q = x$. By (1), $H = p\dot{q} - L = m(\dot{x})^2 - \frac{1}{2}m(\dot{x})^2 = \frac{1}{2}m(\dot{x})^2$, or $H = p^2/2m$. Thus equations (5) take the form

$$\dot{p} = 0, \qquad \dot{q} = \frac{p}{m}.$$

EXERCISES V

1. Show that Eqs. (5) still hold when L is an explicit function of time.

2. Derive Hamilton's equations (5) by applying Hamilton's principle to

$$L = \sum_{k=1}^{n} p_k \dot{q}_k - H(p_k, q_k).$$

3. Show that, for a simple harmonic oscillator of one degree of freedom, $H = (p^2/2m) + (kq^2/2)$, where k is the stiffness of the system. Also, show that $\dot{p} = -kq$, $\dot{q} = p/m$.

4. From the Lagrangian function for a simple pendulum, with q the angle θ made by the pendulum with the vertical, show that p is the angular momentum $ml^2\dot{\theta}$, and hence that $H = (p^2/2ml^2) - mgl \cos q$. Show that Hamilton's equations (5) reduce in this case to the well-known forms.

5. From the Lagrangian function for planetary motion with potential function $V(r)$, verify that $p_r = m\dot{r}$, $p_\theta = mr^2\dot{\theta}$, and that H in (1) gives the total energy of the moving body. Express H in terms of p_r and p_m, and show that (5) reduces to

$$\frac{p_\theta^2}{mr^3} - \frac{dv}{dr} = \frac{dp_r}{dt}, \qquad 0 = \frac{dp_\theta}{dt}; \qquad \frac{p_r}{m} = \dot{r}, \qquad \frac{p_\theta}{mr^2} = \dot{\theta}.$$

Give the physical interpretation of the first two of these equations, noting that $p_\theta^2/mr^3 = mv^2/r$ and that $-dv/dr$ is the gravitational force.

6. Derive Lagrange's and Hamilton's equations in spherical coordinates (r, θ, ϕ). Develop and interpret physically the formulas for generalized forces and momenta in the directions of r, θ, and ϕ.

9. Holonomic and Nonholonomic Systems.

We return to the argument in Sec. 7 where we assumed that the δq_k are completely arbitrary in the time interval between t_0 and t_1, the δq_k all vanishing at t_0 and t_1. It sometimes happens that these variations are subject to certain constraints owing to the fact that (1) the $q_1, \cdots, q_n$ are dependent, or (2) that the restrictions on the δq_k are expressible only between δq's and not between the q's. In case (1), the difficulty is due to the fact that too many coordinates are used and that the number of degrees of freedom is less than the number of coordinates used; we accordingly decrease the number of coordinates and proceed with the Lagrangian method as before. In case (2), when the relations connecting the δq's are expressible only in terms of the δq's, the relations are *nonintegrable*, and it is impossible to obtain the appropriate relations among the q's. A system in which the nonintegrable case (2) appears is said to be *nonholonomic*. If such nonintegrable relations do not exist, the system is termed *holonomic*.

Considering the nonholonomic case (with $n = m$), suppose that there are β ($< n$) relations connecting the δq's, of the form

$$\sum_{k=1}^{n} a_{1k} \, \delta q_k = 0, \quad \sum_{k=1}^{n} a_{2k} \, \delta q_k = 0, \quad \cdots, \quad \sum_{k=1}^{n} a_{\beta k} \, \delta q_k = 0, \quad (1)$$

when the a_{rk} are functions of the q_k. Referring to (8) of Sec. 7, we can be sure only that

$$\sum_{k=1}^{n} \left[\frac{\partial T}{\partial q_k} - \frac{d}{dt}\left(\frac{\partial T}{\partial \dot{q}_k}\right) + Q_k \right] = 0, \qquad (2)$$

subject to the conditions (1). Assuming the existence of a potential function, $Q_k = - \partial V / \partial q_k$, we may write (2) in the form

$$\sum_{k=1}^{n} \left\{ \frac{\partial L}{\partial q_k} - \frac{d}{dt}\left(\frac{\partial L}{\partial \dot{q}_k}\right) \right\} \delta q_k = 0. \qquad (3)$$

Multiplying relations (1) by $\lambda_1, \lambda_2, \cdots, \lambda_\beta$, respectively, and adding to (3), we have

$$\sum_{k=1}^{n} \left[\frac{\partial L}{\partial q_k} - \frac{d}{dt}\left(\frac{\partial L}{\partial \dot{q}_k}\right) + \lambda_1 a_{1k} + \cdots + \lambda_\beta a_{\beta k} \right] \delta q_k = 0. \quad (4)$$

(See Exs. XXVI, 26 and 27 of Chap. I). In (4) set the coefficients of $\delta q_1, \cdots, \delta q_\beta$ successively equal to zero. We obtain

$$\left. \begin{array}{l} \dfrac{\partial L}{\partial q_1} - \dfrac{d}{dt}\left(\dfrac{\partial L}{\partial \dot{q}_1}\right) + \lambda_1 a_{11} + \cdots + \lambda_\beta a_{\beta 1} = 0, \\ \cdots\cdots\cdots\cdots\cdots\cdots\cdots\cdots\cdots\cdots\cdots\cdots \\ \dfrac{\partial L}{\partial q_\beta} - \dfrac{d}{dt}\left(\dfrac{\partial L}{\partial \dot{q}_\beta}\right) + \lambda_1 a_{1\beta} + \cdots + \lambda_\beta a_{\beta\beta} = 0. \end{array} \right\} \quad (5)$$

Since there are only β restrictions upon the δq's, the remaining $(n - \beta)$ of these δq's are arbitrary. So we can write

$$\left. \begin{array}{l} \dfrac{\partial L}{\partial q_{\beta+1}} - \dfrac{d}{dt}\left(\dfrac{\partial L}{\partial \dot{q}_{\beta+1}}\right) + \lambda_1 a_{1,\beta+1} + \cdots + \lambda_\beta a_{\beta,\beta+1} = 0, \\ \cdots\cdots\cdots\cdots\cdots\cdots\cdots\cdots\cdots\cdots\cdots\cdots \\ \dfrac{\partial L}{\partial q_n} - \dfrac{d}{dt}\left(\dfrac{\partial L}{\partial \dot{q}_n}\right) + \lambda_1 a_{1n} + \cdots + \lambda_\beta a_{\beta n} = 0. \end{array} \right\} \quad (6)$$

The values of $\lambda_1, \cdots, \lambda_\beta$, and the n expressions

$$\frac{\partial L}{\partial q_k} - \frac{d}{dt}\left(\frac{\partial L}{\partial \dot{q}_k}\right),$$

$k = 1, \cdots, n$ may be calculated from the equations (1), (5) and (6). Thus for a nonholonomic system, the Lagrangian equations are of the form

$$\frac{d}{dt}\left(\frac{\partial L}{\partial \dot{q}_k}\right) - \frac{\partial L}{\partial q_k} = \sum_{r=1}^{\beta} \lambda_r a_{rk}, \quad (k = 1, \cdots, n). \tag{7}$$

For a detailed treatment of further topics in dynamics, such as contact transformations, see Whittaker, "Analytical Dynamics"; Webster, "Dynamics"; Kemble, "Quantum Mechanics."

10. Theory of Small Oscillations. We shall now study the problem of small vibrations of any system $\mathbf{S}$ of n particles about a configuration of equilibrium.

As before let the system $\mathbf{S}$ be defined by m parameters $q_1, \cdots, q_m$. Suppose that the potential energy $V(q_1, \cdots, q_m)$ of the system depends only on the coordinates $q_1, \cdots, q_m$, and that V is developable by Taylor's theorem into

$$V = V_0 + \sum_{k=1}^{m} q_k\left(\frac{\partial V}{\partial q_k}\right)_0 + \frac{1}{2}\sum_{r=1}^{m}\sum_{s=1}^{m} q_r q_s\left(\frac{\partial^2 V}{\partial q_r\, \partial q_s}\right)_0 + \cdots \tag{1}$$

where the suffix zero denotes the value at

$$q_1 = q_2 = \cdots = q_m = 0$$

of the quantity to which the suffix is attached.

Suppose that the motions of the particles are all small enough that the terms in V of higher order may be neglected. Since the system $\mathbf{S}$ is in equilibrium at $q_1 = \cdots = q_m = 0$, so that V is a minimum (or maximum), $(\partial V/\partial q_k)_0 = 0$ for each k. Then the approximate value of $V - V_0$ is

$$V - V_0 = \tfrac{1}{2}\sum_{r=1}^{m}\sum_{s=1}^{m} V_{rs} q_r q_s, \tag{2}$$

a quadratic form in the q's. [Here $V_{rs} = (\partial^2 V/\partial q_r\, \partial q_s)_0$.] Suppose that $V = 0$ when $q_1 = q_2 = \cdots = q_m = 0$. Then $V_0 = 0$.

If V is a minimum the equilibrium is *stable* so that the terms V_{rs} will be such that V is positive for all positive values of the variables $q_1, \cdots, q_m$.

As before, the kinetic energy is

$$T = \tfrac{1}{2} \sum_{r=1}^{m} \sum_{s=1}^{m} \tau_{rs} \dot{q}_r \dot{q}_s, \tag{3}$$

where the τ_{rs} are functions of q_k alone.

If we assume τ_{rs} to be developable, then

$$\tau_{rs} = \tau_{rs}^{(0)} + \sum_{k=1}^{m} q_k \left(\frac{\partial \tau_{rs}}{\partial q_k} \right)_0 + \cdots \quad (r, s = 1, \cdots, m) \tag{4}$$

Furthermore, if we assume that the $\dot{q}_k$'s are small at the same time as q_k, we may approximate τ_{rs} by $\tau_{rs}^{(0)}$, the value of τ_{rs} at time t_0.

Suppose that besides the conservative forces of restitution arising from the potential energy V, there exist nonconservative resistances which are linear functions of velocities. Denote the *dissipation force* of this character corresponding to q_k by $-\partial R/\partial \dot{q}_r$, where

$$R = \tfrac{1}{2} \sum_{r=1}^{m} \sum_{s=1}^{m} R_{rs} \dot{q}_r \dot{q}_s \tag{5}$$

is a quadratic form which we assume to be non-negative.

Thus we deal with a set of three homogeneous quadratic forms with constant coefficients,

$$T = \tfrac{1}{2} \sum_{r=1}^{m} \sum_{s=1}^{m} \tau_{rs} \dot{q}_r \dot{q}_s, \qquad R = \tfrac{1}{2} \sum_{r=1}^{m} \sum_{s=1}^{m} R_{rs} \dot{q}_r \dot{q}_s,$$

$$V = \tfrac{1}{2} \sum_{r=1}^{m} \sum_{s=1}^{m} V_{rs} q_r q_s. \tag{6}$$

Each of these forms must be nonnegative for all possible values of the variables of which it is a function. The numbers τ_{rs} are called the *coefficients of inertia*, the V_{rs} *coefficients of stiffness*, and the R_{rs} *coefficients of viscosity* or *resistance*.

From Eqs. (9) of Sec. 7, we find Lagrange's equations for our system to be

$$\frac{d}{dt} \left(\frac{\partial T}{\partial \dot{q}_k} \right) - \frac{\partial T}{\partial q_k} = -\frac{\partial V}{\partial q_k} - \frac{\partial R}{\partial \dot{q}_k} + \epsilon_k, \ (k = 1, \cdots, m) \tag{7}$$

where ϵ_k is the total impressed force acting on the kth particle. This is a system of linear differential equations of the second order, which, by means of (6), may be written in the form

$$\sum_{s=1}^{m} (\tau_{rs}p^2 + R_{rs}p + V_{rs})q_s = \epsilon_r, \quad p = \frac{d}{dt}. \quad (r = 1, \cdots, m) \quad (8)$$

From here on the theory proceeds as indicated in Chap. III, Secs. 25 to 28.

CHAPTER IX

INTRODUCTION TO REAL VARIABLE THEORY

1. Introduction. Throughout the earlier chapters of this book, frequent reference has been made to theorems demanding a greater degree of rigor than it seemed advisable to invoke at the time. In the present chapter we shall prove some of these theorems. At the close of the chapter will be found a bibliography which the student may find useful if he continues the studies initiated in the present work.

2. Theory of Real Numbers. The structure of analysis rests upon the theory of real numbers as a foundation. Hence, any rigorous treatment of calculus and related subjects must start with real number theory. Liebnitz and Newton, the creators of infinitesimal calculus, did not realize the necessity for this to insure the security of the foundations of their work. It was not until the beginning of the eighteenth century that serious studies were undertaken—under the influence of Gauss—to examine the fundamental concepts underlying the calculus. Noteworthy advances were made during the last century, the work of Weierstrass, Cantor, and Dedekind being of great importance in the development of the theory.

3. The Rational Numbers. It is assumed that the natural numbers (the positive integers 1, 2, 3, 4, $\cdots$) have been defined and that the arithmetic of positive integers is known. The positive integers are closed under addition and multiplication, for if a and b are any two positive integers, $a + b = c$ and $a \cdot b = d$ are positive integers. However, in the domain of positive integers, there exist equations, such as $x + 3 = 1$ and $x + 5 = 5$, which have no solution, so one is led to adjoin the negative integers and zero. Likewise, equations of the type $ax + b = 0$, a and b being integers, lead one to adjoin further the set of *rational numbers,* i.e., numbers which are ratios of integers. The set of rational numbers is closed under addition, subtraction, multiplication, and division (except by zero).

But the rationals are not closed under algebraic processes. For example, $x^2 - 2 = 0$ has no rational solution; likewise,

$[\sqrt{2} + \sqrt[5]{3}]$ is not a rational number. Evidently there are still gaps in a number system built in this way on the set of rational numbers.

In 1825, Abel discovered that a solution of

$$a_0 x^n + a_1 x^{n-1} + \cdots + a_n = 0, \qquad a_0 \neq 0, \tag{1}$$

where a_i are rational numbers and n is a positive integer, is not always possible in terms of radicals. It was this discovery that lead to Galois' theory of equations which, among other things, uncovered other types of irrationalities.

In 1844, Liouville proved the existence of *transcendental numbers*, i.e., numbers not roots of an equation of type (1). In particular, the number e was shown to be transcendental by Hermite in 1873; and in 1882, Ludermann showed that π is also transcendental.

Thus, mathematicians came to realize that algebraic processes are insufficient to produce all irrational numbers and that some other method must be invoked to round out the complete structure of real numbers. Moreover, this method must not appeal to geometric or other types of intuition.

Three important theories of real numbers have been developed, the theories being named after their founders: (1) *Weierstrass* (1860), (2) *Cantor* (1871), and (3) *Dedekind* (1872). We shall here consider only this last theory.

4. The Dedekind Theory. The Dedekind theory of real numbers had its origin in a course in calculus given by Dedekind in 1858. Dedekind was deeply troubled by the lack of "rigor" in the development of calculus and he traced the trouble largely to the lack of a clear-cut conception of number. The results of his efforts appeared in 1872 in his *Stetigkeit und Irrationale Zahlen*, a book every serious student of mathematics should read.

In this section we shall give an introduction to Dedekind's theory, developing it sufficiently far to be able to use it as a tool in later work.

We consider the set of all rational numbers as known. A *Dedekind cut* (*Schnitt*) in the domain of all rational numbers is a *partition* of *all* the rationals into two classes A and B such that: (1) every rational a of A is less than every rational b of B; (2) the sets A and B must contain elements (rationals). We denote such a partition by $[A, B]$.

(a) A *Dedekind real number* is a symbol attached to a cut [A, B] in the domain of all rational numbers.

(b) A *Dedekind rational number* (in the new sense) is a symbol attached to a cut [A, B] of all rational numbers in which either A has a greatest rational or B a least rational.

(c) A *Dedekind irrational number* is a symbol attached to a cut [A, B] in the domain of rational numbers in which neither A has a greatest rational nor B a least rational.

The *real continuum* is the aggregate of all cuts in the domain of all rational numbers.

Example 1. If A is the set of all rationals a such that $a < \frac{1}{3}$, and if B is the set of all other rationals, then $[A, B]$ is a Dedekind rational real number, B having a least element $\frac{1}{3}$.

If the real number [A, B] is such that A has a greatest element r, and if the real number [A', B'] is such that B' has r for a least element, it can be shown that we can regard [A, B] and [A', B'] as the same Dedekind rational number.

Example 2. If A is the set of all rationals a such that $a^2 < 2$, and if B is the set of all other rationals, then $[A, B]$ is a Dedekind irrational real number, for A has no greatest element and B has no least element (there being no rational r such that $r^2 = 2$). The symbol $\sqrt{2}$ is usually attached to this partition.

(d) *Ordering the Real Numbers.* Let
$$C_1 \equiv [A_1, B_1], \qquad C_2 \equiv [A_2, B_2]$$
denote two real numbers defined by the partitions indicated. The number C_1 is said to precede C_2, i.e., $C_1 < C_2$, if A_1 is included in A_2 (that is, every a_1 of A_1 is in A_2), and if there exist at least two distinct elements in A_2 not in A_1. Similar definitions can be given for $C_1 = C_2$ and $C_1 > C_2$.

(e) *The sum of two real numbers,*
$$C_1 \equiv [A_1, B_1] \text{ and } C_2 \equiv [A_2, B_2]$$
is the cut $C \equiv [A, B]$ where A is the set of all sums $a_1 + a_2$, a_1 ranging through A_1, and a_2 through A_2, and where B is the set of all rationals not in A. That this C is a Dedekind cut follows from the fact that (1) there exist a's in A, and b's in B, (2) if $a = a_1 + a_2$ and if r is any rational less than a, then r belongs to A, for
$$r = a - d = \left(a_1 - \frac{d}{2}\right) + \left(a_2 - \frac{d}{2}\right) = a_1' + a_2'$$

where a_1' belongs to A_1 and a_2' belongs to A_2. Hence every a is less than every b.

Subtraction, multiplication, division, powers, and roots of positive numbers, and other operations may be defined in a similar manner. Thus the domain of all real numbers is closed under these operations. All the well-known properties of real numbers may be proved from these definitions.

If in the definition of a Dedekind cut we replace the word "rational" by "real," then this definition defines a cut of real numbers. From this definition it is possible to prove

FUNDAMENTAL THEOREM 4.1. *Let* $C = [A, B]$ *be a Dedekind cut in the domain of real numbers (i.e., A and B form the class of all real numbers). Then either A has a greatest element or B has a least element.*

It follows from this theorem that no new numbers are obtained by partitioning the set of all real numbers.

5. Axiom of Continuity. Heretofore, we have carefully avoided any reference to geometry. It is occasionally convenient to use a geometric language. Accordingly, while we emphasize the strictly numerical character of our definitions and treatment of real numbers, we shall now set up a correspondence between the real numbers and the points on a line by means of the

Cantor-Dedekind Postulate. There exists a one-to-one correspondence between the real arithmetic continuum and the points on a straight line. (Note, points and lines are undefined.)

We shall frequently use the term *point* (on a line) and *real number* interchangeably, the *real line continuum* being by definition the real arithmetic continuum.

The fundamental theorem states that "all holes in the line are filled up." This theorem is essential in analytical geometry. It is sometimes called the *fundamental axiom of continuity*.

6. Linear Sets. A *real linear set* is an aggregate of real numbers (points). The theory of linear sets originated in the discussion of questions connected with the theory of Fourier series and of functions which can be represented by such a series.

We shall study a few of those elementary properties of linear sets as we shall have need. We must bear in mind that the entire theory of sets of points is essentially an arithmetical theory, the geometrical nomenclature and representation being a convenience, not a necessity. We shall use the word *set* to mean *real linear set* unless otherwise specified.

A set S is a *proper part* of a set S' if each element of S is an element of S', but some element of S' is not in S.

A set S is *infinite* if it can be put into one-to-one correspondence with a proper part of itself.

Thus the set of all positive integers is infinite, for the correspondence

$$1, \quad 2, \quad 3, \quad 4, \quad 5, \cdots$$
$$\updownarrow \quad \updownarrow \quad \updownarrow \quad \updownarrow \quad \updownarrow \tag{1}$$
$$2, \quad 2^2, \quad 2^3, \quad 2^4, \quad 2^5, \cdots,$$

or the correspondence

$$1, \quad 2, \quad 3, \quad 4, \quad 5, \cdots$$
$$\updownarrow \quad \updownarrow \quad \updownarrow \quad \updownarrow \quad \updownarrow \tag{2}$$
$$1!, \quad 2!, \quad 3!, \quad 4!, \quad 5!, \cdots,$$

or the correspondence with the prime numbers

$$1, \quad 2, \quad 3, \quad 4, \quad 5, \quad 6, \quad 7, \quad 8, \quad 9, \cdots$$
$$\updownarrow \quad \updownarrow \quad \updownarrow \quad \updownarrow \quad \updownarrow \quad \updownarrow \quad \updownarrow \quad \updownarrow \quad \updownarrow \tag{3}$$
$$2, \quad 3, \quad 5, \quad 7, \quad 11, \quad 13, \quad 17, \quad 19, \quad 23, \cdots$$

establishes a one-to-one mapping of the set of all positive integers upon a proper part of this set. Again, the set of all real numbers in the closed interval $[0, 1]$ is infinite, for the relation $x' = \frac{1}{3}x$ maps this interval upon a proper part of itself. On the other hand, the set (a, b, c, d, e) cannot be put into one-to-one correspondence with a proper part of itself, and such a set is *finite*.

A set S is *denumerably infinite* if it can be put into one-to-one correspondence with the set of all positive integers. It is evident, for example, that the sets in (1), (2), (3) are denumerably infinite.

THEOREM 6.1. *The set of all rational numbers is denumerably infinite.*

A one-to-one correspondence between the rational numbers and the positive integers is indicated in the following scheme:

$$\left(\frac{0}{1}\right), \left(\frac{1}{1}, \frac{-1}{1}\right), \left(\frac{2}{1}, \frac{1}{2}, \frac{-1}{2}, \frac{-2}{1}\right), \left(\frac{3}{1}, \frac{1}{3}, \frac{-1}{3}, \frac{-3}{1}\right),$$
$$\updownarrow \quad \updownarrow \quad \updownarrow \quad \updownarrow \ \updownarrow \ \updownarrow \ \ \updownarrow \quad \updownarrow \ \updownarrow \ \ \updownarrow \quad \ \updownarrow$$
$$1, \quad 2, \ 3, \quad 4, 5, 6, \quad 7, \quad 8, 9, 10, \quad 11,$$

$$\left(\frac{4}{1}, \frac{3}{2}, \frac{2}{3}, \frac{1}{4}, \frac{-1}{4}, \frac{-2}{3}, \frac{-3}{2}, \frac{-4}{1}\right), \cdots$$
$$\updownarrow \ \updownarrow \ \updownarrow \ \updownarrow \ \ \updownarrow \ \ \ \updownarrow \ \ \ \updownarrow \ \ \updownarrow$$
$$12, \ 13, \ 14, \ 15, \ 16, \ \ 17, \ \ 18, \ \ 19, \cdots,$$

where in each parenthesis the sum of numerator and denominator of each fraction is constant, and where repetitions have been omitted.

THEOREM 6.2. *The set of all real numbers in the interval [0, 1] is nondenumerably infinite.*

Let us represent every number in [0, 1] as an ordinary decimal, where we write, for example, $0.62500000 \cdots$ if the decimal is finite, and where we write $0.62500000 \cdots$ instead of $0.62499999 \cdots$. Suppose all numbers in [0, 1] could be put into a one-to-one correspondence with the positive integers, then:

$$
\begin{aligned}
1 &\leftrightarrow 0.a_1 \, a_2 \, a_3 \, a_4 \cdots , \\
2 &\leftrightarrow 0.b_1 \, b_2 \, b_3 \, b_4 \cdots , \\
3 &\leftrightarrow 0.c_1 \, c_2 \, c_3 \, c_4 \cdots , \\
4 &\leftrightarrow 0.d_1 \, d_2 \, d_3 \, d_4 \cdots , \\
& \quad \cdots \cdots \cdots \cdots
\end{aligned}
\qquad (4)
$$

where $a_1, a_2, \cdots , b_1, \cdots$ are the digits of the respective decimals. Let R be any number

$$ R = 0.\alpha_1 \, \beta_2 \, \gamma_3 \, \delta_4 \cdots , $$

where $\alpha_1 \neq a_1$, $\beta_2 \neq b_2$, $\gamma_3 \neq c_3$, $\cdots$, and where the digits of R are not all 9's after some digit ν_n. It is evident that R is a real number in [0, 1] and that R is distinct from each of the numbers in (4). Hence R was not included in the correspondence (4). It follows that all real numbers in [0, 1] cannot be put into a one-to-one correspondence with the set of positive integers.

EXERCISES I

1. Define the following real numbers by means of a Dedekind cut: $3, 0, e, \sqrt{3}, \sin 3, \pi$.

2. (a) Prove that $x^2 - 2 = 0$ has no rational solution and hence that $\sqrt{2}$ is irrational.

   (b) Prove that $\sqrt[5]{2} + \sqrt{3}$ is irrational.

   (c) Can $\sqrt{2}$ be represented by a repeating infinite decimal? Why not?

3. Show that the real numbers defined by (a) in Sec. 4 obey the properties of simple order.

4. (a) When is the real number c_1 said to be greater than the real c_2?

   (b) When is the real number c_1 said to equal the real c_2?

5. Define the difference, product, and quotient of two real numbers in a manner suggested by (e) in Sec. 4.

6. Show that the two rationals mentioned in the paragraph following Example 1 are essentially the same.

7. Prove Theorem 4.1. (Hint: Consider the cut of rationals determined by the given cut of reals.)

7. Properties of Sets. We shall now formulate certain properties of point sets which we have frequently used in an intuitive manner in the preceding chapters.

An *upper bound* of a linear set S is a number u (if it exists) such that $u \geqq a$ for every number a in S, and a *lower bound* of S is a number l (if it exists) such that $l \leqq a$ for every number a in S. A set S is *bounded* if it has an upper bound and a lower bound. For example, 7, π, and 2 are upper bounds of the set of all numbers less than 2; likewise, 1.5, 1.42, and 1.415 are upper bounds of the set of all positive numbers less than $\sqrt{2}$; 2, $\sqrt{2}$, and 1 are upper bounds of the set of all values of the function e^{-1/x^2}. A function $f(x)$ is *bounded* (over an interval) if the set of all its values (in this interval) is bounded.

Theorem 7.1. *Every bounded set S has a least upper bound U and a greatest lower bound L.*

Partition all real numbers into two classes A and B, A consisting of all numbers x such that x is less than some element of S, and B consisting of all numbers x which are greater than or equal to every element of S. Since S is bounded, A and B have elements. By Theorem 4.1, either A has a greatest element or B a least element. Suppose A had a greatest element X. By definition of A, X is less than some element s of S. It is evident that $X < \frac{1}{2}(X + s) < s$. Hence $\frac{1}{2}(X + s)$ would be in A and X is not the greatest element in A. Thus B has a least element U, and U is the least upper bound of S. The existence of L is proved in a similar manner.

A set S_1 *contains* a set S_2 if each element of S_2 is in S_1.

Let S_1, S_2, S_3, $\cdots$ be sets (finite or infinite in number). The *sum* of S_1, S_2, $\cdots$, denoted by $S_1 + S_2 + \cdots$, is the set consisting of all those elements which are in at least one of the sets S_1, S_2, $\cdots$. The *product* of S_1, S_2, $\cdots$, denoted by $S_1 \cdot S_2 \cdots$, is the set consisting of all those elements which are common to the sets S_1, S_2, $\cdots$. For example, consider the sets (a, b, c), (a, d), (a, e), (a), and (a, c, d, e), where a, b, c, d, e are all distinct. The sum of these sets is the set (a, b, c, d, e) and the product is the single element (a).

A *closed interval* is a set of real numbers x such that $a \leq x \leq b$, or $a \leq x$, or $x \geq b$.   An *open interval* is a set of real numbers x such that $a < x < b$, or $a < x$, or $x > b$.

A point P is a *limit (accumulation) point* of a set S if every open interval I containing P also contains at least one point of S other than P.   It is immaterial whether or not P is an element of S. For example, 0 is a limit point of the set of all numbers $1/n$, where n is a positive integer; again, every real number from 0 to 1 is a limit point of the set of all proper rational fractions.

A set S is *closed* if it contains all its limit points.   Thus, every closed interval is a closed set; the set of numbers $1/n$ is not closed, but if 0 is adjoined to the set it is then closed; the set of all rational numbers is not closed.

A set S is *open* if each point P of S can be inclosed by an open interval which lies entirely in S.   Thus, every open interval is an open set.   The sum of any finite number of open intervals is an open set.

An *interior point* P of a set S is a point which can be inclosed by an open interval which lies entirely in S.   Thus an open set is one such that every point of it is an interior point.

A *neighborhood* of a point P is any open set containing P. Thus, an open interval containing P is a special kind of neighborhood of P.

An element P of a set S which is not an accumulation point of S is an *isolated point* of S.   Thus, if P is an isolated point of S, there exists a neighborhood of P which contains no element of S other than P.

The *closure* $\overline{S}$ of a set S is the set consisting of S together with all its limit points.   Thus, the closure of a closed set is the set itself.   The closure of the set of all rational numbers is the set of all real numbers.

The *complement* of a set S, denoted by $C(S)$, is the set of all points not in S.   It is seen that the complement of a closed (open) set is open (closed).

A point P is an *exterior point* of a set S if it is an interior point of $C(S)$.   Thus, P is exterior to S if P is not an element of $\overline{S}$.

The *boundary* B of a set S is the set of points common to the closure of S and the closure of $C(S)$.   Thus B is given by the formula $B = \overline{S} \cdot \overline{C(S)}$.   It may be shown that the boundary of a set S consists of all those points which are not interior points of either S or $C(S)$.   A closed set contains its boundary. and an open set contains none of its boundary points.

EXERCISES II

1. Show that the isolated points of a linear set are always denumerable.

2. Show that every element of the set S of all rational numbers is a boundary point of S.

3. Prove: The set of all rational numbers is neither closed nor open.

4. Prove: Every neighborhood of a boundary point of a set S contains points of S and points of $C(S)$.

5. Extend all the definitions following Theorem 7.1 to sets of points in the xy-plane; to sets of points in space.   Illustrate with examples.

6. Prove all the comments made in Sec. 7.

8. Certain Theorems on Functions of a Real Variable.   We are now in a position to prove certain theorems quoted in the earlier chapters of this book.

THEOREM 8.1 (*Heine-Borel Theorem*).   *If every point of a closed interval (a, b) is interior to at least one interval of a given set S of intervals, there exists a finite set F of intervals of S, $I_1, I_2, \cdots, I_k$, such that every point of (a, b) is interior to at least one interval of F.*

Divide all real numbers x into two classes A and B as follows: A point x belongs to class A if $x \leqq a$, or if we can cover* the points of the interval (a, x), where $a < x \leqq b$, by a finite set of intervals of S; the number x belongs to class B, if $x > b$, or if we cannot cover the points of the interval (a, x) by a finite number of intervals of S.   Evidently every x_A precedes every x_B.   Consider the Dedekind cut $\xi \equiv [A, B]$.   Now ξ must be b, for suppose ξ precedes b.   Then an interval I of S covers ξ, ξ is an interior point of I, and in I there are numbers of both classes A and B, say x_A and x_B.   There are a finite number of intervals of S covering (a, x_A).   To these intervals adjoin I.   Then there are a finite number of intervals covering (a, x_B).   But this is contrary to our hypothesis.   Thus we conclude that $\xi = b$.

THEOREM 8.2.   *Let (a, b) be a closed interval containing points of the domain of definition of a bounded real function f of a real variable x.   There exists in (a, b) at least one point which has the property that in any arbitrarily small neighborhood of that point, the least upper bound of f is the same as the least upper bound M of f in the whole interval (a, b).*

---

* To *cover* a point P is to select an interval I such that P is an interior point of I.

Divide the real numbers x into two classes A and B as follows: The number x is to belong to class A if $x < a$, or if in the interval (a, x) the least upper bound of f is less than M; x is to belong to class B if $x > b$, or if in (a, x) the least upper bound of f is M. There exist numbers x_A in A and x_B in B, and every x_A precedes every x_B. This partition defines a Dedekind cut $\xi \equiv [A, B]$, such that in every neighborhood of ξ, there are numbers x_A and x_B and thus any arbitrarily small neighborhood of ξ has the same least upper bound M as f has in (a, b).

Proof by the Heine-Borel Theorem. We shall assume that there exists no point p such that, in an arbitrarily small neighborhood of p the least upper bound of f is equal to M. Cover every point x of (a, b) by an interval. Denote by S the set of intervals used to cover the points x of (a, b). Then, by the Heine-Borel theorem, there is a finite number of intervals in the set S such that the least upper bound of f in all the intervals is different from M, and such that every point x of (a, b) is interior to at least one interval of the finite set. We conclude that the least upper bound of f is different from M.

A similar theorem holds with regard to the greatest lower bound of f.

THEOREM 8.3. *If a function $f(x)$ is continuous on the closed interval (a, b), the least upper bound M and the greatest lower bound m of f in (a, b) are both finite, and these bounds are actually attained in each case at least once within the interval (a, b).*

Pick a positive number ϵ. Since f is continuous on (a, b), we can cover each x in (a, b) by an interval I_x such that

$$|f(x) - f(x_1)| < \epsilon$$

when x_1 is in I_x. By the Heine-Borel theorem, there is a finite set F of these intervals I_x such that every point in (a, b) is interior to at least one of the intervals of F. If the number of F's is p, then the greatest variation of f in (a, b) cannot exceed the finite number $2p\epsilon$.

Let ξ be the point discussed in the first proof of Theorem 8.2, and consider the interval $(\xi - \epsilon, \xi + \epsilon)$ in which f has a least upper bound equal to M. Then points can be found in this interval for which the function f differs from M by an amount less than ϵ. Since the interval $(\xi - \delta, \xi + \delta)$ can be taken arbitrarily small, and since f is continuous at ξ, $f(\xi) = M$.

A similar argument may be given in the case of the greatest lower bound.

Theorem 8.4. *If $f(x)$ be continuous on the closed interval (a, b) and if $f(a)$ and $f(b)$ have opposite signs, then there exists at least one value of x in (a, b) for which $f(x)$ vanishes.*

Assume there exists no number x such that $f(x) = 0$. Since f is continuous at every point x in (a, b), there exists a neighborhood of x such that f is either negative (or positive) in that neighborhood. For each x of (a, b) select such an interval, in which f has the same sign for all points interior to it. By the Heine-Borel theorem, there exists a finite set F of these intervals such that every x of (a, b) is in the interior of at least one of the intervals of the set F and having the property that in any one of these intervals, f has the same sign throughout. Let the intervals of F be ordered according to the positions of their left end points. It is evident that successive intervals of F must overlap.

Since, by hypothesis, $f(a)$ and $f(b)$ have opposite signs, we know that there exists at least one interval over which f is always positive and at least one interval over which f is always negative. Hence, there is one pair of successive overlapping intervals over one of which f is positive and over the other of which f is negative. Then the points q common to both intervals are such that $f(q)$ is both positive and negative. This is impossible since f is single-valued. Thus $f(q) = 0$, contrary to hypothesis.

Theorem 8.5. *If $f(x)$ is continuous on the closed interval (a, b) and if C is any real number between $f(a)$ and $f(b)$, there exists on (a, b) at least one value of x for which $f(x)$ is equal to C.*

Let $\varphi(x) = f(x) - C$. Then

$$\varphi(a) = f(a) - C \text{ and } \varphi(b) = f(b) - C$$

have opposite signs. From Theorem 8.4, we know that there exists some value of x in (a, b), say ξ, for which $\varphi(\xi) = 0$, that is, for which $0 = f(\xi) - C = \varphi(\xi)$. Hence $f(\xi) = C$.

Theorem 8.6 (*Rolle's Theorem*). *If $f(x)$ is continuous on the closed interval (a, b), if $f(a) = f(b) = 0$, and if $f'(x)$ exists everywhere in the open interval (a, b), then there exists a point ξ,*

$$a < \xi < b,$$

such that $f'(\xi) = 0$.

Since $f(x)$ is continuous, it follows by Theorem 8.3 that $f(x)$ actually attains its maximum and its minimum somewhere within $[a, b]$. Suppose that $f(x)$ has a maximum point at ξ somewhere within $[a, b]$. Then if $h > 0$,

$$\varphi(h) = \frac{f(\xi + h) - f(\xi)}{h}$$

is negative or zero; and if $h < 0$, $\varphi(h)$ is positive or zero. Since $f'(x)$ exists at each point of (a, b), $\lim_{h \to 0} \varphi(h)$ exists at ξ; in the first case this limit is less than or equal to zero, and in the second case this limit is greater than or equal to zero. Since the derivative is assumed to exist, the two limits must be equal. Hence

$$\lim_{h \to 0} \varphi(h) = f'(\xi) = 0.$$

A function $f(x)$ is said to be *uniformly continuous on* (a, b) if, for every positive number ϵ, there exists a positive number δ such that $|f(x_1) - f(x_2)| < \epsilon$ for every pair of numbers x_1, x_2, on (a, b) closed for which $|x_1 - x_2| < \delta$.

THEOREM 8.7. *If $f(x)$ is continuous on the closed interval (a, b), it is uniformly continuous on (a, b).*

Let ϵ be an arbitrary positive number. Since f is continuous for every point p in (a, b) a neighborhood of p can be determined, such that the oscillation of f in this neighborhood is less than $\epsilon/2$. Determine such a neighborhood for every point in (a, b). By the Heine-Borel theorem, a finite number of intervals can be chosen such that every point in (a, b) is interior to one (at least) of the intervals. The end points of these intervals form a finite set of points in (a, b). Let δ be the smallest distance between consecutive points of this finite set. Any interval whatever in (a, b) of length less than or equal to δ is within at most two of this finite set of nonoverlapping intervals formed by the consecutive points. Hence, in such intervals, the oscillation is at most ϵ.

Let $f(x)$ be a function of x defined over the interval (a, b) closed. Suppose this interval be subdivided by the points $a = x_0 < x_1 < \cdots < x_{n-1} < x_n = b$. The *total variation* of $f(x)$ over (a, b) is the least upper bound of the quantity

$$V = \sum_{i=0}^{n-1} |f(x_{i+1}) - f(x_i)| \tag{1}$$

for all choices of the points x_i and for all finite values of n. If the total variation of $f(x)$ over (a, b) is finite, $f(x)$ is said to be of *bounded variation* over (a, b).

Theorem 8.8. *If $f(x)$ is of bounded variation over (a, b) then $f(x)$ may be represented in the form $\varphi(x) - \psi(x)$, where $\varphi(x)$ and $\psi(x)$ are monotonically increasing bounded functions of x.*

Construct the sum $V(x)$ in (1) for the interval (a, x) where $a \leq x \leq b$. Let $S(x)$ be the sum of the quantities $f(x_{i+1}) - f(x_i)$ which are positive, and $-\sigma(x)$ the sum of these quantities which are negative. Then $V(x) = S(x) + \sigma(x)$ and

$$f(x) - f(a) = S(x) - \sigma(x).$$

Hence,

$$V(x) = 2S(x) + f(a) - f(x) = 2\sigma(x) + f(x) - f(a). \quad (2)$$

Let $\varphi(x)$ and $\psi(x)$ be the least upper bounds of $S(x)$ and $\sigma(x)$ for each x. Hence $f(x) = f(a) + \varphi(x) - \psi(x)$. Since $\varphi(x)$ and $\psi(x)$ are monotonically increasing, we have the theorem.

Theorem 8.9 (*Theorem of Bolzano-Weierstrass*). *An infinite set S of real numbers in a finite interval (a, b) has at least one limit point.*

Suppose S has no limit point. Then for every real number x, there exist a neighborhood of x containing only a finite number of points of S. Let N denote the set of all such neighborhoods. By the Heine-Borel theorem, there exists a finite number I of the intervals of N, having the same property that the N's have and such that every point of (a, b) is interior to at least one interval of I. Since every point of (a, b) is covered and since this covering can be done by a finite number of intervals I, each containing but a finite number of points of S, it follows that S is a finite set. This shows that our assumption of the nonexistence of a limit point to S is incorrect.

EXERCISES III

1. Prove: If a variable is monotonically increasing, it either becomes infinite or approaches a limit.
2. Show that every bounded sequence has a least (greatest) point of accumulation. Does every bounded sequence have a unique limit?
3. Illustrate the fact that Theorem 8.3 is false if the function is not everywhere continuous or if the interval is not closed. Construct a bounded function which has neither a maximum nor a minimum.

4. Prove: *If $f'(x)$ is positive for every value of x on $[a, b]$, an interval for which $f(x)$ is defined, and if x_0 and x_1, $x_1 > x_0$, are any two values of x in $[a, b]$, then $f(x_1) > f(x_0)$; while if $f'(x)$ is negative throughout $[a, b]$, then $f(x_1) < f(x_0)$.*

5. Complete the proofs of Theorems 4.1, 4.2, and 5.1 of Chap. IV.

6. Show that if $f(x)$ is monotonic in $[a, b]$ closed, it is bounded.

7. Prove Theorem 12.1 of Chap. IV (recall Theorems 12.2 and 12.3 of Chap. IV).

BIBLIOGRAPHY

The student who pursues further the various topics initiated in this book may wish to refer to textbooks and original papers. The following selection of references (which is by no means comprehensive and which does not include many excellent treatises) may be found helpful.

ANALYSIS AND FUNCTION THEORY

BIEBERBACH, L.: "Differential- und Integralrechnung," 3. Aufl., 1928.

BURKHARDT, H.: "Einführung in die Theorie der analytischen Funktionen einer komplexen Veränderlichen, 5. Aufl., 1921.

COURANT, R.: "Differential and Integral Calculus," Vols. I, II, 1936.

GOURSAT, E.: "Cours d'analyse mathématique," Vols. I, II, III, 1923.

GREENHILL, A. G.: "The Applications of Elliptic Functions," 1892.

HOBSON, E. W.: "Theory of Functions of a Real Variable," 3d ed., 1927.

HURWITZ, A., und R. COURANT: "Vorlesungen über allgemeine Funktionentheorie und elliptische Funktionen," 3. Aufl., 1929.

JORDAN, C.: "Cours d'analyse," 3d ed., 1915.

KELLOGG, O. D.: "Foundations of Potential Theory," 1929.

KNOPP, K.: "Funktionentheorie," Sammlung Göschen Nr. 668 und 703, 1931.

MacROBERT, T. M.: "Spherical Harmonics," 1927.

OSGOOD, W. F.: "Advanced Calculus," 1925.

OSGOOD, W. F.: "Lehrbuch der Funktionentheorie," 5. Aufl., 1928.

PASCAL, E.: "Repertorium der höheren Mathematik," Bd. I, 2. Aufl., 1910–1929.

ROTHE-OLLENDORFF-POHLHAUSEN: "Funktionentheorie und ihre Anwendung in der Technik," 1931.

STRUTT, M. J. O.: Lamésche, Mathieusche und verwandte Funktionen in Physik und Technik, *Erg. Math.*, Bd. I, H. 3, 1932.

TITCHMARSH, E. C.: "The Theory of Functions," 1932.

TOWNSEND, E. J.: "Functions of a Complex Variable," 1915.

TOWNSEND, E. J.: "Functions of Real Variables," 1928.

VALLÉE POUSSIN, C. J. DE LA: "Cours d'analyse," 6th ed., 1928.

WATSON, G. N.: "A Treatise on the Theory of Bessel Functions," 1922.

WHITTAKER and WATSON: "Modern Analysis," 4th ed., 1927.

WILSON, E. B.: "Advanced Calculus," 1912.

WOODS, F. S.: "Advanced Calculus," 1926.

ORDINARY AND PARTIAL DIFFERENTIAL EQUATIONS

BATEMAN, H.: "Differential Equations," 1918.

BATEMAN, H.: "Partial Differential Equations of Mathematical Physics," 1932.

BIEBERBACH, L.: "Differential Equations."

FORSYTH, A. R.: "Treatise on Differential Equations," 4th ed., 1914.

FRANKLIN, P.: "Differential Equations for Electrical Engineers," 1933.
HORN, J.: "Differentialgleichungen," 2. Aufl., 1927.
INCE, E. L.: "Ordinary Differential Equations," 1927.
PIAGGIO, H. T. H.: "Differential Equations," 1928.
WEBSTER, A. G.: "Partial Differential Equations of Mathematical Physics," 1927.

NUMERICAL ANALYSIS

BENNETT, MILNE, and BATEMAN: Numerical Integration of Differential Equations, *Bull. Nat. Res. Council,* 1933.
SCARBOROUGH, J. B.: "Numerical Mathematical Analysis," 1930.
STEFFENSEN, J. F.: "Interpolation," 1927.
WHITTAKER and ROBINSON, "Calculus of Observations," 1924.

INFINITE SERIES. FOURIER SERIES

BOCHNER, S.: "Fouriersche Integrale," 1932.
BYERLY, W. E.: "Fourier Series and Spherical Harmonics," 1893.
CARSLAW, H. S.: "Fourier Series and Integrals," 3d ed., 1930.
HOBSON, E. W.: "Theory of Functions of a Real Variable and the Theory of Fourier's Series," Vol. II, 1926.
KNOPP, K.: "Theory and Application of Infinite Series," 1928.
WIENER, N.: "The Fourier Integral," 1933.

ALGEBRA, DETERMINANTS, MATRICES

BÔCHER, M.: "Introduction to Higher Algebra," 1907.
DICKSON, L. E.: "Elementary Theory of Equations," 1914.
DICKSON, L. E.: "Modern Algebraic Theories," 1926.
KOWALEWSKI, G.: "Einführung in die Determinantentheorie," 1909.
MACDUFFEE, C. C.: "Theory of Matrices," 1933.
MUIR, T.: "Theory of Determinants," 1930.
WAERDEN, B. L. VAN DER: "Moderne Algebra," 1931.
WEDDERBURN, J. H. M.: "Lectures on Matrices," American Mathematical Society Colloquium Publications, 1934.
WINTNER, A.: "Spektraltheorie der unendlichen Matrizen," 1929.

VECTOR AND TENSOR ANALYSIS. DIFFERENTIAL GEOMETRY

EISENHART, L. P.: "Differential Geometry of Curves and Surfaces," 1909.
EISENHART, L. P.: "Riemannian Geometry," 1926.
GANS, R.: "Vector Analysis," 1932.
GIBBS-WILSON: "Vector Analysis," 1913.
GRAUSTEIN, W. C.: "Differential Geometry," 1935.
McCONNELL, A. J.: "Absolute Differential Calculus," 1931.
PHILLIPS, H. B.: "Vector Analysis," 1933.
SCHOUTEN, J. A.: "Der Ricci-Kalkul," 1924.
WEATHERBURN, C. E.: "Elementary and Advanced Vector Analysis," 1926.
WEATHERBURN, C. E.: "Differential Geometry," 1930.

Calculus of Variations

Bliss, G. A.: "Calculus of Variations," 1925.

Bolza, O.: "Lectures on the Calculus of Variations," 1904.

Applied Mathematics.
Mathematical and Theoretical Physics

Abraham and Becker: "Classical Electricity and Magnetism," 1932.

Ames and Murnaghan: "Theoretical Mechanics," 1929.

Bush, V.: "Operational Circuit Analysis," 1929.

Byerly, W. E.: "Generalized Coordinates," 1916.

Carslaw, H. S.: "Mathematical Theory of Heat Conduction," 1921.

Carson, J. R.: "Electric Circuit Theory and Operational Calculus," 1926.

Courant, R., und D. Hilbert: "Methoden der mathematischen Physik," 1931.

Glauert, H.: "The Elements of Aerofoil and Airscrew Theory."

Frank, Ph., und R. von Mises: "Die Differential und Integralgleichungen der Mechanik und Physik" (zugleich 7. Aufl. von *Riemann-Webers* "Partiellen Differentialgleichungen der mathematischen Physik"), Bd. I, 1931.

Haas, A.: "Introduction to Theoretical Physics," Vols. I, II, 1925.

Houstoun, R. A.: "Introduction to Mathematical Physics," 1912.

Ingersoll and Zobel: "Mathematical Theory of Heat Conduction," 1913.

Jeans, J. H.: "Electricity and Magnetism," 3d ed., 1915.

Lamb, H.: "The Dynamical Theory of Sound."

Lamb, H.: "Hydrodynamics," 5th ed., 1924.

Lindsay and Margenau: "Foundations of Physics," 1936.

Love, A. E. H.: "Mathematical Theory of Elasticity," 1893.

Mason and Weaver: "The Electromagnetic Field," 1929.

Nielsen, J.: "Vorlesungen über elementare Mechanik," 1935.

Page, L.: "Introduction to Theoretical Physics," 1928.

Pierce, G. W.: "Electric Oscillations and Electrical Waves."

Planck, M.: "Introduction to Theoretical Physics."

Prandtl, L., und O. Tietjens: "Hydro- und Aeromechanik," Bd. 2, 1929–1931.

Rayleigh, J. W. S.: "Theory of Sound," 1878.

Schaefer, C.: "Einführung in die Maxwellsche Theorie der Elektrizität und des Magnetismus," 1929.

Slater and Frank: "Introduction to Theoretical Physics," 1933.

Webster, A. G.: "The Dynamics of Particles and of Rigid, Elastic, and Fluid Bodies," 1904.

Whittaker, E. T.: "Analytical Dynamics of Particles and Rigid Bodies, 3d. ed., 1927.

Tables and Handbooks

Adams, E. P.: "Smithsonian Mathematical Formulae and Tables of Elliptic Functions," 1922.

"Handbuch der Experimentalphysik" (Akademische Verlagsgesellschaft).

"Handbuch der Physik" (Springer).

HAHN, BIERENS DE: "Tables des integrales Définies."

JAHNKE, E., und F. EMDE: "Funktionentafeln mit Formeln und Kursen,"
2. Aufl., 1933.

MADELUNG, E.: "Die mathematischen Hilfsmittel des Physikers,"
3. Aufl., 1936.

PEIRCE, B. O.: "A Short Table of Integrals," 1929.

INDEX